Figures available in three downloadable sizes (resolutions)

Citations in text link to references in bibliography

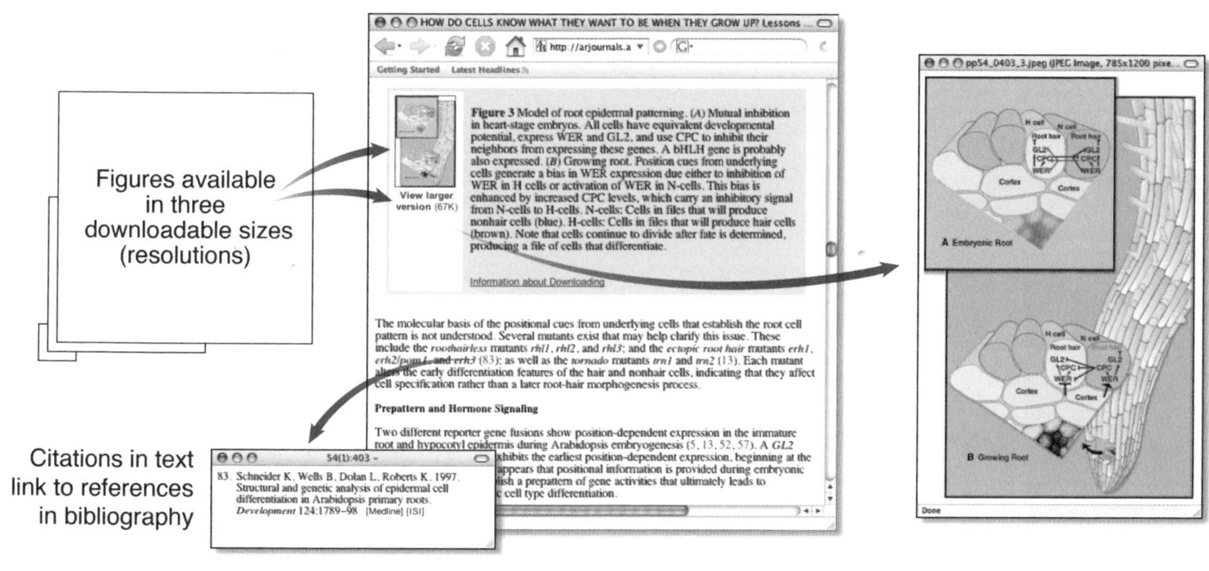

References in Annual Reviews chapter bibliography link out to sources of cited articles online

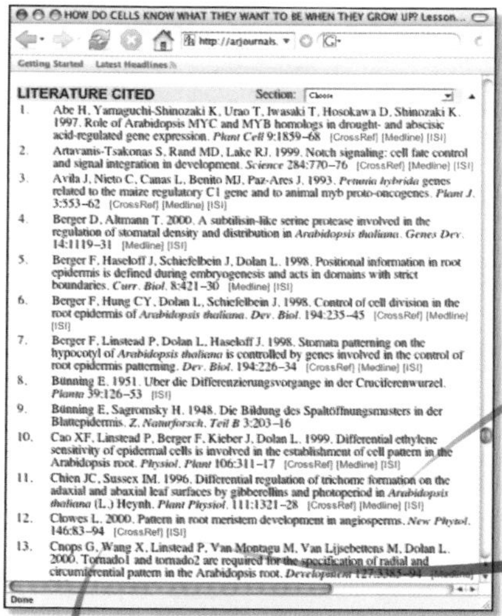

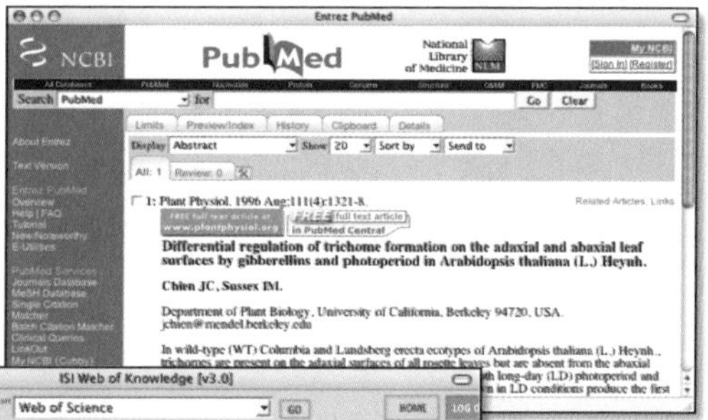

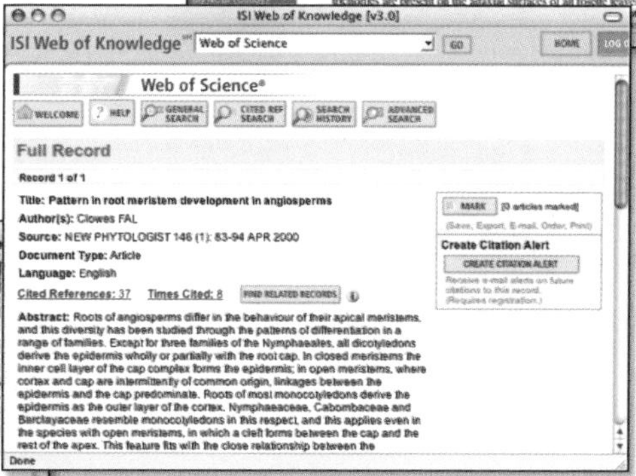

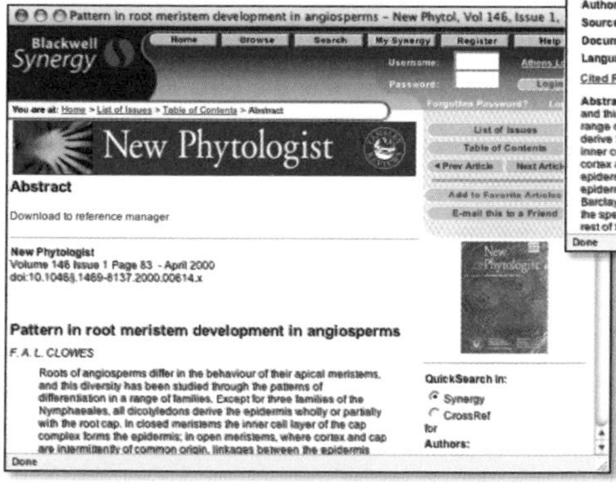

AR
Annual Review of
Plant Biology

Volume 59, 2008

Sabeeha Merchant, *Editor*
University of California, Los Angeles

Winslow R. Briggs, *Associate Editor*
Carnegie Institution of Washington, Stanford, California

Vicki L. Chandler, *Associate Editor*
University of Arizona

www.annualreviews.org • science@annualreviews.org • 650-493-4400

Annual Reviews
4139 El Camino Way • P.O. Box 10139 • Palo Alto, California 94303-0139

Annual Reviews
Palo Alto, California, USA

International Standard Serial Number: 1543-5008
International Standard Book Number: 978-0-8243-0659-5
Library of Congress Catalog Card Number: 50-13143

♾ The paper used in this publication meets the minimum requirements of American National Standards for Information Sciences—Permanence of Paper for Printed Library Materials, ANSI Z39.48-1992.

TYPESET BY APTARA, INC.
PRINTED AND BOUND BY SHERIDAN BOOKS, INC., CHELSEA, MICHIGAN

Annual Review of Plant Biology

Volume 59, 2008

Contents

Indexes

Errata

An online log of corrections to *Annual Review of Plant Biology* articles may be found at http://plant.annualreviews.org/

Related Articles

From the ***Annual Review of Biochemistry***, Volume 76 (2007)

The Machines that Divide and Fuse Mitochondria
Suzanne Hoppins, Laura Lackner, and Jodi Nunnari

From the ***Annual Review of Biophysics and Biomolecular Structure***, Volume 36 (2007)

Structural Mechanisms Underlying Posttranslational Modification by Ubiquitin-Like Proteins
Billy T. Dye and Brenda A. Schulman

Gene Regulation: Gene Control Network in Development
Smadar Ben-Tabou de-Leon and Eric H. Davidson

Living with Noisy Genes: How Cells Function Reliably with Inherent Variability in Gene Expression
Narendra Maheshri and Erin K. O'Shea

Mechanism of DNA Transport Through Pores
Murugappan Muthukumar

Regulation of Actin Filament Assembly by Arp2/3 Complex and Formins
Thomas D. Pollard

From the ***Annual Review of Cell and Developmental Biology***, Volume 23 (2007)

Two Families of Chaperonin: Physiology and Mechanism
Arthur L. Horwich, Wayne A. Fenton, Eli Chapman, and George W. Farr

SNARE-Ware: The Role of SNARE-Domain Proteins in Plant Biology
Volker Lipka, Chian Kwon, and Ralph Panstruga

microRNA Functions
Natascha Bushati and Stephen M. Cohen

Embryonic Patterning in *Arabidopsis thaliana*
Pablo D. Jenik, C. Stewart Gillmor, and Wolfgang Lukowitz

Maintaining Peroxisome Populations: A Story of Division and Inheritance
Andrei Fagarasanu, Monica Fagarasanu, and Richard A. Rachubinski

The Small G Proteins of the Arf Family and Their Regulators
Alison K. Gillingham and Sean Munro

From the ***Annual Review of Genetics***, Volume 41 (2007)

Epigenetic Control of Centromere Behavior
Karl Ekwall

The Origin and Establishment of the Plastid in Algae and Plants
Adrian Reyes-Prieto, Andreas P.M. Weber, and Debashish Bhattacharya

DNA Transposons and the Evolution of Eukaryotic Genomes
Cedric Feschotte and Ellen J. Pritham

Annual Reviews is a nonprofit scientific publisher established to promote the advancement of the sciences. Beginning in 1932 with the *Annual Review of Biochemistry*, the Company has pursued as its principal function the publication of high-quality, reasonably priced *Annual Review* volumes. The volumes are organized by Editors and Editorial Committees who invite qualified authors to contribute critical articles reviewing significant developments within each major discipline. The Editor-in-Chief invites those interested in serving as future Editorial Committee members to communicate directly with him. Annual Reviews is administered by a Board of Directors, whose members serve without compensation.

Annual Reviews of

Analytical Chemistry
Anthropology
Astronomy and Astrophysics
Biochemistry
Biomedical Engineering
Biophysics
Cell and Developmental Biology
Clinical Psychology
Earth and Planetary Sciences
Ecology, Evolution, and Systematics
Entomology
Environment and Resources
Fluid Mechanics
Genetics
Genomics and Human Genetics
Immunology
Law and Social Science
Materials Research
Medicine
Microbiology
Neuroscience
Nuclear and Particle Science
Nutrition
Pathology: Mechanisms of Disease
Pharmacology and Toxicology
Physical Chemistry
Physiology
Phytopathology
Plant Biology
Political Science
Psychology
Public Health
Sociology

SPECIAL PUBLICATIONS
Excitement and Fascination of Science, Vols. 1, 2, 3, and 4

PHOTO CREDIT: UC DAVIS

Eric E. Conn

Our Work with Cyanogenic Plants

Eric E. Conn

Section of Molecular & Cell Biology, University of California, Davis, California 95616; email: eeconn@ucdavis.edu

Annu. Rev. Plant Biol. 2008. 59:1–19

The *Annual Review of Plant Biology* is online at plant.annualreviews.org

This article's doi:
10.1146/annurev.arplant.59.032607.092924

1543-5008/08/0602-0001$20.00

Key Words

cyanogenesis, biosynthesis, localization, compartmentation

Abstract

The author identifies three individuals who played major roles in the development of his scientific career: his chemistry professor at the University of Colorado, Reuben Gustavson; his Ph.D. supervisor at the University of Chicago, Birgit Vennesland; and his friend and departmental colleague of 55 years at the University of California, Paul Stumpf. He also mentions students, postdoctoral scholars, and professional colleagues he encountered during his career of nearly 50 years as a plant biochemist. Finally, the article describes the author's research on cyanogenic plants. These plants contain hydrogen cyanide in a bound form that is usually released when the plant tissue is macerated. Cyanogenic plants contain cyanogenic glycosides in which the hydroxyl groups of cyanohydrins (α-hydroxynitriles) of aldehydes or ketones are covalently linked to a sugar, usually D-glucose. The biosynthesis, localization, and degradation, by hydrolysis, of these compounds have been examined, especially in sorghum and flax seedlings.

Contents

PREFACE

In a prefatory chapter in this series Ian Sussex (37) commented on how "seemingly chance" events influenced his career as a biologist, and that chance is frequently cited as a major influence on the careers of many scientists. The reader of this article can certainly see where chance events clearly shaped my career, especially in the early years. Patrick J. Hannan (18) authored an interesting book on this subject, in which he attributes a large proportion of such chance events to serendipity. Because the online edition of the Merriam-Webster dictionary defines serendipity as "the gift of finding valuable or agreeable things not sought for," the reader should perhaps conclude that chance, more than serendipity, was responsible for most of the events that resulted in the initiation of my career in science. Later, when my career goals were clarified, serendipity, as defined above, may have occasionally played a role in one or two discoveries.

The invitation to write a prefatory article for the *Annual Review of Plant Biology* probably affords many of the plant scientists so honored their first opportunity to put reminiscences of their careers into writing. I am a possible exception because a few years ago Peter Facchini, then secretary of the Phytochemical Society of North America (PSNA) and editor of its newsletter, invited me to write about my career as a plant biochemist. The PSNA is a small organization of scientists especially interested in plant natural products, and the newsletter is distributed to its 300–400 members. I became a member shortly after the PSNA was formed approximately 45 years ago, and for many years I served as the editor of *Recent Advances in Phytochemistry*, which contains papers presented at symposia held at the annual meetings of the Society.

I enjoyed responding to Peter's invitation and tried to produce an interesting article for the newsletter. Now faced with writing the prefatory chapter for this volume, I find that several things I want to include here previously appeared in the PSNA newsletter (13). Rather than trying to restate or rewrite that material, I have arranged for permission to use different parts of that article and acknowledge the original source of the material.

THE EARLY YEARS

I was born in Berthoud, Colorado on January 6, 1923, the fourth son and last child of William and Mary Anna Conn. My father was the assistant manager of a Farmers' Union grain elevator in that small town north of Denver. During the 1920s and 1930s my father managed and/or owned grain elevators in Nebraska and Kansas; he and my mother had started married life on a Kansas farm in 1910. Because my youngest sibling was seven years older than I, in many ways I lived the life of an only child. By the time I started high school, my siblings had all married and started their families. Although our lives have been very different, I remain close to my brothers and their families.

I grew up in a small town in Kansas in the midst of the Great Depression, where my family experienced the dust bowl years and their effects on the Great Plains. When I was seven, my mother arranged for me to take piano lessons. I mention this because that ability, which was not outstanding, nevertheless opened many doors to me socially years later. After my parents lost most of their assets except for their home during the Depression, we moved to Fort Morgan, Colorado. That small town of 5,000 had an excellent high school where I did well academically. I had several outstanding high school teachers, one who taught English Literature, and one who taught Advanced Latin (Cicero and Virgil!) to another student and me. Another fine teacher gave an excellent course in American Problems, a course on contemporary American events as they were being influenced by world affairs, especially in Europe in the late thirties. These women (no men here) simply took it for granted that as the class valedictorian I would go to the University of Colorado at Boulder, and encouraged me in that regard. I won an all-tuition scholarship for four years to study there. Although none of my brothers had been able to go to college, my parents encouraged me to do so.

PHOTO CREDIT: UNIVERSITY OF CHICAGO

Figure 1

Dr. Gus was Professor of Chemistry at the University of Colorado when I entered Boulder in 1940. He was an important mentor for me until I entered graduate school at the University of Chicago in 1946. From 1942 to 1959, he held administrative positions at several institutions (Dean and Acting President, University of Colorado; Vice-President and Dean of Faculties, University of Chicago; President, University of Nebraska; Administrator for the Ford Foundation). In 1959 he retired to Arizona where he passed away in 1974.

THE BOULDER YEARS

A close friend, who had already spent a year at Boulder, urged me to visit the chemistry department there in the spring of 1940. My friend arranged an interview with a professor of chemistry, Dr. Reuben Gustavson (**Figure 1**), who would eventually have a major influence on my career. Dr. Gustavson suggested that I consider majoring in chemistry, which I declared when I enrolled that fall. Although Dr. Gustavson was the chair of the department, he also was my professor in general chemistry, and there I had my first exposure to an outstanding lecturer. Dr. Gus would enter the lecture room with his notes (a few 3 × 5 cards), and deliver highly organized lectures, filling the chalkboard with structures and equations. Moreover, he soon knew the names of most of the hundred or so students in the course, and after a few days started calling on us by name to answer questions and write and balance chemical equations, all in a nonthreatening way. His performance strongly influenced my determination, years later, to perfect my lecturing style and make teaching an important aspect of my academic career.

Courses in analytical and organic chemistry followed; up to this point I had made no overt decision to concentrate on biochemistry. However, Dr. Gus was a steroid chemist—this was before the era of metabolism in biochemistry—and his biochemistry course emphasized sterol structures, chemistry, and their physiological role, if known, in animals. Only a few references to glycolysis and the dicarboxylic acid cycle of Szent-Györgyi were made. Krebs' first detailed review on the tricarboxylic acid cycle had not yet appeared.

During my last two undergraduate years (1942–1944) I served as a teaching assistant in various chemistry courses. Most of the other undergraduate males had enrolled in Army or Navy training programs, which readily guaranteed their military service during the war. Dr. Gustavson arranged for me to be hired by the Manhattan Project as soon as I graduated, and I caught a train for Oak Ridge. There I worked primarily as an inorganic chemist. My first publication, coauthored of course, was on the half-life of an isotope of nickel produced in the experimental, plutonium-producing uranium pile at Site X-10 (5). As the war wound down, I realized that many of my friends in Oak Ridge were planning to go, or return, to graduate school, and I incorporated that objective into my immediate plans. As I look back over those years now, I realize how much was left to chance, at least in my case.

THE CHICAGO YEARS

I again relied on Dr. Gus for advice when planning for graduate study. He was now Vice-President and Dean of Faculties at the University of Chicago, and I stopped in Chicago to see him on a trip to Denver in December 1945, when he advised me to apply to the Biochemistry Department there. I applied to Chicago, as well as to Harvard, and when the offer of a teaching assistantship arrived from Chicago (one day before a similar offer from Harvard appeared in the mail), I accepted. At this point I officially launched my career in biochemistry at the University of Chicago.

Figure 2

Birgit Vennesland and Eric Conn in her garden in Berlin-Dahlem, near her laboratory, Forschungstelle Vennesland, a research unit of the Max-Planck Society.

GRADUATE WORK

Professor Birgit Vennesland (**Figure 2**) was my Ph.D. supervisor, and because she was interested in carbon dioxide fixation as mediated by malic enzyme and other such dark fixation enzymes, I was exposed to higher plants as experimental material. The University of Chicago was an exciting place in those years, and the biochemistry faculty included Konrad Bloch and Albert Lehninger; Frank Westheimer and Henry Taube were nearby in the Department of Chemistry. My entire first year in the Vennesland lab was spent in an attempt to isolate Coenzyme II or triphosphopyridine nucleotide (TPN), as NADP was called in those days, from 50 pounds of hog liver. I was given a procedure authored by Otto Warburg, the discoverer of TPN, that had been brought to the United States by his technician Erwin Hass who had to leave Nazi Germany because he was Jewish. The procedure involved such steps as precipitation of the coenzyme as a mercury salt, and then removal of the mercury with hydrogen sulfide. The first attempt failed; the second resulted in approximately 150 mg of fairly pure TPN. To follow the yield of the coenzyme during purification, I used a Warburg manometer to measure the TPN-dependent rate of glucose-6-phosphate oxidation in the presence of glucose-6-phosphate dehydrogenase (*Zwischenferment*) and "old yellow enzyme." We had to obtain both enzymes from spent brewer's yeast, which necessitated visits to a brewery on Halsted Street behind the Chicago stockyards to get gallons of spent yeast suspension and haul it back to Abbot Hall in several milk cans. Back at the lab, the yeast was centrifuged down and spread out on lab benches to dry and be processed. All the students in the graduate lab knew where I had been and enjoyed the aroma of the drying yeast. When the coenzyme was sufficiently pure, it could then be assayed by the characteristic absorption of the reduced form at 340 nm. As I recall, our preparation was approximately 70% pure after some additional purification with a makeshift counter-current machine. I mention all this because it was a time when biochemical research involved a lot of effort just to obtain the reagents needed.

At that point, Vennesland's laboratory was the sole source of TPN in the country, and she generously provided a few milligrams to several groups, including Severo Ochoa and his young postdoctoral scholar Arthur Kornberg, who were investigating the role of malic enzyme in animal tissues. Vennesland was certainly aware of the effort that I and another of her students had made in isolating and purifying that TPN, and clearly conserved the supply. I do not recall ever doing another TPN prep there but someone must have done so after I left Chicago, because Vennesland's laboratory was involved in plant enzymology until she left for Germany in 1968. I had the pleasure of coauthoring a biography of Birgit Vennesland that is located in the section on Women Pioneers in Plant Biology on the web site of the American Society of Plant Biologists (ASPB) (**http://www.aspb.org/committees/women/pioneers.cfm#Birgit%20Vennesland**).

Figure 3

Helen Stafford joined the Biology Department of Reed College in 1954 and became Emeritus in 1987. At that widely respected undergraduate college, Helen established a highly productive research program in plant biology that was supported by the National Science Foundation.

POSTDOCTORAL WORK

After I finished my Ph.D., I stayed on at Chicago for two years at the request of Dr. Vennesland, who wanted someone to help her graduate students while she was on sabbatical leave. I participated in several research projects and acquired some expertise in supervising less-experienced students. I also taught introductory biochemistry in the Bio-Sci Survey sequence of five courses in the University College. Helen Stafford (**Figure 3**), who had come from David Goddard's lab to work with Vennesland, taught the plant biology quarter in that survey sequence. This course gave Helen and me valuable teaching experience when we moved on to our subsequent careers at Reed College and Berkeley, respectively. Helen established an outstanding research program (funded for many years by NSF) at that excellent undergraduate college, and I authored her biography for the ASPB web site (**http://www.aspb.org/committees/women/pioneers.cfm#Helen%20Stafford**).

One of the projects that I was privileged to participate in during that period went on to become textbook material. This was the thesis research of Harvey Fisher, a graduate student of Vennesland's, who showed that the two hydrogen atoms on the carbon atom at the 4-position in the dihydropyridine ring of reduced diphosphopyridine nucleotide (DPNH, also known as NADH) are nonequivalent enzymatically, and that alcohol dehydrogenase stereospecifically transfers hydrogen, as a hydride ion, between the reduced substrate (deutero-ethanol) and the oxidized NAD (14). The report of this work was recognized as a classic article by the editors of the *Journal of Biological Chemistry* (35) during its centennial celebration a few years ago. Last spring, the American Chemical Society awarded one of its Citations for Chemical Breakthroughs Award program to that paper (39), and installed a plaque in the chemistry department at the University of Chicago. Sadly, Birgit Vennesland, who died in 2001, did not live to see this recognition. Frank Westheimer, who advised Fisher on the chemical syntheses of the deuterated substrates as well as the mechanistic interpretation of the hydride transfer, was able to enjoy the latter acknowledgment a few weeks before his death in 2007.

In addition to providing the highly purified alcohol dehydrogenase used in the first experiments, I also provided emotional support for Harvey Fisher during the early morning hours that he was permitted to use the mass spectrometer in the chemistry department, because chemistry department projects involving mass spectrometry had priority. I recall that Vennesland had instructed us to call her with the results from a particular experiment, no matter what the hour. The results that evening clearly showed that when NADH containing one atom of deuterium (i.e., NAD**D**) is reoxidized by alcohol dehydrogenase in the presence of acetaldehyde, all the deuterium is removed from the reduced coenzyme, which shows that the single deuterium atom in NAD**D** is sterospecifically removed. Our phone call to Vennesland occurred at approximately 3 AM that morning!

Birgit Vennesland was especially thoughtful in introducing her graduate students and postdoctoral scholars to the numerous visitors who came to her laboratory during those years. Usually, these introductions occurred at dinners held in her apartment in University housing on the south side of the Midway. In retrospect I realize that I failed to appreciate the fact that Birgit Vennesland had already achieved an international reputation at that time. In later years, I encountered many of those visitors in my own career. For example, it was at Vennesland's house that I first met Paul Stumpf, as well as the Australian plant physiologist Bob (Rutherford Ness) Robertson, who later hosted me and my family in Adelaide when we were on sabbatical in New Zealand and were visiting Australia. I also recall that Vennesland introduced me to Alan Johns, subsequently director of the Department of Scientific and Industrial Research (DSIR) lab in New Zealand, where I spent my sabbatical in Graham Butler's lab in 1965–66. And of course, I met Severo Ochoa and Arthur Kornberg when they came to discuss the role of malic enzyme in intermediary metabolism in plants and animals.

When Alexander Todd, professor of chemistry at Cambridge, visited the department, I probably made an unfavorable impression—I was asked to oversee the projection of his seminar slides and found that they did not fit the department's projector. I do not recall his specific reaction, and whether it was directed toward me, but I had an opportunity to remind him of that event during my first sabbatical in Cambridge. Our landlady, who rented her ground floor apartment to my wife and me, asked us to join her for sherry one evening, during which she wanted to introduce me to a "biochemical friend" of hers. The friend turned out to be Todd, now Lord Todd, after his recognition for his chemical syntheses of natural products.

Another visitor to Vennesland's laboratory was Daniel Arnon, a member of Dennis Hoagland's famous Department of Soils and Plant Nutrition in Berkeley. Arnon was in Chicago while I was making plans to accept James Bonner's invitation to visit his group at the California Institute of Technology (Caltech) at their expense, ostensibly to be considered for a postdoctoral position. Before I left on the California trip, Arnon called from California to tell me about a tenure-track opening for a plant biochemist in the Hoagland department, and he invited me to spend a few days there on my way to Pasadena. In those days, I had the time and interest to travel by train and so I routed myself out through Denver, where my parents were living at that time, on to Berkeley, down the coast to Los Angeles and then back through Salt Lake City and Denver to Chicago. I presented seminars in both Berkeley and Pasadena, but I do not recall the material I presented.

The open position at Berkeley was to replace Professor J. P. Bennett, whose research field was dormancy in plants. Arnon and Perry Stout, chair of the department at that time, made it clear that this was an independent position and that I would have to undergo the usual procedures for promotion from instructor through assistant professorship to tenure. That comment was both attractive and challenging. At Caltech, James Bonner's group consisted of numerous people who went on to make their marks in plant physiology and biochemistry, including Bob Bandurski, Arthur Galston, Adele Millard, and Paul Saltman. Barney Axelrod was also at Caltech on leave from the USDA lab in Albany, California. At that time, Anton Lange, as director of the phytotron at Caltech, enriched the plant biology community on that campus. I spent a week in Pasadena because one of my older brothers was living there at the time and I was able to spend evenings with him and his family.

The week in Pasadena was stimulating and very enjoyable, but James emphasized that Caltech had few permanent positions in plant biology and that most of the people in his group would go on to other institutions after they spent several years with him. By the time I got back to Chicago, I had job offers from both institutions; the pay at Berkeley would be $3600 for 12 months, and the pay at Caltech would be $5000. After advice from Vennesland and some thought on my part, I decided to accept the position at Berkeley. I also had to explain my decision to my father by telephone, who probably had never earned more than the lesser salary during his lifetime. I hope he understood, because two weeks later he died from a massive heart attack. Years later when I met James Bonner at meetings, he would jokingly bring up the subject of Caltech paying for my interview at Berkeley.

THE BERKELEY YEARS

Because I was hired to replace a faculty member who had worked on dormancy, some members of the Department of Soils and Plant Nutrition expected me to start working in that area. I lacked any background in plant physiology, so I knew it was unrealistic for me to develop a research program in that area. I took my concern to Perry Stout, the chair of the department. Stout stressed that I had been hired because of my biochemical expertise, and that I was expected to progress by demonstrating my skills in that area, although any biochemical collaboration that might develop with other members of the department would be welcomed. I was assigned space in a basement laboratory in Hoagland Hall where there was a cold room available, as well as an early version of the table-top Serval centrifuge with its cage. Eventually a paper appeared on oxidative phosphorylation by mitochondria from etiolated white lupine seedlings, followed by others on other biochemical activities of plant mitochondria. Arnon was working on photosynthetic phosphorylation in the department, but Bob Whatley was a postdoctoral scholar in his group at that time and there was little need for my biochemical expertise. Because at least two other groups independently observed photophosphorylation around then, I had the opportunity on more than one occasion to stress that Arnon's group had certainly made a similar observation independently.

In 1953, Stout was offered the directorship of the newly funded Kearny Foundation for Soil Science, and he wanted very much to have Connie Delwiche join him in the new organization. However, Delwiche at that time was located in a new Department of Plant Biochemistry formed by taking Paul Stumpf, H. A. Barker, W. Z. Hassid, and Delwiche out of the Department of Soils and Plant Nutrition and moving them to the Biochemistry and Virus Laboratory on the opposite side of the campus. Now, a chance event occurred that had an enormous influence on my life. That department suggested a transfer of Delwiche into the Kearney Foundation and my transfer to their department, so as to not lose a faculty position. Needless to say, when Paul Stumpf (**Figure 4**) proposed this exchange to me, it took me approximately three seconds to agree to the transfer.

PHOTO CREDIT: UC DAVIS

Figure 4

Paul Karl Stumpf (1919–2007) Paul Stumpf was a distinguished professor of biochemistry at the University of California from 1948 until he became Emeritus in 1988. He founded the field of plant lipid biochemical research and was a mentor to many researchers in the field of oil seed biochemistry. After retirement, he directed the Competitive Grants Program at the U.S. Department of Agriculture from 1988 until 1991 and helped it develop into the National Research Initiative. He was my colleague and good friend for 55 years.

So, starting in the fall of 1954, I found myself a member of the small (four members) but unbelievably rich environment of the Department of Agricultural Biochemistry. Barker and Hassid were very senior scientists—already members of the National Academy of Sciences—and I had presented seminars on their research while still a graduate student at Chicago. Paul had also welcomed me to Berkeley when I first arrived. I was given Delwiche's laboratory and office next door to Paul's lab, and also was assigned to teach a one-semester biochemistry course for nonmajors.

After a few months of settling into this ideal situation, Paul gave me some friendly advice; he was nearer my age and was becoming my closest colleague in the department. Paul was in the process of initiating his lifelong work on lipid metabolism, and found it to be an exhilarating and rewarding experience after his previous work on glycolytic enzymes as a graduate student with David Green. His advice was to "take up a new field and show what you can accomplish."

I was fortunate to have Tsune Kosuge as my first graduate student; he had a master's degree in plant pathology from Washington State University, and wanted to study plant biochemistry to apply that discipline to plant pathology. Tsune came to Berkeley in 1955 hoping to work with Paul Stumpf, but because Paul was going to Bernie Horecker's lab at the National Institutes of Health (NIH) on his first sabbatical leave, Paul graciously suggested that Tsune work with me. Tsune had presented a seminar on the role of coumarin in the formation of dicoumarol in spoiled sweet clover hay, studied by the legendary K. P. Link at the University of Wisconsin, and decided to investigate the enzymes involved in the biosynthesis of coumarin.

Tsune Kosuge's thesis research, and the papers that resulted from it, together with his work carried out after he joined the

Plant Pathology Department at UC Davis, is probably the first example of a multi-step biosynthetic pathway for a plant natural product described at the enzymatic level. Tsune's papers document the evidence that coumarin is formed in sweet clover as follows: phenylalanine → *trans*-cinnamic acid → *ortho*-coumaric acid → *trans-o*-coumaroyl-β-glucoside → *cis-o*-coumaroyl-β-glucoside → *cis-o*-coumaric acid (coumarinic acid) → coumarin. (Reference 13, p. 6)

The first evidence for the existence of phenylalanine ammonia lyase (PAL) occurred in Kosuge's thesis research when he observed the conversion of phenylalanine to *trans*-cinnamic acid in dialyzed extracts of sweet clover. These experiments were eventually discussed with Arthur Neish, a distinguished Canadian plant biochemist who had already created an impressive body of work on the biosynthesis of lignin from phenylalanine and tyrosine. In a review (29), Art proposed that *trans*-cinnamic acid might be formed by transamination of phenylalanine, followed by reduction of the keto acid to phenyllactic acid, and dehydration to form cinnamic acid. The first two reactions would presumably require stoichiometric amounts of keto acids and reducing agents (DPNH or TPNH) to accomplish the overall conversion. Because Tsune's dialyzed extracts catalyzed the formation of readily detectable amounts of cinnamic acid from phenylalanine, we believed there had to be another reaction. We proposed a single enzyme that catalyzes deamination, analogous to bacterial aspartase.

In 1958 I visited Art at the Prairie Regional Lab in Saskatoon. (Reference 13, p. 7) We discussed the possibility of a simple one-step deamination of phenylalanine and I wound up inviting Art to spend his upcoming study leave in Davis. I also met Stewart Brown on that trip and we have been good friends and correspondents since those days. Stew was recently recognized for his many contributions to the lignin and coumarin literature (4). The Neishs arrived in Davis in September 1959, and Art started looking for the deamination of tyrosine (in grasses) and phenylalanine in a wider range of species.

Art brought his supply of labeled compounds as standards, and we provided our new lab facilities for enzyme work, as well as access to Kosuge, who was located in an adjacent department, for moral support. Art started looking for tyrosine ammonia lyase (TAL) in rice and other grasses. Jane Koukol, a postdoctoral scholar from Vennesland's lab, arrived and started working on PAL, initially in sweet clover and then in barley. Eventually their work on TAL (30) and PAL (20) was published in two different journals. We had decided to call these enzymes tyrase and phenylalanase, similar to the enzyme named aspartase. However, the editors at the *Journal of Biological Chemistry* (*JBC*) insisted that Jane and I adhere to the newly agreed-upon nomenclature rules and use the term phenylalanine deaminase for PAL. The term phenylalanine ammonia lyase reflects a later change in the nomenclature of deaminases. (Reference 13, p. 7)

People ask occasionally about my lack of follow-up on the discovery of PAL as the enzyme gained extraordinary prominence in plant secondary metabolism. Because it was Tsune's finding initially, I urged that he continue working with PAL. However, he was keen to wind up his work on coumarin and start looking at problems in plant pathology that might be amenable to solutions using biochemical approaches. He did just that, in such quantity and quality, that he was elected to our National Academy of Sciences in 1988. Tragically, this was shortly before he died prematurely from colon cancer. Later I learned that he was told a few days before his death that both of us were elected that year. As Tsune took leadership on the coumarin problem in Berkeley, my interests turned to the biochemistry of cyanogenic glycosides. (Reference 13, p. 7)

I had read a review of natural products by Geissman & Hinreiner (16) that noted that many natural compounds consist of an aromatic ring and a side chain of three carbon atoms (i.e., C_6-C_3 phenylpropanes), as well as an aromatic ring and a side chain of a single carbon atom (i.e., C_6-C_1 phenylmethanes), but that C_6-C_2 compounds are far fewer in natural occurrence. Because the cyanogenic glycosides are of the latter type, and also have the triple-bonded nitrile group, I thought these substances might show some interesting enzymology; I therefore concentrated my efforts and limited resources on the study of those compounds.

With the help of Takashi Akazawa, a young graduate student from Ikuzo Uritani's laboratory in Japan, we soon showed that sorghum seedlings should be an ideal tissue in which to study the biosynthesis of dhurrin, the β-glucoside of *p*-hydroxy-(*S*)-mandelonitrile, the cyanogen in sorghum (1). Although sorghum seed contains only traces of dhurrin, the 3- to 5-day-old etiolated seedlings contain approximately 5–10% dhurrin on a dry weight basis. Because tyrosine was the obvious precursor, we fed ^{14}C tyrosine to the seedlings overnight and observed a relatively large incorporation (5–10% of the activity fed) into the glycoside. (Reference 13, p. 7)

We reported these results at the Federation Meetings in April 1948, and were surprised, and somewhat chagrined, to hear John Gander from the University of Minnesota describe almost the same experiments in the following presentation. Because John had the next summer free, I invited him out to Berkeley where we worked hard to identify intermediates between the amino acid fed and the cyanogen. With the large amount of incorporation observed, we both thought that it would be a simple matter to find a few spots on paper chromatograms, identify them, and sort out the pathway. That was not the case, and it eventually took another decade to establish the identities of the intermediates. At the end of the summer John returned home and continued to work on the problem for a few months. But, because success was slow and he had other interests, he stopped working on the problem. At this point, I decided on a dual approach, namely (*a*) to determine whether the tyrosine molecule was incorporated into dhurrin intact except for loss of the carboxyl carbon, and (*b*) to postulate possible intermediates, label them with C^{14}, and feed them to seedlings. However, progress was hindered by my move to the Davis campus in the fall of 1958 and a delayed sabbatical in England in 1960. (Reference 13, p. 7)

I had applied for and received a 3-year U.S. Public Health Service (USPHS) grant in 1957 (for $12,000 per year) entitled "Metabolism of Aromatic Compounds in Plants." It was subsequently renewed in 5-year intervals for a total of 29 years; the final year's amount was $120,000, some of which had to accommodate inflation over those three decades. Approximately 15 years into that period, when the NIH decided that it would no longer fund plant research, someone at the NIH deleted the last two words in the grant title. I wanted to complain about that action, but because I had some people on salary in that grant, I took the coward's way out, and accepted the renewal. In 1973 the National Science Foundation (NSF) also started funding our research, usually in 3-year grants. (Reference 13, p. 8)

In the mid 1950s, the Regents of the University of California approved a major expansion of the university system that included conversion of the Davis campus to a general campus. Paul Stumpf was asked to set up a general biochemistry department in Davis, and I was invited to go with him. We were attracted by the prominence of plant sciences at Davis and the fact that the campus was entering a rapid period of growth. So, in September 1958, Paul and I moved to Davis to initiate our teaching program. We left our students in Berkeley, because the new department's facilities would not be ready until the following summer. (Reference 13, p. 8)

THE DAVIS YEARS

These years started with my marriage to Louise Kachel, a friend from my Chicago days, on October 17, 1959, a few months before we departed for my sabbatical in England. I spent my postponed sabbatical leave at the Low Temperature Station in Cambridge, England with Tony Swain; I hoped to learn more about plant phenolics. I did a few experiments on a project of Swain's and we published a brief note indicating that gallic acid can also be formed without phenylalanine as an intermediate (8). I met Tony's supervisor, the fabled E. C. Bate-Smith, as well as Jeff Harborne, Arthur Bell, Leslie Fowden, and Trevor Goodwin, among others, and attended an early meeting of the Phytochemical Society. These contacts resulted eventually in visits by Fowden and Goodwin to Davis, where they taught in our graduate course in plant biochemistry when either Paul Stumpf or myself was absent on sabbatical. Another fortuitous event in Tony's lab was a visit from Alan Johns, a New Zealander I had met in Chicago years earlier. I invited Alan to our flat for dinner and learned that evening that Graham Butler was working on cyanogenesis in flax seedlings in Johns' department in Palmerston North. I immediately initiated correspondence with Graham that resulted in his spending a year's leave in Davis with us in 1961–1962, and I eventually took my next sabbatical in his lab. (Reference 13, p. 8)

Louise and I left England in June 1960 to spend our summer vacation on the continent; we visited friends she had made while working in Paris during the four years immediately preceding our marriage in 1959. In Germany I called on Hans Grisebach in Freiburg; this was the first of numerous visits in later years to that beautiful city. I had met Hans in Berkeley when he was a postdoctoral scholar with Melvin Calvin, gaining experience in the use of radioisotopes in the study of metabolism. Hans often attended seminars in our department and was aware of Kosuge's enzyme studies on coumarin. When Hans returned to Freiburg he suggested that we keep in touch. In 1960 he was still a docent in the Chemistry Institute, but soon had his own institute where he trained an entire generation of plant biochemists. I have often lectured in our graduate plant biochemistry course on the elegant research done in Hans' Institute, and I am sorry that he did not live to see the many current applications of molecular biology to his field. I am also indebted to Hans for advising some of his students to obtain experience with enzymes in our group. The first person to do so was Klaus Hahlbrock, who came to Davis in 1967. (Reference 13, p. 8)

PHOTO CREDIT: UC DAVIS

Figure 5

Eric meeting with a student in his office at UC Davis.

Back in Davis, I was eager to continue with my teaching and research. Although I performed my share of service on university committees, my primary commitment was to the students and postdoctoral scholars in my lab, and the undergraduates in my courses (**Figure 5**). We made progress on the cyanogen problem; Jane Koukol showed that the carbon bond between the α and β carbons in the side chain of tyrosine was not severed during the conversion of the amino acid to the cyanogen. She also showed that the α carbon atom of tyrosine, labeled with ^{14}C, gives rise to labeled HCN, whereas the β carbon remains in the *p*-hydroxybenzaldehyde moiety of the cyanogen (21). Several years later, my graduate student Ernest Uribe, using tyrosines labeled with ^{14}C in the α position and ^{15}N in the amino nitrogen, showed that the bond between those two atoms is not severed during the synthesis of dhurrin (38). This important result meant that all intermediates in the pathway must contain nitrogen. However, we still did not know the nature of the intermediates. A later experiment by Harold Zilg from Freiburg showed that the glucosyl linkage oxygen atom is derived from molecular O_2 (40). This early result implicated a mixed function oxidase in this pathway. (Reference 13, pp. 8–9)

Graham Butler made several important contributions during his study leave in Davis. Because Gander had shown that dhurrin undergoes metabolic turnover in sorghum seedlings, we wondered whether this process involved the release of HCN in the atmosphere. In an off-the-wall experiment, Graham and Shula Blumenthal fed ^{14}C-labeled HCN to sorghum seedlings in a closed system for several hours and then examined plant extracts for any labeled products. To our great surprise, we observed a single, heavily labeled compound, which we quickly identified as asparagine (3). (Reference 13, p. 9) This experiment probably fits the definition of a serendipitous result. We hoped to find the incorporation of radioactivity into the cyanogenic glycoside dhurrin, and instead observed the intense labeling of asparagine.

Later work by Heinz Floss and Lee Hadwiger (15) and by Jackie Miller (26) showed that many, and probably all, plants contain a mitochondrial β-cyanoalanine synthase that catalyzes the replacement of the –SH group of cysteine with –CN to form β-cyanoalanine. Although we understood why cyanogenic species might have this enzyme, we were surprised to find that noncyanogenic species also contained the enzyme, albeit in lower amounts. Shang-fa Yang and his students (31) eventually solved this anomaly; they showed that one molecule of HCN is formed in the last step of ethylene biosynthesis when 1-aminocyclopropyl-1-carboxylic acid (ACC) is oxidized by ACC oxidase. They could not detect HCN in their experiments, but they showed that the ^{14}C-labeled carbon atom bearing the nitrogen atom in ACC is converted to labeled asparagine in roughly stoichiometric amounts (70% yield). (Reference 13, p. 9) Thus, any plant tissue that produces ethylene also produces an equivalent amount of HCN.

While in Davis, Graham demonstrated the remarkable efficiency of rootless shoots of flax seedlings in the conversion of labeled valine to the cyanogenic glucoside linamarin. The shoots could convert 35% of the labeled valine fed in experiments that lasted only seven hours! Intact seedlings converted, at most, 5% under similar conditions. Various experiments were also designed to detect intermediates in the conversion, but no intermediates were found. Experiments with ^{15}N showed that the nitrogen atom in valine is retained when valine is converted to linamarin. Because sorghum shoots are also much more effective in dhurrin biosynthesis than sorghum seedlings, the two experimental systems are relatively equivalent. When I was in Graham's group (1965–1966), we worked exclusively on flax. (Reference 13, p. 9)

Butler's student, Brian Tapper, was the first to show that oximes are intermediates in the biosynthesis of cyanogenic glucosides. A labeled compound with the properties of an oxime glycoside accumulates in flax seedlings fed ^{14}C-valine and O-methylthreonine, a metabolic inhibitor of valine. Brian prepared the oxime of ^{14}C-labeled isobutyraldehyde, administered it to flax shoots, and found that it is converted to linamarin nearly as efficiently as labeled valine; isobutyraldehyde is not converted. Because oximes can be dehydrated to form nitriles, and the latter might be oxygenated to form cyanohydrins, Brian's results suggested this biosynthetic sequence: amino acid → → aldoxime → nitrile → α-hydroxynitrile (i.e., cyanohydrin) → cyanogenic glycoside, all of which contain one nitrogen atom. (Reference 13, p. 9)

When Klaus Hahlbrock arrived in Davis, he prepared the nitriles and cyanohydrins that correspond to possible intermediates in the biosynthesis of linamarin and prunasin, the cyanogen derived from phenylalanine. When fed to appropriate tissues (flax shoots and petioles of cherry laurel leaves, respectively)

Klaus found that the nitriles are incorporated, although not as efficiently as the amino acids. The aliphatic cyanohydrin is readily converted to linamarin, but the aromatic cyanohydrin is toxic to the leaves. In a joint note with Tapper and Butler that described these findings (17), we put the plausible biosynthetic pathway stated above in writing for the first time. (Reference 13, p. 9)

Klaus soon demonstrated the last step in the pathway. He detected a uridine diphosphoglucose (UDPG)-ketone cyanohydrin glucosyltransferase in flax seedlings and purified it 120-fold, free from β-glucosidase activity. The enzyme is equally active on the cyanohydrins of acetone and butanone, forming linamarin and lotaustralin, respectively. In subsequent work, he concluded that the flax enzyme is responsible for formation of both cyanogenic glucosides in flax, a fact confirmed years later using cloned enzyme. Later Peter Reay (33) purified and characterized the glucosyltransferase in sorghum seedlings. (Reference 13, p. 9)

From 1966 on, research in my group centered on several different aspects of cyanogenesis, with two important exceptions. The first exception was work on cinnamic-4-hydroxylase (C4H) by David Russell. In his thesis research with Arthur Galston, David had studied the increase in kaemperferol derivatives mediated by phytochrome in pea seedlings. He proposed the use of microsomes from such tissue to look for C4H, and was quickly successful. In an important but seldom cited paper (34), David reported numerous properties of the enzyme, including its light-reversible inhibition by carbon monoxide (CO) and the feedback inhibition of its activity by the product, *p*-coumaric acid. David concluded that his enzyme had "all the properties of a P-450 type of cytochrome" and that this required studies of the action spectrum for light reversal of the CO inhibition. My graduate student Rowell Potts subsequently measured the spectrum (32). His spectrum, together with action spectra obtained in Charles West's lab in 1969 for two enzymes involved in gibberellin biosynthesis, were the only data of this kind concerning the many P-450s now demonstrated to exist in plants, before their expression in heterologous hosts became relatively common. Although I coauthored an earlier note in *Archives* with David, I insisted that he be the sole author on the *JBC* paper (34), because he had originally proposed the research and had been completely self-sufficient in his work in the lab. (Reference 13, pp. 9–10)

The other study that did not involve cyanogenesis concerned the role of the nonaromatic amino acid, arogenic acid, in the biosynthesis of tyrosine and phenylalanine in sorghum. Roy Jensen's earlier studies (19) showed that tyrosine is formed in mung bean, maize, and tobacco by transamination of prephenic acid to produce arogenic acid (pretyrosine), followed by oxidative aromatization of the six-membered ring to form tyrosine. Because of the large flow of carbon atoms into the cyanogenic glycoside dhurrin in sorghum, as well as the formation of many phenylpropanoid compounds in all plants, it seemed important to learn more about the final steps of phenylalanine and tyrosine biosynthesis in sorghum. Results obtained by Dan Siehl, Jim Connelley, and Bijay Singh established that the final steps of phenylalanine and tyrosine biosynthesis in sorghum clearly utilize the arogenic acid alternative described by Jensen and coworkers.

A major advance in the cyanogen biosynthetic work occurred when Ian McFarlane arrived from Michael Slaytor's lab in Sydney. By that time, aldoximes, nitriles, and α-hydroxynitriles were considered likely intermediates in cyanogen biosynthesis because of the results from feeding experiments. Because at that time numerous studies in animal tissues, and some in plants, had shown that microsomal enzyme systems catalyze C-hydroxylation reactions, I suggested to Ian that he determine if sorghum microsomes could catalyze the oxidation of *p*-hydroxyphenylacetonitrile to *p*-hydroxymandelonitrile in the presence of NADPH and oxygen. He isolated microsomes from etiolated sorghum seedlings in the presence of thiol reagents, and in an early experiment he included tyrosine as a control, not expecting it to be acted upon. Astonishingly, Ian found that tyrosine was oxidized by the particles to form p-hydroxybenzaldehyde and HCN. Moreover, this reaction was more rapid than the hydroxylation of *p*-hydroxyphenylacetonitrile. The sorghum particles also utilized the aldoxime as a substrate about as well as they utilized the amino acid. The properties of this microsomal system were then extensively studied by Ian and Edith Lees (25); Edith was a faculty member on study leave from the University of Sydney (25). (Reference 13, p. 10)

Because the conversion of tyrosine to p-hydroxyphenylacetaldoxime constitutes a four-electron oxidative decarboxylation, it was likely that an intermediate existed in that conversion. Earlier work on glucosinolate biosynthesis in Ted Underhill's group in Saskatoon indicated N-hydroxyamino acids as intermediates between amino acids and aldoximes in the biosynthesis of glucosinolates. The next step was the synthesis of N-hydroxytyrosine (NHT). (Reference 13, p. 10)

Birger Moller arrived from Copenhagen, just as Ian and Edith were finishing up their work, and decided to work on this problem. He perfected a synthesis of NHT that Ian had initiated, and prepared the ^{14}C-labeled compound. He compared the efficacy of NHT as a substrate with five other compounds that, on paper, could be intermediates between tyrosine and its aldoxime. However, only NHT was metabolized to p-hydroxymandelonitrile by the particles. Moreover, labeled NHT was produced from [U-^{14}C]-tyrosine in tracer experiments when unlabeled NHT was added as a trap (27). Birger made another major contribution to the problem while in Davis; he showed that the biosynthetic sequence catalyzed by the microsomes is highly channeled (28). His experiments explain why, in the early work done in both Butler's and our lab, we never readily detected any intermediates. (Reference 13, p. 10)

Helen Stafford (36) was the first to propose metabolic channeling in the synthesis of natural products. Whereas Birger's paper met many of the criteria listed in Helen's review for a channeled system, research from his group in Copenhagen has gone on to show that the three enzymes involved in the biosynthesis form an organized complex or metabolon.

Work continued on cyanogenesis in plants until I retired in 1993, and many excellent students, postdoctoral scholars, and visiting scientists contributed to that effort. Over the years I have discussed their work in different reviews (9–13) and the interested reader can consult those papers. This research would not have been possible without the essential contributions of all the highly talented people whose work is described in those reviews.

I take great pleasure in the fact that Birger Moller has greatly developed the field of cyanogenesis in plants after his appointment to the Chair of Plant Biochemistry in the Royal Veterinary and Agricultural University in Copenhagen in 1985. He proposed returning to the cyanogenesis field at that time, and I strongly encouraged him to do so. Applying the tools of molecular biology to cyanogenesis and related problems, he and his group have greatly advanced our understanding of these compounds. The progress in Moller's group was recently reviewed (2).

CYANOGENESIS IN TWO LARGE PLANT FAMILIES, ACACIAS AND EUCALYPTUS

Starting in 1974, my research interests broadened significantly owing to a collaboration with David Seigler in the Plant Biology Department at the University of Illinois. At the 1972 PSNA meeting, we discussed the older literature that reported that some South African species of acacia contain cyanogens derived from valine and isoleucine, whereas cyanogens in Australian species are derived from phenylalanine. At that time this was the only example of aliphatic and aromatic cyanogens occurring in the same genus.

David, who teaches plant taxonomy at the University of Illinois, educated me on the taxonomic complexity of the genus, and we decided to check out the earlier work. After confirming those studies, I started testing acacias in the UC Davis arboretum for cyanogenesis, as well as testing herbarium specimens of the species. Leaf material of any positive species was then obtained, extracted, and worked up to identify the cyanogen. This project resulted in the identification of several new cyanogenic glycosides (**Figure 6**). (Reference 13, p. 11)

While testing acacias in California gardens, I also started looking at eucalyptus. Because there was only one documented report of cyanogenesis in that large genus—prunasin in *E. cladocalyx*—I reasoned there should be some additional cyanogenic species of *Eucalyptus*. Initially I found two additional cyanogenic species in California, and this finding led to my last sabbatical in Australia in 1981–1982. (Reference 13, p. 11) My family and I had an apartment in Adelaide, where I had space in Brian Coombe's laboratory at the Waite Institute. I had met Brian in 1955 when he was getting his Ph.D. in plant physiology at Davis.

The Waite Institute has over 300 species of eucalyptus in their botanic garden and that kept me occupied for several weeks. We then started visiting botanic gardens in Adelaide, Brisbane, Canberra, Melbourne, Hobart, Sydney, and Perth, where I arranged for permission to test the eucalyptus and acacia species in those gardens for cyanogenesis. Except for the gardens in Canberra and Perth, I was surprised to see that the other gardens usually had more specimens of northern hemispheric plants than Australian plants. However, Canberra's National Botanic Garden is restricted to Australian species and proved especially useful. (Reference 13, p. 11)

While in Perth, I met Bruce Maslin (**Figure 7**), an authority on the 1000-plus Australian species of acacia, approximately half of which are native to Western Australia. Bruce was interested in my project, and I mentioned one species I had decided was

PHOTO CREDIT: UC DAVIS

Figure 6

Eric Conn admiring Acacia blossoms in the Louise and Eric Conn Acacia Grove in the UC Davis Arboretum.

Figure 7

Bruce Maslin works at the Western Australia Herbarium in South Perth. He is an internationally recognized authority on the systematics (taxonomy) of acacias and continues to find and describe new species of the genus *Acacia*, especially in Western Australia. Bruce played a major role in establishing an internet site called the WorldWideWattle.com that contains much information regarding a group of related genera (*Acacia*, *Senegalia*, and *Vachellia*) that are spread around the world. (Wattle is Aussie-speak for acacia.)

cyanogenic after the results of earlier tests in several gardens. Because of his taxonomic knowledge of the genus, he quickly named several related species and produced herbarium specimens, which we tested. During that first afternoon, we identified more cyanogenic species than I had managed to find during several months of work in gardens! Such results from herbarium specimens require that live species be located in the field, tested for cyanogenesis, and if positive, sampled and processed for identification of the cyanogen. Our results led to several collecting trips with Bruce in subsequent years. (Reference 13, p. 11)

PHOTO CREDIT: UC DAVIS

Figure 8

Eric Conn lecturing to the undergraduate course in General Biochemistry at UC Davis. Courtesy of the University of California at Davis.

Papers in *Phytochemistry* (7, 23), *Kingia* (22), and *Western Australian Herbarium Research Notes* (6) present the results of tests on 96% of the described species of the genus *Acacia*. This work showed that cyanogenic species in the pantropical subgenus *Acacia*, found mainly outside Australia, contain only aliphatic cyanogens, whereas cyanogenic species in the two other subgenera, *Phyllodineae* and *Aculeiferum*, contain aromatic cyanogens. These data support traditional taxonomic evidence that the pantropical subgenus formerly known as *Aculeiferum* (species of this group are now called *Senegalia*, *Mariosousa*, or *Acaciella*) is more closely related to the predominantly Australian subgenus *Phyllodineae* (to which the name *Acacia* is now restricted) than to the pantropical subgenus *Acacia*, now called the genus *Vachellia* (Reference 13, p. 11). Maslin discusses the recent changes in classification of acacias in Reference 24.

The work on eucalyptus involved testing approximately 1400 individual plants and herbarium specimens, which represents 348 species, 22 of which were cyanogenic. (*R*)-prunasin, derived from phenylalanine, was identified as the cyanogen in 10 of those species.

TEACHING

Because Paul Stumpf and I had taught the one-semester biochemistry survey course in Berkeley, we designed a more comprehensive but still introductory course and offered it on the Davis campus. Approximately 60 students enrolled in the course in the fall of 1958. The following fall, there were over 100 students. By the end of the 1960s, I was lecturing to classes approaching 400 students (**Figure 8**). The course became a requirement for numerous undergraduate majors at Davis, and also attracted graduate students who needed biochemistry in their research. We were surprised that this course attracted more students on a campus of four or five thousand than a similar course at UC Berkeley, with its enrollment of 20,000. We attributed this interest to the large amount of activity in various biological sciences at Davis, primarily in the College of Agriculture. The increase in course size over the years was the primary reason that allowed us to hire eight or nine additional faculty and eventually offer a well-rounded selection of biochemistry courses.

That course also led to the writing of our introductory textbook, *Outlines of Biochemistry*. The first edition appeared in 1963 and went though five editions before we "laid it down." *Outlines of Biochemistry* was the first brief biochemistry text that emphasized the principles of intermediary metabolism and did not attempt to be encyclopedic. However, as plant biochemists we made sure to include chapters on photosynthesis and nitrogen fixation that were notoriously lacking in texts written for medical schools. When I returned from my sabbatical in England, Paul and I offered a graduate course in plant biochemistry in which approximately 75–100 students enrolled for many years.

I mentioned above my admiration of Dr. Gus, my first chemistry professor at Boulder, and how I resolved to model my teaching style after his. I apparently was successful in doing so, for I received the Davis Academic Senate teaching award in 1972, the second year it was offered. Later, when the campus established the UC Davis Prize for Undergraduate Teaching and Scholarly Research accompanied by $25,000, I was the recipient in the third year it was offered.

Figure 9

Eric and Louise Conn in the garden of their home in Davis.

DISCLOSURE STATEMENT

The author is not aware of any biases that might be perceived as affecting the objectivity of this review.

ACKNOWLEDGMENTS

Little of this research would have been accomplished without the contributions of the graduate students, postdoctoral scholars, and visiting scientists who collaborated with me over the years. I consider myself extremely fortunate to have been able to attract talented individuals who became both valued scientific colleagues and also treasured friends. I also acknowledge grants from the NSF for 16 years and from the USPHS for 29 years. I also wish to acknowledge the support of my dear wife Louise during the 43 years of our marriage (**Figure 9**). She contributed immeasurably by helping the postdoctoral scholars and scientists and their families settle into life in Davis on their arrival, entertaining them in our home on numerous occasions, and especially on Thanksgiving Day. Louise believed Thanksgiving was a typical American holiday and wanted to share the experience with visitors from overseas. My wife was not a scientist, but her social skills were superb. Sadly, Louise died in March 2002, leaving a great void for my two sons and me.

LITERATURE CITED

1. Akazawa T, Miljanich P, Conn EE. 1960. Studies on the cyanogenic glycoside of *Sorghum vulgare*. *Plant Physiol.* 35:535–38
2. Bak S, Paquette SM, Morant M, Morant AV, Saito S, et al. 2006. Cyanogenic glycosides: a case study for evolution and application of cytochromes P450. *Phytochem. Rev.* 5:309–329
3. Blumenthal-Goldschmidt S, Butler GW, Conn EE. 1963. The incorporation of hydrocyanic acid labeled with carbon-14 into asparagine in seedlings. *Nature* 197:718–19
4. Brown SA. 2007. Dr. Stewart A. Brown (PSNA Phytochemistry Pioneer). *Phytochemistry* 68:1826–29
5. Conn EE, Brosi AR, Swartout JA, Cameron AE, Carter RL, et al. 1946. Confirmation of assignment of 2.6 hr Ni to a mass number of 65. *Phys. Rev.* 70:768
6. Conn EE, Maslin BR, Curry S, Conn ME. 1985. Cyanogenesis in Australian species of *Acacia*: survey of herbarium specimens and living plants. *West. Aust. Herb. Res. Notes* 10:1–60
7. Conn EE, Seigler DS, Maslin BR, Dunn JE. 1989. Cyanogenesis in *Acacia* subgenus *Aculeiferum*. *Phytochemistry* 28:817–20
8. Conn EE, Swain T. 1961. Biosynthesis of gallic acid in higher plants. *Chem. Ind.* 592–93
9. Conn EE. 1973. Biosynthesis of cyanogenic glycosides. *Biochem. Soc. Symp.* 38:277–302
10. Conn EE. 1980. Cyanogenic compounds. *Annu. Rev. Plant Physiol.* 31:433–51
11. Conn EE. 1984. Compartmentation of secondary compounds. In *Membranes and compartmentation in the regulation of plant functions*, eds. AM Boudet, G Alibert, G Marigo, PG Lea, pp. 1–26. Oxford: Oxford Univ. Press
12. Conn EE. 1994. Cyanogenesis-a personal perspective. *Acta Hortic.* 375:1–13
13. Conn EE. 2003. Eric Conn—50 years of plant biochemistry. *Phytochem. Soc. N. Am. Newsl.* 43:5–11
14. Fisher HF, Conn EE, Vennesland B, Westheimer FH. 1953. The enzymatic transfer of hydrogen. I. The reaction catalyzed by alcohol dehydrogenase. *J. Biol. Chem.* 202:687–97
15. Floss HG, Hadwiger L, Conn EE. 1965. Enzymatic formation of β-cyanoalanine from cyanide. *Nature* 208:1207–8
16. Geissman TA, Hinreiner E. 1952. Theories of the biogenesis of flavonoid compounds. *Bot. Rev.* 18:77–244
17. Hahlbrock K, Tapper BA, Butler GW, Conn EE. 1968. Conversion of nitriles and α-hydroxynitriles into cyanogenic glucosides in flax seedling and cherry laurel leaves. *Arch. Biochem. Biophys.* 125:1013–16
18. Hannan PJ. 2006. *Serendipity, luck and wisdom in research*. 221 pp., New York: iUniverse, Inc.
19. Jensen RA. 1986. Tyrosine and phenylalanine biosynthesis: relationship between alternative pathways, regulation and subcellular location. *Recent Adv. Phytochem.* 20:57–61
20. Koukal J, Conn EE. 1961. The metabolism of aromatic compounds in higher plants. IV. Purification and properties of the phenylalanine deaminase of *Hordeum vulgare*. *J. Biol. Chem.* 236:2692–98
21. Koukal J, Miljanich P, Conn EE. 1962. The metabolism of aromatic compounds in higher plants. VI. Studies on the biosynthesis of dhurrin, the cyanogenic glycoside of *Sorghum vulgare*. *J. Biol. Chem.* 237:3223–28
22. Maslin BR, Conn EE, Hall N. 1990. Cyanogenesis in Australian leguminosae: herbarium survey of some *Acacia* and *Papilionoideae* species. *Kingia* 1:283–94
23. Maslin BR, Dunn JE, Conn EE. 1988. Cyanogenesis in Australian species of *Acacia*. *Phytochemistry* 27:421–28

24. Maslin BR. 2008. Generic and subgeneric names in *Acacia* following retypification of the genus. *Muelleria*. In press
25. McFarlane IJ, Lees EM, Conn EE. 1975. The in vivo biosynthesis of dhurrin, the cyanogenic glycoside of *Sorghum bicolor*. *J. Biol. Chem.* 250:4708–13
26. Miller JM, Conn EE. 1980. Metabolism of hydrogen cyanide by higher plants. *Plant Physiol.* 65:1199–1202
27. Moller BL, Conn EE. 1979. The biosynthesis of cyanogenic glucosides in higher plants. N-hydroxytyrosine as an intermediate in the biosynthesis of dhurrin by *Sorghum bicolor* (Linn) Moench. *J. Biol. Chem.* 254:8575–83
28. Moller BL, Conn EE. 1980. The biosynthesis of cyanogenic glucosides in higher plants. Channeling of intermediates in dhurrin biosynthesis by a microsomal system from *Sorghum bicolor* (Linn) Moench. *J. Biol. Chem.* 355:3049–56
29. Neish AC. 1960. Biosynthetic pathways of aromatic compounds. *Annu. Rev. Plant Physiol.* 11:55–80
30. Neish AC. 1961. Formation of *m*- and *p*-coumaric acids by enzymatic deamination of the corresponding isomers of tyrosine. *Phytochemistry* 1:1–24
31. Peiser GD, Wang TT, Hoffman NE, Yang SF, Liu HW, et al. 1984. Formation of cyanide from carbon 1 of 1-aminocyclopropane-1-carboxylic acid during its conversion to ethylene. *Proc. Natl. Acad. Sci. USA* 81:3059–63
32. Potts RM, Weklych R, Conn EE. 1974. The 4-hydroxylation of cinnamic acid by *Sorghum* microsomes and the requirement for cytochrome P-450. *J. Biol. Chem.* 249:5019–26
33. Reay PF, Conn EE. 1974. The purification and properties of a UDP-glucose:aldehyde-cyanohydrin β-glucosyl transferase from *Sorghum* seedlings. *J. Biol. Chem.* 249:5826–30
34. Russell DW. 1971. The metabolism of aromatic compounds in higher plants. X. Properties of the cinnamic acid 4-hydroxylase of pea seedlings and some aspects of its metabolic and developmental control. *J. Biol. Chem.* 246:3870–78
35. Simoni RD, Hill RO, Vaughan M. 2004. JBC Classics: a paper in a series reprinted to celebrate the centenary of the JBC in 2005: The stereochemistry and reaction mechanism of dehydrogenases and their coenzymes, DPN and TPN: The work of Birgit Vennesland. *J. Biol.Chem.* 279(3):e3–4
36. Stafford HA. 1974. Possible multi-enzyme complexes regulating the formation of C_6-C_3 phenolic compounds and lignin in higher plants. *Recent Adv. Phytochem.* 8:53–70
37. Sussex I. 1998. Themes in plant development. *Annu. Rev. Plant Physiol. Plant Molec. Biol.* 49:1–10
38. Uribe EG, Conn EE. 1966. The metabolism of aromatic compounds in higher plants. VII. The origin of the nitrile nitrogen atom of dhurrin (β-D-glucopyranosyloxy-L-p hydroxy-mandelonitrile). *J. Biol. Chem.* 241:92–94
39. Wang L. 2007. Landmark achievements. *Chem. Eng. News* 85:35
40. Zilg H, Tapper BA, Conn EE. 1972. The origin of the glucosidic linkage oxygen of the cyanogenic glucosides linamarin and lotaustralin. *J. Biol. Chem.* 247:2384–86

New Insights into Nitric Oxide Signaling in Plants

Angélique Besson-Bard, Alain Pugin, and David Wendehenne

Unité Mixte de Recherche Institut National de la Recherche Agronomique, Centre National de la Recherche Scientifique, Université de Bourgogne, Plante-Microbe-Environnement, 21065 Dijon Cedex, France;
email: besson@dijon.inra.fr, pugin@dijon.inra.fr, wendehen@dijon.inra.fr

Annu. Rev. Plant Biol. 2008. 59:21–39

The *Annual Review of Plant Biology* is online at plant.annualreviews.org

This article's doi:
10.1146/annurev.arplant.59.032607.092830

1543-5008/08/0602-0021$20.00

Key Words

calcium, nitrosylation, protein kinases, tyrosine nitration

Abstract

A decade-long investigation of nitric oxide (NO) functions in plants has led to its characterization as a biological mediator involved in key physiological processes. Despite the wealth of information gathered from the analysis of its functions, until recently little was known about the mechanisms by which NO exerts its effects. In the past few years, part of the gap has been bridged. NO modulates the activity of proteins through nitrosylation and probably tyrosine nitration. Furthermore, NO can act as a Ca^{2+}-mobilizing messenger, and researchers are beginning to unravel the mechanisms underlying the cross talk between NO and Ca^{2+}. Nonetheless, progress in this area of research is hindered by our ignorance of the pathways for NO production in plants. This review summarizes the basic concepts of NO signaling in animals and discusses new insights into NO enzymatic sources and molecular signaling in plants.

Contents

INTRODUCTION

NO: nitric oxide

Nitric oxide synthase (NOS): consists of a C-terminal reductase and an N-terminal oxygenase domain, separated by a calmodulin-binding site

Nitric oxide (NO) is a free radical reactive gas now recognized in animals as a biological mediator that plays important roles in key physiological processes such as neurotransmission, immunological and inflammatory responses, and relaxation of vascular smooth muscle (72). The identification of the enzymes that catalyze NO synthesis as well as the discovery that NO controls the activity of specific proteins through chemical-based processes within subcellular compartments provided remarkable insights into the way NO exerts its signaling action at the molecular level (for reviews see References 33, 44, 79). Over the past decade, considerable progress has been made in understanding the roles of NO in plants. The emerging picture is that NO functions as a ubiquitous signal involved in diverse physiological processes that include germination, root growth, stomatal closing, and adaptive response to biotic and abiotic stresses (for reviews see References 19, 21, 45, 87). Several laboratories discovered that NO is produced not only from nitrite but also from L-arginine (L-Arg), the main substrate for NO synthesis in animals (16, 79). Notwithstanding these discoveries, our understanding of the mechanisms underlying NO synthesis and signaling activities within cells is still rudimentary. Furthermore, because the appreciation of NO functions and sources relied mainly on pharmacological studies and the use of artificially released NO, the importance of NO as a signaling molecule in plants has been a controversial topic.

To provide a comprehensive overview of the mode of action of NO at the molecular level, this review first summarizes the basic concepts of NO signaling in animals. In light of these concepts, we next discuss recent insights into the mechanisms underlying NO synthesis and its effects in plants. From this analysis we anticipate that NO fulfills the criteria for a signaling molecule.

BASIC CONCEPTS OF NITRIC OXIDE SIGNALING IN ANIMALS

NO is generated mainly by nitric oxide synthase (NOS), which catalyzes the NADPH-dependent oxidation of L-Arg to L-citrulline and NO (79). The mechanism of NO-dependent signaling processes remains a longstanding question. Indeed, in contrast to common signaling molecules, NO is a diffusible gas and, on the basis of its chemistry, is unlikely to interact with a single defined receptor. NO and NO-derived species exert their biological actions through the chemical modification of targets; they mostly act through the binding to transition metals of metalloproteins (metal nitrosylation) and the covalent modification of cysteine (Cys; S-nitrosylation) and tyrosine (Tyr; tyrosine nitration) residues (**Figure 1**). These processes are emerging as specific posttranslational protein modifications; more than 100 proteins have been identified as targets for NO in vitro and/or in vivo. The large panel of functions assigned to NO target proteins essentially concerns all main cellular activities, notably signaling (**Table 1**).

One intriguing issue for which we are still very far from full understanding is NO signal specificity. Indeed, as explained above, the molecular system responsible for producing NO signaling events includes many effectors (target proteins) that regulate a truly remarkable variety of cellular processes. How do the effector systems distinguish the relevant signals? Increasing bodies of evidence indicate that, similarly to Ca^{2+} signaling, NO signals have complex temporal and spatial arrangements (44, 76). That is, the specificity of NO signaling might be governed by the compartmentalization and the dynamic (kinetic, intensity) of its production, and the spatial promiscuity with respect to its effectors and its self-regulation. The finding that NO-signaling components are organized into macromolecular modules highlights this concept (38, 44).

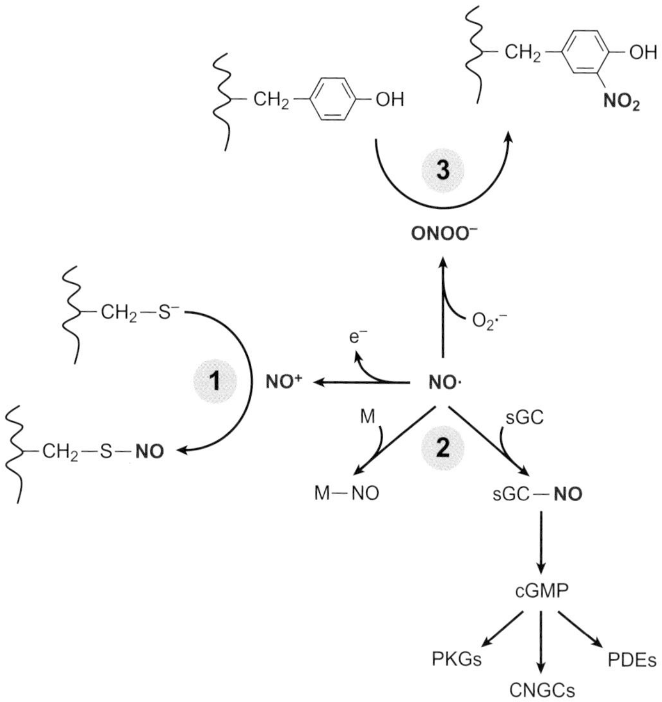

Figure 1

Posttranslational protein modifications by nitric oxide (NO) in animal cells. 1. S-nitrosylation of a Cys residue in a protein leads to the reversible formation of an S-nitrosothiol (e.g., formation of an S-NO bond) and can also promote or inhibit the formation of disulfide bonds within neighboring thiols (38). Mechanistically, S-nitrosylation corresponds to the electrophilic attack of the nitrosonium cation (NO^+, resulting from NO oxidation) on thiolate. Alternative mechanisms have also been proposed (30). 2. The NO radical can donate electrons and therefore reacts with transition metals. Reversible covalent interaction of NO with the centers of iron sulfur clusters, heme, and zinc-finger proteins (M) leads to nitrosylated metalloproteins (M-NO) (33). For instance, the reversible interaction of NO with the heme iron of soluble guanylate cyclase (sGC) increases the catalysis of cyclic GMP (cGMP) synthesis by several hundred-fold. In turn, cGMP mediates NO effects through its binding to cGMP-dependent protein kinases (PKGs), cyclic nucleotide-gated channels (CNGCs), and phosphodiesterases (PDEs) (1). 3. Tyr nitration is mediated by NO-derived species, notably peroxynitrite ($ONOO^-$), formed in the presence of superoxide anions ($O_2\bullet^-$). Nitration occurs in one of the two equivalent carbons (carbon 3) in the aromatic ring of Tyr residues, which results in the formation of 3-nitrotyrosine residues (3-NO_2-Tyr) (33, 73). This process is generally assumed to be irreversible but this subject is controversial (73).

NITRIC OXIDE PRODUCTION IN PLANTS: NO SIMPLE ANSWERS

Currently available data suggest that there are two distinct enzymatic pathways for the generation of NO in plants: a nitrate/nitrite-dependent pathway and an L-Arg-dependent pathway (**Figure 2**). The first pathway involves cytosolic nitrate reductase (NR) (90) and a root-specific plasma membrane nitrite-NO reductase (Ni-NOR) (78). NR catalyzes the in vitro production of NO through a one-electron reduction of nitrite via the use of NAD(P)H as an electron donor (90). In vivo studies highlight that NR might be responsible for the basal level of NO production in the leaves and roots of several plant species (67, 86); this process is controlled by the phosphorylation state of the enzyme (49). A fundamental question arises as to whether NR-derived NO is a signaling compound or a side reaction product of NR activity. A first glimpse into the role of NR as a NO source in transduction processes was provided by the *Arabidopsis thaliana nia1*, *nia2* NR-deficient mutant, in which abscisic acid (ABA) fails to induce NO production and stomatal closure, which indicates that NR-mediated NO synthesis is a major step in ABA signaling in guard cells (10, 21). In addition to NR, Ni-NOR is involved in NO formation from nitrite, but exclusively in roots. Ni-NOR activity is coordinated to that of a plasma membrane-bound NR that reduces nitrate to nitrite (78).

NR: nitrate reductase

Ni-NOR: nitrite-NO reductase

Table 1 Examples of nitric oxide target proteins involved in signaling in animals

Posttranslational modification	Target proteins	Effect on activity
S-nitrosylation	Kinases/phosphatases	
	- tyrosine phosphatase 1B	- inhibition
	- tyrosine kinase Src	- activation
	- Janus kinases	- inhibition
	- apoptosis signaling kinase 1 (ASK1)	- inhibition
	GTPases	
	- $p21^{Ras}$	- activation
	- Dexras	- activation
	Channels/transporters	
	- N-methyl-D-aspartate receptor	- inhibition
	- ryanodine receptors	- activation
	- cyclic nucleotide-gated channels	- activation
	- transient receptor potential channels	- activation
	- L-type Ca^{2+} channels	- activation/inhibition
	- large conductance Ca^{2+}-activated K^{+} channels	- activation
	- Na^{+} channels	- inhibition
	- Ca^{2+}-ATPase	- activation
	Transcription factors	
	- OxyR*	- activation
	- hypoxia-inducible factor	- activation
	- tumor suppressor p53	- activation
	- nuclear factor κB	- inhibition
Metal-nitrosylation	- soluble guanylate cyclase	- activation
	- iron-regulatory proteins (IRP1)	- activation
	- transcription factor SoxR*	- activation
	- nitric oxide synthase	- inhibition
Tyrosine nitration	- tyrosine kinase Src	- activation
	- tyrosine phosphatases	- inhibition

*Reported in bacteria; for references see reviews 1, 14, 33, 38, 44, 73, 76.

Ni-NOR may be involved in several physiological root processes, including development, response to anoxia, and symbiosis (77). The identity of Ni-NOR is currently unknown. Finally, researchers have reported other nitrite-dependent mechanisms for NO synthesis. These include a chemical reduction of nitrite to NO at acidic pH in the apoplasm (9) and a mitochondrial production in which nitrite reduction to NO is driven by electrons from the mitochondrial electron transport chain (64).

Although there is no obvious homolog of animal NOS in the genome of *Arabidopsis* (4), the L-Arg-dependent pathway may involve a plant NOS-like enzyme. Supporting this assumption, NOS-like activities have been detected in several plant tissues and purified organelles, including mitochondria, the nucleus, and peroxisomes (6, 16, 18, 66, 80). Furthermore, mammalian NOS inhibitors could successfully suppress NO synthesis in plants and cell suspensions exposed to hormones (32, 62, 82, 94, 96), pathogens or derived elicitors (20,

27, 43, 47, 60, 85), microsymbionts (7), iron overload (5), and salt stress (95). A search for the enzyme(s) that catalyze(s) these activities in *Arabidopsis* led to the cloning of the *AtNOS1* gene, which encodes a mitochondrial enzyme that shares sequence similarity with a protein involved in NO synthesis in the snail *Helix pomatia* (31, 32). As in the case of its snail counterpart, AtNOS1 is structurally unrelated to classical animal NOSs and the recombinant protein exhibits a NOS activity that is sensitive to mammalian NOS inhibitors. Genetic approaches to elucidate the functions of AtNOS1 have revealed that this enzyme plays a key role in floral transition (36), and is a main NO source in the signaling pathways triggered by ABA (32) and lipopolysaccharides (LPS) (92). Although the AtNOS1-defective mutant *Atnos1* clearly possesses a lower level of NO in particular physiological conditions (e.g., in response to ABA or LPS), the ability of recombinant AtNOS1 to display NOS activity was recently questioned (17, 93). Rather, on the basis of sequence alignment and structural analysis, AtNOS1 may serve as a GTPase involved in mitochondrial ribosome biogenesis and/or translation processes (93). Because mitochondria are an important source of NO (31, 64), such a function might explain why NO synthesis is reduced in the *Atnos1* mutant.

This debate is informative in two respects: First, it highlights the technical limitations of the L-citrulline assay classically used to measure NOS activity. In this assay, protein extracts are incubated in a reaction mixture containing NOS cofactors and radioactive L-Arg. Then, the reaction mixture is loaded on a cation exchange resin, which binds L-Arg but not L-citrulline, the product of NOS activity. In the last step, the radioactivity of the flow-through, which is believed to correspond to radioactive L-citrulline, is counted. The main problem with this method is that other enzymes, distinct from NOS, might use radioactive L-Arg as a substrate. In agreement with this assumption, Tischner and coworkers (81) recently reported that the major product of NOS activity in protein extracts of *Arabidopsis* leaves corresponds to argininosuccinate formed from L-Arg and fumarate by the urea cycle enzyme argininosuccinate lyase. Therefore, interpretations based on the use of the L-citrulline assay should be treated with caution, and a clear demonstration that the radioactive product of the reaction is indeed L-citrulline is definitely required.

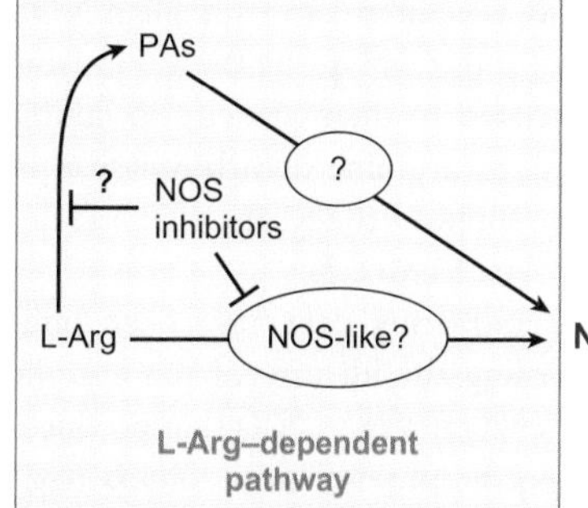

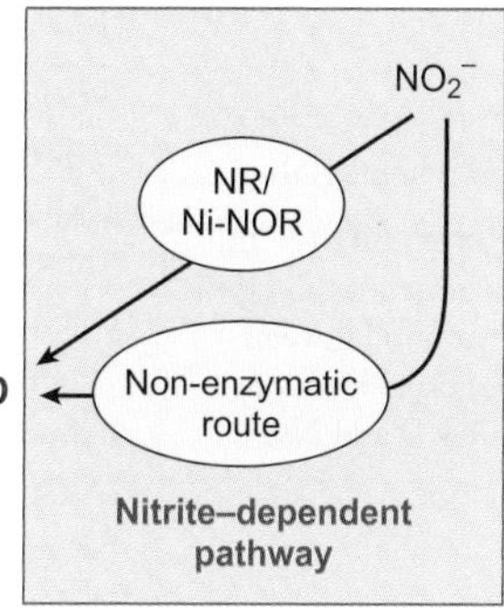

Figure 2

Nitric oxide (NO) synthesis in plants. NO can be produced from nitrite via nonenzymatic or enzymatic pathways, catalyzed by nitrate reductase (NR) or nitrite-NO reductase (Ni-NOR), via a still uncharacterized L-Arg-dependent pathway that involves a nonidentified nitric oxide synthase (NOS)-like enzyme, and via an uncharacterized process that uses polyamines (PAs) as substrates. Mammalian NOS inhibitors (notably competitive inhibitors) might inhibit the NOS-like enzyme as well as the PAs biosynthetic pathway, resulting in decreased NO production.

Second, pharmacological analysis of the occurrence of NOS-like enzymes should be carried out in light of the predictable limited specificity of mammalian NOS inhibitors in plant cells. Here again we should keep in mind that L-Arg derivatives used as NOS inhibitors might affect the activity of other L-Arg-metabolizing enzymes, notably argininosuccinate lyase, but also arginase and/or arginine decarboxylase, the first enzymes of the polyamine (PA) biosynthetic pathway. In this respect, the finding that the PAs spermine and spermidine induce a very fast NO synthesis in various tissues within *Arabidopsis* seedlings is particularly relevant (83). Indeed, as recently discussed by Yamasaki & Cohen (89), this finding suggests the presence of an unknown enzyme that is responsible for the direct conversion of PAs to NO. In

PA: polyamine

Hb: hemoglobin

Peroxynitrite: the product of the rapid reaction between superoxide anions ($O_2\bullet^-$) and NO

this scenario, the ability of mammalian NOS inhibitors to suppress NO synthesis in plants might be related to their capacity to inhibit arginase and/or arginine decarboxylase and, indirectly, to suppress the synthesis of NO derived from PAs (**Figure 2**).

Finally, conflicting data have been published regarding the identity of the enzyme (NOS-like enzyme versus NR) that produces NO in a specific physiological context (e.g., References 47 versus 65, 10 versus 32 or 94). Some of the problems may reflect not only the limited specificity of NOS inhibitors but also the content and availability of L-Arg. Specifically, analysis of the amino acid contents in the leaves of the *Arabidopsis nia1, nia2* NR-deficient mutant grown in the presence of ammonium revealed a tenfold reduced level of L-Arg (58). This observation suggests that NR- or nitrate-deficient plants lack sufficient endogenous substrate to produce NO not only from the nitrate/nitrite-dependent pathway but also from the L-Arg-dependent pathway. Therefore, the general idea that the reduced NO production in those plants reflects the involvement of NR as the main NO source probably needs to be reexamined in light of L-Arg metabolism.

NITRIC OXIDE SIGNALING IN PLANTS

Metal Nitrosylation

It is becoming increasingly clear that NO forms complexes with plant metal-containing proteins. Most work has focused on elucidation of the reactions between NO and hemoglobin (Hb). There are three main types of Hb in plants: symbiotic Hb called leghemoglobin (Lb), which is found in the nitrogen-fixing root nodules of leguminous plants; nonsymbiotic Hb, which consists of two classes of Hbs (class-1 and -2 exhibit a high and a low affinity for oxygen, respectively); and truncated Hb (23). Lb functions to facilitate O_2 transport to the bacteroids via the reversible formation of oxyLb ($HbFe^{II}O_2$) (55). Pioneer studies report the occurrence of an NO nitrosyl-Lb complex ($LbFe^{II}NO$) in intact root nodules or extracts of root nodules from soybean, cowpea, and alfalfa, which suggests that ferrous Lb may interact with the NO formed in functional nodules (55). More recently, Herold & Puppo (37) showed that other Lb forms that are produced in vivo, including oxyLb and ferrylLb ($LbFe^{IV}$), are able to scavenge NO and/or peroxynitrite ($ONOO^-$; See **Figure 1**) in vitro (37), which leads to the formation of nitrate and metLb ($LbFe^{III}$), which could be regenerated to oxyLb. These reactions may exert a protective role in functional nodules and contribute to the recycling of oxyLb (37, 71). The interaction of NO with Hb is not restricted to Lb. In particular, in vitro studies indicate that class-1 Hb from distinct plant species catalyzes the NAD(P)H-dependent conversion of NO to nitrate (63, 74). This scavenging mechanism resembles those described for oxyLb: Class-1 oxyHb converts NO to nitrate, which turns into class-1 metHb, which is subsequently recycled into class-1 oxyHb (40). Interestingly, Perazzolli and coworkers (63) verified that *Arabidopsis* class-1 Hb is also regulated through S-nitrosylation. Recent mutagenesis experiments indicate that this regulation might not be critical for NO scavenging (40). The use of both defective and overexpressing class-1 Hb mutants supports the hypothesis that the functional interaction between NO and class-1 Hb reduces intracellular levels of NO under several physiological conditions, including hypoxia (22, 23, 63) and pathogen attack (74). Accordingly, overexpression of class-1 Hb in transgenic plants results in enhanced tolerance to hypoxic stress and reduced necrotic symptoms in response to avirulent pathogens (e.g., tobacco necrosis virus and *Pseudomonas syringae* pv. *phaseolicola*). Therefore, the main function of class-1 Hb may be to contribute to stress adaptation by protecting plants against deleterious nitrosative stress.

Besides Hb, lipoxygenase, cytosolic and mitochondrial aconitases, catalase, ascorbate peroxidase, and cytochrome c oxidase (COX) are putative targets of NO, regulated via metal nitrosylation in biological systems; the resulting interaction leads to a loss of activity (13, 43, 57, 61). The finding that NO may inhibit the activity of COX is particularly relevant. COX is the terminal electron acceptor of mitochondrial electron transport chains. Via its binding to COX, NO promotes a decline of the proton motive force together with an inhibition of ATP synthesis in purified plant mitochondria (91). In carrot cell suspensions, these modifications are associated with a release of cytochrome c from mitochondria, a hallmark of apoptosis (97). To counteract these deleterious effects of NO, NO-induced inhibition of COX may redirect the electron flow to the alternative pathway to avoid the generation of active oxygen species (39, 57, 91). Here again, a parallel with the situation encountered in animals is informative. Indeed, in animals, NO inhibits COX activity through binding to the heme a_3/Cu_B binuclear center, one of the three redox-active metal sites of the enzyme (see Reference 15 for details). Interestingly, by acting as an intracellular scavenger of NO, myoglobin may prevent COX from the negative effects of NO and the resulting inhibition of respiration in the heart and skeletal muscles (11). Whether plant Hb plays a similar function has not been unraveled yet.

Finally, in animals NO can initiate its biological effects through the activation of soluble guanylate cyclase (sGC) (**Figure 1**; **Table 1**). The interaction of NO with the heme ferrous iron of sGC triggers a conformational change that increases the catalysis of the second messenger cyclic GMP (cGMP), resulting in cell-specific downstream outputs (**Figure 1**). Support for the hypothesis that NO promotes the activation of a plant sGC came through biochemical and pharmacological approaches that showed the ability of NO to induce cGMP synthesis in plant tissues and cell suspensions (see References 19, 21, 45, 87 for reviews). However, an NO-sensitive sGC remains unidentified.

S-Nitrosylation

Although thousands of articles have revealed physiological roles for NO in plants, there has been a delay in appreciating the involvement of S-nitrosylation as a putative post-translational protein modification. This lag was related to the technical limitation in characterizing this modification. Recently, a methodological advance successfully applied in mammalian cells (30) provided a new tool for identifying S-nitrosylated plant proteins. This method, named the Biotin Switch method, involves the substitution of a biotin group at every Cys residue that has been modified by S-nitrosylation in vivo (41). The biotinylated proteins may then be concentrated by affinity chromatography with immobilized streptavidin or neutravidin, and identified by mass spectrometry–based fingerprint analysis. Via the use of the Biotin Switch method, Lindermayr and colleagues (53) reported the first identification of S-nitrosylated proteins in *Arabidopsis* leaf and cell suspension protein extracts treated with artificially released NO. These proteins are involved in a wide array of cellular activities, including metabolism, photosynthesis, redox control, and stress response. Many are known to be S-nitrosylated in vitro and/or in vivo in mammals (76). This group includes the glycolytic enzyme glyceraldehyde 3-phosphate dehydrogenase (GAPDH), whose activity is inhibited by S-nitrosylation in both plants and animals (53, 76). Remarkably, in mammals, once GAPDH is S-nitrosylated it interacts with the E3 ubiquitin ligase Siah1, leading to the translocation of Siah1 into the nucleus. Once it is anchored in the nucleus by S-nitrosylated GAPDH, Siah1 promotes cell death through the ubiquitin-mediated degradation of nuclear target proteins (35). Hancock and colleagues (34) recently discussed whether GAPDH is also a multifunctional protein in plants, particularly involved in the mediation of oxidative and nitrosative signaling. These authors show that similarly to NO, H_2O_2 interacts with and inhibits

cGMP: cyclic GMP

Nitrosoglutathione (GSNO): the most abundant S-nitrosothiol in animals, formed following the interaction of GSH with NO

S-nitrosothiols: endogenous metabolites of NO, usually formed following the interaction of NO^+ with low molecular thiols or Cys residues

GAPDH in *Arabidopsis*. The interaction with H_2O_2, but also NO, is proposed to cause structural changes that allow GAPDH to participate in protein-protein interactions. Identifying proteins that interact with GAPDH in response to H_2O_2 and NO might open interesting roads of research.

The Biotin Switch approach used by Lindermayr and coworkers (53) has also enabled the identification of methionine adenosyltransferase (MAT). MAT is a ubiquitous enzyme that catalyzes the synthesis of S-adenosylmethionine (AdoMet) from methionine and ATP. AdoMet yields its methyl group in a large variety of reactions catalyzed by methyltransferase, and represents a key precursor for the biosynthesis of PAs, glutathione (GSH), and ethylene (52, 56). In vitro S-nitrosylation of recombinant MAT1, MAT2, and MAT3, three *Arabidopsis* isoforms of MAT, resulted in a 30% inhibition of MAT1 activity, whereas MAT2 and MAT3 activities were poorly affected (52). Site-directed mutagenesis and mass spectrometry analysis point to Cys-114, located near the putative substrate binding site of MAT1, as the target site for S-nitrosylation. This Cys residue is absent in MAT2 and MAT3. This finding might provide a molecular explanation for the ability of NO to downregulate ethylene synthesis and subsequent effects such as senescence (51). Thus, MAT1 S-nitrosylation might represent a key mechanism by which plants modulate the cross talk between NO- and ethylene-dependent signals.

New insights into the impact of S-nitrosylation on plant protein activity were recently provided by the analysis of the interaction between NO and the *Arabidopsis* metacaspase 9 (AtMC9) (8). AtMC9 is constitutively S-nitrosylated in vivo, predominantly at the catalytic Cys-147 residue. The S-nitrosylation of Cys-147 maintains AtMC9 in its inactive, unprocessed, zymogenic form. Unexpectedly, AtMC9 is not prone to NO inhibition in its processed, mature form. On the basis of a predicted three-dimensional structure of AtMC9, researchers proposed a hypothetical mechanism explaining this lack of NO inhibition: Once AtMC9 is processed by an upstream activator protease, conformational changes might position a second Cys residue, Cys-29, within the catalytic groove of the enzyme. Consequently, Cys-29, which is insensitive to S-nitrosylation, could substitute for Cys-147 as a nucleophile for catalyzing the proteolytic reaction. Cys-29 is most probably not nitrosylated owing to the absence of surrounding acidic/basic motifs, an environment suspected to facilitate S-nitrosylation (30, 38). This elegant study is highly informative. First, it demonstrates that constitutively produced NO influences the activity of certain proteins. Second, it shows that some Cys residues are more susceptible to NO-mediated modification than others and that protein structural context plays a crucial role.

Importantly, if S-nitrosylation is indeed a physiologically relevant transduction mechanism in plants, it should be reversible. De-S-nitrosylation might occur in reducing environments and might be mediated by GSH, with the subsequent formation of nitrosoglutathione (GSNO), an endogenous NO reservoir and donor (41). Accordingly, evidence now exists for the presence of a GSNO-reductase (GSNOR), conserved between bacteria, animals, and plants (54, 70). GSNOR catalyzes the oxidation of GSNO to glutathione disulfide (GSSG) and ammonia (54). Through this activity, GSNOR plays a crucial role in switching off S-nitrosothiol-mediated effects in plants that are challenged by pathogens (25, 68). Although preliminary, these findings add further impetus to the idea that S-nitrosylation is an important posttranslational reversible mechanism in plants.

Tyrosine Nitration

In animals, Tyr nitration is classically associated with loss of protein functions and is a relevant biomarker of NO-dependent oxidative stress (33). However, recent studies also highlight a role for this posttranslational modification in signaling (33, 73). Tyr nitration rivals Tyr phosphorylation during protein kinase–mediated cell signaling, resulting in the inhibition of Tyr phosphorylation by protein kinases (73) (**Table 1**). In plants, reactions of $ONOO^-$ (**Figure 1**) with Tyr residues in target proteins have drawn the least attention to date as a mechanism of NO signaling. This is partly explained by the extreme reactivity of $ONOO^-$ in biological contexts, which precluded its isolation and detection. Notwithstanding this technical barrier, several groups pointed to the involvement of protein Tyr nitration in plants. Via the use of antibodies raised against 3-NO_2-Tyr residues, Morot-Gaudry-Talarmain and coworkers (59) have demonstrated increased protein Tyr nitration in an antisense nitrite reductase tobacco line that displays a 100-fold higher NR-mediated NO emission rate compared with the wild-type. A similar immunological-based strategy detected protein Tyr nitration in olive leaves exposed to salt stress (84) and in tobacco cells treated with INF1, an elicitor secreted by *Phytophthora infestans* that promotes defense responses (69). All these proteins remain unidentified so far. Interestingly, Saito and coworkers (69) tried to overcome the problem of $ONOO^-$ detection via the use of aminophenyl fluorescein, an $ONOO^-$-sensitive fluorophore, thus allowing its detection and imaging in living cells. Although the use of aminophenyl fluorescein looks promising, it also reacts with active oxygen species or hydroxyl radical (69), which highlights a risk of data misinterpretation.

Interplays Between Nitric Oxide and Ca^{2+}

In animals, NO is one of the key messengers that govern the overall control of Ca^{2+} homeostasis; almost all types of Ca^{2+} channels and transporters are under NO control. NO modulates their activities directly by S-nitrosylation, or indirectly through the second messengers cGMP and/or cyclic ADP ribose (cADPR) (1, 14, 38, 76, 88) (**Table1**). cADPR is a Ca^{2+}-mobilizing second messenger that promotes Ca^{2+} release from intracellular Ca^{2+} stores in a wide variety of animal and plant cells via activation of the Ca^{2+}-permeable channel ryanodine receptors (RYRs) (3, 26).

Cyclic ADP ribose (cADPR): in animals, produced through cyclization of NAD^+ by ADP-ribosyl cyclase

Ryanodine receptors: three isoforms in animals; homotetramer Ca^{2+}-permeable channels localized in the membrane of the endoplasmic reticulum

Early work in plants emphasized the involvement of cADPR in the mediation of NO action on defense gene expression. More precisely, 8-bromo-cADPR, a selective antagonist of cADPR, delays and reduces the accumulation of Pathogenesis-Related (*PR*)-1 transcripts induced by artificially generated NO in tobacco leaves (43). Accordingly, cADPR also triggers the expression of *PR-1*; RYR inhibitors suppress this process (24). These findings paved the way for research into the functional coupling between NO and the second messenger Ca^{2+}. Exposure of *Vicia faba* guard cells or *Nicotiana plumbaginifolia* cell suspensions to NO donors activates a fast and transient rise in cytosolic Ca^{2+} concentrations ($[Ca^{2+}]_{cyt}$) and/or an influx of Ca^{2+} from the extracellular space (28, 47). Pharmacological-based experiments suggested that the NO-induced $[Ca^{2+}]_{cyt}$ changes result from the activation of plasma membrane and/or intracellular Ca^{2+}-permeable channels, depending on the biological model (28, 46, 47). Interestingly, the pharmacology of NO-mediated $[Ca^{2+}]_{cyt}$ increases resembles the pharmacology described in animals. Notably, these experiments commonly designated RYR-like channels as a main target of NO action and cADPR as a key intracellular messenger that mediates NO signals, in agreement with animal studies (1, 14, 88). Importantly, parallel investigation revealed that NO released by the NO donor diethylamine NONOate (DEA/NO) failed to trigger any changes in nuclear free Ca^{2+} concentration in *Nicotiana plumbaginifolia* cells that express the Ca^{2+} reporter apo-aequorin in the nucleus (50). Although preliminary, this finding suggests that the effects of NO on Ca^{2+} homeostasis might be restricted to specific cellular compartments.

CNGC: cyclic nucleotide-gated channel

Exactly how NO contributes to $[Ca^{2+}]_{cyt}$ increases is a subject of recent studies. These studies show that protein kinase inhibitors efficiently suppress the NO-evoked elevation of $[Ca^{2+}]_{cyt}$ in *Vicia faba* guard cells and *Nicotiana plumbaginifolia* cells (46, 75). Therefore, besides or together with cADPR, the signaling cascades that relay NO signals to Ca^{2+}-permeable channels involve protein kinases. Via the use of in-gel kinase assay-based strategies, Lamotte and coworkers (46) tentatively characterized these protein kinases. These authors demonstrated that the rise in $[Ca^{2+}]_{cyt}$ induced by the NO donor DEA/NO in *Nicotiana plumbaginifolia* is preceded by the transient activation of a 42-kDa protein kinase that they identified as NtOSAK (*Nicotiana tabacum* osmotic stress-activated protein kinase). NtOSAK is a Ser/Thr protein kinase that belongs to the SNF1 (sucrose nonfermenting 1)-related protein kinase 2 (SnRK2) family (42). A detailed biochemical characterization of NtOSAK indicated that its activity is Ca^{2+}-independent, is regulated by reversible phosphorylation, and exhibits similar substrate specificity to the yeast SNF1 kinase and the animal AMP-activated protein kinase (12, 42). Similarly to other SnRK2 members, NtOSAK is activated within minutes in response to hyperosmotic stress (42), a treatment that also leads to rapid NO synthesis (29). In agreement with these observations, a predominant role for NO as a mediator of NtOSAK activation was revealed in *Nicotiana plumbaginifolia* cells exposed to hyperosmotic stress (46). So far, there are no data to support the hypothesis that NtOSAK or other SnRK2s are linked to Ca^{2+} mobilization, thus the question remains unanswered.

Evidence for the role of NO as a Ca^{2+}-mobilizing compound in physiological contexts came from the demonstration that in *Nicotiana plumbaginifolia* and grapevine cells, NO scavengers as well as mammalian NOS inhibitors reduced the increase in $[Ca^{2+}]_{cyt}$ triggered by hyperosmotic stress and elicitors of defense responses (29, 46, 47, 85). Interestingly, these studies also revealed that elicitor-induced NO production is stimulated by an upstream influx of extracellular Ca^{2+} (47, 85). In support of this finding, recent work identified CNGC2, a plasma membrane *Arabidopsis* cyclic nucleotide–gated channel (CNGC) member, as a key Ca^{2+}-permeable channel that links elicitor-induced Ca^{2+} influx to downstream NOS-like mediated NO production (2). Indeed, LPS-evoked inward Ca^{2+} current and NO generation in *Arabidopsis* guard cells are abrogated in the *dnd1* (defense no death1) mutant, which is impaired in functional CNGC2. Pharmacological data also pointed to a role for calmodulin or calmodulin-like proteins in the transduction of the LPS-induced Ca^{2+} signal into NOS-like activation. Expanding the complexity of the interplay between NO and Ca^{2+}, dissection of the signaling cascade mediated by the elicitor endopolygalacturonase 1 in grapevine cells led to the proposal that NO might downregulate its own Ca^{2+}-dependent synthesis by inhibition of the elicitor-induced influx of extracellular Ca^{2+} (85). This negative feedback mechanism, which resembles those mechanisms described in several NO-based transduction processes in animals (38, 44), could serve to protect the cells from the deleterious effects of not only excessive NO, but also excessive Ca^{2+}.

The evidence summarized above documents the complexity of the interaction between NO and Ca^{2+}, a remarkable example of cross talk between two signaling compounds (**Figure 3**). Clearly, a substantial effort is still required to understand the mechanisms by which NO modulates Ca^{2+} fluxes. Mechanistically, this may involve not only cGMP, cADPR, and protein kinases as described (28), but also S-nitrosylation of the target channels. Another unresolved issue concerns the impact of the NO/Ca^{2+} interplay on the cell response. According to several studies, by increasing $[Ca^{2+}]_{cyt}$, NO might favor the direct or indirect free Ca^{2+} modulation of signaling proteins. These signaling proteins include Ca^{2+}-dependent protein kinases (CDPKs) (48), mitogen-activated protein

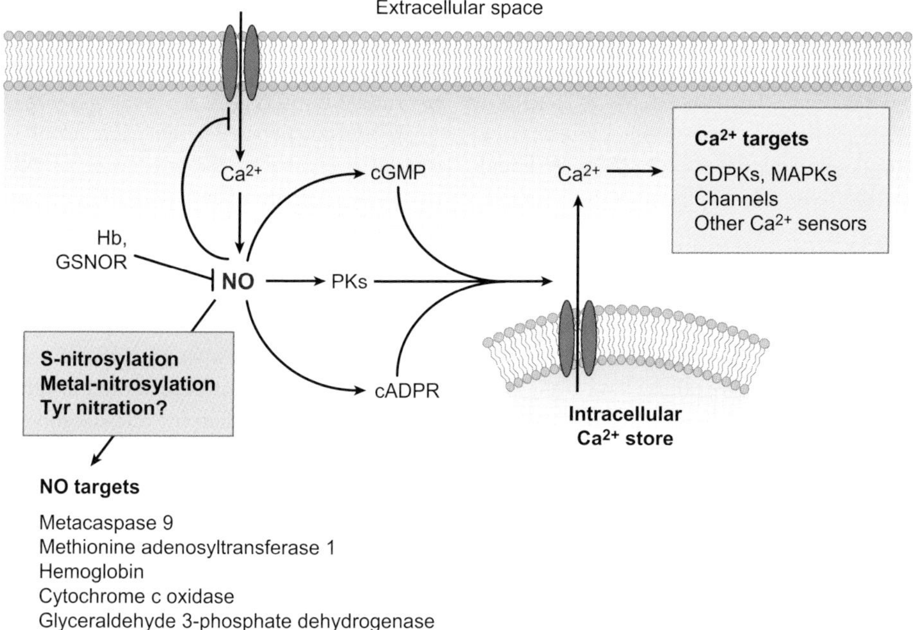

Figure 3

Schematic representation of nitric oxide (NO) signaling in plant cells. NO conveys its effects through various processes. First, NO modulates the activity of target proteins through S- and/or metal-nitrosylation. Well-characterized substrates for these posttranslational modifications include metacaspase 9, methionine adenosyltransferase 1, hemoglobin (Hb), cytochrome c oxidase, and glyceraldehyde 3-phosphate dehydrogenase. Tyr nitration of proteins is proposed but not fully demonstrated. Second, NO induces rises in cytosolic Ca^{2+} concentrations ($[Ca^{2+}]_{cyt}$) by activating intracellular Ca^{2+}-permeable channels that are pharmacologically related to ryanodine receptors. The regulation of other Ca^{2+}-permeable channels, including plasma membrane Ca^{2+}-permeable channels, is not excluded. This process involves cyclic ADP ribose (cADPR), cyclic GMP (cGMP), protein kinases (PKs), and most probably nitrosylation-based mechanisms. The contribution of the SnRK2 protein kinase NtOSAK to NO-induced rises in $[Ca^{2+}]_{cyt}$ has been suggested, but not demonstrated (see text for details). Elevated $[Ca^{2+}]_{cyt}$ modulates the activity of Ca^{2+}-dependent protein kinases (CDPKs), mitogen-activated protein kinases (MAPKs), and Ca^{2+}-sensitive channels, including Cl^- channels and inward-rectifying K^+ channels as reported in guard cells. The negative feedback pathways that switch off NO signals include NO scavenging by Hb, nitrosoglutathione (GSNO) reductase (GSNOR), and attenuation of the Ca^{2+} influx that stimulates NO synthesis, for instance through the inhibition of the cyclic nucleotide-gated channel 2 (CNGC2).

kinases (MAPKs) (C. Courtois, A. Besson-Bard, D. Wendehenne, unpublished observations), and Ca^{2+}-sensitive channels, including Cl^- channels and inward-rectifying K^+ channels as reported in guard cells (28). Clearly, this process enriches the possibilities for NO to trigger its diverse number of responses, such as defense gene expression (43), stomatal closure (21, 28), and adventitious root formation (45).

PERSPECTIVES

The field of NO signaling in plants is at an early but exciting stage. Rapid progress in our knowledge of NO-interacting proteins and second messengers has begun to provide a basis for understanding the molecular mechanisms underlying NO effects (**Figure 3**). Strictly, these mechanisms appear to be conserved with respect to those described in animals: Some of the actions of NO (and probably derived species) appear to be a consequence of posttranslational protein modifications. Furthermore, Ca^{2+} and protein kinases are increasingly recognized as prevalent mediators of NO effects. Although the identification of direct or indirect NO targets is presently a vibrant area of research in NO signaling, several basic questions remain unanswered.

A decade has passed since the first assumption that plants do possess a NOS-like enzyme (18). Although many efforts have been made to discover this enzyme, it remains unidentified. Clearly, this limitation continues to severely hinder rapid progress in our understanding of NO physiological functions in plants. Therefore, identification of this enzyme, or proof that the L-Arg–dependent pathway for NO production is molecularly distinct from the pathways in animals, is the top priority. Another related problem concerns the importance of PAs as a source of NO: Is it a minor or a major pathway for NO synthesis?

Numerous protein candidates for nitrosylation have been identified in vitro and, for a few, the interaction with NO has been finely investigated. These data demonstrate a direct relationship between protein nitrosylation and functional changes. The important challenge that remains is to demonstrate convincingly that protein nitrosylation is a specific and prevalent signaling mechanism occurring in vivo, and not simply a pathway for protein damage. This challenge also applies to protein Tyr nitration.

An all-encompassing question revolves around the issue of the specificity of NO signaling in plants. Several preliminary responses to this question exist. First, NO production is compartmentally localized. For instance, in epidermal tobacco cells challenged by the elicitor cryptogein, NO is first produced within minutes in the plastids and then diffuses to and/or is produced in other compartments, including the nucleus and the cytosol (27). Second, NO functions with second messengers, particularly Ca^{2+}, which operate over temporal and spatial ranges. Third, the dynamics of NO synthesis vary depending on the physiological context. On the basis of these observations, we might assume that NO signaling has temporal and spatial arrangements that determine the specificity of the biological outcome. Establishing this concept will notably require the identification of proteins that interact with NO-generating enzymes as well as NO target proteins, and the analysis of the dynamics of formation and localization of the resulting complexes under physiological conditions.

We are thus at a turning point and answers to these questions should shed new light on the still enigmatic molecular processes underlying NO effects in plants.

SUMMARY POINTS

1. In animals, nitric oxide (NO) serves as a signaling molecule in a wide array of physiological processes. NO is synthesized from L-Arg by nitric oxide synthase (NOS). Biological actions of NO arise as a direct consequence of chemical reactions between NO (and derived species) and transition metals (metal nitrosylation), Cys residues of target proteins (S-nitrosylation), and Tyr residues of target proteins (Tyr nitration).
2. In plants, NO functions as an endogenous mediator in diverse physiological processes. However, as more data accumulate, it becomes evident that our understanding of the mechanisms underlying NO production and its effects in vivo is still rudimentary.

3. NO is produced from nitrite via nonenzymatic and enzymatic routes. The enzymatic process is catalyzed mainly by nitrate reductase. Two other enzymatic pathways that use L-Arg or polyamines as substrates have been reported. The corresponding enzymes remain unidentified and the hypothesis that plants do possess a NOS-like enzyme is highly controversial.
4. Metal nitrosylation as well as S-nitrosylation have been implied in the control of the activity of several plant proteins in vitro and of a few in vivo. These proteins include metacaspase 9, methionine adenosyltransferase 1, cytochrome c oxidase, glyceraldehyde-3-phosphate dehydrogenase, and hemoglobin. The significance of protein Tyr nitration is poorly understood.
5. The formation of a nitrosyl complex between NO and oxyleghemoglobin or class-1 oxyhemoglobin yields nitrate, thereby quenching free NO. This mechanism protects plant cells from the noxious effect of NO. NO signals could also be switched off through the activity of nitrosoglutathione (GSNO) reductase, a key enzyme involved in NO detoxification in animals and bacteria.
6. Endogenous or artificially released NO functions as a Ca^{2+}-mobilizing messenger by promoting rises in cytosolic Ca^{2+} concentrations. NO operates through complex processes that involve cyclic ADP ribose, cyclic GMP, and protein kinases. A candidate protein kinase putatively involved in that process is *Nicotiana tabacum* osmotic stress-activated protein kinase (NtOSAK), a member of the sucrose nonfermenting 1 (SNF1)-related protein kinase 2 (SnRK2) family.
7. By increasing cytosolic Ca^{2+} concentration, NO modulates the activity of protein kinases and Ca^{2+}-sensitive channels, which might be involved in the signaling cascade that leads to defense gene expression, stomatal closure, and adventitious root formation.
8. NO production induced by elicitors of defense responses, especially lipopolysaccharides, is regulated by an upstream Ca^{2+} influx mediated by the cyclic nucleotide-gated channel CNGC2 in *Arabidopsis*.

FUTURE ISSUES

1. Molecular-level elucidation of the pathways by which NO is synthesized from L-Arg and polyamines is required. This will also require the identification of the enzymes targeted by mammalian nitric oxide synthase inhibitors.
2. Novel proteins nitrosylated in vivo need to be identified. The molecular basis by which nitrosylation modulates their activity as well as the physiological relevance of these posttranslational modifications need to be elucidated in detail.
3. The identification of proteins undergoing Tyr nitration in vivo and subsequent structure and function-based analyses are required to investigate the significance of this posttranslational protein modification in plants.

4. We need to identify the molecular components of the NO-dependent pathways that lead to changes in cytosolic Ca^{2+} concentrations and to understand how these pathways guide cells toward a specific response.
5. A crucial future challenge is to understand the specificity of NO signals.

DISCLOSURE STATEMENT

The authors are not aware of any biases that might be perceived as affecting the objectivity of this review.

ACKNOWLEDGMENTS

We apologize to all our colleagues whose work could not be discussed owing to space limitations. We thank Annie Buchwalter for helpful discussions. Work in our lab is supported by grants from the Ministère de l'Education Nationale, de la Recherche et de la Technologie, the Agence Nationale de la Recherche (BLAN07-2-18,4783), the Conseil Régional de Bourgogne (HCP 189), and the Taste, Nutrition, and Health Innovation Pole (VITAGORA).

5. Highlights a major role for NO in the iron-induced signal transduction pathway that leads to the increase of ferritin 1 transcription in *Arabidopsis thaliana*.

7. Shows that NO produced during *Medicago truncatula-Sinorhizobium meliloti* symbiosis is localized in the bacteroid-containing cells of the nodule fixation zone and is sensitive to mammalian nitric oxide synthase inhibitors.

9. Demonstrates that NO is synthesized nonenzymatically at acidic pH through the reduction of nitrite in the apoplast of barley aleurone layers.

LITERATURE CITED

1. Ahern GP, Klyachko VA, Jackson MB. 2002. cGMP and S-nitrosylation: two routes for modulation of neuronal excitability by NO. *Trends Neurosci.* 25:510–17
2. Ali R, Ma W, Lemtiri-Chlieh F, Tsaltas D, Leng Q, et al. 2007. Death don't have no mercy and neither does calcium: *Arabidopsis* CYCLIC NUCLEOTIDE GATED CHANNEL2 and innate immunity. *Plant Cell* 19:1081–95
3. Allen GJ, Muir SR, Sanders D. 1995. Release of Ca^{2+} from individual plant vacuoles by both InsP3 and cyclic ADP-ribose. *Science* 268:735–37
4. *Arabidopsis* Genome Initiative. 2000. Analysis of the genome sequence of the flowering plant *A. thaliana*. *Nature* 408:796–815
5. **Arnaud N, Murgia I, Boucherez J, Briat JF, Cellier F, Gaymard F. 2006. An iron-induced nitric oxide burst precedes ubiquitin-dependent protein degradation for *Arabidopsis AtFer1* ferritin gene expression. *J. Biol. Chem.* 281:23579–88**
6. Barroso JB, Corpas FJ, Carreras A, Sandalio LM, Valderrama R, et al. 1999. Localization of nitric-oxide synthase in plant peroxisomes. *J. Biol. Chem.* 274:36729–33
7. **Baudouin E, Pieuchot L, Engler G, Pauly N, Puppo A. 2006. Nitric oxide is formed in *Medicago truncatula-Sinorhizobium meliloti* functional nodules. *Mol. Plant-Microbe Interact.* 19:970–75**
8. Belenghi B, Romero-Puertas MC, Vercammen D, Brackenier A, Inze D, et al. 2007. Metacaspase activity of *A. thaliana* is regulated by S-nitrosylation of a critical cysteine residue. *J. Biol. Chem.* 282:1352–58
9. **Bethke PC, Badger MR, Jones RL. 2004. Apoplastic synthesis of nitric oxide by plant tissues. *Plant Cell* 16:332–41**

10. Bright J, Desikan R, Hancock JT, Weir IS, Neill SJ. 2006. ABA-induced NO generation and stomatal closure in *Arabidopsis* are dependent on H_2O_2 synthesis. *Plant J.* 45:113–22

11. Brunori M. 2001. Nitric oxide moves myoglobin centre stage. *Trends Biochem. Sci.* 26:209–10

12. Burza AM, Pekala I, Sikora J, Siedlecki P, Malagocki P, et al. 2006. *Nicotiana tabacum* osmotic stress-activated kinase is regulated by phosphorylation on Ser-154 and Ser-158 in the kinase activation loop. *J. Biol. Chem.* 281:34299–311

13. Clark D, Durner J, Navarre DA, Klessig DF. 2000. Nitric oxide inhibition of tobacco catalase and ascorbate peroxidase. *Mol. Plant-Microbe Interact.* 13:1380–84

14. Clementi E. 1998. Role of nitric oxide and its intracellular signalling pathways in the control of Ca^{2+} homeostasis. *Biochem. Pharmacol.* 55:713–18

15. Cooper CE. 2002. Nitric oxide and cytochrome oxidase: substrate, inhibitor or effector? *Trends Biochem. Sci.* 27:33–39

16. Corpas FJ, Barroso JB, Carreras A, Valderrama R, Palma JM, et al. 2006. Constitutive arginine-dependent nitric oxide synthase activity in different organs of pea seedlings during plant development. *Planta* 224:246–54

17. Crawford MN, Galli M, Tischner R, Heimer YM, Okamoto M, Mack A. 2006. Response to Zemojtel et al.: Plant nitric oxide synthase: back to square one. *Trends Plant Sci.* 11:526–27

18. Cueto M, Hernández-Perera O, Martín R, Bentura ML, Rodrigo J, et al. 1996. Presence of nitric oxide synthase activity in roots and nodules of *Lupinus albus*. *FEBS Lett.* 398:159–64

19. Delledonne M. 2005. NO news is good news for plants. *Curr. Opin. Plant Biol.* 8:390–96

20. Delledonne M, Xia Y, Dixon RA, Lamb C. 1998. Nitric oxide functions as a signal in plant disease resistance. *Nature* 394:585–88

21. Desikan R, Cheung MK, Bright J, Henson D, Hancock JT, Neill SJ. 2004. ABA, hydrogen peroxide and nitric oxide signalling in stomatal guard cells. *J. Exp. Bot.* 55:205–12

22. Dordas C, Hasinoff BB, Igamberdiev AU, Manac'h N, Rivoal J, Hill RD. 2003. Expression of a stress-induced hemoglobin affects NO levels produced by alfalfa root cultures under hypoxic stress. *Plant J.* 35:763–70

23. Dordas C, Hasinoff BB, Rivoal J, Hill RD. 2004. Class-1 hemoglobins, nitrate and NO levels in anoxic maize cell-suspension cultures. *Planta* 219:66–72

24. Durner J, Wendehenne D, Klessig DF. 1998. Defense gene induction in tobacco by nitric oxide, cyclic GMP, and cyclic ADP-ribose. *Proc. Natl. Acad. Sci. USA* 95:10328–33

25. Feechan A, Kwon E, Yun BW, Wang Y, Pallas JA, Loake GJ. 2005. A central role for S-nitrosothiols in plant disease resistance. *Proc. Natl. Acad. Sci. USA* 102:8054–59

26. Fliegert R, Gasser A, Guse AH. 2007. Regulation of calcium signalling by adenine-based second messengers. *Biochem. Soc. Trans.* 35:109–14

27. Foissner I, Wendehenne D, Langebartels C, Durner J. 2000. In vivo imaging of an elicitor-induced nitric oxide burst in tobacco. *Plant J.* 23:817–24

28. Garcia-Mata C, Gay R, Sokolovski S, Hills A, Lamattina L, Blatt MR. 2003. Nitric oxide regulates K^+ and Cl^- channels in guard cells through a subset of abscisic acid-evoked signalling pathways. *Proc. Natl. Acad. Sci. USA* 100:11116–21

29. Gould K, Lamotte O, Klinguer A, Pugin A, Wendehenne D. 2003. Nitric oxide production by tobacco leaves: a general stress response? *Plant Cell Environ.* 26:1851–62

30. Greco TM, Hodara R, Parastatidis I, Heijnen HF, Dennehy MK, et al. 2006. Identification of S-nitrosylation motifs by site-specific mapping of the S-nitrosocysteine proteome in human vascular smooth muscle cells. *Proc. Natl. Acad. Sci. USA* 103:7420–25

10. Reports that abscisic acid-induced NO generation, which is catalysed by nitrate reductase, occurs downstream of H_2O_2 and is required for stomatal closure.

20. Along with Reference 24, shows that NO participates in plant defense gene activation and operates through cyclic GMP, cyclic ADP ribose, and salicylic acid.

25. Together with Reference 68, demonstrates a direct correlation between the level of nitrosoglutathione reductase expression and the endogenous content of S-nitrosothiols in plants challenged by pathogens.

31. Guo FQ, Crawford NM. 2005. *Arabidopsis* nitric oxide synthase1 is targeted to mitochondria and protects against oxidative damage and dark-induced senescence. *Plant Cell* 17:3436–50
32. Guo FQ, Okamoto M, Crawford NM. 2003. Identification of a plant nitric oxide synthase gene involved in hormonal signalling. *Science* 302:100–3
33. Hanafy KA, Krumenacker JS, Murad F. 2001. NO, nitrotyrosine, and cyclic GMP in signal transduction. *Med. Sci. Monit.* 7:801–19
34. Hancock JT, Henson D, Nyirenda M, Desikan R, Harrison J, et al. 2005. Proteomic identification of glyceraldehyde 3-phosphate dehydrogenase as an inhibitory target of hydrogen peroxide in *Arabidopsis*. *Plant Physiol. Biochem.* 43:828–35
35. Hara MR, Agrawal N, Kim SF, Cascio MB, Fujimuro M, et al. 2005. S-nitrosylated GAPDH initiates apoptotic cell death by nuclear translocation following Siah1 binding. *Nat. Cell. Biol.* 7:665–74
36. He Y, Tang RH, Hao Y, Stevens RD, Cook CW, et al. 2004. Nitric oxide represses the *Arabidopsis* floral transition. *Science* 305:1968–71
37. Herold S, Puppo A. 2005. Kinetics and mechanistic studies of the reactions of metleghemoglobin, ferrylleghemoglobin, and nitrosylleghemoglobin with reactive nitrogen species. *J. Biol. Inorg. Chem.* 10:946–57
38. **Hess DT, Matsumoto A, Kim SO, Marshall HE, Stamler JS. 2005. Protein S-nitrosylation: purview and parameters. *Nat. Rev. Mol. Cell Biol.* 6:150–66**

38. Provides an excellent survey of the molecular basis of S-nitrosylation in animals, with emphasis on new insights on the spatial and temporal aspects of NO signaling.

39. Huang X, von Rad U, Durner J. 2002. Nitric oxide induces transcriptional activation of the nitric oxide-tolerant alternative oxidase in *Arabidopsis* suspension cells. *Planta* 215:914–23
40. Igamberdiev AU, Bykova NV, Hill RD. 2006. Nitric oxide scavenging by barley hemoglobin is facilitated by a monodehydroascorbate reductase-mediated ascorbate reduction of methemoglobin. *Planta* 223:1033–40
41. Jaffrey SR, Erdjument-Bromage H, Ferris CD, Tempst P, Snyder SH. 2001. Protein S-nitrosylation: a physiological signal for neuronal nitric oxide. *Nat. Cell Biol.* 3:193–97
42. Kelner A, Pekala I, Kaczanowski S, Muszynska G, Hardie DG, Dobrowolska G. 2004. Biochemical characterization of the tobacco 42-kD protein kinase activated by osmotic stress. *Plant Physiol.* 136:3255–65
43. Klessig DF, Durner J, Noad R, Navarre DA, Wendehenne D, et al. 2000. Nitric oxide and salicylic acid signalling in plant defense. *Proc. Natl. Acad. Sci. USA* 97:8849–55
44. Kone BC, Kuncewicz T, Zhang W, Yu ZY. 2003. Protein interactions with nitric oxide synthases: controlling the right time, the right place, and the right amount of nitric oxide. *Am. J. Physiol. Renal. Physiol.* 285:178–90
45. Lamattina L, Garcia-Mata C, Graziano M, Pagnussat G. 2003. Nitric oxide: the versatility of an extensive signal molecule. *Annu. Rev. Plant Biol.* 54:109–36
46. Lamotte O, Courtois C, Dobrowolska G, Besson A, Pugin A, Wendehenne D. 2006. Mechanisms of nitric-oxide-induced increase of free cytosolic Ca^{2+} concentration in *Nicotiana plumbaginifolia* cells. *Free Radic. Biol. Med.* 40:1369–76
47. Lamotte O, Gould K, Lecourieux D, Sequeira-Legrand A, Lebrun-Garcia A, et al. 2004. Analysis of nitric oxide signalling functions in tobacco cells challenged by the elicitor cryptogein. *Plant Physiol.* 135:516–29
48. Lanteri ML, Pagnussat GC, Lamattina L. 2006. Calcium and calcium-dependent protein kinases are involved in nitric oxide- and auxin-induced adventitious root formation in cucumber. *J. Exp. Bot.* 57:1341–51
49. Lea US, ten Hoopen F, Provan F, Kaiser WM, Meyer C, Lillo C. 2004. Mutation of the regulatory phosphorylation site of tobacco nitrate reductase results in high nitrite excretion and NO emission from leaf and root tissue. *Planta* 219:59–65

50. Lecourieux D, Lamotte O, Bourque S, Wendehenne D, Mazars C, et al. 2005. Proteinaceous and oligosaccharidic elicitors induce different calcium signatures in the nucleus of tobacco cells. *Cell Calcium* 38:527–38
51. Leshem YY, Huang JS, Tzeng DDS, Chou CC, eds. 2000. *Nitric Oxide in Plants. Occurrence, Function and Use*. Dordrecht: Kluwer Acad.
52. Lindermayr C, Saalbach G, Bahnweg G, Durner J. 2006. Differential inhibition of *Arabidopsis* methionine adenosyltransferases by protein S-nitrosylation. *J. Biol. Chem.* 281:4285–91
53. Lindermayr C, Saalbach G, Durner J. 2005. Proteomic identification of S-nitrosylated proteins in *Arabidopsis*. *Plant Physiol.* 137:921–30
54. Liu L, Hausladen A, Zeng M, Que L, Heitman J, Stamler JS. 2001. A metabolic enzyme for S-nitrosothiol conserved from bacteria to humans. *Nature* 410:490–94
55. Mathieu C, Moreau S, Frendo P, Puppo A, Davies MJ. 1998. Direct detection of radicals in intact soybean nodules: presence of nitric oxide-leghemoglobin complexes. *Free Radic. Biol. Med.* 24:1242–49
56. Mato JM, Corrales FJ, Lu SC, Avila MA. 2002. S-Adenosylmethionine: a control switch that regulates liver function. *FASEB J.* 16:15–26
57. Millar AH, Day DA. 1996. Nitric oxide inhibits the cytochrome oxidase but not the alternative oxidase of plant mitochondria. *FEBS Lett.* 398:155–58
58. Modolo LV, Augusto O, Almeida IMG, Pinto-Maglio CAF, Oliveira HC, et al. 2006. Decreased arginine and nitric oxide levels in nitrate reductase deficient *A. thaliana* plants impair nitric oxide synthesis and the hypersensitive response to *Pseudomonas syringae*. *Plant Sci.* 171:34–40
59. Morot-Gaudry-Talarmain Y, Rockel P, Moureaux T, Quilleré I, Leydecker MT, et al. 2002. Nitrite accumulation and nitric oxide emission in relation to cellular signalling in nitrite reductase antisense tobacco. *Planta* 215:708–15
60. Mur LA, Santosa IE, Laarhoven LJ, Holton NJ, Harren FJ, Smith AR. 2005. Laser photoacoustic detection allows *in planta* detection of nitric oxide in tobacco following challenge with avirulent and virulent *Pseudomonas syringae* Pathovars. *Plant Physiol.* 138:1247–58
61. Nelson MJ. 1987. The nitric oxide complex of ferrous soybean lipoxygenase-1. Substrate, pH, and ethanol effects on the active-site iron. *J. Biol. Chem.* 262:12137–42
62. Otvos K, Pasternak TP, Miskolczi P, Domoki M, Dorjgotov D, et al. 2005. Nitric oxide is required for, and promotes auxin-mediated activation of, cell division and embryogenic cell formation but does not influence cell cycle progression in alfalfa cell cultures. *Plant J.* 43:849–60
63. Perazzolli M, Dominici P, Romero-Puertas MC, Zago E, Zeier J, et al. 2004. *Arabidopsis* nonsymbiotic hemoglobin AHb1 modulates nitric oxide bioactivity. *Plant Cell* 16:2785–94
64. Planchet E, Jagadis Gupta K, Sonoda M, Kaiser WM. 2005. Nitric oxide emission from tobacco leaves and cell suspensions: rate limiting factors and evidence for the involvement of mitochondrial electron transport. *Plant J.* 41:732–43
65. Planchet E, Sonoda M, Zeier J, Kaiser WM. 2006. Nitric oxide (NO) as an intermediate in the cryptogein-induced hypersensitive response—a critical re-evaluation. *Plant Cell Environ.* 29:59–69
66. Ribeiro EA, Cunha FQ, Tamashiro WM, Martins IS. 1999. Growth phase-dependent subcellular localization of nitric oxide synthase in maize cells. *FEBS Lett.* 445:283–86
67. Rockel P, Strube F, Rockel A, Wildt J, Kaiser WM. 2002. Regulation of nitric oxide (NO) production by plant nitrate reductase in vivo and in vitro. *J. Exp. Bot.* 53:103–10

51. Provides a unique perspective on the early years of NO research in plants.

68. Rustérucci C, Espunya MC, Díaz M, Chabannes M, Martínez MC. 2007. S-nitrosoglutathione reductase affords protection against pathogens in *Arabidopsis*, both locally and systemically. *Plant Physiol.* 143:1282–92
69. Saito S, Yamamoto-Katou A, Yoshioka H, Doke N, Kawakita K. 2006. Peroxynitrite generation and tyrosine nitration in defense responses in tobacco BY-2 cells. *Plant Cell Physiol.* 47:689–97
70. Sakamoto A, Ueda M, Morikawa H. 2002. *Arabidopsis* glutathione-dependent formaldehyde dehydrogenase is an S-nitrosoglutathione reductase. *FEBS Lett.* 515:20–24
71. Sasakura F, Uchiumi T, Shimoda Y, Suzuki A, Takenouchi K, et al. 2006. A class 1 hemoglobin gene from *Alnus firma* functions in symbiotic and nonsymbiotic tissues to detoxify nitric oxide. *Mol. Plant-Microbe Interact.* 19:441–50
72. Schmidt HHHW, Walter U. 1994. NO at work. *Cell* 78:919–25
73. Schopfer FJ, Baker PR, Freeman BA. 2003. NO-dependent protein nitration: a cell signalling event or an oxidative inflammatory response? *Trends Biochem. Sci.* 28:646–54
74. Seregelyes C, Igamberdiev AU, Maassen A, Hennig J, Dudits D, Hill RD. 2004. NO-degradation by alfalfa class 1 hemoglobin (Mhb1): a possible link to *PR-1a* gene expression in Mhb1-overproducing tobacco plants. *FEBS Lett.* 571:61–66
75. Sokolovski S, Hills A, Gay R, Garcia-Mata C, Lamattina L, Blatt MR. 2005. Protein phosphorylation is a prerequisite for intracellular Ca^{2+} release and ion channel control by nitric oxide and abscisic acid in guard cells. *Plant J.* 43:520–29
76. Stamler JS, Lamas S, Fang FC. 2001. Nitrosylation: the prototypic redox-based signalling mechanism. *Cell* 106:675–83
77. Stohr C, Stremlau S. 2006. Formation and possible roles of nitric oxide in plant roots. *J. Exp. Bot.* 57:463–70
78. Stohr C, Strube F, Marx G, Ullrich WR, Rockel P. 2001. A plasma membrane-bound enzyme of tobacco roots catalyses the formation of nitric oxide from nitrite. *Planta* 212:835–41
79. Stuehr DJ, Santolini J, Wang ZQ, Wei CC, Adak S. 2004. Update on mechanism and catalytic regulation in the NO synthases. *J. Biol. Chem.* 279:36167–70
80. Tian QY, Sun DH, Zhao MG, Zhang WH. 2007. Inhibition of nitric oxide synthase (NOS) underlies aluminium-induced inhibition of root elongation in *Hibiscus moscheutos*. *New Phytol.* 174:322–31
81. Tischner R, Galli M, Heimer YM, Bielefeld S, Okamoto M, et al. 2007. Interference with the citrulline-based nitric oxide synthase assay by argininosuccinate lyase activity in *Arabidopsis* extracts. *FEBS J.* 274:4238–45
82. Tun NN, Holk A, Scherer GF. 2001. Rapid increase of NO release in plant cell cultures induced by cytokinin. *FEBS Lett.* 509:174–76
83. Tun NN, Santa-Catarina C, Begum T, Silveira V, Handro W, et al. 2006. Polyamines induce rapid biosynthesis of nitric oxide (NO) in *A. thaliana* seedlings. *Plant Cell Physiol.* 47:346–54
84. Valderrama R, Corpas FJ, Carreras A, Fernandez-Ocana A, Chaki M, et al. 2007. Nitrosative stress in plants. *FEBS Lett.* 581:453–61
85. Vandelle E, Poinssot B, Wendehenne D, Bentejac M, Pugin A. 2006. Integrated signalling network involving calcium, nitric oxide, and active oxygen species but not mitogen-activated protein kinases in BcPG1-elicited grapevine defenses. *Mol. Plant-Microbe Interact.* 19:429–40
86. Vanin AF, Svistunenko DA, Mikoyan VD, Serezhenkov VA, Fryer MJ, et al. 2004. Endogenous superoxide production and the nitrite/nitrate ratio control the concentration of bioavailable free nitric oxide in leaves. *J. Biol. Chem.* 279:24100–7

87. Wendehenne D, Durner J, Klessig DF. 2004. Nitric oxide: a new player in plant signalling and defense responses. *Curr. Opin. Plant Biol.* 7:449–55

88. Willmott N, Sethi JK, Walseth TF, Lee HC, White AM, Galione A. 1996. Nitric oxide-induced mobilization of intracellular calcium via the cyclic ADP-ribose signalling pathway. *J. Biol. Chem.* 271:3699–705

89. Yamasaki H, Cohen MF. 2006. NO signal at the crossroads: polyamine-induced nitric oxide synthesis in plants? *Trends Plant Sci.* 11:522–24

90. Yamasaki H, Sakihama Y. 2000. Simultaneous production of nitric oxide and peroxynitrite by plant nitrate reductase: in vitro evidence for the NR-dependent formation of active nitrogen species. *FEBS Lett.* 468:89–92

91. Yamasaki H, Shimoji H, Ohshiro Y, Sakihama Y. 2001. Inhibitory effects of nitric oxide on oxidative phosphorylation in plant mitochondria. *Nitric Oxide* 5:261–70

92. Zeidler D, Zahringer U, Gerber I, Dubery I, Hartung T, et al. 2004. Innate immunity in *A. thaliana*: lipopolysaccharides activate nitric oxide synthase (NOS) and induce defense genes. *Proc. Natl. Acad. Sci. USA* 101:15811–16

93. Zemojtel T, Fröhlich A, Palmieri MC, Kolanczyk M, Mikula I, et al. 2006. Plant nitric oxide synthase: a never-ending story? *Trends Plant Sci.* 11:524–25

94. **Zhang A, Jiang M, Zhang J, Ding H, Xu S, et al. 2007. Nitric oxide induced by hydrogen peroxide mediates abscisic acid-induced activation of the mitogen-activated protein kinase cascade involved in antioxidant defense in maize leaves. *New Phytol.* 175:36–50**

94. Together with References 46 and 48, demonstrates that endogenous NO regulates the activation of protein kinases involved in hyperosmotic stress, and auxin and abscisic acid signalings.

95. Zhao MG, Tian QY, Zhang WH. Nitric oxide synthase-dependent nitric oxide production is associated with salt tolerance in *Arabidopsis*. *Plant Physiol.* 144:206–17

96. Zottini M, Costa A, De Michele R, Ruzzene M, Carimi F, Lo Schiavo F. 2007. Salicylic acid activates nitric oxide synthesis in *Arabidopsis*. *J. Exp. Bot.* 58:1397–405

97. Zottini M, Formentin E, Scattolin M, Carimi F, Lo Schiavo F, Terzi M. 2002. Nitric oxide affects plant mitochondrial functionality in vivo. *FEBS Lett.* 515:75–78

Plant Immunity to Insect Herbivores

Gregg A. Howe[1] and Georg Jander[2]

[1]Department of Energy-Plant Research Laboratory and Department of Biochemistry and Molecular Biology, Michigan State University, East Lansing, Michigan 48824; email: howeg@msu.edu

[2]Boyce Thompson Institute for Plant Research, Cornell University, Ithaca, New York 14853; email: gj32@cornell.edu

Annu. Rev. Plant Biol. 2008. 59:41–66

The *Annual Review of Plant Biology* is online at plant.annualreviews.org

This article's doi:
10.1146/annurev.arplant.59.032607.092825

1543-5008/08/0602-0041$20.00

Key Words

plant-insect interaction, plant defense, jasmonate, COI1, secondary metabolism

Abstract

Herbivorous insects use diverse feeding strategies to obtain nutrients from their host plants. Rather than acting as passive victims in these interactions, plants respond to herbivory with the production of toxins and defensive proteins that target physiological processes in the insect. Herbivore-challenged plants also emit volatiles that attract insect predators and bolster resistance to future threats. This highly dynamic form of immunity is initiated by the recognition of insect oral secretions and signals from injured plant cells. These initial cues are transmitted within the plant by signal transduction pathways that include calcium ion fluxes, phosphorylation cascades, and, in particular, the jasmonate pathway, which plays a central and conserved role in promoting resistance to a broad spectrum of insects. A detailed understanding of plant immunity to arthropod herbivores will provide new insights into basic mechanisms of chemical communication and plant-animal coevolution and may also facilitate new approaches to crop protection and improvement.

Contents

Secondary metabolites: compounds that are not required for normal plant growth or reproduction and are often unique to, or characteristic of, specific plant lineages

INTRODUCTION

Terrestrial plants are a food source for an estimated one million or more insect species from diverse taxonomic groups. Insects use various feeding strategies to obtain nutrients from all above- and belowground plant parts. Although all phytophagous insects inflict mechanical damage on plant tissues, the quantity and quality of injury vary greatly, depending on the feeding tactic. Approximately two-thirds of all known herbivorous insect species are leaf-eating beetles (Coleoptera) or caterpillars (Lepidoptera) that cause damage with mouthparts evolved for chewing, snipping, or tearing (116). Piercing-sucking herbivores such as thrips and spider mites use tube-like structures to suck the liquid content from lacerated cells, whereas leafminers develop and feed on soft tissue between epidermal cell layers. Aphids, whiteflies, and other Hemiptera insert specialized stylets between cells to establish a feeding site in the phloem. In each of these insect-plant relationships, both partners send and receive chemical cues that determine the outcome of the interaction. Contact chemoreceptors on the insect mouthparts, antennae, and tarsi (feet), for example, gauge the suitability of the host as a food source. Conversely, plant cells recognize and respond to insect movement, wound trauma inflicted by feeding, and compounds in insect oral secretions.

A recurring theme in all spheres of plant-insect biology is variation in the extent to which herbivores exercise dietary specialization. Generalist (i.e., polyphagous) insects feed on many hosts from different plant families. Specialists (i.e., monophagous and oligophagous insects) subsist on one or a few plants from the same family. An insect's decision to accept or reject a host is determined in large part by a myriad of chemical deterrents and attractants. There is good reason to believe that much of the extraordinary diversity of specialized plant compounds, so-called secondary metabolites, results from the coevolutionary struggle of herbivores and plants to eat or not be eaten (13). As sessile organisms, plants rely heavily on chemical defenses to thwart insect attack. Compounds that exert repellent, antinutritive, or toxic effects on herbivores are commonly referred to as direct defenses. Physical barriers such as leaf toughness and trichomes that increase plant fitness in the presence of herbivores are also direct defenses. A second layer of indirect protection is afforded by herbivore-induced plant volatiles and nectar rewards that attract natural enemies of the herbivore (67). The combined effects of direct and indirect defense provide durable resistance to a broad spectrum of arthropod herbivores in natural ecosystems (33, 68).

Plant traits that confer resistance to insect pests may also be classified according to the manner in which they are regulated. Some traits are expressed constitutively under the control of hard-wired developmental programs, irrespective of the herbivore threat level. Reproductive tissues, for example, typically accumulate large amounts of defensive proteins and metabolites. In contrast to these preformed barriers, herbivore-challenged plants mount active defense responses at the site of tissue damage and, in many cases, systemically in undamaged tissues (14). This highly dynamic form of induced resistance has been documented in species throughout the plant kingdom (61). Evidence indicates that induced defenses evolved because they have lower resource allocation costs than constitutive resistance traits (10, 60). In addition to induced defensive traits, plants can minimize the fitness consequences of tissue loss by activating physiological processes, such as sequestration of sugars in below-ground tissues, that allow the plant to better tolerate herbivory (118).

The ability of plants to recognize and respond defensively to insect attack constitutes a form of immunity. Unlike the highly specific adaptive immune system of vertebrates in which mobile defender cells recognize and eliminate pathogenic challenges, plant immunity to insects relies on the innate ability of each cell to perceive "danger" signals, to transmit this information systemically to fend off future attacks, and to mount direct and indirect defenses that reduce insect performance. Our current understanding of the mechanisms and evolutionary origins of immune recognition in plants comes mainly from studies of plant-pathogen interactions (55). Basal resistance to pathogen infection is triggered by transmembrane receptors that recognize pathogen-associated molecular patterns. These ancient microbial molecules, which include fragments of bacterial cell walls, flagellin, and EF-Tu (elongation factor Tu), alert the host to the presence of intruding microorganisms (37, 148). As a second line of defense, the plant immune system relies on disease resistance (R) proteins to detect effector molecules (i.e., virulence factors) that pathogens secrete into plant cells to counteract or weaken host defense. A unifying theme in plant immunity to pathogens is the involvement of receptors that recognize pathogen-derived molecules or, in the case of most R proteins, pathogen-modified host proteins.

Relatively little is known about the molecular recognition events that trigger plant immunity to insect herbivores. However, plants appear to use multiple surveillance systems to recognize insects with a wide range of lifestyles and feeding behaviors. One of these recognition systems is conceptually similar to pathogen-triggered immunity because it involves the perception of exogenous molecules that, when delivered to plant cells via insect secretions, elicit a host defense response. These elicitors can be insect-derived molecules or plant compounds that are modified by the insect. The notion that plants recognize insect-modified compounds of plant origin is consistent with the so-called guard hypothesis, which postulates that R proteins recognize damage to endogenous plant proteins and subsequently initiate a defense response (55). That plants activate many anti-insect defenses in response to mechanical tissue damage indicates that endogenous signals produced by distressed cells also play a critical role in plant perception of herbivory; the concept of wound trauma as a trigger for defense is analogous to danger signal models of the vertebrate immune system (86). The plant hormone jasmonic acid (JA) and related signaling compounds (collectively referred to as jasmonates) are ubiquitous signals for tissue injury and for the subsequent activation of defense responses to many, if not most, insect herbivores.

Direct defense: a toxin, antifeedant, physical barrier, or other plant defensive trait that deters herbivory

Indirect defense: a plant defensive trait that protects against herbivory by enhancing the attraction of predators of the herbivore

Constitutive defense: toxins and other defensive barriers that are produced irrespective of whether herbivores are present

Induced defense: toxins and other defensive traits that are only expressed in response to herbivory

Elicitor: insect- or plant-derived compound that, upon recognition by the host plant, activates a defensive response

JA: jasmonic acid

Here, we review recent advances in our understanding of the molecular and biochemical mechanisms of plant immunity to insect herbivores. First, we discuss early signaling events at the plant-insect interface and their involvement in insect recognition. Second, we describe the central role of jasmonates in the regulation of defense responses to herbivory and discuss important new developments regarding the mechanism of jasmonate action. Finally, we highlight specific examples of direct and indirect defensive traits that impact host-plant selection by, or resistance to, insect herbivores.

EARLY SIGNALING EVENTS AT THE PLANT-INSECT INTERFACE

Successful implementation of an induced defense response requires that plants respond to herbivory both rapidly and accurately. Early signaling events at the plant-insect interface, which occur well before changes in host plant gene expression and defense-related metabolism, are critical for the process of herbivore recognition (83). Several studies have identified insect elicitors that allow plants to distinguish herbivory from mechanical damage. In the case of hemipteran herbivores, there is evidence for the involvement of *R* genes in the control of host plant resistance.

Mechanical Wounding Versus Herbivory

Although all herbivory results in plant tissue damage, tissue disruption per se is not always a reliable indicator of insect attack. Therefore, to avoid wasting defensive resources, plants must differentiate insect feeding and simple mechanical damage, such as that caused by hail or wind in natural settings. Some responses, including the upregulation of genes required for cell repair and response to osmotic stress, would likely occur as a result of either herbivory or mechanical wounding. However, the production of toxic secondary metabolites and other defensive responses would presumably benefit only herbivore-challenged plants.

Changes in gene expression underlie the induced synthesis of most defensive secondary metabolites and proteins, as well as other changes in plant metabolism that occur during herbivory. Microarray experiments with several plant species, including *Arabidopsis thaliana* (Arabidopsis) (23, 102), *Nicotiana attenuata* (coyote tobacco) (137), *Populus trichocarpa* × *Populus deltoides* (hybrid poplar) (84, 99), and *Picea sitchensis* (Sitka spruce) (100), compared gene expression patterns induced by mechanical wounding with that induced by insect feeding or simulated herbivory. Although there is considerable overlap in the induced expression patterns, there are also transcriptional responses that appear to be specific to insect feeding or the application of insect oral secretions to wound sites. In some cases, these responses have been associated with the production of specific insect-deterrent compounds such as nicotine (52) and glucosinolates (88).

There are two main theories to explain how plants discriminate insect herbivory from mechanical damage. The first is that plants recognize compounds in insect oral secretions. This view is supported by the identification of several insect-derived factors that elicit defense responses when applied to artificial wounds (see below). Plants may also differentiate mechanical wounding from herbivory through the use of as yet unknown mechanisms that gauge the quantity and quality of tissue damage. Caterpillar feeding, for example, involves the action of specialized mandibles that remove similarly sized pieces of leaf tissue in a highly choreographed and predictable manner. Most studies showing that mechanical wounding and herbivory (or simulated herbivory) elicit different responses have relied on wound treatments that do not approximate tissue injury caused by insect grazing (90). Recognizing this limitation, researchers have developed novel approaches to disentangle the effects of mechanical damage from the effects of oral secretions. One approach in studying the role of insect saliva in plant-lepidopteran interactions, for example, is to challenge plants with larvae in which the labial salivary gland is removed. Such experiments with *Helicoverpa zea* (corn earworm) provided evidence that salivary secretions qualitatively affect plant defense responses to caterpillar feeding (93). A second approach is to challenge plants with mechanical caterpillar devices that more accurately mimic tissue injury caused by caterpillar feeding (90). These experiments have shown that repetitive mechanical wounding of *Phaseolus lunatus* (lima bean) leaves elicits a pattern of volatile emission that is qualitatively similar to that induced by caterpillar attack. It is thus clear that the temporal and spatial patterns of mechanical injury are a critical determinant of the host defense response.

Insect Oral Secretions

One of the best-studied plant responses to herbivory is the elevated release of volatiles, which include terpenes, green leafy volatiles, ethylene, and other volatile organic compounds. Studies with several plant-insect combinations have demonstrated that insect feeding or application of oral secretions to wound sites elicits a different or more intense volatile response than mechanical damage alone (7, 8, 22, 112, 135). Plants can benefit from herbivory-specific volatile production through direct deterrent effects on the herbivores, attraction of predators to the site of insect feeding, and intraplant signaling events that poise uninfested tissue for more rapid defense induction. Because of the relative ease of volatile collection and the nondestructive nature of the assay, induced volatile production has been used to identify insect-derived elicitors of plant defense responses.

N-17-hydroxylinolenoyl-L-glutamine (volicitin) (**Figure 1**) was identified in *Spodoptera exigua* (beet armyworm) oral secretions through its ability to induce volatile release in *Zea mays* (maize) seedlings (5). This compound was the first example of what appears to be a widely prevalent production of fatty acid–amino acid conjugates (FACs) (**Figure 1**) by lepidopteran larvae (3, 40, 92, 98). Specific responses to FACs in lepidopteran oral secretions, including changes in gene expression, alteration of the plant proteome, and induced production of nicotine and protease inhibitors, have been studied most extensively in *N. attenuata* (35, 39). Selective binding of volictin to plasma membrane preparations from maize suggests the existence of an FAC receptor (134). Other workers have suggested that the detergent-like properties of FACs may account for some of the biological activities of these amphiphilic compounds (81).

FAC: fatty acid–amino acid conjugate

Some plants, including *P. lunatus* and *Gossypium hirsutum* (cotton), do not respond to FACs (120). However, the release of volatiles by FAC-insensitive plants in response to caterpillar feeding indicated that other elicitors are present in the oral secretions. A bioassay-guided search for elicitors of ethylene production in *Vigna unguiculata* (cowpea) led to the identification of proteolytic fragments of plastidic ATP synthase γ-subunit in the oral secretions of *Spodoptera frugiperda* (fall armyworm) (112). At least four of these disulfide-bonded peptides, called inceptins (**Figure 1**), are produced through the digestion of plant proteins in the *S. frugiperda* gut (113). Although *Phaseolus vulgaris* (common bean) responded similarly to inceptin, *Z. mays* and *Nicotiana tabacum* (cultivated tobacco) did not (112). The proposed mechanism of action of inceptin is consistent with the guard hypothesis of plant immunity, but plant receptors for these elictors remain to be identified.

Oral secretions from orthopteran insects also use an FAC-independent mechanism to elicit volatile release in the host plants of these insects. Recently, a new class of sulfated fatty acids called caeliferins (**Figure 1**) was identified in the oral secretions of *Shistocerca americana* (American bird grasshopper) and other grasshopper species (4). Like FACs, caeliferins elicit the release of volatile terpenes

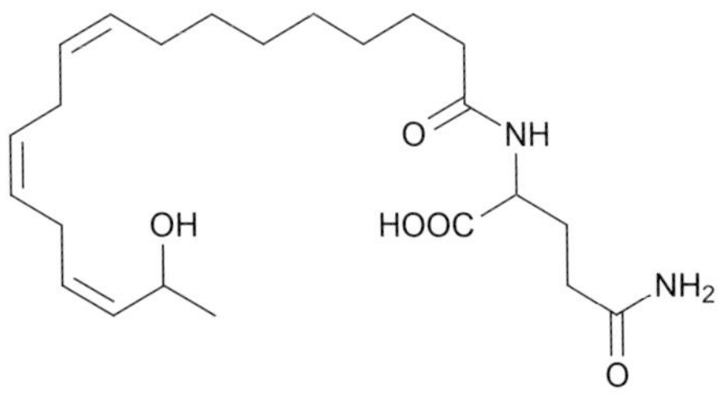

N-17-Hydroxylinolenoyl-L-glutamine (volicitin)

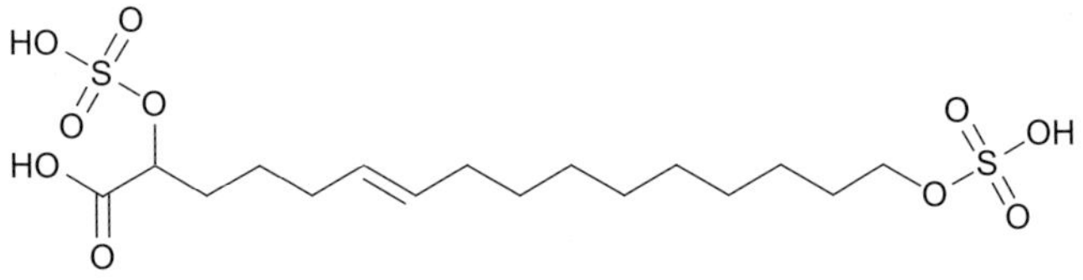

Caeliferin A 16:1

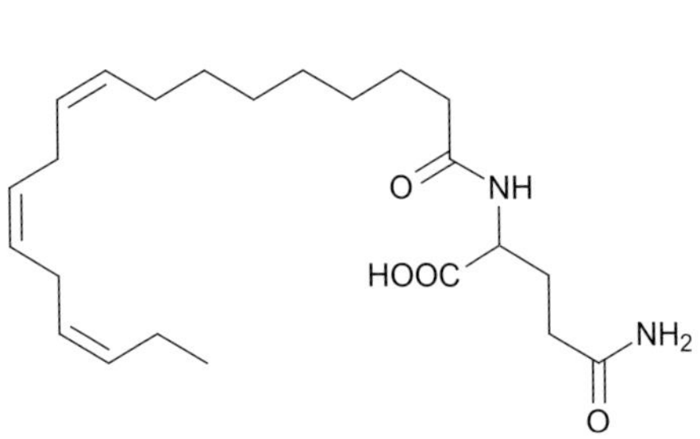

N-Linolenoyl-L-glutamine

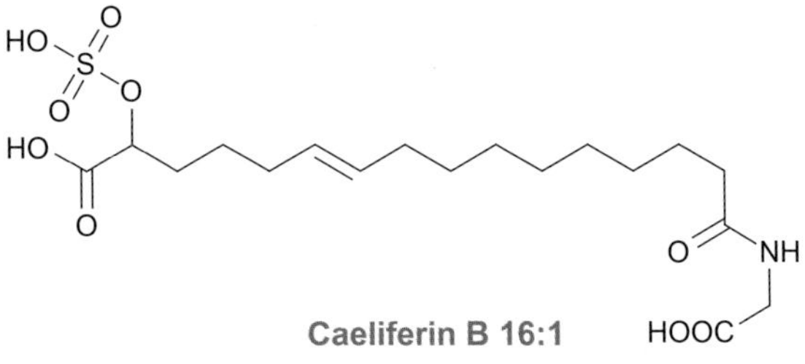

Caeliferin B 16:1

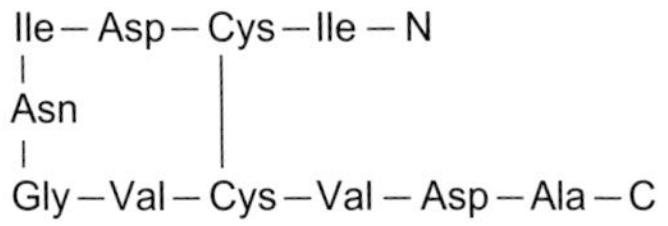

Inceptin

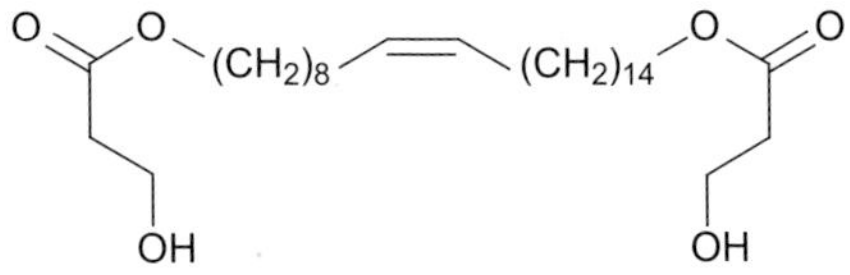

Bruchin C

Figure 1

Insect-derived elicitors of host plant defense responses. Volicitin and *N*-linolenoyl-L-glutamine belong to the family of fatty acid–amino acid conjugates (FACs) found in oral secretions of lepidopteran larvae. The fatty acid and amino acid moieties of FACs are derived from the insect and host plant, respectively (95). Inceptin, which was also isolated from oral secretions of lepidopteran larvae, is produced by proteolytic degradation of chloroplast ATP synthase in the insect gut. FACs and inceptin thus represent examples of elicitors that are produced by modification of plant compounds within the insect. Caeliferins were isolated from the oral secretions of the grasshopper species *Schistocerca americana*. Bruchins, which are produced by pea weevils and related bruchids, stimulate neoplastic growth at the site of weevil oviposition.

from maize seedlings. It is not known whether this response functions to deter grasshopper feeding directly, attracts predators, or provides some other benefit to the host plant. Further research is also necessary to determine whether the abundantly produced caeliferins provide an essential defensive or digestive benefit to the grasshoppers.

Given the numerous insect herbivores that trigger defense responses and the comparatively small number of plant-insect combinations that have been examined in detail, the discovery of additional components of insect oral secretions that elicit host defense responses can be anticipated. Other types of insect secretions also elicit defense responses. For instance, plants can respond to insect oviposition fluids, either in anticipation of imminent herbivory or to attract egg-eating predators (48). Bruchins (**Figure 1**) in the oviposition fluid of *Bruchis pisorum* (pea weevil) elicit tumor-like growths beneath the egg on *Pisum sativum* (pea), which inhibits entry of the larvae into the pod. Oviposition by the sawfly *Diprion pini* on *Pinus sylvestris* (Scots pine) increases the production of terpenoid volatiles and decreases ethylene release (117). Similarly, oviposition by *Pieris brassicae* (large white butterfly) on *A. thaliana* triggers the expression of defense-related genes (80). The plant signaling compounds JA and salicylic acid (SA) accumulate in insect eggs and may contribute to the elicitation of defense responses (133).

R Genes Mediate Aphid Resistance

Insect-derived elicitors have not yet been identified for aphids, whiteflies, or other phloem-feeding Hemiptera. Although these insects cause comparatively little tissue damage when feeding from phloem sieve elements, plants are nevertheless able to mount distinctive metabolic and transcriptional responses to hemipteran attack (23, 65, 88, 137). Aphid salivary enzymes such as peroxidase and pectinase may be elicitors of plant defense responses (89), but this hypothesis remains to be tested rigorously.

Genetic evidence from several monocot and dicot crop species supports the idea that *R* gene products mediate resistance to phloem-feeding insects (119). In two cases, specific plant NBS-LRR (nucleotide binding site–leucine rich repeat) proteins that contribute to the recognition of hemipteran herbivores have been identified. The tomato *Mi-1* gene provides resistance to some isolates of *Macrosiphum euphorbiae* (potato aphid) and *Bemisia tabaci* (silverleaf whitefly), although not to *Myzus persicae* (green peach aphid) (94, 106). Another NBS-LRR protein, encoded by the melon *Vat* gene, confers increased resistance to both *Aphis gossypii* (cotton aphid) and the transmission of plant viruses by this aphid species (26). By analogy to plant defense against pathogens, these findings suggest a gene-for-gene interaction between the plant and the aphid. However, the presumed avirulence proteins in aphid saliva have not yet been identified.

SA: salicylic acid

MAPK: mitogen-activated protein kinase

Calcium Flux, Membrane Potential, and Mitogen-Activated Protein Kinases

Relatively little is known about the signal transduction pathways that connect insect-specific elicitors to the plant defense responses they evoke. The calcium ion (Ca^{2+}) has been implicated as a second messenger in many plant signaling pathways, including responses to herbivory (83). Under normal conditions, the cytosolic Ca^{2+} content is several orders of magnitude lower than that in organelles or apoplastic fluid. Transient increases in cytosolic Ca^{2+} levels activate calmodulin and other calcium-sensing proteins that subsequently promote downstream signaling events, including protein phosphorylation and transcriptional responses. Feeding by *Spodoptera littoralis* (Egyptian cotton worm) on *P. lunatus* causes a transient increase in cytosolic Ca^{2+} in cells adjacent to the insect bite (82). In other experiments with *P. lunatus*, treatment with a Ca^{2+} chelator prevented defense gene induction in response to feeding by *Tetranychus urticae* (two-spotted spider mite) and volatiles from mite-infested neighboring plants (9). In *A. thaliana*, the nuclear protein IQD1 binds calmodulin in a Ca^{2+}-dependent manner and thereby affects the transcription of genes involved in glucosinolate biosynthesis (75). IQD1 overexpression reduces herbivory by *M. persicae* and *Trichoplusia ni* (cabbage looper), suggesting that this protein is involved in perceiving Ca^{2+} signals to modulate plant defense responses.

R gene–mediated resistance to pathogens and other plant responses to environmental stress involve mitogen-activated protein kinase (MAPK) signaling cascades (42). Although no complete MAPK pathway leading to insect resistance has been identified, there is evidence that such pathways play a role in some plant-insect interactions. In

Jasmonate pathway: a hormone signaling pathway that plays an essential and central role in regulating plant responses to herbivory

Priming: metabolic preparation for a more rapid or robust response to subsequent herbivory

JA-Ile: jasmonoyl-isoleucine

JAC: jasmonoyl–amino acid conjugate

Solanum lycopersicum (tomato), *Mi-1* mediated resistance was attenuated when expression of certain MAPKs and MAPK kinases was reduced by virus-induced gene silencing (VIGS) (78). VIGS studies in tomato also showed that at least three MAPKs are required for systemin-mediated defense responses to *Manduca sexta* (tobacco hornworm) (58). FACs in *M. sexta* oral secretions increase wound-induced expression of SA-induced MAPK and wound-induced MAPK in *N. attenuata* (142). Furthermore, reducing expression of these two kinases by VIGS demonstrated that they are important for characteristic responses of *N. attenuata* to caterpillar oral secretions. In the wild rice *Oryza minuta*, expression of a putative MAPK kinase, *OmMKK1*, is induced by *Nilaparvata lugens* (brown planthopper) feeding, as well as by treatment with JA and SA (144).

REGULATION OF DEFENSE RESPONSES BY JASMONATES

Evidence has accumulated over the past few years to indicate that the jasmonate family of signaling compounds functions in endogenous regulation of plant resistance to arthropod herbivores. Below, we discuss the various roles of jasmonates in anti-insect defense, the mechanism by which herbivore-induced jasmonate synthesis promotes global reprogramming of defense gene expression, and the regulation of this response.

Jasmonates Serve Multiple Roles in Plant Immunity to Insects

Jasmonates play a central role in regulating defense responses to herbivores that inflict various types of tissue damage. This conclusion is based on numerous laboratory and field studies showing that jasmonate mutants are compromised in resistance to a wide range of arthropod herbivores, including caterpillars (Lepidoptera), beetles (Coleoptera), thrips (Thysanoptera), leafhoppers (Homoptera), spider mites (Acari), fungal gnats (Diptera), and mirid bugs (Heteroptera) (14, 50, 67). DNA microarray studies show that the jasmonate pathway has a dominant role in regulating global changes in gene expression in response to both mechanical wounding and herbivory (23, 24, 39, 84, 99, 100, 102, 103). Jasmonates are also involved in the regulation of tritrophic interactions (28, 128, 136), host plant resistance to phloem-feeding insects (27, 32, 87, 145), trichome-based defenses (15, 77), priming of direct and indirect defenses (28, 132), pathogen resistance (36), and systemic transmission of defense signals (109). In addition to these defense-related processes, jasmonates regulate several aspects of plant development; the hormone generally promotes defensive and reproductive processes while inhibiting the growth and photosynthetic output of vegetative tissues (25, 35). These juxtaposing activities suggest a broader role for jasmonates in managing the "dilemma of plants to grow or defend" (47) in rapidly changing and hostile environments.

Wound trauma inflicted by chewing insects or mechanical damage results in rapid (<30 min) accumulation of JA at the site of wounding. In higher plants, JA is synthesized via the octadecanoid pathway (**Figure 2**). Genes encoding nearly all jasmonate biosynthetic enzymes have been identified (108). It is now clear that further metabolism of newly synthesized JA plays a critical role in regulating downstream transcriptional responses. Among the routes of JA metabolism that modulate plant responses to biotic stress are (*a*) synthesis of the volatile compound methyl-JA (MeJA) by JA-carboxymethyl transferase (108) and (*b*) formation of jasmonoyl-isoleucine (JA-Ile) and other JA–amino acid conjugates (JACs) by JASMONATE RESISTANT 1 (JAR1) and related conjugating enzymes (59, 121) (**Figure 2**). A strict requirement for JA synthesis in anti-insect defense was demonstrated by the use of mutants that are impaired in the β-oxidation stage of the octadecanoid pathway (76, 110). This conclusion is consistent with the fact that conjugation of JA

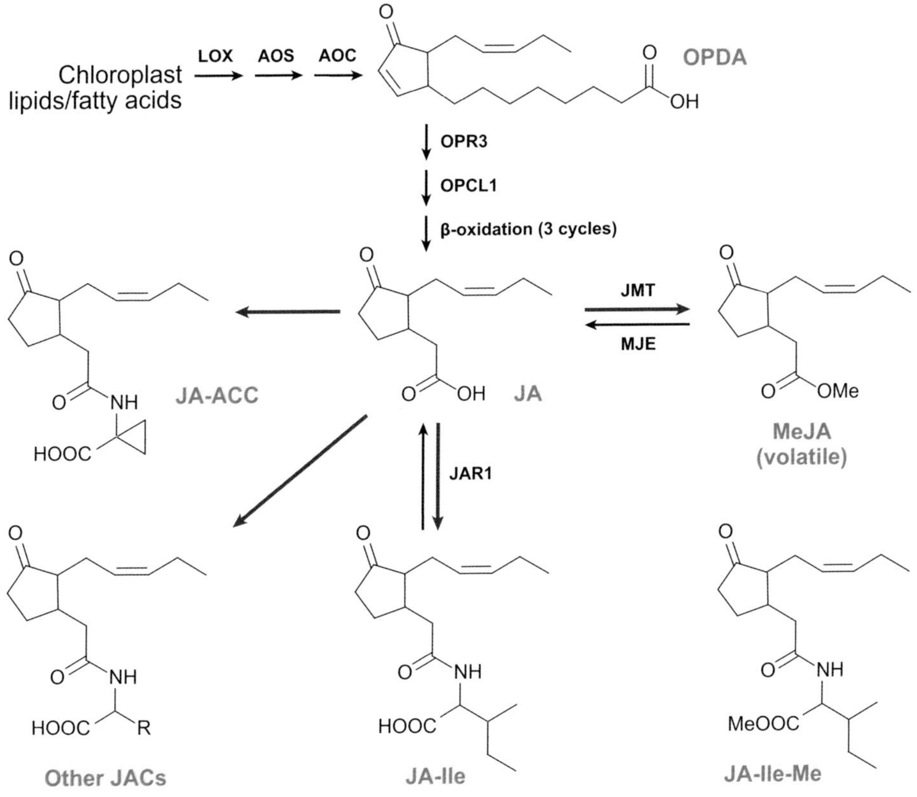

Figure 2

The octadecanoid pathway for the biosynthesis of jasmonic acid (JA) and bioactive conjugates of JA. JA synthesis is initiated in the chloroplast, where linolenic acid is converted to 12-oxo-phytodienoic acid (OPDA) by the sequential action of lipoxygenase (LOX), allene oxide synthase (AOS), and allene oxide cyclase (AOC). Following transport to the peroxisome, OPDA is reduced to OPC-8:0 (not shown) by OPDA reductase 3 (OPR3). OPC-8:0 CoA ligase (OPLC1) converts OPC-8:0 to its corresponding CoA derivative, which is the entry substrate for three cycles of β-oxidation that yield (+)-7-iso-JA (JA). JA is metabolized to several biologically active derivatives (*red arrows*). JA carboxyl methyltransferase (JMT) converts JA to the volatile compound MeJA. The reverse reaction is catalyzed by MeJA esterase (MJE). Conjugation of JA to isoleucine (Ile) by JASMONATE RESISTANT 1 (JAR1) produces JA-Ile, which promotes CORONATINE INSENSITIVE 1 (COI1) interaction with JAZ repressor proteins. JA-Ile can be methylated to produce JA-Ile-Me (44), the biological role of which is not known. As yet unidentified enzymes conjugate JA to ACC (1-aminocyclopropane-1-carboxylic acid, an ethylene biosynthetic intermediate) and other amino acids to generate JA-ACC and other jasmonoyl–amino acid conjugates (JACs), respectively.

to isoleucine (Ile) is required for direct defense against caterpillar feeding (59). Plastid-derived 12-oxo-phytodienoic acid (OPDA) is implicated as a signal per se (i.e., in the absence of its conversion to JA) for a limited range of direct (123) and indirect (71) defense responses to herbivory. Recent studies provide evidence that the mechanism of OPDA signaling is distinct from that involved in the perception of JA-derived signals such as JA-Ile (124, 129).

Jasmonate Perception

Much of our understanding of the role of jasmonates in plant-insect interactions has

COI1: CORONATINE-INSENSITIVE 1

JAZ: jasmonate ZIM domain

come from the analysis of mutants that fail to perceive JA/MeJA (25). In particular, mutants that are defective in the *CORONATINE INSENSITIVE 1* (*COI1*) gene are impaired in all jasmonate-signaled processes and, as a consequence, are highly susceptible to a wide range of arthropod herbivores (18, 77, 87, 96, 102, 123, 145). COI1 is the F-box component of a multi-protein E3-ubiquitin ligase called SCF^{COI1}, which is named for the SKP1-like, cullin, and F-box proteins of the complex. This finding led to the proposal that jasmonate signaling involves SCF^{COI1}-mediated ubiquitination of regulatory proteins that control the transcription of jasmonate-responsive genes (25).

A major step toward elucidating the mechanism of jasmonate action came from the recent discovery of jasmonate ZIM domain (JAZ) proteins that are targeted by SCF^{COI1} for degradation during jasmonate signaling (19, 129). Several lines of evidence indicate that at least some members of the JAZ family act as repressors of jasmonate-responsive genes. First, JAZ proteins are degraded in a COI1- and 26S proteasome–dependent manner in response to JA treatment. Second, dominant mutations in the conserved C-terminal domain of JAZ proteins stabilize them against SCF^{COI1}-mediated degradation and, as a consequence, reduce the plant's responsiveness to JA/MeJA (19, 129, 143). Finally, physical interaction of COI1 and JAZ1 is stimulated in a dose-dependent manner by JA-Ile and, to a lesser extent, by JA-Leu (129). That JA, MeJA, and OPDA failed to promote this interaction indicates that the COI1-dependent biological activity of these compounds requires their conversion to a bioactive JAC (e.g., JA-Ile) or that these JA derivatives promote COI1 interaction with different JAZ substrates. The ability of JA-Ile to stimulate the COI1-JAZ1 interaction in the yeast two-hybrid system (i.e., in the absence of other plant proteins) implicates the COI1-JAZ complex as a receptor for JA-Ile (129). Although ligand-binding studies are needed to test this hypothesis, it is worth noting that the emerging picture of jasmonate action is analogous to the auxin signaling pathway, in which auxin binding to the LRR domain of the TRANSPORT INHIBITOR 1 (TIR1) receptor promotes the degradation of Aux/IAA transcriptional repressors (126). It will be interesting to determine whether the concept of auxin as a molecular glue that promotes TIR1-substrate interactions extends to JA-Ile as a ligand for the LRR domain of COI1.

These new insights into the mechanism of jasmonate action suggest that the core signal transduction chain for wound- and herbivore-induced expression of defensive genes is composed of relatively few links. In healthy undamaged leaves, low JA-Ile levels presumably allow JAZs to accumulate and repress the transcription of target genes (**Figure 3*a***). Establishment of this repressed state involves direct interaction of JAZ proteins with transcription factors, such as MYC2, that promote the expression of jasmonate-responsive genes (19). In response to tissue injury, rapid accumulation of JA-Ile would trigger SCF^{COI1}-mediated degradation of JAZ proteins and subsequent derepression of defense-related genes (**Figure 3*b***). A noteworthy feature of most *JAZ* transcripts is their rapid accumulation in response to jasmonate treatment (129) or wound trauma (H.S. Chung & G.A. Howe, unpublished data). Rapid resynthesis of JAZ repressors presumably provides a mechanism to restrain the expression of energetically demanding and potentially cell-damaging defensive processes when jasmonate levels decline, for example, upon cessation of insect feeding. Such a mechanism of negative feedback control suggests that the expression of jasmonate-based defenses should be viewed more as a continuum than as discrete induced and uninduced states. The key role of JA-Ile in regulating the strength of the response highlights the need to study further the cellular mechanisms of JAC homeostasis in healthy and injured tissues. It can be anticipated that a combination of negative and positive feedback mechanisms allows the plant to mount a defense response that is

a Unchallenged host plant

SCF^COI1

JAZ

TF

Early genes

Low

Low JA-Ile

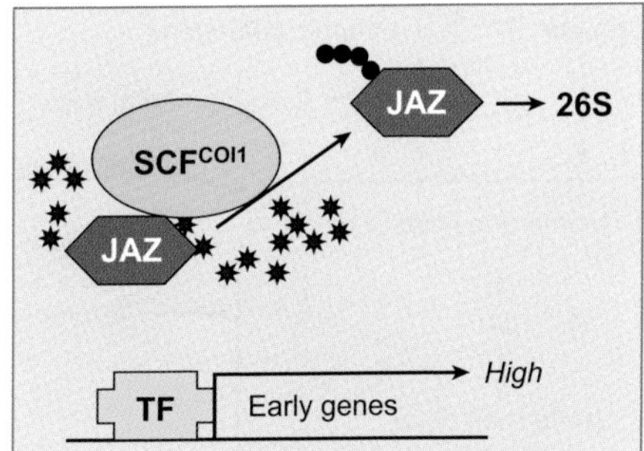

Figure 3

The JAZ repressor model of jasmonate signaling. (*a*) Low intracellular levels of jasmonoyl-isoleucine (JA-Ile) (*red stars*) favor the accumulation of jasmonate ZIM domain (JAZ) proteins, which bind to and repress the activity of transcription factors (TF) such as MYC2 that positively regulate jasmonate-responsive early genes. (*b*) Tissue injury, such as that caused by chewing insects, results in rapid accumulation of JA-Ile. These high levels of JA-Ile promote SCF^{COI1}-mediated ubiquitination (*black circles*) and subsequent degradation of JAZ repressor proteins via the 26S proteasome (26S), resulting in the derepression of transcription factors and the expression of early response genes. See text for more details.

commensurate with the intensity and duration of the attack.

Specificity of Jasmonate-Based Defenses

An important question concerning jasmonate-regulated defenses is whether the response is specific for different herbivores and, if so, how this specificity is achieved. Reymond and colleagues showed that crucifer specialist (*Pieris rapae*, small white butterfly) and generalist (*S. littoralis*) caterpillars elicit nearly identical gene expression patterns in *A. thaliana* (102). Much more divergent patterns were observed in plants challenged with insects from different feeding guilds (23, 45). For example, although the transcriptional response of *A. thaliana* to chewing (*P. rapae*) and piercing-sucking (*Frankliniella occidentalis*, western flower thrips) insects was dominated by jasmonate-regulated genes, the majority of these genes (61%) exhibited an expression pattern that was specific to one of the two attackers (23). Transcript profiles elicited by phloem-feeding insects are markedly different from those induced by attackers from other feeding guilds and are generally associated with the activation of SA-responsive genes and weak expression of JA-responsive genes (23, 32, 65, 131). Induction of the jasmonate pathway by aphid feeding likely reflects cell damage caused by stylet probing (57, 131). The phloem-feeding *B. tabaci*, which causes much less mechanical damage than do aphids, does not activate JA-responsive genes (145). Emerging evidence indicates that phloem feeders actively suppress jasmonate-based defenses (131, 145). In summary, insects from different feeding guilds tend to elicit distinct (but overlapping) patterns of gene expression, whereas attackers from the same guild evoke very similar responses. Because most insects betray their presence by triggering jasmonate synthesis in damaged tissues, jasmonate-signaled defenses may have evolved as a relatively nonspecific strategy to deter a large variety of different herbivores.

Relatively little is known about the early signaling events involved in herbivore-induced production of bioactive jasmonates.

Feeding guild: a group of insect herbivores that use one of various types of feeding behavior (e.g., chewing or piercing-sucking) to obtain nutrients from host plant tissue

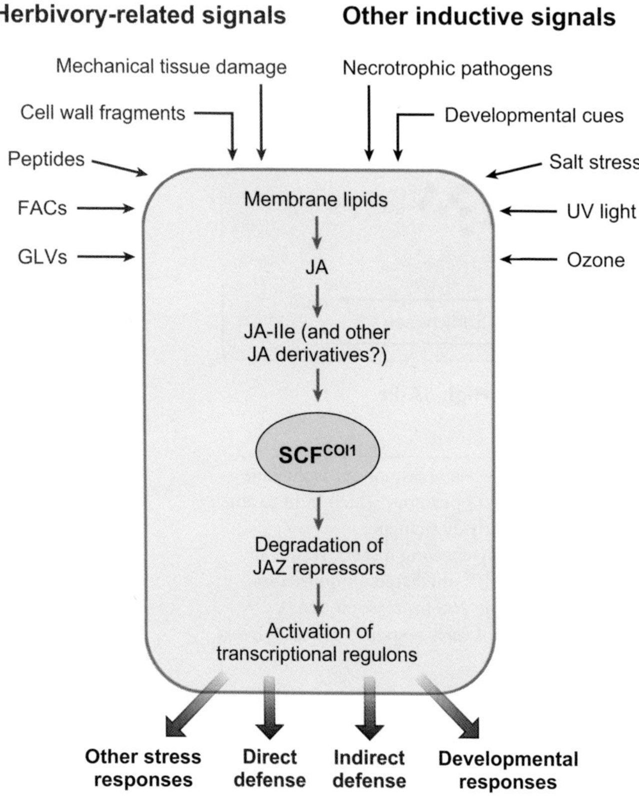

Figure 4

Regulation of jasmonate-based defenses in response to herbivory. Herbivore-induced signals (*red arrows*) activate the production of bioactive jasmonates such as jasmonoyl-isoleucine (JA-Ile). JA-Ile promotes SCF^{COI1}-mediated degradation of jasmonate ZIM domain (JAZ) repressor proteins, resulting in derepression of transcriptional regulons that control direct and indirect defensive traits. The jasmonate signaling pathway also regulates plant responses to developmental cues and other stress conditions (*black arrows*). FACs, fatty acid—amino acid conjugates; GLVs, green leafy volatiles [e.g., (*Z*)-3-hexenal]; JA, jasmonic acid.

That severe mechanical tissue damage, abiotic stress, and developmental cues activate jasmonate synthesis and many associated defenses indicates that insect-derived factors are not strictly required for these responses (**Figure 4**). Rather, it would appear that insect-derived elicitors such as FACs and inceptin (see above), which stimulate JA synthesis when applied to artificial wounds, reinforce or amplify the jasmonate pathway (67, 112). In addition to modulation by herbivore-derived factors, jasmonate-regulated defenses may be positively or negatively modulated by other phytohormones (14, 105). SA, for example, is well known for its ability to antagonize induced defense responses to lepidopteran insects (14, 21). Ethylene also affects the expression of defensive proteins and secondary metabolites (43, 51, 141). In comparison to the jasmonates, however, ethylene production during herbivore attack is considered to play a relatively minor role in the active defense response (138).

The specificity of induced defense responses to herbivory may also be influenced by differential interactions between various bioactive jasmonates, COI1, JAZ proteins, and the downstream transcription factors they regulate. For example, specific members of the JAZ family may control distinct sets of herbivore-responsive genes in different cell types or in response to different ligands. Phosphorylation of JAZ proteins by a MAPK (64) suggests a mechanism to modify the specificity of responses or integrate the jasmonate pathway with other signals. The recent discovery (121) that JA is conjugated to the ethylene precursor 1-aminocyclopropane-1-carboxylic acid (ACC) is of interest because JA and ethylene accumulate simultaneously and act synergistically in response to herbivory (49, 111, 138). The hypothesis that JA-ACC (**Figure 2**) is involved in the control of defenses that are coordinately regulated by the jasmonate and ethylene pathways deserves further attention.

Systemic Signaling

Many inducible defenses are expressed rapidly (i.e., within hours) in undamaged leaves of herbivore-challenged plants. This fascinating systemic response, which has been documented in a wide range of plant species, provides effective resistance to future insect attacks (14, 61). Since the discovery of this phenomenon more than 35 years ago (38), considerable research effort has been devoted to the identification of systemic wound signals and the underlying mechanisms by which they are produced, transported, and perceived. Classical grafting experiments indicate that systemic proteinase inhibitor (PI) expression in *S. lycopersicum* depends both on JA synthesis at the site of wounding and on jasmonate perception in distal undamaged leaves. These and other findings support a model in which JA (or a derivative of JA) acts as a phloem-mobile signal (109). Systemin, which is a potent peptide elicitor of PI expression in *S. lycopersicum*, appears to strengthen systemic defenses by amplifying jasmonate synthesis in damaged leaves (109). Notably, however, the systemin homolog in *Solanum nigrum* (black nightshade) does not mediate PI expression or other direct defense responses (114). The divergent role of systemin in closely related species suggests that different plants may employ distinct mechanisms to regulate jasmonate synthesis and systemic responses to herbivory (50).

Recent studies with *N. attenuata* indicate that FACs in oral secretions of *M. sexta* elicit rapid activation of MAPK activity and defense-related genes in undamaged areas of the attacked leaf (142). FAC binding to a hypothetical receptor was proposed to generate a rapidly acting, short-distance mobile signal that triggers MAPK cascades in the damaged leaf. This intraleaf systemic response is followed by the production of a second mobile signal (e.g., jasmonate) that initiates PI expression in distal undamaged leaves. These findings are consistent with the idea that multiple intercellular signals, acting over a range of distances, mediate the complex spatiotemporal responses of plants to herbivory. That both *S. lycopersicum* systemin and FACs positively regulate jasmonate synthesis via a MAPK cascade (58, 142) suggests that parallel signaling pathways initiated at the plant-insect interface may converge on the jasmonate pathway (**Figure 4**).

DIRECT DEFENSE RESPONSES

Secondary Metabolites

It is likely that all plants exhibit constitutive or induced accumulation of toxic secondary metabolites as part of their defense against herbivory. Research with numerous plant species has revealed a great variety of small molecules with toxic or antifeedant effects on insect herbivores. Many terpenoids, the most metabolically diverse class of plant secondary metabolites (>40,000 known structures), play a role in plant defense (2). The alkaloids, widely distributed secondary metabolites that are best known for their metabolic effects in mammals (e.g., caffeine, nicotine, morphine, strychnine, and cocaine), likely evolved as a defense against insect herbivory. Other well-studied classes of plant secondary metabolites with defensive properties include the furanocoumarins, cardenolides, tannins, saponins, glucosinolates, and cyanogenic glycosides.

PI: proteinase inhibitor

Recent advances in plant molecular biology have made it possible to identify the biosynthetic pathways leading to the production of defensive toxins. For example, Frey and coworkers (30) discovered genes encoding all five enzymes involved in the biosynthesis of 2,4-dihydroxy-1,4-benzoxazin-3-one (DIBOA), a toxin found in maize, wheat, and other Gramineae. Almost all genes required for the production of glucosinolates, a diverse class of metabolites found in the model plant *A. thaliana* and other Cruciferae, have been identified (41). As an example of how such knowledge of biochemical pathways can be applied to change plant immunity to herbivory, *A. thaliana* was engineered with three enzymes from *Sorghum bicolor* (grain sorghum) to produce the cyanogenic glycoside dhurrin, thereby enhancing resistance to *Phyllotreta nemorum* (yellow-striped flea beetle) (127).

Many defensive compounds are potentially toxic to the plants that produce them. Therefore, the storage of relatively benign precursors that are activated by herbivory is a recurring theme in plant biology. For instance, all three of the defensive systems mentioned in the previous paragraph include compounds that are sequestered in plants, but not activated until the onset of herbivory. DIBOA is stored as inactive DIBOA-glucoside, glucosinolates are enzymatically activated to produce toxic breakdown products, and the respiratory inhibitor hydrogen cyanide is released from cyanogenic glycosides during herbivory.

The complex mixture of toxins found in many plants may provide synergistic effects in defense against herbivory. For instance, a combination of two monoterpenoids is almost ten times more toxic to *Spodoptera litura* (tobacco cutworm) than would have been predicted from a simple additive effect (53). Similarly, exposure of *Callosobruchus maculatus* (cowpea bruchid) to PIs shows synergistic effects; growth inhibition by several PIs is more effective than the sum of the individual inhibitors (6). Although some herbivores can compensate for the presence of PIs by consuming additional plant tissue (140), increased food consumption may be constrained by the deleterious effects of increased exposure to toxins. Steppuhn & Baldwin (122) recently verified this experimentally by silencing PI expression and/or nicotine production in *N. attenuata* and demonstrating that compensatory feeding by *M. sexta* in response to PIs was prevented by the presence of nicotine in the diet.

In addition to possible synergistic effects, metabolic diversity in toxin production by individual plants can also provide defense against multiple herbivores with different feeding styles or resistance mechanisms. Recent work on glucosinolates demonstrates how natural selection for a diverse profile of secondary metabolites can provide defensive specificity. Nearly 40 different glucosinolates have been found in *A. thaliana*, and more than 100 breakdown products are likely formed after activation by the enzyme myrosinase. Experiments with four insect herbivores showed that tryptophan-derived indole and methionine-derived aliphatic glucosinolates have differing effects on Hemiptera and Lepidoptera (87). Indole glucosinolates, which break down in the absence of the activating enzyme myrosinase (11), provide a better defense against *M. persicae* than do the more stable aliphatic glucosinolates (70). The *EPITHIOSPECIFIER* (*ESP*) and *EPITHIOSPECIFIER MODIFIER 1* (*ESM1*) loci, which were identified by means of natural variation in insect resistance (73, 147), control the breakdown of aliphatic glucosinolates to either nitriles or isothiocyanates. Isothiocyanates provide better resistance to *T. ni*, *S. littoralis*, and *P. rapae* than do nitriles (1, 16, 73). Nevertheless, the continued presence of the nitrile-generating ESP protein in many *A. thaliana* land races (73) suggests that nitrile production benefits plants in nature.

Defensive Proteins

Insect feeding triggers the expression of plant defensive proteins that exert direct effects on the attacker. PIs, which impair various mechanistic classes of digestive proteases in the insect midgut, have been thoroughly studied for their role in the active defense response (38, 107). Inhibition of gut proteases by PIs results in amino acid deficiencies that negatively affect the growth and development of the herbivore (79, 146). The effectiveness of PIs as a defense is often thwarted by the insect's adaptive ability to express digestive proteases that are insensitive to the host plant complement of PIs or that inactivate PIs (12, 34, 56, 104). The diversity and rapid evolution of certain *PI* gene families may reflect the evolution of insect counter-adaptations that have led to the chemical arms race between plants and herbivores (125).

The plant's defensive protein arsenal also includes enzymes that disrupt insect digestive physiology and other aspects of food consumption. Members of the cysteine protease family of enzymes, for example, disrupt the chitin-rich peritrophic membrane that protects the gut epithelium (72, 91). Plant lectins and chitinases may also target carbohydrate-containing components of the insect gut (74, 97). Oxidative enzymes such as polyphenol oxidase (PPO) and lipoxygenase (LOX) covalently modify dietary protein through the production of reactive *o*-quinones and lipid peroxides, respectively (20, 29, 139). Because catalysis by O_2-dependent enzymes is limited by low oxygen levels in the foregut and midgut of some insect species (54), an alternative possibility is that PPO and LOX act rapidly (i.e., within seconds) during tissue mastication by insect mouthparts. This hypothesis is particularly germane in the case of plants such as potato and tomato that express high levels of PPO (130) and LOX (A. Schilmiller, R. Last & C. Wilkerson, unpublished observation) in glandular trichomes.

The discovery of novel defensive proteins has been facilitated by proteomic analysis of gut content and feces (frass) of insect herbivores. This approach is based on the premise that defensive proteins are relatively resistant to gut proteases and, as a consequence, are highly enriched during passage of the food bolus through the insect. Application of this procedure to the tomato-reared *M. sexta* larvae led to the identification of isoforms of arginase and threonine deaminase (TD), which degrade the essential amino acids arginine and threonine, respectively, in the lepidopteran midgut (18). Arginase and TD appear to be components of a multitiered defensive system that functions to deplete amino acid availability in the alkaline environment of the lepidopteran gut; the low protein (i.e., amino acid) content of plant tissue is often a limiting factor for the growth of insect herbivores (85). TD's ability to degrade threonine is activated during herbivore attack by proteolytic removal of the enzyme's C-terminal regulatory domain (17). An emerging concept from this and other recent studies (112, 139) is that limited proteolysis of plant proteins in the insect gut provides a level of regulation in the overall control of induced host defenses. In summary, wound-induced postingestive defenses likely involve synergistic interactions between PIs, oxidative enzymes, amino acid–degrading enzymes, and metabolites that exert a combination of toxic and antifeedant effects. The central role of proteins in this process broadens the traditional view that secondary metabolites are the major determinants of host plant utilization by insects.

Induced expression of many anti-insect proteins is tightly regulated by the jasmonate signaling pathway. Examples of jasmonate-inducible proteins that have an established or putative role in direct defense include PPO, arginase, TD, leucine amino peptidase, acid phosphatase (VSP2), and a broad spectrum of PIs (17, 18, 20, 29, 79). The abundance of many of these proteins in the insect gut correlates with high-level accumulation of the corresponding transcripts in insect-damaged leaves (17, 18). Jasmonate-induced transcription and high protein stability appear to provide complementary mechanisms to maximize the effectiveness of protein-based defenses while minimizing the high allocation costs associated with the production of protein-based defenses. The lack of expression of jasmonate-inducible proteins in *coi1* mutants (18, 77) indicates that these proteins are dispensable for plant vegetative growth in the laboratory. This observation, together with the sporadic occurrence of jasmonate-inducible proteins (e.g., TD) in specific plant lineages, suggests that midgut-active defensive enzymes evolved from preexisting housekeeping enzymes that catabolize essential nutrients during normal plant development.

TD: threonine deaminase

VOLATILE COMMUNICATION DURING HERBIVORY

Volatile-Mediated Direct and Indirect Defenses

The release of volatiles in response to herbivory can provide a direct defensive benefit by deterring further conspecific oviposition (22) or an indirect benefit by attracting predators (66). The attraction of parasitoid wasps by damage-induced volatiles is a well-studied phenomenon in many plant species. Parasitoids associate plant-derived odors with the presence of prey, which provides a defensive benefit to the emitting plants as long as volatile production is a reliable beacon of herbivory. The specificity of this interaction has been demonstrated with the expression of *Z. mays* TPS10, an herbivore-induced terpene synthase that forms (*E*)-β-farnesene, (*E*)-α-bergamotene, and other sesquiterpenes, in *A. thaliana* (115). Females of the parasitoid *Cotesia marginiventris*, which had learned to associate this odor with their prey, *S. littoralis*, were subsequently attracted to TPS10-producing *A. thaliana*. Because wild-type *A. thaliana* does not produce significant amounts of volatile terpenes, this experiment demonstrates that a single herbivore-induced gene from *Z. mays* is sufficient to elicit this indirect defense.

Other recent work with *Z. mays* shows that the release of volatiles provides an indirect defense against underground herbivory. In response to attack by larvae of *Diabrotica virgifera* (western corn rootworm), maize roots release (*E*)-β-caryophyllene, which attracts *Heterorhabditis megidis* nematodes that feed on the beetle larvae (101). Treatment of nonproducing plants with (*E*)-β-caryophyllene attracted *H. magidis* and reduced herbivory.

Inter- and Intraplant Volatile Communication

In addition to mediating interactions with herbivores and their predators, damage-induced volatiles can provide a signal that allows neighboring plants to prepare for imminent herbivory. This process, called priming, results in a more rapid or a more robust response to subsequent herbivory (9, 28, 62). Although early experiments relied on laboratory setups with unrealistically high volatile concentrations, there are now good examples of interplant signaling through the release of endogenous volatiles. Green leafy volatiles (primarily degradation products of linoleic and linolenic acids) released by *Z. mays* primed neighboring plants to respond more vigorously to subsequent mechanical damage and application of caterpillar oral secretions (28). *N. attenuata* planted adjacent to clipped *Artemisia tridentata* (sagebrush) received a blend of volatile organic compounds that altered gene expression and caused more rapid induction of PI production upon subsequent feeding by *M. sexta* (69).

At first glance, it would appear that eavesdropping on volatile signals should provide a defensive benefit only to the receiving plant. However, in a tree or other large plant, volatiles transferred between branches or leaves of the same individual would potentially allow faster communication of imminent threats than would phloem-mediated propagation of a systemic signal (described above). Recent studies with three plant-insect interaction systems provide evidence of such intraplant volatile-mediated priming. Field experiments with mechanically clipped *A. tridentata* showed that defense priming depends on the movement of an airborne signal between damaged and undamaged branches (63). In laboratory experiments with *P. deltoides* × *P. nigra* (hybrid poplar), volatiles released by *Lymantria dispar* (gypsy moth)-challenged leaves primed a nearby leaf on the same plant to release terpene volatiles more rapidly in response to subsequent attack by *L. dispar* (31). Extrafloral nectar production, which can attract insect predators, was both induced and primed by volatiles released from *P. lunatus* leaves on the same plant under natural conditions (46).

PERSPECTIVES AND FUTURE DIRECTIONS

As described in this review, there has been considerable recent progress in deciphering the molecular basis of plant immunity to insect herbivores. Nevertheless, knowledge of how plants perceive and respond to herbivory lags far behind our understanding of plant responses to pathogen invasion. Although both insect-derived elicitors (**Figure 1**) and NBS-LRR receptors involved in insect recognition have been identified independently, there are as yet no known receptor-ligand interactions or direct links from these to the induction of plant defense pathways. Calcium flux, phosphorylation cascades, and other early signaling events are necessary for full defense induction, but the order of these signals, feedback loops that augment or attenuate responses, and connections to downstream transcriptional and metabolic changes remain relatively uninvestigated. Identification of the JAZ family of proteins will permit experiments that lead to a deeper mechanistic understanding of jasmonate signaling and its role in controlling the outcome of a myriad of plant-pest interactions. Rather than being a set of linear pathways, jasmonate and other signals that regulate the expression of plant defenses clearly involve a complex mesh of interactions that provide the flexibility needed to respond to multiple herbivores and pathogens in a natural setting. The inevitable tradeoffs that occur during plant responses to simultaneous attacks and the possible manipulation of the plant defense network (e.g., phytohormone synthesis and action) by herbivores are important research areas that deserve further attention.

Research on plant-pathogen interactions provides a good model for approaches that can also be used to study plant interactions with herbivores. Many of the key pathogen defense genes in plants were discovered by means of mutant screens. Similarly, genetic mapping of plant mutations that alter herbivore resistance, or perhaps responses to purified insect elicitors, will almost certainly lead to the identification of previously unknown defense pathways. Research on plant-pathogen interactions has also benefited greatly from experimental systems in which it is possible to study responses and perform genetic manipulations on both sides of the interaction (e.g., *A. thaliana* and *Pseudomonas syringae*). Ongoing genome projects for *Medicago truncatula* (barrel medic) and *Acyrthosiphon pisum* (pea aphid) will provide the first plant-insect system in which it is possible to study broad-scale gene expression on both sides of the interaction. Beyond genome sequencing, additional effort should be placed on identifying insect genetic markers, studying natural variation in host plant utilization, and developing methods such as RNA interference for manipulating insect gene expression. The development of such research tools will facilitate studies on both sides of the plant-insect interaction and thereby achieve a more complete understanding of plant immunity to insect herbivores.

SUMMARY POINTS

1. Terrestrial plants use a combination of constitutive and inducible defensive traits to resist challenge by herbivorous insects; in natural ecosystems, any given plant species is consumed by only a small fraction of the herbivores in that environment.
2. Initial signaling events at the plant-insect interface (i.e., the bite zone), which include rapid changes in Ca^{2+} flux, membrane potential, and phosphorylation status, play an important role in the control of defensive processes but remain poorly understood.
3. Defense responses to insect attack are elicited by compounds in insect oral secretions. In the case of plant interactions with some hemipteran insects, there is evidence for the involvement of *R* genes in the control of host plant resistance.
4. Temporal and spatial patterns of mechanical tissue injury resulting from herbivory play a critical role in the production of endogenous signals that promote host defense responses.
5. The jasmonate signaling pathway is an evolutionarily conserved mechanism to regulate the expression of direct and indirect defenses. As relatively nonspecific sentinels of cellular injury, jasmonates promote resistance to a wide variety of biotic aggressors.

6. Herbivore attack results in rapid accumulation of JA and its bioactive conjugate, JA-Ile. Recent studies support a model in which binding of JA-Ile to COI1 triggers the degradation of JAZ repressor proteins and subsequent derepression of defensive genes.
7. Plant defensive metabolites and proteins thwart herbivory by exerting direct repellent, antifeedant, and toxic effects on the insect. Synergistic interactions between these compounds strengthen the host defense response.
8. Herbivore-induced plant volatiles serve several important functions in plant immunity to insect herbivores, including the attraction of insect predators and priming of defense responses.

DISCLOSURE STATEMENT

The authors are not aware of any biases that might be perceived as affecting the objectivity of this review.

ACKNOWLEDGMENTS

This review is dedicated to the memory of Clarence "Bud" Ryan, whose pioneering research inspired several generations of plant biologists to pursue the study of plant-insect interactions. The authors wish to thank Eric Schmelz, Peter Constabel, Martin de Vos, and Gary Felton for helpful comments on the manuscript. We also thank Jim Tumlinson, Tony Schilmiller, Rob Last, and Curtis Wilkerson for sharing unpublished information. Plant-insect interaction research in G.H.'s laboratory is currently supported by the National Institutes of Health (R01GM57795), the U.S. Department of Energy (DE-FG02-91ER20021), the U.S. Department of Agriculture (2007-35604-17791), and the National Science Foundation (DBI-0604336). Plant-insect interaction research in G.J.'s laboratory is supported by the U.S. Department of Agriculture (2005-35604-15446) and the National Science Foundation (IOS-0718733, DBI-0500550, and OISE-0436554).

LITERATURE CITED

1. Agrawal AA, Kurashige NS. 2003. A role for isothiocyanates in plant resistance against the specialist herbivore *Pieris rapae*. *J. Chem. Ecol.* 29:1403–15
2. Aharoni A, Jongsma MA, Bouwmeester HJ. 2005. Volatile science? Metabolic engineering of terpenoids in plants. *Trends Plant Sci.* 10:594–602
3. Alborn HT, Brennan EB, Tumlinson JH. 2003. Differential activity and degradation of plant volatile elicitors in regurgitant of tobacco hornworm (*Manduca sexta*) larvae. *J. Chem. Ecol.* 29:1357–72
4. Alborn HT, Hansen TV, Jones TH, Bennett DC, Tumlinson JH, et al. 2007. Novel disulfoxy fatty acids from the American bird grasshopper *Shistocerca americana*, elicitors of plant volatiles. *Proc. Natl. Acad. Sci. USA* 104:12976–81
5. Alborn HT, Turlings TCJ, Jones TH, Stenhagen G, Loughrin JH, Tumlinson JH. 1997. An elicitor of plant volatiles from beet armyworm oral secretion. *Science* 276:945–49

6. Amirhusin B, Shade RE, Koiwa H, Hasegawa PM, Bressan RA, et al. 2007. Protease inhibitors from several classes work synergistically against *Callosobruchus maculatus*. *J. Insect Physiol.* 53:734–40
7. Arimura G, Huber DP, Bohlmann J. 2004. Forest tent caterpillars (*Malacosoma disstria*) induce local and systemic diurnal emissions of terpenoid volatiles in hybrid poplar (*Populus trichocarpa* × *deltoides*): cDNA cloning, functional characterization, and patterns of gene expression of (-)-germacrene D synthase, *PtdTPS1*. *Plant J.* 37:603–16
8. Arimura G, Ozawa R, Kugimiya S, Takabayashi J, Bohlmann J. 2004. Herbivore-induced defense response in a model legume. Two-spotted spider mites induce emission of (*E*)-β-ocimene and transcript accumulation of (*E*)-β-ocimene synthase in *Lotus japonicus*. *Plant Physiol.* 135:1976–83
9. Arimura G, Ozawa R, Shimoda T, Nishioka T, Boland W, Takabayashi J. 2000. Herbivory-induced volatiles elicit defence genes in lima bean leaves. *Nature* 406:512–15
10. Baldwin IT. 1998. Jasmonate-induced responses are costly but benefit plants under attack in native populations. *Proc. Natl. Acad. Sci. USA* 95:8113–18
11. Barth C, Jander G. 2006. Arabidopsis myrosinases TGG1 and TGG2 have redundant function in glucosinolate breakdown and insect defense. *Plant J.* 46:549–62
12. Bayes A, Comellas-Bigler M, de la Vega MR, Maskos K, Bode W, et al. 2005. Structural basis of the resistance of an insect carboxypeptidase to plant protease inhibitors. *Proc. Natl. Acad. Sci. USA* 102:16602–7
13. Becerra JX. 2007. The impact of herbivore-plant coevolution on plant community structure. *Proc. Natl. Acad. Sci. USA* 104:7483–88
14. Bostock RM. 2005. Signal crosstalk and induced resistance: straddling the line between cost and benefit. *Annu. Rev. Phytopathol.* 43:545–80
15. Boughton AJ, Hoover K, Felton GW. 2005. Methyl jasmonate application induces increased densities of glandular trichomes on tomato, *Lycopersicon esculentum*. *J. Chem. Ecol.* 31:2211–16
16. Burow M, Muller R, Gershenzon J, Wittstock U. 2006. Altered glucosinolate hydrolysis in genetically engineered *Arabidopsis thaliana* and its influence on the larval development of *Spodoptera littoralis*. *J. Chem. Ecol.* 32:2333–49
17. Chen H, Gonzales-Vigil E, Wilkerson CG, Howe GA. 2007. Stability of plant defense proteins in the gut of insect herbivores. *Plant Physiol.* 143:1954–67
18. Chen H, Wilkerson CG, Kuchar JA, Phinney BS, Howe GA. 2005. Jasmonate-inducible plant enzymes degrade essential amino acids in the herbivore midgut. *Proc. Natl. Acad. Sci. USA* 102:19237–42
19. Chini A, Fonseca S, Fernández G, Adie B, Chico JM, et al. 2007. The JAZ family of repressors is the missing link in jasmonate signalling. *Nature* 448:666–71
20. Constabel CP, Bergey DR, Ryan CA. 1995. Systemin activates synthesis of wound-inducible tomato leaf polyphenol oxidase via the octadecanoid defense signaling pathway. *Proc. Natl. Acad. Sci. USA* 92:407–11
21. Cui JP, Jander G, Racki LR, Kim PD, Pierce NE, Ausubel FM. 2002. Signals involved in Arabidopsis resistance to *Trichoplusia ni* caterpillars induced by virulent and avirulent strains of the phytopathogen *Pseudomonas syringae*. *Plant Physiol.* 129:551–64
22. De Moraes CM, Mescher MC, Tumlinson JH. 2001. Caterpillar-induced nocturnal plant volatiles repel conspecific females. *Nature* 410:577–80
23. De Vos M, Van Oosten VR, Van Poecke RMP, Van Pelt JA, Pozo MJ, et al. 2005. Signal signature and transcriptome changes of *Arabidopsis* during pathogen and insect attack. *Mol. Plant-Microbe Interact.* 18:923–37

24. Devoto A, Ellis C, Magusin A, Chang HS, Chilcott C, et al. 2005. Expression profiling reveals COI1 to be a key regulator of genes involved in wound- and methyl jasmonate-induced secondary metabolism, defence, and hormone interactions. *Plant Mol. Biol.* 58:497–513
25. Devoto A, Turner JG. 2005. Jasmonate-regulated Arabidopsis stress signalling network. *Physiol. Plant.* 123:161–72
26. Dogimont C, Bendahmane A, Pitrat M, Burget-Bigeard E, Hagen L, et al. 2007. *U.S. Patent No. 20,070,016,977*
27. Ellis C, Karafyllidis I, Turner JG. 2002. Constitutive activation of jasmonate signaling in an *Arabidopsis* mutant correlates with enhanced resistance to *Erysiphe cichoracearum*, *Pseudomonas syringae*, and *Myzus persicae*. *Mol. Plant-Microbe Interact.* 15:1025–30
28. Engelberth J, Alborn HT, Schmelz EA, Tumlinson JH. 2004. Airborne signals prime plants against insect herbivore attack. *Proc. Natl. Acad. Sci. USA* 101:1781–85
29. Felton GW, Bi JL, Summers CB, Mueller AJ, Duffey SS. 1994. Potential role of lipoxygenases in defense against insect herbivory. *J. Chem. Ecol.* 20:651–66
30. Frey M, Chomet P, Glawischnig E, Stettner C, Grun S, et al. 1997. Analysis of a chemical plant defense mechanism in grasses. *Science* 277:696–99
31. Frost CJ, Appel HM, Carlson JE, De Moraes CM, Mescher MC, Schultz JC. 2007. Within-plant signalling via volatiles overcomes vascular constraints on systemic signalling and primes responses against herbivores. *Ecol. Lett.* 10:490–98
32. Gao LL, Anderson JP, Klingler JP, Nair RM, Edwards OR, Singh KB. 2007. Involvement of the octadecanoid pathway in bluegreen aphid resistance in *Medicago truncatula*. *Mol. Plant-Microbe Interact.* 20:82–93
33. Gatehouse JA. 2002. Plant resistance towards insect herbivores: a dynamic interaction. *New Phytol.* 156:145–69
34. Giri AP, Harsulkar AM, Deshpande VV, Sainani MN, Gupta VS, Ranjekar PK. 1998. Chickpea defensive proteinase inhibitors can be inactivated by podborer gut proteinases. *Plant Physiol.* 116:393–401
35. Giri AP, Wunsche H, Mitra S, Zavala JA, Muck A, et al. 2006. Molecular interactions between the specialist herbivore *Manduca sexta* (Lepidoptera, Sphingidae) and its natural host *Nicotiana attenuata*. VII. Changes in the plant's proteome. *Plant Physiol.* 142:1621–41
36. Glazebrook J. 2005. Contrasting mechanisms of defense against biotrophic and necrotrophic pathogens. *Annu. Rev. Phytopathol.* 43:205–27
37. Gómez-Gómez L, Boller T. 2002. Flagellin perception: a paradigm for innate immunity. *Trends Plant Sci.* 7:251–56
38. Green TR, Ryan CA. 1972. Wound-induced proteinase inhibitor in plant leaves: a possible defense mechanism against insects. *Science* 175:776–77
39. Halitschke R, Gase K, Hui D, Schmidt DD, Baldwin IT. 2003. Molecular interactions between the specialist herbivore *Manduca sexta* (Lepidoptera, Sphingidae) and its natural host *Nicotiana attenuata*. VI. Microarray analysis reveals that most herbivore-specific transcriptional changes are mediated by fatty acid-amino acid conjugates. *Plant Physiol.* 131:1894–902
40. Halitschke R, Schittko U, Pohnert G, Boland W, Baldwin IT. 2001. Molecular interactions between the specialist herbivore *Manduca sexta* (Lepidoptera, Sphingidae) and its natural host *Nicotiana attenuata*. III. Fatty acid-amino acid conjugates in herbivore oral secretions are necessary and sufficient for herbivore-specific plant responses. *Plant Physiol.* 125:711–17
41. Halkier BA, Gershenzon J. 2006. Biology and biochemistry of glucosinolates. *Annu. Rev. Plant Biol.* 57:303–33

42. Hamel LP, Nicole MC, Sritubtim S, Morency MJ, Ellis M, et al. 2006. Ancient signals: comparative genomics of plant MAPK and MAPKK gene families. *Trends Plant Sci.* 11:192–98
43. Harfouche AL, Shivaji R, Stocker R, Williams PW, Luthe DS. 2006. Ethylene signaling mediates a maize defense response to insect herbivory. *Mol. Plant-Microbe Interact.* 19:189–99
44. Hause B, Stenzel I, Miersch O, Maucher H, Kramell R, et al. 2000. Tissue-specific oxylipin signature of tomato flowers: Allene oxide cyclase is highly expressed in distinct flower organs and vascular bundles. *Plant J.* 24:113–26
45. Heidel AJ, Baldwin IT. 2004. Microarray analysis of salicylic acid- and jasmonic acid-signalling in responses of *Nicotiana attenuata* to attack by insects from multiple feeding guilds. *Plant Cell Environ.* 27:1362–73
46. Heil M, Silva Bueno JC. 2007. Within-plant signaling by volatiles leads to induction and priming of an indirect plant defense in nature. *Proc. Natl. Acad. Sci. USA* 104:5467–72
47. Herms DA, Mattson WJ. 1992. The dilemma of plants: to grow or defend. *Q. Rev. Biol.* 67:283–335
48. Hilker M, Meiners T. 2006. Early herbivore alert: Insect eggs induce plant defense. *J. Chem. Ecol.* 32:1379–97
49. Horiuchi J, Arimura G, Ozawa R, Shimoda T, Takabayashi J, Nishioka T. 2001. Exogenous ACC enhances volatiles production mediated by jasmonic acid in lima bean leaves. *FEBS Lett.* 509:332–36
50. Howe GA. 2004. Jasmonates as signals in the wound response. *J. Plant Growth Regul.* 23:223–37
51. Hudgins JW, Franceschi VR. 2004. Methyl jasmonate-induced ethylene production is responsible for conifer phloem defense responses and reprogramming of stem cambial zone for traumatic resin duct formation. *Plant Physiol.* 135:2134–49
52. Hui DQ, Iqbal J, Lehmann K, Gase K, Saluz HP, Baldwin IT. 2003. Molecular interactions between the specialist herbivore *Manduca sexta* (Lepidoptera, Sphingidae) and its natural host *Nicotiana attenuata*. V. Microarray analysis and further characterization of large-scale changes in herbivore-induced mRNAs. *Plant Physiol.* 131:1877–93
53. Hummelbrunner LA, Isman MB. 2001. Acute, sublethal, antifeedant, and synergistic effects of monoterpenoid essential oil compounds on the tobacco cutworm, *Spodoptera litura* (Lep., Noctuidae). *J. Agric. Food Chem.* 49:715–20
54. Johnson KS, Barbehenn RV. 2000. Oxygen levels in the gut lumens of herbivorous insects. *J. Insect Physiol.* 46:897–903
55. Jones JD, Dangl JL. 2006. The plant immune system. *Nature* 444:323–29
56. Jongsma MA, Bakker PL, Peters J, Bosch D, Stiekema WJ. 1995. Adaptation of *Spodoptera exigua* larvae to plant proteinase inhibitors by induction of gut proteinase activity insensitive to inhibition. *Proc. Natl. Acad. Sci. USA* 92:8041–45
57. Kaloshian I, Walling LL. 2005. Hemipterans as plant pathogens. *Annu. Rev. Phytopathol.* 43:491–521
58. Kandoth PK, Ranf S, Pancholi SS, Jayanty S, Walla MD, et al. 2007. Tomato MAPKs LeMPK1, LeMPK2, and LeMPK3 function in the systemin-mediated defense response against herbivorous insects. *Proc. Natl. Acad. Sci. USA* 104:12205–10
59. Kang JH, Wang L, Giri A, Baldwin IT. 2006. Silencing threonine deaminase and JAR4 in *Nicotiana attenuata* impairs jasmonic acid-isoleucine-mediated defenses against *Manduca sexta*. *Plant Cell* 18:3303–20
60. Karban R, Agrawal AA, Mangel M. 1997. The benefits of induced defenses against herbivores. *Ecology* 78:1351–55

61. Karban R, Baldwin IT. 1997. *Induced Responses to Herbivory*. Chicago, IL: Univ. Chicago Press
62. Karban R, Baldwin IT, Baxter KJ, Laue G, Felton GW. 2000. Communication between plants: induced resistance in wild tobacco plants following clipping of neighboring sagebrush. *Oecologia* 125:66–71
63. Karban R, Shiojiri K, Huntzinger M, McCall AC. 2006. Damage-induced resistance in sagebrush: Volatiles are key to intra- and interplant communication. *Ecology* 87:922–30
64. Katou S, Yoshioka H, Kawakita K, Rowland O, Jones JDG, et al. 2005. Involvement of PPS3 phosphorylated by elicitor-responsive mitogen-activated protein kinases in the regulation of plant cell death. *Plant Physiol.* 139:1914–26
65. Kempema LA, Cui X, Holzer FM, Walling LL. 2007. Arabidopsis transcriptome changes in response to phloem-feeding silverleaf whitefly nymphs. Similarities and distinctions in responses to aphids. *Plant Physiol.* 143:849–65
66. Kessler A, Baldwin IT. 2001. Defensive function of herbivore-induced plant volatile emissions in nature. *Science* 291:2141–44
67. Kessler A, Baldwin IT. 2002. Plant responses to insect herbivory: the emerging molecular analysis. *Annu. Rev. Plant Biol.* 53:299–328
68. Kessler A, Halitschke R, Baldwin IT. 2004. Silencing the jasmonate cascade: induced plant defenses and insect populations. *Science* 305:665–68
69. Kessler A, Halitschke R, Diezel C, Baldwin IT. 2006. Priming of plant defense responses in nature by airborne signaling between *Artemisia tridentata* and *Nicotiana attenuata*. *Oecologia* 148:280–92
70. Kim JH, Jander G. 2007. *Myzus persicae* (green peach aphid) feeding on Arabidopsis induces the formation of a deterrent indole glucosinolate. *Plant J.* 49:1008–19
71. Koch T, Krumm T, Jung V, Engelberth J, Boland W. 1999. Differential induction of plant volatile biosynthesis in the lima bean by early and late intermediates of the octadecanoid-signaling pathway. *Plant Physiol.* 121:153–62
72. Konno K, Hirayama C, Nakamura M, Tateishi K, Tamura Y, et al. 2004. Papain protects papaya trees from herbivorous insects: role of cysteine proteases in latex. *Plant J.* 37:370–78
73. Lambrix V, Reichelt M, Mitchell-Olds T, Kliebenstein DJ, Gershenzon J. 2001. The Arabidopsis epithiospecifier protein promotes the hydrolysis of glucosinolates to nitriles and influences *Trichoplusia ni* herbivory. *Plant Cell* 13:2793–807
74. Lawrence SD, Novak NG. 2006. Expression of poplar chitinase in tomato leads to inhibition of development in Colorado potato beetle. *Biotech. Lett.* 28:593–99
75. Levy M, Wang Q, Kaspi R, Parrella MP, Abel S. 2005. Arabidopsis IQD1, a novel calmodulin-binding nuclear protein, stimulates glucosinolate accumulation and plant defense. *Plant J.* 43:79–96
76. Li C, Schilmiller AL, Liu G, Lee GI, Jayanty S, et al. 2005. Role of β-oxidation in jasmonate biosynthesis and systemic wound signaling in tomato. *Plant Cell* 17:971–86
77. Li L, Zhao Y, McCaig BC, Wingerd BA, Wang J, et al. 2004. The tomato homolog of *CORONATINE-INSENSITIVE1* is required for the maternal control of seed maturation, jasmonate-signaled defense responses, and glandular trichome development. *Plant Cell* 16:126–43
78. Li Q, Xie QG, Smith-Becker J, Navarre DA, Kaloshian I. 2006. *Mi-1*-mediated aphid resistance involves salicylic acid and mitogen-activated protein kinase signaling cascades. *Mol. Plant-Microbe Interact.* 19:655–64
79. Lison P, Rodrigo I, Conejero V. 2006. A novel function for the cathepsin D inhibitor in tomato. *Plant Physiol.* 142:1329–39

80. Little D, Gouhier-Darimont C, Bruessow F, Reymond P. 2007. Oviposition by pierid butterflies triggers defense responses in Arabidopsis. *Plant Physiol.* 143:784–800
81. Maffei M, Bossi S, Spiteller D, Mithöfer A, Boland W. 2004. Effects of feeding *Spodoptera littoralis* on lima bean leaves. I. Membrane potentials, intracellular calcium variations, oral secretions, and regurgitate components. *Plant Physiol.* 134:1752–62
82. Maffei ME, Mithöfer A, Arimura G, Uchtenhagen H, Bossi S, et al. 2006. Effects of feeding *Spodoptera littoralis* on lima bean leaves. III. Membrane depolarization and involvement of hydrogen peroxide. *Plant Physiol.* 140:1022–35
83. Maffei ME, Mithöfer A, Boland W. 2007. Before gene expression: early events in plant-insect interaction. *Trends Plant Sci.* 12:310–16
84. Major IT, Constabel CP. 2006. Molecular analysis of poplar defense against herbivory: comparison of wound- and insect elicitor-induced gene expression. *New Phytol.* 172:617–35
85. Mattson WJ. 1980. Herbivory in relation to plant nitrogen-content. *Annu. Rev. Ecol. System.* 11:119–61
86. Matzinger P. 2002. The danger model: a renewed sense of self. *Science* 296:301–5
87. Mewis I, Appel HM, Hom A, Raina R, Schultz JC. 2005. Major signaling pathways modulate Arabidopsis glucosinolate accumulation and response to both phloem-feeding and chewing insects. *Plant Physiol.* 138:1149–62
88. Mewis I, Tokuhisa JG, Schultz JC, Appel HM, Ulrichs C, Gershenzon J. 2006. Gene expression and glucosinolate accumulation in *Arabidopsis thaliana* in response to generalist and specialist herbivores of different feeding guilds and the role of defense signaling pathways. *Phytochemistry* 67:2450–62
89. Miles PW. 1999. Aphid saliva. *Biol. Rev.* 74:41–85
90. Mithöfer A, Wanner G, Boland W. 2005. Effects of feeding *Spodoptera littoralis* on lima bean leaves. II. Continuous mechanical wounding resembling insect feeding is sufficient to elicit herbivory-related volatile emission. *Plant Physiol.* 137:1160–68
91. Mohan S, Ma PWK, Pechan T, Bassford ER, Williams WP, Luthe DS. 2006. Degradation of the *S. frugiperda* peritrophic matrix by an inducible maize cysteine protease. *J. Insect Physiol.* 52:21–28
92. Mori N, Alborn HT, Teal PEA, Tumlinson JH. 2001. Enzymatic decomposition of elicitors of plant volatiles in *Heliothis virescens* and *Helicoverpa zea*. *J. Insect Physiol.* 47:749–57
93. Musser RO, Farmer E, Peiffer M, Williams SA, Felton GW. 2006. Ablation of caterpillar labial salivary glands: technique for determining the role of saliva in insect-plant interactions. *J. Chem. Ecol.* 32:981–92
94. Nombela G, Williamson VM, Muniz M. 2003. The root-knot nematode resistance gene *Mi-1.2* of tomato is responsible for resistance against the whitefly *Bemisia tabaci*. *Mol. Plant-Microbe Interact.* 16:645–49
95. Pare PW, Alborn HT, Tumlinson JH. 1998. Concerted biosynthesis of an insect elicitor of plant volatiles. *Proc. Natl. Acad. Sci. USA* 95:13971–75
96. Paschold A, Halitschke R, Baldwin IT. 2007. Co(i)-ordinating defenses: NaCOI1 mediates herbivore-induced resistance in *Nicotiana attenuata* and reveals the role of herbivore movement in avoiding defenses. *Plant J.* 51:79–91
97. Peumans WJ, Vandamme EJM. 1995. Lectins as plant defense proteins. *Plant Physiol.* 109:347–52
98. Pohnert G, Jung V, Haukioja E, Lempa K, Boland G. 1999. New fatty acid amides from regurgitant of Lepidopteran (Noctuidae, Geometridae) caterpillars. *Tetrahedron* 55:11275–80

99. Ralph S, Oddy C, Cooper D, Yueh H, Jancsik S, et al. 2006. Genomics of hybrid poplar (*Populus trichocarpa* × *deltoides*) interacting with forest tent caterpillars (*Malacosoma disstria*): normalized and full-length cDNA libraries, expressed sequence tags, and a cDNA microarray for the study of insect-induced defences in poplar. *Mol. Ecol.* 15:1275–97
100. Ralph SG, Yueh H, Friedmann M, Aeschliman D, Zeznik JA, et al. 2006. Conifer defence against insects: Microarray gene expression profiling of Sitka spruce (*Picea sitchensis*) induced by mechanical wounding or feeding by spruce budworms (*Choristoneura occidentalis*) or white pine weevils (*Pissodes strobi*) reveals large-scale changes of the host transcriptome. *Plant Cell Environ.* 29:1545–70
101. Rasmann S, Köllner TG, Degenhardt J, Hiltpold I, Toepfer S, et al. 2005. Recruitment of entomopathogenic nematodes by insect-damaged maize roots. *Nature* 434:732–37
102. Reymond P, Bodenhausen N, Van Poecke RM, Krishnamurthy V, Dicke M, Farmer EE. 2004. A conserved transcript pattern in response to a specialist and a generalist herbivore. *Plant Cell* 16:3132–47
103. Reymond P, Weber H, Damond M, Farmer EE. 2000. Differential gene expression in response to mechanical wounding and insect feeding in *Arabidopsis*. *Plant Cell* 12:707–20
104. Rivard D, Cloutier C, Michaud D. 2004. Colorado potato beetles show differential digestive compensatory responses to host plants expressing distinct sets of defense proteins. *Arch. Insect Biochem. Physiol.* 55:114–23
105. Robert-Seilaniantz A, Navarro L, Bari R, Jones JD. 2007. Pathological hormone imbalances. *Curr. Opin. Plant Biol.* 10:372–79
106. Rossi M, Goggin FL, Milligan SB, Kaloshian I, Ullman DE, Williamson VM. 1998. The nematode resistance gene *Mi* of tomato confers resistance against the potato aphid. *Proc. Natl. Acad. Sci. USA* 95:9750–54
107. Ryan CA. 1990. Protease inhibitors in plants: Genes for improving defenses against insects and pathogens. *Annu. Rev. Phytopathol.* 28:425–49
108. Schaller F, Schaller A, Stintzi A. 2005. Biosynthesis and metabolism of jasmonates. *J. Plant Growth Regul.* 23:179–99
109. Schilmiller AL, Howe GA. 2005. Systemic signaling in the wound response. *Curr. Opin. Plant Biol.* 8:369–77
110. Schilmiller AL, Koo AJ, Howe GA. 2007. Functional diversification of acyl-CoA oxidases in jasmonic acid biosynthesis and action. *Plant Physiol.* 143:812–24
111. Schmelz EA, Alborn HT, Tumlinson JH. 2003. Synergistic interactions between volicitin, jasmonic acid and ethylene mediate insect-induced volatile emission in *Zea mays*. *Physiol. Plant.* 117:403–12
112. Schmelz EA, Carroll MJ, LeClere S, Phipps SM, Meredith J, et al. 2006. Fragments of ATP synthase mediate plant perception of insect attack. *Proc. Natl. Acad. Sci. USA* 103:8894–99
113. Schmelz EA, Leclere S, Carroll MJ, Alborn HT, Teal PEA. 2007. Cowpea (*Vigna unguiculata*) chloroplastic ATP synthase is the source of multiple plant defense elicitors during insect herbivory. *Plant Physiol.* 144:793–805
114. Schmidt S, Baldwin IT. 2006. Systemin in *Solanum nigrum*. The tomato-homologous polypeptide does not mediate direct defense responses. *Plant Physiol.* 142:1751–58
115. Schnee C, Köllner TG, Held M, Turlings TC, Gershenzon J, Degenhardt J. 2006. The products of a single maize sesquiterpene synthase form a volatile defense signal that attracts natural enemies of maize herbivores. *Proc. Natl. Acad. Sci. USA* 103:1129–34
116. Schoonhoven LM, Jermey T, van Loon JJA. 1998. *Insect-Plant Biology: From Physiology to Evolution*. London: Chapman & Hall

117. Schroder R, Cristescu SM, Harren FJ, Hilker M. 2007. Reduction of ethylene emission from Scots pine elicited by insect egg secretion. *J. Exp. Bot.* 58:1835–42
118. Schwachtje J, Minchin PE, Jahnke S, van Dongen JT, Schittko U, Baldwin IT. 2006. SNF1-related kinases allow plants to tolerate herbivory by allocating carbon to roots. *Proc. Natl. Acad. Sci. USA* 103:12935–40
119. Smith CM, Boyko EV. 2007. The molecular bases of plant resistance and defense responses to aphid feeding: current status. *Entomol. Exp. Appl.* 122:1–16
120. Spiteller D, Pohnert G, Boland G. 2001. Absolute configuration of volicitin, an elicitor of plant volatile biosynthesis from lepidopteran larvae. *Tetrahedron Lett.* 42:1483–85
121. Staswick PE, Tiryaki I. 2004. The oxylipin signal jasmonic acid is activated by an enzyme that conjugates it to isoleucine in Arabidopsis. *Plant Cell* 16:2117–27
122. Steppuhn A, Baldwin IT. 2007. Resistance management in a native plant: Nicotine prevents herbivores from compensating for plant protease inhibitors. *Ecol. Lett.* 10:499–511
123. Stintzi A, Weber H, Reymond P, Browse J, Farmer EE. 2001. Plant defense in the absence of jasmonic acid: the role of cyclopentenones. *Proc. Natl. Acad. Sci. USA* 98:12837–42
124. Taki N, Sasaki-Sekimoto Y, Obayashi T, Kikuta A, Kobayashi K, et al. 2005. 12-oxo-phytodienoic acid triggers expression of a distinct set of genes and plays a role in wound-induced gene expression in Arabidopsis. *Plant Physiol.* 139:1268–83
125. Talyzina NM, Ingvarsson PK. 2006. Molecular evolution of a small gene family of wound inducible Kunitz trypsin inhibitors in *Populus*. *J. Mol. Evol.* 63:108–19
126. Tan X, Calderon-Villalobos LI, Sharon M, Zheng C, Robinson CV, et al. 2007. Mechanism of auxin perception by the TIR1 ubiquitin ligase. *Nature* 446:640–45
127. Tattersall DB, Bak S, Jones PR, Olsen CE, Nielsen JK, et al. 2001. Resistance to an herbivore through engineered cyanogenic glucoside synthesis. *Science* 293:1826–28
128. Thaler JS. 1999. Jasmonate-inducible plant defences cause increased parasitism of herbivores. *Nature* 399:686–88
129. Thines B, Katsir L, Melotto M, Niu Y, Mandaokar A, et al. 2007. JAZ repressor proteins are targets of the SCFCOI1 complex during jasmonate signalling. *Nature* 448:661–65
130. Thipyapong P, Joel DM, Steffens JC. 1997. Differential expression and turnover of the tomato polyphenol oxidase gene family during vegetative and reproductive development. *Plant Physiol.* 113:707–18
131. Thompson GA, Goggin FL. 2006. Transcriptomics and functional genomics of plant defence induction by phloem-feeding insects. *J. Exp. Bot.* 57:755–66
132. Ton J, D'Alessandro M, Jourdie V, Jakab G, Karlen D, et al. 2007. Priming by airborne signals boosts direct and indirect resistance in maize. *Plant J.* 49:16–26
133. Tooker JF, De Moraes CM. 2005. Jasmonate in lepidopteran eggs and neonates. *J. Chem. Ecol.* 31:2753–59
134. Truitt CL, Wei HX, Pare PW. 2004. A plasma membrane protein from *Zea mays* binds with the herbivore elicitor volicitin. *Plant Cell* 16:523–32
135. Turlings TCJ, Tumlinson JH, Lewis WJ. 1990. Exploitation of herbivore-induced plant odors by host-seeking parasitic wasps. *Science* 250:1251–53
136. van Poecke RM, Dicke M. 2002. Induced parasitoid attraction by *Arabidopsis thaliana*: involvement of the octadecanoid and the salicylic acid pathway. *J. Exp. Bot.* 53:1793–99
137. Voelckel C, Weisser WW, Baldwin IT. 2004. An analysis of plant-aphid interactions by different microarray hybridization strategies. *Mol. Ecol.* 13:3187–95
138. von Dahl CC, Baldwin IT. 2007. Deciphering the role of ethylene in plant-herbivore interactions. *J. Plant Growth Regul.* 26:201–9

139. Wang JH, Constabel CP. 2004. Polyphenol oxidase overexpression in transgenic *Populus* enhances resistance to herbivory by forest tent caterpillar (*Malacosoma disstria*). *Planta* 220:87–96
140. Winterer J, Bergelson J. 2001. Diamondback moth compensatory consumption of protease inhibitor-transformed plants. *Mol. Ecol.* 10:1069–74
141. Winz RA, Baldwin IT. 2001. Molecular interactions between the specialist herbivore *Manduca sexta* (Lepidoptera, Sphingidae) and its natural host *Nicotiana attenuata*. IV. Insect-induced ethylene reduces jasmonate-induced nicotine accumulation by regulating putrescine *N*-methyltransferase transcripts. *Plant Physiol.* 125:2189–202
142. Wu J, Hettenhausen C, Meldau S, Baldwin IT. 2007. Herbivory rapidly activates MAPK signaling in attacked and unattacked leaf regions but not between leaves of *Nicotiana attenuata*. *Plant Cell* 19:1096–122
143. Yan Y, Stolz S, Chetelat A, Reymond P, Pagni M, et al. 2007. A downstream mediator in the growth repression limb of the jasmonate pathway. *Plant Cell* 19:2470–83
144. You MK, Oh SI, Ok SH, Cho SK, Shin HY, et al. 2007. Identification of putative MAPK kinases in *Oryza minuta* and *O. sativa* responsive to biotic stresses. *Mol. Cells* 23:108–14
145. Zarate SI, Kempema LA, Walling LL. 2007. Silverleaf whitefly induces salicylic acid defenses and suppresses effectual jasmonic acid defenses. *Plant Physiol.* 143:866–75
146. Zavala JA, Patankar AG, Gase K, Hui DQ, Baldwin IT. 2004. Manipulation of endogenous trypsin proteinase inhibitor production in *Nicotiana attenuata* demonstrates their function as antiherbivore defenses. *Plant Physiol.* 134:1181–90
147. Zhang Z, Ober JA, Kliebenstein DJ. 2006. The gene controlling the quantitative trait locus *EPITHIOSPECIFIER MODIFIER1* alters glucosinolate hydrolysis and insect resistance in Arabidopsis. *Plant Cell* 18:1524–36
148. Zipfel C, Kunze G, Chinchilla D, Caniard A, Jones JDG, et al. 2006. Perception of the bacterial PAMP EF-Tu by the receptor EFR restricts *Agrobacterium*-mediated transformation. *Cell* 125:749–60

Patterning and Polarity in Seed Plant Shoots

John L. Bowman[1,2] and Sandra K. Floyd[1]

[1]School of Biological Sciences, Monash University, Melbourne, Victoria 3800, Australia

[2]Section of Plant Biology, University of California, Davis, California 95616; email: john.bowman@sci.monash.edu.au, sandra.floyd@sci.monash.edu.au

Annu. Rev. Plant Biol. 2008. 59:67–88

The *Annual Review of Plant Biology* is online at plant.annualreviews.org

This article's doi:
10.1146/annurev.arplant.57.032905.105356

1543-5008/08/0602-0067$20.00

Key Words

embryogenesis, auxin, shoot apical meristem, hypocotyl, cotyledon, leaf

Abstract

Leaves and stems are ultimately derived from the shoot apical meristem (SAM); leaves arise from the peripheral zone of the SAM and stem tissue is derived from both the peripheral and central zones of the SAM. Both the peripheral and central regions of the SAM are formed during embryogenesis when the basic body plan of the plant is established. Interplay between points of maximal concentration of auxin and specific patterns of transcription of both auxin-responsive transcription factors and other patterning genes subdivide the embryo along both the apical-basal and central-peripheral axes. Differential gene expression along these axes leads to the differentiation of tissues, lateral organs, meristems, and boundary regions, each with varying responsiveness to auxin. Subsequent shoot growth and development is a reiteration of basic patterning processes established during embryogenesis.

Contents

THE DEVELOPMENT AND EVOLUTIONARY CONTEXT FOR ANALYSIS OF PATTERNING OF THE SHOOT SYSTEM

Seed plants have been the dominant component of land plant floras since the Middle Triassic (approximately 230 Mya) (72) and their foliage defines and colors our landscapes, marking the seasons in many regions of the world. The living seed plants include cycads, *Ginkgo*, conifers, the Gnetales, and flowering plants. Living seed plants range from small herbaceous annuals to succulent cacti to massive long-lived giant sequoia. The leaves of seed plants also vary tremendously, from needle-like to frond-like and everything in between. Despite this enormous variability in form, the basic building blocks of which the shoot systems of the 300,000 or so seed plant species are constructed, radial stems and dorsiventral leaves, are similar due to common ancestry. All living seed plants have a complex shoot apical meristem (SAM) that is unique among vascular plants. The seed plant SAM consists of distinct populations of cells, including one or more layers of initial cells below which are a group of relatively quiescent central mother cells that are surrounded by actively dividing cells of the peripheral zone (**Figure 1**). Cells in the central zone are larger in diameter and vacuolated compared with the small, densely cytoplasmic cells of the peripheral zone. Leaves arise from the peripheral zone of the SAM whereas stem tissue is derived from both the peripheral and central zones of the SAM. The reiterative production of leaves in a specific pattern, termed phyllotaxy, results in modular shoots composed of lateral leaves spaced along a central radial stem. Nearly all angiosperm leaves and some gymnosperm leaves have an associated axillary meristem from which additional shoot systems (i.e., branches) are generated. The phyllotaxy, rate of leaf production, and stem elongation, combined with the size and shape of leaves produced, give a species its characteristic morphology.

There has been tremendous interest in recent years in understanding the underlying processes that control the functioning of the SAM in seed plants, including the maintenance of stem cells, initiation and polarity

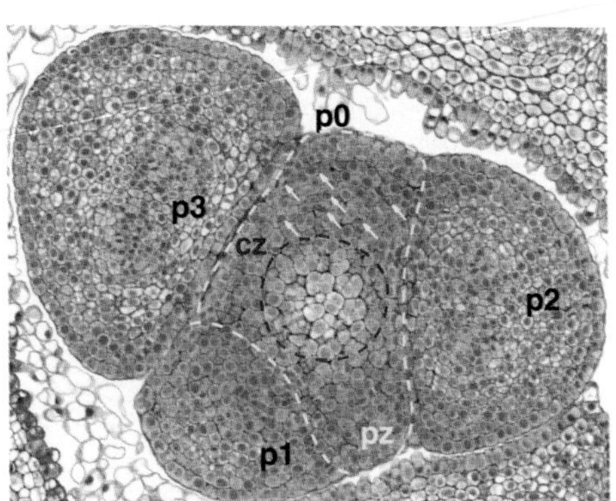

Figure 1

Shoot apex of *Ginkgo biloba*. The shoot apical meristem includes the central zone (cz) of larger vacuolate cells and the peripheral zone (pz) of smaller, less vacuolate cells. Leaves are derived from the peripheral zone whereas both the peripheral and central zone contribute to the stem. Leaf primordia are labeled youngest (p0) to oldest (p3). Note the many mitotic figures (*yellow arrows*) in the peripheral zone associated with p0.

of leaf primordia from the peripheral zone, and control of phyllotaxy. This work has focused on the model system *Arabidopsis*, which is amenable to genetic analysis and manipulation. The sporophyte (diploid) generation of seed plants (like all vascular plants) is capable of continuous development through the activities of shoot and root meristems. The stage of development where the basic body plan of the seed plant sporophyte is established is often referred to as embryogenesis, although the reiterative nature of plant development renders the demarcation between embryogenesis and postembryonic development nebulous (16, 56). The developmental patterning that is established during embryogenesis is repeated throughout the life of the plant. Thus, analyses focusing on the initial patterning events may be informed by findings from the study of the SAM and conversely, the study of embryogenesis contributes to our understanding of the SAM (56). For the purposes of this review we will use the term embryogenesis to encompass the developmental period in which the basic apical-basal, radial, and proximo-distal axes of the plant and its first lateral organs, the cotyledons, are established. For many species, this corresponds to the time between the formation of the zygote by fertilization of the female gametophyte and seed dormancy, when seeds are shed from the parent plant and dispersed. It must be noted that this is not always the case because some species do not undergo a 'dormant stage', and the seeds of many species contain 'embryos' with several leaves in addition to the cotyledons. Nonetheless, it is often convenient to think of seed development as embryogenesis.

Here we attempt to survey a limited number of recent findings that contribute toward understanding the development of the shoot system, and highlight a few key events about which little is presently known. We then attempt to extrapolate as to how generally applicable the developmental processes discovered in *Arabidopsis* are likely to be for other flowering plants and seed plants. Finally we discuss the significance of the emerging developmental genetic data for understanding the nature of some of the concepts in plant development, such as cytohistological zonation in the SAM, symmetry in the embryo, and the establishment of differential growth. Other excellent reviews highlight additional aspects of body plan establishment in *Arabidopsis* (12, 25, 54) and aspects of leaf development (7, 22, 95) and the ideas and experimental data in this review need to be considered in light of these other recent reviews on related topics.

ORIGIN OF PATTERN FORMATION IN *ARABIDOPSIS* SPOROPHYTES

In *Arabidopsis*, all the major pattern elements of the sporophyte body plan are established during the time between fertilization of the female gametophyte by the male gametophyte and the onset of seed dormancy. The basic patterns set up during this developmental window, including the apical-basal axis, the radial axis, and the programs necessary for the generation of lateral organs, are propagated during the remainder of the sporophytic phase of the life cycle. Thus, an understanding of the underlying molecular processes of these early stages can, to a large degree, be extrapolated to the rest of the growth and development of the sporophyte.

In general terms, development is the process by which different cells of a multicellular organism attain different fates. Although cell lineages are often visually conspicuous in plants, as in the files of cells readily apparent in the epidermises of stems, leaves, and roots, it is clear that position largely determines cell fate in most contexts, implicating a role for signaling molecules. Unlike animals, where many small, secreted, peptide signaling molecules have been identified as critical for developmental patterning, few such molecules have been identified in plants. Although this may merely be due to our present ignorance of the molecular mechanisms of plant development, it is also possible that molecules other than peptides may be more important. One such molecule that has a pervasive role in plant development is auxin (12, 13, 25, 53, 60, 98). Indeed, three major patterning events in angiosperm embryogenesis, establishment of the apical-basal axis, establishent of the central-peripheral axes, and initation of lateral organs (cotyledons), are correlated with dynamic patterns of auxin concentration and flux. Thus, auxin may act in an instructive manner, with the potential for concentration gradients to pattern developmental events. Determining how these gradients are established and how they are modulated is critical to understanding pattern formation in plants.

The Flow of Auxin

In *Arabidopsis* apical-basal polarity of the sporophyte correlates with a polarity already established in the female gametophyte (**Figure 2**). Following fertilization, the

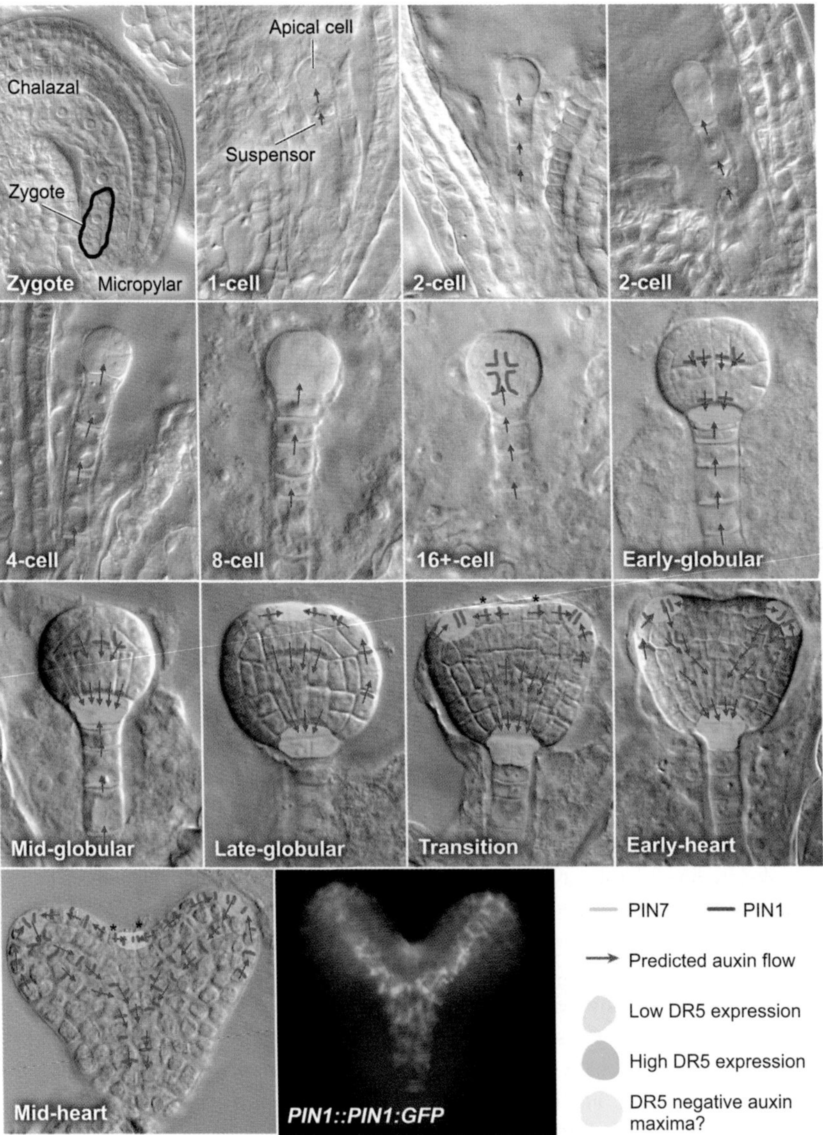

Figure 2

PIN FORMED (PIN) expression, auxin maxima, and predicted auxin flow during *Arabidopsis* embryogenesis. *PIN1::PIN1:GFP* in a late heart stage wild-type embryo. Reversals in PIN1 polarity marking the establishment of the cotyledons, and subsequently, auxin flow back toward the meristem following cotyledon formation are demarcated with asterisks.

zygote elongates and divides asymmetrically to produce a smaller apical cell, which will give rise to most of the embryo proper, and a larger micropylar basal cell that gives rise to the extraembryonic suspensor and the root meristem of the embryo. Thus, the polarity established at the first zygotic division of the embryo corresponds with the polarity of the embryo sac. Apical-basal axis formation is also marked by an asymmetric distribution of members of the PIN FORMED (PIN) family of proteins that mediate cellular auxin efflux from cells (39, 76, 102). Dynamic changes in auxin flux and maxima are mediated by both transcriptional control of PIN genes and the regulation of polar localization of PIN proteins (15, 99). The basal cell of the two-celled zygote expresses PIN7 protein at its apical end, presumably facilitating auxin flow into the apical cell (36). Although auxin has been difficult to detect directly, experiments using reporter genes, such as DR5::GFP, that respond positively to auxin suggest that auxin accumulates in the apical cell (reviewed in Reference 42). Although loss of *PIN7* activity has only minor effects on axis formation, this is likely due to extensive compensatory redundancy among PIN genes, in which the expression patterns of other family members change as a response to loss-of-function PIN alleles. Severe embryonic phenotypes, including embryos lacking apical-basal polarity and consisting of a file of suspensor-like cells, are observed in *pin1 pin3 pin4 pin7* quadruple mutants, suggesting that the early auxin asymmetry observed at the two-cell stage may be instructive with respect to apical cell fate (15, 36, 99).

The correspondence between embryo sac polarity and maternal sporophyte polarity brings up the question of how much instruction the maternal sporophyte provides with regard to embryonic polarity. Two observations suggest that embryonic patterning may be largely autonomous. Firstly, development of a second embryo, derived from cells normally fated to be extraembryonic suspensor cells, with an opposite polarity as compared with that derived from the apical cell, suggest that embryonic polarity can be established independently of maternal inputs (96). Secondly, the production of somatic embryos, free from the influence of any maternal sporophyte, indicates that embryonic polarity can be established autonomously. It is tempting to speculate that an asymmetric distribution of auxin between two daughter cells whose chromatin status reflects an embryonic cell fate may be sufficient to result in a progression into an embryonic developmental program. Embryo polarity could be established in the egg cell prior to fertilization because *Arabidopsis* egg cells are distinctly polar with a large vacuole at the micropylar end and the nucleus positioned at the chalazal end (66). These two poles correspond to the asymmetric first division of the zygote that results in a smaller apical cell and a larger basal cell that receives the egg vacuole (**Figure 2**).

Dynamic changes in auxin flow correlate with subsequent major events in embryonic development as described in **Figure 2** (36). First, auxin is thought to be drained from the embryo during the globular stage owing to the basal expression of PIN1. Second, an establishment of upward flow of auxin in the protodermal layer and thence downwards through the center contributes to axial elongation of the future procambium in the late globular embryo. This pattern presages much of what follows and highlights the need for understanding the establishment of the role of the epidermis in general patterning processes. Third, the establishment of bilateral symmetry and the SAM is correlated with a reversal in PIN polarity at the apex of the globular embryo. Finally, there is evidence that auxin is shunted back toward the meristem following the formation of lateral organ primordia (24, 50). That the dynamic flow of auxin and the creation of maxima is, if not instructive, at least necessary for proper embryo development is demonstrated by mutations in genes regulating PIN protein localization that result in abnormal auxin flow and embryonic patterning. GNOM (GN), a membrane-associated guanine nucleotide exchange factor, regulates vesicle budding, an important process for recycling of PIN proteins between endosomal compartments and the plasma membrane (90). The *gn* mutant resembles the severe embryo phenotype of *pin1 pin3 pin4 pin7*, suggesting that dynamic recycling of PIN proteins is important for embryo development (15, 17, 67, 86, 99). However, the random changes in PIN1 distribution observed in *gn* mutants imply that GN does not determine the polarity of PIN localization (40, 90).

The creation of auxin maxima can be determined either by changing the direction of auxin flow such that opposing flows result in an accumulation of auxin, or alternatively, by localized synthesis of auxin. What little is known about the control of reversals in the polar localization of PIN proteins revolves around the activity of the *PINOID* (*PID*) gene. *PID* encodes a serine-threonine protein kinase, and may directly regulate PIN1 polarity because loss of PID activity leads to basal PIN1 localization and gain of PID function leads to apical PIN1 localization in cells of cotyledon primordia (23, 37). Phosphorylation of PIN proteins by PID is counteracted by the activity of PROTEIN PHOSPHATASE 2A (PP2A), such that phosphorylation of PIN1 promotes its apical cellular localization, whereas reduction in phosphorylation of PIN1 results in a basal cellular localization (70). Auxin maxima directing the initiation of organs are altered in plants lacking PID function; *pid* mutants often possess three cotyledons and fail to initiate floral organs (8, 10, 23). Furthermore, *pid pin1* and *pid enhancer of pinoid* (*enp*) double mutants lack cotyledons (38, 94). In these double mutant combinations, a transition stage embryo appears to develop, but the polar localization of PIN1 protein is not oriented normally and the cotyledons fail to develop appropriately. Thus, PID controls some aspects of polar PIN1 localization, but much of embryonic pattern formation occurs normally in *pid* mutants, indicating the existence of other controls. Furthermore, the loss of cotyledons in *pid pin1* mutants can be suppressed by mutations in CUP-SHAPED COTYLEDON (CUC) genes (38).

What is the origin of embryonic auxin? This is a question that has been largely neglected thus far, primarily owing to the incomplete knowledge of auxin biosynthesis and its sequestration via conjugation. Localized synthesis of auxin within the developing embryo could also play a role in creating auxin maxima and influencing auxin flows. This is especially relevant because *PIN1* expression is responsive to auxin concentration, suggesting the dynamic changes of auxin flux will include feedback regulation (50, 74, 84, 85, 99). At least two biochemical pathways can lead to auxin synthesis, one based on the products of the YUCCA genes (20, 104) and another via nitrilase (reviewed in Reference 73), and auxin can be inactivated via conjugation pathways (reviewed in Reference 103). Although increases in auxin concentration through exogenous application or expression of bacterial biosynthetic genes can often be accommodated, presumably through conjugative processes and increasing auxin flow, ectopic expression of YUCCA genes has severe morphological effects, suggesting that the control of auxin synthesis needs to be considered (104). At least four YUCCA genes are expressed during embryogenesis (21). *YUC1* and *YUC4* expression is detected as early as the transition stage in the apical regions of the embryo, with later expression primarily at the tips of the cotyledons, the SAM, and incipient leaf primordia (21). *YUC10* and *YUC11* are expressed in similar patterns during the heart stage. The expression of YUCCA genes in the presumptive SAM supports the hypothesis that elevated levels of auxin are present in the the SAM (**Figure 2**). *YUC4* is positively regulated by *STYLISH1* (*STY1*), and and multiple loss of function mutations in *STYLISH*-related genes result in similar carpel and leaf phenotypes as *YUCCA* loss-of-function mutant combinations (20, 58, 59, 88). On the basis of the coincident expression patterns of *STY1* and YUCCA genes during embryogenesis, STYLISH genes are likely involved in embryonic YUCCA gene regulation. At present, the relative contributions of auxin synthesis and auxin flux in generating auxin maxima are not clear, but it is likely that a combination of localized auxin synthesis and directional auxin flow is required to generate and maintain auxin maxima.

One consequence of auxin maxima created by convergent auxin flow and localized auxin synthesis is the activation of AUXIN RESPONSE FACTORS (ARFs), transcription factors that activate and/or repress target genes (reviewed in References 61 and 82). ARF proteins are negatively regulated by AUXIN/INDOLE ACETIC ACID (AUX/IAA) proteins, which are targeted for degradation in response to auxin via a transport inhibitor resistant (TIR)-mediated targeting of the AUX/IAA protein to the proteasome (reviewed in References 26, 60, 82, 93, and 103). The release of the ARF proteins from their AUX/IAA partner allows their binding to auxin response elements (AREs) and the regulation (positive or negative) of target genes. Two members of the ARF gene family, *MONOPTEROS* (*MP/ARF5*) and *NONPHOTOTROPIC HYPOCOTYL 4* (*NPH4/ARF7*) have demonstrated roles in embryo axis patterning, with double mutants lacking both apical and basal embryonic development (11, 46, 47, 101). Specifically, the double mutants lack both the axial elongation of central cells and cotyledon initiation, suggesting that MP/NPH4 are required to interpret auxin maxima directing these two developmental processes. Because these processes, the initiation of lateral organ primordia and the establishment of procambial precursors, require different gene expression patterns, MP/NPH4 must interact with other cell type–specific factors to regulate morphogenesis. Dominant gain-of-function alleles in an AUX/IAA partner, *BODENLOS* (*BDL*), result in a similar loss of embryonic apical-basal polarity, suggesting that MP/NPH4 and BDL are the primary ARF-AUX/IAA proteins involved in early embryonic development (44, 45, 101). However, this does not preclude the participation of other family members in other aspects of embryonic pattern formation; *ETTIN*, *ARF2*, and *ARF4* are likely candidates for contributing to cotyledon patterning (4, 75).

Several significant morphological transitions during embryogenesis remain enigmatic. First, the establishment of the protoderm by periclinal divisions at the eight-cell stage sets the stage for signaling events between cell layers. The behavior of auxin flow differs significantly between the epidermal and internal cell layers. The establishment of auxin maxima that mark the cotyledons, and subsequently leaf primordia, occurs through changes in auxin flow within the epidermal layer and likely localized synthesis of auxin. Subsequent flow into the internal cells from sites of auxin maxima establishes the path of provascular tissue. How is the protodermal layer initated and differentated? Second, changes in auxin flow, from initially pumping auxin into the embryo, to a state where auxin is drained from the embryo at the early globular stage, imply that embryonic pattern formation requires both dynamic changes in PIN protein expression patterns and subcellular localization. During the transition from the early to late globular stages auxin is thought to flow upward in the epidermis and then downward through the central region instead of being drained from the embryo. The control and initation of this process is also unknown, although it is likely related to the origin of the protodermal layer. Third, the mechanism of reversal of *PIN1* polarity in the epidermis at the apex of the embryo that establishes the positions of cotyledon primordia is largely unknown. Fourth, how is auxin flow shifted from being primarily epidermal to an internal flow into subepidermal layers at sites of PIN1 convergence? Such changes result in a draining of auxin from the site of the epidermal maxima and mark the initial establishment of routes of vascular patterning. Finally, concomitant with the initiation of cotyledons is the formation of the SAM, which completes the establishment of all the major pattern elements of the apical portion of the embryo. How are these dynamic changes achieved?

Interplay

What is known about the transcriptional control of the auxin synthesis, flux, and response machinery? Unfortunately, not much. Although the direct transcriptional control of PIN, PID, and ARF genes is a largely unknown territory, the expression patterns of several classes of transcription factors have been correlated with aspects of auxin biology. Here we describe a few, not to be comprehensive, but to highlight how little is known about their precise roles, even of those genes that have been subjected to significant analyses.

The activity of the CUC class of NAC [no apical meristem (NAM), *Arabidopsis* transcription activation factor (ATAF), and CUC] transcription factors causes a repression of growth between organs that creates boundaries, and their expression is correlated with low auxin levels (38). CUC genes are initially expressed in a domain extending across the upper region of the globular embryo, dividing the embryo into two halves (2, 89, 92, 100) (**Figure 3**). Once *SHOOT MERISTEMLESS (STM)* is activated in the center of the embryo (65) to mark the future SAM, CUC expression becomes limited to the marginal regions, effectively forming a boundary between the cotyledons (92). Loss of CUC

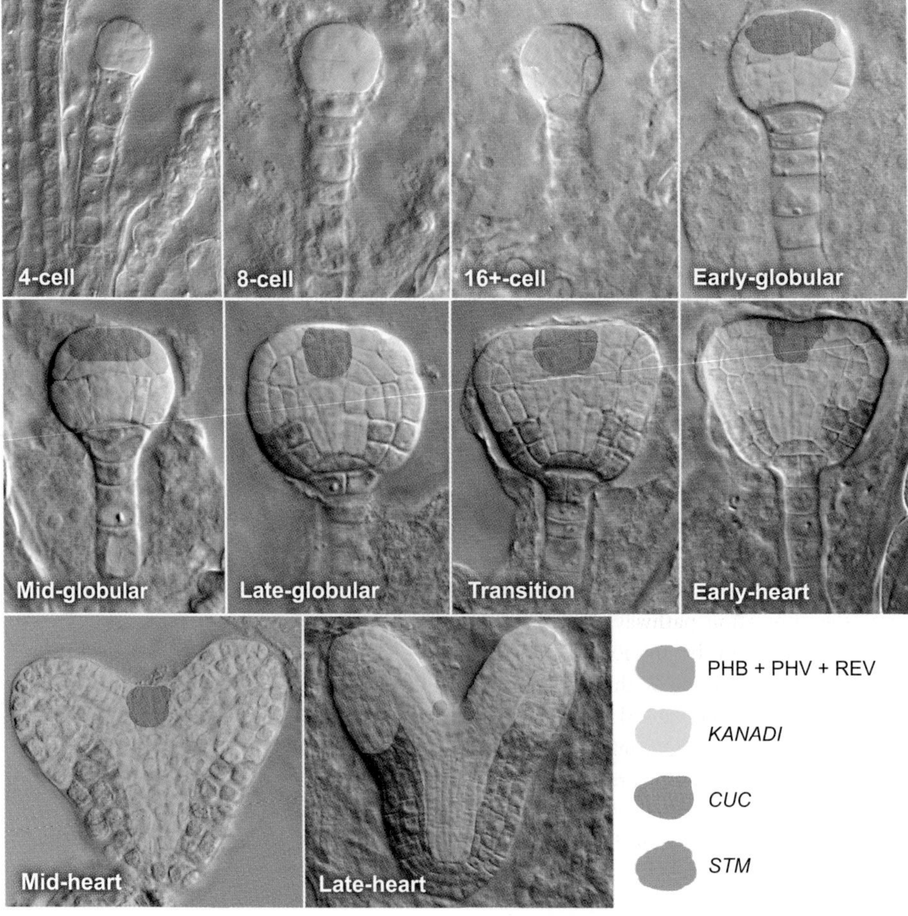

Figure 3
Expression patterns of four classes of transcription factors [*PHABULOSA* (*PHB*) + *PHAVOLUTA* (*PHV*) + *REVOLUTA* (*REV*) in green, *KANADI* in yellow, *CUP-SHAPED COTYLEDON* (*CUC*) in red, *SHOOT MERISTEMLESS* (*STM*) in blue] during early embryogenesis. Note that both the spatial and temporal patterns are approximate because the observations of expression for each gene were done independently, without multiple labeling of individual embryos.

activity results in a loss of separation between the cotyledons, such that the entire periphery of the embryo develops as a single cup-shaped cotyledon, a phenotype that can be phenocopied by application of auxin transport inhibitors to developing embryos (1, 62). In addition, *STM* is not activated appropriately in *cuc1 cuc2* embryos, such that a SAM is not formed (1). Conversely, ectopic CUC expression is correlated with a repression of growth. For example, CUC genes are ectopically expressed throughout the apical periphery of *pin1 pid* embryos and cotyledon primordia fail to initiate appropriately, but removal of CUC activity in this background results in the restoration of cotyledon development (38). The observation that some of the CUC genes are initially activated in a border domain suggests that they are in some respects responding to a preexisting boundary, but what establishes this boundary remains unclear. Are CUC genes activated in response to low auxin levels (e.g., at sites of PIN polarity reversal where auxin appears to be drained from a point), or does the activation of CUC genes result in a subsequent reduction in the response to auxin? These scenarios do not have to be mutually exclusive, and perhaps the variability in the initial expression patterns of *CUC1* and *CUC2* reflects an interplay between CUC and PIN gene regulation.

Analyses of CUC genes highlight two significant questions with respect to pattern formation. First, CUC gene expression defines boundaries, which can provide a separation between organs so that they can subsequently develop autonomously (reviewed in Reference 3). In addition, boundaries may facilitate communication pathways between the two separated organs by providing a third cell type distinct from each of the entities that the boundary defines, and thus boundaries may be instructive during developmental processes. Second, the nebulous relationship between CUC gene expression and the regulation of auxin synthesis and flow highlights the paucity of our knowledge about the relative temporal relationships of change in gene expression during embryonic pattern formation. Observations in real time of living inflorescence apices have been pivotal in providing insight into these processes, as described below (50).

One consequence of CUC expression in the central apical region of the embryo is the activation of *STM*, a Class I knotted1-like homeobox (KNOX) gene (1) (**Figure 3**). Class I KNOX gene activity is hypothesized to suppress differentiation within the SAM and the formation of organ boundaries (6, 52, 64). Several lines of evidence indicate that Class I KNOX genes may act to regulate and be regulated by plant hormones to promote maintenance or formation of the SAM (43, 49). Hay and coworkers (49) propose a model in which Class I KNOX genes in the SAM [such as *STM* and *BREVIPEDICELLUS* (*BP*) in *Arabidopsis* and *KNOTTED 1* (*KN1*) in maize] promote cytokinin synthesis and downregulate gibberellic acid (GA) levels, promoting meristematic activity. Class I KNOX genes are excluded from the positions of auxin maxima associated with the site of leaf initiation within the SAM, and it has been suggested that Class I KNOX genes are downregulated by high levels of auxin and may also act to repress auxin transport (48, 49). *BP* is also expressed in the cortex of the hypocotyl and in young internodal regions that become cortex, and directly downregulates components of the lignin biosynthetic pathway (69). In *bp* mutant plants, premature and increased levels of lignification occur in cortical and interfascicular regions of the stem, whereas overexpression of *BP* leads to a reduction in lignification throughout the stem (69). The accumulated evidence suggests that Class I KNOX genes are expressed in regions of low auxin concentration and low PIN-mediated transport and act to inhibit processes of growth and differentiation that are associated with auxin action.

In contrast to the Class I KNOX genes, members of the Class III homeodomain-leucine zipper (HD-Zip) gene family have expression patterns that correlate with known pathways of auxin flow out of the apex toward

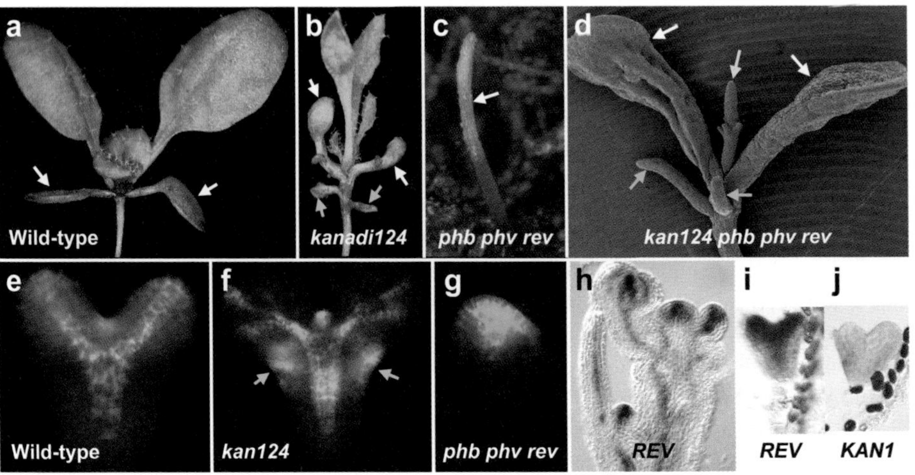

Figure 4

(*a–d*) Seedlings. White arrows denote cotyledons, blue arrows show 'hypocotyl leaves', and the yellow arrow shows the 'central' leaf. (*e–g*) *PIN1::PIN1:GFP*; blue arrows mark ectopic expression in *kan124* embryos. (*h–i*) *REV* expression in the inflorescence shoot and heart stage embryo. (*j*) *KAN1* expression in the heart stage embryo. Abbreviations: *phb*, *phabulosa*; *phv*, *phavulota*; *rev*, *revoluta*; *kan*, *kanadi*; *PIN*, *PIN FORMED*.

incipient leaf primordia and in the provasculature (27, 50, 78, 106) (**Figure 3**, **4*h–i***). Loss of Class III HD-Zip activity, as in *phabulosa* (*phb*) *phavoluta* (*phv*) *revoluta* (*rev*) mutants, results in a loss of central shoot identity (27, 78). The apical regions of mutant seedlings lack a SAM, and instead comprise a single radialized cotyledon, lacking adaxial cell types, with a small, radial vascular bundle (**Figure 4*c***). In this background, the reversals in PIN1 polarity that establish the divergent flow of auxin away from the center of the embryo and demarcate bilateral symmetry do not occur (51). Instead, the pattern of presumed auxin flow in the early globular embryo, upward through the epidermis and down centrally, continues such that an embryo with a single central auxin maximum is formed (**Figure 4*g***). Although the mechanistic relationship between presumptive pathways of auxin flow and Class III HD-Zip gene expression is unknown, that dynamic patterns of auxin flow appear to be established in a *phb phv rev* background in which KANADI activity (see below) is also removed suggests that that Class III HD-Zip activity may largely respond to, rather than direct, patterns of auxin flux. However, it has been reported that Class III HD-Zip genes influence polar auxin transport. Zhong & Ye (106) showed that auxin polar transport is reduced in *rev* plants and that the expression of two of the PIN genes is reduced. Class III HD-Zip genes may respond to auxin by promoting the differentiation of cell types (e.g., procambium) that further facilitate auxin polar transport away from the SAM and in the vasculature, and that by disrupting Class III HD-Zip activity reduced auxin flow occurs owing to a loss of proper conduits. Loss- and gain-of-function *REV* mutations lead to a reduction or expansion, respectively, of lignified tissues in the stem, which is consistent with a role for this gene in directing the normal flow of auxin within the shoot (27, 68, 105, 107).

Loss of *DORNRÖSCHEN* (*DRN*) and *DRN-LIKE* (*DRNL*) activity results in an embryonic mutant phenotype similar to that of loss of Class III HD-Zip gene activity (19). DRN and DRNL proteins physically interact with Class III HD-Zip proteins and the embryonic expression pattterns of *DRN* and *DRNL* overlap with those of Class III HD-Zip genes, suggesting they may act in a common protein complex (19, 71).

Another class of gene that has been proposed to regulate auxin biology is the KANADI group of GARP transcription factors, named for maize Golden 2, ARR (*Arabidopsis* response regulators) and Psr1 (phosphorous stress response1 from *Chlamydomonas*). Loss- and gain-of-function phenotypes of KANADI activity are largely the converse of those of Class III HD-Zip genes (29, 30, 57). However, one phenotypic feature of loss of KANADI activity that is not observed in gain-of-function alleles of Class III HD-Zip genes is the formation of leaves from the hypocotyl of *kan1 kan2 kan4* plants (51) (**Figure 4*b***). The 'hypocotyl' leaves that develop during embryogenesis are associated with ectopic auxin maxima that form during the heart stage; PIN1 is already ectopically expressed during the globular stage. During the globular stage PIN1 normally becomes restricted to the apical portion of the embryo, but in KANADI mutants, PIN1 is expressed more basally around the entire circumference of the embryo (**Figure 4*j***). The ectopic auxin maxima are generated by ectopic reversals in PIN1 localization below the cotyledons as well as by the ectopic maintenance of PIN1 localization at the apical end of protodermal cells of the hypocotyl (**Figure 4*f***). One hypothesis for the origin of the ectopic reversal lies in what has been observed by live imaging of the dynamic changes in *PIN1* localization in the flowering shoot apices of *Arabidopsis* (50). Once a flower primordium is established, the orientation of PIN1 reverses such that auxin is transported away from the newly initiated flower primordium back toward the meristem (50). If this reversal is a general process, not limited to the establishment of flower meristems, one might expect to see a reversal of PIN1 from leaf/cotyledon primordia toward the SAM. Because *PIN1* is positively regulated by auxin (50, 85), such a reversal could account for the high expression levels of *PIN1* in the L1 layer of the meristem in late heart and torpedo stage embryos (51). In *kan1 kan2 kan4* embryos, if this reversal is not limited to the regions adaxial to the cotyledons, but also occurs below the cotyledons owing to the ectopic expression of PIN1 there, ectopic auxin maxima form in the hypocotyl.

Leaf primordia are initiated from the peripheral region when exogenous auxin is applied, but they are not initiated from the central zone even if auxin is applied to the center of the meristem (80). However, in *phb phv rev kan1 kan2 kan4* hextuple mutants, radial leaf-like organs also initiate from the hypocotyl and the shoot apex (**Figure 4*d***). These results suggest that auxin-mediated organ outgrowth can occur wherever opposing, PIN1-mediated auxin flow converges and appropriate auxin response factors are expressed. Normally this occurs only in the peripheral zone of the meristem. Following cotyledon formation, the flow of auxin back toward the center of the embryo in the hextuple *kan1 kan2 kan4 phv phb rev* mutant would create an auxin maximum in the position normally occupied by the SAM in the wild-type, but because *PHB*, *PHV*, and *REV* are required for normal SAM development (27, 78), the ectopic auxin maximum induces an ectopic leaf-like organ in the hextuple mutant.

The interactions between these four families of transcription factors and auxin biology highlight that the response to auxin maxima is context dependent, as was shown by the application of exogenous auxin to shoot apices (80). The lack of response in the central zone of the SAM to auxin requires the function of the Class III HD-Zip genes, perhaps acting through downstream genes, and the Class I KNOX genes likely play some role. Likewise, cells of the developing hypocotyl are initially competent to form and respond to auxin maxima, but this capability is restricted during the globular stages by the peripheral expression of KANADI. The idea that the meristem may also be a point of high auxin concentration (24, 50) also cautions against the use of using only DR5 to define auxin maxima, because this method depends on the distribution of ARFs that act as activators of transcription (reviewed in Reference 42). DR5 is a synthetic promoter composed of four repeats of a composite auxin response element, whose regulation is thought to reflect ARF activity in cells. Because the distribution of ARF activation is dependent on auxin, patterning is a complex interplay between ARFs and other transcription factors within a cell, and these combinations feed back to further influence auxin biology as well as other transcriptional patterns.

The KANADI genes provide an example of a likely negative feedback loop involving ARF activity. Loss of *ARF2*, *ETTIN* (*ETT*; *ARF3*), and *ARF4* activity results in adaxialized leaves with outgrowths on their abaxial sides, a phenotype that resembles loss of KANADI activity (4, 75). Mutations in *ETT* also enhance the phenotypic effects of *kan1* mutations and suppress the effects of ectopic KANADI activity. Epistasis experiments suggest neither activity is upstream or downstream of the other, leading Pekker and colleagues (75) to speculate that KANADI and ARF proteins act together. The induction of ETT/ARF4 in response to auxin abaxially, in a domain in which KANADI activity is already present, could lead to the downregulation of auxin responses via their combined activity. Although the KANADI/ETT/ARF4 system exhibits a role only in the cotyledons and leaves, similar feedback modules could act in different cells on the basis of the different combinations of ARF proteins and other transcription factors expressed in particular cell types. In *Arabidopsis* the ARF gene family consists of 23 members and the AUX/IAA family consists of 29 members, a large fraction of which is expressed (based on microarray data) in the embryo or in the shoot tips (reviewed in References 61 and 82). A greater understanding of the expression patterns and loss-of-function phenotypes of ARF gene family members in addition to those of *MP* and *NPH4* is required to begin to understand the role of these genes in embryonic patterning.

The formation of auxin maxima exhibits hallmarks of a self-organizing system, both in the phyllotaxy of the shoot and in the development of leaf vascular patterns (9, 24, 55, 81, 85, 87). This could be extrapolated to the formation of auxin maxima in the embryo; auxin maxima form sequentially in the embryo proper, the root pole, the shoot pole, and finally at the sites of cotyledon primordia. Conceptually a self-organizing system could be established by the initation of auxin synthesis at sites of auxin maxima, perhaps at a certain threshold level of auxin; the increased auxin synthesis could then lead to a change in the flow of auxin away from the site of synthesis, perhaps at a second threshold level of auxin. Although some changes could occur in the absence of transcription, the action of ARFs in conjunction with other transcription factors is likely instrumental in coordinating these events. Again, the need for an understanding of the spatial and temporal patterns of auxin biosynthesis and ARF gene expression is highlighted, as well as a need for integrating these with the expression of other developmentally important genes.

Insights into Temporal Aspects of Auxin Biology and Gene Expression

A major limiting factor in our understanding of pattern formation is the lack of knowledge about the relative temporal relationships between the dynamic changes in auxin flow and gene expression of transcriptional regulators of patterning. Although in theory this could be accomplished by observing developing embryos, difficulties arise owing to their embedded position within the maternal sporophyte. However, recent technical advances in microscopy have allowed such observations in the *Arabidopsis* inflorescence meristem (41, 79) (**Figure 5**). The primary difference between the developmental dynamics of the inflorescence meristem and the establishment of embryonic patterning and subsequent functioning of the vegetative shoot meristem is that primordia formed on the periphery of the inflorescence meristem represent a reduced bract and its axillary meristem (the flower), whereas the primordia produced on the

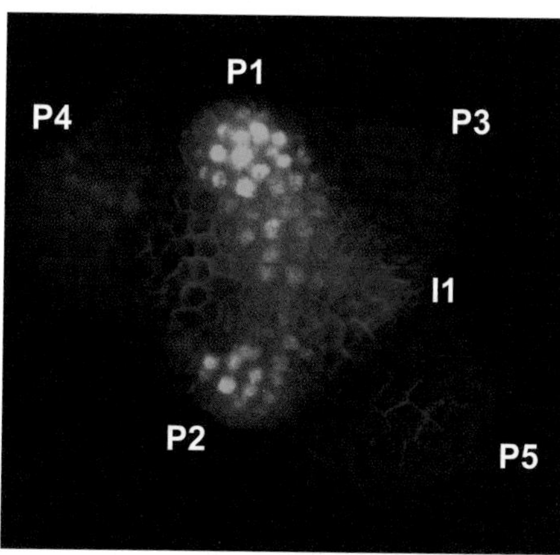

Figure 5

Arabidopsis inflorescence apex with PIN FORMED 1 (PIN1) (*blue*), REVOLUTA (REV) (*green*) and FILAMENTOUS FLOWER (FIL) (*magenta*) proteins labeled. Flower primordia (Pn) and incipient positions (In) where flower primordia will next arise are labeled.

periphery of the globular embryo or the vegetative meristem are leaf-like organs, with or without associated axillary meristems (63). Despite this caveat, studies on the dynamics of gene expression in the inflorescence and flower meristems obtained by live imaging (50) can likely be extrapolated to other stages of shoot development.

The dynamics of PIN1 protein expression observed with live imaging of inflorescence apices resembles that observed during embryogenesis (50). Expression of PIN1 marks the initiation of flower meristems in two respects. First, the polarity of PIN1 protein in the shoot apex is toward the position of the incipient flower meristem, suggesting that auxin is flowing from the meristem toward the position of the next flower primordium. On the basis of DR5 reporter gene expression, auxin maxima are formed in the periphery of the meristem at the positions predicted by the polarity of PIN1 within the meristem. Second, because PIN1 is positively regulated by increases in auxin concentration, the expression levels of PIN1 are highest at the sites of flower initiation (50, 74, 99). Following the formation of auxin maxima in the peripheral zone, the cells adaxial to the newly formed primordium exhibit a reversal in the polarity of PIN1 protein, suggesting the auxin adaxial to the primordium flows back toward the center of the meristem. In most respects this is similar to what has been observed during the globular to heart stages of embryogenesis, with the exception of the lack of an established shoot meristem in the embryo that could act as a source of auxin to be funneled to the sites of cotyledon initiation, further highlighting the need for information about the sites of auxin synthesis, both in the embryo and at later stages of development.

Concomitant with the formation of peripheral auxin maxima, both *CUC2* and *STM* are downregulated in regions predicted to have a high auxin concentration (50), suggesting both these genes may be regulated by ARF-mediated transcriptional responses. In addition, following the observed reversal of auxin flow back toward the meristem (presumably from where auxin is being drained), both genes are upregulated in a band of cells just adaxial to the region of downregulation; *CUC2* expression forms a boundary between the newly established flower primordium and the inflorescence meristem. *CUC2* and *STM* are downregulated in response to high auxin, whereas *REV* exhibits the converse expression pattern. *REV* is initially expressed in the central region of the shoot meristem, and its expression pattern expands within the epidermis in a ray from the center of the meristem toward the site of primordium initiation, as if following the flow of auxin predicted by the polar expression of *PIN1* protein. However, *REV* expression extends only to the abaxial edge of *PIN1* maximum expression and not all the way to the abaxial margin of the peripheral zone, suggesting that *PIN1* and *REV* expression interact to define a boundary, or that both *PIN1* and *REV* may be responding to a preexisting abaxial-adaxial boundary (50). At approximately the time when *CUC2* and *STM* are upregulated in a boundary region adaxial to the primordium, *REV* expression disappears from this region such that the *REV* expression in the primordium is cut off from the *REV* expression in the meristem center. It is not clear at present what is cause and effect, but this event likely represents the beginning of autonomous development of the flower primoridum. Finally, *FILAMENTOUS FLOWER* (*FIL*) expression marks the abaxial region of the primordium, peripheral to the maximal region of *PIN1* expression; a slight overlap in the expression domains of *FIL* and *REV* is detected.

The significance of these results is that for the first time we have a glimpse into the temporal relationships between the establishment of auxin maxima and some gene expression patterns, allowing cause to be separated from effect with respect to some developmental events. The examination of additional genes, such as the YUCCA genes, *STY*, *MP*, and *KANADI*, and further multiple combinations of fluorescently labeled proteins will continue to provide additional insights into these developmental processes, and application of these techniques to embryo development and vegetative meristems will allow the identification of the common mechanisms of organ establishment and meristem function in *Arabidopsis*.

EXTRAPOLATING THE *ARABIDOPSIS* MODEL TO OTHER SEED PLANTS

What evidence exists for commonality in mechanisms of patterning and polarity among diverse seed plants? All seed plants exhibit a SAM with similar patterns of cytohistological zonation and spiral phyllotaxis. It seems reasonable to predict that PIN-mediated auxin maxima may be responsible for the initiation of organs from the peripheral zone. Although there is no direct evidence to date about expression and function of PIN genes in shoot apices of plants other than *Arabidopsis*, the PIN gene family seems to be ancient in land plants, with homologs identified in the lycophyte *Selaginella* and the moss *Physcomitrella* (32). Likewise, the Class III HD-Zip gene family is present in the genome of all land plants (33, 77, 83). Gymnosperms have a single ortholog of *PHB*, *PHV*, and *REV*, which is expressed in the peripheral zone, provascular tissue, and adaxially in leaves (31, 33). This suggests a conserved role for Class III HD-Zip function in establishing central shoot identity and adaxial leaf identity as well as promoting vascular development in seed plants. The KANADI gene family is also ancient, with homologs present in lycophytes and moss (32), although to date there is no evidence for the function of KANADI homologs in nonflowering plants. Class I KNOX genes are also ancient, and map to the common ancestor of mosses and vascular plants (18). The first to be identified, *KNOTTED-1* (*KN1*) in maize, is expressed in the SAM and is excluded from the sites of leaf initiation, as is *STM*, and loss of both genes leads to loss of SAM (reviewed in Reference 43). Class I KNOX genes are also expressed in the apices of gymnosperms, where they are excluded from the sites of leaf initiation (14, 91). Thus, the presumed role of Class I KNOX genes in suppressing growth and response to auxin in the *Arabidopsis* SAM may be conserved in seed plants. Although there are no published data, a search of the rice genome indicates that there is a single gene that is the likely ortholog of *CUC1* and *CUC2* (S.K. Floyd, unpublished data). It is not known if *CUC1/CUC2* orthologs exist in gymnosperms, but Axtell & Bartel (5) identified miR164, a microRNA that targets *CUC1* and *CUC2*, in a conifer. These data are consistent with the presence of at least one CUC1/CUC2 gene in all seed plants. Thus, patterning in the seed plant SAM likely involves conserved genes with conserved functions that evolved in a common ancestor.

Can we extend the model for patterning the *Arabidopsis* embryo to embryos of other flowering plants and seed plants and account for variability among them? One immediately obvious difference within flowering plants is the lack of bilateral symmetry of the monocot embryo, suggesting there is a single auxin maximum during embryogenesis resulting in an asymmetrical embryo. In maize, leaf primordia are broader than in *Arabidopsis*, encircling the SAM, and *KN1* is excluded in an encircling zone on the SAM prior to the emergence of the leaf primordium (52). This suggests a broader auxin maximum throughout a larger arc of the peripheral zone in maize than in *Arabidopsis*. In conifers, a whorl of cotyledons is formed, suggesting numerous auxin maxima are formed in those embryos. Cycads and *Ginkgo* both have two cotyledons, but in cycads each cotyledon has a base that encircles the meristem much like a grass leaf base (35). Much emphasis is placed on the onset of bilateral symmetry in *Arabidopsis* embryogenesis. However, it is clear that seed plant embryos vary in terms of the number, position, and insertion of cotyledons so that cotyledon initiation leads to asymmetry (monocots, cycads), bilateral symmetry (dicotyledonous plants), or radial symmetry (conifers). The underlying commonality is that cotyledon initiation represents the onset of organogenesis from the shoot apex (56). Bilateral symmetry and heart stage are descriptive terms that apply to some seed plants and it is more broadly meaningful to focus on the developmental process of organogenesis (56). On the basis of the model for *Arabidopsis* we would predict that the differences in cotyledon number and arrangement among seed plants reflect spatial and temporal differences in PIN-mediated maxima and CUC-mediated boundaries. Expression and functional data are needed to confirm or reject these predictions.

Finally, embryogenesis in flowering plants begins with asymmetrical division of the zygote as in *Arabidopsis*. However, most gymnosperm embryos begin with a phase of free-nuclear division; the clearly bipolar embryos contain hundreds of nuclei (in cycads and *Ginkgo*). Most nuclei are aggregated at what will become the apical end and cellularization begins there as well. The shoot apex becomes organized even in the absence of complete cellularization of the basal end in cycads (35). PIN-mediated auxin flux occurs through polar localization of PIN proteins at the plasma membrane, which can happen only in multicellular tissue. Although auxin gradients may be involved, zygotic PIN-mediated polar transport cannot establish polarity within the free-nuclear embryo of gymnosperms (on the basis of our understanding of PIN function in *Arabidopsis*). The tightly controlled movement of auxin through particular cells and cell layers of the early embryo that occurs in *Arabidopsis* to create the shoot pole, create the root pole, and initiate the provasculature of the hypocotyl cannot occur in the gymnosperm embryo and may reflect a heterochronic shift to engage shoot patterning mechanisms at an earlier stage in development in the flowering plant lineage.

CONCLUDING REMARKS

A model is emerging in which auxin gradients and auxin transporters (PINs, PINOID) influence and are influenced by transcription factors, some of which are associated with high auxin concentration and flux (ARFs, Class III HD-Zips) and some of which are associated with low auxin concentrations (KNOX, CUC, KANADI). Together these transcription factors create patterns of differential growth in the shoot to maintain a meristem and produce lateral organs. As we mentioned at the beginning of this review, the SAM of seed plants is unique among land plants in that it exhibits cytohistological zonation that is associated with maintenance of stem cells (the central zone) and the production of lateral organs (the peripheral zone) (28, 34). The central zone includes the initial cells and their subadjacent derivatives, in which cell division is infrequent and the cells are larger and more vacuolate than in the peripheral zone (**Figure 1**). Auxin maxima form in the peripheral zone to determine where leaf primordia will emerge. Other genes that are expressed in the peripheral zone include *PHB*, *PHV*, and *REV* in the adaxial side of the entire peripheral zone,

KANADI in the abaxial side of the peripheral zone, *CUC1* and *CUC2* between adjacent primordia, and *STM* everywhere except the auxin maxima. The real-time analyses of Heisler and coworkers (50) suggest that the peripheral zone is already polarized with adaxial and abaxial domains when auxin maxima are formed and when elevated levels of *REV* expression occur. The fact that a ring of tissue with adaxial and abaxial characters develops in the *pin1* mutant inflorescence meristem and the *cuc1 cuc2* mutant embryo indicates that ad/abaxial polarity does not depend on the formation of auxin maxima or leaf primordia in the peripheral zone (1, 97). In the globular embryo, *PHB*, *PHV*, and *REV* are initially expressed throughout the embryo and then their expression becomes restricted to the apical and central regions (27, 68). At the same time, *KAN1* expression is evident around the periphery of the hypocotyl (57). The first auxin maxima forms at the boundary of *KANADI* and *PHB*, *PHV*, *REV* expression where there is no *STM* expression (50). Together this suggests that the peripheral zone is a region that represents the boundary of peripheral and central shoot expression domains in which auxin maxima form, with auxin flow converging from outer and inner domains. In both embryos and growing shoot apices organs form at the boundary of an abaxial/outer domain and an adaxial/inner domain of *PHB*, *PHV*, *REV* expression (50). This supports the view of Kaplan & Cooke (56) that the apical pole of the globular proembryo is the SAM and *STM* activity is required to maintain a population of stem cells, not establish them. However, cells at the center of the meristem do not acquire the larger, more vacuolate character that defines the central zone until after *STM* expression, which indicates that the peripheral zone is defined and functional prior to the establishment of the central zone and that in *stm* mutant plants the peripheral zone is established but the central zone is not. The data merging from detailed analyses of *Arabidopsis* are beginning to provide new insights into the developmental genetics of some longstanding questions, such as the developmental origin of the SAM in seed plants and the manner in which the SAM functions. There are still many gaps in the *Arabidopsis* model, such as the role of auxin biosynthesis and the causal relationship of auxin maxima, minima, and the transcription factors that are expressed in those regions. We also have still more to learn about how broadly the *Arabidopsis* model can be applied to understand seed plant shoot patterning in general. However, plant developmental genetics is beginning to address the fundamental issues of patterning in plants that we can apply to long-standing concepts from comparative anatomy to achieve a better understanding of seed plant development and evolution.

ACKNOWLEDGMENTS

We thank Gabriela Pagnussat for the images of embryo development in **Figures 2** and **3**, and Marcus Heisler for the image in **Figure 5**. We thank members of our lab, Marcus Heisler, and Yuval Eshed for helpful discussions over the years. We apologize for citing reviews in some cases rather than the primary literature owing to a lack of space. The authors' research is funded by the Australian Research Council (DP0771232, FF0561326), the United States National Science Foundation (IOB-0515435), and Monash University.

LITERATURE CITED

1. Aida M, Ishida T, Fukaki H, Fujisawa H, Tasaka M. 1997. Genes involved in organ separation in *Arabidopsis*: An analysis of the cup-shaped cotyledon mutant. *Plant Cell* 9:841–57

2. Aida M, Ishida T, Tasaka M. 1999. Shoot apical meristem and cotyledon formation during *Arabidopsis* embryogenesis: interaction among the *CUP-SHAPED COTYLEDON* and *SHOOT MERISTEMLESS* genes. *Development* 126:1563–70
3. Aida M, Tasaka M. 2006. Morphogenesis and patterning at the organ boundaries in the higher plant shoot apex. *Plant Mol. Biol.* 60:915–28
4. Alvarez JP, Pekker I, Goldshmidt A, Blum E, Amsellem Z, Eshed Y. 2006. Endogenous and synthetic microRNAs stimulate simultaneous, efficient, and localized regulation of multiple targets in diverse species. *Plant Cell* 18:1134–51
5. Axtell MJ, Bartel DP. 2005. Antiquity of microRNAs and their targets in land plants. *Plant Cell* 17:1658–73
6. Barton MK, Poethig RS. 1993. Formation of the shoot apical meristem in *Arabidopsis thaliana*—an analysis of development in the wild-type and in the shoot meristemless mutant. *Development* 119:823–31
7. Beerling DJ, Fleming AJ. 2007. Zimmermann's telome theory of megaphyll leaf evolution: a molecular and cellular critique. *Curr. Opin. Plant Biol.* 10:4–12
8. Benjamins R, Quint A, Weijers D, Hooykaas P, Offringa R. 2001. The PINOID protein kinase regulates organ development in *Arabidopsis* by enhancing polar auxin transport. *Development* 128:4057–67
9. Benkova E, Michniewicz M, Sauer M, Teichmann T, Seifertova D, et al. 2003. Local, efflux-dependent auxin gradients as a common module for plant organ formation. *Cell* 115:591–602
10. Bennett SRM, Alvarez J, Bossinger G, Smyth DR. 1995. Morphogenesis in pinoid mutants of *Arabidopsis thaliana*. *Plant J.* 8:505–20
11. Berleth T, Jürgens G. 1993. The role of the *monopteros* gene in organizing the basal body region of the *Arabidopsis* embryo. *Development* 118:575–87
12. Berleth T, Scarpella E, Prusinkiewicz P. 2007. Towards the systems biology of auxin-transport-mediated patterning. *Trends Plant Sci.* 12:151–59
13. Bhalerao RP, Bennett MJ. 2003. The case for morphogens in plants. *Nat. Cell Biol.* 5:939–43
14. Bharathan G, Goliber TE, Moore C, Kessler S, Pham T, Sinha NR. 2002. Homologies in leaf form inferred from *KNOX1* gene expression during development. *Science* 296:1858–60
15. Blilou I, Xu J, Wildwater M, Willemsen V, Paponov I, et al. 2005. The PIN auxin efflux facilitator network controls growth and patterning in *Arabidopsis* roots. *Nature* 433:39–44
16. Bower FO. 1908. *Origin of a Land Flora: A Theory Based on the Facts of Alternation*. London: Macmillan
17. Busch M, Mayer U, Jürgens G. 1996. Molecular analysis of the *Arabidopsis* pattern formation gene *GNOM*: Gene structure and intragenic complementation. *Mol. Gen. Genet.* 250:681–91
18. Champagne C, Ashton N. 2001. Ancestry of *KNOX* genes revealed by bryophyte (*Physcomitrella patens*) homologs. *New Phytol.* 150:23–36
19. Chandler JW, Cole M, Flier A, Grewe B, Werr W. 2007. The AP2 transcription factors DÖRNROSCHEN and DÖRNROSCHEN-LIKE redundantly control Arabidopsis embryo patterning via interaction with PHAVOLUTA. *Development* 134:1653–62
20. Cheng Y, Dai X, Zhao Y. 2006. Auxin biosynthesis by the YUCCA flavin monooxygenases controls the formation of floral organs and vascular tissues in *Arabidopsis*. *Genes Dev.* 20:1790–99
21. Cheng Y, Dai X, Zhao Y. 2007. Auxin synthesized by the YUCCA flavin monooxygenases is essential for embryogenesis and leaf fromation in *Arabidopsis*. *Plant Cell* 19:2430–39

22. Chitwood DH, Guo MJ, Nogueira FTS, Timmermans MCP. 2007. Establishing leaf polarity: the role of small RNAs and positional signals in the shoot apex. *Development* 134:813–23
23. Christensen SK, Dagenais N, Chory J, Weigel D. 2000. Regulation of auxin response by the protein kinase PINOID. *Cell* 100:469–78
24. de Reuille PB, Bohn-Courseau I, Ljung K, Morin H, Carraro N, et al. 2006. Computer simulations reveal properties of the cell-cell signaling network at the shoot apex in *Arabidopsis*. *Proc. Natl. Acad. Sci. USA* 103:1627–32
25. de Smet I, Jürgens G. 2007. Patterning the axis in plants—auxin in control. *Curr. Opin. Genet. Dev.* 17:1–7
26. Dharmasiri N, Estelle M. 2004. Auxin signaling and regulated protein degradation. *Trends Plant Sci.* 9:302–8
27. Emery JF, Floyd SK, Alvarez J, Eshed Y, Hawker NP, et al. 2003. Radial patterning of *Arabidopsis* shoots by class III HD-Zip and *KANADI* genes. *Curr. Biol.* 13:1768–74
28. Esau K. 1977. *Anatomy of Seed Plants*. New York: Wiley
29. Eshed Y, Baum SF, Perea JV, Bowman JL. 2001. Establishment of polarity in lateral organs of plants. *Curr. Biol.* 11:1251–60
30. Eshed Y, Izhaki A, Baum SF, Floyd SK, Bowman JL. 2004. Asymmetric leaf development and blade expansion in *Arabidopsis* are mediated by KANADI and YABBY activities. *Development* 131:2997–3006
31. Floyd SK, Bowman JL. 2006. Distinct developmental mechanisms reflect the independent origins of leaves in vascular plants. *Curr. Biol.* 16:1911–17
32. Floyd SK, Bowman JL. 2007. The ancestral developmental toolkit of land plants. *Int. J. Plant Sci.* 168:1–35
33. Floyd SK, Zalewski CS, Bowman JL. 2006. Evolution of class III homeodomain leucine zipper genes in streptophytes. *Genetics* 173:373–88
34. Foster AS. 1938. Structure and growth of the shoot apex in *Ginkgo biloba*. *Bull. Torrey Bot. Club* 65:531–56
35. Foster AS, Gifford EM Jr. 1974. *Comparative Morphology of Vascular Plants*. San Francisco: Freeman
36. Friml J, Vieten A, Sauer M, Weijers D, Schwarz H, et al. 2003. Efflux-dependent auxin gradients establish the apical-basal axis of *Arabidopsis*. *Nature* 426:147–53
37. Friml J, Yang X, Michniewicz M, Weijers D, Quint A, et al. 2004. A PINOID-dependent binary switch in apical-basal PIN polar targeting directs auxin efflux. *Science* 306:862–65
38. Furutani M, Vernoux T, Traas J, Kato T, Tasaka M, Aida M. 2004. PIN-FORMED1 and PINOID regulate boundary formation and cotyledon development in *Arabidopsis* embryogenesis. *Development* 131:5021–30
39. Galweiler L, Guan CH, Muller A, Wisman E, Mendgen K, et al. 1998. Regulation of polar auxin transport by AtPIN1 in *Arabidopsis* vascular tissue. *Science* 282:2226–30
40. Geldner N, Anders N, Wolters H, Keicher J, Kornberger W, et al. 2003. The *Arabidopsis* GNOM ARF-GEF mediates endosomal recycling, auxin transport, and auxin-dependent plant growth. *Cell* 112:219–30
41. Grandjean O, Vernoux T, Laufs P, Belcram K, Mizukami Y, Traas J. 2004. In vivo analysis of cell division, cell growth, and differentiation at the shoot apical meristem in arabidopsis. *Plant Cell* 16:74–87
42. Hagen G, Guilfoyle T. 2002. Auxin-responsive gene expression: genes, promoters and regulatory factors. *Plant Mol. Biol.* 49:373–85
43. Hake S, Smith HMS, Holtan H, Magnani E, Mele G, Ramirez J. 2004. The role of *KNOX* genes in plant development. *Annu. Rev. Cell Dev. Biol.* 20:125–51

44. Hamann T, Benkova E, Bäurle I, Kientz M, Jürgens G. 2002. The *Arabidopsis BODENLOS* gene encodes an auxin response protein inhibiting MONOPTEROS-mediated embryo patterning. *Genes Dev.* 16:1610–15
45. Hamann T, Mayer U, Jürgens G. 1999. The auxin-insensitive *bodenlos* mutation affects primary root formation and apical-basal patterning in the *Arabidopsis* embryo. *Development* 126:1387–95
46. Hardtke CS, Berleth T. 1998. The *Arabidopsis* gene *MONOPTEROS* encodes a transcription factor mediating embryo axis formation and vascular development. *EMBO J.* 17:1405–11
47. Hardtke CS, Ckurshumova W, Vidaurre DP, Singh SA, Stamatiou G, et al. 2004. Overlapping and nonredundant functions of the *Arabidopsis* auxin response factors MONOPTEROS and NONPHOTOTROPIC HYPOCOTYL 4. *Development* 131:1089–100
48. Hay A, Barkoulas M, Tsiantis M. 2006. ASYMMETRIC LEAVES1 and auxin activities converge to repress BREVIPEDICELLUS expression and promote leaf development in *Arabidopsis*. *Development* 133:3955–61
49. Hay A, Craft J, Tsiantis M. 2004. Plant hormones and homeoboxes: bridging the gap. *BioEssays* 26:395–404
50. Heisler MG, Ohno C, Das P, Sieber P, Reddy GV, et al. 2005. Patterns of auxin transport and gene expression during primordium development revealed by live imaging of the *Arabidopsis* inflorescence meristem. *Curr. Biol.* 15:1899–911
51. Izhaki A, Bowman JL. 2007. KANADI and class IIIHD-zip gene families regulate embryo patterning and modulate auxin flow during embryogenesis in *Arabidopsis*. *Plant Cell* 19:495–508
52. Jackson D, Veit B, Hake S. 1994. Expression of maize *KNOTTED1* related homeobox genes in the shoot apical meristem predicts patterns of morphogenesis in the vegetative shoot. *Development* 120:405–13
53. Jenik PD, Barton MK. 2005. Surge and destroy: the role of auxin in plant embryogenesis. *Development* 132:3577–85
54. Jenik PD, Gillmor CS, Lukowitz W. 2007. Embryonic patterning in *Arabidopsis thaliana*. *Annu. Rev. Cell Dev. Biol.* 23:207–36
55. Jönsson H, Heisler MG, Shapiro BE, Meyerowitz EM, Mjolsness E. 2006. An auxin-driven polarized transport model for phyllotaxis. *Proc. Natl. Acad. Sci. USA* 103:1633–38
56. Kaplan DR, Cooke TJ. 1997. Fundamental concepts in the embryogenesis of dicotyledons: a morphological interpretation of embryo mutants. *Plant Cell* 9:1903–19
57. Kerstetter RA, Bollman K, Taylor RA, Bomblies K, Poethig RS. 2001. KANADI regulates organ polarity in *Arabidopsis*. *Nature* 411:706–9
58. Kuusk S, Sohlberg JJ, Eklund DM, Sundberg E. 2006. Functionally redundant *SHI*-family genes regulate Arabidopsis gynoecium development in a dose dependent manner. *Plant J.* 47:99–111
59. Kuusk S, Sohlberg JJ, Long JA, Fridborg I, Sundberg E. 2002. *STY1* and *STY2* promote the formation of apical tissues during Arabidopsis gynoecium development. *Development* 129:4707–17
60. Leyser O. 2006. Dynamic integration of auxin transport and signalling. *Curr. Biol.* 16:R424–33
61. Liscum E, Reed JW. 2002. Genetics of Aux/IAA and ARF action in plant growth and development. *Plant Mol. Biol.* 49:387–400
62. Liu CM, Xu ZH, Chua NH. 1993. Auxin polar transport is essential for the establishment of bilateral symmetry during early plant embryogenesis. *Plant Cell* 5:621–30

63. Long J, Barton MK. 2000. Initiation of axillary and floral meristems in *Arabidopsis*. *Dev. Biol.* 218:341–53
64. Long JA, Barton MK. 1998. The development of apical embryonic pattern in *Arabidopsis*. *Development* 125:3027–35
65. Long JA, Moan EI, Medford JI, Barton MK. 1996. A member of the KNOTTED class of homeodomain proteins encoded by the *STM* gene of *Arabidopsis*. *Nature* 379:66–69
66. Mansfield SG, Briarty LG. 1991. Early embryogenesis in *Arabidopsis thaliana*. II. The developing embryo. *Can. J. Bot.* 69:461–76
67. Mayer U, Buttner G, Jürgens G. 1993. Apical-basal pattern-formation in the *Arabidopsis* embryo—studies on the role of the *gnom* gene. *Development* 117:149–62
68. McConnell JR, Emery J, Eshed Y, Bao N, Bowman J, Barton MK. 2001. Role of PHABULOSA and PHAVOLUTA in determining radial patterning in shoots. *Nature* 411:709–13
69. Mele G, Ori N, Sato Y, Hake S. 2003. The knotted-like homeobox gene *BREVIPEDICELLUS* regulates cell differentiation by modulating metabolic pathways. *Genes Dev.* 17:2088–93
70. Michniewicz M, Zago MK, Abas L, Weijers D, Schweighofer A, et al. 2007. Antagonistic regulation of PIN phosphorylation by PP2A and PINOID directs auxin flux. *Cell* 130:1044–56
71. Nag A, Yang YZ, Jack T. 2007. *DÖRNROSCHEN-LIKE*, an AP2 gene, is necessary for stamen emergence in Arabidopsis. *Plant Mol. Biol.* 65:219–32
72. Niklas KJ, Tiffney BH, Knoll AH. 1985. Patterns in vascular plant diversification: an analysis at the species level. In *Phanerozoic Diversity Patterns: Profiles in Microevolution*, ed. JW Valentine, pp. 97–128. Princeton, NJ: Princeton Univ. Press
73. Normanly J, Bartel B. 1999. Redundancy as a way of life—IAA metabolism. *Curr. Opin. Plant Biol.* 2:207–13
74. Paciorek T, Zazimalová E, Ruthardt N, Petrásek J, Stierhof YD, et al. 2005. Auxin inhibits endocytosis and promotes its own efflux from cells. *Nature* 435:1251–56
75. Pekker I, Alvarez JP, Eshed Y. 2005. Auxin response factors mediate *Arabidopsis* organ asymmetry via modulation of KANADI activity. *Plant Cell* 17:2899–910
76. Petrásek J, Mravec J, Bouchard R, Blakeslee JJ, Abas M, et al. 2006. PIN proteins perform a rate-limiting function in cellular auxin efflux. *Science* 312:914–18
77. Prigge MJ, Clark SE. 2006. Evolution of the class III HD-Zip gene family in land plants. *Evol. Dev.* 8:350–61
78. Prigge MJ, Otsuga D, Alonso JM, Ecker JR, Drews GN, Clark SE. 2005. Class III homeodomain-leucine zipper gene family members have overlapping, antagonistic, and distinct roles in *Arabidopsis* development. *Plant Cell* 17:61–76
79. Reddy GV, Heisler MG, Ehrhardt DW, Meyerowitz EM. 2004. Real-time lineage analysis reveals oriented cell divisions associated with morphogenesis at the shoot apex of *Arabidopsis thaliana*. *Development* 131:4225–37
80. Reinhardt D, Mandel T, Kuhlemeier C. 2000. Auxin regulates the initiation and radial position of plant lateral organs. *Plant Cell* 12:507–18
81. Reinhardt D, Pesce ER, Stieger P, Mandel T, Baltensperger K, et al. 2003. Regulation of phyllotaxis by polar auxin transport. *Nature* 426:255–60
82. Remington DL, Vision TJ, Guilfoyle TJ, Reed JW. 2004. Contrasting modes of diversification in the *Aux/IAA* and *ARF* gene families. *Plant Physiol.* 135:1738–52
83. Sakakibara K, Nishiyama T, Kato M, Hasebe M. 2001. Isolation of homeodomain-leucine zipper genes from the moss *Physcomitrella patens* and the evolution of homeodomain-leucine zipper genes in land plants. *Mol. Biol. Evol.* 18:491–502

84. Sauer M, Balla J, Luschnig C, Wisniewska J, Reinöhl V, et al. 2006. Canalization of auxin flow by Aux/IAA-ARF-dependent feedback regulation of PIN polarity. *Genes Dev.* 20:2902–11
85. Scarpella E, Marcos D, Friml J, Berleth T. 2006. Control of leaf vascular patterning by polar auxin transport. *Genes Dev.* 20:1015–27
86. Shevell DE, Leu WM, Gillmor CS, Xia GX, Feldmann KA, Chua NH. 1994. Emb30 is essential for normal-cell division, cell expansion, and cell-adhesion in *Arabidopsis* and encodes a protein that has similarity to Sec7. *Cell* 77:1051–62
87. Smith RS, Guyomarc'h S, Mandel T, Reinhardt D, Kuhlemeier C, Prusinkiewicz P. 2006. A plausible model of phyllotaxis. *Proc. Natl. Acad. Sci. USA* 103:1301–6
88. Sohlberg JJ, Myrenås M, Kuusk S, Lagercrantz U, Kowalczyk M, et al. 2006. STY1 regulates auxin homeostasis and affects apical-basal patterning of the Arabidopsis gynoecium. *Plant J.* 47:112–23
89. Souer E, van Houwelingen A, Kloos D, Mol J, Koes R. 1996. The *no apical meristem* gene of Petunia is required for pattern formation in embryos and flowers and is expressed at meristem and primordia boundaries. *Cell* 85:159–70
90. Steinmann T, Geldner N, Grebe M, Mangold S, Jackson CL, et al. 1999. Coordinated polar localization of auxin efflux carrier PIN1 by GNOM ARF GEF. *Science* 286:316–18
91. Sundås-Larsson A, Svenson M, Liao H, Engström P. 1998. A homeobox gene with potential developmental control function in the meristem of the conifer *Picea abies*. *Proc. Natl. Acad. Sci. USA* 95:15118–22
92. Takada S, Hibara K, Ishida T, Tasaka M. 2001. The *CUP-SHAPED COTYLEDON1* gene of *Arabidopsis* regulates shoot apical meristem formation. *Development* 128:1127–35
93. Teale WD, Paponov IA, Palme K. 2006. Auxin in action: signalling, transport and the control of plant growth and development. *Nat. Rev. Mol. Cell Biol.* 7:847–59
94. Treml BS, Winderl S, Radykewicz R, Herz M, Schweizer G, et al. 2005. The gene *ENHANCER OF PINOID* controls cotyledon development in the *Arabidopsis* embryo. *Development* 132:4063–74
95. Tsukaya H. 2006. Mechanism of leaf-shape determination. *Annu. Rev. Plant Biol.* 57:477–96
96. Vernon DM, Meinke DW. 1994. Embryogenic transformation of the suspensor in *twin*, a polyembryonic mutant of *Arabidopsis*. *Dev. Biol.* 165:566–73
97. Vernoux T, Kronenberger J, Grandjean O, Laufs P, Traas J. 2000. PIN-FORMED 1 regulates cell fate at the periphery of the shoot apical meristem. *Development* 127:5157–65
98. Vieten A, Sauer M, Brewer PB, Friml J. 2007. Molecular and cellular aspects of auxin-transport-mediated development. *Trends Plant Sci.* 12:160–68
99. Vieten A, Vanneste S, Wisniewska J, Benková E, Benjamins R, et al. 2005. Functional redundancy of PIN proteins is accompanied by auxin-dependent cross-regulation of PIN expression. *Development* 132:4521–31
100. Vroemen CW, Mordhorst AP, Albrecht C, Kwaaitaal M, de Vries SC. 2003. The *CUP-SHAPED COTYLEDON3* gene is required for boundary and shoot meristem formation in *Arabidopsis*. *Plant Cell* 15:1563–77
101. Weijers D, Sauer M, Meurette O, Friml J, Ljung K, et al. 2005. Maintenance of embryonic auxin distribution for apical-basal patterning by PIN-FORMED-dependent auxin transport in *Arabidopsis*. *Plant Cell* 17:2517–26
102. Wisniewska J, Xu J, Seifertová D, Brewer PB, Ruzicka K, et al. 2006. Polar PIN localization directs auxin flow in plants. *Science* 312:883

103. Woodward AW, Bartel B. 2005. Auxin: Regulation, action, and interaction. *Ann. Bot.* 95:707–35
104. Zhao YD, Christensen SK, Fankhauser C, Cashman JR, Cohen JD, et al. 2001. A role for flavin monooxygenase-like enzymes in auxin biosynthesis. *Science* 291:306–9
105. Zhong R, Ye Z-H. 1999. *IFL1*, a gene regulating interfascicular fiber differentiation in *Arabidopsis*, encodes a homeobox-leucine zipper protein. *Plant Cell* 11:2139–52
106. Zhong R, Ye Z-H. 2001. Alteration of auxin polar transport in the *Arabidopsis ifl1* mutants. *Plant Physiol.* 126:549–63
107. Zhong RQ, Ye Z-H. 2004. *amphivasal vascular bundle 1*, a gain-of-function mutation of the *IFL1/REV* gene, is associated with alterations in the polarity of leaves, stems and carpels. *Plant Cell Physiol.* 45:369–85

Chlorophyll Fluorescence: A Probe of Photosynthesis In Vivo

Neil R. Baker

Department of Biological Sciences, University of Essex, Colchester, CO4 3SQ, United Kingdom; email: baken@essex.ac.uk

Annu. Rev. Plant Biol. 2008. 59:89–113

The *Annual Review of Plant Biology* is online at plant.annualreviews.org

This article's doi:
10.1146/annurev.arplant.59.032607.092759

1543-5008/08/0602-0089$20.00

Key Words

carbon dioxide assimilation, electron transport, imaging, metabolism, photosystem II photochemistry, stomata

Abstract

The use of chlorophyll fluorescence to monitor photosynthetic performance in algae and plants is now widespread. This review examines how fluorescence parameters can be used to evaluate changes in photosystem II (PSII) photochemistry, linear electron flux, and CO_2 assimilation in vivo, and outlines the theoretical bases for the use of specific fluorescence parameters. Although fluorescence parameters can be measured easily, many potential problems may arise when they are applied to predict changes in photosynthetic performance. In particular, consideration is given to problems associated with accurate estimation of the PSII operating efficiency measured by fluorescence and its relationship with the rates of linear electron flux and CO_2 assimilation. The roles of photochemical and nonphotochemical quenching in the determination of changes in PSII operating efficiency are examined. Finally, applications of fluorescence imaging to studies of photosynthetic heterogeneity and the rapid screening of large numbers of plants for perturbations in photosynthesis and associated metabolism are considered.

Contents

INTRODUCTION

The use of chlorophyll *a* fluorescence measurements to examine photosynthetic performance and stress in algae and plants is now widespread in physiological and ecophysiological studies. This has come about owing to the development of a sound understanding of the relationships between fluorescence parameters and photosynthetic electron transport in vivo and the commercial availability of a range of affordable, easy to use portable fluorimeters. Fluorescence can be a very powerful tool to study photosynthetic performance, especially when coupled with other noninvasive measurements such as absorption spectroscopy, gas analyses, and infrared thermometry. This review examines how some key fluorescence parameters can be used to assess photosynthetic performance in vivo and to identify possible causes of changes in photosynthesis and plant performance; it is aimed at plant biologists who seek to use fluorescence as a tool in their research. However, the underlying theoretical bases of fluorescence changes in vivo are complex and correct interpretation of changes in fluorescence parameters can often be difficult. Consideration is given to some problems associated with the measurement of these parameters and the assumptions made when using these parameters to evaluate changes in photosynthetic performance.

Heat loss: occurs when excitation energy within pigments is lost as heat; often termed nonradiative decay or thermal deactivation

Excitation energy: energy within a pigment molecule after a photon is absorbed and generates an excited state of the molecule

Q_A: primary quinone electron acceptor of PSII

Photochemical quenching: results from using excitation energy within photosystem II (PSII) to drive electron transport from P680 to Q_A

BACKGROUND

Following the observation by Kautsky & Hirsch (55) that changes in fluorescence induced by illumination of dark-adapted leaves are qualitatively correlated with changes in CO_2 assimilation, it became evident that under some circumstances fluorescence emissions in photosynthetic organisms could be correlated to their photosynthetic rates (54, 56, 77). Butler (21) developed a simple model for photosystem II (PSII) photochemistry in which photochemistry competes with the processes of fluorescence and heat loss for excitation energy in the pigment antenna of PSII (**Figure 1**). This model followed from the proposal that electron transfer from the reaction center chlorophyll of PSII (P680) to the primary quinone acceptor of PSII (Q_A) quenches fluorescence (28), a process termed photochemical quenching. Increases in the rate of heat loss result in nonphotochemical quenching of fluorescence. The model predicts that PSII fluorescence emission could be used to monitor changes in photochemistry, provided that the rate constants for fluorescence and heat loss do not change (21). However, it is now well established that large changes can occur in the rate constant for heat loss from the PSII antenna (61, 65). Consequently, to estimate PSII photochemistry from fluorescence, it is essential to determine the fluorescence quenching that results from both photochemical and nonphotochemical processes.

Separation of fluorescence quenching into photochemical and nonphotochemical components was first achieved by the addition of 3-(3,4-dichlorophenyl)-1,1-dimethylurea

(DCMU) to intact chloroplasts and *Chlorella* cells at points throughout the fluorescence induction curve (64, 66). DCMU inhibits electron transfer from Q_A to the secondary quinone acceptor of PSII (Q_B), which results in a rapid reduction of Q_A and an increase in fluorescence as photochemical quenching is prevented. A slower increase in fluorescence follows, which is associated with the decay of nonphotochemical quenching. Unfortunately, this DCMU technique is not suitable for analyzing fluorescence quenching in leaves owing to the slow and uneven penetration of DCMU into leaf tissues. Also, the irreversibility of the DCMU inhibition of electron transport makes the technique unsuitable for continuous measurements on individual leaves. However, maximal Q_A reduction in leaves in the light can be achieved by rapidly exposing leaves to a very large increase in light (17). This light-addition technique is used to quantitatively determine the fraction of fluorescence quenching that is attributable to photochemical and nonphotochemical quenching processes (18). The development of fluorimeters that use weak modulated measuring beams in which phase and frequency decoding are used to detect fluorescence yield changes enabled the routine, nondestructive, quantitative determination of photochemical and nonphotochemical processes in leaves by the application of a brief (less than 1 s) saturating flash of light sufficiently intense as to maximally reduce the Q_A pool in the sample (26, 102). The value of the modulated technique is that it provides a continuous measure of the relative quantum yield of fluorescence (101). This technique was used to demonstrate that the quantum yield of PSII photochemistry of a leaf at a given actinic light intensity can be estimated from the modulated fluorescence yield prior to the application of the saturating flash and the maximum modulated fluorescence yield during the flash (37). In the absence of photorespiration, which competes with CO_2 assimilation for the products of electron transport, the quantum yield of PSII photochemistry is directly related to the quantum yield of CO_2 assimilation by the leaf, ϕ_{CO_2} (37), thus allowing, under certain conditions, the application of fluorescence measurements to provide a rapid, nondestructive probe of CO_2 assimilation. A list of the fluorescence parameters used in this review, their definitions, and comments on their physiological relevance are given in **Table 1**.

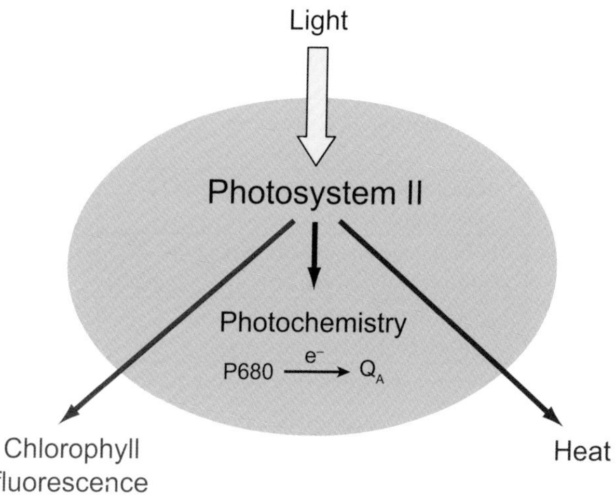

Figure 1

Simple model of the possible fate of light energy absorbed by photosystem II (PSII). Light energy absorbed by chlorophylls associated with PSII can be used to drive photochemistry in which an electron (e^-) is transferred from the reaction center chlorophyll, P680, to the primary quinone acceptor of PSII, Q_A. Alternatively, absorbed light energy can be lost from PSII as chlorophyll fluorescence or heat. The processes of photochemistry, chlorophyll fluorescence, and heat loss are in direct competition for excitation energy. If the rate of one process increases the rates of the other two will decrease.

Nonphotochemical quenching: occurs when there is an increase in the rate at which excitation energy within photosystem II is lost as heat

Quantum yield (quantum efficiency) of a process: number of molecules undergoing the process divided by the number of photons absorbed by the system

Actinic light: light that is absorbed by the photosynthetic apparatus and will drive electron transport

PHOTOSYSTEM II PHOTOCHEMISTRY

Dark-Adapted State

When a leaf is kept in the dark, Q_A becomes maximally oxidized and the PSII reaction centers are referred to as being ‘open’, i.e., capable of performing photochemical reduction of Q_A. Exposure of a dark-adapted leaf to a weak modulated measuring beam [photosynthetically active photon flux density (PPFD) of *ca.* 0.1 $\mu mol\ m^{-2}\ s^{-1}$] results in the minimal level of fluorescence, F_o (**Figure 2**). The intensity of the measuring beam must be nonactinic

Table 1 **Chlorophyll fluorescence parameters frequently used in studies of photosystem II photochemistry**

Parameter	Definition	Physiological relevance
F, F'	Fluorescence emission from dark- or light-adapted leaf, respectively.	Provides little information on photosynthetic performance because these parameters are influenced by many factors. F' is sometimes referred to as F_s' when at steady state
F_o, F_o'	Minimal fluorescence from dark- and light-adapted leaf, respectively	Level of fluorescence when Q_A is maximally oxidized (PSII centers open)
F_m, F_m'	Maximal fluorescence from dark- and light-adapted leaf, respectively	Level of fluorescence when Q_A is maximally reduced (PSII centers closed)
F_v, F_v'	Variable fluorescence from dark- and light-adapted leaves, respectively	Demonstrates the ability of PSII to perform photochemistry (Q_A reduction)
F_q'	Difference in fluorescence between F_m' and F'	Photochemical quenching of fluorescence by open PSII centers.
F_v/F_m	Maximum quantum efficiency of PSII photochemistry	Maximum efficiency at which light absorbed by PSII is used for reduction of Q_A.
F_q'/F_m'	PSII operating efficiency	Estimates the efficiency at which light absorbed by PSII is used for Q_A reduction. At a given photosynthetically active photon flux density (PPFD) this parameter provides an estimate of the quantum yield of linear electron flux through PSII. This parameter has previously been termed $\Delta F/F_m'$ and ϕ_{PSII} in the literature.
F_v'/F_m'	PSII maximum efficiency	Provides an estimate of the maximum efficiency of PSII photochemistry at a given PPFD, which is the PSII operating efficiency if all the PSII centers were 'open' (Q_A oxidized).
F_q'/F_v'	PSII efficiency factor	Relates the PSII maximum efficiency to the PSII operating efficiency. Nonlinearly related to the proportion of PSII centers that are 'open' (Q_A oxidized). Mathematically identical to the coefficient of photochemical quenching, q_P.
NPQ	Nonphotochemical quenching	Estimates the nonphotochemical quenching from F_m to F_m'. Monitors the apparent rate constant for heat loss from PSII. Calculated from $(F_m/F_m') - 1$.
q_E	Energy-dependent quenching	Associated with light-induced proton transport into the thylakoid lumen. Regulates the rate of excitation of PSII reaction centers.
q_I	Photoinhibitory quenching	Results from photoinhibition of PSII photochemistry.
q_L	Fraction of PSII centers that are 'open'	Estimates the fraction of 'open' PSII centers (with Q_A oxidized) on the basis of a lake model for the PSII photosynthetic apparatus. Given by $(F_q'/F_v')(F_o'/F')$
q_T	Quenching associated with a state transition	Results from phosphorylation of light-harvesting complexes associated with PSII
ϕ_F	Quantum yield of fluorescence	Number of fluorescent events for each photon absorbed

PPFD: photosynthetically active photon flux density

to ensure that Q_A remains maximally oxidized. If the period used for dark adaptation is not long enough Q_A may not become maximally oxidized. Then a pulse of weak far-red light, which preferentially excites photosystem I (PSI) and removes electrons from Q_A, should be applied prior to the measurements of F_o. In some leaves (32) and algae (10) significant accumulation of reduced Q_A can occur in the dark owing to nonphotochemical reduction of plastoquinone by chlororespiration; the reduced plastoquinone must be reoxidized by a pulse of weak red light before measurement of F_o. If after reaching F_o the

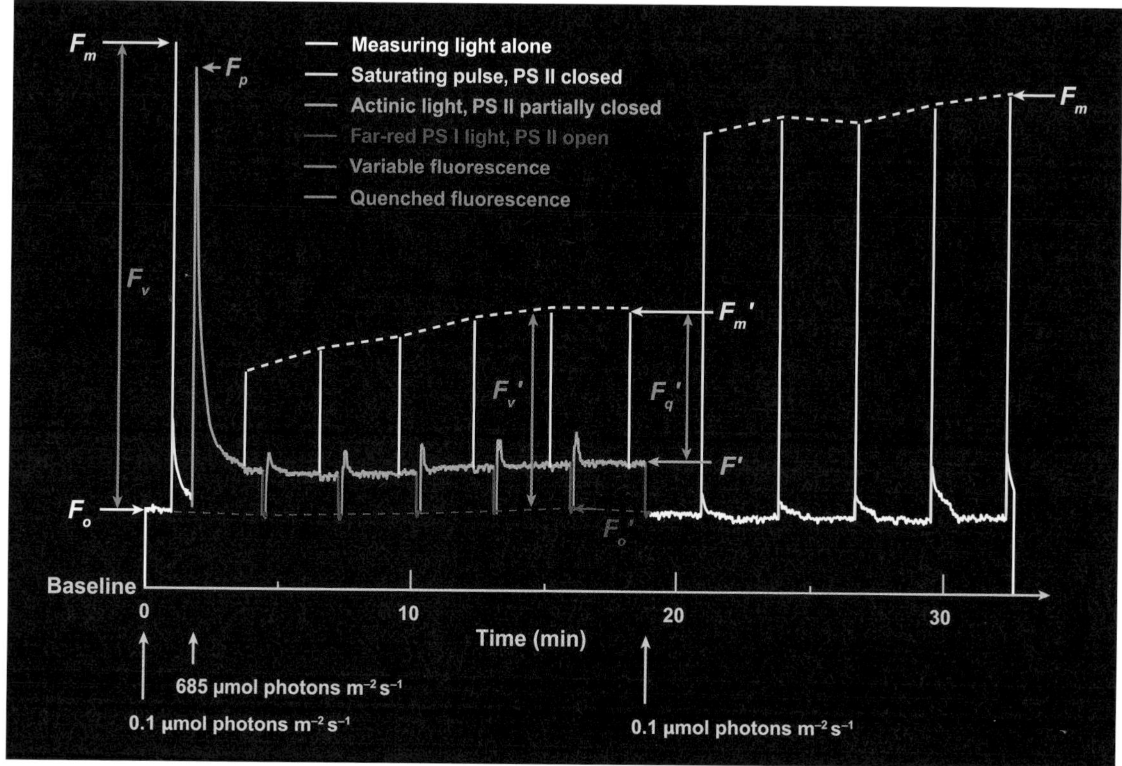

Figure 2

Fluorescence quenching analysis using modulated fluorescence. A dark-adapted leaf is exposed to various light treatments. The parameters denoted with a prime (′) are from the leaf exposed to actinic light. The parameters without a prime are obtained from the leaf in the dark-adapted state. The different colors of the trace denote different light treatments. White: weak measuring light alone (0.1 μmol photons m^{-2} s^{-1}) that gives F_o. An important feature of this measuring beam is that its intensity must be low enough so it does not drive significant PSII photochemistry. Yellow: saturating light pulse ($\leq$1 s duration, >6000 μmol photons m^{-2} s^{-1}) that gives F_m in darkness and F_m' in light. Blue: actinic light (685 μmol photons m^{-2} s^{-1}) that drives photosynthesis and gives F'. Red: far-red light (30 μmol photons m^{-2} s^{-1} at 720–730 nm for 4 s) that excites photosystem I (PSI) preferentially, and thus oxidizes the plastoquinone and Q_A pools associated with PSII and gives Fo'. Orange: variable fluorescence calculated as $F_v = F_m - F_o$ from the dark-adapted leaf and $F_v' = F_m' - F_o'$ from the illuminated leaf. Green: fluorescence that is quenched from F_m' to F' by PSII photochemistry in the illuminated leaf, calculated as $F_q' = F_m' - F'$. All parameters, except F_q', F_v, and F_v', are measured from the baseline. Figure reproduced from Reference 8, with permission.

leaf is now exposed to a short actinic pulse of high PPFD (typically less than 1 s at several thousand μmol m^{-2} s^{-1}), Q_A will be maximally reduced and the maximal fluorescence level, F_m, is observed (**Figure 1**). PSII reaction centers with reduced Q_A are referred to as being 'closed'. The difference between F_m and F_o is defined as the variable fluorescence, F_v. The ratio of F_v/F_m can be used to estimate the maximum quantum yield of Q_A reduction, i.e., PSII photochemistry, from the simple model of Butler (21). The fluorescence emission from a leaf, F, is defined by $I.A_{leaf}.fraction_{PSII}.\phi_F$, where I is the incident PPFD on the leaf, A_{leaf} is the proportion of incident PPFD that is absorbed by the leaf, $fraction_{PSII}$ is the fraction of absorbed PPFD that is received by PSII and ϕ_F is the quantum

Open center: photosystem II (PSII) reaction center in which the primary quinone acceptor of PSII, Q_A, is oxidized and capable of photoreduction

Closed center: PSII reaction center in which Q_A is reduced and unable to perform photochemistry

I: PPFD incident on the leaf

A_{leaf}: proportion of incident PPFD on the leaf that is absorbed by the leaf

$fraction_{PSII}$: fraction of absorbed PPFD that is received by PSII

yield of fluorescence. ϕ_F is defined by $k_F/(k_F + k_H + k_P P)$, where k_F, k_H, and k_P are the rate constants for the decay of excitation energy in PSII by fluorescence, heat loss, and photochemistry, respectively, and *P* is the fraction of PSII reaction centers that are open. At F_o, PSII reaction centers are maximally open, $P = 1$, and the fluorescence quantum yield, ϕ_{Fo}, is given by $k_F/(k_F + k_H + k_P)$. At F_m, the PSII reaction centers are maximally closed, $P = 0$, and photochemistry cannot occur, thus $k_P P = 0$ and the fluorescence quantum yield, ϕ_{F_m}, is given by $k_F/(k_F + k_H)$. Thus, ϕ_{F_v}/ϕ_{F_m} is given by $(\phi_{F_m} - \phi_{F_o})/\phi_{F_m} = k_P/(k_F + k_H + k_P)$, which shows that this ratio estimates the maximum quantum yield of PSII photochemistry. Assuming that I, A_{leaf}, and $fraction_{PSII}$ are constant for measurements of F_o and F_m, then F_v/F_m can be used to estimate the maximum quantum yield of PSII photochemistry. This simple model requires a number of other assumptions that are not necessarily correct for all situations (15). For example, fluorescence at both F_o and F_m is assumed to be emitted from a homogeneous system where all the excited states of the chlorophylls are the same. Clearly this is generally not the case; consequently, F_v/F_m should not be considered to provide a rigorous quantitative value of the quantum yield of PSII photochemistry (15). However, F_v/F_m does provide a very useful relative measure of the maximum quantum yield of PSII primary photochemistry; F_v/F_m values for nonstressed leaves are remarkably consistent at *ca.* 0.83 (14).

When plants are exposed to abiotic and biotic stresses in the light, decreases in F_v/F_m are frequently observed. This is such a widespread phenomenon that F_v/F_m measurements provide a simple and rapid way of monitoring stress. Unfortunately, the reasons for stress-induced decreases in F_v/F_m are often complex. Stressing photosynthetic tissues in the light can result in increases in nonphotochemical quenching processes, which decrease F_m. Such quenching may not recover during a short period of dark adaptation, or even overnight, and results in decreases in F_v/F_m (1, 2). However, identification of the intrinsic causes of such decreases can often be difficult. In many stress situations increases in nonphotochemical quenching can often be accompanied by photoinactivation of PSII reaction centers, which then dissipate excitation energy as heat rather than as photochemistry (79). Photoinactivation can lead to oxidative damage and loss of PSII reaction centers (4), both of which are associated with an increase in F_o (19, 90). However, caution must be exercised when attempting to interpret the significance of decreases in F_m or increases in F_o that occur as a result of a stress treatments. These fluorescence levels are determined both by the physicochemical properties of PSII and the optical properties of the leaf. Unfortunately, during many stress treatments, especially when changes in leaf water status occur, the optical properties of the leaf can change markedly and modify A_{leaf}. Changes in $fraction_{PSII}$ can occur owing to changes in thylakoid membrane structure and organization. Such modifications will result in changes in F_o and F_m that are independent of changes in ϕ_{F_o} and ϕ_{F_m}. In such situations, absolute changes in F_o and F_m cannot be used with confidence to indicate loss of PSII reaction centers or increases in nonphotochemical quenching. However, when ratios of fluorescence parameters, such as F_v/F_m, are considered, the influence of changes in A_{leaf} and $fraction_{PSII}$ are canceled out and changes in the ratio are indicative of changes in the ratio of quantum yields of the two parameters; for example F_v/F_m is defined by $(I.A_{leaf}.fraction_{PSII}.\phi_{F_v})/(I.A_{leaf}.fraction_{PSII}.\phi_{F_m}) = (\phi_{F_v}/\phi_{F_m})$.

In many ecophysiological studies it is suggested that stress-induced decreases in F_v/F_m imply that the photosynthetic efficiency of the leaves under ambient light conditions is compromised. This is not necessarily the case, because the quantum yield of PSII photochemistry under ambient light may be considerably below the observed F_v/F_m value, which estimates the maximum quantum yield of PSII photochemistry, not the yield at which PSII is operating under the ambient light (see below). The maximum quantum yield of PSII photochemistry is only achieved at very low ambient light levels.

Light-Adapted State

A leaf in continuous actinic light has a fluorescence level termed F', which rises to the maximal fluorescence level, F_m', when the leaf is exposed to a brief saturating light pulse that maximally reduces Q_A (**Figure 2**). A prime notation (′) used after a fluorescence parameter indicates that the sample is exposed to light that will drive photosynthesis, i.e., actinic light. The difference between F_m' and F' is designated F_q' and results from quenching of F_m' by PSII photochemistry. The ratio F_q'/F_m' is theoretically proportional to the quantum yield of PSII photochemistry prior to application of the saturating light pulse (37). Genty and coworkers empirically confirmed this theory from mass spectrometric measurements of oxygen evolution (38). For leaves exposed to actinic light the quantum yield of PSII photochemistry is equivalent to the quantum yield of linear electron flux (LEF) through PSII reaction centers, and hereafter is referred to as the PSII operating efficiency. Measurements of F_q'/F_m' provide a rapid method to determine the PSII operating efficiency under different light and other environmental conditions; F_q'/F_m' has previously been termed $\Delta F/F_m'$ and ϕ_{PSII} in the literature.

There are a number of potential sources of error associated with measurements of F_q'/F_m', which can be important when evaluating changes in PSII operating efficiency. These sources of error can also be a problem when measuring dark-adapted F_v/F_m. The relationship between F_q'/F_m' and the true quantum yield of PSII photochemistry can be affected if PSI contributes significantly to the measurements of the fluorescence parameters (41, 57, 97). When using F_q'/F_m' to determine the quantum yield of PSII photochemistry all the measured fluorescence is assumed to originate from PSII. Although this is true for variable fluorescence, it is not the case for F_o if fluorescence is monitored at wavelengths above 700 nm (70, 85). PSI is generally assumed to make a negligible contribution to fluorescence at wavelengths below 700 nm. Unfortunately, most commercial instruments measure a significant amount of fluorescence at wavelengths above 700 nm. The PSI contribution to F_o at wavelengths above 700 nm has been estimated at *ca*. 30% and 50% for C_3 and C_4 leaves, respectively (41, 97). Consequently, decreases in F_q'/F_m' will occur and therefore give estimates of PSII operating efficiency that are lower than the true values. As PPFD increases F_q'/F_m' decreases (**Figure 3**), but PSI fluorescence yield remains reasonably constant (25), thus the PSI contributions that result in depression of F_q'/F_m' and the consequent errors that lead to underestimation of PSII operating efficiency become proportionally greater. Measurement of fluorescence at wavelengths below 700 nm minimizes such errors by markedly reducing the PSI contribution to the signals (41, 97). However, measurements at these shorter wavelengths result in an increase in the contribution of fluorescence from the upper regions of the leaf because the probability of reabsorption of emissions at the shorter wavelengths is greater than for emissions above 700 nm (71).

LEF: linear electron flux

Another error can arise in estimations of F_q'/F_m' via the use of saturating light pulses that induce multiple turnovers of PSII reaction centers, as is the case with most commercial instruments. Such saturating pulses can result not only in the reduction of Q_A, but also in the reduction of plastoquinone to plastoquinol. Plastoquinone, but not plastoquinol, is a quencher of chlorophyll fluorescence. A decrease in plastoquinone during the application of the saturating light pulse will result in a decrease in quenching and an overestimation of F_m' that can be as large as 20% (62, 105). Such errors are significant only in leaves with high plastoquinone/plastoquinol ratios prior to application of the saturating light pulse,

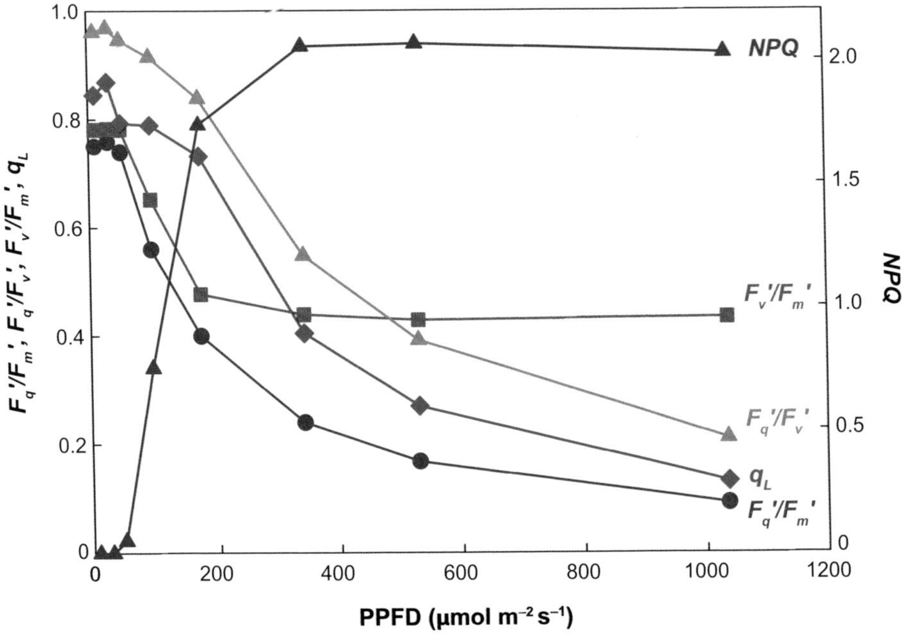

Figure 3

The responses of photosystem II (PSII) operating efficiency (F_q'/F_m'), maximum PSII quantum efficiency (F_v'/F_m'), the fraction of the maximum PSII efficiency that is realized in the light (F_q'/F_v'), the fraction of PSII reaction centers that are open (q_L), and nonphotochemical quenching (*NPQ*) in a tobacco leaf to increasing photosynthetically active photon flux density (PPFD). The leaf was kept in an atmosphere containing 100 μmol mol^{-1} CO_2 and 2% O_2 to reduce CO_2 assimilation and eliminate photorespiration, respectively. Data taken from Reference 63 with permission.

which is the case at very low light levels, and even then overestimates of F_q'/F_m' will be less than 10% (6).

Fortunately, errors in the measurement of F_q'/F_m' due to PSI fluorescence and plastoquinone quenching are small in many cases. The frequently observed linear relationship between F_q'/F_m' and the quantum yield of CO_2 assimilation with increasing light in leaves from a wide range of species in which photorespiration was absent or suppressed (e.g., 23, 24, 27, 29, 37, 39, 40, 51, 58, 59, 60) matches what is theoretically predicted (see below). Also, the yield of oxygen evolution from PSII determined by mass spectrometry is linearly related to F_q'/F_m' (38). If large errors in the measurement of F_q'/F_m' existed, then such linear relationships would not be observed. However, it is possible that errors could be more significant in leaves with unusual pigment or plastoquinone contents and caution should be exercised in such situations.

RELATIONSHIP BETWEEN PHOTOSYSTEM II OPERATING EFFICIENCY, LINEAR ELECTRON FLUX, AND CO_2 ASSIMILATION

The operation of linear electron flux (LEF) from water through PSII and PSI to electron acceptors requires similar electron fluxes through the reaction centers of both PSII and PSI. When the quantum yield of PSI photochemistry and PSII operating efficiency are measured simultaneously over a range of light intensities, linear relationships between the two parameters are observed frequently (34, 35, 39, 43, 44, 45, 57). In mature C_4 leaves, where CO_2 assimilation is the main sink for the products of LEF (i.e., ATP and NADPH) (29), the PSII operating efficiency should be directly related to the quantum yield of CO_2 assimilation, ϕ_{CO_2} (37). Such linear relationships between the PSII operating efficiency and ϕ_{CO_2} have been observed over a range of light intensities (37, 58, 59, 60, 103), over a range of atmospheric CO_2 concentrations (37, 103), and during induction of photosynthesis when dark-adapted leaves are exposed to actinic light (37). When photorespiration is inhibited in mature C_3 leaves by reduction of the atmospheric oxygen from 21% to 2% and CO_2 assimilation is the only major sink for ATP and NADPH, a linear relationship is also observed between PSII operating efficiency and ϕ_{CO_2} (23, 24, 27, 39, 40, 51). These observations demonstrate that PSII operating efficiency is a very good monitor of LEF.

In principle, the linear relationship between PSII operating efficiency and LEF allows the use of F_q'/F_m' to estimate the noncyclic electron transport rate through PSII (ETR), where ETR $= I.A_{leaf}.fraction_{PSII}.(F_q'/F_m')$. As discussed above, care should be taken when determining and interpreting F_q'/F_m', but often difficulties arise in the accurate determination of the other parameters involved in the estimation of ETR. A_{leaf} is frequently assumed to be 0.84, i.e., 84% of incident PPFD is assumed to be absorbed by leaves. This assumption may be reasonable for many mature green leaves, but is not always the case and large deviations from this value can frequently occur (30, 47, 53). A_{leaf} should be measured using a integrating sphere with a light source similar to that used to drive photosynthesis and a spectroradiometer or quantum sensor. Similarly, $fraction_{PSII}$ for leaves is frequently assumed to be 0.5, which is unlikely to be the case in many situations. Although $fraction_{PSII}$ has been estimated for leaves, the procedure is not straightforward and involves numerous assumptions (67, 68, 83). Another problem is that leaves of many species accumulate nonphotosynthetic pigments, such as anthocyanins, which can markedly modify not only A_{leaf} but also $fraction_{PSII}$; this is often the case when leaves experience environmental stresses during development. Unfortunately, commercial modulated fluorometers automatically calculate values of ETR by assuming that leaves have values of A_{leaf} and $fraction_{PSII}$ of 0.84 and 0.5, respectively, often leading to substantial errors in calculations of ETR. ETR values calculated by such instruments should not be used unless the assumed values of A_{leaf} and $fraction_{PSII}$ have been validated for the leaves being measured. In cases where such validations have not been made, changes in F_q'/F_m' should be used only to determine changes in the relative quantum yield of LEF and not used to estimate differences in ETR.

ETR: electron transport rate through photosystem II

If the allocation of the ATP and electrons that result from LEF to sinks other than CO_2 assimilation is negligible or constant, then PSII operating efficiency also provides a good relative measure of the quantum yield of CO_2 assimilation. The relationship between the PSII operating efficiency and the quantum yield of CO_2 assimilation (ϕ_{CO_2}) is defined by $\phi_{CO_2} = (F_q'/F_m').fraction_{PSII}.(1/k)$, where k is the number of electron equivalents produced by LEF required to reduce one molecule of CO_2. For C_3 leaves in which photorespiration is inhibited and other electron sinks are negligible k is assumed to be 4. If k and $fraction_{PSII}$ are constant then F_q'/F_m' is a good indicator of changes in ϕ_{CO_2}. In many cases k and $fraction_{PSII}$ will not remain constant between treatments and F_q'/F_m' should not be used to monitor changes in ϕ_{CO_2}. The value of k is dependent upon the proportion of reductants produced by LEF used for CO_2 assimilation. k will change when other sinks for these reductants change relative to CO_2 assimilation. Differences in k occur in leaves at different stages of growth and in response to environmental stresses. In C_3 leaves large changes in k occur with changes in intracellular CO_2 and O_2 concentrations, which modify the relative rates of CO_2 assimilation and photorespiration. The difficulties in the accurate determination of k and $fraction_{PSII}$ preclude the use of estimations of ϕ_{CO_2} from F_q'/F_m' to calculate actual rates of CO_2 assimilation from $(I. A_{leaf}. \phi_{CO_2})$. However, relative changes in rates of CO_2 assimilation can be evaluated from estimations of ϕ_{CO_2} provided that k and $fraction_{PSII}$ are constant.

A linear relationship between PSII operating efficiency and ϕ_{CO_2} is not found in many situations. Linearity is lost if the proportion of electrons consumed by CO_2 assimilation relative to other metabolic processes changes. In such cases F_q'/F_m' should not be used to estimate changes in ϕ_{CO_2} unless the relationship between F_q'/F_m' and ϕ_{CO_2} has been determined for the particular system under investigation. This is the case for C_3 leaves when photorespiration is operating; the ratio of PSII operating efficiency to ϕ_{CO_2} increases with increasing photorespiratory activity relative to carbon assimilation (39, 42, 45). Environmental stresses can induce large increases in the PSII operating efficiency:ϕ_{CO_2} ratio. For example, when the leaves of some C_4 species develop at suboptimal growth temperatures, PSII operating efficiency:ϕ_{CO_2} is increased significantly (31, 36). These increases are accompanied by increases in the levels of antioxidants and activities of enzymes involved in scavenging reactive oxygen species, which suggests that an increased electron flux to oxygen, relative to CO_2 assimilation, is occurring via the Mehler reaction (31, 36). Similar increases in PSII operating efficiency:ϕ_{CO_2} were observed in leaves of mangrove, a C_3 species, growing at high temperatures in tropical Australia (22).

FACTORS THAT DETERMINE PHOTOSYSTEM II OPERATING EFFICIENCY

PSII operating efficiency, F_q'/F_m', is given by the product of two important fluorescence parameters, F_v'/F_m' and F_q'/F_v' (37), where F_v' is equal to $F_m' - F_o'$ and is the variable fluorescence of the light-adapted leaf and F_o' is the minimal fluorescence level in the light when Q_A is maximally oxidized (**Figure 2**). F_v'/F_m' estimates the maximum quantum yield of PSII photochemistry (hereafter termed maximum PSII efficiency) that can be achieved in the light-adapted leaf when Q_A is maximally oxidized. Consequently, this parameter can be used to assess the contributions of nonphotochemical quenching to changes in the PSII operating efficiency of leaves in the light. F_q'/F_v' provides an estimate of the fraction of the maximum PSII efficiency that is actually realized in the leaf under the environmental conditions during the measurement, and is hereafter termed the PSII efficiency factor. The PSII efficiency factor is nonlinearly related to the fraction of PSII reaction centers with Q_A oxidized, i.e., the fraction of PSII centers that are open, and is mathematically identical to the frequently used coefficient of photochemical quenching, q_P. F_q'/F_v' is determined by the ability of the photosynthetic apparatus to maintain Q_A in the oxidized state, which is a function of the relative rates of Q_A reduction and oxidation. Determination of F_v'/F_m' and F_q'/F_v' makes it possible to assess whether changes in PSII operating efficiency are attributable to changes in nonphotochemical quenching or the ability of an excited PSII reaction center to drive electron transport.

Calculation of F_v'/F_m' and F_q'/F_v' requires determination of F_o', which can often be difficult. F_o' is usually measured by exposing the leaf to a pulse of weak far-red light, after removing the actinic light, to maximally oxidize Q_A (101). However, in many situations maximal oxidation of Q_A may not be achieved during the far-red pulse and also nonphotochemical quenching can partially relax, thus resulting in an overestimation of F_o' (6). This problem can be overcome by calculating F_o' from values of F_m' at the point of measurement and dark-adapted values of F_o and F_m using $F_o' = F_o/[(F_v/F_m) + (F_o/F_m')]$ (92). Maxwell & Johnson (78) suggested that this calculation should not be used if leaves are stressed and significant photoinhibition has occurred. However, a problem exists only if F_m is measured after F_m' and recovery from photoinhibition occurs during the dark adaptation period prior to measurement of F_m (6).

The PSII operating efficiency of a leaf decreases as PPFD increases owing to decreases in both F_v'/F_m' and F_q'/F_v' (**Figure 3**). However, the relative contributions of these two parameters can change markedly with increasing PPFD. Generally, increases in nonphotochemical quenching, indicated by decreases in F_v'/F_m', saturate at much lower light levels than decreases in F_q'/F_v', which demonstrates that a decrease in the ability to oxidize Q_A, not an increase in nonphotochemical quenching, is the major factor that determines the large changes in PSII operating efficiency at high light intensities. Also, increases in the PSII operating efficiency during induction of photosynthesis when a dark-adapted maize leaf is exposed to actinic light are primarily associated with increases in F_q'/F_v' and not changes in F_v'/F_m' (92). This finding demonstrates that the ability of processes downstream of PSII to utilize the products of LEF, rather than nonphotochemical quenching, is most important in the regulation of the induction of photosynthesis in this leaf.

The rate of consumption of NADPH and ATP are major factors that determine PSII operating efficiency in many situations. Changes in carboxylation efficiency, the rate of regeneration of ribulose 1,5-bisphosphate, the supply of CO_2 from the atmosphere to the sites of carboxylation via the stomata, photorespiration, and the rate of transport of carbohydrates out of the cell can all influence the rate of NADPH and ATP utilization (**Figure 4**), and consequently the PSII operating efficiency. Many environmental stresses impact on CO_2 assimilation, although the sites of photosynthesis limitation during these stresses can be quite varied. Stress-induced decreases in stomatal conductance, carbon metabolism, and transport processes can all decrease PSII efficiency. The specific mechanisms by which a restriction in metabolic turnover can result in decreases in PSII operating efficiency are not fully understood. Increases in NADPH and ATP decrease LEF and the rate of Q_A oxidation, which can be monitored by decreases in F_q'/F_v'. However, acidification of the thylakoid lumen as ATP levels increase also results in an increase in nonphotochemical quenching and a decrease in F_v'/F_m' (see section on Nonphotochemical Quenching, below).

Photochemical Quenching

An important factor in determining the probability of PSII photochemistry is the redox state of Q_A, i.e., the fraction of PSII reaction centers that are open and capable of photochemistry. Frequently, the PSII efficiency factor (or the mathematically equivalent q_P) is used to estimate the redox state of Q_A. Unfortunately, in most situations the relationship between the PSII efficiency factor and the fraction of PSII centers in the open state is not linear and consequently changes in F_q'/F_v' (or q_P) cannot simply be used to estimate the redox state of Q_A. The relationship between the PSII efficiency factor and the fraction of open PSII centers is only linear if there is negligible excitation energy transfer among individual PSII complexes and associated antennae. This is the 'puddle model' in which each PSII reaction center and its associated antenna cannot transfer excitation energy to the antennae of other PSII reaction centers. It is widely accepted that this is not the case and excitation in PSII antennae can be competed for by a number of reaction centers (21, 69, 72). If all the PSII reaction centers are considered to be embedded within a single antennae matrix and are capable of receiving excitation energy from antenna pigments throughout the matrix ('lake model'), then the relationship between F_q'/F_v' and the redox state of Q_A is curvilinear (7, 52). However, the degree of curvilinearity is dependent not only upon the fraction of PSII centers that are open but also on the amount of light-induced nonphotochemical quenching that is occurring; for a fixed oxidation state of Q_A increases in nonphotochemical quenching decrease the curvilinearity (7).

Assuming a lake model for PSII, the redox state of Q_A is linearly related to the fluorescence parameter $(F_q'/F_v')(F_o'/F')$, which has been termed q_L (63). Consequently, if an accurate assessment of the redox state of the Q_A pool is required then q_L, and not F_q'/F_v' (or q_P), should be used. When the PSII operating efficiency is modified by exposing leaves to a range of PPFDs, although the patterns of change of F_q'/F_v' and q_L with increasing PPFD are similar, values of q_L are always lower than for F_q'/F_v' (or q_P), and at high PPFDs q_L values can be almost half of F_q'/F_v' (63) (**Figure 3**). Consequently, large errors can occur when

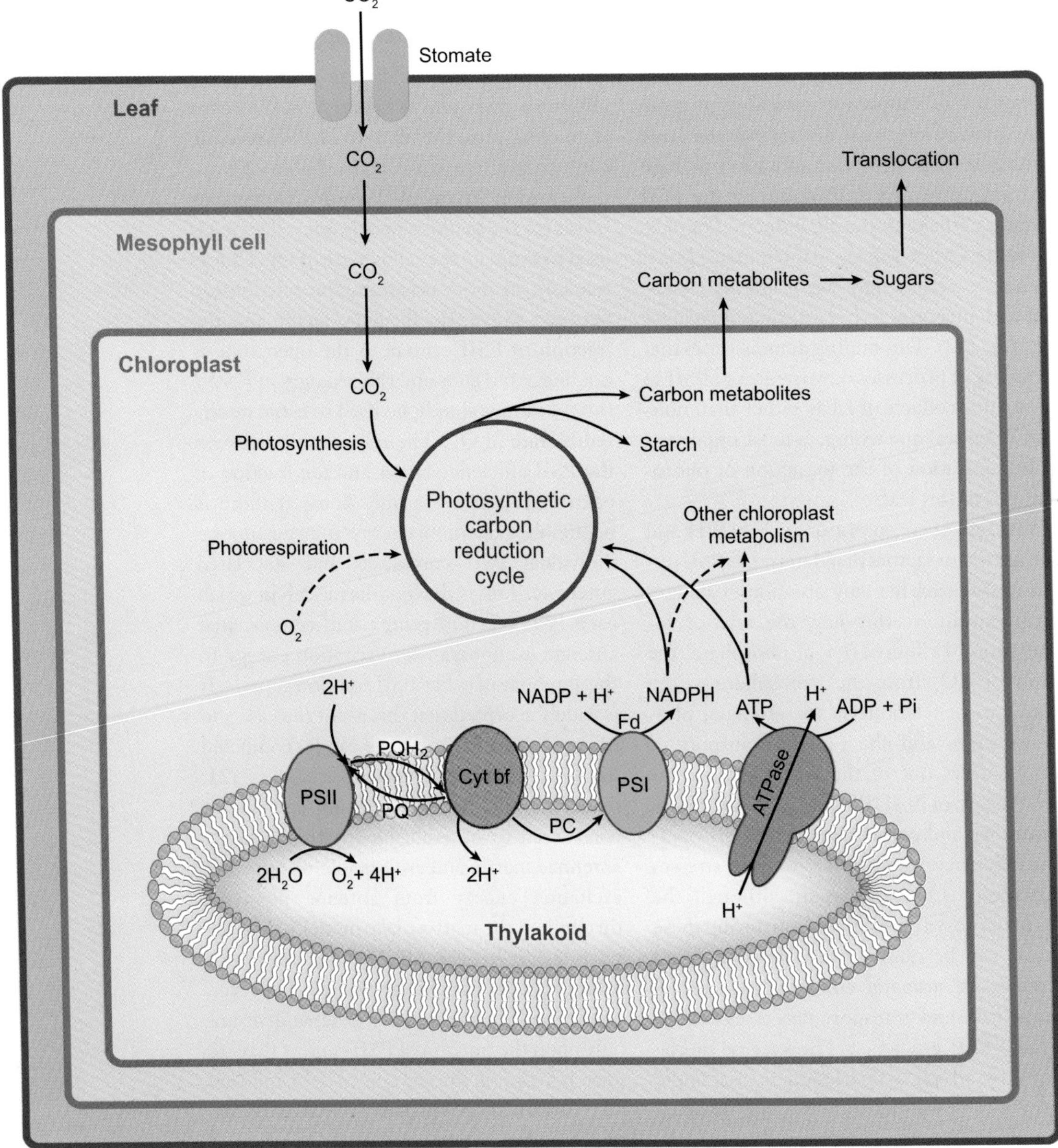

estimating changes in the redox state of Q_A using F_q'/F_v', rather than q_L, especially at high light intensities.

Nonphotochemical Quenching

Although F_v'/F_m' can be used to evaluate the contribution of changes in nonphotochemical quenching to changes in PSII operating efficiency, levels of nonphotochemical quenching are often assessed by the parameter *NPQ*. *NPQ* is calculated from $(F_m/F_m') - 1$ (13) and estimates changes in the apparent rate constant for excitation decay by heat loss induced by light relative to this rate constant in the dark (65). Because *NPQ* compares nonphotochemical quenching from a dark-adapted leaf at F_m to that at F_m' for the leaf exposed to actinic light, *NPQ* values can only be compared for leaves that have similar nonphotochemical quenching characteristics in the dark-adapted state, e.g., leaves with similar F_v/F_m values. Changes in *NPQ* are nonlinearly related to and rise to higher values than F_v'/F_m' for a given change in nonphotochemical quenching (**Figure 3**). Consequently, changes in *NPQ* do not allow evaluation of the proportion of changes in PSII operating efficiency that are attributable to changes in nonphotochemical quenching.

Nonphotochemical quenching in leaves can consist of three components: energy-dependent quenching, q_E, photoinhibitory quenching, q_I, and state transition quenching, q_T (65). Researchers have resolved nonphotochemical quenching into q_E, q_I, and q_T from analyses of the relaxation kinetics of these quenching components in the dark (49, 98, 106). However, care must be taken when attempting to quantify the contributions of these components because the characteristics of their relaxation kinetics can vary as a result of changing environmental conditions imposed on leaves. Generally, in nonstressed leaves under moderate to saturating light q_E is the major component, and q_I becomes prominent at light levels well in excess of that required to saturate photosynthesis or when stresses severely restrict the consumption of reductants produced by photosynthetic electron transport. Quenching associated with state transitions, q_T, is important only at low light levels, but can be very significant in algae (3, 33). Development of q_E is associated with quenching in the PSII antennae owing to the acidification of the thylakoid lumen resulting from electron transport (66). This acidification results in activation of violaxanthin de-epoxidase (109) and protonation of some carboxylic acid residues of the PsbS, a protein associated with the PSII antennae (74, 75) (**Figure 5**). Protonation of PsbS and binding of zeaxanthin to PSII produces conformational changes in the antennae that result in increases in the quantum yield of thermal dissipation of excitation

←

Figure 4

Relationships between photosynthetic electron transport, carbon metabolism and transport, and CO_2 supply. Electron transport, driven by the excitation of photosystem I (PSI) and photosystem II (PSII), results in the reduction of NADP to NADPH and the accumulation of protons in the thylakoid lumen. The resulting proton motive force is used to make ATP by driving protons back across the membrane through ATP synthase (ATPase). Ribulose 1,5-bisphosphate carboxylase/oxygenase (Rubisco) catalyzes the assimilation of CO_2 with ribulose 1,5-bisphosphate (RuBP) in the carboxylation reaction of the photosynthetic carbon reduction cycle in the chloroplast stroma. Stomata regulate the diffusion of CO_2 from the atmosphere to the sites of carboxylation. Other reactions of the photosynthetic carbon reduction cycle utilize NADPH and ATP to produce triose phosphates, which are required for the synthesis of carbohydrates. NADPH and ATP are also used in a range of other chloroplast metabolic activities, e.g., nitrogen and sulfur metabolism and lipid and pigment synthesis. Rubisco can also catalyze the oxygenation of RuBP in the process of photorespiration, which also involves consumption of NADPH and ATP by the photosynthetic carbon reduction cycle. Abbreviations: Cyt bf, cytochrome b_6f complex; Fd, ferredoxin; PC, plastocyanin; PQ, plastoquinone; PQH_2, plastoquinol.

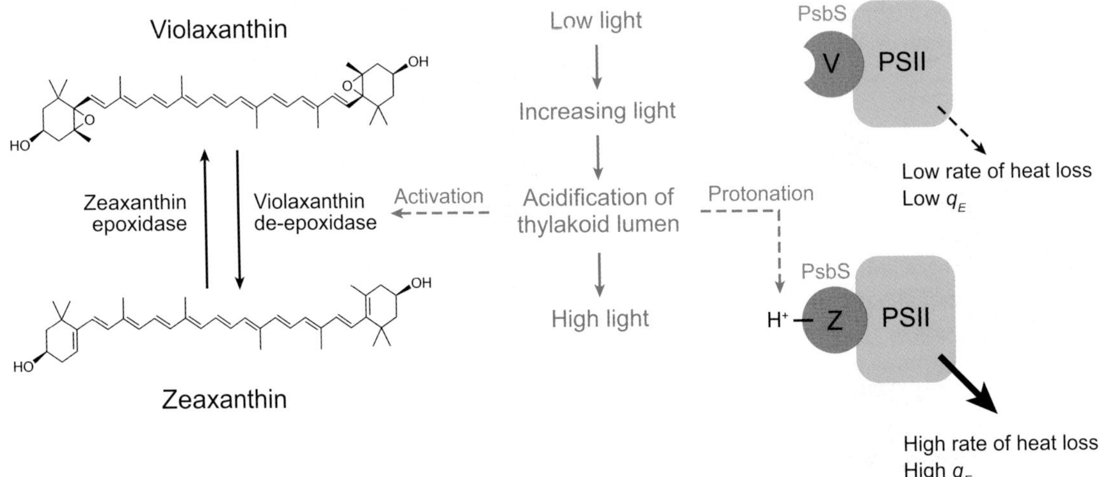

Figure 5

Mechanism of light-induced energy-dependent quenching of excitation energy in photosystem II (PSII). At low light that is limiting for photosynthesis a xanthophyll pigment, violaxanthin (V), is associated with the PSII antenna and PSII has a low rate of heat loss and consequently a low level of energy-dependent quenching, q_E, which is an important component of nonphotochemical quenching (NPQ). At higher light intensities increased electron transport results in acidification of the thylakoid lumen. When the lumen pH drops below *ca*. 6 violaxanthin de-epoxidase is activated and converts violaxanthin to zeaxanthin (Z) and PsbS becomes protonated. The zeaxanthin associated with PSII is an efficient quencher of excitation energy in the PSII antenna and the rate of heat loss from PSII increases, which increases q_E. When light intensity decreases deprotonation of PsbS occurs and zeaxanthin epoxidase converts zeaxanthin back to violaxanthin, which decreases q_E.

energy (50, 65, 95). Photoinactivation of PSII and zeaxanthin-related quenching can be involved in the development of q_I (65).

More detailed analyses of nonphotochemical quenching can resolve the excitation energy fluxes into light-induced quenching processes and non–light-induced quenching

Figure 6

Imaging the heterogeneity of photosynthetic activities of leaves, individual cells, and chloroplasts. (*a*) Image of F_q'/F_m' for a mildly water-stressed leaf of a Japanese anemone (*Anemone* × *hybrida*) collected from a local park on a warm and windy day and exposed to an actinic photosynthetically active photon flux density (PPFD) of 200 μmol m^{-2} s^{-1}. This image demonstrates the large heterogeneity in photosynthetic activity across the leaf. The colored bar indicates the range of F_q'/F_m' values. (*b*) Image of F_q'/F_m' of chloroplasts in pair of stomatal guard cells of an attached leaf of *Tradescantia albiflora* exposed to a PPFD of 250 μmol m^{-2} s^{-1}. Values of F_q'/F_m', F_v'/F_m', and F_q'/F_v' shown for two individual chloroplasts demonstrate the heterogeneity of photosynthetic activity between chloroplasts in similar cells; this is primarily attributable to differences in F_q'/F_v'. (*c--h*) Images taken from a pair of guard cells of an attached leaf of *Commelina communis* with the stomate open (*c–e*) and after closure by decreasing the relative humidity (*f–h*). (*c, f*) are reflected light images; (*d, g*) are images of F_m'. (*e, h*) Images of F_q'/F_m' at a PPFD of 150 μmol m^{-2} s^{-1} showing the large decrease in PSII operating efficiency that occurs on closure of the stomata. (*j*) Reflected light image from an intertidal benthic biofilm collected from a salt marsh mud flat at Colne Point, Essex, UK and (*k*) image of F_q'/F_m' from these cells demonstrating the very large differences in the PSII operating efficiency between species. A number of different species can be identified in the biofilm: *Gyrosigma limosum* (1); *Euglena* sp. (2); *Plagiotropis vitrea* (3); *Pleurosigma angulatum* (4); and *Navicula* sp. (5). Images in (*b–h*) are taken from Reference 7, with permission; images in (*j*) and (*k*) are taken from Reference 94 with permission of copyright holder, American Society of Limnology and Oceanography.

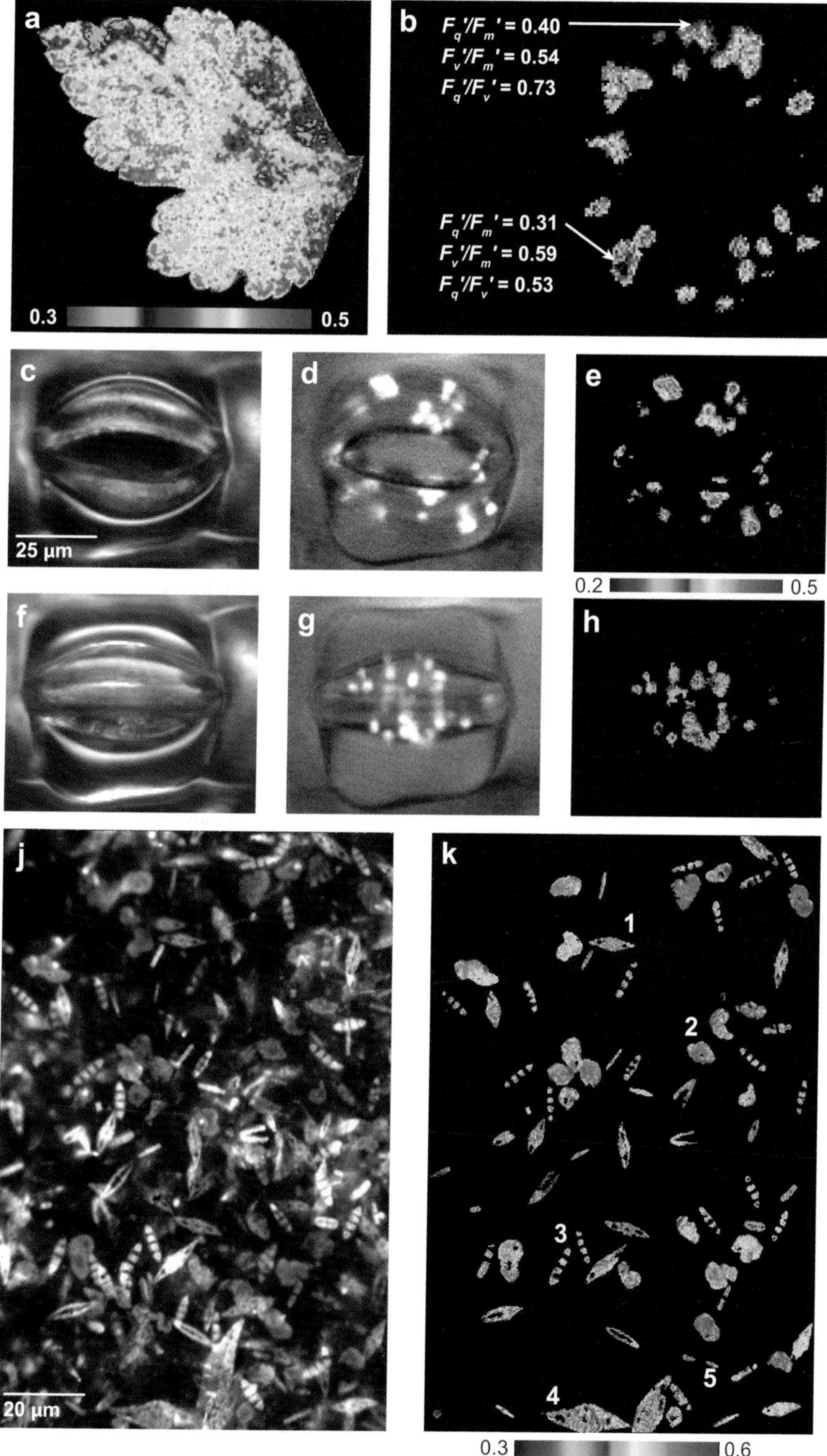
a
0.3
0.5
b
F_q'/F_m' = 0.40
F_v'/F_m' = 0.54
F_q'/F_v' = 0.73
F_q'/F_m' = 0.31
F_v'/F_m' = 0.59
F_q'/F_v' = 0.53
c
25 µm
d
e
0.2
0.5
f
g
h
j
20 µm
k
1
2
3
4
5
0.3
0.6

processes (46, 63). The quantum yield of quenching due to light-induced processes, ϕ_{NPQ}, can be calculated (63):

$$\phi_{NPQ} = 1 - \frac{F'_q}{F'_m} - \frac{1}{\frac{F_m - F'_m}{F'_m} + 1 + \frac{F'_q}{F'_v} \cdot \frac{F'_o}{F'} \cdot \left(\frac{F_m}{F_o} - 1\right)} \tag{1}$$

Because the sum of the quantum yields of PSII photochemistry (ϕ_{PSII}), light-induced quenching processes, and non–light-induced quenching processes is assumed to equal 1, the quantum yield of non–light-induced quenching processes, ϕ_{NO}, can be estimated from $\phi_{\mathrm{NO}} = 1 - (F_q'/F_m') - \phi_{\mathrm{NPQ}}$ (63).

IMAGING OF FLUORESCENCE

The development of instruments capable of imaging chlorophyll fluorescence has provided a powerful tool to resolve spatial heterogeneity of leaf photosynthetic performance (86, 91). Photosynthetic heterogeneity has been identified in many situations, e.g., during induction of photosynthesis (20, 92), with changes in carbohydrate translocation (80), at the onset of senescence (108), in response to changes in leaf water status (82, 87, 107) (**Figure 6*a***), chilling (48) and ozone (73) stresses, wounding (99), and infection with bacteria (12, 16) and fungi (100, 104). Nonimaging fluorescence measurements would often not detect such heterogeneity. Imaging of appropriate fluorescence parameters can provide information about the causes of the heterogeneity. During induction of photosynthesis in a maize leaf, large changes in the degree of heterogeneity of the PSII operating efficiency occur (7). Similar patterns of heterogeneity are found in the images of F_q'/F_m' and F_q'/F_v', which are not seen in the F_v'/F_m' images. Consequently, the heterogeneity is attributable to differences in the ability of cells to oxidize Q_A, which results from an inability to consume NADPH and ATP in CO_2 assimilation.

For C_3 leaves in which photorespiration is inhibited, the mean PSII operating efficiency (determined from images of F_q'/F_m') is linearly related to ϕ_{CO_2} (determined from gas exchange), which allows quantitative visualization of the spatial distribution of photosynthesis (40). From gas exchange measurements made in conjunction with fluorescence imaging, Meyer & Genty (81) determined the relationship between PSII operating efficiency and intercellular CO_2 concentration (C_i) and constructed images of C_i from images of F_q'/F_m'. This approach has made it possible to map the two-dimensional distribution of C_i across leaves to study the lateral diffusion of CO_2 in leaf tissues (84). However, this procedure requires the assumption of spatially homogenous light absorption across the leaf area under study, which may not be the case in many leaves, such as when leaves have developed under stress or have been infected with pathogens.

High-resolution imaging has been used to examine the photosynthetic activities of single cells and even individual chloroplasts (93). The responses of electron transport in individual stomatal guard cells and adjacent mesophyll cells in intact leaves to changes in light, atmospheric CO_2 concentration, and humidity have been studied by imaging F_q'/F_m' (71) (**Figure 6*c–h***). The isolation of individual chloroplasts from images of the guard cells of *Tradescantia albiflora* exposed to a PPFD of 250 μmol m^{-2} s^{-1} indicates that they show a wide range of mean F_q'/F_m' values, ranging from 0.27 to 0.43 (7). Such differences in the PSII operating efficiencies of individual chloroplasts are primarily attributed to differences in the ability to utilize ATP and reductants, not to differences in nonphotochemical quenching, because differences in F_q'/F_v' are considerably greater than those for F_v'/F_m' (7) (**Figure 6*b***). Imaging has also resolved large differences in photosynthetic performance among benthic diatom species in biofilms (94) (**Figure 6*j,k***). One problem in the production of images of F_q'/F_m' of such biofilms is that some of the cells can move between the time that the images of F' and F_m' are captured, and therefore these cells must be moved within one image to allow them to be superimposed before calculation of the F_q'/F_m' image (91, 94).

Fluorescence imaging can be used in screening procedures to identify organisms with modified photosynthetic performance, as has been done for algae (11, 88) and *Arabidopsis* (89) mutants. Perturbations of metabolic processes not directly involved in photosynthetic metabolism often induce changes in fluorescence parameters (9, 96), which can be used to screen for such perturbations. The development of commercial fluorescence imaging instruments that can image areas greater than 100 cm^2 allows the screening of large numbers of plants simultaneously. High-throughput screening of metabolic perturbations in *Arabidopsis* seedlings can be achieved by growing plants in the wells of 96-well microtiter plates (9) (**Figure 7**). Fluorescence imaging can also be used to estimate leaf area and consequently estimate growth; one application is the early growth of seedlings that have planophile, nonoverlapping leaves, such as *Arabidopsis*, from images of F_m. The total area from which the fluorescence is emitted is directly related to the leaf area that contains chlorophyll (9). However, for plants in

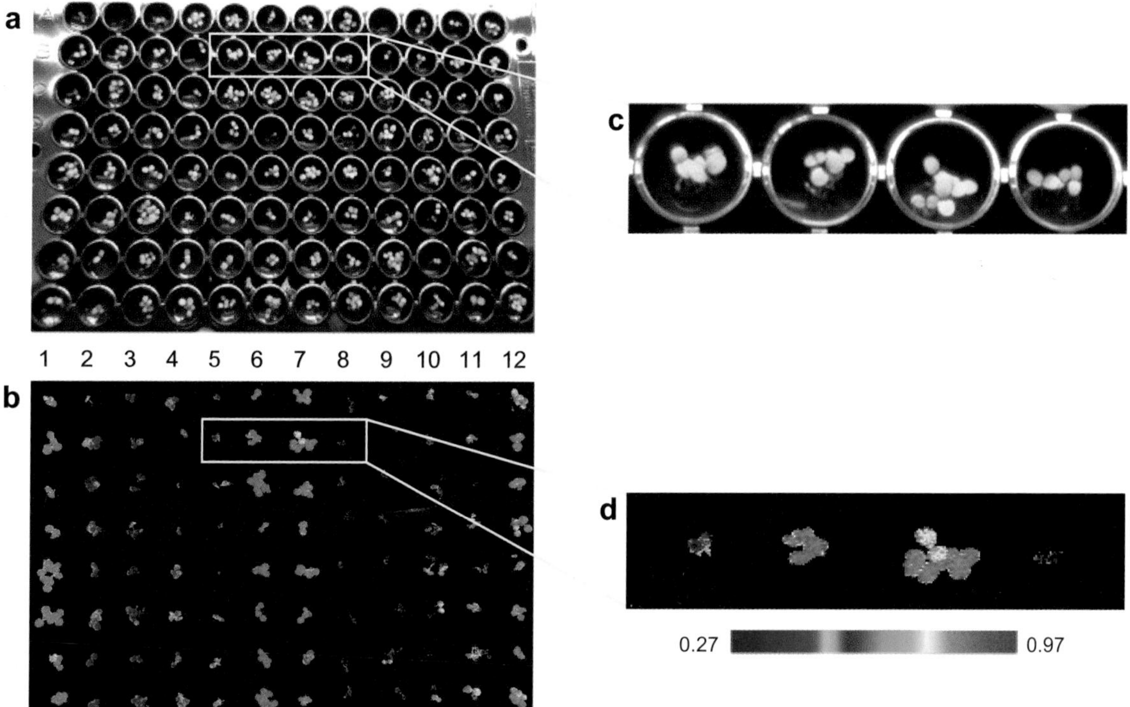

Figure 7

High-throughput screening for metabolic perturbations in *Arabidopsis*. (*a*) Five-day-old *Arabidopsis* plants in a 96-well plate 24 h after being treated with 0.4 (rows 5 and 11), 0.8 (rows 4 and 10), 4 (rows 3 and 9), and 8 (rows 2 and 8) mM Imazapyr, a herbicide that inhibits acetolactase synthase and consequently the synthesis of branched chain amino acids. Untreated controls are in rows 1, 6, 7, and 12. (*b*) Images of F_v/F_m for these plants. (*c,d*) Enlargements of the plants and images outlined by the yellow boxes in (*a*) and (*b*) respectively. Although differences in growth cannot be detected by visual observation, there are very large differences in the images of F_v/F_m between the control and herbicide-treated plants. Taken from Reference 9 with permission of copyright holder, American Society of Plant Biologists.

which the leaves overlap significantly or the leaves cannot be positioned normal to the camera this relationship does not necessarily hold. In such cases examination of the relationship between the area of fluorescence and leaf growth is required before the use of fluorescence to screen for differences in growth.

SUMMARY POINTS

1. Dark-adapted F_v/F_m is a useful relative measure of the maximum quantum yield of photosystem II (PSII) photochemistry, but does not provide an accurate quantitative value of this quantum yield.
2. F_q'/F_m' is a useful relative measure of the quantum yields of PSII photochemistry and linear electron flux through PSII.
3. F_q'/F_m' can be used to estimate the rate of linear electron transport. This requires accurate determination of the photosynthetically active photon flux density (PPFD) incident on the leaf, the proportion of incident PPFD that is absorbed by the leaf, and the fraction of absorbed PPFD that is received by PSII.
4. In certain circumstances F_q'/F_m' is a good indicator of changes in the quantum yield of CO_2 assimilation by the leaf, ϕ_{CO_2}, but it should not be used to estimate absolute rates of CO_2 assimilation.
5. Many metabolic and physiological factors influence F_q'/F_m' by determining the rate of consumption of ATP and NADPH.
6. Fluorescence imaging can identify spatial heterogeneity of photosynthetic performance and offers new possibilities for understanding the operation and regulation of photosynthesis. Fluorescence imaging can also be used to image other physiological phenomena indirectly if they interfere with the operation of photosynthesis and its associated metabolism, e.g., herbicide effects and stomatal heterogeneity.

FUTURE DIRECTIONS

1. Chlorophyll fluorescence parameters can now be easily measured and provide useful probes of photosynthetic performance in vivo and the extent to which performance is limited by photochemical and nonphotochemical processes.
2. Coupling of appropriate fluorescence measurements with other noninvasive techniques, such as absorption spectroscopy (5), gas exchange (76), and thermal imaging (107), can provide insights into the limitations to photosynthesis under given conditions.
3. Fluorescence imaging has great potential in future plant screening programs and other areas of applied plant physiology. The selection of appropriate fluorescence parameters and careful calibration of their changes with key plant performance indicators is important. Once a satisfactory calibration has been achieved, fluorescence can offer rapid, high-throughput screening. The use of automated sampling devices in conjunction with increases in the areas than can be imaged will enhance the rates of screening procedures even further.

DISCLOSURE STATEMENT

The author is not aware of any biases that might be perceived as affecting the objectivity of this review.

ACKNOWLEDGMENTS

I would to thank the many colleagues with whom I have had discussions during the preparation of this review, in particular Steven Driever, Jeremy Harbinson, David Kramer, Tracy Lawson, James Morison, Phil Mullineaux, and Don Ort. Many of my studies using chlorophyll fluorescence have been supported by the Biotechnology and Biological Research Council and the Natural Environment Research Council in the UK.

LITERATURE CITED

1. Adams WW III, Demmig-Adams B. 2004. Chlorophyll fluorescence as a tool to monitor plant response to the environment. In *Chlorophyll a Fluorescence: A Signature of Photosynthesis*, ed. GC Papageorgiou, Govindjee, pp. 583–604. Dordrecht: Springer
2. Adams WW III, Demmig-Adams B. 2006. Energy dissipation and photoinhibition: a continuum of photoprotection. In *Photoprotection, Photoinhibition, Gene Regulation and Environment*, ed. B Demmig-Adams, WW Adams III, AK Mattoo, pp. 49–64. Dordrecht: Springer
3. Allen JF, Mullineaux CW. 2004. Probing the mechanism of state transitions in oxygenic photosynthesis by chlorophyll fluorescence spectroscopy, kinetics and imaging. In *Chlorophyll a Fluorescence: A Signature of Photosynthesis*, ed. GC Papageorgiou, Govindjee, pp. 447–61. Dordrecht: Springer
4. Aro E-M, Virgin I, Anderson B. 1994. Photoinhibition of photosystem II. Inactivation, protein damage and turnover. *Biochim. Biophys. Acta* 1143:113–34
5. Baker NR, Harbinson J, Kramer DM. 2007. Determining the limitations and regulation of photosynthetic energy transduction in leaves. *Plant Cell Environ.* 30:1107–25
6. Baker NR, Oxborough K. 2004. Chlorophyll fluorescence as a probe of photosynthetic productivity. In *Chlorophyll a Fluorescence: A Signature of Photosynthesis*, ed. GC Papageorgiou, Govindjee, pp. 65–82. Dordrecht: Springer
7. Baker NR, Oxborough K, Lawson T, Morison JIL. 2001. High resolution imaging of photosynthetic activities of tissues, cells and chloroplasts in leaves. *J. Exp. Bot.* 52:615–21
8. Baker NR, Rosenqvist E. 2004. Applications of chlorophyll fluorescence can improve crop production strategies: an examination of future possibilities. *J. Exp. Bot.* 55:1607–21
9. Barbagallo RP, Oxborough K, Pallett KE, Baker NR. 2003. Rapid noninvasive screening for perturbations of metabolism and plant growth using chlorophyll fluorescence imaging. *Plant Physiol.* 132:485–93
10. Bennoun P. 1982. Evidence for a respiratory chain in the chloroplast. *Proc. Natl. Acad. Sci. USA* 79:4352–56
11. Bennoun P, Béal D. 1997. Screening algal mutant colonies with altered thylakoid electrochemical gradient through fluorescence and delayed luminescence digital imaging. *Photosynth. Res.* 51:161–65
12. Berger S, Benediktyová Z, Matouŝ K, Bonfig K, Mueller MJ, et al. 2007. Visualization of dynamics of plant-pathogen interaction by novel combination of chlorophyll fluorescence imaging and statistical analysis: differential effects of virulent and avirulent strains of *P. syringae* and of oxylipins on *A. thaliana*. *J. Exp. Bot.* 58:797–806

13. Bilger W, Björkman O. 1990. Role of the xanthophylls cycle in photoprotection elucidated by measurements of light-induced absorbance changes, fluorescence and photosynthesis in *Hedera canariensis*. *Photosynth. Res.* 25:173–85
14. Björkman O, Demmig B. 1987. Photon yield of O_2 evolution and chlorophyll fluorescence characteristics at 77 K among vascular plants of diverse origins. *Planta* 170:489–504
15. Blankenship RE. 2002. *Molecular Mechanisms of Photosynthesis*, pp. 149–51. Oxford: Blackwell Sci. 321 pp.
16. Bonfig KB, Schreiber U, Gabler A, Roitsch T, Berger S. 2006. Infection with virulent and avirulent *P. syringae* strains differentially affects photosynthesis and sink metabolism in *Arabidopsis* leaves. *Planta* 225:1–12
17. Bradbury M, Baker NR. 1981. Analysis of the slow phases of the in vivo chlorophyll fluorescence induction curve. Changes in the redox state of photosystem II electron acceptors and fluorescence emission from photosystems I and II. *Biochim. Biophys. Acta* 635:542–51
18. Bradbury M, Baker NR. 1984. A quantitative determination of photochemical and non-photochemical quenching during the slow phase of the chlorophyll fluorescence induction curve of bean leaves. *Biochim. Biophys. Acta* 765:275–81
19. Bradbury M, Baker NR. 1986. The kinetics of photoinhibition of the photosynthetic apparatus in pea chloroplasts. *Plant Cell Environ.* 9:289–97
20. Bro E, Meyer S, Genty B. 1996. Heterogeneity of leaf assimilation during photosynthetic induction. *Plant Cell Environ.* 19:1349–58
21. Butler WL. 1978. Energy distribution in the photochemical apparatus of photosynthesis. *Annu. Rev. Plant. Physiol.* 29:345–78
22. Cheeseman JM, Herendeen LB, Cheeseman AT, Clough BF. 1997. Photosynthesis and photoprotection in mangroves under field conditions. *Plant Cell Environ.* 20:579–88
23. Cornic G. 1994. Drought stress and high light effects on leaf photosynthesis. In *Photoinhibition of Photosynthesis*, ed. NR Baker, JR Bowyer, pp. 297–313. Oxford: BIOS Scientific Publishers Ltd.
24. Cornic G, Ghashghaie J. 1991. Effect of temperature on net CO_2 assimilation and photosystem II quantum yield on electron transfer of French bean leaves (*Phaseolus vulgaris* L.) during drought stress. *Planta* 183:178–84
25. Dau H. 1994. Molecular mechanisms and quantitative models of variable photosystem II fluorescence. *Photochem. Photobiol.* 60:1–23
26. Dietz K-J, Schreiber U, Heber U. 1985. The relationship between the redox state of Q_A and photosynthesis in leaves at various carbon dioxide, oxygen and light regimes. *Planta* 166:219–26
27. DiMarco G, Manes FS, Tricoli D, Vitale E. 1990. Fluorescence parameters measured concurrently with net photosynthesis to investigate chloroplastic CO_2 concentration in leaves of *Quercus silex* L. *J. Plant Physiol.* 136:538–43
28. Duysens LNM, Sweers HE. 1963. Mechanism of two photochemical reactions in algae as studied by means of fluorescence. In *Studies on Microalgae and Photosynthetic Bacteria*, ed. H Tamiya, pp. 353–72. Tokyo: Univ. Tokyo Press
29. Edwards GE, Baker NR. 1993. Can CO_2 assimilation in maize leaves be predicted accurately from chlorophyll fluorescence analysis? *Photosyn. Res.* 37:89–102
30. Ehleringer JR. 1991. Temperature and energy budgets. In *Plant Physiological Ecology*, ed. RW Pearcy, J Ehleringer, HA Mooney, PW Rundel, pp. 97–135. London: Chapman and Hall

31. Farage PK, Blowers D, Long SP, Baker NR. 2006. Low growth temperatures modify the efficiency of light use by photosystem II for CO_2 assimilation in leaves of two chilling-tolerant C_4 species, *Cyperus longus* L. and *Miscanthus* × *giganteus*. *Plant Cell Environ.* 29:720–28
32. Field TS, Nedbal L, Ort DR. 1998. Nonphotochemical reduction of the plastoquinone pool in sunflower leaves originates from chlororespiration. *Plant Physiol.* 116:1209–18
33. Finazzi G. 2004. The central role of the green alga *Chlamydomonas reinhardtii* in revealing the mechanism of state transitions. *J. Exp. Bot.* 56:383–88
34. Foyer C, Furbank R, Harbinson J, Horton P. 1990. The mechanisms contributing to control of electron transport by carbon assimilation in leaves. *Photosynth. Res.* 25:83–100
35. Foyer C, Lelandais M, Harbinson J. 1992. Control of quantum efficiencies of Photosystems I and II electron flow and enzyme activation following dark-to-light transitions in pea leaves. Relationship between NADP/NADPH ratios and NADP-malate dehydrogenase activation state. *Plant Physiol.* 99:979–86
36. Fryer MJ, Andrews JR, Oxborough K, Blowers DA, Baker NR. 1998. Relationship between CO_2 assimilation, photosynthetic electron transport and active O_2 metabolism in leaves of maize in the field during periods of low temperature. *Plant Physiol.* 116:571–80
37. Genty B, Briantais J-M, Baker NR. 1989. The relationship between the quantum yield of photosynthetic electron transport and quenching of chlorophyll fluorescence. *Biochim. Biophys. Acta* 990:87–92
38. Genty B, Goulas Y, Dimon B, Peltier JM, Moya I. 1992. Modulation of efficiency of primary conversion in leaves, mechanisms involved at PSII. In *Research in Photosynthesis, Volume 4*, ed. N Murata, pp. 603–10. Dordrecht: Kluwer Academic Publishers
39. Genty B, Harbinson J, Baker NR. 1990. Relative quantum efficiencies of the two photosystems of leaves in photorespiratory and nonphotorespiratory conditions. *Plant Physiol. Biochem.* 28:1–10
40. Genty B, Meyer S. 1994. Quantitative mapping of leaf photosynthesis using chlorophyll fluorescence imaging. *Aust. J. Plant Physiol.* 22:277–84
41. Genty B, Wonders J, Baker NR. 1990. Non-photochemical quenching of F_o in leaves is emission wavelength dependent. Consequences for quenching analysis and its interpretation. *Photosynth. Res.* 26:133–39
42. Ghannoum O, Siebke K, von Caemmerer S, Conroy JP. 1998. The photosynthesis of young *Panicum* C_4 leaves is not C_3-like. *Plant Cell Environ.* 21:1123–31
43. Habash DZ, Genty B, Baker NR. 1994. The consequences of chlorophyll deficiency for photosynthetic light use efficiency in a single gene mutation of cowpea. *Photosynth. Res.* 42:17–25
44. Harbinson J, Genty B, Baker NR. 1989. The relationship between the quantum efficiencies of photosystems I and II in pea leaves. *Plant Physiol.* 90:1029–34
45. Harbinson J, Genty B, Baker NR. 1990. The relationship between CO_2 assimilation and electron transport in leaves. *Photosynth. Res.* 25:213–24
46. Hendrikson L, Furbank RT, Chow WS. 2004. A simple alternative approach to assessing the fate of absorbed light energy using chlorophyll fluorescence. *Photosynth. Res.* 82:73–81
47. Hodáňová D. 1985. Leaf optical properties. In *Photosynthesis during Leaf Development*, ed. Z Šesták, pp. 107–127. Praha: Academia
48. Hogewoning SW, Harbinson J. 2007. Insights into the development, kinetics and variation of photoinhibition using chlorophyll fluorescence imaging of a chilled, variegated leaf. *J. Exp. Bot.* 58:453–63

49. Horton P, Hague A. 1988. Studies on the induction of chlorophyll fluorescence in isolated barley protoplasts: IV. Resolution of nonphotochemical quenching. *Biochim. Biophys. Acta* 932:107–15
50. Horton P, Ruban A. 2005. Molecular design of the photosystem II light-harvesting antenna: photosynthesis and photoprotection. *J. Exp. Bot.* 56:365–73
51. Hymus GJ, Ellsworth DS, Baker NR, Long SP. 1999. Does free-air carbon dioxide enrichment affect photochemical energy use by evergreen trees in different seasons? A chlorophyll fluorescence study of mature loblolly pine. *Plant Physiol.* 120:1183–91
52. Joliot P, Joliot A. 1964. Études cinétiques de la réaction photochimique libérant l'oxygene au cours de la photosynthese. *C. R. Acad. Sci. Paris* 258:4622–25
53. Jones HG. 1992. *Plants and Microclimate* (2nd edition). Cambridge: Cambridge Univ. Press. 428 pp.
54. Kautsky H, Apel W, Amann H. 1960. Chlorophyllfluoreszenz und Kohlensäureassimilation. XIII. Die Fluoreszenkurve und die Photochemie der Pflanze. *Biochem. Zeit.* 322:277–92
55. Kautsky H, Hirsch A. 1931. Neue Versuche zur Kohlensäureassimilation. *Naturwissenschaften* 19:964
56. Kautsky H, Zedlitz W. 1941. Fluoreszenzkurven von Chloroplasten-Grana. *Naturwiss* 29:101–2
57. Klughammer C, Schreiber U. 1994. An improved method, using saturating pulses, for the determination of Photosystem I quantum yield via $P700^+$-absorbance changes at 830 nm. *Planta* 192:261–68
58. Krall JP, Edwards GE. 1990. Quantum yields of photosystem II electron transport and CO_2 fixation in C_4 plants. *Aust. J. Plant Physiol.* 17:579–88
59. Krall JP, Edwards GE. 1991. Environmental effects on the relationship between quantum yield of carbon assimilation and in vivo PS II electron transport in maize. *Aust. J. Plant Physiol.* 18:267–78
60. Krall JP, Edwards GE, Ku MSB. 1991. Quantum yield of photosystem II and efficiency of CO_2 fixation in *Flaveria* (Asteraceae) species under varying light and CO_2. *Aust. J. Plant Physiol.* 18:369–83
61. Kramer DM, Avenson TJ, Kanazawa A, Cruz JA, Ivanov B, Edwards GE. 2004. The relationship between photosynthetic electron transfer and its regulation. In *Chlorophyll a Fluorescence: A Signature of Photosynthesis*, ed. GC Papageorgiou, Govindjee, pp. 251–78. Dordrecht: Springer
62. Kramer DM, DiMarco G, Loreto F. 1995. Contribution of plastoquinone quenching to saturation pulse-induced rise of chlorophyll fluorescence in leaves. In *Photosynthesis from Light to the Biosphere, Vol I*, ed. P Mathis, pp. 147–50. Dordrecht: Kluwer Academic Publishers
63. Kramer DM, Johnson G, Kiirats O, Edwards GE. 2004. New fluorescence parameters for determination of Q_A redox state and excitation energy fluxes. *Photosynth. Res.* 79:209–18
64. Krause GH, Briantais J-M, Vernotte C. 1980. Two mechanisms of reversible fluorescence quenching in chloroplasts. In *Photosynthesis. I. Photophysical Processes and Membrane Energization*, ed. G Akoyunoglou, pp. 575–84. Philadelphia: Balaban International Services
65. Krause GH, Jahns P. 2004. Non-photochemical energy dissipation determined by chlorophyll fluorescence quenching: characterization and function. In *Chlorophyll a Fluorescence: A Signature of Photosynthesis*, ed. GC Papageorgiou, Govindjee, pp. 463–95. Dordrecht: The Netherlands: Springer

66. Krause GH, Vernotte C, Briantais J-M. 1982. Photoinduced quenching of chlorophyll fluorescence in intact chloroplasts and algae. Resolution into two components. *Biochim. Biophys. Acta* 679:116–24
67. Laisk A, Loreto F. 1996. Determining photosynthetic parameters from leaf CO_2 exchange and chlorophyll fluorescence. Ribulose-1,5-bisphosphate carboxylase/oxygenase specificity factor, dark respiration in the light, excitation distribution between photosystems, alternative electron transport rate, and mesophyll diffusion resistance. *Plant Physiol.* 110:903–12
68. Laisk A, Eichelmann H, Oja V, Rasulov B, Rämma H. 2006. Photosystem II cycle and alternative electron flow in leaves. *Plant Cell Physiol.* 47:972–83
69. Lavergne J, Trissl HW. 1995. Theory of fluorescence induction in photosystem II: Derivation of analytical expressions in a model including exciton-radical-pair equilibrium and restricted energy transfer between photosynthetic units. *Biophys. J.* 68:2474–92
70. Lavorel J. 1962. Hétérogenéité de la chlorophylle in vivo. I, Spectres d'emission de fluorescence. *Biochim. Biophys. Acta* 60:510–23
71. Lawson T, Oxborough K, Morison JIL, Baker NR. 2002. Responses of photosynthetic electron transport in stomatal guard cells and mesophyll cells in intact leaves to light, CO_2 and humidity. *Plant Physiol.* 128:1–11
72. Lazár D. 1999. Chlorophyll *a* fluorescence induction. *Biochim. Biophys. Acta* 1412:1–28
73. Leipner J, Oxborough K, Baker NR. 2001. Primary sites of ozone-induced perturbations of photosynthesis in leaves: identification and characterization in *Phaseolus vulgaris* using high resolution chlorophyll fluorescence imaging. *J. Exp. Bot.* 52:1689–96
74. Li XP, Björkman O, Shih C, Grossman AR, Rosenqvist M, et al. 2000. A pigment-binding protein essential for regulation of photosynthetic light harvesting. *Nature* 403:391–95
75. Li XP, Gilmore AM, Caffarri S, Bassi R, Golan T, et al. 2004. Regulation of photosynthetic light harvesting involves intrathylakoid lumen pH sensing by the PsbS protein. *J. Biol. Chem.* 279:22866–74
76. Long SP, Bernacchi CJ. 2003. Gas exchange measurements, what can they tell us about underlying limitations to photosynthesis? Procedures and sources of error. *J. Exp. Bot.* 54:2392–401
77. MacAllister ED, Myers J. 1940. The time course of photosynthesis and fluorescence observed simultaneously. *Smithson. Inst. Misc. Collect.* 99:1–37
78. Maxwell K, Johnson GN. 2000. Chlorophyll fluorescence—a practical guide. *J. Exp. Bot.* 51:659–68
79. Melis A. 1999. Photosystem II damage and repair cycle in chloroplasts: what modulates the rate of photodamage in vivo? *Trends Plant Sci.* 4:130–35
80. Meng Q, Siebke K, Lippert P, Baur B, Mukherjee U, Weis E. 2001. Sink-source transition in tobacco leaves visualized using chlorophyll fluorescence imaging. *New Phytol.* 151:585–95
81. Meyer S, Genty B. 1998. Mapping intercellular CO_2 mole fraction (C_i) in *Rosa rubiginosa* leaves fed with abscisic acid by using chlorophyll fluorescence imaging. *Plant Physiol.* 116:947–57
82. Meyer S, Genty B. 1999. Heterogeneous inhibition of photosynthesis over the leaf surface of *Rosa rubiginosa* L. during water stress and abscisic acid treatment: induction of a metabolic component by limitation of CO_2 diffusion. *Planta* 210:126–31
83. Miyake C, Shinzaki Y, Miyata M, Tomizawa K. 2004. Enhancement of cyclic electron flow around PSI at high light and its contribution to the induction of nonphotochemical quenching of chl fluorescence in intact leaves of tobacco plants. *Plant Cell Physiol.* 45:1426–33

84. Morison JIL, Gallouët, Lawson T, Cornic G, Herbin R, Baker NR. 2005. Lateral diffusion of CO_2 in leaves is not sufficient to support photosynthesis. *Plant Physiol.* 139:254–66
85. Moya I, Mullet JE, Briantais J-M, Garcia R. 1981. Comparison between lifetime spectra of chloroplasts and subchloroplast particles at −196°C and 20°C. In *Photosynthesis. I. Photophysical Processes and Membrane Energization*, ed. G Akoyunoglou, pp 163–72. Philadelphia: Balaban International Services
86. Nedbal L, Whitmarsh J. 2004. Chlorophyll fluorescence imaging of leaves and fruits. In *Chlorophyll a Fluorescence: A Signature of Photosynthesis*, ed. GC Papageorgiou, Govindjee, pp. 389–407. Dordrecht: Springer
87. Nejad AR, Harbinson J, van Meeteren U. 2006. Dynamics of spatial heterogeneity of stomatal closure in *Tradescantia virginiana* altered by growth at high relative humidity. *J. Exp. Bot.* 57:3669–78
88. Niyogi KK, Björkman O, Grossman AR. 1997. *Chlamydomonas* xanthophylls cycle mutants identified by video imaging of chlorophyll fluorescence quenching. *Plant Cell* 9:1369–80
89. Niyogi KK, Grossman AR, Björkman O. 1998. *Arabidopsis* mutants define a central role for the xanthophyll cycle in the regulation of photosynthetic energy conversion. *Plant Cell* 10:1121–34
90. Osmond CB. 1994. What is photoinhibition? Some insights from comparisons of shade and sun plants. In *Photoinhibition of Photosynthesis from Molecular Mechanisms to the Field*, ed. NR Baker, JR Bowyer, pp. 1–24. Oxford: BIOS Scientific Publishers
91. Oxborough K. 2004. Using chlorophyll *a* fluorescence imaging to monitor photosynthetic performance. In *Chlorophyll a Fluorescence: A Signature of Photosynthesis*, ed. GC Papageorgiou, Govindjee, pp. 409–28. Dordrecht: Springer
92. Oxborough K, Baker NR. 1997. Resolving chlorophyll *a* fluorescence images of photosynthetic efficiency into photochemical and nonphotochemical components—calculation of qP and F_v'/F_m' without measuring F_o'. *Photosynth. Res.* 54:135–42
93. Oxborough K, Baker NR. 1997. An instrument capable of imaging chlorophyll *a* fluorescence from intact leaves at very low irradiance and at cellular and subcellular levels of organization. *Plant Cell Environ.* 20:1473–83
94. Oxborough K, Hanlon ARM, Underwood GJC, Baker NR. 2000. In vivo estimation of photosystem II photochemical efficiency of individual microphytobenthic cells using high-resolution imaging of chlorophyll *a* fluorescence. *Limnol. Oceanogr.* 45:1420–25
95. Pascal AA, Liu Z, Broess K, van Oort B, van Amerongen H, et al. 2005. Molecular basis of photoprotection and control of photosynthetic light-harvesting. *Nature* 436:134–37
96. Percival MP, Baker NR. 1991. Herbicides and photosynthesis. In *Herbicides*, ed. NR Baker, MP Percival, pp. 1–26. Amsterdam: Elsevier Science Publishers
97. Pfündel E. 1998. Estimating the contribution of photosystem I to total leaf chlorophyll fluorescence. *Photosynth. Res.* 56:185–95
98. Quick WP, Stitt M. 1989. An examination of factors contributing to nonphotochemical quenching of chlorophyll fluorescence in barley leaves. *Biochim. Biophys. Acta* 977:287–96
99. Quilliam RS, Swarbrick PJ, Scholes JD, Rolfe SA. 2006. Imaging photosynthesis in wounded leaves of *Arabidopsis thaliana*. *J. Exp. Bot.* 57:55–69
100. Scharte J, Schön H, Weis E. 2005. Photosynthesis and carbohydrate metabolism in tobacco leaves during an incompatible interaction with *Phytophthora nicotianae*. *Plant Cell Environ.* 28:1421–35
101. Schreiber U. 2004. Pulse-Amplitude-Modulation (PAM) fluorometry and saturation pulse method: an overview. *Chlorophyll a Fluorescence: A Signature of Photosynthesis*, ed. GC Papageorgiou, Govindjee, pp. 279–319. Dordrecht, The Netherlands: Springer

102. Schreiber U, Schliwa U, Bilger W. 1986. Continuous recording of photochemical and nonphotochemical fluorescence quenching with a new type of modulation fluorometer. *Photosynth. Res.* 10:51–62
103. Siebke K, von Caemmerer S, Badger M, Furbank RT. 1997. Expressing an RbcS antisense gene in transgenic *Flaveria bidentis* leads to an increased quantum requirement for CO_2 fixed in photosystems I and II. *Plant Physiol.* 115:1163–74
104. Swarbrick PJ, Schulze-Lefert P, Scholes JD. 2006. Metabolic consequences of susceptibility and resistance (race-specific and broad-spectrum) in barley leaves challenged with powdery mildew. *Plant Cell Environ.* 29:1061–76
105. Vernotte C, Etienne A-L, Briantais J-M. 1979. Quenching of the system II chlorophyll fluorescence by the plastoquinone pool. *Biochim. Biophys. Acta* 545:519–27
106. Walters RG, Horton P. 1991. Resolution of components of nonphotochemical chlorophyll fluorescence quenching in barley leaves. *Photosynth. Res.* 27:121–33
107. West JD, Peak D, Peterson JQ, Mott KA. 2005. Dynamics of stomatal patches for a single surface of *Xanthium strumarium* L. leaves observed with fluorescence and thermal images. *Plant Cell Environ.* 28:633–41
108. Wingler A, Brownhill E, Portau. 2005. Mechanisms of the light-dependent induction of cell death in tobacco plants with delayed senescence. *J. Exp. Bot.* 56:2897–905
109. Yamamoto HY, Bugos RC, Hieber AD. 1999. Biochemistry and molecular biology of the zanthophyll cycle. In *The Photochemistry of Carotenoids*, ed. HA Frank, AJK Young, G Britton, RJ Cogdell, pp. 293–303. Dordrecht, The Netherlands: Kluwer Academic Publishers

Seed Storage Oil Mobilization

Ian A. Graham

Centre for Novel Agricultural Products, Department of Biology, University of York, York YO10 5YW, United Kingdom; email: iag1@york.ac.uk

Annu. Rev. Plant Biol. 2008. 59:115–42

The *Annual Review of Plant Biology* is online at plant.annualreviews.org

This article's doi:
10.1146/annurev.arplant.59.032607.092938

1543-5008/08/0602-0115$20.00

Key Words

storage lipid mobilization, glyoxysomes/peroxisomes, fatty acid catabolism, β-oxidation, glyoxylate cycle, gluconeogenesis

Abstract

Storage oil mobilization starts with the onset of seed germination. Oil bodies packed with triacylglycerol (TAG) exist in close proximity with glyoxysomes, the single membrane–bound organelles that house most of the biochemical machinery required to convert fatty acids derived from TAG to 4-carbon compounds. The 4-carbon compounds in turn are converted to soluble sugars that are used to fuel seedling growth. Biochemical analysis over the last 50 years has identified the main pathways involved in this process, including β-oxidation, the glyoxylate cycle, and gluconeogenesis. In the last few years molecular genetic dissection of the overall process in the model oilseed species *Arabidopsis* has provided new insight into its complexity, particularly with respect to the specific role played by individual enzymatic steps and the subcellular compartmentalization of the glyoxylate cycle. Both abscisic acid (ABA) and sugars inhibit storage oil mobilization and a substantial degree of the control appears to operate at the transcriptional level.

Contents

INTRODUCTION

Oil, in the form of triacylglycerol (TAG), is a major seed storage reserve in many plant species including oilcrops such as sunflower, oilseed rape, soybean, and maize. The TAG accumulates during seed maturation and is then stored in the seed until germination, after which it is used to fuel seedling growth. During seed maturation TAGs are synthesized within the endoplasmic reticulum (ER) and are packaged into immature oil bodies, which subsequently bud off from the ER to form the mature organelle [Reviewed by Murphy & Vance (99); Hsieh & Huang (67)]. Depending on the plant species, storage protein and carbohydrate reserves (most frequently in the form of starch) also accumulate (8). These storage reserves are typically large insoluble compounds that can remain intact in desiccated seeds for extended periods. Upon seed germination these reserves need to be rapidly converted to soluble metabolites that can be transported throughout the seedling and used to support growth, which enables photoautotrophism to be achieved before reserves are exhausted.

TAG: triacylglycerol

Germination: complete when the root tip or radicle has emerged through the seed coat

FA: fatty acid

Specialized metabolic programs have evolved to ensure the rapid and efficient use of storage reserves upon the initiation of seed germination. The mobilization of storage oil involves the coordinated induction of a number of biochemical pathways in different subcellular locations. The first step in oil breakdown is catalyzed by lipases (70), which hydrolyze TAG to produce free fatty acids (FAs) and glycerol. The FAs then enter single membrane–bound organelles termed glyoxysomes where β-oxidation and part of the glyoxylate cycle occurs (15, 16). Glyoxysomes are structurally similar but metabolically distinct from the more ubiquitous peroxisomes—glyoxysomes contain two enzymes that are unique to the glyoxylate cycle, malate synthase (MLS) and isocitrate lyase (ICL). β-oxidation converts FAs to acetyl-CoA, which is subsequently condensed into 4-carbon compounds via the glyoxylate cycle. These 4-carbon compounds are then transported to the mitochondria, where they can either be converted to malate and transported to the cytosol for gluconeogenesis, or used as substrates for respiration. Traditional biochemical studies carried out on a number of oilseed species, in particular castor bean, resulted in the definition of the main pathways and enzymatic activities of the storage oil mobilization process. More recently, these studies have been extended through the use of biochemical genetics in the model oilseed species *Arabidopsis*. These studies have also led to new insights into additional roles of peroxisomal β-oxidation, including, for example, the synthesis of the wound signal jasmonic acid (JA), the synthesis of the auxin indole-3-acetic acid (IAA), and the breakage of seed dormancy (see References 4 and 106 for reviews).

Intriguingly, although the major period of oil breakdown occurs during postgerminative seedling growth, activities of enzymes and/or mRNA transcripts associated with this process have also been detected in developing seeds of various species including cotton (94), castor bean (72), cucumber (39), and *Brassica napus* (14). In a number of species, including *Arabidopsis* and *Brassica napus*, seed oil content actually falls during the final stages of seed maturation (5, 13). Furthermore, the breakdown of significant amounts of medium chain–length FAs in developing seeds of *Brassica napus* engineered to produce these valuable compounds effectively results in futile cycling (33). Controlling the degradation of oil and FAs during embryo development could therefore be a useful strategy to improve oil yield in existing crops or in those engineered to produce other industrial FAs.

Efficient storage oil breakdown is essential for successful seedling establishment, which in turn is of paramount importance for plant fitness in the field. Knowledge of the underlying biochemistry and metabolism of the breakdown as well as the synthesis of storage oil is essential for the development of new and improved oilseed crops that not only accumulate high levels of the desired oil, but also use it efficiently to support vigorous seedling growth. (See Oilseed Crops as Factories for Industrial Feedstocks.)

OILSEED CROPS AS FACTORIES FOR INDUSTRIAL FEEDSTOCKS

Humankind relies heavily on plant-derived oils for both food and animal feed applications. In addition, because the fatty acid constituents of triacylglycerols are structurally similar to the hydrocarbon chains that give functionality to petrochemicals, plant-derived oils also have great potential for the replacement of finite fossil fuels in application areas ranging from lubricants, polymers, paints, and solvents to inks, dyes, cosmetics, and surfactants (93). Currently, plant-derived oils are also increasingly being used for the production of biodiesel transportation fuel (62). The demand for plant-derived oils is set to grow even further with biotechnology promising to deliver a new generation of oilcrops with added functionalities ranging from long chain polyunsaturated fatty acids as sustainable replacements for fish oil to hydroxy, epoxy, and conjugated fatty acids as renewable industrial feedstocks (9, 49, 100). Seed plants collectively produce more than 500 different types of fatty acids, which differ by chain length, the presence of different unsaturated bonds, and functional groups (128); these represent further opportunities for the development of new oilseed crops as renewable industrial feedstocks.

OIL BODIES AND LIPOLYSIS

Oil bodies are relatively simple spherical organelles consisting of a TAG matrix covered by a phospholipid monolayer embedded with proteins (98). The most abundant of these proteins are the oleosins, which are usually present as two or more highly conserved isoforms (136). Oil body size typically correlates with oleosin protein levels in vivo (133, 135). This observation, coupled with in vitro studies that indicate the oleosin coat promotes steric hindrance and electrical repulsion between oil bodies (137), has led to the assumption that the function of oleosins is to prevent these organelles from coalescing during seed maturation, desiccation, and germination (20, 83). Direct evidence that oleosins do indeed determine the size of oil bodies in seeds recently came from studies in which the gene encoding the major (18-kD) oleosin in *Arabidopsis* seeds was disrupted, resulting in enlarged oil bodies, an alteration in accumulation of lipids and proteins, and a delay in seed germination (125). Presumably, maintaining a high surface-to-volume ratio by preventing oil body coalescence is important for TAG mobilization, because it provides sufficient surface area for lipase action and/or interaction with glyoxysomes.

As shown in **Figure 1**, oil bodies and glyoxysomes are in close proximity. A number

Glyoxysomes: single membrane–bound organelles that host two enzymes of the glyoxylate cycle, malate synthase and isocitrate lyase; also referred to as peroxisomes

Glyoxylate cycle: operates to accept acetyl-CoA units derived from β-oxidation and results in the net production of 4-carbon compounds

Table 1 Molecular genetic dissection of storage oil mobilization in *Arabidopsis*. All mutants shown here are discussed in the text. The background colors are consistent with those of Figure 2, apart from citrate synthase, which here is shown as completely green, reflecting its major role in β-oxidation: Yellow signifies a cytosolic/oil body location, green shows a direct involvement in glyoxysomal β-oxidation, gray shows the glyoxylate cycle, and blue signifies gluconeogenesis.

Protein Function	Subcellular location	Gene number	*Arabidopsis* mutant	Mutant Phenotype: Impaired oil breakdown	Mutant Phenotype: Impaired seedling establishment	References
Patatin-like TAG lipase	Oil body	At4g04040	*sdp1*	Yes	Yes	26
Glycerol kinase	Cytosol		*gli1*	No	No	25
			gli1 icl1	No	Yes	
ABC transporter	Glyoxysome membrane	At4g39850	*cts/ped3/pxa1*	Yes	Yes	38, 59, 147
Acyl-CoA synthetase	Glyoxysome	At3g05970	*lacs6*	No	No	41
		At5g27600	*lacs7*	No	No	
			lac6 lac7	Yes	Yes	
Acyl-CoA oxidase	Glyoxysome	At4g16760	*acx1*	No	No	2, 32, 108, 121
		At5g65110	*acx2*	No	No	
		At1g06290	*acx3*	No	No	
		At3g51840	*acx4*	No	No	
			acx1 acx2	Yes	Yes	
			acx3 acx4	Embryo lethal	-	
Multifunctional protein	Glyoxysome	At4g29010	*aim1*	No	No	116
Multifunctional protein 2 (MFP)	Glyoxysome	At3g06860	*mfp2*	Yes (partial)	Yes	119
3-keto-acyl-CoA thiolase	Glyoxysome	At2g33150	*kat2*	Yes (severe)	Yes	43, 57
Malate dehydrogenase	Glyoxysome	At2g22780	*pmdh1*	No	No	111
		At5g09660	*pmdh2*	No	No	
			pmdh1 pmdh2	Yes	Yes	
Citrate synthase	Glyoxysome	At3g58750	*csy2*	No	No	110
		At2g42790	*csy3*	No	No	
			csy2 csy3	Yes	Yes	
Monodehydro ascorbate reductase (MDAR4)	Glyoxysome membrane (matrix side)	At3g27820	*sdp2*	Yes	Yes	27
Malate synthase	Glyoxysome	At5g03860	*mls*	No	Partial	17, 26
Isocitrate lyase	Glyoxysome	At3g21720	*icl*	No	Partial	28
PEP-carboxykinase	Cytosol	At4g37870	*pck1*	No	Partial	107

of electron micrographic studies have suggested that oil bodies are in actual physical contact with glyoxysomes (60, 142) and invagination has been proposed as a direct mechanism to transport lipids from the oil bodies into glyoxysomes during FA β-oxidation (60). Biochemical data demonstrating that neutral lipids are transferred directly from the oil body into the glyoxysomal membrane of cotton (*Gossypium hirsutum*) seedlings further support the importance of physical contact between the organelles. (12).

Lipases are interfacial enzymes that cleave mono-, di-, and triacylglycerol into free FAs and glycerol at the oil/water interface. Lipase activities are typically membrane-associated and can be found in the oil body, glyoxysome, or microsomal fractions of seed extracts, depending on the species (69, 96). Lipases have been purified from the seeds of many different plant species (69) and genes encoding proteins with TAG lipase activity have been cloned from castor (24), tomato (91), and *Arabidopsis* (34). However, we lack conclusive evidence that these genes encode the bona fide TAG lipase for storage oil mobilization. For example, the pH optimum and peak of expression during seed development of the acid lipase cloned from castor bean endosperm make it an unlikely candidate (24), and gene knockouts in a candidate TAG lipase from *Arabidopsis* still retain wild-type TAG lipase activity and break TAG down at the normal rate (34).

A breakthrough in the search for the true TAG lipase was recently achieved via the use of an *Arabidopsis* seedling mutant screen (26). The screen was based on the observation that the impaired postgerminative growth phenotype found in a number of FA catabolism mutants can be rescued by provision of an alternative carbon source, such as sucrose (4, 17, 28, 57, 107, 108). Eastmond (26) used the sucrose rescue as a strategy to screen EMS-mutagenized seed, and identified multiple recessive mutations that fell into 17 complementation groups, six of which represent new *sugar dependent* (*sdp*) loci; the remainder are allelic to previously characterized mutants. Three of the new loci (*sdp1*, *sdp2*, and *sdp3*) are deficient in oil body lipase activity. Cloning of *sdp1* revealed that the corresponding protein is a member of an unorthodox class of patatin-like TAG lipases (PTLs) that contain a patatin-like serine esterase domain, previously described in animal and yeast TAG lipases, which are required for TAG breakdown (3, 52, 145). SDP1 is active against long chain TAGs in vitro, and GFP fusions show that it is associated with oil bodies during germination as depicted in **Figure 2**. SDP1 homologues are found in a wide range of plant species (26). This class of TAG lipases therefore appears to be conserved across eukaryotic evolution for the function of hydrolyzing TAG from oil bodies.

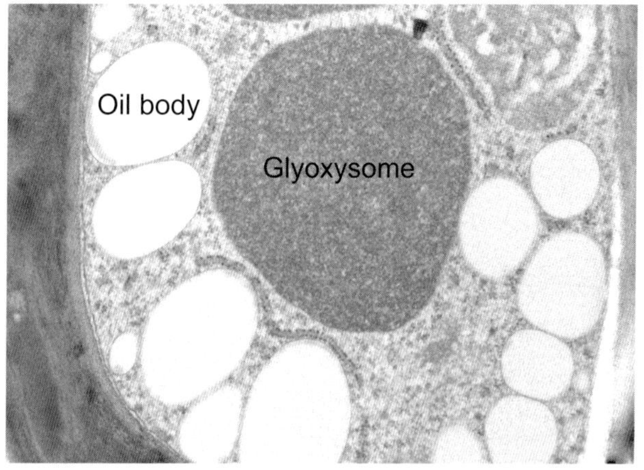

Figure 1

Transmission electron micrograph of a section through an imbibed *Arabidopsis* seed showing the close proximity of oil bodies and glyoxysomes.

β-oxidation: enzymatic steps that involve oxidation of fatty acyl-CoAs followed by thiolytic cleavage of a two-carbon acetyl-CoA unit

MLS: malate synthase

ICL: isocitrate lyase

Gluconeogenesis: synthesis of hexose sugars from tricarboxylic acid (TCA) cycle intermediates

Seedling establishment: the stage at which seedlings gain photosynthetic competence and switch from heterotrophic to photoautotrophic growth

GLYCEROL UTILIZATION

Lipolysis of TAG results in the production of FAs and glycerol in a 3:1 ratio; the three-carbon (3C) glycerol represents

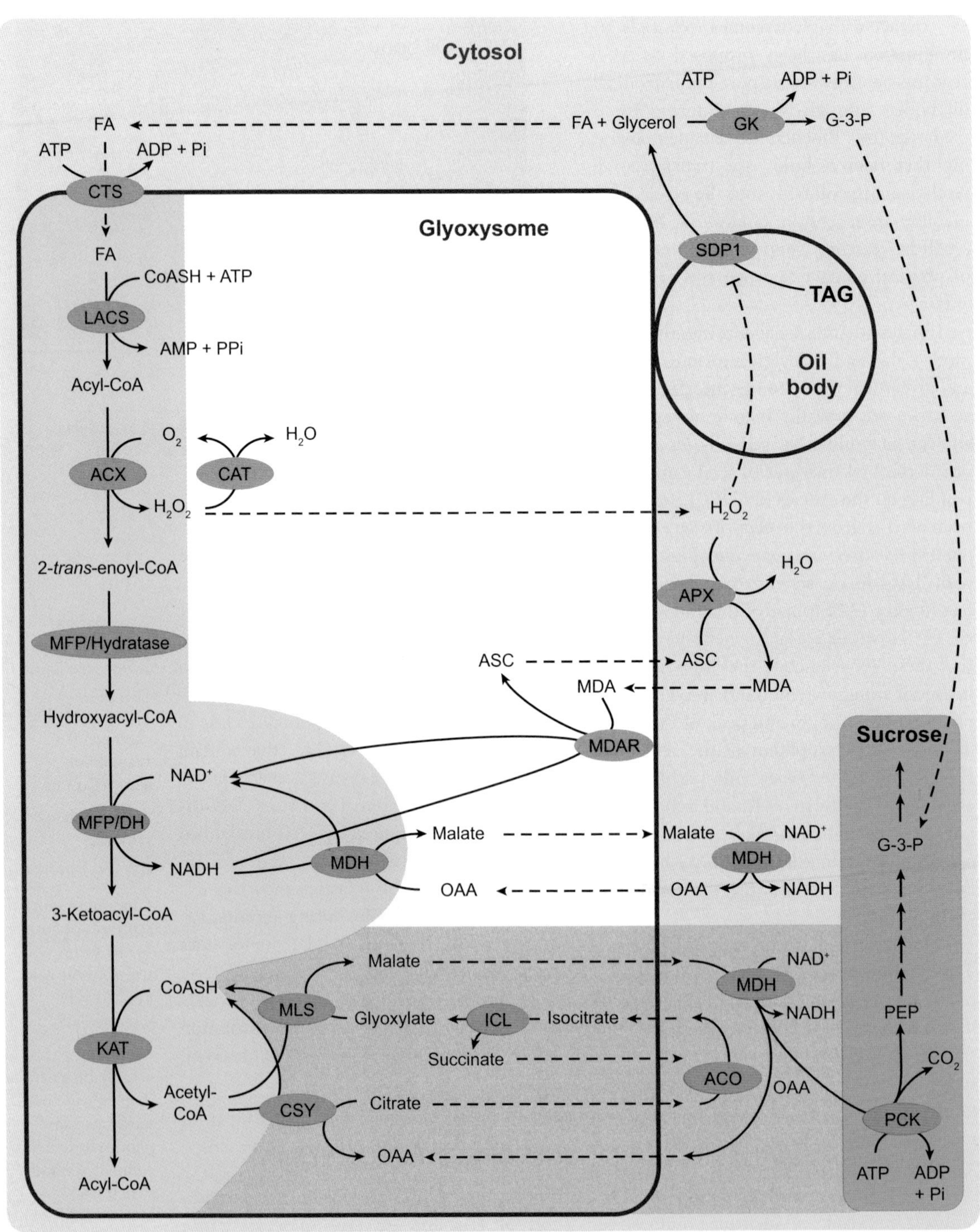
Cytosol
ATP
ADP + Pi
FA
FA + Glycerol
GK
G-3-P
ATP
ADP + Pi
CTS
Glyoxysome
FA
CoASH + ATP
LACS
AMP + PPi
Acyl-CoA
SDP1
TAG
Oil body
O_2
H_2O
ACX
CAT
H_2O_2
H_2O_2
2-*trans*-enoyl-CoA
H_2O
APX
MFP/Hydratase
ASC
ASC
MDA
MDA
Hydroxyacyl-CoA
MDAR
Sucrose
NAD^+
MFP/DH
Malate
Malate
NAD^+
MDH
MDH
G-3-P
NADH
OAA
OAA
NADH
3-Ketoacyl-CoA
Malate
NAD^+
MDH
CoASH
MLS
Glyoxylate
ICL
Isocitrate
NADH
PEP
KAT
Succinate
ACO
CO_2
Acetyl-CoA
CSY
Citrate
OAA
PCK
OAA
Acyl-CoA
ATP
ADP + Pi

approximately 5% of the total carbon released (assuming an average chain length of 18C for each FA). Two alternate pathways for glycerol utilization have been described in mammals and microbes, one involves the production of glycerol-3-phosphate (G-3-P) by glycerol kinase prior to conversion to dihydroxyacetone phosphate (DHAP), and the other involves the production of dihydroxyacetone by glycerol dehydrogenase before production of DHAP (84, 85). Biochemical studies suggested 30 years ago that the first pathway involving glycerol kinase predominates in plants (64, 68). This has been confirmed more recently by the identification of an *Arabidopsis* glycerol kinase, *GLI1*, which is upregulated during early postgerminative seedling growth (25). Disruption of this gene results in accumulation of glycerol and increased resistance to a variety of dehydration-related abiotic stresses, but it does not compromise germination or postgerminative seedling growth (25). However, the contribution of significant carbon equivalents by glycerol for either gluconeogenesis or respiration can be demonstrated through the production of a double mutant that lacks the ability to utilize glycerol and is also disrupted in the glyoxylate cycle (25). Characterization of plants carrying the *icl1* mutation, in which the key glyoxylate cycle enzyme ICL is disrupted, surprisingly showed that under optimal growth conditions this pathway is not essential for seedling establishment; an essential role becomes evident only when the light intensity or duration is reduced (28). However, the *gli1–1 icl2* double mutant arrests shortly after seed germination irrespective of the light conditions (25). This result demonstrates that, although relatively small, the contribution of carbon skeletons from the glycerol kinase pathway is essential in the absence of a functional glyoxylate cycle, and this contribution along with other sources of carbon skeletons from, for example, photosynthesis and storage protein breakdown, is sufficient to compensate for the lack of FA-derived carbon skeletons delivered via the glyoxylate cycle.

Acyl-CoA: fatty acid esterified to Coenzyme-A

ABC transporter: ATP binding cassette transporter protein

Figure 2

Pathways and processes involved in the mobilization of storage oil to sucrose that have been functionally characterized by molecular genetic analysis in *Arabidopsis*. The background color scheme is consistent with **Table 1** and distinguishes different subcellular locations and/or pathways as follows: Yellow signifies a cytosolic/oil body location, green signifies a direct involvment in glyoxysomal β-oxidation, gray denotes the glyoxylate cycle, and blue shows gluconeogenesis. The triacylglycerol (TAG) lipase, sugar dependent 1(SDP1), hydrolyzes TAG to fatty acids (FAs) and glycerol (26). Glycerol kinase (GK) produces glycerol-3-phosphate (G-3-P) which can enter gluconeogenesis (25). FAs are imported directly into the glyoxysome via the COMATOSE (CTS) ATP-binding cassette (ABC) transporter (38, 59, 147). Alternate import models consistent with existing data are discussed in the text. FAs are activated by a long chain Acyl-CoA synthetase (LACS) (41) and enter the core reactions of β-oxidation: Acyl-CoA oxidase (ACX) (32, 108, 121), multifunctional protein (116) hydratase (MFP/Hydratase) and multifunctional protein dehydrogenase (MFP/DH), and 3-ketoacyl-CoA thiolase (KAT) (43, 57). Hydrogen peroxide (H_2O_2) is broken down in the glyoxysome matrix by catalase (CAT), or is broken down as it passes through the membrane by an ascorbate peroxidase (APX)/monodehydroascorbate reductase (MDAR) electron transfer system. Disruption of MDAR results in inhibition of SDP1 owing to H_2O_2 escape (27). Glyoxysomal malate dehydrogenase (MDH) operates in the reverse direction to convert oxaloacetate (OAA) to malate and is dedicated to regenerating NAD^+ from NADH for the continued operation of β-oxidation (111). Citrate synthase (CSY) is also essential for β-oxidation and plays a role in the glyoxylate cycle (110). Malate synthase (MLS) (17) and isocitrate lyase (ICL) (28) are unique to the glyoxylate cycle and localize to the glyoxysome. The aconitase (ACO) and MDH reactions of the glyoxylate cycle are cytosolic (19, 58, 111); MDH operates in the forward direction to produce OAA and NADH. Phosphoenolpyruvate (PEP) carboxykinase (PCK) is the major controlling step of gluconeogenesis, producing PEP from OAA. The contribution of the mitochondrial tricarboxylic acid (TCA) cycle to the production of OAA is not included. MDA, monodehydroascorbate; ASC, ascorbate.

STORAGE OIL–DERIVED FATTY ACID CATABOLISM

Peroxisomes are the Site of Straight-Chain Fatty Acid Catabolism in Higher Plants

In higher plants and most fungi straight-chain FA catabolism via the β-oxidation pathway takes place in the peroxisomes, whereas in mammals it occurs in both peroxisomes and mitochondria (48, 109). However, plant mitochondria harbor a number of enzymes associated with the breakdown of the branched-chain amino acids (BCAAs) leucine, isoleucine, and valine (21, 123, 130); components of the mitochondrial electron-transfer flavoprotein:ubiquinone oxidoreductase associated with this process have also recently been described (73, 74). However, at least some of the core β-oxidation reactions in BCAA catabolism also appear to take place in plant peroxisomes (48, 81, 146), which suggests that BCAA breakdown intermediates are transported between the two organelles.

Fatty Acid Activation and Entry into Peroxisomes

Fatty acids released from TAG by lipolysis must be transported across the single membrane of the peroxisome to be catabolized via β-oxidation. Studies in *Saccharomyces cerevisiae* suggest that FAs can enter the peroxisome either as nonesterified FAs or as acyl-CoA esters. Medium-chain FAs can be imported as free FAs, which are activated inside the peroxisome by a peroxisomal acyl-CoA synthase, Faa2p (61). Long-chain FAs (LCFAs) are activated in the cytosol and transported as acyl-CoA esters across the peroxisomal membrane by two half-ABC (ATP-binding cassette) transporters, Pxa1p and Pxa2p, that are thought to dimerize to produce a functional transporter (61, 141). In mammals the orthologous half-ABC transporter is called adrenoleukodystrophy protein (ALDP) (95), which when mutated in humans results in the debilitating disorder of the same name. The *Arabidopsis* ALDP homologue was identified from three different genetic screens and independently named *PEROXISOMAL ABC TRANSPORTER 1* (*PXA1*), *PEROXISOME DEFICIENT 3* (*PED3*), and *COMATOSE* (*CTS*) (38, 59, 147). *PXA1/PED3/CTS* (hereafter referred to as *CTS*) is a whole-ABC transporter that presumably does not require dimerization to be functional; colocalization with catalase and other peroxisomal β-oxidation enzymes confirms its peroxisomal location (38). Mutation of the CTS locus results in seeds that are blocked in FA breakdown, which strongly suggests that CTS is important in the transport of TAG-derived carbon into peroxisomes (38, 59, 147). Seeds of *cts* mutants also show increased dormancy—this is the basis of one of the screens that led to its identification (38, 118). This dormant seed phenotype, which is also exhibited by several other peroxisomal β-oxidation mutants, can be rescued to various degrees by after-ripening, nitrate, cold treatments, and nicking of the seed coat (38, 108). However, without an exogenous carbon source to compensate for the block in storage oil mobilization the germinated *cts* seeds are unable to establish photoautotrophic growth (38, 59, 147). (See Peroxisomal β-oxidation but Not Storage Oil Breakdown Is Required for Seed Germination) Acyl-CoA profiling of *cts-1* and *cts-2* seeds rescued on exogenous sucrose showed that the levels of long-chain acyl-CoAs, particularly the predominantly TAG-derived C20 and C22 acyl-CoAs, increased significantly above those found in wild-type seedlings over a developmental series from imbibed seeds to 5-day-old seedlings (38). This finding provided evidence that the CTS transporter is involved in the transport of fatty acyl-CoAs into peroxisomes.

The acyl-CoA transport model was called into question by the demonstration that two peroxisomal long-chain acyl-CoA synthetases (LACS6 and LACS7) are essential for TAG-derived FA breakdown in *Arabidopsis* seeds

(41). The activation of FAs to fatty acyl-CoAs is essential for FA catabolism to proceed through β-oxidation. The reaction occurs in two steps: First, FAs are converted to adenylate acyl-AMP via the use of ATP; the carbonyl carbon of the adenylate then reacts with the thiol group of Coenzyme A (CoA) to yield acyl-CoA and AMP and PPi are released (53) (**Figure 2**). Fulda and coworkers (41) found that two functionally redundant peroxisome-localized LACS together are essential for FA breakdown, which is surprising given that the CTS transporter was thought to deliver already activated acyl-CoAs from the cytosol into the peroxisome. This led Fulda and coworkers (41) to propose that, in contrast with *S. cerevisiae*, peroxisomal LACS activity is essential for the transport of FAs into the organelle, with LAC6 and LAC7 acting in the same pathway as the CTS ABC transporter. The accumulation of long-chain acyl-CoAs in *cts* mutants may not be a consequence of a block in acyl-CoA transport, but instead could be due to a block in FA transport into peroxisomes; the untransported FAs may be converted to acyl-CoAs by cytosolic LACS (of which there are multiple isoforms in *Arabidopsis*) (124).

A number of alternative models for FA transport into peroxisomes have been proposed (41, 105). The model depicted in **Figure 2** shows transport of free FAs rather than acyl-CoA esters via the CTS transporter and activation by LACS in the peroxisomal lumen. This model accounts for the data of Fulda and coworkers (41), and is also consistent with the demonstration that jasmonic acid (JA) biosynthesis, which relies on peroxisomal β-oxidation for the catalytic conversion of OPC8-CoA to JA-CoA, is compromised in both *cts* and *OPC8 CoA ligase 1* (*opcl1*) mutants of *Arabidopsis* (77, 131). OPCL1 is a peroxisomal acyl-activating enzyme involved in the biosynthesis of JA in *Arabidopsis* (77). Other models for transport are also consistent with the existing data. For example, acyl-CoA substrates could be transported and at the same time cleaved by CTS and peroxisomal LACS activity may be required to reactivate them. An alternative route of entry for free FAs into the peroxisome may also operate in addition to CTS-mediated transport: The free FAs may be activated by LACS in the peroxisomal lumen. In support of an alternative route, both the *lac6 lac7* double mutant and *cts* mutants can slowly degrade their storage oil when provided with exogenous sugar (38, 41). However, if an alternate route does exist, it alone is not sufficient to support the catabolism of long-chain FAs required to fuel seedling growth. Finally, CTS could be involved in the transport of a cofactor, such as CoA, adenine nucleotides, or phosphate, required for the intraperoxisomal activation of free FAs by LACS enzymes. The mechanism of cofactor transport into plant peroxisomes remains uncharacterized, but precedent exists because the yeast homologue of CTS can transport free CoA (61). A much better

PEROXISOMAL β-OXIDATION BUT NOT STORAGE OIL BREAKDOWN IS REQUIRED FOR SEED GERMINATION

The isolation of mutants disrupted in different steps in the storage oil mobilization process revealed that peroxisomal β-oxidation is required for the termination of dormancy and initiation of germination in *Arabidopsis* seeds [(Reviewed in Penfield et al. (106)]. Increased seed dormancy is observed in *Arabidopsis* mutants disrupted in either the peroxisomal ATP-binding cassette (ABC) transporter (38, 118) or in the peroxisomal β-oxidation process (108, 110). This phenotype cannot be rescued by exogenous sugars, unlike the seedling establishment phenotype of these same mutants, which is due to a block in storage oil breakdown (106, 108). However, other mutants disrupted in storage oil breakdown, including *sdp1* (26) and *lac6 lac7* (41, 118), remain unaffected in seed germination but do exhibit the typical compromised seedling establishment phenotype. Thus, seedling establishment requires carbon from fatty acid breakdown but seed germination does not. The COMATOSE (CTS) ABC transporter and the core peroxisomal β-oxidation pathway play an as yet undefined role in the breakage of seed dormancy and initiation of seed germination.

understanding of the substrate specificity and transport mechanism of the CTS transporter is needed to clarify this key step in storage oil mobilization and peroxisome function.

ACX: Acyl-CoA oxidase

Multifunctional protein (MFP): a single protein that exhibits core hydratase and dehydrogenase activities, and possibly additional auxiliary activities, of β-oxidation

KAT: 3-ketoacyl-CoA thiolase

We now know the substrate specificity of CTS extends well beyond straight-chain FAs. Characterization of *Arabidopsis* mutants disrupted in CTS showed that it is involved in the transport of 12-oxo-phytodienoic acid (OPDA), which is converted to the wound-signaling hormone, JA, by peroxisomal β-oxidation (131). CTS is also involved in the transport of indole butyric acid (IBA), a naturally occurring auxin, and the proherbicide 2,4-dichlorophenoxy butyric acid (2,4 DB), which are converted by a single round of β-oxidation to the more biologically active indole acetic acid (IAA) and the herbicide 2,4-dichlorophenoxy acetic acid (2,4 D), respectively (59, 147). 2,4 DB and IBA bioactivation provided the basis of two genetic screens in *Arabidopsis* that led to the isolation of mutations in the peroxisomal ABC transporter, as discussed above, and a number of other mutants compromised either directly or indirectly in the overall process of peroxisomal β-oxidation (57, 81, 148). Additional substrates for β-oxidation may also be imported via the CTS transporter, including, for example, intermediates in chlorophyll degradation such as phytanoyl-CoA, which is initially catabolized in the mitochondria (73), and branched-chain amino acid metabolism (48, 81, 146).

Peroxisomal β-Oxidation

The esterification of FAs to acyl-CoAs activates them for oxidative attack at the C-3 or β-carbon position, which involves a series of enzymatic steps known as the β-oxidation pathway or spiral (**Figure 2**). This process was first described in a landmark study by Franz Knoop (76) in 1904; he fed synthetically labeled even- and odd-numbered FAs to dogs and monitored the breakdown products in their urine. Work performed on endospermic castor bean seeds defined the role of β-oxidation in the mobilization of storage oil reserves in oilseeds (15); a substantial body of literature on the related enzymatic processes and associated genes has accumulated and is the subject of a number of reviews (4, 42, 45, 48, 105, 109) (**Table 1**).

In each round of the β-oxidation spiral, acetyl-CoA (C_2) is cleaved from acyl-CoA (C_n) and the remaining acyl-CoA (C_{n-2}) reenters the β-oxidation spiral to repeat the process (**Figure 2**). This core pathway requires the enzymes acyl-CoA oxidase (ACX), multifunctional protein (MFP), and 3-ketoacyl-CoA thiolase (KAT) to catalyze oxidation, hydration and dehydrogenation, and thiolytic cleavage, respectively, of acyl-CoA. The complete degradation of long-chain acyl-CoAs to C_2 acetyl units requires the enzymes responsible for catalyzing each step to accept substrates with diminishing carbon chain length with each passage through the β-oxidation spiral. As we shall see, two alternative strategies have evolved in the core group of β-oxidation enzymes to cope with this range of substrates: either multiple isoforms with different chain-length specificities or enzymes with broad substrate specificity/low carbon chain-length substrate selectivity. Peroxisomal thioesterases that cleave acyl-CoAs and divert them from the β-oxidation spiral have been reported in a wide range of organisms but the role of these enzymes is still not fully understood. (See The Enigmatic Role of Peroxisomal Acyl-CoA Thioesterases.)

Acyl-CoA Oxidases

The Acyl-CoA oxidases (ACXs; IUBMB Enzyme Nomenclature: EC 1.3.3.6) catalyze the first step of oxidation of acyl-CoA to Δ^2-*trans*-enoyl-CoA. The reaction requires flavin adenine dinucleotide (FAD) as a cofactor to generate $FADH_2$, which is then oxidized by flavoprotein dehydrogenase to produce hydrogen peroxide. Six ACX genes have been identified in the *Arabidopsis* genome (31, 48) and of these, four have been characterized and encode proteins with overlapping but distinct substrate specificities. ACX1 exhibits medium- to long-chain activity, with a substrate optimum between C12:0 and C16:0, whereas ACX2 has optimum activity with long-chain saturated and unsaturated acyl-CoAs (C14:0 to C20:0) (66). ACX3 exhibits medium-chain (C8:0 to C14:0) substrate specificity (32, 40); ACX4 shows short-chain (C4:0 to C8:0) substrate specificity (56). Two additional putative *Arabidopsis* ACX genes, ACX5 (At2g35690) and ACX6 (At1g06310), remain uncharacterized biochemically, but are expressed at extremely low or undetectable levels in germinating seeds. The ACX1, ACX2, ACX3, and ACX4 genes are all upregulated coordinately during *Arabidopsis* seed germination and early postgerminative growth (120), which correlates with the period of most rapid FA breakdown in *Arabidopsis*.

The crystal structures of the ACX1 and ACX4 proteins have been determined (87, 103). ACX1 is active as a dimer, which is typical of other acyl-CoA oxidases; the structure determination reveals a substrate-binding architecture that explains the observed preference for long-chain, monounsaturated substrates (103). Conversely, ACX4 exhibits little similarity with any of the other ACXs and is instead more similar to mitochondrial acyl-CoA dehydrogenases (ACADS), which share its tetrameric state (56). Determination of the structure of ACX4 and comparison with the structures of ACADs and ACX1 revealed that the extra C-terminal domain, present in dimer-forming oxidases such as ACX1, prevents the formation of a tetramer and functions to stabilize a large acyl-binding pocket that can accommodate the longer chain substrates (87).

Mutants with disruptions in all six ACX genes have been described (2, 32, 108, 121). Single gene mutations result in large reductions in endogenous enzyme activities that correspond to the substrate specificities determined by heterologous expression of the corresponding proteins. Consistent with this, metabolite profiling of acyl-CoA levels show an accumulation of specific chain lengths consistent with a bottleneck in the related enzyme activity (32, 108, 121). However, storage oil breakdown and seedling establishment is largely unaffected in any of the single mutants, presumably because the overlapping substrate specificities of the remaining isoforms compensate sufficiently to allow continued operation of the pathway. However, double mutants do exhibit strong phenotypes. The *acx3-1 acx4-1* double mutant aborts during the first phase of embryo development, presumably owing to a complete lack of short-chain acyl-CoA oxidase activity (121). The early stage embryo lethality could be due to any one of a number of factors, including the accumulation of acyl-CoAs or short chain FAs to toxic levels, sequestration of CoA to the acyl-CoA pool, or disruption in the production of FA or lipid-based signaling

THE ENIGMATIC ROLE OF PEROXISOMAL Acyl-CoA THIOESTERASES

Acyl-CoA thioesterases (ACHs) are a large group of enzymes that catalyze the hydrolysis of acyl-CoA to free fatty acid and CoASH (reduced form of Coenzyme A). ACHs are present across phyla and are localized in almost all cellular compartments, including the endoplasmic reticulum, cytosol, mitochondria, and peroxisomes (71). The precise physiological role of peroxisomal ACHs has been difficult to define. In mammalian peroxisomes ACHs may play a role in the regulation of lipid metabolism by maintaining CoASH at optimal levels during periods of increased fatty acid oxidation (71). Recently a peroxisomal acyl-CoA thioesterase in *S. cerevisiae* was shown to play an essential role in the breakdown of short straight-chain and branched-chain fatty acids (88). Two peroxisomal acyl-CoA thioesterases from *Arabidopsis*, ACH1 and ACH2, have been characterized, but their physiological role is unknown and not easy to fit into the current model of peroxisomal β-oxidation (132). A variety of substrates are oxidized at the β-carbon position in addition to fatty acids, including, for example, intermediates in the synthesis of JA and IAA and the catabolism of branched chain amino acids and phytanic acid. The role of ACH1 and ACH2 could be to maintain optimal flux through β-oxidation in the presence of these unusual substrates, as was proposed for *S. cerevisiae* (88).

molecules. The *acx1-2 acx2-1* double mutant lacks medium and long chain activity in postgerminative tissue but undergoes normal embryo development (108). However, *acx1-2 acx2-1* is blocked in storage oil breakdown, accumulates long chain acyl-CoAs, and has a sucrose-dependent seedling establishment phenotype (2, 108). Oil bodies persist and the size of peroxisomes increases significantly in 4-day-old *acx1–1 acx2-1* seedlings rescued on sucrose (108). A similar enlarged peroxisome phenotype is present in *mfp2-1* and *ped1/kat2* seedlings disrupted in the two other core enzymes of peroxisomal β-oxidation (43, 57, 119), but not in *cts* or the *lacs6-1 lacs7-1* double mutant (38, 41). As previously suggested, the altered acyl-CoA levels in *Arabidopsis* mutants disrupted in FA breakdown may play a role in regulating various cellular processes, including peroxisome size and storage oil breakdown (50). It will be important to establish the mechanism by which the disruption of peroxisomal β-oxidation results in a block in storage oil mobilization from the oil body and whether the elevation of acyl-CoA levels is involved. In vitro activity of a neutral TAG lipase from castor bean is inhibited by oleoyl-CoA and CoA (63), which raises the possibility of a regulatory role for SDP1.

MULTIFUNCTIONAL PROTEIN

Two of the core β-oxidation pathway reactions, 2-*trans*-enoyl-CoA hydratase (EC 4.2.1.17) and l-3-hydroxyacyl-CoA dehydrogenase (EC 1.1.1.35), are contained on the MFP, as well as additional auxiliary activities necessary for the β-oxidation of certain unsaturated FAs [reviewed in Graham & Eastmond (48), Poirier et al. (109)]. Two different types of multifunctional protein that are not related in sequence or structure, but catalyze the same set of reactions via mirror image stereochemistry, have been described: The type 1 MFEs (multifunctional enzymes), found in mammals, bacteria, and plants, mediate the conversion of 2-*trans*-enoyl-CoA to 3-ketoacyl-CoA via a 3S-hydroxyacyl-CoA isomer, and the type 2 MFEs, found in mammals and fungi, mediate the same conversion but through the 3R-hydroxyacyl CoA isomer (109). As described below, this is an important distinction for the ability to utilize intermediates in unsaturated FA catabolism. MFP enzyme activities have been studied extensively in cucumber, where four different isozymes have been reported, three of which are present in the glyoxysomes of germinating seedlings and a fourth peroxisomal form found in leaves (7, 54, 55). The 79-kDa glyoxysomal MFP was cloned and it comprises four domains, with 2-*trans*-enoyl-CoA hydratase, 3S-hydroxyacyl-CoA dehydrogenase, 3-hydroxyacyl-CoA epimerase, and Δ3,Δ2-enoyl-CoA isomerase activities (112). The role of these latter two auxiliary activities is discussed further below.

Arabidopsis contains two isoforms of MFP. The first (MFP1) has been characterized genetically as the *abnormal inflorescence meristem1* (*aim1*) locus (116). This mutant shows aberrant vegetative and reproductive development, a unique phenotype among the comprehensive set of β-oxidation mutants now described in *Arabidopsis* (4, 105). The molecular basis of this developmental phenotype is not understood. Germination and seedling establishment is normal in the *aim1* mutant, which is not surprising given that *AIM1* is expressed at a low level in germinating seedlings, in contrast to the gene encoding the second isoform, MFP2, which is strongly induced during postgerminative seedling growth (29). *Arabidopsis* mutations in *MFP2* require an exogenous supply of sucrose for seedling establishment and are compromised in storage oil breakdown, but the phenotype is not as severe as in *Arabidopsis* mutants that lack the other core β-oxidation enzyme activities, ACX or KAT (43, 57, 108, 119). Acyl-CoA feeding experiments on extracts of wild-type and *mfp2* seedlings demonstrate that the 2-*trans*-enoyl-CoA hydratase is active only against long-chain (C18:0) substrates, whereas the l-3-hydroxyacyl-CoA dehydrogenase is active on C6:0, C12:0, and C18:0 substrates

(119). Thus, MFP2 contains one enzyme activity (2-*trans*-enoyl-CoA hydratase) that shows a narrow substrate specificity similar to the ACXs and a second enzyme activity (l-3-hydroxyacyl-CoA dehydrogenase) that has broad substrate specificity. As with the *acx3 acx4* double mutant, the *mfp2-1 aim1* double mutant aborts during the early stages of embryo development, which is consistent with a specific requirement for short-chain β-oxidation activity during this critical stage in the life cycle (112).

3-KETOACYL-COA THIOLASE

The enzyme 3-ketoacyl-CoA thiolase (KAT; *EC 2.3.1.16*) catalyzes the last step of FA β-oxidation, which involves the thiolytic cleavage of 3-ketoacyl-CoA to acyl-CoA (C_{n-2}) and acetyl-CoA (C_2). *KAT* homologs have been cloned from a number of plant species and recombinant proteins from *Brassica napus* and *Arabidopsis* exhibit KAT activity with the C4 substrate acetoacetyl-CoA (43, 101). Unfortunately, more extensive substrate specificity determination has not been performed because of the difficulty in synthesizing longer chain substrates.

The *Arabidopsis* genome contains three loci that encode KAT enzymes, annotated as KAT1, KAT2, and KAT5 on the basis of the chromosome on which they occur (At1g04710, At2g33150, and At5g48880, respectively) (43). An investigation of public domain cDNA sequences has revealed that *KAT5* produces two polypeptides, KAT5.1 and KAT5.2, apparently as a consequence of alternate RNA splicing (11). KAT5.1 lacks the N-terminal region, which contains the predicted PTS2 peroxisome targeting signal and, unlike the other three KAT proteins, it is targeted to the cytosol rather than peroxisomes (11). *KAT2* is the only one of the three KAT genes expressed at significant levels during seed germination in *Arabidopsis*, and *kat2* mutants are blocked in storage oil breakdown and are dependent on exogenous sucrose for seedling establishment (43). Allelic mutants in *KAT2* have been isolated by screening for 2,4-DB resistance and by reverse genetics approaches (43, 57). Long-chain (C16 to C20) fatty acyl-CoAs accumulate in *kat2* seedlings, which indicates that the mutant lacks long-chain thiolase activity. This, along with the fact that extracts from *kat2* seedlings have significantly decreased activity with C4 acetoacetyl-CoA substrate compared with wild-type, suggests that the KAT2 protein has broad substrate specificity (43). Similar to the *acx1 acx2* double mutant and *mfp2*, the peroxisomes in cotyledons of *kat2* seedlings are enlarged (43, 108, 119).

The crystal structure of the *Arabidopsis* KAT2 protein has recently been determined under nonreducing conditions that resulted in a disulfide linkage at the catalytic site, which gave rise to an inactive form of the enzyme (129). This result, along with the fact that optimal KAT activity in in vitro assays is obtained under reducing conditions, led these authors to suggest that in vivo peroxisomal β-oxidation is regulated by redox state. If this is the case, then mechanisms that regulate peroxisomal redox state, such as the membrane-associated ascorbate-dependent electron transfer system, could play a key role in controlling the flux of FAs through the β-oxidation pathway. In this context it is noteworthy that the *Arabidopsis sdp2* mutant, disrupted in the monodehydroascorbate reductase component of the ascorbate-dependent redox system located in the peroxisomal membrane, has a functional β-oxidation pathway on the basis of the fact that *sdp2* seedlings remain as sensitive as wild-type seedlings to 2,4 DB (27). Clearly, more work needs to be done in this area to establish the extent to which redox state controls FA β-oxidation.

AUXILIARY PEROXISOMAL β-OXIDATION ACTIVITIES

Many FAs, particularly those found in seed storage oils, have unsaturated bonds in the *cis*-configuration at even-numbered carbons

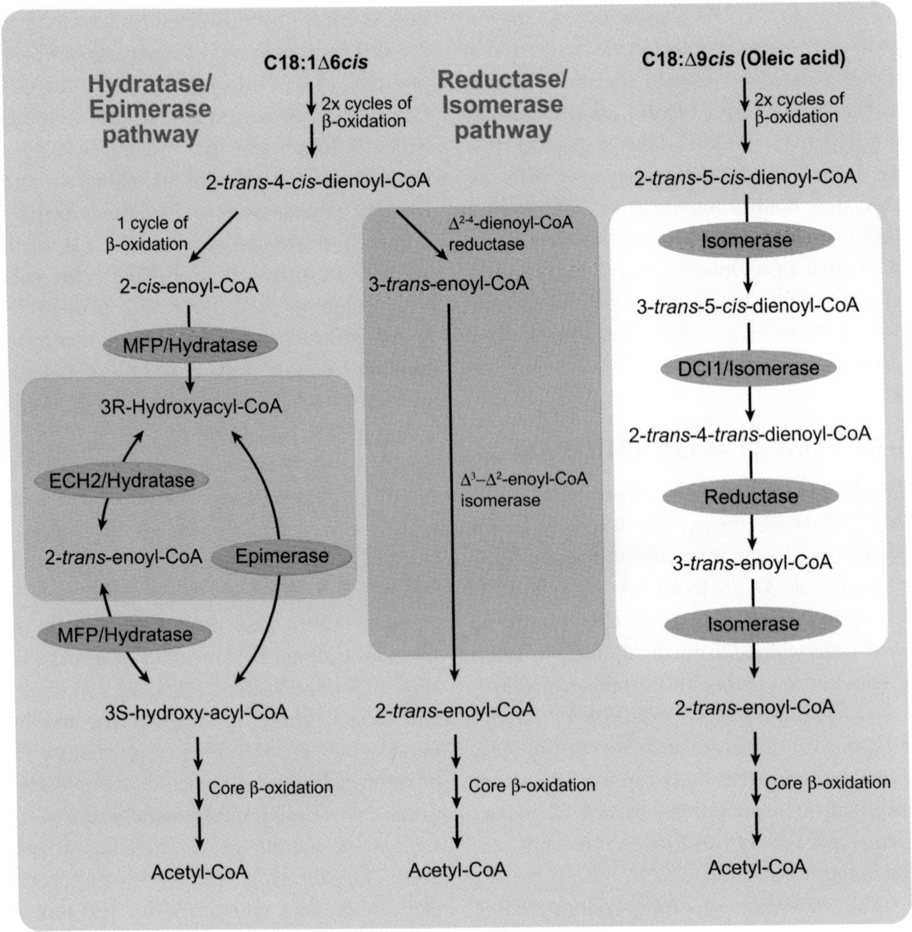

Figure 3

Pathways involved in the β-oxidation of fatty acids that contain unsaturated double bonds in the *cis*-configuration at even- and odd-numbered carbons. Two alternate pathways are proposed to operate in the complete degradation of C18:1Δ6*cis* (*left*). In the hydratase/epimerase pathway, 3R-Hydroxyacyl-CoA is converted to 3S-Hydroxyacyl-CoA either by an epimerase activity or an auxiliary enzyme, enoyl-CoA hydratase 2 (ECH2/Hydratase) (44) and the resulting 2-*trans*-enoyl-CoA then re-enters the normal set of core reactions of β-oxidation. For the complete breakdown of fatty acids with *cis* double bonds at odd-numbered carbons such as C18:1Δ9*cis* (oleic acid) (*right*) the enzyme Δ3,5,Δ2,4-dienoyl-CoA isomerase (DCI/Isomerase) is essential (46). Background colors depict the different pathways: Green shows core β-oxidation reactions, blue shows the hydratase/epimerase pathway for the breakdown of C18:1Δ6*cis*, brown shows the reductase/isomerase pathway for the breakdown of C18:1Δ6*cis*, and yellow shows the pathway for the breakdown of 2-*trans*-5*cis*-Dienoyl-CoA, an intermediate of oleic acid β-oxidation.

or unsaturated bonds at odd-numbered carbons. Both of these arrangements result in metabolic blocks for the β-oxidation pathway if only the core set of enzymes is considered. β-oxidation of unsaturated FAs with a *cis* double bond on an even-numbered carbon eventually produces the intermediate 2-*trans*,4-*cis*-dienoyl-CoA (**Figure 3**). Two alternative pathways have been proposed for the continued β-oxidation of this intermediate (122) (**Figure 3**). In the hydratase/epimerase pathway a further round of β-oxidation produces

2-*cis*-enoyl-CoA that is in turn hydrated to 3R-hydroxyacyl-CoA by the enoyl-CoA hydratase activity of MFP. Conversion of 3R-hydroxyacyl-CoA to the 3S isomer for re-entry to core β-oxidation can be achieved either via a one-step epimerase activity or a two-step reaction involving an enoyl CoA hydratase 2 activity and the core hydratase activity of the MFP (**Figure 3**). Epimerase activity has been detected on one of the cucumber MFP proteins (112) and a homologous domain is present on the *Arabidopsis* MFP2 (29), which indicates that this route most probably operates in plants. Recently a gene from *Arabidopsis*, *ECH2*, that encodes a monofunctional enzyme with enoyl-CoA hydratase 2 activity was reported (44). The corresponding enzyme is localized to peroxisomes and analysis of the carbon flux through the β-oxidation cycle in plants that underexpress the *AtECH2* gene demonstrated its involvement in the degradation of unsaturated FAs (44) (**Figure 3**).

In the alternative reductase/isomerase pathway, the 2-*trans*,4-*cis*-dienoyl-CoA is converted to 3-*trans*-enoyl-CoA by another auxiliary enxyme, 2,4-dienoyl-CoA reductase. A Δ3,Δ2-enoyl-CoA isomerase then converts the 3-*trans*-enoyl-CoA (or 3-*cis*-enoyl-CoA) into 2-*trans*-enoyl-CoA, which can re-enter the core β-oxidation reactions. Both 2,4-dienoyl-CoA reductase and Δ3,Δ2-enoyl-CoA isomerase activities have been detected in plants, but the corresponding genes have not been characterized (7, 35). Δ3,Δ2-enoyl-CoA isomerase activity is present on the multifunctional protein of many organisms, including cucumber (112), but as yet there are no experimental data to prove that the homologous domain present in the *Arabidopsis* MFP2 is functional (29).

β-oxidation of FAs with *cis* double bonds at odd-numbered carbons, such as oleic acid (C18:1Δ9*cis*), produces 2-*trans*,5-*cis*-dienoyl-CoA; the continued catabolism back to 2-*trans*-enoyl-CoA involves two different routes in mammals and yeast (109). The enzyme Δ3,5,Δ2,4-dienoyl-CoA isomerase (DCI) is essential for one of these routes and an *Arabidopsis* gene encoding this enzyme has recently been described (46) (**Figure 3**). The *AtDCI1* gene is expressed constitutively in all tissues, but is particularly induced during seed germination. The protein appears to be localized to peroxisomes, and proteins with high sequence identity can be found in a broad range of plants including gymnosperms and angiosperms (46). This enzyme is nonessential for the degradation of unsaturated FAs in both yeast and mammals and it will therefore be interesting to establish, through the isolation of mutants, what role *AtDCI1* plays in plants.

MDAR: monodehydroascorbate reductase

PRODUCTS OF PEROXISOMAL FATTY ACID β-OXIDATION

Hydrogen Peroxide

The major end products of the peroxisomal β-oxidation spiral are H_2O_2, NADH, and acetyl-CoA. H_2O_2 is potentially damaging to proteins, lipids, and DNA. The catalase enzyme present in the peroxisomal matrix plays an essential protective role by breaking down H_2O_2 to molecular oxygen and water in higher plants and other organisms (138, 143). As shown in **Figure 2**, plant peroxisomes also contain an ascorbate-dependent membrane-bound electron transfer system that involves the oxidation and reduction of ascorbate by ascorbate peroxidase (APX) and monodehydroascorbate reductase (MDAR), respectively, which results in the breakdown to water of H_2O_2 that escapes the peroxisomes (4, 97, 144). This membrane-bound system has a much higher affinity for H_2O_2 than catalase, and the suggestion that it acts as a cordon to limit the escape of H_2O_2 into the cytosol (75, 97, 144) was recently confirmed by the characterization of an *Arabidopsis* mutant, *sdp2*, disrupted in the MDAR component of the system (27). Disruption of the APX/MDAR system results in leakage of H_2O_2 from peroxisomes and inactivation of TAG hydrolysis on closely associated oil bodies (27). Thus, during storage oil mobilization catalase protects

MDH: malate dehydrogenase

CSY: citrate synthase

constituents of the peroxisomal matrix from oxidative damage and the APX/MDAR system prevents H_2O_2 from escaping beyond the outer surface of the peroxisomal membrane and causing lethal oxidative damage.

NADH REGENERATION

Reoxidation of peroxisomal NADH, produced through the L-3-hydroxyacyl-CoA dehydrogenase core activity of β-oxidation, must occur inside the organelle because the peroxisomal membrane is impermeable to NAD(H) (114, 139). A number of mechanisms operate in plants to reoxidize peroxisomal NADH. The first is linked to the MDAR component of the APX/MDAR system, and its activity is expected to be dependent on the amount of H_2O_2 being broken down at the peroxisomal membrane (**Figure 2**). A membrane-bound MDAR also has the potential to take electrons from NADH and donate these to molecular oxygen either directly, or through a *b*-type cytochrome (23), which can in turn produce H_2O_2 (18). *Arabidopsis* peroxisomes also contain a soluble matrix isoform, MDAR1, distinct from the membrane bound isoform, MDAR4 (86), and this could also participate in reoxidation of NADH.

The second mechanism involves oxidation of NADH by peroxisomal malate dehydrogenase (MDH). This mechanism requires peroxisomal MDH to operate in the reverse direction, converting oxaloacetate to malate, which is shuttled outside the peroxisome to be reoxidized (92). This mechanism has remained controversial until recently, because it was thought that peroxisomal MDH operating in the forward direction is required in the conversion of malate to oxaloacetate in the glyoxylate cycle. An *Arabidopsis* double mutant in which both of the peroxisomal *MDH* genes are disrupted results in severe impairment of storage oil breakdown, peroxisomal FA β-oxidation, and seedling establishment, but has no significant impact on the operation of the glyoxylate cycle as monitored by [^{14}C]acetate feeding experiments (111). *S. cerevisiae* mutants without peroxisomal MDH are also unable to carry out peroxisomal FA β-oxidation (139). A malate shuttle appears to operate across the glyoxysomal/peroxisomal membrane and obviates the need for peroxisomal MDH as part of the glyoxylate cycle (**Figure 2**). Malate is shuttled out of the organelle and oxidized before returning, most probably as oxaloacetate, but the alternate aspartate/2-oxoglutarate shuttle also proposed by Mettler & Beevers (92) is still not ruled out by the current evidence.

FATE OF ACETYL-COA DERIVED FROM STORAGE OIL BREAKDOWN

Acetyl-CoA derived from FA β-oxidation is metabolized via the glyoxylate cycle (**Figure 2**). Two enzymes, ICL (*EC 4.1.3.1*) and MLS (*EC 4.1.3.2*), are unique to the glyoxylate cycle, and the other three enzymes, citrate synthase (CSY; *EC 4.1.3.7*), aconitase (ACO; *EC 4.2.1.3*) and MDH (*EC 1.1.1.37*), also appear in the TCA cycle. ICL, MLS, and CSY are localized in plant peroxisomes, whereas the ACO and MDH enzymatic reactions required for the glyoxylate cycle are extraperoxisomal (19, 58, 111). MLS and CSY both use acetyl-CoA as a substrate in the peroxisome to produce malate and citrate, respectively (**Figure 2**). Even in the absence of MLS, acetyl-CoA can still be used to support gluconeogenesis and seedling growth because the glyoxylate produced by ICL can be utilized through part of the photorespiratory pathway (17). A sugar-dependent (*sdp*) hypocotyl elongation in the dark phenotype has been reported for *mls* mutants (26), but overall they are not as compromised in seedling establishment as *icl* mutants, which are unable to use acetyl-CoA for gluconeogenesis but can break down storage oil and directly respire the resulting acetyl units through the TCA cycle (28). Seedling establishment in *icl* mutants requires optimal day length and light intensity to support photosynthesis, which demonstrates that these mutants are close to the threshold levels of sugars required for growth (28). Disruption of either ICL or MLS is therefore likely to be selected against in the field, where the action of the glyoxylate cycle would be vital for the successful establishment of buried seeds or those in competition with other seedlings.

In *S. cerevisiae* a carnitine shuttle transfers acetyl units directly to the mitochondrion for entry into the TCA cycle (140). Characterization of the *à bout de souffle* (*bou*) *Arabidopsis* mutant, which is disrupted in a putative acylcarnitine carrier in the mitochondrial membrane, led to the proposal that a carnitine shuttle also operates between peroxisomes and mitochondria in plants (82). Seedling establishment in the light but not in the dark is compromised in *bou* mutants and this light-dependent phenotype can be rescued by sugars. A role for BOU in acetyl-CoA transport from the peroxisome is not consistent with the dark treatment rescue of the growth phenotype. More recent work demonstrates that the story in plants is different from that in *S. cerevisiae*: Acetyl units are only exported from the peroxisome for respiration in the mitochondria after conversion to citrate (110). The double mutant, *csy2 csy3*, disrupted in the two peroxisomal *CSY* genes expressed in germinating *Arabidopsis* seedlings, is blocked in storage oil breakdown, seedling establishment requires exogenous sugar, and seedling growth is resistant to 2,4 DB, all traits shared with *Arabidopsis* mutants disrupted in peroxisomal β-oxidation (43, 57, 108, 119). This phenotype is therefore distinct from that of the *icl* and *mls* glyoxylate cycle mutants, which can break down and respire seed storage oil (17, 28). Peroxisomal β-oxidation can be induced in response to carbohydrate starvation or senescence (22, 65). To further demonstrate that peroxisomal CSY has a role in FA catabolism that is distinct from its role in the glyoxylate cycle, Pracharoenwattana and coworkers (110) showed that the expression of *CSY2* and *CSY3* genes is induced, along with genes that encode enzymes of peroxisomal β-oxidation, in detached dark-treated leaves (assumed to mimic carbohydrate starvation), whereas the *MLS* and *ICL* genes are not expressed. Therefore, peroxisomal CSY plays an essential role in the respiration of FAs in all plant tissues, and is not required only for the operation of the glyoxylate cycle and gluconeogenesis during seed germination and seedling establishment (**Figure 2**).

Glyoxylate cycle enzymes are located both inside and outside the glyoxysome and consequently the operation of the cycle requires transport of several intermediates across the glyoxysomal membrane. Characterization of the transport mechanisms involved is a major challenge that should be addressed.

PCK: phosphoenolpyruvate (PEP) carboxykinase

GLUCONEOGENESIS

Four-carbon compounds from the glyoxylate cycle can be converted into hexose by gluconeogenesis and subsequently used for cell wall biosynthesis, or converted into sucrose for transport to the growing seedling tissue (10). This process is important in both endospermic oilseed species such as castor and nonendospermic species such as *Arabidopsis*, which store the bulk of their seed oil reserves in the embryo (30). *Arabidopsis* seedlings disrupted in the glyoxylate cycle enzymes ICL or MLS (17, 28) or the gluconeogenesis enzyme phosphoenolpyruvate (PEP) carboxykinase (PCK) (107) show a reduced ability for hypocotyl elongation in the dark. This phenotype, which can be rescued by an exogenous sugar supply, is mimicked by the removal of the single cell endosperm layer (107). The demonstration that *PCK1* gene expression is high in the *Arabidopsis* endosperm, along with the fact that removal of the endosperm from *pck1* mutant seeds does not further compromise hypocotyl elongation in the dark, confirms the critical role of PCK activity in endospermic gluconeogenesis (107). Interestingly, in *Arabidopsis* endospermic lipid reserves are required for one-third of the total hypocotyl elongation in the dark, but represent only one-tenth of the total available lipid (107). This suggests that the ultimate fate of lipid-derived carbon in the embryo is inflexible to some extent, and that carbon is committed to fuel other vital processes, even when sucrose is limiting for the expanding hypocotyl. One possible fate of this carbon could be chloroplast development. Therefore, the commitment of oil reserves to different end uses is regulated differentially in the embryo and endosperm.

REGULATION OF STORAGE OIL BREAKDOWN

Following seed imbibition, a coordinated induction of many of the genes involved in storage lipid mobilization occurs, and this induction is closely reflected at the level of protein and enzyme activity. For example, the *Arabidopsis ACX1*, *ACX2*, *ACX3*, and *ACX4* genes that encode the family of acyl-CoA oxidase enzymes (32, 40, 66, 121), the *MFP2* gene that encodes the multifunctional protein (29, 116, 119), and the thiolase-encoding *KAT2* gene (43, 57) all show an increase in mRNA levels during germination that corresponds with an increase in enzyme activity. In *Arabidopsis*, this expression peaks two days after imbibition and subsequently declines, and this induction is coordinately regulated with genes that encode the glyoxylate cycle enzymes MLS and ICL and the key gluconeogenesis enzyme PCK1 (120). Promoter-reporter gene studies of *Arabidopsis* genes involved in β-oxidation, the glyoxylate cycle, and gluconeogenesis (32, 107, 113) and glyoxylate cycle genes from *Brassica napus* (14) and cucumber (51, 115) all consistently conclude that regulation operates predominantly at the level of transcription. In cucumber cell cultures and mature plant tissues sugars play an important role in the regulation of glyoxylate cycle gene expression through a form of carbon catabolite repression (47). The underlying mechanism that controls the expression of any of these genes is not understood.

A number of treatments decrease or block storage oil mobilization during postgerminative seedling growth. For example, depending on the concentration, exogenous sugars result in a decrease or total block in oil breakdown (28, 134). The nitrogen status of the seedlings has a major impact on this effect; a reduction of nitrate in the media leads to the enhancement of sucrose repression of oil breakdown (90). Thus, the carbon to nitrogen ratio, rather than the carbohydrate status alone, plays the predominant role in the regulation of storage oil mobilization. The phytohormone abscisic acid (ABA) blocks seed germination in *Arabidopsis* but does not completely inhibit lipid breakdown or the expression of genes that encode the key enzymes of FA β-oxidation or the glyoxylate cycle (113). ABA-treated seeds accumulate sucrose, but ABA-treated *icl* and *kat2* mutants do not, which shows that the accumulated sucrose is derived from lipid breakdown (113). The effect of ABA is tissue-specific in *Arabidopsis* seeds; reserve mobilization in the embryo is inhibited by ABA, whereas the single cell layer of endosperm tissue surrounding the embryo shows little or no response (107). This same tissue-specific effect of ABA on storage lipid mobilization has also been observed in tobacco seeds, which suggests wide conservation among flowering plants (89). The ABA insensitivity of lipid breakdown in the endosperm can be attributed specifically to the lack of expression of the *ABSCISIC ACID INSENSITIVE 4* (*ABI4*) transcription factor (104). ABI4 is an AP2 domain–containing transcription factor involved in seed and abscisic acid response signaling networks (36, 127). *ABI4* is expressed in the embryo but not the endosperm of *Arabidopsis* and regulation of lipid breakdown in the embryo is absent in the *abi4* mutant, thus confirming that ABI4 is a key regulator of lipid catabolism in response to ABA (104).

In addition to an involvement in the response to ABA, ABI4 also plays an important role in plant responses to carbohydrate availability. The *abi4* mutant has been isolated in a number of genetic screens for sugar signaling mutants (126) and recent analysis of a number of photosynthetic and starch biosynthetic gene promoters suggest a direct role for ABI4 in their control (1, 117). ABI4 also plays an important role in integrating retrograde signaling to coordinate nuclear gene expression with chloroplast function and carbohydrate status (79, 102). Hence, ABI4 plays a central role in coupling metabolic status to the regulation of primary carbon metabolism in plants. Defining the targets of ABI4 in germinating seeds and establishing how these either directly or indirectly regulate storage oil mobilization in response to ABA and carbohydrate status will be an important next step in our understanding of the regulation of storage oil mobilization.

CONCLUSIONS

Storage oil mobilization during seed germination involves the coordinated regulation of a defined metabolic network of enzymes and associated proteins. *Arabidopsis* molecular genetics has been used to great effect to perturb this network at different points to establish the role of individual steps and determine the specific role of subcellular compartmentation in the overall process. This review focused on the steps involved in the conversion of oil to sugar. No doubt this defined network will be substantially integrated with the rest of cellular metabolism. Nutritional homeostasis involving the feedback regulation of storage oil mobilization is likely to be a key player, could operate at different levels, and will determine the fate of individual metabolites as well as the extent to which TAG lipolysis, β-oxidation, the glyoxyate cycle, and gluconeogenesis operate. Gaps remain in our knowledge, particularly with respect to the mechanism of action of the CTS ABC transporter, the identity of other transporters that shuttle metabolites between the glyoxysome and the cytosol, and the mechanism by which the overall process is regulated. Regulation is likely to involve both transcriptional and posttranscriptional processes, and the involvement of the ABI4 transcription factor raises the possibility of integration with other aspects of cellular metabolism.

SUMMARY POINTS

1. Triacylglycerols (TAGs) are broken down to free fatty acids (FA) and glycerol by an oil body–associated lipase, which is a member of the patatin-like TAG lipase family previously described in animals and yeast.
2. FA transport into glyoxysomes is dependent on the activity of an ATP-binding cassette (ABC) transporter protein located in the glyoxysomal membrane.
3. Storage oil mobilization is severely compromised in *Arabidopsis* mutants disrupted in either lipolysis of TAG, transport of FA into the glyoxysomes, activation of FA inside the glyoxysome, or in any of the core reactions of β-oxidation.
4. Storage oil mobilization is not essential for seed germination but is essential for seedling establishment in *Arabidopsis*.
5. H_2O_2 produced by the first step in FA β-oxidation is broken down by catalase activity in the glyoxysomal matrix and a high-affinity ascorbate-dependent membrane-bound electron transfer system that prevents the H_2O_2 from escaping beyond the outer surface of the glyoxysomal membrane and causing lethal damage.
6. Glyoxysomal malate dehydrogenase (MDH) operates in the reverse direction to regenerate NAD^+ from NADH, which is essential for the continued operation of FA

β-oxidation; a cytosolic MDH operates in the forward direction as part of the glyoxylate cycle.

7. Extensive shuttling of glyoxylate cycle intermediates across the glyoxysomal membrane is necessary because three of the enzymatic reactions of the cycle occur inside and two outside the organelle.
8. Both abscisic acid (ABA) and sugars repress storage oil mobilization and in *Arabidopsis* the ABSCISIC ACID INSENSITIVE 4 (ABI4) transcription factor is responsible for the differential sensitivity of endosperm and embryo tissues to ABA.

FUTURE ISSUES

1. The relationship between oil bodies and glyoxysomes requires further investigation to establish the dynamics of this process and whether oil body vesicles are encapsulated in the glyoxysomes, as suggested in the literature.
2. The mechanism of transport of FAs into the glyoxysome should be resolved. Detailed *in vitro* biochemical characterization of the substrate specificity and mode of action of the COMATOSE (CTS) ABC transporter is required.
3. Our knowledge of auxiliary enzymes involved in FA β-oxidation is far from complete, particularly with respect to various unusual FAs. Characterization of auxiliary enzymes in native plant species is necessary to support future efforts at metabolic engineering of novel oil production.
4. Transport of glyoxylate cycle intermediates across the glyoxysomal membrane could play an important role in regulating the partition of carbon skeletons to different processes. Progress in this area requires the identification of metabolite transporters associated with the glyoxysomal membrane.
5. Glyoxysomal/peroxisomal β-oxidation plays multiple roles throughout plant development, among which the breaking of seed dormancy/initiation of seed germination is one of the most intriguing—particularly because it is distinct from the role played in storage oil mobilization and seedling establishment. Establishing the mechanism behind this role is a major target in the seed dormancy field.
6. Defining the mechanisms that regulate storage oil mobilization is a major future challenge. ABA and sugar-mediated inhibition of storage oil mobilization is known and the ABI4 transcription factor may play a universal role in the integration of ABA-mediated stress responses and carbohydrate status, so that storage oil is broken down only when needed. Posttranscriptional processes could also be involved, and the role of metabolites such as acyl-CoAs in the control of key enzymatic steps, such as the SUGAR DEPENDENT 1 (SDP1) TAG lipase, should be established.

DISCLOSURE STATEMENT

The author is not aware of any biases that might be perceived as affecting the objectivity of this review.

ACKNOWLEDGMENTS

Financial support for the work on storage oil mobilization in the author's laboratory comes primarily from The UK Biotechnology and Biological Sciences Research Council and the Garfield Weston Foundation. This, along with the research contribution of past and present members of the Graham laboratory, is gratefully acknowledged.

LITERATURE CITED

1. Acevedo-Hernández GJ, León P, Herrera-Estrella LR. 2005. Sugar and ABA responsiveness of a minimal RBCS light-responsive unit is mediated by direct binding of ABI4. *Plant J.* 43:506–19
2. Adham AR, Zolman BK, Millius A, Bartel B. 2005. Mutations in *Arabidopsis* acyl-CoA oxidase genes reveal distinct and overlapping roles in β-oxidation. *Plant J.* 41:859–74
3. Athenstaedt K, Daum G. 2003. YMR313c/TGL3 encodes a novel triacylglycerol lipase located in lipid particles of *Saccharomyces cerevisiae*. *J. Biol. Chem.* 278:23317–23
4. Baker A, Graham IA, Holdsworth M, Smith SM, Theodoulou FL. 2006. Chewing the fat: β-oxidation in signalling and development. *Trends Plant Sci.* 11:124–32
5. Baud S, Boutin J-P, Miquel M, Lepiniec L, Rochat C. 2002. An integrated overview of seed development in *Arabidopsis thaliana* ecotype WS. *Plant Physiol. Biochem.* 40:151–60
6. Beevers H. 1961. Metabolic production of sucrose from fat. *Nature* 191:433–36
7. Behrends W, Engeland K, Kindl H. 1988. Characterization of two forms of the multifunctional protein acting in fatty acid β-oxidation. *Arch. Biochem. Biophys.* 263:161–69
8. Bewley JD, Black M. 1994. *Seeds: Physiology of Development and Germination*. New York: Plenum. 2nd ed.
9. Cahoon EB, Shockey JM, Dietrich CR, Gidda SK, Mullen RT, Dyer JM. 2007. Engineering oilseeds for sustainable production of industrial and nutritional feedstocks: solving bottlenecks in fatty acid flux. *Curr. Opin. Plant Biol.* 10:236–44
10. Canvin DT, Beevers H. 1961. Sucrose synthesis from acetate in the germinating castor bean: kinetics and pathway. *J. Biol. Chem.* 236:988–95
11. Carrie C, Murcha MW, Millar AH, Smith SM, Whelan J. 2007. Nine 3-ketoacyl-CoA thiolases (KATs) and acetoacetyl-CoA thiolases (ACATs) encoded by five genes in *Arabidopsis thaliana* are targeted either to peroxisomes or cytosol but not to mitochondria. *Plant Mol. Biol.* 63:97–108
12. Chapman KD, Trelease RN. 1991. Acquisition of membrane lipids by differentiating glyoxysomes: role of lipid bodies. *J. Cell Biol.* 115:995–1007
13. Chia TY, Pike MJ, Rawsthorne S. 2005. Storage oil breakdown during embryo development of *Brassica napus*. *J. Exp. Bot.* 56:1285–96
14. Comai L, Dietrich RA, Maslyar DJ, Baden CS, Harada JJ. 1989. Coordinate expression of transcriptionally regulated isocitrate lyase and malate synthase genes in *Brassica napus*. *Plant Cell* 1:293–300
15. Cooper TG, Beevers H. 1969. β-oxidation in glyoxysomes from castor bean endosperm. *J. Biol. Chem.* 244:3514–20
16. Cooper TG, Beevers H. 1969. Mitochondria and glyoxysomes from castor bean endosperm. Enzyme constitutents and catalytic capacity. *J. Biol. Chem.* 244:3507–13
17. Cornah JE, Germiane V, Ward JL, Beale MH, Smith SM. 2004. Lipid utilization, gluconeogenesis and seedling growth in *Arabidopsis* mutants lacking the glyoxylate cycle enzyme malate synthase. *J. Biol. Chem.* 279:42916–23

18. Corpas FJ, Barroso JB, del Rio LA. 2001. Peroxisomes as a source of reactive oxygen species and nitric oxide signal molecules in plant cells. *Trends Plant Sci.* 6:145–50

19. Courtois-Verniquet F, Douce R. 1993. Lack of aconitase in glyoxysomes and peroxisomes. *Biochem. J.* 294:103–7

20. Cummins I, Hills MJ, Ross JH, Hobbs DH, Watson MD, Murphy DJ. 1993. Differential, temporal and spatial expression of genes involved in storage oil and oleosin accumulation in developing rapeseed embryos: Implications for the role of oleosins and the mechanisms of oil-body formation. *Plant Mol. Biol.* 23:1015–27

21. Daschner K, Couee I, Binder S. 2001. The mitochondrial isovaleryl-coenzyme A dehydrogenase of *Arabidopsis* oxidizes intermediates of leucine and valine catabolism. *Plant Physiol.* 126:601–12

22. Dieuaide M, Brouquisse R, Pradet A, Raymond P. 1992. Increased fatty acid β-oxidation after glucose starvation in maize root tips. *Plant Physiol.* 99:595–600

23. Donaldson RP. 2002. Peroxisomal membrane enzymes. In *Plant Peroxisomes, Biochemistry, Cell Biology and Biotechnological Applications*, ed. A Baker, IA Graham, 8:259–78. Dordrecht, The Netherlands: Kluwer Acad.

24. Eastmond PJ. 2004. Cloning and characterization of the acid lipase from castor beans. *J. Biol. Chem.* 279:45540–45

25. Eastmond PJ. 2004. Glycerol-insensitive *Arabidopsis* mutants: *gli1* seedlings lack glycerol kinase, accumulate glycerol and are more resistant to abiotic stress. *Plant J.* 37:617–25

26. Eastmond PJ. 2006. SUGAR-DEPENDENT1 encodes a patatin domain triacylglycerol lipase that initiates storage oil breakdown in germinating *Arabidopsis* seeds. *Plant Cell* 18:665–75

26. The first description of a true TAG lipase involved in storage oil hydrolysis from higher plants.

27. Eastmond PJ. 2007. MONODEHYROASCORBATE REDUCTASE4 is required for seed storage oil hydrolysis and postgerminative growth in *Arabidopsis*. *Plant Cell* 19:1376–87

28. Eastmond PJ, Germain V, Lange PR, Bryce JH, Smith SM, Graham IA. 2000. Postgerminative growth and lipid catabolism in oilseeds lacking the glyoxylate cycle. *Proc. Natl. Acad. Sci. USA* 97:5669–74

28. Demonstrated for the first time that seedlings could still break down storage oil and respire carbon skeletons in the absence of a complete glyoxylate cycle.

29. Eastmond PJ, Graham IA. 2000. The multifunctional protein AtMFP2 is coordinately expressed with other genes of fatty acid β-oxidation during seed germination in *Arabidopsis thaliana*. *Biochem. Soc. Trans.* 28:95–99

30. Eastmond PJ, Graham IA. 2001. Re-examining the role of the glyoxylate cycle in oilseeds. *Trends Plant Sci.* 6:72–78

31. Eastmond PJ, Hooks M, Graham IA. 2000. The *Arabidopsis* acyl-CoA oxidase gene family. *Biochem. Soc. Trans.* 28:755–57

32. Eastmond PJ, Hooks MA, Williams D, Lange P, Bechtold N, et al. 2000. Promoter trapping of a novel medium-chain acyl-CoA oxidase, which is induced transcriptionally during *Arabidopsis* seed germination. *J. Biol. Chem.* 275:34375–81

33. Eccleston VS, Ohlrogge JB. 1998. Expression of lauroyl-acyl carrier protein thioesterase in *Brassica napus* seeds induces pathways for both fatty acid oxidation and biosynthesis and implies a set point for triacylglycerol accumulation. *Plant Cell* 10:613–22

34. El-Kouhen K, Blangy S, Ortiz E, Gardies AM, Ferte N, Arondel V. 2005. Identification and characterization of a triacylglycerol lipase in *Arabidopsis* homologous to mammalian acid lipases. *FEBS Lett.* 579:6067–73

35. Engeland K, Kindl H. 1991. Purification and characterization of a plant peroxisomal Δ2, Δ3-enoyl-CoA isomerase acting on 3-*cis*-enoyl-CoA and 3-*trans*-enoyl-CoA. *Eur. J. Biochem.* 196:699–705

36. Finkelstein RR, Wang ML, Lynch TJ, Rao S, Goodman HM. 1998. The *Arabidopsis* abscisic acid response locus ABI4 encodes an APETALA 2 domain protein. *Plant Cell* 10:1043–54

37. Footitt S, Marquez J, Schmuths H, Baker A, Theodoulou FL, Holdsworth M. 2006. Analysis of the role of COMATOSE and peroxisomal β-oxidation in the determination of germination potential in *Arabidopsis*. *J. Exp. Bot.* 57:2805–14

38. Footitt S, Slocombe SP, Larner V, Kurup S, Wu Y, et al. 2002. Control of germination and lipid mobilization by COMATOSE, the *Arabidopsis* homologue of human ALDP. *EMBO J.* 21:2912–22

38. Demonstrated the role of a glyoxysomal/peroxisomal ABC-transporter protein in both seed germination and lipid mobilization.

39. Frevert J, Köller E, Kindl H. 1980. Occurrence and biosynthesis of glyoxysomal enzymes in ripening cucumber seeds. *Hoppe-Seyler's Z. Physiol. Chem.* 361:1557–65

40. Froman BE, Edwards PC, Bursch AG, Dehesh K. 2000. ACX3, a novel medium-chain acyl-coenzyme A oxidase from *Arabidopsis*. *Plant Physiol.* 123:733–42

41. Fulda M, Schnurr J, Abbadi A, Heinz E, Browse J. 2004. Peroxisomal acyl-CoA synthetase activity is essential for seedling development in *Arabidopsis thaliana*. *Plant Cell* 16:394–405

41. The demonstration that LACS activity inside the organelle is essential for fatty acid breakdown called into question the model for FA uptake via the ABC-transporter protein.

42. Gerhardt B. 1992. Fatty acid degradation in plants. *Prog. Lipid Res.* 31:417–46

43. Germain V, Rylott EL, Larson TR, Sherson SM, Bechtold N, et al. 2001. Requirement for 3-ketoacyl-CoA thiolase-2 in peroxisome development, fatty acid β-oxidation and breakdown of triacylglycerol in lipid bodies of *Arabidopsis* seedlings. *Plant J.* 28:1–12

44. Goepfert S, Hiltunen JK, Poirier Y. 2006. Identification and functional characterization of a monofunctional peroxisomal enoyl-CoA hydratase 2 that participates in the degradation of even *cis*-unsaturated fatty acids in *Arabidopsis thaliana*. *J. Biol. Chem.* 281:35894–903

45. Goepfert S, Poirier Y. 2007. β-oxidation in fatty acid degradation and beyond. *Curr. Opin. Plant Biol.* 10:245–51

46. Goepfert S, Vidoudez C, Rezzonico E, Hiltunen JK, Poirier Y. 2005. Molecular identification and characterization of the *Arabidopsis* Δ(3,5), Δ(2,4)-dienoyl-coenzyme A isomerase, a peroxisomal enzyme participating in the β-oxidation cycle of unsaturated fatty acids. *Plant Physiol.* 138:1947–56

47. Graham IA, Denby KJ, Leaver CJ. 1994. Carbon catabolite repression regulates glyoxylate cycle gene expression in cucumber. *Plant Cell* 6:761–72

48. Graham IA, Eastmond PJ. 2002. Pathways of straight and branched chain fatty acid catabolism in higher plants. *Prog. Lipid Res.* 41:156–81

49. Graham IA, Larson T, Napier JA. 2007. Rational metabolic engineering of transgenic plants for biosynthesis of ω-3 polyunsaturates. *Curr. Opin. Biotechnol.* 18:142–47

50. Graham IA, Li Y, Larson TR. 2002. Acyl-CoA measurements in plants suggest a role in regulating various cellular processes. *Biochem. Soc. Trans.* 30:1095–99

51. Graham IA, Smith LM, Leaver CJ, Smith SM. 1990. Developmental regulation of expression of the malate synthase gene in transgenic plants. *Plant Mol. Biol.* 15:539–49

52. Gronke S, Mildner A, Fellert S, Tennagels N, Petry S, et al. 2005. Brummer lipase is an evolutionary conserved fat storage regulator in *Drosophila*. *Cell Metab.* 1:323–30

53. Groot PH, Scholte HR, Hulsmann WC. 1976. Fatty acid activation: specificity, localization, and function. *Adv. Lipid Res.* 14:75–126

54. Gühnemann-Schäfer K, Kindl H. 1995. Fatty acid β-oxidation in glyoxysomes. Characterization of a new tetrafunctional protein (MFP III). *Biochim. Biophys. Acta* 1256:181–86

55. Gühnemann-Schäfer K, Kindl H. 1995. The leaf peroxisomal form (MFP IV) of multifunctional protein functioning in fatty acid β-oxidation. *Planta* 196:642–46

56. Hayashi H, De Bellis L, Ciurli A, Kondo M, Hayashi M, Nishimura M. 1999. A novel acyl-CoA oxidase that can oxidize short-chain acyl CoA in plant peroxisomes. *J. Biol. Chem.* 274:12715–21

57. Hayashi H, Toriyama K, Kondo M, Nishimura M. 1998. 2,4-Dichlorophenoxybutyric acid-resistant mutants of *Arabidopsis* have defects in glyoxysomal fatty acid β-oxidation. *Plant Cell* 10:183–95

57. Employed a novel genetic screen in *Arabidopsis* and led to the identification of the first mutant disrupted in storage oil mobilization.

58. Hayashi M, De Bellis L, Alpi A, Nishimura M. 1995. Cytosolic aconitase participates in the glyoxylate cycle in etiolated pumpkin cotyledons. *Plant Cell Physiol.* 36:669–80

59. Hayashi M, Nito K, Takei-Hoshi R, Yagi M, Kondo M, et al. 2002. Ped3p is a peroxisomal ATP-binding cassette transporter that might supply substrates for fatty acid β-oxidation. *Plant Cell Physiol.* 43:1–11

60. Hayashi Y, Hayashi M, Hayashi H, Hara-Nishimura I, Nishimura M. 2001. Direct interaction between glyoxysomes and lipid bodies in cotyledons of the *Arabidopsis thaliana* ped1 mutant. *Protoplasma* 218:83–94

61. Hettema EH, van Roermund CW, Distel B, van den Berg M, Vilela C, et al. 1996. The ABC transporter proteins Pat1 and Pat2 are required for import of long-chain fatty acids into peroxisomes of *Saccharomyces cerevisiae*. *EMBO J.* 15:3813–22

62. Hill J, Nelson E, Tilman D, Polasky S, Tiffany D. 2006. Environmental, economic, and energetic costs and benefits of biodiesel and ethanol biofuels. *Proc. Natl. Acad. Sci. USA* 103:11206–10

63. Hills MJ, Murphy DJ, Beevers H. 1989. Inhibition of neutral lipase from castor bean lipid bodies by Coenzyme A (CoA) and Oleoyl-CoA. *Plant Physiol.* 89:1006–10

64. Hippman H, Heinz E. 1976. Glycerol kinase in leaves. *Z. Pflanzenphysiol.* 79:408–18

65. Hooks MA, Bode K, Couée I. 1995. Regulation of acyl-CoA oxidases in maize seedlings. *Phytochemistry* 40:657–60

66. Hooks MA, Kellas F, Graham IA. 1999. Long-chain acyl-CoA oxidases of *Arabidopsis*. *Plant J.* 20:1–13

67. Hsieh K, Huang AH. 2004. Endoplasmic reticulum, oleosins, and oils in seeds and tapetum cells. *Plant Physiol.* 136:3427–34

68. Huang AHC. 1975. Enzymes of glycerol metabolism in the storage tissues of fatty seedlings. *Plant Physiol.* 55:555–58

69. Huang AHC. 1983. Plant lipases. In *Lipases*, ed. HL Brockman, D Borgstrom, pp. 419–42. Amsterdam: Elsevier

70. Huang AHC. 1992. Oil bodies and oleosins in seeds. *Annu. Rev. Plant Physiol. Plant Mol. Biol.* 43:177–200

71. Hunt MC, Alexson SE. 2002. The role Acyl-CoA thioesterases play in mediating intracellular lipid metabolism. *Prog. Lipid Res.* 41:99–130

72. Hutton D, Stumpf PK. 1969. Fat metabolism in higher plants. Characterization of the ß-oxidation systems from maturing and germinating castor bean seeds. *Plant Physiol.* 44:508–16

73. Ishizaki K, Larson TR, Schauer N, Fernie AR, Graham IA, Leaver CJ. 2005. The critical role of *Arabidopsis* electron-transfer flavoprotein:ubiquinone oxidoreductase during dark-induced starvation. *Plant Cell* 17:2587–600

74. Ishizaki K, Schauer N, Larson TR, Graham IA, Fernie AR, Leaver CJ. 2006. The mitochondrial electron transfer flavoprotein complex is essential for survival of *Arabidopsis* in extended darkness. *Plant J.* 47:751–60

75. Karyotou K, Donaldson RP. 2005. Ascorbate peroxidase, a scavenger of hydrogen peroxide in glyoxysomal membranes. *Arch. Biochem. Biophys.* 434:248–57

76. Knoop F. 1904. Der Abbau aromatischer Fettsöuren im Tierkörper. *Beitr. Chem. Physiol. Pathol.* 6:150–62
77. Koo AJK, Chung HS, Kobayashi Y, Howe GA. 2006. Identification of a peroxisomal acyl-activating enzyme involved in the biosynthesis of jasmonic acid in *Arabidopsis*. *J. Biol. Chem.* 281:33511–20
78. Kornberg HL, Beevers H. 1957. A mechanism of conversion of fat to carbohydrate in castor beans. *Nature* 180:35
79. Koussevitzky S, Nott A, Mockler TC, Hong F, Sachetto-Martins G, et al. 2007. Signals from chloroplasts converge to regulate nuclear gene expression. *Science* 316:700–1
80. Kunze M, Pracharoenwattana I, Smith SM, Hartig A. 2006. A central role for the peroxisomal membrane in glyoxylate cycle function. *Biochim. Biophys. Acta* 1763:1441–52
81. Lange PR, Eastmond PJ, Madagan K, Graham IA. 2004. An *Arabidopsis* mutant disrupted in valine catabolism is also compromised in peroxisomal fatty acid β-oxidation. *FEBS Lett.* 571:147–53
82. Lawand S, Dorne AJ, Long D, Coupland G, Mache R, Carol P. 2002. *Arabidopsis* A BOUT DE SOUFFLE, which is homologous with mammalian carnitine acyl carrier, is required for postembryonic growth in the light. *Plant Cell* 14:2161–73
83. Leprince O, van Aelst AC, Pritchard HW, Murphy DJ. 1998. Oleosins prevent oil-body coalescence during seed imbibition as suggested by a low-temperature scanning electron microscope study of desiccation-tolerant and -sensitive oilseeds. *Planta* 204:109–19
84. Lin EC. 1976. Glycerol dissimilation and its regulation in bacteria. *Annu. Rev. Microbiol.* 30:535–78
85. Lin EC. 1977. Glycerol utilization and its regulation in mammals. *Annu. Rev. Biochem.* 46:765–95
86. Lisenbee CS, Lingard MJ, Trelease RN. 2005. *Arabidopsis* peroxisomes possess functionally redundant membrane and matrix isoforms of monodehydroascorbate reductase. *Plant J.* 43:900–14
87. Mackenzie J, Pedersen L, Arent S, Henriksen A. 2006. Controlling electron transfer in acyl-CoA oxidases and dehydrogenases: a structural view. *J. Biol. Chem.* 281:31012–20
88. Maeda I, Delessert S, Hasegawa S, Seto Y, Zuber S, Poirier Y. 2006. The peroxisomal Acyl-CoA thioesterase Pte1p from *Saccharomyces cerevisiae* is required for efficient degradation of short straight chain and branched chain fatty acids. *J. Biol. Chem.* 281:11729–35
89. Manz B, Muller K, Kucera B, Volke F, Leubner-Metzger G. 2005. Water uptake and distribution in germinating tobacco seeds investigated in vivo by nuclear magnetic resonance imaging. *Plant Physiol.* 138:1538–51
90. Martin T, Oswald O, Graham IA. 2002. *Arabidopsis* seedling growth, storage lipid mobilization, and photosynthetic gene expression are regulated by carbon:nitrogen availability. *Plant Physiol.* 128:472–81
91. Matsui K, Fukutomi S, Ishii M, Kajiwara T. 2004. A tomato lipase homologous to (DAD1 LeLID1) is induced in postgerminative growing stage and encodes a triacylglycerol lipase. *FEBS Lett.* 569:195–200
92. Mettler IJ, Beevers H. 1980. Oxidation of NADH in glyoxysomes by a malate-aspartate shuttle. *Plant Physiol.* 66:555–60
93. Metzger JO, Bornscheuer U. 2006. Lipids as renewable resources: current state of chemical and biotechnological conversion and diversification. *Appl. Microbiol. Biotechnol.* 71:13–22
94. Miernyk JA, Trelease RN. 1981. Control of enzyme activities in cotton cotyledons during maturation and germination. IV. ß-oxidation. *Plant Physiol.* 67:341–46

95. Mosser J, Douar A-M, Sarde CO, Kioschis P, Feil R, et al. 1993. Putative X-linked adrenoleukodystrophy gene shares unexpected homology with ABC transporters. *Nature* 361:726–30
96. Mukherjee KD. 1994. Plant lipases and their application in lipid biotransformations. *Prog. Lipid Res.* 33:165–74
97. Mullen RT, Trelease RN. 1996. Biogenesis and membrane properties of peroxisomes: Does the boundary membrane serve and protect? *Trends Plant Sci.* 1:389–94
98. Murphy DJ. 1993. Structure, function and biogenesis of storage lipid bodies and oleosins in plants. *Prog. Lipid Res.* 32:247–80
99. Murphy DJ, Vance J. 1999. Mechanisms of lipid-body formation. *Trends Biochem. Sci.* 24:109–15
100. Napier JA. 2007. The production of unusual fatty acids in transgenic plants. *Annu Rev. Plant Biol.* 58:295–319
101. Olesen C, Thomsen KK, Svendsen I, Brandt A. 1997. The glyoxysomal 3-ketoacyl-CoA thiolase precursor from *Brassica napus* has enzymatic activity when synthesized in *Escherichia coli*. *FEBS Lett.* 412:138–40
102. Oswald O, Martin T, Dominy PJ, Graham IA. 2001. Plastid redox state and sugars: interactive regulators of nuclear-encoded photosynthetic gene expression. *Proc. Natl. Acad. Sci. USA* 98:2047–52
103. Pedersen L, Henriksen A. 2005. Acyl-CoA oxidase 1 from *Arabidopsis thaliana*. Structure of a key enzyme in plant lipid metabolism. *J. Mol. Biol.* 345:487–500
104. **Penfield S, Li Y, Gilday AD, Graham S, Graham IA. 2006. *Arabidopsis* ABA INSENSITIVE4 regulates lipid mobilization in the embryo and reveals repression of seed germination by the endosperm. *Plant Cell* 18:1887–99**
105. Penfield S, Pinfield-Wells HM, Graham IA. 2006. Storage reserve mobilisation and seedling establishment in *Arabidopsis*. In *The Arabidopsis Book*, ed. CR Somerville, EM Meyerowitz. Rockville, MD: Am. Soc. Plant Biol. **http://www.aspb.org/publications/arabidopsis/index.cfm**
106. Penfield S, Pinfield-Wells HM, Graham IA. 2007. Lipid metabolism and seed dormancy. In *Seed Development, Dormancy and Germination, Annu. Plant Rev.*, ed. K Bradford, H Nonogaki, 27:133–52. Oxford: Blackwell
107. **Penfield S, Rylott EL, Gilday AD, Graham S, Larson TR, Graham IA. 2004. Reserve mobilization in the *Arabidopsis* endosperm fuels hypocotyl elongation in the dark, is independent of abscisic acid, and requires *PHOSPHOENOLPYRUVATE CARBOXYKINASE1*. *Plant Cell* 16:2705–18**
108. Pinfield-Wells H, Rylott EL, Gilday AD, Graham S, Job K, et al. 2005. Sucrose rescues seedling establishment but not germination of *Arabidopsis* mutants disrupted in peroxisomal fatty acid catabolism. *Plant J.* 43:861–72
109. Poirier Y, Antonenkov VD, Glumoff T, Hiltunen JK. 2006. Peroxisomal β-oxidation—a metabolic pathway with multiple functions. *Biochim. Biophys. Acta* 1763:1413–26
110. **Pracharoenwattana I, Cornah JE, Smith SM. 2005. *Arabidopsis* peroxisomal citrate synthase is required for fatty acid respiration and seed germination. *Plant Cell* 17:2037–48**
111. **Pracharoenwattana I, Cornah JE, Smith SM. 2007. *Arabidopsis* peroxisomal malate dehydrogenase functions in β-oxidation but not in the glyoxylate cycle. *Plant J.* 50:381–90**
112. Preisig-Müller R, Guhnemann-Schafer K, Kindl H. 1994. Domains of the tetrafunctional protein acting in glyoxysomal fatty acid β-oxidation. Demonstration of epimerase and isomerase activities on a peptide lacking hydratase activity. *J. Biol. Chem.* 269:20475–81

104. The first report of a transcription factor that regulates storage oil mobilization during seed germination.

107. Demonstrated that reserve mobilization is differentially regulated by ABA in endosperm and embryo tissues and highlighted the role played by the endosperm in the provision of carbon to the growing embryo.

110. Demonstrates that the mechanism involved in exporting carbon skeletons from glyoxysomes/peroxisomes is different in plants and yeast.

111. Led to a major revision of how the reactions of the glyoxylate cycle are partitioned between the glyoxysome and the cytosol in higher plants.

113. Pritchard SL, Charlton WL, Baker A, Graham IA. 2002. Germination and storage reserve mobilization are regulated independently in *Arabidopsis*. *Plant J.* 31:639–47

114. Reumann S. 2002. The photorespiratory pathway of leaf peroxisomes. In *Plant Peroxisomes*, ed. A Baker, IA Graham, pp. 141–90. London: Kluwer

115. Reynolds SJ, Smith SM. 1995. Regulation of expression of the cucumber isocitrate lyase gene in cotyledons upon seed germination and by sucrose. *Plant Mol. Biol.* 29:885–96

116. Richmond TA, Bleecker AB. 1999. A defect in β-oxidation causes abnormal inflorescence development in *Arabidopsis*. *Plant Cell* 11:1911–24

117. Rook F, Hadingham SA, Li Y, Bevan MW. 2006. Sugar and ABA response pathways and the control of gene expression. *Plant Cell Environ.* 29:426–34

118. Russell L, Larner V, Kurup S, Bougourd S, Holdsworth M. 2000. The *Arabidopsis* COMATOSE locus regulates germination potential. *Development* 127:3759–67

119. Rylott EL, Eastmond PJ, Gilday AD, Slocombe SP, Larson TR, et al. 2006. The *Arabidopsis thaliana* multifunctional protein gene (*MFP2*) of peroxisomal β-oxidation is essential for seedling establishment. *Plant J.* 45:930–41

120. Rylott EL, Hooks MA, Graham IA. 2001. Co-ordinate regulation of genes involved in storage lipid mobilization in *Arabidopsis thaliana*. *Biochem. Soc. Trans.* 29:283–87

121. Rylott EL, Rodgers CA, Gilday AD, Edgell T, Larson TR, Graham IA. 2003. *Arabidopsis* mutants in short- and medium-chain acyl-CoA oxidase activities accumulate acyl-CoAs and reveal that fatty acid β-oxidation is essential for embryo development. *J. Biol. Chem.* 278:21370–77

122. Schulz H, Kunau W-H. 1987. β-oxidation of unsaturated fatty acids—a revised pathway. *Trends Biochem. Sci.* 12:403–6

123. Schuster J, Binder S. 2005. The mitochondrial branched-chain aminotransferase (AtBCAT-1) is capable to initiate degradation of leucine, isoleucine and valine in almost all tissues in *Arabidopsis thaliana*. *Plant Mol. Biol.* 57:241–54

124. Shockey JM, Fulda MS, Browse JA. 2002. *Arabidopsis* contains nine long-chain acyl-coenzyme a synthetase genes that participate in fatty acid and glycerolipid metabolism. *Plant Physiol.* 129:1710–22

125. Siloto RM, Findlay K, Lopez-Villalobos A, Yeung EC, Nykiforuk CL, Moloney MM. 2006. The accumulation of oleosins determines the size of seed oilbodies in *Arabidopsis*. *Plant Cell* 18:1961–74

126. Smeekens S. 2000. Sugar-induced signal transduction in plants. *Annu. Rev. Plant Physiol. Plant Mol. Biol.* 51:49–81

127. Soderman EM, Brocard IM, Lynch TJ, Finkelstein RR. 2000. Regulation and function of the *Arabidopsis* ABA-insensitive4 gene in seed and abscisic acid response signaling networks. *Plant Physiol.* 124:1752–65

128. Somerville CR, Bonetta D. 2001. Plants as factories for technical materials. *Plant Physiol.* 125:168–71

129. Sundaramoorthy R, Micossi E, Alphey MS, Germain V, Bryce JH, et al. 2006. The crystal structure of a plant 3-ketoacyl-CoA thiolase reveals the potential for redox control of peroxisomal fatty acid β-oxidation. *J. Mol. Biol.* 359:347–57

130. Taylor NL, Heazlewood JL, Day DA, Millar AH. 2004. Lipoic acid-dependent oxidative catabolism of α-keto acids in mitochondria provides evidence for branched-chain amino acid catabolism in *Arabidopsis*. *Plant Physiol.* 134:838–48

131. Theodoulou FL, Job K, Slocombe SP, Footitt S, Holdsworth M, et al. 2005. Jasmonic acid levels are reduced in COMATOSE ATP-binding cassette transporter mutants. Implications for transport of jasmonate precursors into peroxisome. *Plant Physiol.* 137:835–40

116. Highlights the fact that peroxisomal β-oxidation plays many other important roles in plant development, some of which are still poorly understood.

132. Tilton GB, Shockey JM, Browse J. 2004. Biochemical and molecular characterization of ACH2, an acyl-CoA thioesterase from *Arabidopsis thaliana*. *J. Biol. Chem.* 279:7487–94
133. Ting JTL, Lee KY, Ratnayake C, Platt KA, Balsamo RA, Huang AHC. 1996. Oleosin genes in maize kernels having diverse oil contents are constitutively expressed independent of oil contents—Size and shape of intracellular oil bodies are determined by the oleosins oils ratio. *Planta* 199:158–65
134. To JP, Reiter WD, Gibson SI. 2002. Mobilization of seed storage lipid by *Arabidopsis* seedlings is retarded in the presence of exogenous sugars. *BMC Plant Biol.* 2:4
135. Tzen JTC, Cao YZ, Laurent P, Ratnayake C, Huang AHC. 1993. Lipids, proteins, and structure of seed oil bodies from diverse species. *Plant Physiol.* 101:267–76
136. Tzen JTC, Lai YK, Chan KL, Huang AHC. 1990. Oleosin isoforms of high and low molecular weights are present in the oil bodies of diverse seed species. *Plant Physiol.* 94:1282–89
137. Tzen JTC, Lie GC, Huang AH. 1992. Characterization of the charged components and their topology on the surface of plant seed oil bodies. *J. Biol. Chem.* 267:15626–34
138. van den Bosch H, Schutgens RB, Wanders RJ, Tager JM. 1992. Biochemistry of peroxisomes. *Annu. Rev. Biochem.* 61:157–97
139. van Roermund CW, Elgersma Y, Singh N, Wanders RJ, Tabak HF. 1995. The membrane of peroxisomes in *Saccharomyces cerevisiae* is impermeable to NAD(H) and acetyl-CoA under in vivo conditions. *EMBO J.* 1414:3480–86
140. van Roermund CW, Hettema EH, van den Berg M, Tabak HF, Wanders RJ. 1999. Molecular characterization of carnitine-dependent transport of acetyl-CoA from peroxisomes to mitochondria in *Saccharomyces cerevisiae* and identification of a plasma membrane carnitine transporter, Agp2p. *EMBO J.* 18:5843–52
141. Verleur N, Hettema EH, van Roermund CW, Tabak HF, Wanders RJ. 1997. Transport of activated fatty acids by the peroxisomal ATP-binding-cassette transporter Pxa2 in a semi-intact yeast cell system. *Eur. J. Biochem.* 249:657–61
142. Wanner G, Theimer RR. 1978. Membranous appendices of spherosomes (oleosomes). Possible role in fat utilization in germinating oil seeds. *Planta* 140:163–69
143. Willekens H, Chamnongpol S, Davey M, Schraudner M, Langebartels C, et al. 1997. Catalase is a sink for H_2O_2 and is indispensable for stress defense in C3 plants. *EMBO J.* 16:4806–16
144. Yamaguchi K, Mori H, Nishimura M. 1995. A novel isoenzyme of ascorbate peroxidase localized on glyoxysomal and leaf peroxisomal membranes in pumpkin. *Plant Cell Physiol.* 36:1157–62
145. Zimmermann R, Strauss JG, Haemmerle G, Schoiswohl G, Birner-Gruenberger R, et al. 2004. Fat mobilization in adipose tissue is promoted by adipose triglyceride lipase. *Science* 306:1383–86
146. Zolman BK, Monroe-Augustus M, Thompson B, Hawes JW, Krukenberg KA, et al. 2001. *chy1*, an *Arabidopsis* mutant with impaired β-oxidation, is defective in a peroxisomal β-hydroxyisobutyrylCoA hydrolase. *J. Biol. Chem.* 276:31037–46
147. Zolman BK, Silva ID, Bartel B. 2001. The *Arabidopsis pxa1* mutant is defective in an ATP-binding cassette transporter-like protein required for peroxisomal fatty acid β-oxidation. *Plant Physiol.* 127:1266–78
148. Zolman BK, Yoder A, Bartel B. 2000. Genetic analysis of indole-3-butyric acid responses in *Arabidopsis thaliana* reveals four mutant classes. *Genetics* 156:1323–37

The Role of Glutathione in Photosynthetic Organisms: Emerging Functions for Glutaredoxins and Glutathionylation

Nicolas Rouhier,[1] Stéphane D. Lemaire,[2] and Jean-Pierre Jacquot[1]

[1]Unité Mixte de Recherches, 1136 INRA-UHP Interaction Arbres-Microorganismes, IFR 110 GEEF, Nancy University, Faculté des Sciences, 54506 Vandoeuvre Cedex, France; email: nrouhier@scbiol.uhp-nancy.fr, j2p@scbiol.uhp-nancy.fr

[2]Institut de Biotechnologie des Plantes, Université de Paris Sud, 91405 Orsay Cedex, France; email: stephane.lemaire@u-psud.fr

Annu. Rev. Plant Biol. 2008. 59:143–66

The *Annual Review of Plant Biology* is online at plant.annualreviews.org

This article's doi:
10.1146/annurev.arplant.59.032607.092811

1543-5008/08/0602-0143$20.00

Key Words

cysteine, iron sulfur, oxidative stress, redox, signaling

Abstract

Glutathione, a tripeptide with the sequence γ-Glu-Cys-Gly, exists either in a reduced form with a free thiol group or in an oxidized form with a disulfide between two identical molecules. We describe here briefly the pathways involved in the synthesis, reduction, polymerization, and degradation of glutathione, as well as its distribution throughout the plant and its redox buffering capacities. The function of glutathione in xenobiotic and heavy metal detoxification, plant development, and plant-pathogen interactions is also briefly discussed. Several lines of evidence indicate that glutathione and glutaredoxins (GRXs) are implicated in the response to oxidative stress through the regeneration of enzymes involved in peroxide and methionine sulfoxide reduction. Finally, emerging functions for plant GRXs and glutathione concern the regulation of protein activity via glutathionylation and the capacity of some GRXs to bind iron sulfur centers and for some of them to transfer FeS clusters into apoproteins.

Contents

INTRODUCTION

Glutathione: the major nonprotein cellular thiol

GSH: reduced glutathione

GSSG: oxidized glutathione

Glutathionylation: the binding of a glutathione to a thiol group to protect the protein from irreversible inactivation or to regulate protein activity

Glutaredoxin (GRX): small-molecular-weight thiol oxidoreductase

Glutathione is a tripeptide with the sequence γ-L-glutamyl-L-cysteinyl-glycine that plays an important role in a wide range of organisms. Glutathione is nearly ubiquitous, although it is absent in some organisms that use different thiol cofactors such as coenzyme A, mycothiol, or ergothioneine (58). Glutathione can exist either in the reduced state (GSH) or in an oxidized state (GSSG), in which two glutathione molecules are linked via a disulfide bond. In plants, glutathione is necessary not only for maintaining the redox balance, but also for xenobiotic detoxification, heavy metal detoxification, and more generally for cell signaling (**Figure 1**). Because GSH and its derivatives are involved in numerous developmental processes and because it is a major player in the cell redox chemistry, it has been studied extensively over the past decades. Recent reviews have described the synthesis and degradation of this compound, its role in xenobiotic elimination, its role in cell signaling in interaction with other redox systems such as ascorbate or peroxides, and also its role in signaling pathways induced by jasmonic acid and other plant hormones (25, 65, 73, 77, 78). We give a brief overview of these aspects but describe more extensively the emerging importance of glutathionylation reactions in plants and the recent exciting developments concerning glutaredoxins (GRXs), the catalysts of these deglutathionylation/glutathionylation reactions that are also involved in stress response and in iron sulfur assembly reactions.

GLUTATHIONE AND HOMOLOGS IN PLANTS

Structure, Chemical Properties, Synthesis, Reduction, Polymerization, and Degradation

The redox buffering properties and the intracellular concentrations of GSH are conditioned by its chemical properties, its mode of synthesis, and reduction. Likewise, the formation of GSH polymers (phytochelatins), and the degradation of GSH are reactions that control the intracellular GSH pool and GSH/GSSG ratios. These various reactions are discussed in the following sections.

Structure of the oxidized and reduced forms. The linear structure of GSH reveals an anomaly in the organization of this compound. Unlike in traditional proteins or peptides the glutamate residue is linked to the neighboring cysteine via its side chain carboxylate, resulting in a pseudopeptide bond. In its oxidized form, GSSG, the two chains of glutathione are linked via a disulfide bond with elimination of two protons and two electrons.

It is a gross simplification to represent glutathione, either oxidized or reduced, as a linear molecule. In reality GSH or GSSG adopts

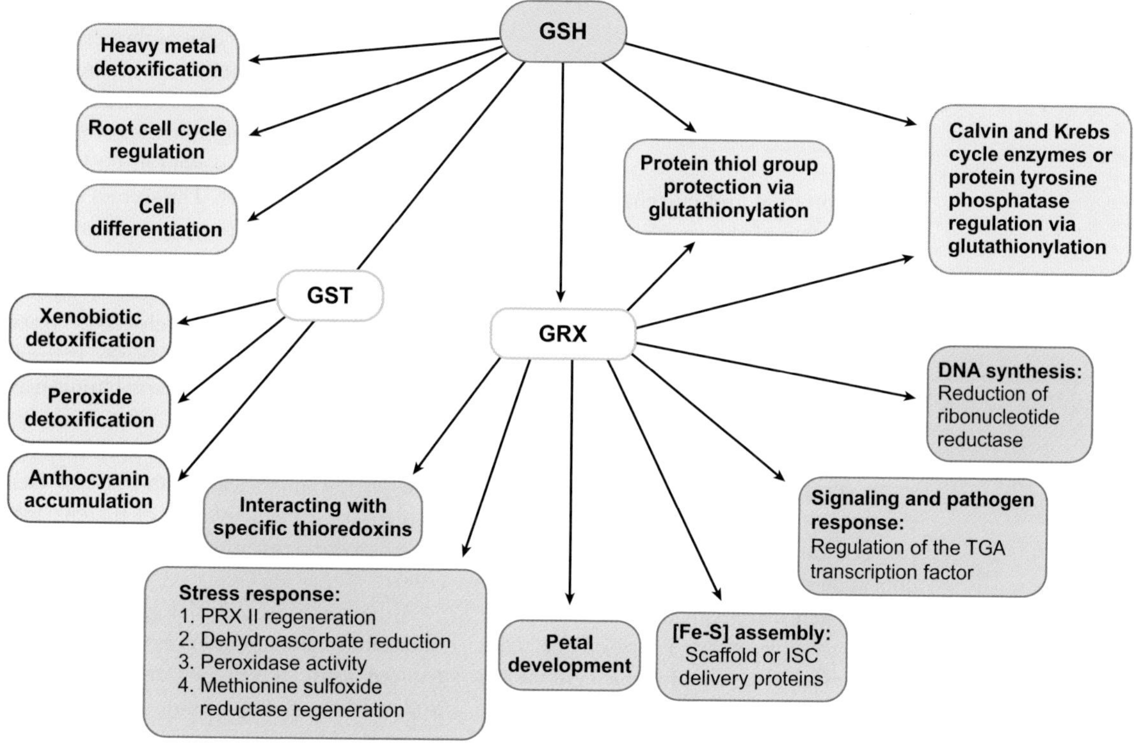

Figure 1

Reduced glutathione (GSH)-, glutathione-*S*-transferase (GST)-, and glutaredoxin (GRX)-linked processes. Abbreviations: ISC, iron sulfur cluster; PRX, peroxiredoxin.

three-dimensional structures that are far from linear. Although several protein structures contain bound glutathione, data regarding the structure of this compound in solution are scarce. The crystal structure of GSH was solved a long time ago and later refined (32), but surprisingly only recently have Klochkov and coworkers (54) succeeded in solving the structure of GSH by NMR and residual dipolar coupling analysis. To solve this structure, the authors aligned the molecules in a lyotropic crystalline medium. This certainly indicates that glutathione is a flexible molecule with few structural constraints, presumably because of its small size. The examination of several protein structures containing bound GSSG (1GRA, 2GRT, and 1YKC) also indicates that even in its more complex oxidized form, glutathione is flexible, it can adopt many conformations, and thus the glutathione binding sites present in enzymes that utilize this compound are varied. As a result, the analysis of the primary sequences of glutathione-dependent enzymes does not reveal any similarity in the glutathione binding sites.

Glutathione and its variants. There are homologs of glutathione in some plants and especially legumes; the most frequently observed is homoglutathione (hGSH) in legumes. hGSH is similar to glutathione, but the glycine residue is replaced by a β-alanine. Its synthesis requires the participation of a specific hGSH synthetase (62). In soybean, for example, hGSH is preferred to GSH for the glutathione-*S*-transferase (GST)-linked detoxification of the xenobiotic acifluorfen (100). Hydroxymethylglutathione is another alternative compound to GSH in which the glycine residue is replaced by a serine; this

TRX: thioredoxin

compound is found in graminae, including rice, wheat, and barley (82). A vacuolar carboxypeptidase of the Y type may be involved in the synthesis of hydroxymethylglutathione (82).

Redox potential and cysteine pKa values. The E_m value of the couple GSH/GSSG is –240 mV at pH 7.0 (65). This value is actually close to the value determined for many thioredoxins (TRXs) (from –280 to –330 mV), which constitute alternative reducing systems in plants and elsewhere. However, as GSSG dissociates upon reduction into two separate GSH units, its influence on the cellular redox status depends on both the total glutathione concentration and the GSH/GSSG ratio (65, 73). The unusual chemical nature of the pseudopeptide bond between γ-Glu and Cys influences only marginally the pKa value of the cysteine residue, which is critical for redox activity. The pKa value for this cysteine has been determined experimentally to be ~8.6–9 compared to the value of 8.3 for free cysteine (50).

Synthesis, reduction, and degradation. Being a pseudopeptide, glutathione is produced not via classical protein synthesis, but rather through the operation of two successive enzymes: γ-glutamyl-cysteine ligase or γ-glutamyl-cysteine synthase (γ-GCL or GSH1) and glutathione synthetase (GS or GSH2). The first of these enzymes catalyzes the formation in the chloroplast of the pseudopeptide bond between Glu and Cys in the presence of ATP, leading to γ-Glu-Cys (also known as γ-EC). Plant γ-GCL are monomeric enzymes of ~450 amino acids in the processed form, whereas the mammalian proteins are composed of a large catalytic subunit associated with a small regulatory subunit (46). Plant γ-GCL contain one or two disulfide bonds and are inhibited by reduction. The reduction of one of the disulfides, conserved in all plant species, governs the dimer-to-monomer transition of the enzyme, whereas the reduction of the second disulfide, present only in some plant species including Brassicaceae, shields access to the active site, thereby decreasing catalytic efficiency (41). The significance of this redox effect, its existence in different species, and the nature of its in vivo effector (TRX system or GSH/GRX system) are still unclear. The second enzyme of the synthesis pathway, glutathione synthetase, catalyzes the ATP-dependent formation of glutathione from γ-EC and glycine (45). This second step likely takes place both in the chloroplast and in the cytosol, but some variations in this distribution may occur between plants (107). The *Arabidopsis thaliana* glutathione synthetase is composed of 480 amino acids, with a glycine-rich loop covering the active site of the enzyme, but no redox regulation has been reported (108).

Although in most physiological conditions intracellular glutathione is essentially in the reduced form, it can be converted to the oxidized form, GSSG, in an oxidizing environment. The regeneration of GSH is performed by glutathione reductase, a NADPH-dependent dimeric flavoprotein that contains one FAD and one disulfide per subunit. The three-dimensional structure of human glutathione reductase reveals that the FAD is facing the disulfide, and thus an intramolecular electron flow from NADPH to FAD and then to the disulfide is facilitated (52). After reduction of the catalytic disulfide of glutathione reductase, a classical dithiol disulfide exchange reaction takes place between the reductase and GSSG, and two GSH molecules are released. There are no structural data available concerning plant glutathione reductases to date, but the high sequence similarities to other reductases from different biological origin suggest that they should be structurally similar. Glutathione reductase exhibits some similarity to other flavin-containing disulfide oxidoreductases such as TRX reductase and lipoamide dehydrogenase, but generally these other enzymes cannot reduce the same substrates. However, in *Drosophila melanogaster*, which lacks a functional glutathione reductase, GSSG is reduced by a TRX reductase in the presence of TRX, indicating some overlap between the two major reducing systems (51).

Glutathione is a cellular redox buffer, but it can also be considered as a reservoir of cysteine for the cell. If cysteine is needed, it is then necessary to degrade the glutathione molecule. This is achieved via the successive operation of two different enzymes, γ-glutamyl transferase (γ-GT) and dipeptidase (99). The degradation process conforms to the following equations, where AA stands for any amino acid:

$$\gamma \text{Glu} - \text{Cys} - \text{Gly} + \text{AA} \rightarrow \gamma \text{Glu} - \text{AA} + \text{Cys} - \text{Gly}. \quad 1.$$

$$\text{Cys} - \text{Gly} + 2\text{H}_2\text{O} \rightarrow \text{Cys} + \text{Gly}. \quad 2.$$

Several γ-GT in plants transfer the γ-Glu residue to a variety of amino acids with the release of the dipeptide Cys-Gly (Equation 1), which in turn is cleaved by a dipeptidase to release the required cysteine (Equation 2). L-Glu is regenerated from γ-Glu-AA via the action of γ-glutamyl cyclotransferase and 5-oxoprolinase. γ-GT can also degrade xenobiotic-conjugated glutathione derivatives. Two forms of the enzyme have been detected in many plants; one enzyme is located outside the plasma membrane facing the cell wall and the other enzyme is soluble (61, 74). The soluble enzymes are heterodimers (subunits of 21 and 42 kDa) originating from a single precursor that is cleaved during biogenesis, whereas the bound γ-GTs are either heterodimers or monomers of 61 kDa. In plants the activity of γ-GT is believed to be linked to secondary metabolism and fruit ripening (99).

Distribution in Planta and Tissular and Subcellular Localization

Glutathione is present in many tissues and subcellular compartments, with concentrations in the millimolar range. In chloroplasts, the concentration of glutathione is estimated to be between 1 and 4.5 mM (78). Labeling with monochlorobimane and confocal microscopy were used to quantify cytoplasmic glutathione in *Arabidopsis* cells, with estimates of its concentration in the 3-mM range (66). Similar labeling in the main cell types of poplar gave values ranging between 0.2 and 0.3 mM in both photosynthetic and nonphotosynthetic cells (35). Using this same technology, Meyer & Fricker (64) estimated the rates of in vivo synthesis of glutathione in *Arabidopsis* cell culture suspensions. An alternative method for the detection of glutathione is the use of specific antibodies, although in general they also recognize the dipeptide γ-glutamylcysteine (40). Recently, a redox-sensitive GFP (roGFP2) has been engineered to estimate in vivo the intracellular redox potential (34), and it will constitute an important tool in the future to estimate the glutathione redox state in different tissues and subcellular compartments. Experiments performed with roGFP2 in *A. thaliana* demonstrated that the redox potential in the cytosol of non-stressed cells is −320 mV (63). In addition, in vitro characterization of this roGFP2 showed that it monitors the redox potential of the cellular glutathione buffer via GRX-linked reactions but not through the TRX-dependent pathways (63).

Glutathione and glutathione reductase have been detected in mitochondria; in addition, GSH and ascorbate are present in peroxisomes, suggesting that these organelles contain a full complement of these antioxidant systems (47). Glutathione is also present in the apoplast and endoplasmic reticulum. It remains unanswered how glutathione is transported between organelles or compartments that do not possess the ability to synthesize it. Some plasma membrane-localized transporters transport glutathione and especially import GSSG from the apoplast to the cytosol (44, 114), but to date, experimental evidence for a glutathione transport mechanism from the cytosol to organelles or vice versa is scarce. Selective antibodies versus glutamate, cysteine, and glycine together with gold labeling have been used to detect the glutathione precursors in *Cucurbita pepo* roots by using transmission electron microscopy, leading to the conclusion that glutathione degradation occurs in the vacuole or the tonoplast but not at the plasmalemma and/or apoplast (113).

PRX: peroxiredoxin

Physiological Roles

GSH has physiological roles in reactive oxygen species detoxification, heavy metal detoxification, xenobiotic conjugation, and also in a variety of cellular and tissular functions. These roles are discussed in the following sections.

Redox buffer and reactive oxygen species detoxification. Glutathione is the most abundant low-molecular-weight thiol in cells and it constitutes a redox buffer that keeps the intracellular environment reduced. Glutathione plays a major role in the detoxification of reactive oxygen species (ROS). GSH can be oxidized to GSSG by some ROS, such as H_2O_2; GSH can react with nitric oxide to form the GSNO derivative, but it also participates in the glutathione/ascorbate cycle, in which GSH allows regeneration of reduced ascorbate, the other major antioxidant in plant cells. GSH also provides electrons to diverse peroxidases. Indeed, although plant glutathione peroxidases are reduced by TRX rather than by glutathione and should thus be renamed thioredoxin-peroxidases (37, 75), other peroxidases of the peroxiredoxin (PRX) family use glutathione alone or with GRX (23, 27, 91). Other enzymes, such as some GSTs or GRXs, also possess a glutathione-dependent peroxidase activity (14, 55).

Phytochelatins and heavy metal detoxification. One of the most documented systems for eliminating heavy metals comprises metallothioneins, small-molecular-weight proteins containing a high density of cysteine residues. Similar to other organisms, plants contain multiple metallothioneins, but they also possess an alternative system of detoxification, phytochelatins (PCs) (12). These compounds are characterized by a general structure of the type $(\gamma\text{-Glu-Cys})_n\text{-Gly}$, but in some plant species the terminal Gly is sometimes replaced by an Ala, Gln, Glu, or Ser, leading to the formation of isophytochelatins (21). In *A. thaliana*, GSH is the in vivo precursor to PC synthesis, which also occurs independently of the protein synthesis machinery. PCs are synthesized through PC synthase. This enzyme is a ~50-kDa polypeptide that catalyzes the net transfer of a γ-EC unit of GSH to another GSH molecule or a PC molecule, mediating its extension from the C to N terminus. Toxic metals such as nickel, cadmium, mercury, or arsenate are efficiently detoxified via glutathione and PCs owing to the high affinity of these polymers for heavy metals (12, 42). Nickel hyperaccumulators produce PC constitutively and increase glutathione synthesis, leading to a better tolerance for this metal (26). The glutathione S-conjugates can be sequestered in the vacuole via γ-glutamyl transpeptidase (33).

Glutathione conjugates. When plant cells need to eliminate xenobiotics, they first conjugate them to glutathione to target the molecules that need to be removed. The enzymes that perform the ligation of glutathione to external molecules are called GSTs and they are found in nearly all living organisms. There are several classes in the plant GST superfamily, including the ϕ (phi), τ (tau), θ (theta), ζ (zeta), λ (lambda), and dehydroascorbate reductase (DHAR) classes; the ϕ and τ classes are specific to plants (19). The glutathione conjugates are then transferred to the vacuole by ATP-dependent GS-X pumps and degraded.

Other physiological functions. Glutathione is involved in many diverse biological processes in plants such as the G1/S transition of the cell cycle during postembryonic root development (105), tracheary cell differentiation (36), anthocyanin accumulation

(110), programmed cell death, and pathogen resistance (16, 24, 71). Most of these suggested functions are based on the analysis of plants containing low levels of glutathione, such as *Arabidopsis* γ-GCL mutants *rax1–1* (4), *cad2–1* (13), and *rml1* (105) or wild-type plants treated with buthionine sulfoximine, a specific inhibitor of γ-GCL. However, such low levels of glutathione are likely to affect the function of GRXs by impairing their reduction and to alter the regulation of protein activities by precluding, for example, glutathionylation. Therefore, the requirement of GSH in all these processes may be linked to the existence of proteins that are regulated by GRX and/or by glutathionylation.

GLUTATHIONYLATION

Glutathionylation/ Deglutathionylation Reactions

In addition to its well-established roles described above, glutathione is involved in a posttranslational modification called glutathionylation. This reversible modification consists of the formation of a mixed disulfide bond between a cysteine residue and glutathione (**Figure 2**). Theoretically, glutathionylation can occur spontaneously by different reaction mechanisms (68). The most widely accepted mechanisms occur in the presence of GSSG or in the presence of GSH and oxidants. Thus, in the cell, protein

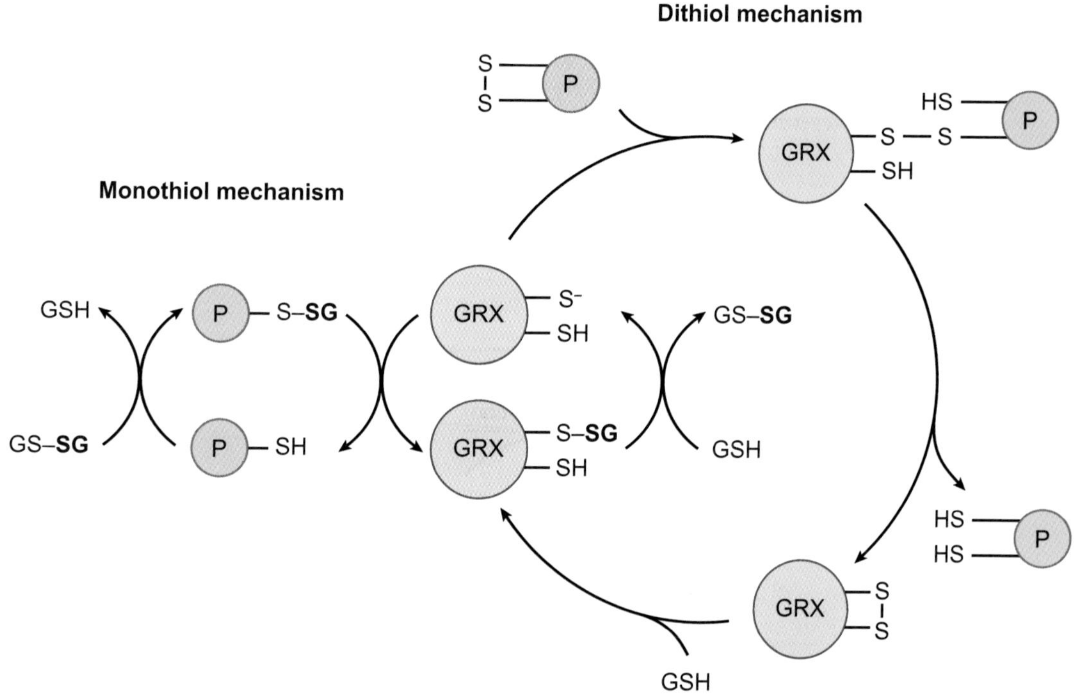

Figure 2

Monothiol and dithiol glutaredoxin (GRX)-dependent catalytic mechanisms. GRX can reduce both disulfide bridges or protein-glutathione adducts with the help of two glutathione molecules; these reactions have different mechanisms. In the dithiol mechanism, two thiol groups of GRXs are required and form an intramolecular disulfide bond between the two active-site cysteines that is subsequently reduced by reduced glutathione (GSH). In the monothiol mechanism used for deglutathionylation reactions, only one active-site cysteine is generally needed to reduce the mixed disulfide between the target protein (P) and glutathione. The glutathionylated GRX form is regenerated by another glutathione molecule. Abbreviation: GSSG, oxidized glutathione.

glutathionylation is favored under conditions of enhanced ROS production. The mechanism prevailing in vivo remains unknown. However, in vitro studies have suggested that GSH and ROS promote glutathionylation much more efficiently than GSSG alone (15, 67, 112). Starke and coworkers (98) reported that a human GRX could catalyze glutathionylation in the presence of glutathione-thiyl radicals. In contrast, the reverse reaction, deglutathionylation, is likely catalyzed by GRX. Other disulfide oxidoreductases, such as TRX or protein disulfide isomerases (PDI), are poorly efficient in catalyzing deglutathionylation compared with CPYC-GRX (49, 81, 83; M. Zaffagnini & S.D. Lemaire, manuscript in preparation). The reaction is based on a monothiol mechanism because it only requires the most N-terminal cysteine of the active site of CPYC-GRX (**Figure 2**) and an external GSH for the GRX regeneration (8). Nevertheless, CGFS-GRXs from yeast or *Chlamydomonas reinhardtii*, which contain a disulfide, can also catalyze deglutathionylation, likely through a dithiol mechanism but without external GSH (102; M. Zaffagnini & S.D. Lemaire, manuscript in preparation) (**Figure 3**).

Glutathionylation Targets

Most studies on glutathionylation have been performed in mammals. Proteomic studies, based mainly on the use of ^{35}S-labeling or biotinylated glutathione, have allowed the identification of approximately 150 targets of glutathionylation involved in diverse processes such as glycolysis, signal transduction, protein degradation, intracellular trafficking, and protein folding. Glutathionylation can protect protein thiols from irreversible inactivation but can also alter, either positively or negatively, the activity of many proteins. Mammalian carbonic anhydrase III is one

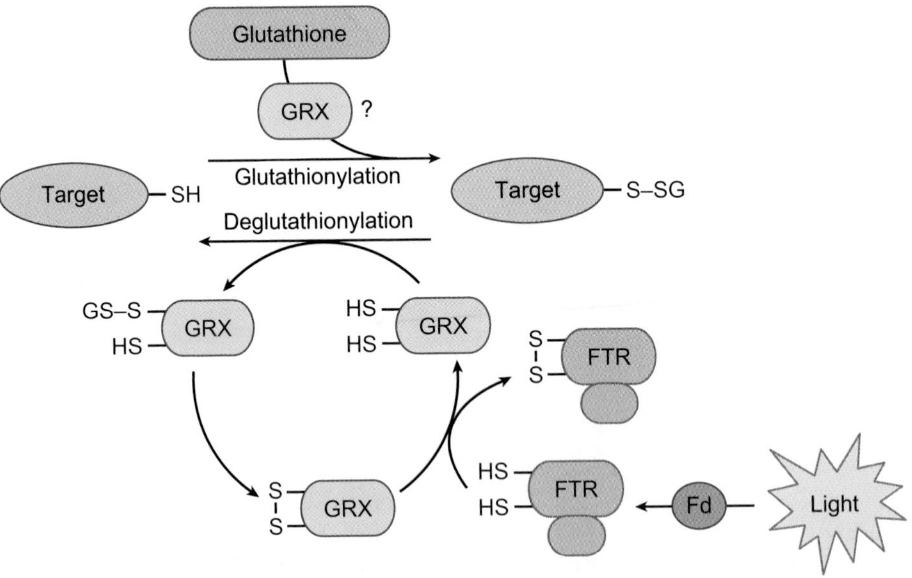

Figure 3

CGFS-GRX-dependent mechanism for deglutathionylation reactions. This mechanism, demonstrated for *Chlamydomonas reinhardtii* GRX3, a homolog of GRXS14, differs from those described in **Figure 2** in that the glutathionylated catalytic cysteine of GRX is attacked by an extra active-site C terminus cysteine. The resulting disulfide is then reduced by FTR in chloroplasts. Abbreviations: GRX, glutaredoxin; FTR, ferredoxin-thioredoxin reductase; Fd, ferredoxin.

of the first enzymes for which regulation by glutathionylation has been demonstrated (9).

The studies on glutathionylation in mammals, yeast, and bacteria have been reviewed recently (30, 42, 68, 96). In contrast, little is known so far about glutathionylation in plants. We focus on the most recent studies that suggest that glutathionylation is also a mechanism of regulation and redox signaling in plants. The first report of a plant protein undergoing glutathionylation concerned *A. thaliana* GSTs that possess a DHAR activity and/or a glutathione-dependent thioltransferase activity (17). These enzymes, which contain a catalytically essential cysteine, are glutathionylated in vitro in the presence of GSSG with a concomitant loss of enzymatic activity. This form would constitute an intermediary step of the catalytic mechanism, allowing glutathione-dependent reduction of dehydroascorbic acid (DHA). The second study, based on the in vivo use of biotinylated glutathione with *A. thaliana* cell suspensions, reported the glutathionylation of two enzymes: cytosolic triose-phosphate isomerase, a glycolytic enzyme, and fructose-1,6-bisphosphate (FBP) aldolase, a Calvin cycle enzyme (43). In vitro, the activity of recombinant cytosolic triose-phosphate isomerase is inhibited by GSSG. More recently, the inactivation of a soybean protein tyrosine phosphatase (PTP) by glutathionylation was also reported (18). Although a similar inactivation of several animal PTPs has been described (5, 104), in the case of soybean PTP, glutathionylation was suggested to involve a different mechanism implicating the catalytic cysteine and two additional cysteines (18).

In human cells, one of the three extra active-site cysteines of TRX was also identified as a glutathionylation target in vivo under oxidative stress (10). Plant TRXs also undergo glutathionylation in vitro. The glutathionylation of mitochondrial TRX h2 from poplar leads to an increase in the redox potential of the active-site disulfide and is thus likely to affect the activity of the protein (28). Among the four types of TRX (f, m, x, and y) present in chloroplasts, the f-type TRXs can undergo glutathionylation (67). These f-type TRXs are reduced in the light by way of photoreduced ferredoxin and ferredoxin-thioredoxin reductase (FTR) and are involved mainly in the light-dependent regulation of carbon metabolism enzymes, including several Calvin cycle enzymes (7, 57). Glutathionylation of *Arabidopsis* TRX f strongly decreases its reduction by FTR and thus its ability to activate target enzymes in the light (67). Cytosolic glyceraldehyde-3-phosphate dehydrogenase (GAPDH) is a glycolytic enzyme inactivated by glutathionylation (69). In higher-plant chloroplasts, two types of GAPDH, A_2B_2 and A_4, participate in the Calvin cycle. *Arabidopsis* A_4-GAPDH is inactivated by glutathionylation in vitro, whereas A_2B_2-GAPDH is not (112). However, the activity of A_2B_2-GAPDH is regulated by TRX f, whereas A_4-GAPDH is not. Consequently, under conditions leading to protein glutathionylation in chloroplasts, the activity of both types of GAPDH is likely to be decreased. More generally, the results obtained about the glutathionylation of TRX f, GAPDH, and FBP aldolase suggest that this posttranslational modification could constitute a new mechanism of regulation of Calvin cycle enzymes under oxidative stress (57, 67).

FTR: ferredoxin-thioredoxin reductase

Using biotinylated glutathione and dark-grown *Arabidopsis* cell suspensions, Dixon and coworkers (20) identified 10 glutathionylated proteins in vivo (sucrose synthase, tubulin α and β, acetyl-CoA carboxylase, actin, cytosolic GAPDH, transducin, and Hsc70–1) and 71 glutathionylated proteins in vitro. However, these techniques did not distinguish glutathionylated proteins from those interacting with glutathionylated proteins. Using denaturing treatments, Dixon and colleagues have shown that among the targets identified in vitro, only 22 are likely to be glutathionylated, but unfortunately the identity of these 22 proteins was not revealed. In vitro analyses on methionine synthase and alcohol dehydrogenase revealed that a protein present in *Arabidopsis* extracts was required to trigger glutathionylation of these enzymes (20). The first in vivo proteomic study on photosynthesizing cells was recently performed in *Chlamydomonas* using ^{35}S-radiolabeling and allowed the identification of more than 20 glutathionylated proteins, most of which are located in the chloroplast (L. Michelet, S.D. Lemaire & P. Decottignies, manuscript in preparation). These proteins are involved in diverse processes such as photosynthesis, chloroplast translation, amino acid and ATP metabolism, protein folding, acetate metabolism, and oxidative stress. Many enzymes related to stress were identified, such as chloroplast chaperones or PRXs. Two new Calvin cycle enzymes, distinct from those known to undergo glutathionylation, were also identified. Glutathionylation was confirmed in vitro for three of these targets: the chloroplastic enzymes HSP70B and 2-Cys PRX and also isocitrate lyase, an enzyme involved in acetate metabolism.

GLUTAREDOXINS

The Glutaredoxin Family

Approximately 30 different GRX isoforms have been identified in higher plants, whereas only 6 are found in the eukaryotic green alga *C. reinhardtii* and 3 in the cyanobacterium *Synechocystis* sp. (56, 87, 90). In land plants, including mosses, GRX isoforms can be classified into three distinct subgroups. All these GRXs share several conserved motives, a conserved three-dimensional structure, and they possess a cysteine or a serine in the fourth position of the active-site motif (CxxC or CxxS) (90). The first class, or CPYC-type, which contains GRXs with C[P/G/S][Y/F][C/S] motifs, is homologous to the classical dithiol GRXs such as *Escherichia coli* GRX1 and GRX3, yeast GRX1 and GRX2, and mammalian GRX1 and GRX2. The second class, or CGFS-type, has a strictly conserved CGFS active-site sequence and includes GRXs homologous to yeast GRX3, GRX4, and GRX5 and to *E. coli* GRX4 (38). Plants have generally four different members in this group (GRXS14 to GRXS17). GRXS14 and GRXS15 are small proteins (approximately 170 amino acids) with a single repeat of the GRX module, GRXS16 is larger (around 290 amino acids) with the GRX module linked to an N-terminal extension, and GRXS17 possesses a TRX-like module in the N-terminal part followed by two to three GRX domains depending on the organisms. The third class, or CC-type, which regroups proteins with CC[M/L][C/S/G/A/I] active sites, is apparently restricted to land plants, because it is absent in the genomes of lower photosynthetic organisms such as *Chlamydomonas* or *Synechocystis* and also in bacteria and mammals. The only functional data reported for CC-type GRX isoforms concern their involvement in petal development (111) and pathogen responses through jasmonic acid/salicylic acid signaling (76), two processes specific to higher plants.

Subcellular Localization

Predictions of subcellular localizations suggest that most CC-type GRXs are cytosolic. It is also the case for several GRXs containing a CPYC active site, although in plants two or three of these GRXs (GRXC2, GRXC3, or GRXC4) are predicted to be secreted and might correspond to GRXs highly abundant in the phloem sap (101). In addition, two *Arabidopsis* GRXs (GRXC5 and GRXS12) belonging to the CPYC-type but containing an altered active site (WCSYC or WCSYS, respectively) are predicted to be targeted to chloroplasts. In contrast, CGFS-type GRXs are predicted to be localized in the cytosol/nucleus (GRXS17), the mitochondria (GRXS15), or the chloroplast (GRXS14 and GRXS16). The chloroplastic localization of GRXS14 and GRXS16 and the mitochondrial localization of GRXS15 have been confirmed experimentally (11; S. Bandyopadhyay, F. Gama, M. Molina-Navarro, J. M. Gualberto, R. Claxton, S. G. Naik, B. H. Huynh,

E. Herrero, J. P. Jacquot, M. K. Johnson, N. Rouhier, manuscript in revision).

Structural and Biochemical Properties

GRXs use two different catalytic mechanisms that involve one or two conserved cysteines to reduce a mixed disulfide between a protein and glutathione or a disulfide bridge. One catalytic dithiol mechanism is similar to that employed by TRXs, i.e., the N-terminal cysteine forms a transient disulfide with the oxidized target protein and the second resolving cysteine is required to reduce this disulfide and generate the reduced target protein. In the monothiol mechanism, a cysteine of a target protein reacts with glutathione and the first N-terminal active-site cysteine of GRX reduces this mixed disulfide. Another glutathione molecule is then needed to regenerate the reduced GRX (**Figure 2**). In addition, a third mechanism used by some CGFS-GRXs at least is depicted in **Figure 3**. Following the deglutathionylation reaction, an intramolecular disulfide bridge is formed between the catalytic cysteine and an extra active-site cysteine. The regeneration of this oxidized GRX is dependent on FTR but not on glutathione (M. Zaffagnini & S.D. Lemaire, manuscript in preparation).

The high number of GRX genes in plants compared with other organisms and the low conservation of the primary sequences, especially near the active site, suggest that some of the GRXs should possess different structural and biochemical properties. GRXs are generally considered to be disulfide oxidoreductases of the TRX family that are reduced by glutathione and have a redox potential ranging from −170 to −230 mV. These general features are likely conserved in all CPYC-type GRXs, which possess DHAR and disulfide reductase activities but can also catalyze deglutathionylation (88; M. Zaffagnini & S.D. Lemaire, manuscript in preparation). Site-directed mutagenesis has shown that these dithiol GRXs can use a monothiol mechanism with some substrates such as hydroxylethyl disulfide, dehydroascorbate, or PRX IIB (88, 89). However, the recent biochemical characterization of *Chlamydomonas* GRX3, a chloroplastic CGFS-GRX homologous to GRXS14, revealed unique properties. This GRX3 exhibits a lower midpoint redox potential, closer to that of TRXs, and is efficiently reduced by FTR in the light but not by glutathione. It has no disulfide reductase or DHAR activities but catalyzes deglutathionylation efficiently (M. Zaffagnini & S.D. Lemaire, manuscript in preparation). This finding suggests that the numerous GRX isoforms present in plants may indeed exhibit different biochemical properties that will have to be explored.

ISC: iron sulfur cluster

To date, only two plant GRX structures, poplar GRXC1 and GRXC4, have been solved (22, 79). The previously solved GRX structures of other organisms indicated a monomeric organization and a typical TRX fold. From NMR data, it appears that GRXC4, which displays a CPYC active site, has a typical TRX fold, but it is in equilibrium between a monomeric and a dimeric form; the auto-association surface comprises both the active site and the GSH binding site (**Figure 4**). In the dimer, this creates a small free pocket that could accommodate the presence of a prosthetic group such as an iron sulfur center were it not prevented by the side chain of the Pro residue of the active site (79). This observation was later confirmed by the description of a dimeric poplar GRXC1 (active site CGYC) bridging an iron sulfur cluster (ISC) around the active site (**Figure 4**) (22).

Functions of Glutaredoxins

The structural and redox properties of plant glutaredoxins govern their biochemical reactivities. We describe in the following section the present knowledge concerning the physiological functions of glutaredoxins in photosynthetic organisms.

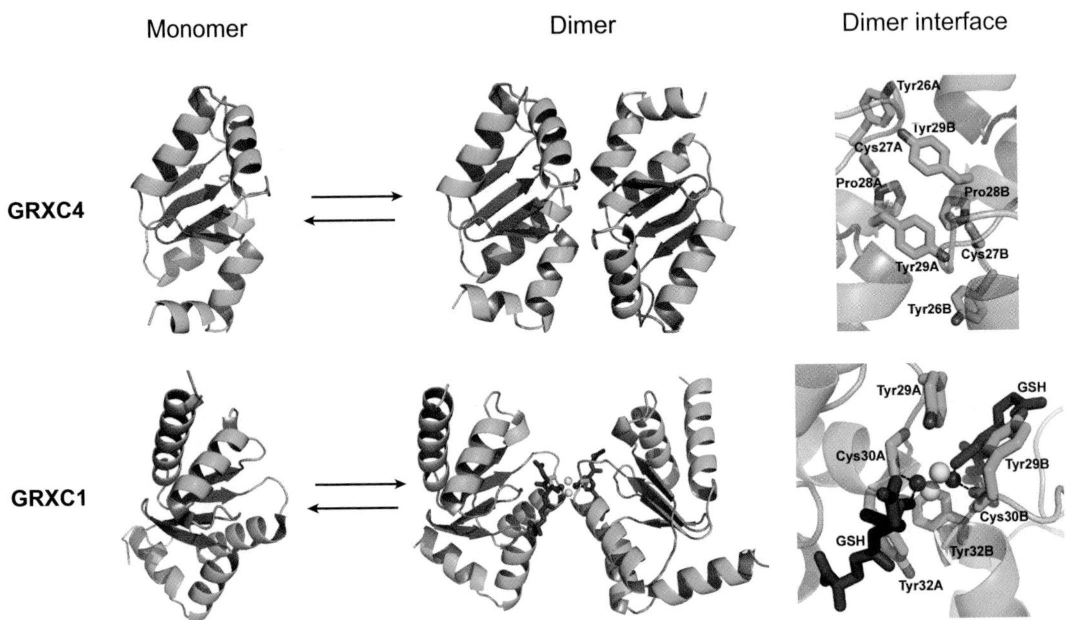

Figure 4

Monomer-to-dimer transition of poplar glutaredoxin homologs GRXC1 and GRXC4. The two proteins oscillate between a monomeric and a dimeric state. In GRXC4, the monomers are arranged in a head-to-tail orientation (79), whereas in GRXC1 (Accession numbers 1Z7R, 2E7P) they are in a mirror conformation and the two subunits are bridged by a [2Fe-2S] cluster (22, 93). In GRXC4, the side chain of the active-site proline residue (replaced by a glycine in GRXC1) likely prevents the incorporation of an iron sulfur cluster (ISC). The iron atoms are colored red, the heterosulfur atoms are colored yellow, and the ligand glutathione molecules are colored dark blue. The figure was drawn with PyMOL.

Role in oxidative stress response. To date, the most documented functions of GSH and GRXs in plants are their involvement in oxidative stress responses. GSH is crucial, especially in the chloroplast and in the cytosol, serving as an electron donor to DHAR for the maintenance of a reduced pool of ascorbate, which itself is used by ascorbate peroxidase for the removal of H_2O_2. GRXs are implicated in many different ways, for example, by directly reducing peroxides (55) or dehydroascorbate (88; M. Zaffagnini & S.D. Lemaire, manuscript in preparation), or by reducing PRXs, a group of thiol-dependent peroxidases (23, 27, 91). Peroxiredoxins are thiol containing enzymes that have the capacity to reduce not only hydrogen peroxide but also more complex alkyl hydroperoxides. The interaction between GRXC4 and PRX IIB has been well described. Mutagenesis studies on the cysteines of both partners indicate that the sulfenic acid formed on the peroxidatic cysteine of PRX IIB after the reduction of the peroxide can likely be attacked either by GRX or by GSH, forming a glutathionylated PRX IIB, the latter efficiently reduced by GRXC4 but not by glutathione alone (89). The second hypothesis has been inferred from NMR studies on PRX IIB, which showed that this protein oscillates between a dimeric reduced form and a monomeric glutathionylated form (80). These type II PRXs are the only glutathione- or GRX-dependent peroxidases; other PRXs and GPXs, contrary to their initial denomination based on their homology to mammalian glutathione peroxidases, use TRXs but not glutathione for their regeneration (37, 75, 92). Thus, the glutathione-dependent peroxidase activities observed in many studies on plant extracts are probably due to peroxidase activities linked either to the direct peroxide reduction by GSH or to GRXs, GSTs, or some specific PRXs.

Another aspect concerning the roles of GRXs in oxidative stress response is the capacity of some CPYC-GRXs to replace TRXs as reductants to methionine sulfoxide reductases, a group of enzymes that reduce methionine sulfoxide back to methionine (106). Methionine is one of the most oxidation-sensitive amino acids, but this oxidation does not necessary lead to the inactivation of the protein. Random oxidation of methionine could constitute a sink for ROS and thus constitute a process of detoxification (97).

The *Arabidopsis* knockout mutant of chloroplastic GRXS14 presents defects in early seedling growth under oxidative stress and increased protein carbonylation in the chloroplast (11). Although its precise mechanism of action is not known, this GRX is involved in the stress response. One hypothesis might be that part of the iron sulfur assembly machinery is defective in this mutant (see below), liberating free iron, which could lead to an oxidative stress situation. A GRXC2 from the extremophile *Deschampsia antarctica*, identified as a gene involved in cold acclimation, is likely also involved in the response to an osmotic stress (31).

Roles in iron sulfur cluster assembly. Yeast mutant cells in which the *grx5* gene has been deleted (*a*) are impaired in mitochondrial ISC biogenesis and thus in respiratory growth, (*b*) accumulate free iron, and (*c*) are more sensitive to oxidative stress (86). Some prokaryotic and eukaryotic monothiol CGFS-GRXs are effective functional substitutes for yeast GRX5 (70). Although the specific role of yeast GRX5 in ISC biogenesis remains to be elucidated, studies of knockout mutants suggest that it likely facilitates the transfer of clusters preassembled on the Isu1p scaffold protein onto acceptor proteins (72). Another hypothesis formulated from in silico analysis suggests that GRX5 may rather serve in the initial assembly of ISC into scaffold proteins (2). The recent discovery that GRX5 is also required for vertebrate heme synthesis raises the possibility that cluster-bound GRX5 plays a direct role in regulating heme biosynthesis in mammals by facilitating the assembly of a [4Fe-4S] cluster on iron regulatory protein 1 or by activating ferrochelatase through the insertion of the catalytically essential [2Fe-2S] cluster (109). Moreover, some *E. coli* GRXs increase ISC incorporation into the oxygen sensor fumarate nitrate reductase regulator, a protein that requires a [4Fe-4S] cluster for its function, presumably by reducing disulfides involving the ligand cysteines and formed in the apoprotein (1).

In other respects, poplar GRXC1 (CGYC active site) and human GRX2 (CSYC active site) are holodimers in which the subunit-bridging [2Fe-2S] cluster is ligated by one active-site cysteine of each monomer and the cysteines of two glutathione molecules (22, 48, 93) (**Figure 4**). The ISC was proposed to function as a redox sensor for the activation of GRX2 during conditions of oxidative stress. Nevertheless, whereas human GRX2 is localized both in the cytosol and mitochondria, poplar GRXC1 is essentially a cytosolic protein. Although ISC assembly machineries are located in the organelles, some iron sulfur (Fe-S) proteins (e.g., aconitase) are present in the cytosol and in the nucleus (103). A system involving the mitochondrial ISC assembly machinery, a few other proteins, and glutathione is required in *Saccharomyces cerevisiae* both for the export of ISC from mitochondria and for the assembly of cytosolic ISC-containing proteins, but many components that contribute to this process have not been identified (60). Initial cluster transfer experiments between holo-GRXC1 and a chloroplastic apo-ferredoxin were not successful, suggesting either that this GRX does not efficiently transfer ISC or that it has specific cytosolic partners not yet identified (S. Bandyopadhyay and M.K. Johnson, unpublished results).

An additional argument for the involvement of GRX in general and of GRXs with a

CGFS active site in ISC biogenesis/assembly derives from mutagenesis studies on poplar GRXC1 that indicate that incorporation of an ISC is likely to be a general feature of plant GRXs possessing a glycine or a small amino acid adjacent to the catalytic cysteine. Especially, the GRX with natural CGFS active sites (such as yeast GRX5) might incorporate an ISC as the mutation of the GRXC1 active site (CGYC) into CGFS still allows the incorporation of an ISC (93). Preliminary work with plant CGFS-GRXs indicates that two chloroplastic GRXs (GRXS14 and GRXS16) out of four CGFS-GRXs stably incorporate a [2Fe-2S] cluster during an anaerobic purification and that the fastest transfer observed to date occurs between GRXS14 and *Synechocystis* apo-ferredoxin (S. Bandyopadhyay, F. Gama, M. Molina-Navarro, J. M. Gualberto, R. Claxton, S. G. Naik, B. H. Huynh, E. Herrero, J.P. Jacquot, M. K. Johnson, N. Rouhier, manuscript in revision). These results strongly suggest that these proteins would function as scaffold proteins for de novo synthesis and transfer of Fe-S clusters, as Fe-S cluster delivery proteins for mediating the transfer of Fe-S clusters from Isc or sulfur mobilization (Suf) scaffold proteins to acceptor proteins, or as a regulator of the Suf machinery by interacting with SufE1 (**Figure 5**).

To date, although Fe-S proteins are required for many essential processes for life, such as photosynthesis, respiration, and nitrogen and sulfur assimilation, the different pathways involved in iron sulfur assembly and biogenesis in plants are poorly characterized (3). However, some proteins (cysteine desulfurase and scaffold proteins) homologous to those of bacterial, yeast, and mammalian assembly machineries have been characterized both in mitochondria and chloroplasts (4), and the finding that GRX may be involved in iron sulfur assembly is a new and exciting area of research.

Other functions. In addition to their role in oxidative stress responses, in ISC assembly, and for the two CC-type GRXs characterized so far in petal development and in pathogen response, GRXs might be involved in several other processes and metabolic pathways, in particular through the regulation of proteins by deglutathionylation/glutathionylation. GRX affinity columns allowed the identification of 94 putative targets in *A. thaliana*, *Solanum tuberosum*, *Pisum sativum*, and *Populus trichocarpa* × *deltoides* and 42 in *Synechocystis* (59, 94). There is an apparent overlap between the numerous putative targets of TRX and GRX identified by proteomics and the proteins that undergo glutathionylation (68). Although dual regulation by TRX/GRX and glutathionylation is possible for some of the targets, and despite the low specificity of TRX and GRX affinity columns, some targets may be specifically redox regulated by TRX or GRX or glutathionylation. Bacterial or mammalian GRXs have also been detected primarily through their ability to sustain the activity of ribonucleotide reductase and 3′-phosphoadenosine-5′-phosphosulfate (PAPS) reductase (39), and similar activities have been reported for poplar GRXC4, the most studied protein with the canonical CPYC active site (95). In addition, in plants the bacterial PAPS reductase is replaced by an adenosine-5′-phosphosulfate reductase, which contains a GRX module in the C terminus of the reductase domain (6).

GRX/TRX cross talk. Whereas GRXs are normally reduced by NADPH, glutathione reductase, and GSH, some GRXs can be alternatively reduced by TRX reductase, such as *Chlamydomonas* GRX3 (M. Zaffagnini & S.D. Lemaire, manuscript in preparation); some TRXs are reduced by the GSH/GRX system rather than by TRX reductases (29). The glutathionylation of some plant TRXs represents another area of interaction between TRX and GRX. In addition, the analysis of an *Arabidopsis* mutant deficient in mitochondrial and cytosolic TRX reductase indicated that some cytosolic TRXs are still partially reduced

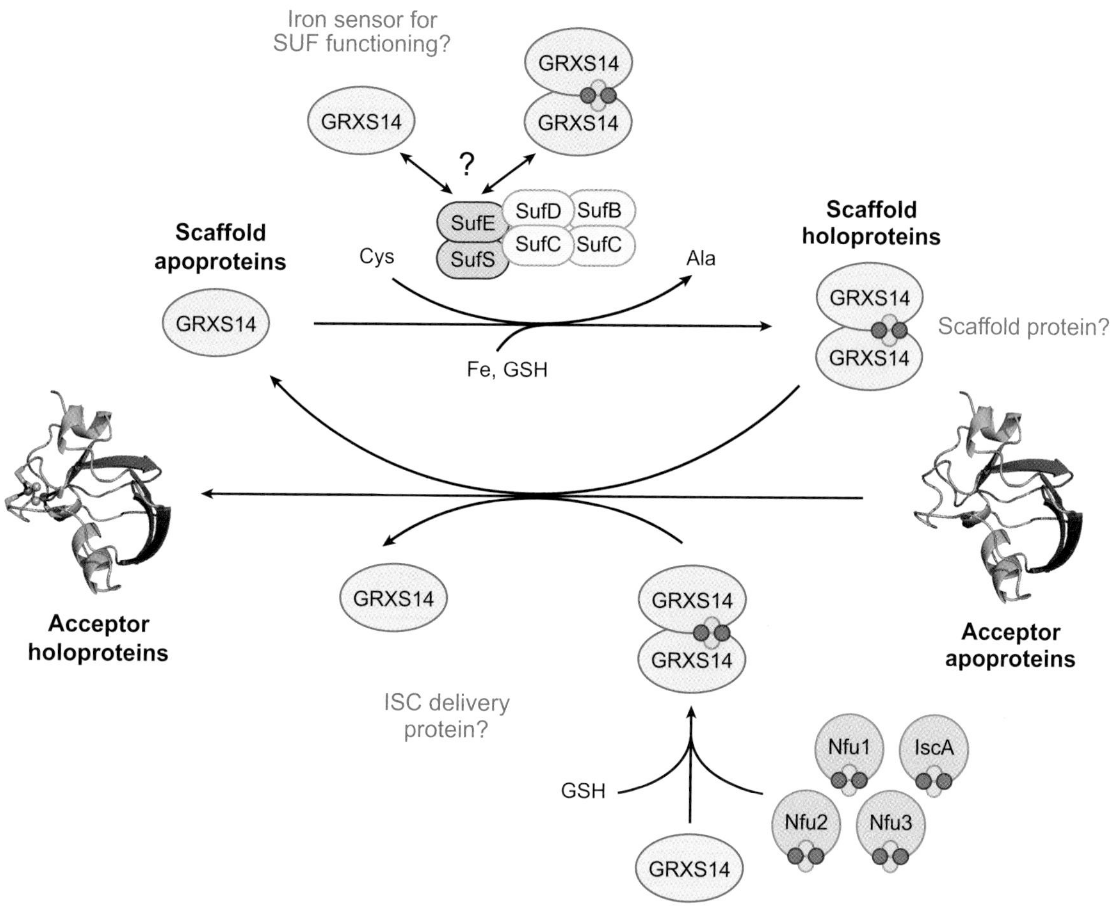

Figure 5

Proposed roles for chloroplastic CGFS-glutaredoxins (GRXs) in iron sulfur assembly. In addition to other known chloroplastic scaffold proteins (IscA, Nfu1, Nfu2, and Nfu3), GRXS14 and others could function as scaffold proteins for de novo synthesis and transfer of Fe-S clusters, as Fe-S cluster delivery proteins for mediating the transfer of Fe-S clusters from Isc or Suf scaffold proteins to acceptor proteins, or as a regulator of the Suf machinery by interacting with SufE1 via the BolA domain. In ISC, the iron atoms are colored red and the heterosulfur atoms are colored yellow. The acceptor protein represented here is a spinach ferredoxin (Accession number 1OFF). Abbreviations: ISC, iron sulfur cluster; GSH, reduced glutathione; Suf, sulfur mobilization.

through an unknown glutathione-dependent pathway that might involve some GRXs (84).

FUTURE DEVELOPMENTS

Several questions concerning the roles of GSHs and GRXs in plants remain to be answered. The importance of the cross talk between TRXs, GRXs, and glutathionylation reactions needs to be addressed in the future, especially because the number of redox-regulated or glutathionylated proteins in plants is likely to increase with the development of proteomic studies. The factors involved in glutathionylation regulation, the role of GRXs, and the functional importance of glutathionylation will also have to be addressed. The emergence of posttranslational regulation of TRXs and GRXs by glutathionylation or nitrosylation could also

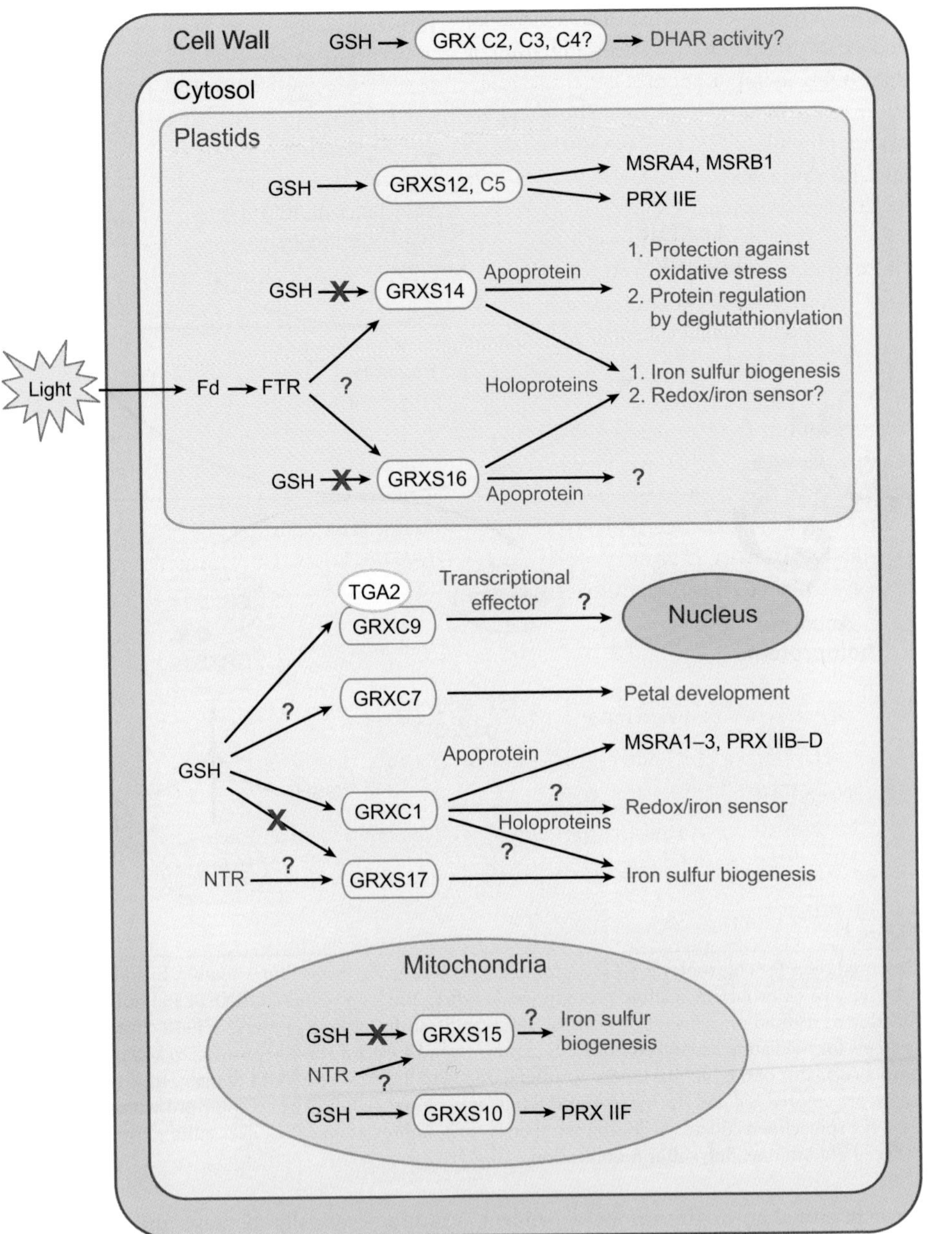

Figure 6

Putative localization and function of glutaredoxins (GRXs) in plant cells. Compartments, such as the vacuole, endoplasmic reticulum, or peroxisomes, for which the presence of GRX has not been established have been omitted. The phloem is also omitted in this scheme, although a GRXC2 from *Ricinus communis* was identified in this compartment (101). GRXC1, GRXC2, GRXC3, GRXC4, GRXC5, and GRXS12 belong to the first GRX subgroup; GRXS14, GRXS15, GRXS16, and GRXS17 belong to the second subgroup, and GRXC7, GRXC9, and GRXS10 belong to the third subgroup. Abbreviations: DHAR, dehydroascorbate reductase; MSR, methionine sulfoxide reductase; NTR, NADPH thioredoxin reductase; PRX, peroxiredoxin; GSH, reduced glutathione; FTR, ferredoxin-thioredoxin reductase; Fd, Ferredoxin; TGA2, TGA2 transcription factor.

constitute regulatory mechanisms of these reductases. In this respect, S-nitrosoglutathione (GSNO) is an important messenger molecule in animal cells and its role is still obscure in plants. The role of GSH in cell signaling is established but whether GRX also plays a role needs to be evaluated. Especially, the recent advances showing that phosphatases, kinases, and transcription factors can be redox regulated, sometimes by glutathionylation reactions, suggest important roles for GRXs in cell signaling (53, 76, 85).

Another point of interest will be to study systematically the reducing systems needed for each class of GRX. Indeed, the conventional CPYC-GRXs probably use GSH, but nothing is known in particular about the mode of reduction of the CC group, and only preliminary studies suggest that oxidized CGFS-GRXs are regenerated via TRX reductase. A possible involvement of TRXs for the reduction of the CGFS proteins is also an open question.

Overall, the functions of all the plant GRX isoforms are far from established. The present knowledge is summarized in **Figure 6**. The results obtained from organisms with fewer GRX genes, which can be easily deleted or disrupted, can serve as a working model for those organisms that have a more complex GRX organization. The high number of GRX genes present in land plants certainly suggests that they should be involved in a broad spectrum of processes. The question of the specificity or redundancy within the GRX family remains unanswered, and the study of GRX knockout lines and possibly of multiple knockouts should shed some light on this domain.

SUMMARY POINTS

1. Glutathione is a major redox buffer in the cell.
2. Glutathione and its derivatives are involved in the detoxification of xenobiotics and heavy metals.
3. Photosynthetic organisms contain a broad multigenic glutaredoxin (GRX) family.
4. GRXs and glutathione are involved in deglutathionylation/glutathionylation reactions.
5. Some GRXs bind an ISC (iron sulfur center); glutathione and iron-sulfur-containing GRXs are involved in iron sulfur assembly.

DISCLOSURE STATEMENT

The authors are not aware of any biases that might be perceived as affecting the objectivity of this review.

ACKNOWLEDGMENTS

The authors would like to thank C.S. Koh for her help in drawing structural pictures, and V. Noguera Mazon and M. Kusunoki for providing the structural coordinates of poplar GRXC1 and GRXC4.

LITERATURE CITED

1. Achebach S, Tran QH, Vlamis-Gardikas A, Müllner M, Holmgren A, Unden G. 2004. Stimulation of Fe-S cluster insertion into apoFNR by *Escherichia coli* glutaredoxins 1, 2 and 3 in vitro. *FEBS Lett.* 565:203–6

2. Alves R, Herrero E, Sorribas A. 2004. Predictive reconstruction of the mitochondrial iron-sulfur cluster assembly metabolism. II. Role of glutaredoxin Grx5. *Proteins* 57:481–92
3. Balk J, Lobreaux S. 2005. Biogenesis of iron-sulfur proteins in plants. *Trends Plant Sci.* 10:324–31
4. Ball L, Accotto GP, Bechtold U, Creissen G, Funck D, et al. 2004. Evidence for a direct link between glutathione biosynthesis and stress defense gene expression in *Arabidopsis. Plant Cell* 16:2448–62
5. Barrett WC, DeGnore JP, König S, Fales HM, Keng YF, et al. 1999. Regulation of PTP1B via glutathionylation of the active site cysteine 215. *Biochemistry* 38:6699–705
6. Bick JA, Aslund F, Chen Y, Leustek T. 1998. Glutaredoxin function for the carboxyl-terminal domain of the plant-type 5′-adenylylsulfate reductase. *Proc. Natl. Acad. Sci. USA* 95:8404–9
7. Buchanan BB, Balmer Y. 2005. Redox regulation: a broadening horizon. *Annu Rev. Plant Biol.* 56:187–220
8. Bushweller JH, Aslund F, Wuthrich K, Holmgren A. 1992. Structural and functional characterization of the mutant *Escherichia coli* glutaredoxin (C14–S) and its mixed disulfide with glutathione. *Biochemistry* 31:9288–93
9. Cabiscol E, Levine RL. 1996. The phosphatase activity of carbonic anhydrase III is reversibly regulated by glutathiolation. *Proc. Natl. Acad. Sci. USA* 93:4170–74
10. Casagrande S, Bonetto V, Fratelli M, Gianazza E, Eberini I, et al. 2002. Glutathionylation of human thioredoxin: a possible crosstalk between the glutathione and thioredoxin systems. *Proc. Natl. Acad. Sci. USA* 99:9745–49
11. Cheng NH, Liu JZ, Brock A, Nelson RS, Hirschi KD. 2006. AtGRXcp, an *Arabidopsis* chloroplastic glutaredoxin, is critical for protection against protein oxidative damage. *J. Biol. Chem.* 281:26280–88
12. Cobbett C, Goldsbrough P. 2002. Phytochelatins and metallothioneins: roles in heavy metal detoxification and homeostasis. *Annu. Rev. Plant Biol.* 53:159–82
13. Cobbett CS, May MJ, Howden R, Rolls B. 1998. The glutathione-deficient, cadmium-sensitive mutant, cad2–1, of *Arabidopsis thaliana* is deficient in gamma-glutamylcysteine synthetase. *Plant J.* 16:73–78
14. Cummins I, Cole DJ, Edwards R. 1999. A role for glutathione transferases functioning as glutathione peroxidases in resistance to multiple herbicides in black-grass. *Plant J.* 18:285–92
15. Dalle-Donne I, Giustarini D, Colombo R, Milzani A, Rossi R. 2005. S-glutathionylation in human platelets by a thiol-disulfide exchange-independent mechanism. *Free Radic. Biol. Med.* 38:1501–10
16. Després C, Chubak C, Rochon A, Clark R, Bethune T, et al. 2003. The *Arabidopsis* NPR1 disease resistance protein is a novel cofactor that confers redox regulation of DNA binding activity to the basic domain/leucine zipper transcription factor TGA1. *Plant Cell* 15:2181–91
17. Dixon DP, Davis BG, Edwards R. 2002. Functional divergence in the glutathione transferase superfamily in plants. Identification of two classes with putative functions in redox homeostasis in *Arabidopsis thaliana. J. Biol. Chem.* 277:30859–69
18. Dixon DP, Fordham-Skelton AP, Edwards R. 2005. Redox regulation of a soybean tyrosine-specific protein phosphatase. *Biochemistry* 44:7696–703
19. Dixon DP, Lapthorn A, Edwards R. 2002. Plant glutathione transferases. *Genome Biol.* 3:REVIEWS3004.1–3004.10

20. Dixon DP, Skipsey M, Grundy NM, Edwards R. 2005. Stress-induced protein S-glutathionylation in *Arabidopsis*. *Plant Physiol.* 138:2233–44

21. Ducruix C, Junot C, Fievet JB, Villiers F, Ezan E, Bourguignon J. 2006. New insights into the regulation of phytochelatin biosynthesis in *A. thaliana* cells from metabolite profiling analyses. *Biochimie* 88:1733–42
22. Feng Y, Shong N, Rouhier N, Hase T, Kusunoki M, et al. 2006. Structural insight into poplar glutaredoxin C1 with a bridging iron sulfur center near the active site. *Biochemistry* 45:7998–8008
23. Finkemeier I, Goodman M, Lamkemeyer P, Kandlbinder A, Sweetlove LJ, Dietz KJ. 2005. The mitochondrial type II peroxiredoxin F is essential for redox homeostasis and root growth of *Arabidopsis thaliana* under stress. *J. Biol. Chem.* 280:12168–80
24. Foyer CH, Noctor G. 2005. Oxidants and antioxidants signalling in plants: a re-evaluation of the concept of oxidative stress in a physiological context. *Plant Cell Environ.* 28:1056–71
25. Foyer CH, Noctor G. 2005. Redox homeostasis and antioxidant signaling: a metabolic interface between stress perception and physiological responses. *Plant Cell* 17:1866–75
26. Freeman JL, Persans MW, Nieman K, Albrecht C, Peer W, et al. 2004. Increased glutathione biosynthesis plays a role in nickel tolerance in thlaspi nickel hyperaccumulators. *Plant Cell* 16:2176–91
27. Gama F, Keech O, Eymery F, Finkemeier I, Gelhaye E, et al. 2007. The mitochondrial type II peroxiredoxin from poplar. *Physiol. Plant.* 129:196–206
28. Gelhaye E, Rouhier N, Gerard J, Jolivet Y, Gualberto J, et al. 2004. A specific form of thioredoxin h occurs in plant mitochondria and regulates the alternative oxidase. *Proc. Natl. Acad. Sci. USA* 101:14545–50
29. Gelhaye E, Rouhier N, Jacquot JP. 2003. Evidence for a subgroup of thioredoxin h that requires GSH/Grx for its reduction. *FEBS Lett.* 555:443–48
30. Ghezzi P. 2005. Regulation of protein function by glutathionylation. *Free Radic. Res.* 39:573–80
31. Gidekel M, Destefano-Beltrán L, Garcia P, Mujica L, Leal P, et al. 2003. Identification and characterization of three novel cold acclimation-responsive genes from the extremophile hair grass *Deschampsia antarctica* Desv. *Extremophiles* 7:459–69
32. Gorbitz CH. 1987. A redetermination of the crystal and molecular structure of glutathione (L-glutamyl-L-cysteinylglycine) at 120 K. *Acta Chem. Scand. Ser. B* 41:362–66
33. Grzam A, Martin MN, Hell R, Meyer AJ. 2007. γ-Glutamyl transpeptidase GGT4 initiates vacuolar degradation of glutathione S-conjugates in *Arabidopsis*. *FEBS Lett.* 581:3131–38
34. Hanson GT, Aggeler R, Oglesbee D, Cannon M, Capaldi RA, et al. 2004. Investigating mitochondrial redox potential with redox-sensitive green fluorescent protein indicators. *J. Biol. Chem.* 279:13044–53
35. Hartmann TN, Fricker MD, Rennenberg H, Meyer AJ. 2003. Cell-specific measurement of cytosolic glutathione in poplar leaves. *Plant Cell Environ.* 26:965–75
36. Henmi K, Demura T, Tsuboi S, Fukuda H, Iwabuchi M, Ogawa K. 2005. Change in the redox state of glutathione regulates differentiation of tracheary elements in *Zinnia* cells and *Arabidopsis* roots. *Plant Cell Physiol.* 46:1757–65
37. Herbette S, Lenne C, Leblanc N, Julien JL, Drevet JR, Roeckel-Drevet P. 2002. Two GPX-like proteins from *Lycopersicon esculentum* and *Helianthus annuus* are antioxidant enzymes with phospholipid hydroperoxide glutathione peroxidase and thioredoxin peroxidase activities. *Eur. J. Biochem.* 269:2414–20

20. The first extensive proteomic analysis of glutathionylated proteins in plants.

38. Herrero E, de la Torre-Ruiz MA. 2007. Monothiol glutaredoxins: a common domain for multiple functions. *Cell Mol. Life Sci.* 64:1518–30
39. Holmgren A. 2000. Antioxidant function of thioredoxin and glutaredoxin systems. *Antioxid. Redox Signal.* 2:811–20
40. Horibe T, Furuya R, Iwai A, Yosho C, Tujimoto Y, Kikuchi M. 2001. The dipeptide, gamma-glutamylcysteine, is recognized by the antiglutathione antibody single chain Fv fragment 20C9. *Biochem. Biophys. Res. Commun.* 281:1321–24
41. Hothorn M, Wachter A, Gromes R, Stuwe T, Rausch T, Scheffzek K. 2006. Structural basis for the redox control of plant glutamate cysteine ligase. *J. Biol. Chem.* 281:27557–65
42. Howe G, Merchant S. 1992. Heavy metal-activated synthesis of peptides in *Chlamydomonas reinhardtii*. *Plant Physiol.* 98:127–36
43. **Ito H, Iwabuchi M, Ogawa K. 2003. The sugar-metabolic enzymes aldolase and triose-phosphate isomerase are targets of glutathionylation in *Arabidopsis thaliana*: detection using biotinylated glutathione. *Plant Cell Physiol.* 44:655–60**
44. Jamai A, Chollet JF, Delrot S. 1994. Proton-peptide co-transport in broad bean leaf tissues. *Plant Physiol.* 106:1023–31
45. Jez JM, Cahoon RE. 2004. Kinetic mechanism of glutathione synthetase from *Arabidopsis thaliana*. *J. Biol. Chem.* 279:42726–31
46. Jez JM, Cahoon RE, Chen S. 2004. *Arabidopsis thaliana* glutamate-cysteine ligase: functional properties, kinetic mechanism, and regulation of activity. *J. Biol. Chem.* 279:33463–70
47. Jimenez A, Hernandez JA, Del Rio LA, Sevilla F. 1997. Evidence for the presence of the ascorbate-glutathione cycle in mitochondria and peroxisomes of pea leaves. *Plant Physiol.* 114:275–84
48. Johansson C, Kavanagh KL, Gileadi O, Oppermann U. 2007. Reversible sequestration of active site cysteines in a 2Fe-2S-bridged dimer provides a mechanism for glutaredoxin 2 regulation in human mitochondria. *J. Biol. Chem.* 282:3077–82
49. Jung CH, Thomas JA. 1996. S-glutathiolated hepatocyte proteins and insulin disulfides as substrates for reduction by glutaredoxin, thioredoxin, protein disulfide isomerase, and glutathione. *Arch. Biochem. Biophys.* 335:61–72
50. Jung G, Breitmaier E, Voelter W. 1972. Dissociation equilibrium of glutathione. A Fourier transform-13C-NMR spectroscopic study of pH-dependence and of charge densities. *Eur. J. Biochem.* 24:438–45
51. Kanzok SM, Fechner A, Bauer H, Ulschmid JK, Müller HM, et al. 2001. Substitution of the thioredoxin system for glutathione reductase in *Drosophila melanogaster*. *Science* 291:643–46
52. Karplus PA, Schulz GE. 1989. Substrate binding and catalysis by glutathione reductase as derived from refined enzyme: substrate crystal structures at 2 Å resolution. *J. Mol. Biol.* 210:163–80
53. Klatt P, Molina EP, Lamas S. 1999. Nitric oxide inhibits c-Jun DNA binding by specifically targeted S-glutathionylation. *J. Biol. Chem.* 274:15857–64
54. Klochkov AV, Khairutdinov BI, Tagirov MS, Klochkov VV. 2005. Determination of the spatial structure of glutathione by residual dipolar coupling analysis. *Magn. Res. Chem.* 43:948–51
55. Lee KO, Lee JR, Yoo JY, Jang HH, Moon JC, et al. 2002. GSH-dependent peroxidase activity of the rice (*Oryza sativa*) glutaredoxin, a thioltransferase. *Biochem. Biophys. Res. Commun.* 296:1152–56
56. Lemaire SD. 2004. The glutaredoxin family in oxygenic photosynthetic organisms. *Photosynth. Res.* 79:305–18

43. The first report on the identification of glutathionylated proteins in vivo in plants.

57. Lemaire SD, Michelet L, Zaffagnini M, Massot V, Issakidis-Bourguet E. 2007. Thioredoxins in chloroplasts. *Curr. Genet.* 51:343–65
58. Li H, Xu H, Graham DE, White RH. 2003. Glutathione synthetase homologs encode alpha-L-glutamate ligases for methanogenic coenzyme F420 and tetrahydrosarcinapterin biosyntheses. *Proc. Natl. Acad. Sci. USA* 100:9785–90
59. Li M, Yang Q, Zhang L, Li H, Cui Y, Wu Q. 2007. Identification of novel targets of cyanobacterial glutaredoxin. *Arch. Biochem. Biophys.* 458:220–28
60. Lill R, Muhlenhoff U. 2005. Iron-sulfur-protein biogenesis in eukaryotes. *Trends Biochem. Sci.* 30:133–41
61. Martin MN, Saladores PH, Lambert E, Hudson AO, Leustek T. 2007. Localization of members of the γ-glutamyl transpeptidase family identifies sites of glutathione and glutathione S-conjugate hydrolysis. *Plant Physiol.* 144:1715–32
62. Matamoros MA, Moran JF, Iturbe-Ormaetxe I, Rubio MC, Becana M. 1999. Glutathione and homoglutathione synthesis in legume root nodules. *Plant Physiol.* 121:879–88
63. Meyer AJ, Brach T, Marty L, Kreye S, Rouhier N, et al. 2007. Redox-sensitive GFP in *Arabidopsis thaliana* is a quantitative biosensor for the redox potential of the cellular glutathione redox buffer. *Plant J.* 52:973–86
64. Meyer AJ, Fricker MD. 2002. Control of demand-driven biosynthesis of glutathione in green *Arabidopsis* suspension culture cells. *Plant Physiol.* 130:1927–37
65. Meyer AJ, Hell R. 2005. Glutathione homeostasis and redox-regulation by sulfhydryl groups. *Photosynth. Res.* 86:435–57
66. Meyer AJ, May MJ, Fricker M. 2001. Quantitative in vivo measurement of glutathione in *Arabidopsis* cells. *Plant J.* 27:67–78
67. Michelet L, Zaffagnini M, Marchand C, Collin V, Decottignies P, et al. 2005. Glutathionylation of chloroplast thioredoxin f is a redox signaling mechanism in plants. *Proc. Natl. Acad. Sci. USA* 102:16478–83
68. Michelet L, Zaffagnini M, Massot V, Keryer E, Vanacker H, et al. 2006. Thioredoxins, glutaredoxins, and glutathionylation: new crosstalks to explore. *Photosynth. Res.* 89:225–45
69. Mohr S, Hallak H, de Boitte A, Lapetina EG, Brune B. 1999. Nitric oxide-induced S-glutathionylation and inactivation of glyceraldehyde-3-phosphate dehydrogenase. *J. Biol. Chem.* 274:9427–30
70. Molina MM, Belli G, de la Torre MA, Rodríguez-Manzaneque MT, Herrero E. 2006. Nuclear monothiol glutaredoxins of *Saccharomyces cerevisiae* can function as mitochondrial glutaredoxins. *J. Biol. Chem.* 279:51923–30
71. Mou Z, Fan W, Dong X. 2003. Inducers of plant systemic acquired resistance regulate NPR1 function through redox changes. *Cell* 113:935–44
72. Muhlenhoff U, Gerber J, Richhardt N, Lill R. 2003. Components involved in assembly and dislocation of iron-sulfur clusters on the scaffold protein Isu1p. *EMBO J.* 22:4815–25
73. Mullineaux PM, Rausch T. 2005. Glutathione, photosynthesis and the redox regulation of stress-responsive gene expression. *Photosynth. Res.* 86:459–74
74. Nakano Y, Okawa S, Yamauchi T, Koizumi Y, Sekiya J. 2006. Purification and properties of soluble and bound γ-glutamyltransferases from radish cotyledon. *Biosci. Biotechnol. Biochem.* 70:369–76
75. Navrot N, Collin V, Gualberto J, Gelhaye E, Hirasawa M, et al. 2006. Plant glutathione peroxidases are functional peroxiredoxins distributed in several subcellular compartments and regulated during biotic and abiotic stresses. *Plant Physiol.* 142:1364–79
76. Ndamukong I, Abdallat AA, Thurow C, Fode B, Zander M, et al. 2007. SA-inducible *Arabidopsis* glutaredoxin interacts with TGA factors and suppresses JA-responsive PDF1.2 transcription. *Plant J.* 50:128–39

65. A complete review on glutathione.

67. Reports the glutathionylation of TRX f and suggests that glutathionylation could constitute a mechanism of regulation of photosynthetic metabolism.

77. Noctor G. 2006. Metabolic signalling in defence and stress: the central roles of soluble redox couples. *Plant Cell Environ.* 29:409–25

78. Noctor G, Foyer CH. 1998. ASCORBATE AND GLUTATHIONE: keeping active oxygen under control. *Annu. Rev. Plant Physiol. Plant Mol. Biol.* 49:249–79

79. Noguera V, Walker O, Rouhier N, Jacquot JP, Krimm I, Lancelin JM. 2005. NMR reveals a novel glutaredoxin-glutaredoxin interaction interface. *J. Mol. Biol.* 353:629–41

80. Noguera-Mazon V, Lemoine J, Walker O, Rouhier N, Salvador A, et al. 2006. Glutathionylation induces the dissociation of 1-Cys D-peroxiredoxin noncovalent homodimer. *J. Biol. Chem.* 281:31736–42

81. Nulton-Persson AC, Starke DW, Mieyal JJ, Szweda LI. 2003. Reversible inactivation of α-ketoglutarate dehydrogenase in response to alterations in the mitochondrial glutathione status. *Biochemistry* 42:4235–42

82. Okumura R, Koizumi Y, Sekiya J. 2003. Synthesis of hydroxymethylglutathione from glutathione and L-serine catalyzed by carboxypeptidase Y. *Biosci. Biotechnol. Biochem.* 67:434–37

83. Peltoniemi MJ, Karala AR, Jurvansuu JK, Kinnula VL, Ruddock LW. 2006. Insights into deglutathionylation reactions. Different intermediates in the glutaredoxin and protein disulfide isomerase catalyzed reactions are defined by the γ-linkage present in glutathione. *J. Biol. Chem.* 281:33107–14

84. Reichheld JP, Khafif M, Riondet C, Droux M, Bonnard G, Meyer Y. 2007. Inactivation of thioredoxin reductases reveals a complex interplay between thioredoxin and glutathione pathways in *Arabidopsis* development. *Plant Cell* 19:1851–65

85. Reynaert NL, Van Der Vliet A, Guala AS, McGovern T, Hristova M, et al. 2006. Dynamic redox control of NF-κB through glutaredoxin-regulated S-glutathionylation of inhibitory κB kinase β. *Proc. Natl. Acad. Sci. USA* 103:13086–91

86. Rodríguez-Manzaneque MT, Tamarit J, Belli G, Ros J, Herrero E. 2002. Grx5 is a mitochondrial glutaredoxin required for the activity of iron/sulfur enzymes. *Mol. Biol. Cell* 13:1109–21

87. Rouhier N, Couturier J, Jacquot JP. 2006. Genome wide analysis of plant glutaredoxin systems. *J. Exp. Bot.* 57:1685–96

88. Rouhier N, Gelhaye E, Jacquot JP. 2002. Exploring the active site of plant glutaredoxin by site-directed mutagenesis. *FEBS Lett.* 511:145–49

89. Rouhier N, Gelhaye E, Jacquot JP. 2002. Glutaredoxin-dependent peroxiredoxin from poplar: protein-protein interaction and catalytic mechanism. *J. Biol. Chem.* 277:13609–14

90. Rouhier N, Gelhaye E, Jacquot JP. 2004. Glutaredoxin: the still mysterious alternative reducing system of plants. *Mol. Cell. Life Sci.* 61:1266–77

91. Rouhier N, Gelhaye E, Sautiere PE, Brun A, Laurent P, et al. 2001. Isolation and characterization of a new peroxiredoxin from poplar sieve tubes that uses either glutaredoxin or thioredoxin as a proton donor. *Plant Physiol.* 127:1299–309

92. Rouhier N, Jacquot JP. 2005. The plant multigenic family of thiol peroxidases. *Free Radic. Biol. Med.* 38:1413–21

93. Rouhier N, Unno H, Bandyopadhay S, Masip L, Kim SK, et al. 2007. Functional, structural and spectroscopic characterization of a glutathione-ligated [2Fe-2S] cluster in poplar glutaredoxin C1. *Proc. Natl. Acad. Sci. USA* 104:7379–84

94. Rouhier N, Villarejo A, Srivastava M, Gelhaye E, Keech O, et al. 2005. Identification of plant glutaredoxin targets. *Antioxid. Redox Signal.* 7:919–29

95. Rouhier N, Vlamis-Gardikas A, Lillig CH, Berndt C, Schwenn JD, et al. 2003. Characterization of the redox properties of poplar glutaredoxin. *Antioxid. Redox Signal.* 5:15–22

78. A review on the role of glutathione together with ascorbate in plant metabolism and stress tolerance.

91. The first target of GRX characterized in plants.

93. This study reports the presence of an iron-sulfur cluster in a plant glutaredoxin.

96. Shackelford RE, Heinloth AN, Heard SC, Paules RS. 2005. Cellular and molecular targets of protein S-glutathiolation. *Antioxid. Redox Signal.* 7:940–50
97. Stadtman ER, Moskovitz J, Berlett BS, Levine RL. 2002. Cyclic oxidation and reduction of protein methionine residues is an important antioxidant mechanism. *Mol. Cell. Biochem.* 234/235:3–9
98. Starke DW, Chock PB, Mieyal JJ. 2003. Reversible inactivation of α-ketoglutarate dehydrogenase in response to alterations in the mitochondrial glutathione status. *Biochemistry* 42:4235–42
99. Storozhenko S, Belles-Boix E, Babiychuk E, Herouart D, Davey MW, et al. 2002. γ-glutamyl transpeptidase in transgenic tobacco plants. Cellular localization, processing, and biochemical properties. *Plant Physiol.* 128:1109–19
100. Sugiyama A, Sekiya J. 2005. Homoglutathione confers tolerance to acifluorfen in transgenic tobacco plants expressing soybean homoglutathione synthetase. *Plant Cell Physiol.* 46:1428–32
101. Szederkenyi J, Komor E, Schobert C. 1997. Cloning of the cDNA for glutaredoxin, an abundant sieve-tube exudate protein from *Ricinus communis* L. and characterisation of the glutathione-dependent thiol-reduction system in sieve tubes. *Planta* 202:349–56
102. Tamarit J, Belli G, Cabiscol E, Herrero E, Ros J. 2003. Biochemical characterization of yeast mitochondrial Grx5 monothiol glutaredoxin. *J. Biol. Chem.* 278:25745–51
103. Tong WH, Rouault TA. 2007. Metabolic regulation of citrate and iron by aconitases: role of iron-sulfur cluster biogenesis. *Biometals* 20:549–64
104. van Montfort RL, Congreve M, Tisi D, Carr R, Jhoti H. 2003. Oxidation state of the active-site cysteine in protein tyrosine phosphatase 1B. *Nature* 423:773–77
105. Vernoux T, Wilson RC, Seeley KA, Reichheld JP, Muroy S, et al. 2000. The ROOT MERISTEMLESS1/CADMIUM SENSITIVE2 gene defines a glutathione-dependent pathway involved in initiation and maintenance of cell division during postembryonic root development. *Plant Cell* 12:97–110
106. Vieira Dos Santos C, Laugier E, Tarrago L, Massot V, Issakidis-Bourguet E, et al. 2007. Specificity of thioredoxins and glutaredoxins as electron donors to two distinct classes of Arabidopsis plastidial methionine sulfoxide reductases B. *FEBS Lett.* 581:4371–6
107. Wachter A, Wolf S, Steininger H, Bogs J, Rausch T. 2005. Differential targeting of GSH1 and GSH2 is achieved by multiple transcription initiation: implications for the compartmentation of glutathione biosynthesis in the Brassicaceae. *Plant J.* 41:15–30
108. Wang CL, Oliver DJ. 1997. Identification of a putative flexible loop in *Arabidopsis* glutathione synthetase. *Biochem. J.* 322:241–44
109. Wingert RA, Galloway JL, Barut B, Foott H, Fraenkel P, et al. Tübingen 2000 Screen Consort. 2005. Deficiency of glutaredoxin 5 reveals Fe-S clusters are required for vertebrate haem synthesis. *Nature* 436:1035–39
110. Xiang C, Werner BL, Christensen EM, Oliver DJ. 2001. The biological functions of glutathione revisited in *Arabidopsis* transgenic plants with altered glutathione levels. *Plant Physiol.* 126:564–74
111. Xing S, Rosso MG, Zachgo S. 2005. ROXY1, a member of the plant glutaredoxin family, is required for petal development in *Arabidopsis thaliana*. *Development* 132:1555–65
112. Zaffagnini M, Michelet L, Marchand C, Sparla F, Decottignies P, et al. 2007. The thioredoxin-independent isoform of chloroplastic glyceraldehyde-3-phosphate dehydrogenase is selectively regulated by glutathionylation. *FEBS J.* 274:212–26

113. Zechmann B, Zellnig G, Müller M. 2006. Immunocytochemical localization of glutathione precursors in plant cells. *J. Electron Microsc.* 55:173–81
114. Zhang MY, Bourbouloux A, Cagnac O, Srikanth CV, Rentsch D, et al. 2004. A novel family of transporters mediating the transport of glutathione derivatives in plants. *Plant Physiol.* 134:482–91

Algal Sensory Photoreceptors

Peter Hegemann

Institute of Biology, Experimental Biophysics, Humboldt Universität zu Berlin, 10115 Berlin, Germany; email: Hegemann@rz.hu-berlin.de

Annu. Rev. Plant Biol. 2008. 59:167–89

The *Annual Review of Plant Biology* is online at plant.annualreviews.org

This article's doi: 10.1146/annurev.arplant.59.032607.092847

1543-5008/08/0602-0167$20.00

Key Words

aureochrome, blue-light photoreceptors, BLUF-proteins, channelrhodopsin, enzymerhodopsin, neochrome, phototropin, photoactivated cyclase

Abstract

Only five major types of sensory photoreceptors (BLUF-proteins, cryptochromes, phototropins, phytochromes, and rhodopsins) are used in nature to regulate developmental processes, photosynthesis, photoorientation, and control of the circadian clock. Sensory photoreceptors of algae and protists are exceptionally rich in structure and function; light-gated ion channels and photoactivated adenylate cyclases are unique examples. During the past ten years major progress has been made with respect to understanding the function, photochemistry, and structure of key sensory players of the algal kingdom.

Contents

INTRODUCTION

The photobiology of algae is extremely rich, unusual, and a gold mine for new proteins that may be far from our traditional thinking, which is based on knowledge from prokaryotes, higher plants, or animals. Animals are motile organisms that use their photoreceptors preferentially for orientation when they move fast, search for food, or need to avoid obstacles, enemies, etc. Plants, in contrast, are usually immobile and use their photoreceptors to adjust photosynthesis and developmental steps to optimize the photosynthetic apparatus according to the available light. Algae are photosynthetic and either mobile per se or at least during some developmental stages as gametes or zoospores. Algae need photoreceptors for their general development, as is the case in plants, for the switch between different stages of the life cycle, for the release of gametes, for controlling the photosynthetic apparatus, and for orientation during their motile life stages. Microalgae and related flagellates are especially convenient to work with owing to their fast life cycle, the ease of quantifying their behavioral responses, and in some selected cases the well-established genetics. In contrast to prokaryotes, unicellular algae are large enough to harbor optical devices for the detection of light direction, which opens attractive evolutionary aspects for the study of eye development. Thus, photoreceptors of at least some microalgae are much better suited for study than those of macroalgae.

This review does not give an overview of the general photobiology of algae; I leave this task to more qualified botanists or plant physiologists. I instead focus on the reaction mechanisms of only a few selected algal photoreceptors. Our understanding of these photoreceptors has grown tremendously during the past ten years, and their study might have a broad impact on the understanding of algal physiology and/or promote applications in other nonrelated scientific areas.

Phototaxis and Photoactivated Electrical Processes in *Volvocaceae*

Phototaxis is the ability of motile microbes to track a light source—normally the sun—and move toward or away from it depending on the amount of light that is actually required for photosynthesis. True phototaxis requires an optical system that allows detection of the direction of the light source. The direction of the sun must be determined when light is very weak. But, it is equally important to record the light direction in conditions of intense diffuse background light. Classical tools for the study of phototaxis are microalgae with two or four flagella and a bright orange eyespot. Most studies were carried out on Volvocales such as *Chlamydomonas*, *Volvox*, and *Dunaliella*, but *Dinophyceae* such as *Gonyaulax* and *Peridinium* were also investigated quite carefully (28). Mast (59) originally recognized the eyespot in 1916 as the organelle cells use to orient their

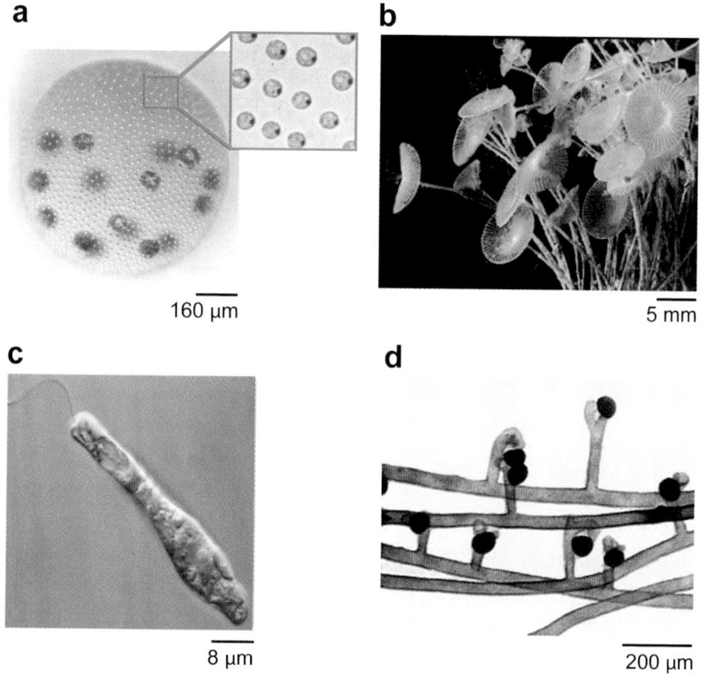

Figure 1

Photographs of (*a*) the colonial alga *Volvox carteri* (courtesy of Armin Hallmann); (*b*) the marine alga *Acetabularia acetabulum* (**http://hoopermuseum.earthsci.carleton.ca/Bermuda/maralga/BERM7.HTML**); (*c*) the unicellular flagellate *Euglena gracilis* (**http://www.fortunecity.de/lindenpark/hundertwasser/517/Euglena.html**); and (*d*) the filamentous alga *Vaucheria terrestris* (*Xanthophyceae*, *Chrysophyta*) (**http://www.biol.tsukuba.ac.jp/~inouye/ino/st/x/vauch.jpg**).

swimming with respect to light incidence. Macroalgae release motile spores or gametes that are quite similar to unicellular microalgae in behavior. Phototaxis of gametes from *Ulva mutabilis* or *Acetabularia mediteranea* (**Figure 1*b***) was studied as early as a century ago (see Reference 28 and included literature).

Algae developed eyes to monitor the light direction; apparent pigmented eyespots serve as the optical system. Algal eyes may operate as simple shading devices or screens (Chrysophyceae, Xanthophyceae, Phaeophyceae, Eustigmatophyceae, Dinophyceae), quarter wave layers or quarter wave stack antennas (Chlorophyceae), lens antennas (Dinophyceae), or dielectric slab wave guides (Chryptophyceae). Foster & Smyth (19) elucidated and summarized the relevant optical principles in their fundamental review titled "Light antennas in phototactic algae."

Because algae lack a brain, the photoreceptor system must be directly connected to an output system that modulates the swimming direction according to the deviation from the desired tracking direction. Most unicellular Chlorophyceae accomplish this by placing their eye in a position that advances the beating plane of the flagella by $\approx 30^\circ$ during rotational swimming. If they swim perpendicular to the light source, they receive a modulated signal owing to the contrast of the eyespot, and correct their swimming until the modulation amplitude is small (19). The cells modulate the flagellar beating plane, the beat frequency, and the three dimensional beating pattern in an anticyclic manner depending on changes of the light intensity (74, 75) and the

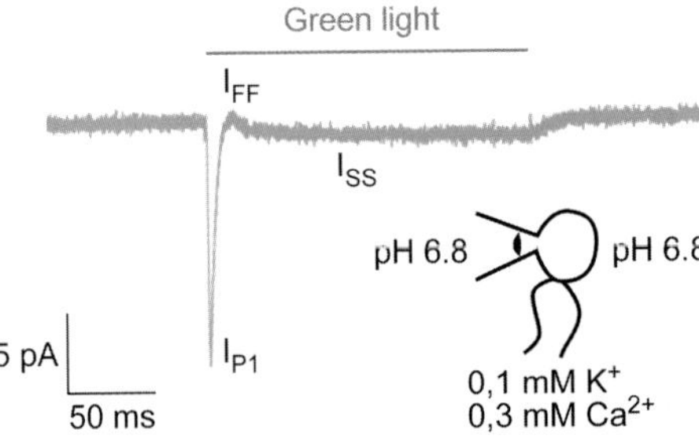

Figure 2

Photocurrents recorded from the eye of a *Chlamydomonas* cell at pH = 6.8. The green bar indicates the duration of the light pulse. I_{P1}, fast photoreceptor current; I_{SS}, stationary current; I_{FF}, fast flagellar current.

direction the cell swims with respect to the light source. The flagellar beating pattern is regulated by Ca^{2+} but the exact mechanism remains unclear.

Light excitation of a *Chlorophycean* alga results in a cascade of electrical events that may be recorded from individual cells or from a cell population. Photocurrents are similar in all chlorophyceae analyzed so far, namely *Haematococcus pluvialis* (58), *Chlamydomonas reinhardtii* (33), *Volvox carteri* (5), *Polytomella* and *Spermatozopsis similis* (25), and even the freshwater cryptophyte, *Cryptomonas sp.* (85). The initial event after light excitiation is always a cation influx across the eyespot overlaying part of the plasma membrane (photoreceptor current) (**Figures 2** and **3**). A flash results in a single transient peak I_P, whereas the signal seen upon step-up stimulation I_P is followed by a small stationary current I_{SS} [reviewed by Sineshchekov & Govorunova (82)]. The most amazing and most discussed property of the photoreceptor current is that it starts without any detectable delay ($\tau <$ 50 μs). The photocurrent peaks after 1–2 ms and decays within approximately $\tau \leq 20$ ms, depending on the flash energy (12, 40, 85, 87).

Direct coupling model (DCM): implies that the photoreceptor current of a chlophyceaen eye is carried by cations conducted by channelrhodopsins

Remote coupling model (RCM): implies that the charge movement within channelrhodopsin is only the trigger for activation of a secondary ion channel

In a *Chlamydomonas* cell, the amplitude of the photoreceptor current I_P may reach 40 pA, which is 50% of the total current, if it is recorded directly from the eye. This value corresponds to 10^6 elementary charges entering the eyespot area. Taking a membrane capacity of 1 μF/cm^2 into account, the cell is transiently depolarized by approximately 80 mV (34). If the number of rhodopsin molecules per eye is in the range of 10^4 to 10^5, as determined from freeze fracture images of the eye (63), by retinal extraction (1), and recent calculations of the number of rhodopsin molecules per cell (26), each photoreceptor channel would carry only 10 to 100 charges after a saturating flash. Thus, it is more than sufficient for the cell if one photon activates a single ion channel. There is simply no need for any chemical signal amplification, as in animal vision, as we pointed out many years ago (34).

Several aspects of the recorded photocurrents are still a matter of debate, resulting mainly from different recording techniques used in the different laboratories. One such aspect is the rise of the photoreceptor current, which is a critical issue for understanding the mechanism of ion channel activation. In single cell experiments at saturating light flashes (>10^{21} photon m^{-2}s^{-1} green light), the photoreceptor current I_P rises monoexponentially with a time constant τ of 0.2 ms and reaches the peak after 1.5 ms (11). There is no indication of a second component (12, 40) (**Figure 3**). This extremely fast rise led to the direct coupling model (DCM), which proposes that the rhodopsin and ion channel are directly coupled, forming a single protein complex (34). Photocurrents of chlorophycean algae were also retrieved from free-swimming cells in populations (83, 84). The advantage of this technique is that currents can be recorded from wild-type cells, whereas single cell measurements are restricted to cell wall–deficient mutants (82). In population experiments the photoreceptor current rises biphasically, which the Sineshchekov group (86, 88) interpreted as follows: The initial slow rise is a charge movement within the photoreceptor molecules, whereas the second component is the current that flows through a secondary channel (remote coupling model, RCM). However, the population assay is a

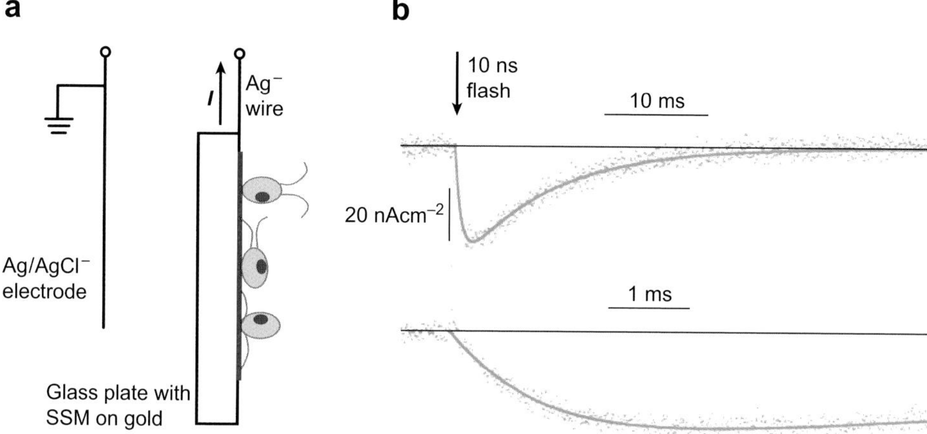

Figure 3

(*a*) Schematic representation of *Chlamydomonas* cells adsorbed to a solid supported membrane (SSM), prepared according to Reference 80 (1.5% phosphatidylcholine, 0.1% phosphatidylserine).
(*b*) Flash-induced photocurrents recorded at higher time resolution ($\lambda = 530$ nm). Only one fifth of the recorded data points are shown. Exponential function is shown as a solid line, taken from Reference 44.

differential assay; it records differences between cells oriented differently with respect to the light source or between cells of different sensitivity. The resulting current is less than 0.01% of the total current (1 nA from $>10^7$ cells) (83). This extremely small fraction makes an interpretation of the signals extremely difficult.

Another so far underestimated approach for recording photoreceptor currents with excellent time resolution from *Chlamydomonas* cells is the use of black lipid membranes (BLM) or solid supported membranes (SSM) (**Figure 3*a***). An SSM consists of a lipid monolayer on a gold-sputtered glass substrate, coated with a long-chained mercaptan [$CH_3(CH_2)_nSH$, n = 15, 17] (80). *Chlamydomonas* cells were adsorbed to the SSM and photocurrents recorded in a capacitive mode from a few hundred cells with high time resolution. The rise of the photocurrent is clearly monoexponential (44) (**Figure 3*b***), consistent with the DC-model.

The kinetics of the photocurrent does not necessarily reflect the kinetics of the photoreceptor, nor does it parallel the conductance change of the plasma membrane, especially not at high light intensities. The ion influx transiently depolarizes the cell and causes a rapid reduction of the influx. Thus, the current peaks earlier and decays faster at high flash energies. The key properties of the current are as follows: (*a*) high light saturation, (*b*) extremely fast rise, and (*c*) voltage-dependent decay; these properties were explained by the presence of a directly light-activated rhodopsin–ion channel complex (40). The DCM was the basis for the identification of light-gated channels (see below).

The identity of the ions that carry the algal photoreceptor current is also a matter of debate since the discovery of photocurrents in *Haematococcus* (58). In *Chlamydomonas* at neutral pH the photoreceptor current is mostly carried by Ca^{2+}, but H^+ and K^+ also contribute when the driving force is high enough, i.e., at low pH or high extracellular K^+ (12, 40, 70). Meanwhile, it is clear that H^+ is by far the best-conducted ion but owing to low H^+ abundance, Ca^{2+} contributes the most to the current under nearly all physiological conditions.

Upon step-up stimulation, photoreceptor currents show a transient phase that decays to

SSM: solid supported membranes

Channelrhodopsin (ChR): rhodopsin with intrinsic cation conductance that is regulated/gated by retinal isomerization (after light absorption)

a stationary level, I_{SS}, of a few pA, which is only a percent of the transient current. This adaptation makes sense for an alga that may be permanently exposed to high light intensities during the day. Despite our knowledge from in vitro studies of photoreceptor inactivation in stationary light (see below), the more extreme adaptation of the photoreceptor current in vivo remains quite unclear.

After a light flash a secondary K^+ efflux repolarizes the cell toward the K^+ equilibrium potential; this secondary K^+ efflux is in equilibrium with the local Ca^{2+}/H^+ influx in continuous light. Steady state currents deserve more attention because modulated stationary currents constitute the basis for phototaxis at high light levels. Owing to the extremely small amplitude steady-state currents have not yet been studied in detail.

Flagellar currents. When the integral of the photoreceptor current exceeds a critical level in unicellular algae, flagellar currents are triggered. Because unicellular flagellates are nearly isopotential, the flagellar channels sense the primary depolarization originating from the eye. Thus, flagellar current activation does not require signal amplification or a transmitter. In *C. reinhardtii* and *H. pluvialis* researchers observed a fast action potential–like flagellar current, I_{FF}. I_{FF} is the trigger for switching from forward to backward swimming (phobic response) (78), as shown by simultaneous detection of photocurrents and flagellar beating (41). At low intensity flashes or dim continuous light, when no I_{FF} currents appear, flagella undergo only weak beating changes without changing the beating mode. The signaling that occurs between the eyespot and the flagella under these low-light conditions remains unclear. Because depolarization is in the range of only 1 mV at 1% rhodopsin bleaching, modulation of the flagellar beat frequency and the beating plane might be supported by intracellular signaling from the eye to the flagellar base (88).

Freshwater algae have developed special mechanisms for surviving in conditions of low extracellular ionic strength. At low extracellular Cl^-, a Cl^--efflux I_{Cl} can be observed between I_P and I_F. Because photocurrents are conventionally recorded at a few mM Cl^-, which inhibits the Cl^- efflux, this current is hidden in most experiments (11, 32).

CHANNELRHODOPSIN

Physiology

The clear demonstration that the photoreceptor for phototaxis is rhodopsin came originally from action spectroscopy on white chlorophyll- and carotenoid-deficient strains. After complementation of these blind cells with retinal or analogous compounds, phototaxis recovered within one minute and the action spectrum shifted depending on the retinoid used (18). After researchers excluded the two animal rhodopsin–related proteins chlamyrhodopsin-1 and chlamyrhodopsin-2, which occur in the algal eyespot as dominant proteins, as phototaxis photoreceptors (20), three research groups independently identified two microbial rhodopsin–related sequences in the *Chlamydomonas* cDNA database. The encoded proteins were named channelrhodopsin 1 and 2 (ChR1 and ChR2), *Chlamydomonas* sensory rhodopsin A and B (CSRA and CSRB), or archaeal-related sensory rhodopsin 1 and 2 (ASR1 and ASR2); the genes in the *Chlamydomonas* database are known simply as *Chlamyopsin 3* and *4* (*COP3* and *COP4*). This confusion is a consequence of the closed deposition of gene names into the genome database. Sineshchekov and colleagues (26, 86) immediately employed an antisense approach. Cells with reduced ChR1 or ChR2 content showed small photoreceptor currents and were less light sensitive than wild-type. The authors recorded action spectra with two maxima; in cells with reduced ChR1 content the photocurrent action spectra reshaped in favor of the 470 nm side peak. Although the action spectrum bands are quite narrow compared with rhodopsin absorption spectra, the initial conclusion that ChR1 absorption peaks at approximately 500 nm whereas the ChR2 absorption peaks at 470 nm is correct and has been confirmed by in vitro studies. The second important finding that resulted from these early experiments on ChRs was that phobic responses are impaired in cells with reduced ChR content, independent of the species or the ChR isoform used (26, 86). The extent to which phototaxis is supported by ChR1 and ChR2 remains unclear, and more behavioral studies that employ strains completely lacking one of the ChRs are urgently needed. But as long as nuclear gene targeting is not routinely possible in *Chlamydomonas*, such mutants might remain an unrealistic dream. In any case, the finding that two similar photoreceptor proteins are involved in behavioral responses explains the broad-banded high-intensity *Chlorophycaean* action spectra of earlier times (28).

ChRs are light-gated ion channels that belong to the class of microbial-type rhodopsins because they occur in archaea, eubacteria, and fungi; bacteriorhodopsin (BR) is the prototype of this class. Amino acids that form the H^+-conducting network in BR are conserved, but are not connected to the intracellular or extracellular bulk phases. Thus, the conserved H^+-network was considered to be part of the switch between the closed and open states of the channel, but was not considered as the conducting pore (51, 90). ChRs exhibit some striking features that distinguish them from other microbial rhodopsins (ion pumps and sensors). ChRs contain six glutamates in helix two as well as many cysteines and serines distributed all over the hypothetical transmembrane regions. This increase in polar residues is partially compensated for by an excess of aromatic amino acids. The increase in polarity leads to the expectation of higher water content in the transmembrane region, which is necessary for a functional channel. In the 3D models that were calculated on the basis of the bacteriorhodopsin X-ray structure, the polar groups of helix two point to the outside of the ring formed by the seven transmembrane (7TM) helices, toward the lipid face (37). A ChR trimer may be the functional unit and the conducting pore may be formed at the contact site between three monomers. However, a trimer as a functional unit would suggest cooperativity in ChR activation, which has not been found (36, 72). Thus, on the basis of the experimental results, the channel is most likely a monomer and the 3D models are probably incorrect with respect to helix two.

Transport Activity

Two channelrhodopsins from *Chlamydomonas* and one from *Volvox carteri* (GenBank Accession No. DQ094781) were functionally studied in host cell systems such as *Xenopus* oocytes, HEK cells, and PC12 cells (36, 48, 66, 67). Flash stimulation generates a photocurrent that rises with a time constant of roughly 200 μs, peaks after 1.5–2 ms, and decays with $\tau \approx 15$ ms under standard conditions (**Figure 4*a***). The photocurrent kinetics resemble photocurrents from intact algae, although the latter decay faster owing to the unclamped potential. Stimulation of ChR with light pulses in host cells under voltage clamp generates photocurrents that relax toward a stationary level, as seen in **Figure 4*b***. Compared with ChR1, ChR2 inactivates more strongly in constant light and especially at high extracellular pH (pHo) and low membrane voltage. All three known ChRs conduct primarily protons and, to a lower extent, cations, with variable efficiency. In the first publication the cation conductance of ChR1 was overlooked (66). The calculated unitary conductance (for example, defined for 1 mM substrate and –100 mV) is more than 100-fold larger for H^+ compared with Na^+ or K^+. In freshwater algae, Ca^{2+} is in most cases more available than any other cation, and because ChR binds Ca^{2+} very tightly (k_M = 100 μM), Ca^{2+} needs specific consideration. Larger photocurrents recorded from ChR2-expressing cells compared with those from ChR1-expressing counterparts (68) are due to higher expression levels and are not caused

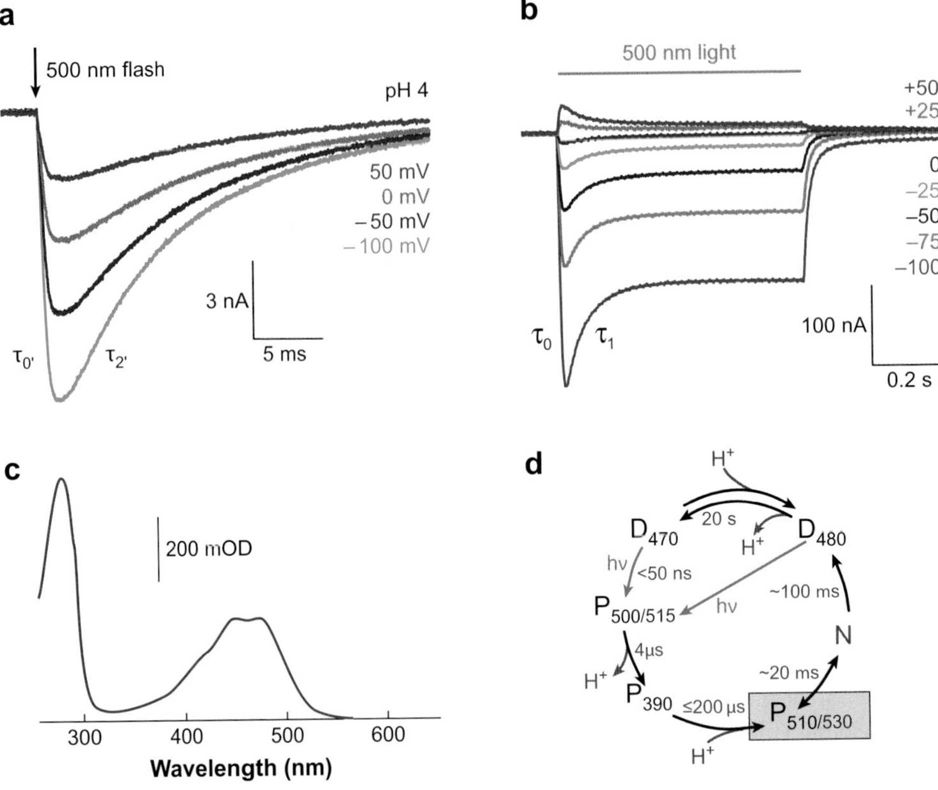

Figure 4

(*a*) Flash-induced currents recorded from *Volvox carteri* channelrhodopsin (VChR1/2)-expressing *Xenopus* oocytes (10 ns). (*b*) Photocurrents in response to 600 ms light pulses at variable membrane voltage. (*c*) Absorption spectrum of ChR2 (purified from COS cells) at pH 6. (*d*) Simplified reaction scheme of VChR from spectroscopic data. P_{510} is the conducting state that absorbs maximally at 530 nm under acidic conditions (adapted from Reference 16).

by a higher unitary conductance (S.Tsunoda, unpublished data).

Photochromism and Photoactivation

Although ChR2 was functionally expressed in a variety of mammalian cell culture systems and used for the generation of action potentials with light (see below), ChR only very recently could be expressed and purified in sufficient amounts to allow a preliminary spectroscopic analysis. VChR was expressed in COS1 cells (green monkey kidney cells) and functionally purified, which made it possible to record absorption spectra of the dark states. The VChR spectrum is vibrationally fine-structured with a maximum at 470 nm (D_{470}) (**Figure 4*c***). D_{470} is in equilibrium with a D_{480} species in a pH-dependent manner. The ratio P_{480}/P_{470} increases at low pH and after preillumination (light-adaptation). Excitation of D_{470} with laser flashes causes immediate absorbance changes ($\tau \leq 100$ ns) and the appearance of a red-shifted photoproduct. This early photoproduct, P_{500}, deprotonates with $\tau = 4$ µs owing to the formation of P_{390}, which reacts further to form P_{510} with $\tau = 200$ µs. P_{510} is considered to be the main conducting state, G1. If this is true, the channel should be gated within 200 µs after light absorption (16). P_{480} undergoes a photocycle with P_{530} as the dominant intermediate but without visible deprotonated species. The photocycle model, as seen in **Figure 4*d***, unifies photocurrents measured under different light, pH, and voltage conditions with spectroscopic data.

Despite the enormous progress made toward understanding ChR1 and ChR2 since the appearance of the two sequences in the expressed sequence tags (EST) database, we cannot make a clear discrimination between the DCM and the RCM from the experiments carried out so far. J.L. Spudich and colleagues (26, 50, 86) argued that ChR might not work as a channel in vivo but instead may activate a transducer or a remote channel, as sensory rhodopsins do in archaea and eubacteria. This hypothesis cannot be ruled out and would not even be possible to test via the use of ChR knockout mutants. Only the extreme similarity of flash-induced ChR photocurrents in oocytes or HEK cells to the photocurrents measured from single *Chlamydomonas* or *Volvox* cells makes it quite unlikely that ChR does not carry the photocurrents in the living alga. That other signaling systems may contribute to the phototactic response at low light is certainly not in doubt.

Application to Neuroscience

Originally, three groups tested the potential of ChR to control nerve cell firing (2, 4, 48, 57). They all used ChR2 because no cation conductance has yet been reported for ChR1 and the photocurrents in ChR2-expressing oocytes were larger than their ChR1-expressing counterparts (68). All three groups demonstrated that in cultured hippocampal neurons, as well as in hippocampal slices, light pulses of only a few ms in duration are sufficient to trigger action potentials. Moreover, neurons can follow light protocols with action potential firing up to 30 Hz. These observations nicely correlate with the decay of the photocurrent ($\tau = 20$ ms). "It is a very simple system, because all you have to do is express this one protein, and now you can control the activity of neurons with light," said the neurophysiologist Edward Callaway (64). Retinal is made in most mammalian cells on demand and there is no need to add retinal to the culture. Meanwhile, researchers have expressed ChR2 in *C. elegans* (65), chicken embryos (57), and mouse neurons (95), and action potentials could be specifically generated in neurons from all species by the application of light, either directly or via thin optical fibers. When Bi and coworkers (2) delivered ChR2 to the retina of a blind mouse using lentivirus as a vector, they found that light could elicit electrical activity similar to that of a seeing animal (prosthetic vision).

By combining ChR2 with halorhodopsin (HR), an eubacterial light-driven Cl^- pump that absorbs light red-shifted 100 nm compared with ChR2 and hyperpolarizes the cells in the light, the cellular membrane voltage could be controlled even more precisely and driven in both directions by changing the intensity and the ratio of 470/570 nm light (29) (**Figure 5**). Applications of ChR were already discussed in a larger context in References 38 and 98. Two limitations exist for the wider application of ChR in neuroscience and technology: First, ChR conducts only up to a few hundred ions per absorbed photon, summing up to a current of a few femtosiemens per ChR in continuous high intensities. This limitation can be overcome by high expression levels, by tailoring ChR toward a larger conductance, or possibly by purifying ChR from larger algal cells that require larger cation influxes for depolarization. Second, ChRs that absorb green or even red light would be extremely desirable. This could be achieved through modification of the retinal binding pocket (39) or the expression of ChR from algae with red-shifted action spectra, such as *Prorocentrum* (maximum at 570 nm) (28).

Ion Pumps and Enzyme Rhodopsins

The first algal rhodopsin purified in sufficient amounts for direct flash photolysis analysis

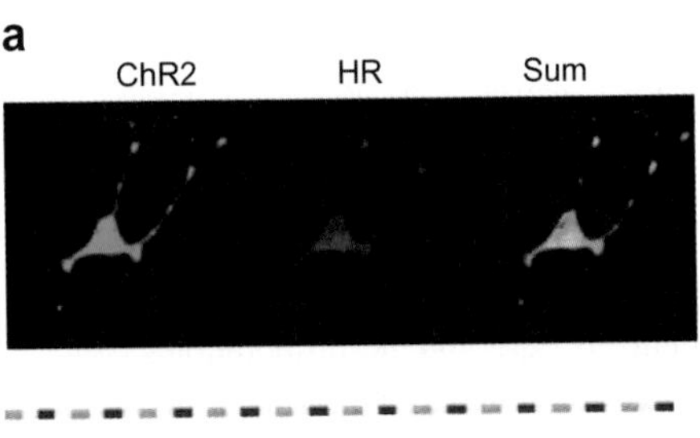

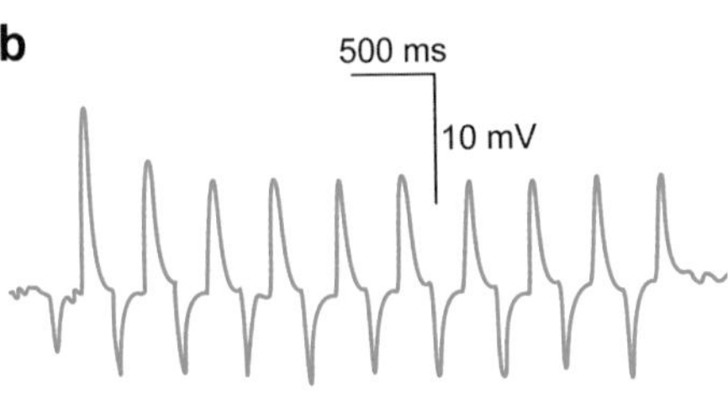

Figure 5

(*a*) Expression of algal channelrhodopsin 2 (ChR2), fused to the red fluorophore mCherry, and bacterial halorhodopsin (HR), fused to GFP, in a hippocampal neuronal cell. (*b*) The cells were stimulated alternatively with yellow and blue light; the graph shows hyperpolarization (downward signal) and depolarization depending on HR and ChR activation. (adapted from Reference 29, under provision of the Creative Commons Attribution License).

was a rhodopsin from the marine cryptophyta *Guillardia theta* (GtR1) (85). *Guillardia theta* is a protist and is not classified as a plant. The plastid originates from a rhodophyte. The rhodopsin was functionally expressed in *E.coli*. In flash photolysis experiments GtR1 behaves similarly to the well-characterized archean rhodopsins in that it shows K-, M-, and O-like photocycle intermediates and a photocycle turnover time with $\tau = 80$ ms. GtR1 lacks proton pumping activity (or passive channel activity), although the amino acids specific for a light-driven proton pump are conserved. A microbial-type rhodopsin gene was also found in the dinoflagellate *Pyrocystis*. This rhodopsin is controlled by the internal clock but no information about other functions is available (71). A rhodopsin with proven proton pumping activity was found in the marine Ulvophyceaen alga *Acetabularia acetabulum* (**Figure 1*b***). In *Xenopus* oocytes *Acetabularia* rhodopsin (AR) pumped protons out of the cell in the light under all tested conditions, with an action spectrum maximum at 518 nm (94). AR is the first ion-pumping rhodopsin found in a green plant organism; it is very similar to bacteriorhodopsin and its eubacterial relatives. Discouragingly, no information could be collected regarding the in vivo function of either rhodopsin from *Guillardia* or *Acetabularia*. Mechanistically these rhodopsins may prove uninteresting because they represent no new principle, but it would be intriguing to discover why photosynthetic algae need a light-driven proton pump.

Another new subfamily of algal rhodopsins is defined by rhodopsin sequences that contain extremely long C-terminal extensions. These sequences encode large proteins that comprise a microbial sensory rhodopsin, a histidine kinase, a response regulator, and an effector protein, such as a nucleotide cyclase [adenylate or guanylate cyclase (AC or GC)] (**Figure 6**). These rhodopsins present a classical two-component system, which is widely used in prokaryotes for a variety of signaling processes and in eukaryotes, including plants, for very selected purposes (45). The unusual feature of the algal sequences is that all the elements, from the photoreceptor to the final enzymatic output domain, are assembled in one protein. Examples include chlamyrhodopsin-5, -6, and -7 (CR5, CR6, and CR7) (51). CR5 and CR6 contain cyclase domains, whereas the function of the terminal enzyme domain of CR7 remains unclear. Researchers have found related enzyme rhodopsins in the genome of *Ostreococcus taurii*. *O. taurii* belongs to the *Prasinophyceae*, an early diverging class within the green plant lineage, and is a globally abundant, single-celled alga thriving in the upper (illuminated) water column of the oceans. The most striking feature of *O. tauri* and related species is their minimal cellular organization: They consist of a naked, nearly 1 micron cell without flagella, but with a single

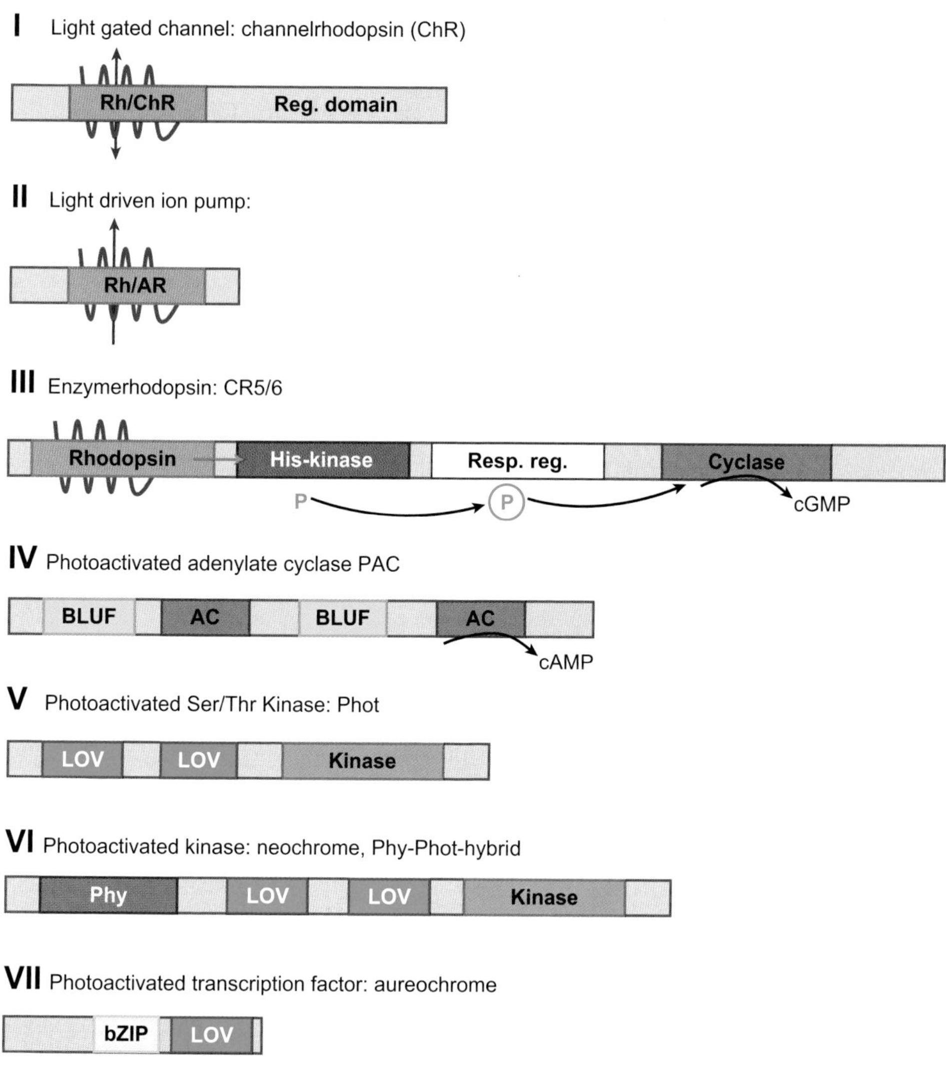

Figure 6

Seven principal sensory photoreceptor types as they occur in algae and/or flagellates (protists). Rh, rhodopsin; ChR, channelrhodopsin; AR, Acetabularia rhodopsins; Resp.reg, response regulator; BLUF, blue-light receptor using flavin adenine dinucleotide (FAD); AC, adenylate cyclase; LOV, light, oxygen, voltage sensor; Phy, phytochrome; CR, chlamyrhodopsin; AUREO, Aureochrome; bZIP, basic-region/leucine-zipper.

chloroplast and mitochondrion. Researchers have defined three different ecotypes or potential species on the basis of their adaptation to light intensity. One ecotype (*O. lucimarinus*) is adapted to high light intensities and corresponds to surface-isolated strains. The second (RCC141) is a low-light species that prefers deep areas of the water column. The third (*O. tauri*) belongs to a group of strains isolated from a coastal lagoon and is considered to be light polyvalent. All three enzyme rhodopsin sequences are highly interesting but so far their function is unknown (S. Kateriya, personal communication).

PHOTOACTIVATED ENZYMES FROM *EUGLENOPHYTA*

FAD: flavin adenine dinucleotide

PAC: photoacivated adenylate cyclase

Light-regulated enzyme: Fusion of photoreceptor and enzyme; the photoreceptor domains activate or drastically stimulate the activity of the enzyme in the light

Function and Physiology

Besides chlorophycean algae, the flagellate *Euglena* (especially *E. gracilis*) (**Figure 1*c***) is the classical organism for the study of photomovement responses in lower eukaryotes (6, 13, 60). *Euglenozoa* are protists and are not considered to be plants. In *Euglena* the sensory photoreceptor for behavioral responses is concentrated in the swelling at the base of the long flagella, called the paraflagellar swelling (PFS) (**Figure 7*a***). The PFS is a three-dimensional crystal; Piccinni & Mammi (73) recorded refractive reflexes of the flagellar membrane many years ago. After 20 years of unsuccessful attempts by many research groups to functionally purify the photoreceptor, the Watanabe group (47) finally succeeded. Their breakthrough involved denaturation and subsequent acidification of the *Euglena* samples. Flavin adenine dinucleotide (FAD) becomes brightly fluorescent at low pH, allowing easy quantification of the photoreceptor complex. The photoreceptor is a heterotetrameric complex of two homologous photoactivated adenylate cyclases (PAC), PACα and PACβ. The purified complex shows basic adenylate cyclase activity that is stimulated 80-fold by light (47, 96). PAC proteins define a new family of directly light-stimulated enzymes.

To gain insight into the evolution of this unique light-regulated enzyme, researchers

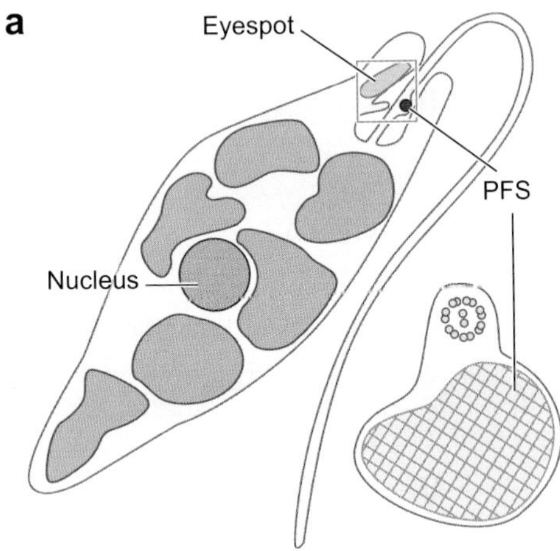

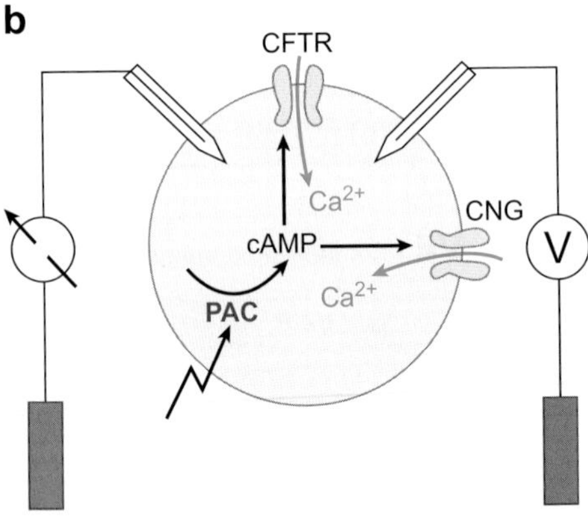

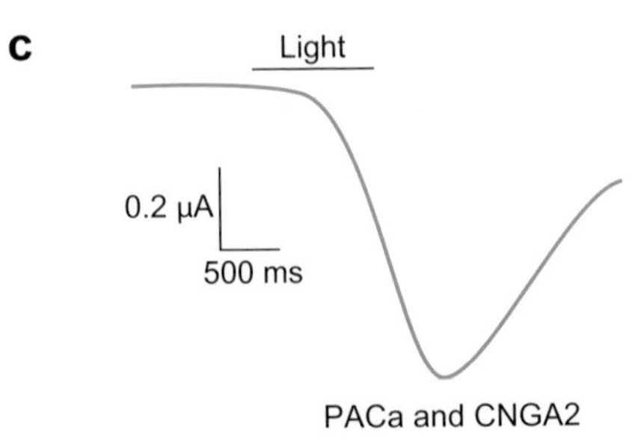

Figure 7

(*a*) Scheme of *Euglena*. The crystalline paraflagellar swelling (PFS) is attached to the base of the long flagellum as seen from the magnified view. (*b*) Time-resolved studies on photoactivated adenylate cyclase (PAC) in *Xenopus* oocytes. Broken arrow depicts light pulse. In this assay, PAC is expressed in conjunction with the cystic fibrosis transmembrane conductance regulator (CFTR) in such a way that cyclic adenosine monophosphate (cAMP) activates a cAMP-dependent protein kinase (PKA), which subsequently modifies and activates CFTR. This assay is highly sensitive but relatively slow. Alternatively, PAC can be expressed along with a cAMP-sensitive cation channel from olfactory neurons that directly opens upon binding of cAMP. The latter approach is faster but less sensitive; an example result is given in *c*. Adapted from Reference 79, with permission from the Nature Publishing Group. Abbreviation: CNG, cyclic nucleotide–gated channel.

searched for related sequences in various euglenoids by RT-PCR. Two PAC-like transcripts were found in four phototrophic euglenoids: *E. sideropus*, *E. viridis*, *E. gymnastica*, and the osmotrophic species *Khawkinea quartana*. All the encoded proteins are expected to function as light-activated cyclases. Because a phylogenetic analysis revealed that the cyclase domains all belong to a bacterial cluster, the authors proposed that PAC might have been transferred to Euglenoids during secondary endosymbiosis (55).

In Vitro Analysis of Photoactivated Adenylate Cyclase and Related Proteins

Photoactivated cyclases are modular proteins; each comprises two photoreceptor domains (F1 and F2) as well as two catalytic domains (C1 and C2) (**Figure 6**). The F domains bind FAD and belong to a group of blue light receptors using FAD (BLUF) that is widely distributed in prokaryotes but rare in eukaryotes (24). The first identified BLUF member is AppA (for activation of photopigment and puc expression), which functions as a blue light–dependent derepressor of photosynthesis genes in *Rhodobacter sphaeroides* (23). The photochemistry of BLUF is radically different from that of traditional sensory photoreceptors such as rhodopsins and phytochromes. In rhodopsin and phytochrome the isomerizing chromophores react similarly in solution and in the protein, whereas flavoproteins generally transfer electrons and the reaction is quite variable depending on the protein environment or the reaction partner. Upon light excitation BLUF undergoes a conformational change (seen as a *ca*. 10 nm red-shift in absorption) but the chromophore remains in its oxidized state (49, 61). The photocycle is slow and requires several seconds to recover to the dark state. In contrast, the primary photochemistry of BLUF domains is ultrafast and the red-shifted signaling state is reached after a few picoseconds (22). Excitation of FAD from the electronic S_0 to the S_1 state is followed by an electron transfer from a conserved Tyr in the chromophore binding pocket to FAD to form the radical anion $FAD^{*\bullet-}$. Next, a H^+ is transferred, most likely onto N5 to form the neutral radical $FADH^{*\bullet}$. This neutral radical causes isomerization of a conserved Gln and subsequent modification of the hydrogen bonding network between FAD and associated amino acid residues (62). The positions of the reactive Tyr and Gln are conserved in the different species and are precisely known from four available X-ray structures (97). The radical species were visualized only in the BLUF domain of the Slr1694 protein from *Synechocystis sp.* PCC6803 (21), but there is no doubt that the results are valid for all BLUF-domains, including those of the PAC.

BLUF: blue light photoreceptors using FAD

cAMP: cyclic adenosine monophosphate

Unfortunately, neither electrical measurements nor fluorescence imaging of Ca^{2+} has been successful on any *Euglenoid* flagellate. The invaginated cell wall and the underlying plasma membrane make the cell surface inaccessible for a suction pipette and impermeable for Ca^{2+}-dyes such as Fura or Fluo. To study PAC function further, researchers injected PAC complementary RNAs into *Xenopus* oocytes. Oocytes are wonderful systems for studying algal proteins because the proteins are generally well expressed even if expression in prokaryotes and yeast is impossible. The kinetics were monitored electrically by the coexpression of various cAMP-sensitive ion channels (**Figure 7*b*** and ***c***). Both PAC variants are active but PACα is 100-fold more active than PACβ (79). The reason why PACβ is less active remains unclear and more detailed studies are needed to determine how the BLUF-domains activate the enzyme.

Light-activated enzymes such as PAC are as valuable for applied science as ChRs, because cAMP is a key messenger in all eukaryotes. The PAC expression level needed for light stimulation of cAMP in the host cell is small. Nagahama and coworkers (47) carried out the first experiments in this direction. Serotonergic modulation of sensory neurons

Phototropin protein (Phot): photoreceptor comprising two FMN-binding LOV-domains and a C-terminal kinase; regulates hypocotyl phototropism, chloroplast relocation and guard cell opening in higher plants as well as sexual differentiation in algae in blue light

LOV: light, oxygen, voltage

FMN: flavin mononucleotide

in *Aplysia* increases intracellular cAMP levels and promotes synaptic transmission by increasing the spike width. Expression of PAC in motor neurons and subsequent illumination with blue light decreases the spike amplitude and increases the spike width, which demonstrates that PAC successfully modulates cAMP levels in living animals.

What is the next step? To gain a profound understanding of the primary processes of BLUF at the same level of detail as is available for the primary processes of photosynthesis or retinal proteins (bacteriorhodopsin), we first need molecular dynamic (MD) calculation of the flavin in its protein environment on the basis of available X-ray structures. Second, to gain a deeper insight into the dynamics of the amino acid side chains that interact with the isoalloxacine, femtosecond stimulated Raman experiments (56) and femtosecond infrared spectroscopy (27) are required. No other photoreceptor shows such a complex behavior on an ultrafast time scale and so little change on a longer time scale. To study the signal transfer to the effector domains, the PACs from protists are ideal, because most other BLUFs act on partner proteins, most of which are unknown and/or are only in transient contact with the photoreceptor.

PHOTOTROPIN

Phototropins (Phot) are light-activated serine/threonine kinases. These proteins were originally discovered in *Arabidopsis* and other higher plants, where they control phototropism, chloroplast relocation, and stomatal opening, among other functions (8). Phot sequences were found in many algae but these proteins were studied functionally only in *Chlamydomonas* to some extent. In this alga, differentiation from the vegetative state into the sexually active state (gametic state) is mediated by nitrogen starvation in combination with blue light (76). Gametes of different mating types fuse to form zygotes and when the conditions are appropriate, zygotes germinate to release the progenies. However, the progeny release is again light-dependent and blue light is more efficient than other colors. Beck and colleagues (42, 43) localized Phot in the cell body and the flagella (4%). By comparing the development of wild-type and Phot-antisense strains at low photon irradiance, they showed that Phot is the photoreceptor responsible for both developmental processes (42, 43). Unlike higher plant phototropins, the activation of *Chlamydomonas* Phot causes major changes in expression of specific gene targets, in particular genes encoding chlorophyll and carotenoid biosynthesis enzymes (42, 43, 46). The formation of mating-competent gametes is accompanied by a loss of chemotaxis toward ammonia (7). Phototropin in *Chlamydomonas* gametes also seems to mediate the light control of this type of chemotaxis (14, 15). Whereas vegetative cells move toward the ammonium source in the light and in darkness, chemotaxis is switched off in the late phase of gamete formation, and this is mediated by phototropin (14).

Phot proteins comprise two light sensor domains, LOV1 and LOV2, and a C-terminal kinase. LOV (light, oxygen, voltage) domains are a subclass of the much larger family of PAS (Per-ARNT-Sim, where PER stands for *Drosophila* period clock protein, ARNT stands for aryl hydrocarbon receptor nuclear translocator and SIM is *Drosophila* single-minded protein) proteins, which participate in a diverse array of biological signaling pathways. In vitro studies on LOV1 from *Chlamydomonas* Phot, LOV2 from *Avena sativa*, and Neochrome from the fern *Adiantum capillus-veneris* (discussed below) contributed the most to our knowledge about the reaction mechanism of LOV photoreceptors. Upon illumination, LOV domains undergo a photocycle that comprises a triplet state, LOV-715, which converts within one or a few microseconds into the signaling state to form a thioadduct between a formerly protonated Cys and the C(4a) position of the flavin mononucleotide (FMN)-isoalloxacine ring (**Figure 8*a***). The resulting LOV-390 reconverts to the dark state within many seconds to minutes (54, 91). The X-ray crystal structures of dark state LOV-447 and the photoproduct LOV-390 were determined for both LOV1 and LOV2 (9, 10, 17). The *Chlamydomonas* LOV1 dark state is shown in **Figure 8*b***. The transition from the dark state to the signaling state is accompanied by surprisingly minimal changes in the surrounding protein. However, the contact between LOV2 and the downstream Jα-helix is interrupted upon formation of the thioadduct in the light (31). If the Jα-LOV contact is prevented by mutation, the kinase is permanently active, which demonstrates the relevance of this particular interaction (30).

The mechanism of thioaddict formation is not yet completely clear. Results from ultrafast spectroscopy originally suggested that a H^+ transfer from the thiol to the N(5) position leads to a protonated triplet state that is subsequently attacked by the thiolate (52). However, theoretical studies on a model system via the use of ab initio formalism showed that a radical mechanism via transfer of a hydrogen atom from the Cys to the flavin is energetically favored (69). The preference of an electron over a H^+ transfer was supported by studies on a mutant in which the reactive Cys was replaced by Met (3, 53). Likewise, time-resolved electron paramagnetic resonance (EPR) measurements on several LOV domains supported the conclusion that a radical pair mechanism dominates the pathway under most conditions (3, 77). However, depending on the conditions, the radical pair may be formed by a hydrogen atom transfer or in a two-step process that transfers an electron first and a H^+ in a second step (77), as shown in **Figure 9**.

NEOCHROME

Photoorientation of the giant chloroplast in *Mougeotea* has been known for a long time to be regulated by light (81). Experiments using microbeams and polarized light implied that the gradient of a phytochrome in Pfr

a

b

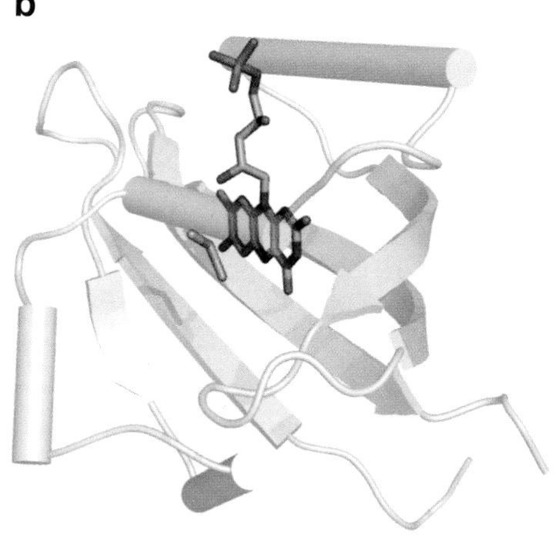

Figure 8

(*a*) Simplified representation of the phototropin (Phot)-LOV1 photocycle from *Chlamydomonas reinhardtii* (54). LOV1*T is the excited triplet state. (*b*) *Chlamydomonas* Phot-LOV1 with flavin mononucleotide (FMN) and the reactive cysteine (*yellow*). Protein Data Bank id: 1n9I. Reproduced with permission from *Biophysical Journal*.

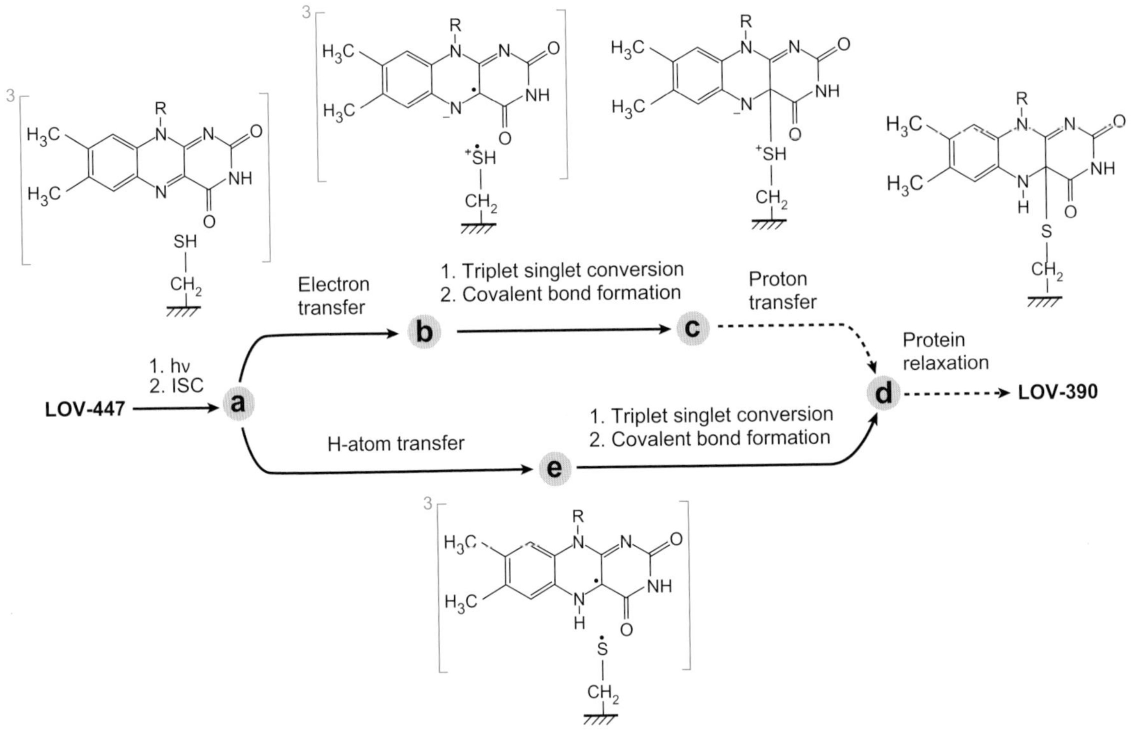

Figure 9

Suggested reaction pathway and intermediates of photoadduct (LOV-390) formation in wild-type LOV domains. Reaction steps that are inhibited at t < 80° K are shown by dashed arrows. Reprinted with permission from Reference 77. Copyright 2004 American Chemical Society.

form bound at the cell periphery controls chloroplast orientation (35). Low levels of blue light mimicked this behavior, which led Haupt (35) to propose that a chimeric photoreceptor for blue and red light absorption mediates chloroplast movement. Suetsugu and coworkers (89) identified two genes in *Mougeotea* that encode hybrid proteins that resemble phytochrome 3 (phy3) from *Adiantum cappillus veneris*. These hybrid proteins comprise two LOV domains, a kinase, and an N-terminal phytochrome domain (Phy-Phot-hybrid). The authors named these members of the recently discovered photoreceptor class neochrome1 and neochrome2 (MSNeo1 and MSNeo2). The recombinant proteins show typical phytochrome bilin binding and red/far-red–reversible photochromism but no FMN binding could be achieved. Both genes are able to rescue red light–induced chloroplast movement in *Adiantum* phy3 mutants, which indicates functional equivalence with respect to red light sensing. As phytochrome-phototropin chimeras, neochromes originally seemed to verify Haupt's old prediction exactly. However, this has now been called into question, because MsNeo cannot perceive blue light in planta. More likely, blue light–mediated chloroplast photoorientation is achieved by the phototropins MsPhot1 and MsPhot2 in this alga. More conventional phytochromes were identified in *Mesotenium* (McPhy1b) (U31283, U31284 in the NCBI Nucleotide Database), *Mougeotia scalaris* (MsPhy1) (Gb:S52048), and *Chara foetida* (Gb:X80291), but they were not studied functionally in any detail.

EPR: electron paramagnetic resonance

AUREOCHROME

The most recent blue light receptor family to be discovered was functionally characterized in the stramenopile algae *Vaucheria frigida* (Xanthophyceae) and *Fucus distichus* (Phaeophyceae) (93). Two homologs were identified in *Vaucheria*; each has one basic-region/leucine-zipper (bZIP) domain and one LOV-sensing domain. The authors have named these chromoproteins AUREOCHROMEs (AUREO1 and AUREO2) because stramenopiles species are typically golden-yellow in color. AUREO1 binds FMN via its LOV domain and forms a 390 nm–absorbing form, indicative of formation of a cysteinyl adduct to the C(4a) carbon of the FMN upon blue light irradiation. The adduct decays to the ground state in approximately 5 min. The bZIP domain binds the target sequence TGACGT. AUREO1-target binding is strongly enhanced by blue light treatment, implying that AUREO1 functions as a blue light–regulated transcription factor. The function of AUREO1 as photoreceptor for light-induced branching (92) was elucidated through RNA interference (RNAi) experiments. RNAi of AUREO2 unexpectedly induces the formation of sex organ primordia instead of branches, implicating AUREO2 as a sub-switch to initiate development of a branch, but not a sex organ. AUREO sequences are also found in the genome of the marine diatom *Thalassiosira pseudonana* (Bacillariophyceae), but are not present in green plants. AUREOCHROME therefore represents a blue-light receptor of photosynthetic stramenopiles.

FUTURE ISSUES

1. With respect to flavin-based photoreceptors such as phototropin (Phot) and phytochromes, the work in algae is lagging behind the work that has been done in higher plants. This is because no photoreceptor mutants are available in algae. This deficit can only be partially compensated for by the application of RNAi, because the reduction of the photoreceptor content is stage-dependent, a target of silencing, and not specific in cases where several genes with overlapping function occur in the alga. Only clean gene targeting can solve this problem and more effort should be invested into this goal. The microalga in which clean gene targeting is first possible will become the leading model species.
2. Algae are exceptionally rich in sensory photoreceptors and the study of their genomes, especially those of freshwater algae, will bring more light-gated enzymes to our knowledge.
3. The molecular analysis of the unusual algal sensory photoreceptors has only recently begun, but tight collaboration of biologists, biochemists, physicists, and theoreticians will guarantee fast progress.
4. Applications for light-activated enzymes that metabolize or produce universal metabolic key compounds will soon be discovered and will support science in other fields.
5. The challenge lies in the study of the biology and the biophysics in or on the living alga. Only these studies will allow the discovery of new natural treasures.

DISCLOSURE STATEMENT

The author is not aware of any biases that might be perceived as affecting the objectivity of this review.

ACKNOWLEDGMENTS

I thank all my coworkers who worked with great patience on the characterization of algal photoreceptors, especially during the years from 1985 to 1996 when the molecular identification was not in sight. I thank Tilo Mathes and Oliver Ernst for discussion during preparation of the manuscript and for sharing unpublished data. The author also gratefully acknowledges the continuous support by the Deutsche Forschungsgemeinschaft.

LITERATURE CITED

1. Beckmann M, Hegemann P. 1991. In vitro identification of rhodopsin in the green-alga *Chlamydomonas*. *Biochemistry* 30:3692–97
2. Bi AD, Cui JJ, Ma YP, Olshevskaya E, Pu ML, et al. 2006. Ectopic expression of a microbial-type rhodopsin restores visual responses in mice with photoreceptor degeneration. *Neuron* 50:23–33
3. Bittl R, Kay CWM, Weber S, Hegemann P. 2003. Characterization of a flavin radical product in a C57M mutant of a LOV1 domain by electron paramagnetic resonance. *Biochemistry* 42:8506–12
4. Boyden ES, Zhang F, Bamberg E, Nagel G, Deisseroth K. 2005. Millisecond-timescale, genetically targeted optical control of neural activity. *Nat. Neurosci.* 8:1263–68
5. Braun FJ, Hegemann P. 1999. Two light-activated conductances in the eye of the green alga *Volvox carteri*. *Biophys. J.* 76:1668–78
6. Buder J. 1917. Zur Kenntnis der phototaktischen Richtungsbewegung. *Jahrbuch wiss. Botanik* 58:106–220
7. Byrne TE, Wells MR, Johnson CH. 1992. Circadian-rhythms of chemotaxis to ammonium and of methylammonium uptake in *Chlamydomonas*. *Plant Physiol.* 98:879–86
8. Christie JM. 2007. Phototropin blue-light receptors. *Annu. Rev. Plant Biol.* 58:21–45
9. Crosson S, Moffat K. 2001. Structure of a flavin-binding plant photoreceptor domain: Insights into light-mediated signal transduction. *Proc. Natl. Acad. Sci. USA* 98:2995–3000
10. Crosson S, Moffat K. 2002. Photoexcited structure of a plant photoreceptor domain reveals a light-driven molecular switch. *Plant Cell* 14:1067–75
11. Ehlenbeck S. 2002. Licht-induzierte H^+ und Cl^--Ströme in *Chlamydomonas reinhardtii*. Diss. Universität Regensburg
12. Ehlenbeck S, Gradmann D, Braun FJ, Hegemann P. 2002. Evidence for a light-induced H^+ conductance in the eye of the green alga *Chlamydomonas reinhardtii*. *Biophys. J.* 82:740–51
13. **Engelmann W. 1882. Über Sauerstoffausscheidung von Pflanzenzellen im Mikrospektrum. *Bot. Ztg.* 40:419–26**

13. Shows that the paraflagellar swelling (PFS) and not the eyespot is the photosensitive organelle in Euglena.

14. Ermilova EV, Zalutskaya ZM, Huang KY, Beck CF. 2004. Phototropin plays a crucial role in controlling changes in chemotaxis during the initial phase of the sexual life cycle in *Chlamydomonas*. *Planta* 219:420–27
15. Ermilova EV, Zalutskaya ZM, Lapina TV, Nikitin MM. 2003. Chemotactic behavior of *Chlamydomonas reinhardtii* is altered during gametogenesis. *Curr. Microbiol.* 46:261–64
16. Ernst OP, Sànchez Murcia PA, Daldrop P, Tsunoda SP, Kateriya S, and Hegemann P. 2007. Photoactivation of channelrhodopsin. *J. Biol. Chem.* doi: 10.1074/jbc.M708039200

17. Fedorov R, Schlichting I, Hartmann E, Domratcheva T, Fuhrmann M, Hegemann P. 2003. Crystal structures and molecular mechanism of a light-induced signaling switch: The Phot-LOV1 domain from *Chlamydomonas reinhardtii*. *Biophys. J.* 84:2474–82

18. Foster KW, Saranak J, Patel N, Zarilli G, Okabe M, et al. 1984. A rhodopsin is the functional photoreceptor for phototaxis in the unicellular eukaryote *Chlamydomonas*. *Nature* 311:756–59

19. Foster KW, Smyth RD. 1980. Light antennas in phototactic algae. *Microbiol. Rev.* 44:572–630

20. Fuhrmann M, Stahlberg A, Govorunova E, Rank S, Hegemann P. 2001. The abundant retinal protein of the *Chlamydomonas* eye is not the photoreceptor for phototaxis and photophobic responses. *J. Cell Sci.* 114:3857–63

21. Gauden M, van Stokkum IHM, Key JM, Lührs DC, van Grondelle R, et al. 2006. Hydrogen-bond switching through a radical pair mechanism in a flavin-binding photoreceptor. *Proc. Natl. Acad. Sci. USA* 103:10895–900

22. Gauden M, Yeremenko S, Laan W, van Stokkum IHM, Ihalainen JA, et al. 2005. Photocycle of the flavin-binding photoreceptor AppA, a bacterial transcriptional antirepressor of photosynthesis genes. *Biochemistry* 44:3653–62

23. Gomelsky M, Kaplan S. 1998. AppA, a redox regulator of photosystem formation in *Rhodobacter sphaeroides* 2.4.1, is a flavoprotein—Identification of a novel FAD binding domain. *J. Biol. Chem.* 273:35319–25

24. Gomelsky M, Klug G. 2002. BLUF: a novel FAD-binding domain involved in sensory transduction in microorganisms. *Trends Biochem. Sci.* 27:497–500

25. Govorunova EG, Jung KH, Sineshchekov OA. 2004. Rhodopsin-mediated photomotility in *Chlamydomonas* and related algae. *Biofizika* 49:278–93

26. Govorunova EG, Jung KH, Sineshchekov OA, Spudich JL. 2004. *Chlamydomonas* sensory rhodopsins A and B: Cellular content and role in photophobic responses. *Biophys. J.* 86:2342–49

27. Groot ML, van Wilderen LJGW, Larsen DS, van der Horst MA, van Stokkum IHM, et al. 2003. Initial steps of signal generation in photoactive yellow protein revealed with femtosecond mid-infrared spectroscopy. *Biochemistry* 42:10054–59

28. Halldal P. 1958. Action spectra of phototaxis and related problems in Volvocales, Ulva-gametes and Dinophyceae. *Physiol. Plantarum* 11:118–53

29. Han X, Boyden ES. 2007. Multiple color optical activation, silencing, and desynchronisation of neural activity with single-spike temporal resolution. *PLoS* ONE 2:e299

30. Harper SM, Neil LC, Day IJ, Hore PJ, Gardner KH. 2004. Conformational changes in a photosensory LOV domain monitored by time-resolved NMR spectroscopy. *J. Am. Chem. Soc.* 126:3390–91

31. Harper SM, Neil LC, Gardner KH. 2003. Structural basis of a phototropin light switch. *Science* 301:1541–44

32. Harris EH. 2008. *The Chlamydomonas Sourcebook*, Vol. 3. New York: Elsevier. 2nd ed. In press

33. Harz H, Hegemann P. 1991. Rhodopsin-regulated calcium currents in *Chlamydomonas*. *Nature* 351:489–91

34. Harz H, Nonnengasser C, Hegemann P. 1992. The photoreceptor current of the green-alga *Chlamydomonas*. *Philos. Trans. R. Soc. London Ser. B* 338:39–52

35. Haupt W. 1999. Chloroplast movement: From phenomenology to molecular biology. *Prog. Bot.* 60:3–36

36. Hegemann P, Ehlenbeck S, Gradmann D. 2005. Multiple photocycles of channelrhodopsin. *Biophys. J.* 89:3911–18

18. The authors rescued phototaxis in white cells by addition of retinoids and presented action spectra showing that the photoreceptor is rhodopsin.

19. Extended study and survey of the optical principles of algal eyes.

33. Recording of photocurrents from *Chlamydomonas* and demonstration that they are mediated by rhodopsin.

37. Hegemann P, Tsunoda S. 2007. Light tools for neuroscience: *Channelrhodopsin* and light-activated enzymes. *Cell Sci. Rev.* 3:108–23
38. Herlitze S, Landmesser LT. 2007. New optical tools for controlling neuronal activity. *Curr. Opin. Neurobiol.* 17:87–94
39. Hoffmann M, Wanko M, Strodel P, König PH, Frauenheim T, et al. 2006. Color tuning in rhodopsins: The mechanism for the spectral shift between bacteriorhodopsin and sensory rhodopsin II. *J. Am. Chem. Soc.* 128:10808–18
40. Holland EM, Braun FJ, Nonnengasser C, Harz H, Hegemann P. 1996. Nature of rhodopsin-triggered photocurrents in *Chlamydomonas*.1. Kinetics and influence of divalent ions. *Biophys. J.* 70:924–31
41. Holland EM, Harz H, Uhl R, Hegemann P. 1997. Control of phobic behavioral responses by rhodopsin-induced photocurrents in *Chlamydomonas*. *Biophys. J.* 73:1395–401
42. Huang KY, Beck CF. 2003. Photoropin is the blue-light receptor that controls multiple steps in the sexual life cycle of the green alga *Chlamydomonas reinhardtii*. *Proc. Natl. Acad. Sci. USA* 100:6269–74
43. Huang KY, Kunkel T, Beck CF. 2004. Localization of the blue-light receptor phototropin to the flagella of the green alga *Chlamydomonas reinhardtii*. *Mol. Biol. Cell* 15:3605–14
44. Hufnagel P. 1993. *Messung der photoströme der Chlamydomonas-Zellen an planaren Lipidmembranen*. Diss. Ludwig-Maximilians-Universität München
45. Hwang I, Sheen J. 2001. Two-component circuitry in *Arabidopsis* cytokinin signal transduction. *Nature* 413:383–89
46. Im CS, Eberhard S, Huang KY, Beck CF, Grossman AR. 2006. Phototropin involvement in the expression of genes encoding chlorophyll and carotenoid biosynthesis enzymes and LHC apoproteins in *Chlamydomonas reinhardtii*. *Plant J.* 48:1–16
47. **Iseki M, Matsunaga S, Murakami A, Ohno K, Shiga K, et al. 2002. A blue-light-activated adenylyl cyclase mediates photoavoidance in *Euglena gracilis*. *Nature* 415:1047–51**

47. Purification of the paraflagellar photoreceptor from Euglena, and evidence that it is a heterotetrameric complex of two photoactivated cyclases.

48. Ishizuka T, Kakuda M, Araki R, Yawo H. 2006. Kinetic evaluation of photosensitivity in genetically engineered neurons expressing green algae light-gated channels. *Neurosci. Res.* 54:85–94
49. Ito S, Murakami A, Sato K, Nishina Y, Shiga K, et al. 2005. Photocycle features of heterologously expressed and assembled eukaryotic flavin-binding BLUF domains of photoactivated adenylyl cyclase (PAC), a blue-light receptor in *Euglena gracilis*. *Photochem. Photobiol. Sci.* 4:762–69
50. Jung KH. 2007. The distinct signaling mechanisms of microbial sensory rhodopsins in Archaea, Eubacteria and Eukarya. *Photochem. Photobiol.* 83:63–69
51. Kateriya S, Nagel G, Barnberg E, Hegemann P. 2004. "Vision" in single-celled algae. *News Physiol. Sci.* 19:133–37
52. Kennis JTM, Crosson S, Gauden M, van Stokkum IHM, Moffat K, van Grondelle R. 2003. Primary reactions of the LOV2 domain of phototropin, a plant blue-light photoreceptor. *Biochemistry* 42:3385–92
53. Kottke T, Dick B, Fedorov R, Schlichting I, Deutzmann R, Hegemann P. 2003. Irreversible photoreduction of flavin in a mutated Phot-LOV1 domain. *Biochemistry* 42:9854–62
54. Kottke T, Heberle J, Hehn D, Dick B, Hegemann P. 2003. Phot-LOV1: Photocycle of a blue-light receptor domain from the green alga *Chlamydomonas reinhardtii*. *Biophys. J.* 84:1192–201
55. Koumura Y, Suzuki T, Yoshikawa S, Watanabe M, Iseki M. 2004. The origin of photoactivated adenylyl cyclase (PAC), the Euglena blue-light receptor: phylogenetic analysis

of orthologues of PAC subunits from several euglenoids and trypanosome-type adenylyl cyclases from *Euglena gracilis*. *Photochem. Photobiol. Sci.* 3:580–86

56. Kukura P, McCamant DW, Mathies RA. 2007. Femtosecond stimulated Raman spectroscopy. *Annu. Rev. Phys. Chem.* 58:461–88
57. Li X, Gutierrez DV, Hanson MG, Han J, Mark MD, et al. 2005. Fast noninvasive activation and inhibition of neural and network activity by vertebrate rhodopin and green algae channelrhodopsin. *Proc. Natl. Acad. Sci. USA* 102:17816–21
58. **Litvin FF, Sineshchekov OA, Sineshchekov VA. 1978. Photoreceptor electric-potential in phototaxis of alga *Haematococcus pluvialis*. *Nature* 271:476–78**
59. **Mast SO. 1916. The process of orientation in the colonial organism, *Gonium pectorale*, and a study of the structure and function of the eye-spot. *J. Exp. Zool.* 20:1–17**
60. Mast SO, Gover M. 1922. Relation between intensity of light and rate of locomotion in *Phacus pleuronectes* and *Euglena gracilis* and its bearing on orientation. *Biol. Bull.* 43:203–9
61. Masuda S, Bauer CE. 2002. AppA is a blue light photoreceptor that antirepresses photosynthesis gene expression in *Rhodobacter sphaeroides*. *Cell* 110:613–23
62. Masuda S, Hasegawa K, Ishii A, Ono T. 2004. Light-induced structural changes in a putative blue-light receptor with a novel FAD binding fold sensor of blue-light using FAD (BLUF); Slr1694 of *Synechocystis sp* PCC6803. *Biochemistry* 43:5304–13
63. Melkonian M, Robenek H. 1980. Eyespot membranes of *Chlamydomonas reinhardii*—a freeze-fracture study. *J. Ultrastruct. Res.* 72:90–102
64. Miller G. 2006. Optogenetics: Shining new light on neural circuits. *Science* 314:1674–76
65. Nagel G, Brauner M, Liewald JF, Adeishvili N, Bamberg E, Gottschalk A. 2005. Light activation of channelrhodopsin-2 in excitable cells of *Caenorhabditis elegans* triggers rapid behavioral responses. *Curr. Biol.* 15:2279–84
66. **Nagel G, Ollig D, Fuhrmann M, Kateriya S, Mustl AM, et al. 2002. Channelrhodopsin-1: A light-gated proton channel in green algae. *Science* 296:2395–98**
67. Nagel G, Szellas T, Huhn W, Kateriya S, Adeishvili N, et al. 2003. Channelrhodopsin-2, a directly light-gated cation-selective membrane channel. *Proc. Natl. Acad. Sci. USA* 100:13940–45
68. Nagel G, Szellas T, Kateriya S, Adeishvili N, Hegemann P, Bamberg E. 2005. Channelrhodopsins: directly light-gated cation channels. *Biochem. Soc. Trans.* 33:863–66
69. Neiss C, Saalfrank P. 2003. Ab initio quantum chemical investigation of the first steps of the photocycle of phototropin: A model study. *Photochem. Photobiol.* 77:101–9
70. Nonnengasser C, Holland EM, Harz H, Hegemann P. 1996. The nature of rhodopsin-triggered photocurrents in *Chlamydomonas*. 2. Influence of monovalent ions. *Biophys. J.* 70:932–38
71. Okamoto OK, Hastings JW. 2003. Novel dinoflagellate clock-related genes identified through microarray analysis. *J. Phycol.* 39:519–26
72. Petreanu L, Huber D, Sobczyk A, Svoboda K. 2007. Channelrhodopsin-2-assisted circuit mapping of long-range callosal projections. *Nat. Neurosci.* 10:663–68
73. Piccinni E, Mammi M. 1978. Motor apparatus of *Euglena gracilis:* ultrastructure of the basal portion of the flagellum and the paraflagellar body. *Boll. Zool.* 45:405–14
74. Rüffer U, Nultsch W. 1990. Flagellar photoresponses of *Chlamydomonas* cells held on micropipettes: I. Change in flagellar beat frequency. *Cell Motil Cytoskelet.* 15:162–67
75. Rüffer U, Nultsch W. 1991. Flagellar photoresponses of *Chlamydomonas* cells held on micropipettes: II. Change in flagellar beat pattern. *Cell Motil. Cytoskelet.* 18:269–78
76. Sager R, Granick S. 1954. Nutritional control of sexuality in *Chlamydomonas reinhardii*. *J. Gen. Physiol.* 37:729–42

58. The first recording of electrical responses from a green alga, *Haematococcus pluvialis*.

59. Demonstrated convincingly that the pigmented spot of single-celled algae is the light sensitive organelle that controls behavioral light responses.

66. ChR1 is the first example of a light-gated ion channel; it causes inward directed photocurrents and can depolarize the cell enough to trigger secondary voltage-gated channels at high light intensities.

77. Schleicher E, Kowalczyk RM, Kay CWM, Hegemann P, Bacher A, et al. 2004. On the reaction mechanism of adduct formation in LOV domains of the plant blue-light receptor phototropin. *J. Am. Chem. Soc.* 126:11067–76
78. Schmidt JA, Eckert R. 1976. Calcium couples flagellar reversal to photostimulation in *Chlamydomonas reinhardtii*. *Nature* 262:713–15
79. Schröder-Lang S, Schwärzel M, Seifert R, Strünker T, Kateriya S, et al. 2007. Fast manipulation of cellular cAMP level by light in vivo. *Nat. Methods* 4:39–42
80. Seifert K, Fendler K, Bamberg E. 1993. Charge transport by ion translocating membrane-proteins on solid supported membranes. *Biophys. J.* 64:384–91
81. Senn G. 1908. Die Gestaltungs- und Lageveränderungen der Pflanzenchromatophoren. Leipzig, Ger: Engelmann
82. Sineshchekov OA, Govorunova EG. 1999. Rhodopsin-mediated photosensing in green flagellated algae. *Trends Plant Sci.* 4:58–63
83. Sineshchekov OA, Govorunova EG, Der A, Keszthelyi L, Nultsch W. 1992. Photoelectric responses in phototactic flagellated algae measured in cell-suspension. *J. Photochem. Photobiol. B* 13:119–34
84. Sineshchekov OA, Govorunova EG, Der A, Keszthelyi L, Nultsch W. 1994. Photoinduced electric currents in carotenoid-deficient *Chlamydomonas* mutants reconstituted with retinal and its analogs. *Biophys. J.* 66:2073–84
85. Sineshchekov OA, Govorunova EG, Jung KH, Zauner S, Maier UG, Spudich JL. 2005. Rhodopsin-mediated photoreception in cryptophyte flagellates. *Biophys. J.* 89:4310–19
86. **Sineshchekov OA, Jung KH, Spudich JL. 2002. Two rhodopsins mediate phototaxis to low- and high-intensity light in *Chlamydomonas reinhardtii*. *Proc. Natl. Acad. Sci. USA* 99:8689–94**

86. ChR1 and ChR2 antisense transformants were generated; showed that both channelrhodopsins contribute to photocurrents and phobic responses in *Chlamydomonas*.

87. Sineshchekov OA, Litvin FF, Keszthelyi L. 1990. Two components of the photoreceptor potential in phototaxis of the flagellated green alga *Haematococcus*. *Biophys. J.* 57:33–39
88. Sineshchekov OA, Spudich JL. 2006. Sensory rhodopsin signaling in green flagellate algae. In *Handbook of Photosensory Receptors*, ed. WR Brigg, JL Spudich, pp. 25–42. Weinheim, Ger: Wiley-VCH
89. Suetsugu N, Mittmann F, Wagner G, Hughes J, Wada M. 2005. A chimeric photoreceptor gene, NEOCHROME, has arisen twice during plant evolution. *Proc. Natl. Acad. Sci. USA* 102:13705–9
90. Suzuki T, Yamasaki K, Fujita S, Oda K, Iseki M, et al. 2003. Archaeal-type rhodopsins in *Chlamydomonas*: model structure and intracellular localization. *Biochem. Biophys. Res. Commun.* 301:711–17
91. Swartz TE, Corchnoy SB, Christie JM, Lewis JW, Szundi I, et al. 2001. The photocycle of a flavin-binding domain of the blue light photoreceptor phototropin. *J. Biol. Chem.* 276:36493–500
92. Takahashi F, Hishinuma T, Kataoka H. 2001. Blue light-induced branching in *Vaucheria*. Requirement of nuclear accumulation in the irradiated region. *Plant Cell Phys.* 42:274–85
93. Takahashi F, Yamagata D, Ishikawa M, Fukamatsu Y, Ogura Y, et al. 2007. AUREOCHROME: a newly found novel photoreceptor required for photomorphogenesis in stramenopiles. *Proc. Natl. Acad. Sci USA*. In press
94. Tsunoda SP, Ewers D, Gazzarrini S, Moroni A, Gradmann D, Hegemann P. 2006. H^+ pumping rhodopsin from the marine alga *Acetabularia*. *Biophys. J.* 91:1471–79
95. Wang H, Peca J, Matsuzaki M, Matsuzaki K, Noguchi J, et al. 2007. High-speed mapping of synaptic connectivity using photostimulation in Channelrhodopsin-2 transgenic mice. *Proc. Natl. Acad. Sci. USA*. 104:8143–48

96. Yoshikawa S, Suzuki T, Watanabe M, Iseki M. 2005. Kinetic analysis of the activation of photoactivated adenylyl cyclase (PAC), a blue-light receptor for photomovements of *Euglena*. *Photochem. Photobiol. Sci.* 4:727–31
97. Yuan H, Anderson S, Masuda S, Dragnea V, Moffat K, Bauer C. 2006. Crystal structures of the *Synechocystis* photoreceptor Slr1694 reveal distinct structural states related to signaling. *Biochemistry* 45:12687–94
98. Zhang F, Wang LP, Boyden ES, Deisseroth K. 2006. Channelrhodopsin-2 and optical control of excitable cells. *Nat. Methods* 3:785–92

Plant Proteases: From Phenotypes to Molecular Mechanisms

Renier A. L. van der Hoorn

Plant Chemetics Lab, Max Planck Institute for Plant Breeding Research, Cologne, Germany 50829 and Chemical Genomics Center of the Max Planck Society, Dortmund, Germany 44227; email: hoorn@mpiz-koeln.mpg.de

Annu. Rev. Plant Biol. 2008. 59:191–223

The *Annual Review of Plant Biology* is online at plant.annualreviews.org

This article's doi:
10.1146/annurev.arplant.59.032607.092835

1543-5008/08/0602-0191$20.00

Key Words

phytocalpain, papain-like cysteine proteases, deconjugating proteases, subtilases, serine carboxypeptidase-like proteases, pepsin-like aspartic proteases

Abstract

Plant genomes encode hundreds of proteases, which represent dozens of unrelated families. The biological role of these proteases is mostly unknown, but mutant alleles, gene silencing, and overexpression studies have provided phenotypes for a growing number of proteases. The aim of this review is to show the diversity of the processes that are regulated by proteases, and to summarize the current knowledge of the underlying molecular mechanisms. The emerging picture is that plant proteases are key regulators of a striking variety of biological processes, including meiosis, gametophyte survival, embryogenesis, seed coat formation, cuticle deposition, epidermal cell fate, stomata development, chloroplast biogenesis, and local and systemic defense responses. The functional diversity correlates with the molecular data: Proteases are specifically expressed in time and space and accumulate in different subcellular compartments. Their substrates and activation mechanisms are elusive, however, and represent a challenging topic for further research.

Contents

INTRODUCTION

As in the case of all other organisms, plants use proteases to degrade nonfunctional proteins into amino acids. This is common textbook knowledge, but there is more to proteases than this housekeeping function. Proteases are also key regulators. By irreversibly determining the fate of other proteins, they regulate different processes in response to developmental and environmental cues. This implies that proteases are substrate specific, and that their activity is tightly regulated, both in time and space. Testimony for the existence of regulatory proteases in plants is relatively recent and is summarized in this review.

Proteases cleave peptide bonds that can be internal (for endopeptidases), N-terminal (for aminopeptidases), or C-terminal (for carboxypeptidases). All proteases polarize the carbonyl group of the substrate peptide bond by stabilizing the oxygen in an oxyanion hole, which makes the carbon atom more vulnerable for attack by an activated nucleophile (**Figure 1*a***). Proteases can do this in four major ways, which gives the names to four catalytic classes: cysteine proteases, serine proteases, metalloproteases, and aspartic proteases (30) (**Figure 1*b***).

MEROPS: protease database, named after a tropical bird living in families and clans

Clan: group of protease families that share the same ancestor

Family: group of proteases that share a certain level of sequence homology

Proteases in the MEROPS protease database have been subdivided into families and clans on the basis of evolutionary relationships (**http://merops.sanger.ac.uk**) (69). The *Arabidopsis* genome encodes over 800 proteases, which are distributed over almost 60 families, which belong to 30 different clans (**Figure 2*b***). The distribution and the family size are well conserved within the plant

a

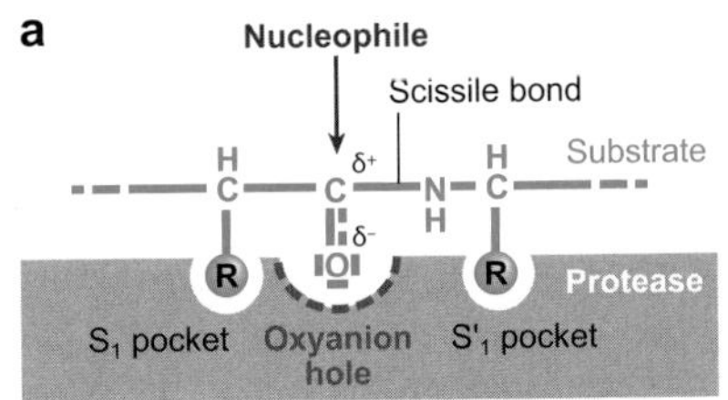

b

Catalytic class	Nucleophile	Oxyanion stabilizer
Cysteine proteases	**Cys**-His	-NH-(2x)
Serine proteases	**Ser**-His	-NH-(2x)
Metalloproteases	**H_2O**-Me^{2+}	Me^{2+}
Aspartic proteases	**H_2O**-Asp	H^+-Asp

Figure 1

Cleavage mechanisms of the four major catalytic classes of proteases. (*a*) The substrate protein (*green*) binds via amino acid residues (R) to the substrate binding site of the protease (*gray*) by interacting with substrate (S) pockets of the enzyme. The scissile peptide bond is adjacent to a carbonyl group, which is polarized by the enzyme by stabilizing the oxyanion hole (*blue*); this makes the carbonyl carbon vulnerable for nucleophilic attack. (*b*) The major differences between the catalytic classes are the nature of the nucleophile and oxyanion stabilizer. Cysteine and serine proteases use a Cys or Ser residue as nucleophile, activated by histidine (His) in the active site. The oxyanion hole is usually stabilized by two residues in the backbone of the protease. Metalloproteases and aspartic proteases use water as nucleophile, activated by electrostatic interactions with the metal ion (Me^{2+}) or aspartate (Asp), respectively. The oxyanion of these proteases is stabilized by Me^{2+} and Asp, respectively.

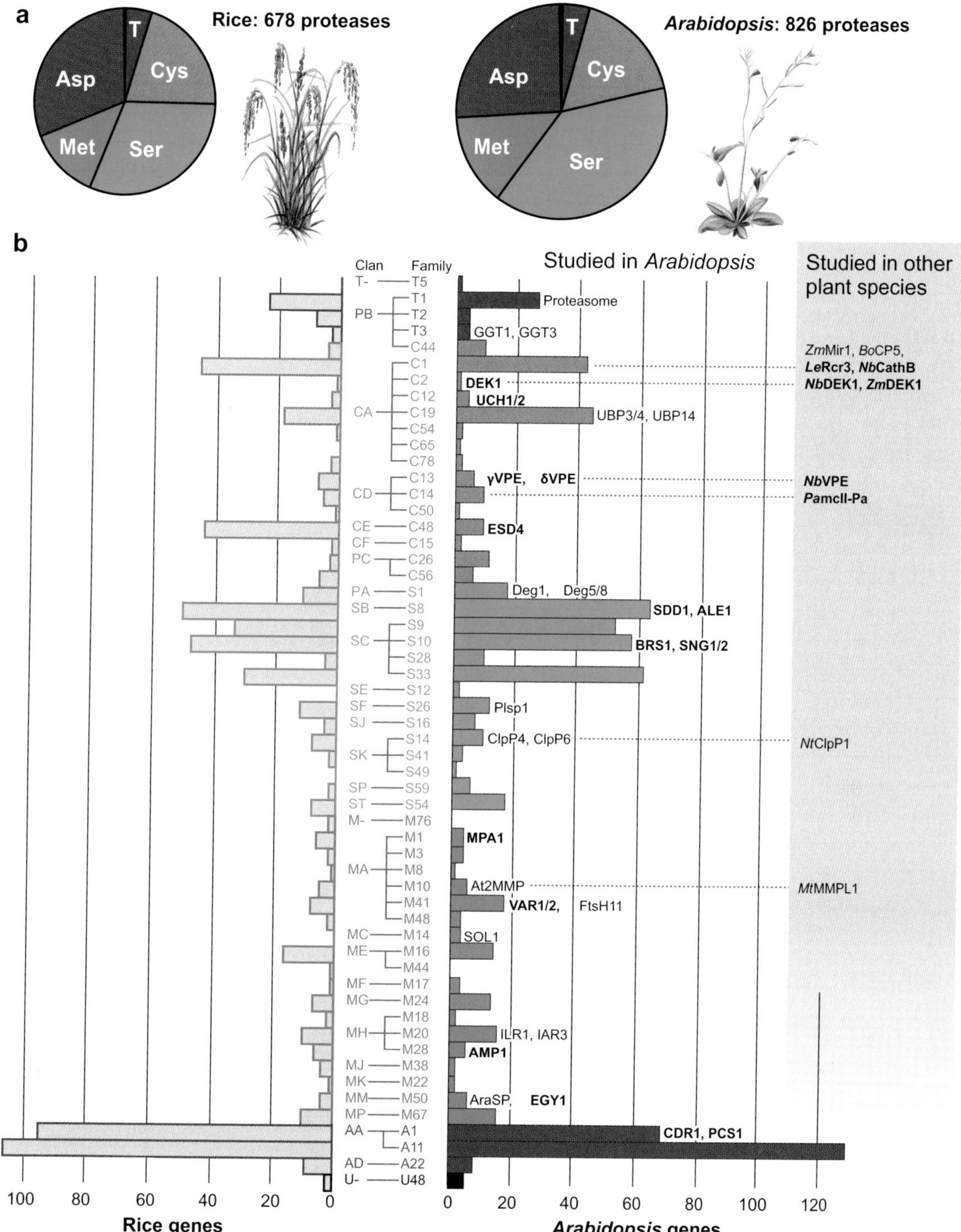

Figure 2

Distribution of rice (*left*) and *Arabidopsis* (*right*) protease genes over (*a*) the different catalytic classes, and (*b*) the different families (*right*) and clans (*left*). Proteases for which biological roles are known from genetic experiments are indicated on the right (see also **Table 1**). Proteases discussed in this article are indicated in bold.

Table 1 Proteases with known phenotypes

Name of protease[a]	Accession	Species[b]	Family	Phenotype observed[c]	Reference
GGT1	At4g39640	*At*	T3	KO: premature senescence after flowering	59
GGT3	At1g69820	*At*	T3	KO: reduced number of siliques and seeds	59
Rcr3	AF493234	*Le*	C1A	KO: loss of recognition of fungal pathogen	49
***Nb*CathB**	DQ492297	*Nb*	C1A	KD: suppressed hypersensitive cell death	35
Mir1	AAB70820	*Zm*	C1A	OE: inhibits caterpillar growth	67
*Bo*CP5	AF454960	*Bo*	C1A	KD: suppresses broccoli postharvest senescence	31
DEK1	AY061804	*Zm*	C2	KO: no/reduced aleurone on kernels	7
***Nb*DEK1**	AY450851	*Nb*	C2	KD: callus-like surface on all organs	1
***At*DEK1**	At1g55350	*At*	C2	KD: altered epidermal cell fate	43
UCH1/2	At5g16310	*At*	C12	KO: more branches; OE: less branches	101
UBP1/2	At1g177110	*At*	C19	KO: enhanced susceptibility to canavanine	100
UBP3/4	At4g39910	*At*	C19	KO: impaired pollen development	26
UBP14	At3g20630	*At*	C19	KO: embryos arrest at the globular stage	27
***Nb*VPE**	AB181187	*Nb*	C13	KD: blocked hypersensitive cell death	38
γVPE	At4g32940	*At*	C13	KO: reduced toxin-induced cell death	51
δVPE	At3g20210	*At*	C13	KO: delayed cell death in seed coat	65
mcII-Pa	AJ534970	*Pa*	C14	KD: reduced cell death during embryogenesis	12
ESD4	At4g15880	*At*	C48	KO: early flowering, pleiotropic effects	64
Deg1	At3g27925	*At*	S1	KD: reduced growth, early flowering	46
Deg5(/8)	At4g18370	*At*	S1	KO: reduced growth under high light	85
SDD1	At1g04110	*At*	S8	KO: altered stomata density and distribution	9
ALE1	At1g62340	*At*	S8	KO: lacks embryo cuticle	88
BRS1	At4g30610	*At*	S10	OE: enhanced BR sensitivity	54
SNG1	At2g22990	*At*	S10	KO: no sinapoylmalate biosynthesis in leaves	52
SNG2	At5g09640	*At*	S10	KO: no sinapoylcholine biosynthesis in seeds	82
Plsp1	At3g24590	*At*	S26	KO: reduced plastid internal membranes, lethal	42
ClpP4	At5g45390	*At*	S14	KD: bleached leaves; OE: chlorotic rosette leaves	80, 105
ClpP1	Z00044	*Nt*	S14	KO: ablation of shoot system	50
ClpP6	At1g11750	*At*	S14	KD: chlorotic young rosette leaves	83
MPA1	At1g63770	*At*	M1	KO: disturbed meiotic chromosome segregation	78
At2MMP	At1g70170	*At*	M10	KO: slow growth, late flowering, early senescence	36
MMPL1	Y18249	*Mt*	M10	KD: larger infection threads; OE: aborted infection	21
VAR1	At5g42270	*At*	M41	KO: variegated leaves, stems, and siliques	76
VAR2	At2g30950	*At*	M41	KO: variegated leaves, stems, and siliques	18
FtsH11	At5g53170	*At*	M41	KO: loss of thermotolerance	16
SOL1	At1g71696	*At*	M14	KO: suppressor of restricted root meristem	13
ILR1	At3g02875	*At*	M20	KO: insensitive to exogenous IAA-Leu	4
IAR3	At1g51760	*At*	M20	KO: reduced sensitivity to exogenous IAA-Ala	23
AMP1	At3g54720	*At*	M28	KO: oversized meristems, polycotyly, etc.	39
AraSP	At2g32480	*At*	M50	KD/KO: impaired chloroplast and seedling development	10
EGY1	At5g35220	*At*	M50	KO: reduced chlorophyl and gravitropism	15

(Continued)

Table 1 (*continued*)

Name of protease[a]	Accession	Species[b]	Family	Phenotype observed[c]	Reference
CDR1	At5g33340	*At*	A1	OE: constitutive disease resistance; dwarfing	98
PCS1	At5g02190	*At*	A1	KO: lethality in gametophytes and embryos	34

[a]Proteases discussed in text are indicated in bold.

[b]*At*, *Arabidopsis thaliana*; *Bo*, *Brassica oleracea*; *Le*, *Lycopersicon esculentum*; *Mt*, *Medicago trunculata*; *Nb*, *Nicotiana benthamiana*; *Nt*, *Nicotiana tabacum*; *Os*, *Oryza sativa*; *Pa*, *Picea abies*; *Zm*, *Zea mays*.

[c]KO, knockout; KD, knockdown/silencing/RNAi; OE, overexpression; IAA, indole acetic acid.

kingdom because poplar and rice have similar distributions (33) (**Figure 2*b***).

The biological functions of at least 40 proteases have been revealed through genetic studies (**Table 1**). The diversity of the biological functions is tremendous and stretches out over the entire spectrum of proteases. The proteases functionally described so far belong to ~20 different families of 14 clans (**Figure 2*b***). Although the phenotypes associated with altered expression of these proteases have been well described, research addressing their molecular mechanisms has only just begun. Interestingly, not all annotated proteases cleave peptide bonds in proteins. MEROPS peptidase T3 family members γ-glutamyltransferase 1 and 2 (GGT1 and GGT2), for example, hydrolyze the tripeptide glutathione and glutathione S-conjugates (59), whereas the MEROPS peptidase M20 family members indole acetic acid (IAA)-amino acid hydrolase (ILR1) and IAA-alanine resistant 3 (IAR3) hydrolyze auxin–amino acid conjugates (4, 23). One subclass of the S10 carboxypeptidases catalyzes acyltransferase reactions, rather than proteolysis (SNG1/2, discussed below).

This review summarizes the phenotypic data for a broad spectrum of plant proteases and discusses their molecular mechanisms. I focus on seventeen proteases that are relatively well described at a phenotypic level. The biological function of each of these proteases is so distinct that I choose to treat them separately and group them on the basis of the MEROPS classification. The summarized data illustrate that proteases play strikingly diverse regulatory roles in a broad spectrum of processes essential for a plant's life.

CYSTEINE PROTEASES

Cysteine proteases use a catalytic Cys as a nucleophile during proteolysis. Plant genomes encode for approximately 140 cysteine proteases that belong to 15 families of 5 clans (69). The structures of proteases from different clans are distinct, which implicates convergent evolution. Clans CA and CE contain proteases with a papain-like fold, whereas CD proteases have a caspase-like fold (explained below). Many cysteine proteases play a role in programmed cell death (PCD), in response to both developmental cues and pathogens. Other cysteine proteases regulate epidermal cell fate, flowering time, inflorescence architecture, and pollen or embryo development (**Table 1**). Seven of these proteases have been studied in detail and are discussed here.

Phytocalpain DEK1

Calpains (family C2, clan CA) are well studied calcium-dependent proteases in animals that usually act in the cytoplasm (74). Calpains are evolutionarily related to papain because they share the same fold and order of catalytic residues (Cys, His, Asn) (40). Calpains are folded as two lobes, one carries the catalytic Cys and the other carries His and Asn residues, and the catalytic triad is assembled between the lobes. In calpains, the distance between the lobes, and thereby the functionality of the catalytic triad, is regulated by calcium binding (40). Plant genomes

Convergent evolution: independent evolution toward a similar functional endpoint

Programmed cell death (PCD): cell death in which cell signaling is required for cells to die

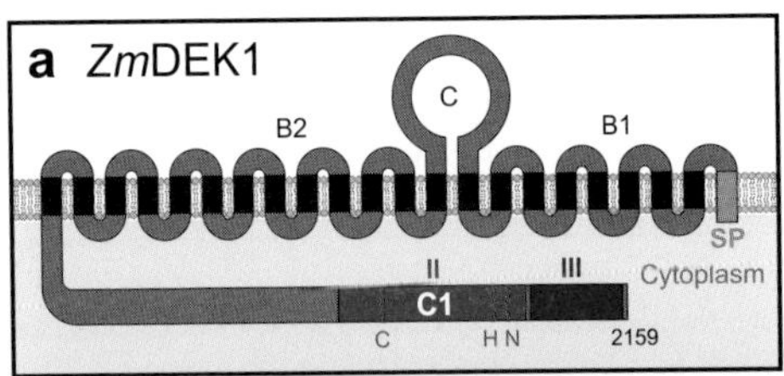

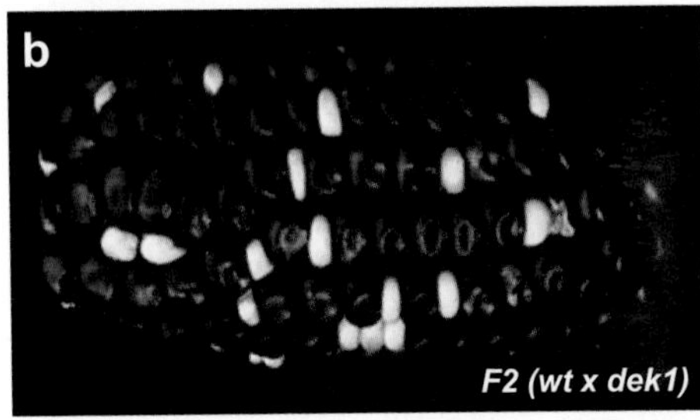

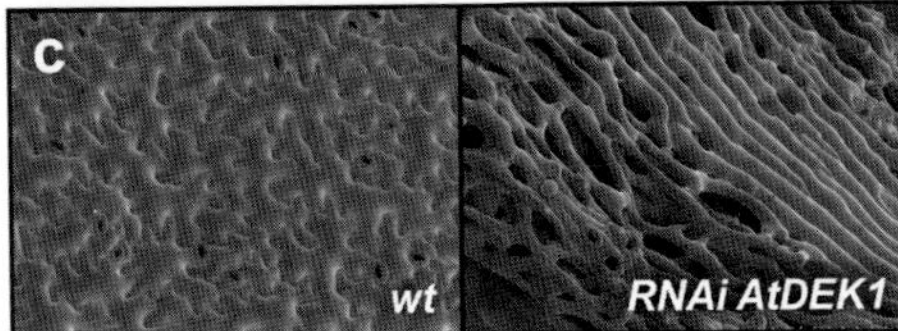

Figure 3

DEK1 (*a*) Predicted topology of the *Zea mays* defective kernel 1 (DEK1) protein. SP, signal peptide; B1, B2, transmembrane domains (*black*); C, extracytoplasmic loop; II, calpain protease domain (*red*); III, calpain domain III (*dark blue*); C, H, N, catalytic residues Cys, His, and Asn (*purple*). (*b*) Phenotype of a maize ear of a heterozygous *dek1* mutant in a genetic background that stains the aleurone layer black. The *dek1* mutation is recessive and causes loss of the aleurone layer in the homozygous state. Reprinted with permission from Reference 55, Copyright 2002, National Academy of Sciences, U.S.A. (*c*) Silencing of AtDEK1 in *Arabidopsis* results in loss of epidermal cell identity: Epidermal cells are gradually replaced by mesophyll-like cells. Pictures kindly provided by Dr. G. Ingham (Institute for Molecular Plant Sciences, Edinburgh, UK).

contain only one calpain, also called phytocalpain, which is unique in its structure (**Figure 3*a***) and essential for plant epidermis development.

DEK1. Defective kernel 1 (DEK1) (**Table 2**) is required for epidermal cell identity. The *dek1* mutation was originally identified in maize where it causes defective kernels that lack an aleurone cell layer (6) (**Figure 3*b***). Although the aleurone is initiated in young endosperm, it is not maintained in *dek1* mutants (55). A series of twelve maize *dek1* alleles was described with phenotypes that range from aborted embryos to viable plants that have crinkled leaves, shortened internodes, and bent nodes (7). Revertant sector analysis revealed that DEK1 functions cell-autonomously because wild-type cells cannot rescue the phenotype of adjacent *dek1* mutant cells, and *dek1* mutant cells cannot impose their phenotype onto adjacent wild-type cells (7). The maize *dek1* phenotypes are similar to those described in other plant species. *Arabidopsis dek1* mutants develop only a partial aleurone and the embryos abort during development (43, 56). Mutant embryos that develop to the globular stage show uncontrolled planes of cell division in the suspensor and embryo proper (43, 56). Suppression of *AtDek1* transcript levels via the use of RNAi permits the growth of viable plants. The phenotypes vary in severity from fused cotyledons to leaf epidermal cells that are gradually replaced by mesophyl-like cells that contain chloroplasts (43) (**Figure 3*c***). Suppression of *NbDek1* transcript levels via the use of virus-induced gene silencing in *Nicotiana benthamiana* results in hyperproliferation of epidermal cells and the formation of callus-like surfaces on leaves, stems, and flowers (1). Interestingly, despite the severe epidermal phenotypes caused by the loss of Dek1, the basic organization of inner leaf tissues is maintained, with normal palisade and mesophyll cells (1, 7, 56). *AtDEK1*-overexpressing *Arabidopsis* plants lack trichomes and show altered surface structures of leaves, ovules, and seeds (56). Taken together, these phenotypes indicate that *DEK1* is essential for epidermal cell identity, and epidermal cell identity is essential for the development of the embryo, the suspensor, and the shoot apical meristem, but not the endosperm and mesophyll (43).

The DEK1 protein contains an exceptionally high number of transmembrane domains (21), interrupted by a putative extracytoplasmic domain (55). The C-terminal domain is presumably cytoplasmic and shares homology with calpain (55). Apart from its unusual structure, DEK1 is also unique because it is highly

Table 2 Phytocalpain DEK1 (defective kernel 1)

Gene name	*DEK1*	*AtDEK1*	*NbDEK1*
Described alleles	*Dek1–1...12* (7)	*Dek1–1...4* (43, 56)	
Knockout phenotype	Aleurone deficient, embryo abortion (6, 7, 55)	Aleurone deficient, embryo abortion (43, 56)	Not reported
Knockdown phenotype	Not reported	Deformed plants lacking epidermis (43)	Callus formation on all surfaces (1)
Overexpression phenotype	Not reported	Loss of trichomes, different epidermal cell shape, but not in all ecotypes (56)	Not reported
Endogenous expression	Low levels, ubiquitous (55, 96)	Low levels, ubiquitous (56)	Low levels, ubiquitous (1)
Subcellular localization	Membrane (predicted)	Membrane (predicted)	Possibly in nuclear membrane (1)
Genetic interactors	Function of receptor-like kinase CR4 depends on Dek1 (7)	Receptor-like kinase ACR4 acts independent of Dek1 (56)	Not reported
Proteolytic activity	Domains II and III cleave casein in vitro, stimulated by Ca^{2+} (96)	Not reported	Not reported
Putative mechanism	May cleave transcription factors in response to signals from the surface of the organism (43)		

conserved throughout the plant kingdom and is encoded by a single copy of the gene in each sequenced plant genome (55). The protease domain of DEK1 has proteolytic activity in vitro that can be enhanced by calcium (96). Different models exist for DEK1 function. An initial model proposed a role for maize DEK1 in the release of signals that are perceived by receptor-like kinase CR4, because maize *cr4* mutants share some of the *dek1* phenotypes, and *cr4*/*dek1* double mutants show *dek1* phenotypes (6). In *Arabidopsis*, however, *Arabidopsis thaliana homolog of crinkly 4* (*acr4*)/*dek1* double mutants show additive effects, which suggests that *dek1* and *acr4* act in different pathways of epidermis specification (43). In another model, DEK1 cleaves homeodomain–leucine zipper IV (HDZipIV) transcription factors, which regulate epidermal cell fate (43). This model is consistent with the cell-autonomous function of DEK1 and the fact that DEK1 carries nuclear targeting signals (1). However, the true subcellular localization of DEK1 remains to be investigated.

Papain-Like Proteases Rcr3 and *Nb*CathB

Papain-like proteases (family C1, clan CA) contain catalytic residues in the order Cys, His, Asn. As with calpain (family C2, clan CA), the fold consists of two domains (lobes) and the catalytic site lies between them (29). Family C1 has been subdivided into subfamily C1A, which comprises proteases that contain disulfide bridges and accumulate in vesicles, the vacuole, or the apoplast, and family C1B, which comprises proteases that lack disulfide bridges and are located in the cytoplasm (69). Plants only have C1A proteases. There are approximately 30 papain-like proteases in subfamily C1A encoded by *Arabidopsis*, subdivided into 8 subfamilies (8). These C1A proteases are produced as preproproteases (**Figure 4*a***). The autoinhibitory prodomain folds back onto the catalytic site cleft and is removed during the activation of the protease (90). Papain-like proteases are implicated in pathogen perception, disease resistance signaling, defense against insects, and senescence (**Table 1**).

Suspensor: connection between embryo and endosperm

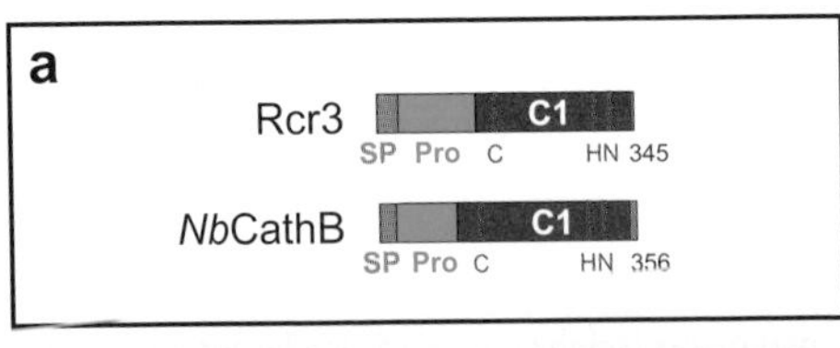

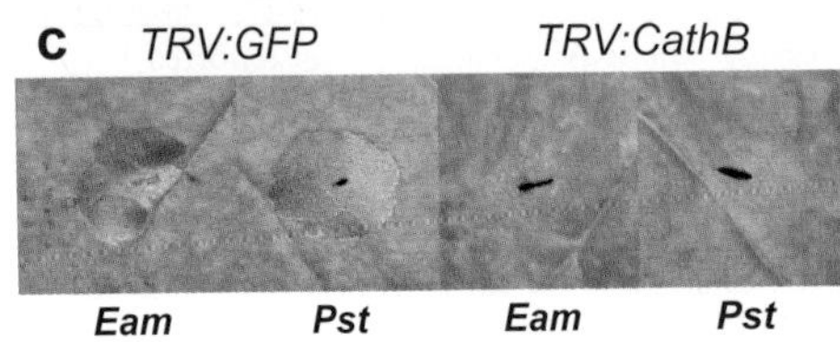

Figure 4

Rcr3 and NbCathB (*a*) Domains of Rcr3 (required for *Cladosporium* resistance 3) and *Nb*CathB (*Nicotiana benthamiana* cathepsin B) proteins. SP, signal peptide (*orange*); pro, autoinhibitory prodomain (*blue*); C1, protease domain (*red*); C, H, N, catalytic residues Cys, His, and Asn (*purple*). (*b*) Mutant *rcr3–2* plants have lost *Cladosporium fulvum* resistance gene-2 (*Cf-2*)-mediated resistance for the leaf mold fungus *Cladosporium fulvum*. Reprinted with permission from Reference 24, Copyright 2000, National Academy of Sciences, U. S. A. (*c*) Silencing of *NbCatB* suppresses the hypersensitive response induced by the nonhost bacterial pathogens *Erwinia amylovora* (*Eam*) and *Pseudomonas syringae* pv. *tomato* DC3000 (*Pst*). Figures kindly provided by Dr. E. Gilroy (Scottish Crop Research Institute, Dundee, Scotland).

Biotrophic: pathogen that feeds on living plant tissues

Hypersensitive response (HR): rapid programmed cell death that occurs at the site of pathogen infection

Nonhost resistance: when all genotypes of a host are resistant against all genotypes of a pathogen

Rcr3. Required for *Cladosporium* resistance 3 (Rcr3) (**Table 3**) is essential for the function of the resistance gene *Cf-2* in tomato. The *Cf-2* resistance gene was introgressed from wild tomato plants into cultivated tomato (*Lycopersicon esculentum*) by plant breeders to generate tomato plants that are resistant to the biotrophic leaf mold fungus *Cladosporium fulvum* carrying the avirulence gene *Avr2*. The resistance response involves a hypersensitive response (HR) of cell death at the site of infection, which prevents further pathogen growth. *Avr2* encodes a small, secreted, cysteine-rich protein without obvious homology to other proteins, and *Cf-2* encodes a receptor-like membrane protein (25, 58). *Rcr3* was identified in a forward genetic screen for *Cf-2* tomato plants that are susceptible to *C. fulvum* carrying *Avr2* (24) (**Figure 4*b***). *Rcr3* encodes a secreted papain-like cysteine protease with proven proteolytic activity (49) (**Figure 4*a***). Surprisingly, *Cf-2* plants contain the *Rcr3* allele from the wild tomato *Lycopersicon pimpinellifolium* ($Rcr3^{pim}$), which differs from the *Lycopersicon esculentum* allele ($Rcr3^{esc}$) in one amino acid deletion and six amino acid substitutions. $Rcr3^{esc}$ triggers necrotic responses in combination with *Cf-2*, but $Rcr3^{pim}$ does not (49). This explained a peculiar observation made by plant breeders in the early twentieth century. A necrosis-suppressing gene (*Ne*), whose identity was unkown, was introgressed from *L. pimpinellifolium* together with *Cf-2* to suppress autonecrotic responses induced by *Cf-2*. *Ne* proved to be $Rcr3^{pim}$ (49). Studies of the role of Rcr3 in Avr2 recognition revealed that Avr2 physically interacts with Rcr3 and inhibits its activity (72). Inhibition of Rcr3 by protease inhibitor E-64 or the absence of Rcr3 activity in *rcr3* mutants cannot trigger the resistance response mediated by Cf-2, suggesting that neither the product nor substrates of Rcr3, but the Avr2-Rcr3 complex or a specific conformational change in Rcr3, is required to trigger the resistance response (72). These data are consistent with the guard hypothesis, which predicts that resistance proteins (e.g., Cf-2) are guarding the virulence targets (e.g., Rcr3) of pathogen effector proteins (e.g., Avr2) (72, 91, 92). The upregulation of Rcr3 transcript levels during pathogen infection is consistent with a role in defense (49). However, whether Rcr3 contributes to pathogen resistance and how the Avr2-Rcr3 complex is recognized by Cf-2 remains to be investigated.

NbCathB. *Nicotiana benthamiana* Cathepsin B (*Nb*CathB) (**Table 3**) is required for the HR induced by nonhost pathogens. The potato *CathB* transcript level increases early during infection with the oomycete pathogen *Phytophthora infestans* (2). A similar quick transcriptional induction occurs with *NbCathB* in

Table 3 Papain-like proteases Rcr3 (required for *C. fulvum* resistance 3) and *Nb*CathB (*N. benthamiana* Cathepsin B)

Gene name	*Rcr3*	*NbCathB*
Described alleles	*rcr3—1...4* (24)	None
Knockout phenotype	Loss of resistance for fungus *Cladosporium fulvum* carrying Avr2 (24)	Not reported
Knockdown phenotype	Not reported	Suppresses hypersensitive cell death (35)
Overexpression phenotype	Not reported	Not reported
Endogenous expression	Higher expression in older plants, upregulated during pathogen infection (49)	Induced during hypersensitive cell death (2, 35)
Subcellular localization	Secreted into leaf apoplast (49)	Secreted (35)
Genetic interactors	Requires receptor-like protein Cf-2 (24)	Not reported
Proteolytic activity	Degrades casein and gelatin (49)	Not reported
Putative mechanism	May trigger activation of Cf-2-induced resistance response by complex formation with fungal inhibitor protein Avr2 (72)	May act in extracellular signaling to regulate hypersensitive cell death (35)

N. benthamiana during the HR (35). Virus-induced gene silencing of *NbCathB* prevents the HR induced by two distinct nonhost bacterial pathogens (**Figure 4*c***). This loss of the HR is associated with further growth of the bacteria, which indicates that nonhost resistance is hampered. The HR induced by the combined expression of avirulence protein Avr3a with resistance protein R3a was also suppressed in silenced plants, but the HR induced by coexpression of avirulence protein Avr4 and resistance protein Cf-4 was unaltered (35). This indicates that *Nb*CathB is required for some, but not for all, resistance signaling pathways. *Nb*CathB is activated during secretion and is also active in noninfected plants. The data indicate that *Nb*CathB is an extracellular protease that acts in the transduction of signals during recognition of some, but not all, avirulent pathogens. How this protease mediates HR signaling is unknown, but it represents an exciting area for further research.

Deconjugating Enzymes UCH1/2 and ESD4

The conjugation of ubiquitin and small ubiquitin-like modifiers (SUMO) to lysine residues of target proteins is an important way to regulate the location, activity, and degradation of these proteins (28). Conjugation of ubiquitin and SUMO is mediated by specific E3 ligases, whereas deconjugation is catalyzed by different proteases that belong to MEROPS families C12, C19, and C48. Ubiquitin-specific proteases (UBPs; family C19, clan CA) and ubiquitin C-terminal hydrolases (UCHs; family C12, clan CA) interact with ubiquitin through electrostatic interactions and hydrolyze the bonds formed by the C-terminal glycine of ubiquitin in a highly selective manner, releasing ubiquitin from its precursors or from ubiquitinated proteins. SUMO-deconjugating enzymes (family C48, clan CE) are specific for the C-terminal glycine of SUMO and release SUMO from both precursors and conjugates. Most C12, C19, and C48 proteins are produced in the cytoplasm without a prodomain and move to the nucleus via nuclear localization signals (NLS) (**Figure 5*a***).

Although the C12/C19 and C48 families belong to different clans, the structure of the lobes and the position of the catalytic residues are similar between CA and CE clan proteases. However, the difference between CA and CE clan proteases is that the lobes are swapped in the primary sequence, possibly owing to an ancient gene rearrangement

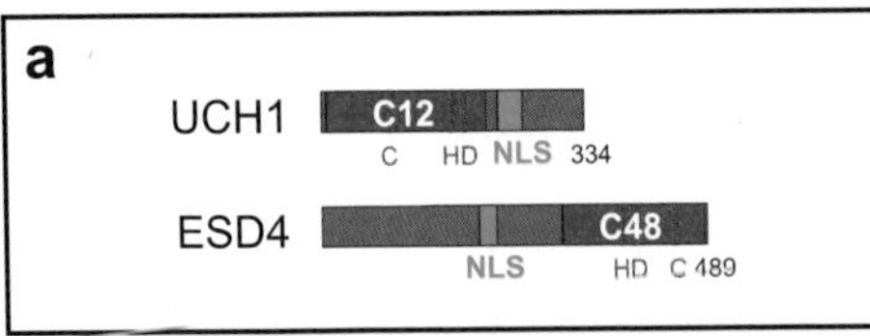

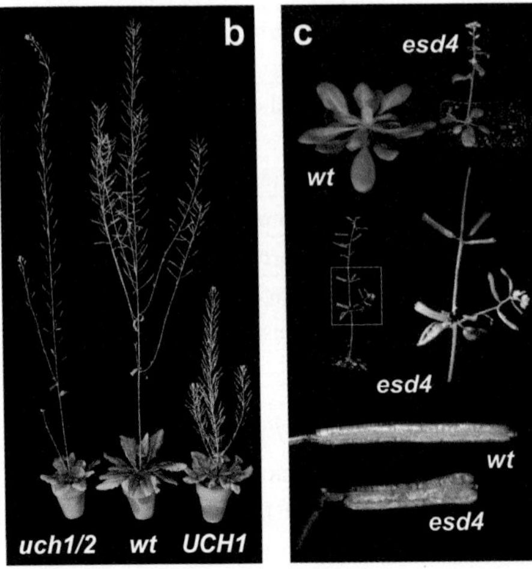

Figure 5

UCH1 and ESD4 (*a*) Domains of ubiquitin C-terminal hydrolase 1 (UCH1) and early in short days 4 (ESD4) proteins. NLS, nuclear localization signal (*green*); C12/C48, protease domain (*red*); C, H, D, catalytic residues Cys, His, and Asn (*purple*). (*b*) The *uch1–1/uch2–1* double mutant (*uch1/2*) shows less branching than wild-type, whereas the *UCH1*-overexpressing strain shows more branching than wild-type under short day conditions. The picture was kindly provided by Dr. R. Vierstra (University of Wisconsin, Madison). (*c*) *esd4–1* mutant plants flower earlier than wild-type when grown under short day conditions (*top*). *esd4–1* mutants develop siliques at unexpected positions (*middle*), and siliques are shorter and broader at the tip (*bottom*). Pictures kindly provided by Dr. N. Elrouby (Max-Planck-Institut für Züchtungsforschung, Cologne, Germany).

(63, 69). Members of the C19 family are required for pollen and embryo development (26, 27).

UCH1 and UCH2. Ubiquitin C-terminal hydrolase 1 and 2 (UCH1 and UCH2) (**Table 4**) regulate shoot architecture, probably by rescuing specific ubiquitinated proteins from degradation. Among the few UCHs encoded in the *Arabidopsis* genome, UCH1 and UCH2 share strong sequence similarity and were chosen for functional analysis. Although *uch1* and *uch2* single mutants have no phenotypes, the *uch1/uch2* double mutants show phenotypes that are often the opposite to those observed for *UCH1*-overexpressing (*35S:UCH1*) plants (101). Phenotypes in the rosette size, leaf shape, and flower organs were observed, but the strongest phenotype is displayed in the shoot architecture under short day conditions. *35S:UCH1* plants are short bushy plants covered with siliques, whereas *uch1/uch2* plants develop a less-branched primary inflorescence when compared with wild-type (101) (**Figure 5*b***). The specific phenotypes suggest that UCHs act on distinct ubiquitinated conjugates. Indeed, UCH2 can release ubiquitin from polyubiquitin precursors and from polyubiquitin conjugates, but the levels of ubiquitin conjugates are unaltered in the *35S:UCH1* and *uch1/uch2* plants (101). The phenotypes in shoot architecture suggest a possible link to auxin signaling. The phenotype of the auxin-insensitive mutants *axr1–3* and *axr2–1* is strongly enhanced by UHC1 overexpression, which indicates that auxin signaling may be affected by *UCH1/2*. Indeed, the stability of an AXR3/IAA17 reporter is stabilized in *35S:UHC1* lines (101). This result leads to the hypothesis that UCH1/2 proteins directly or indirectly rescue auxin/IAA proteins from degradation to dampen auxin signal strength or restore normal plant growth after auxin signaling. In addition, UCH1/2 proteins may also deubiquitinate proteins that are not related to auxin signaling.

ESD4. Early in short days 4 (ESD4) (**Table 4**) regulates many developmental processes, including flowering time, by modifying the sumoylation status of various proteins. The *esd4* mutant was identified in a screen for mutants that flower earlier in short day conditions. In addition to an earlier flowering time, the *esd4* mutant also has shorter internodes, smaller leaves, altered phylotaxy, fewer solitary flowers, and shorter siliques compared with wild-type (70) (**Figure 5*c***). The early flowering phenotype is partly explained by the fact that transcript levels of the floral repressor *FLOWERING LOCUS C* (*FLC*)

Table 4 Deconjugating enzymes UCH1/2 (ubiquitin C-terminal hydrolase 1/2) and ESD4 (early in short days 4)

Gene name	*UCH1/2*	*ESD4*
Described alleles	*uch1–1*, *uch2–1* (101)	*esd4–1,2* (64, 70)
Knockout phenotype	Shorter petioles, smaller leaves, deformed petals, large stigmas, less fertile, less branched (101)	Early flowering in short days, smaller leaves, shorter internodes and siliques, altered phylotaxy, fewer leaves and flowers (64, 70)
Knockdown phenotype	Not reported	Not reported
Overexpression phenotype	Shorter petioles, smaller leaves, bushy plants covered with siliques (101)	No phenotype (64)
Endogenous expression	Ubiquitous (101)	Ubiquitous (64)
Subcellular localization	Nuclear and cytoplasmic (UCH1/2-GFP) (101)	Inner surface of nuclear envelope (ESD4-GFP) (64)
Genetic interactors	UCH1 overexpression enhances *axr1/2* auxin mutant phenotypes (101)	In same pathway as nuclear pore anchor NUA (99)
Proteolytic activity	Cleaves ubiquitin from polyubiquitin and from ubiquitin conjugates (101)	Cleaves *At*SUMO1/2 from its precursor and from conjugates (20, 64)
Putative mechanism	May rescue specific ubiquitin-tagged proteins (e.g., AXR3) from degradation (101)	Regulates sumoylation status of different proteins involved in diverse developmental processes (64)

are reduced in *esd4* mutants, which causes an upregulation of the flowering time genes *SUPPRESSOR OF OVEREXPRESSION OF CONSTANS 1* (*SOC1*) and *FLOWERING LOCUS T* (*FT*) (70). However, analysis of *flc/esd4* double mutants indicated that *ESD4* also regulates flowering time genes independently of *FLC* (70). *ESD4* encodes a desumoylating enzyme that can cleave certain *Arabidopsis* SUMO proteins from their precursor and from conjugates (20, 64). Consistent with the presumed role of ESD4 in desumoylating other proteins, SUMO conjugates accumulate in *esd4* mutants, and SUMO overexpression in *esd4* plants further enhances the accumulation of SUMO conjugates and the *esd4* mutant phenotype (64). ESD4 proteins localize to the inner surface of the nuclear envelope (64) and physically interact with a nuclear pore anchor (NUA) (99). *nua* mutants phenocopy *esd4* mutants and *nua/esd4* double mutants are indistinguishable from single mutants, which suggests that both genes act in the same pathway (99). Interestingly, besides an increased level of SUMO conjugates and a reduced *FLC* transcript level, *nua* mutants accumulate more mRNA in the nucleus, consistent with the role of NUA proteins as determined in yeast (99). Given the spectrum of different phenotypes of *esd4* mutants and the range of proteins that are regulated by sumoylation, ESD4 probably acts in multiple pathways to desumoylate different substrates, each involved in different processes, including flowering time.

Caspase-Like Proteases MCAs and VPEs

Caspases (family C14, clan CD) have been intensively investigated in animals because they regulate apoptotic cell death (73). Their fame is also a source of confusion because the hunt for caspase activities (cleavage after Asp) in plants resulted in the description of many "caspase-like proteases" that are probably not related to caspases (93). In this review, caspase-like proteases are defined as sharing sequence homology or at least structural homology to the animal caspases. Proteases that share sequence homology with animal caspases are absent from plant

Apoptotic cell death: a form of programmed cell death in animals

Caspase: cysteine protease that cleaves substrates after aspartic acid residues

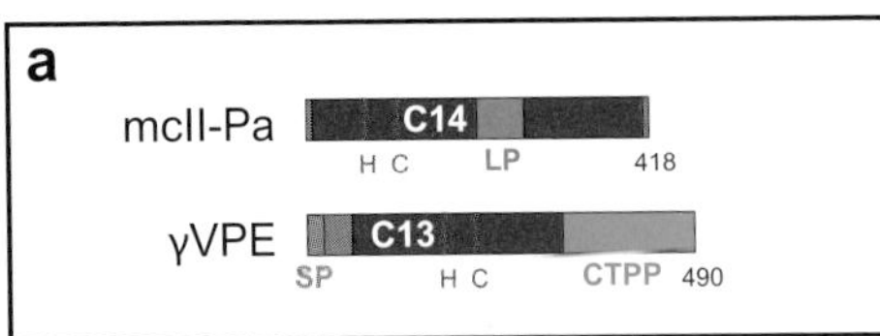

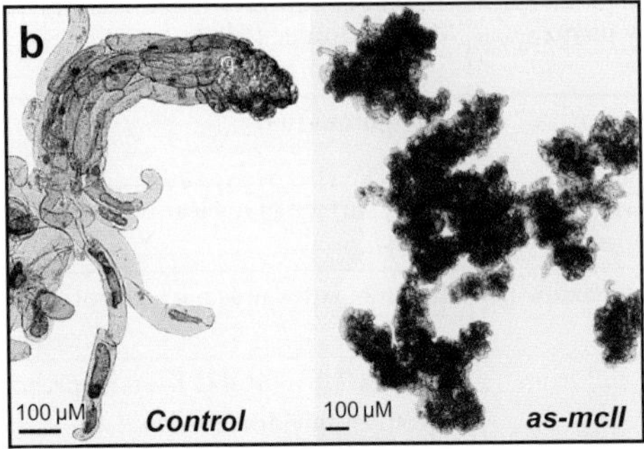

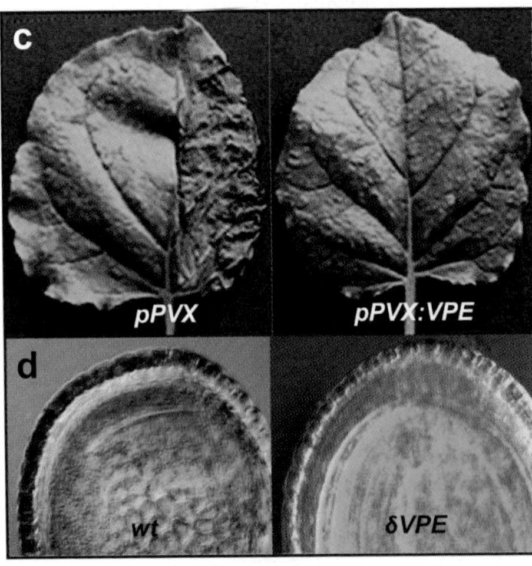

Figure 6

mcII-Pa and VPE (*a*) Domains of metacaspase type II of *Picea abies* (mcII-Pa) and γ vacuolar processing enzymes (γVPE) proteins. SP, signal peptide (*orange*); CTPP, autoinhibitory C-terminal propeptide (*blue*); C13/C14, protease domain (*red*); H, C, catalytic residues His and Cys (*purple*); LP, linker peptide (*green*). (*b*) Silencing of *mcII-Pa* prevents cell death induced during somatic embryogenesis, visualized by staining with acetocarmine (*red*, viable cells) and Evans blue (*blue*, dead cells). Picture kindly provided by Dr. P. Bozhkov (Sveriges Lantbruksuniversitet, Uppsala, Sweden). (*c*) *NbVPE* silencing blocks the hypersensitive response (HR), cell death induced by tobacco mosaic virus (TMV), in plants containing the *N* resistance gene. Collapsed tissue is visible 24 h after triggering HR. Reprinted from Reference 45 with permission from the American Association for the Advancement of Science. (*d*) Cell death in two cell layers during seed coat formation is delayed in Δ*vpe* mutants. Reprinted from Reference 65 with permission from the American Society of Plant Biologists.

genomes, but plants do contain metacaspases (MCAs; family C14) and vacuolar processing enzymes (VPEs; family C13). These caspase-like enzymes are unified in clan CD and use a catalytic Cys that is activated by the catalytic His for nucleophilic attack. Caspase-like enzymes are folded as an $\alpha/\beta/\alpha$ sandwich (17). Clan CD proteases are highly selective for cleavage after specific residues: Asp for animal caspases, Arg for MCAs, and Asn for VPEs (69). Most CD clan proteases are produced with N- and C-terminal propeptides (**Figure 6*a***). Caspases and MCAs (family C14) are usually cytoplasmic or nuclear, whereas VPEs (family C13) are located in vesicles or in the vacuole. (Meta)caspases are produced with a linker protein that is proteolytically removed, which results in a heterocomplex of a p20 chain and a p10 chain (**Figure 6*a***). Given the evolutionary relationship with caspases, caspase-like enzymes in plants have long been suspected to regulate PCD. Published work from the past few years indicates that this is indeed the case (summarized below).

mcII-Pa. Metacaspase type II of *Picea abies* (mcII-Pa) (**Table 5**) mediates PCD during somatic embryogenesis in Norway spruce (*Picea abies*). Somatic embryogenesis of Norway spruce is an elegant system in which to study embryogenesis because embryo development can be synchronized by changing the hormone balance, and the embryos have large suspensor cells that undergo gradual, successive PCD (11). The fact that this PCD is accompanied by caspase activity and can be inhibited by a caspase inhibitor led to the identification of *mcII-Pa*, a metacaspase that is specifically expressed in suspensor cells that undergo PCD (84). Silencing *mcII-Pa* prevents PCD and suppresses caspase activity and the frequency of nuclear degradation (84) (**Figure 6*b***). However, biochemical characterization of the mcII-Pa protein revealed that it cleaves after Arg but not after Asp, which suggests that the caspase activity is not caused by mcII-Pa activity, but by enzymes activated by mcII-Pa. Interestingly, mcII-Pa

Table 5 Caspase-like proteases mcII-Pa (metacaspase type II of *Picea abies*) and VPE (vacuolar processing enzyme)

Gene name	*mcII-Pa*	*VPE*
Described alleles	None	*αβγδvpe* (51); *γvpe-1* (71); *δvpe-1*, *δvpe-4* (65)
Knockout phenotype	Not reported	*αβγδvpe*: abolished toxin-induced cell death (51)
		γvpe: slightly decreased pathogen resistance (71)
		δvpe: delayed cell death during seed coat development (65)
Knockdown phenotype	No cell death in somatic embryos, no embryonic pattern formation (84)	*NbVPE:* blocks virus-induced hypersensitive cell death (38)
Overexpression phenotype	Not reported	Not reported
Endogenous expression	Only in somatic embryo cells that are committed to cell death and in procambial strands that lead to xylem differentiation (84)	*NbVPE*: upregulated during hypersensitive cell death (38)
		γVPE: upregulated during programmed cell death (PCD) and pathogen infection (51, 71) *δVPE*: only in maternal cell layers during seed development (65)
Subcellular localization	Cytoplasmic and nuclear (immunolocalization) (12)	In vacuole and vesicles (immunolocalization) (27)
Genetic interactors	Not reported	Not reported
Proteolytic activity	Cleaves after Arg, but not after Asp in vitro (12)	Cleaves after Asn (48)
Putative mechanism	May cleave nuclear structural proteins to disassemble the nuclear envelope during PCD (12)	May activate vacuolar enzymes and disintegrate the vacuolar membrane to release hydrolytic enzymes during PCD (37, 38, 51, 65)

translocates from the cytoplasm into the nucleus during PCD and associates with chromatin and disassembling nuclear pore complexes (12). Nuclear disintegration can be induced by adding mcII-Pa protein to nuclei isolated from PCD-deficient cell lines (12). This nuclear disintegration can be inhibited by a mcII-Pa inhibitor and is absent if a catalytic mutant of mcII-Pa is added instead (12). The data lead to a hypothesis in which cytoplasmic metacaspases participate in PCD by degrading the nuclear envelope, which leads to nuclear degradation (12).

VPEs. Vacuolar processing enzymes (VPEs) (**Table 5**) are essential for PCD induced during disease resistance responses, by a fungal toxin, and during seed coat development. VPEs were initially studied for their role in the maturation of seed storage proteins, but the upregulation of these genes during different kinds of PCD prompted further phenotype investigation. Silencing of VPEs in *N. benthamiana* abolishes the hypersensitive cell death triggered by tobacco mosaic virus (TMV) in plants carrying the TMV-resistance gene *N* (38) (**Figure 6*c***). Cytological studies revealed that vacuolar collapse precedes PCD and both are prevented in VPE-silenced plants (38). *Arabidopsis* has four VPEs: α, β, γ, and δ. *δVPE* is expressed specifically in two cell layers of the maternal inner integument of developing seed coats (65). These cell layers normally undergo PCD early during seed development, which results in the degradation of nuclei and shrinkage of the inner integument. However, this PCD is absent in *δvpe* mutants, although the final seed coat is normal (**Figure 6*d***). In contrast to *δVPE*, the *γVPE* gene is expressed throughout the plant, and *γvpe* mutant plants show a weak reduced resistance toward various pathogens

Metacaspases: proteases that share certain conserved sequence motifs with caspases

Integument: covering of an organ, in this case a seed

(71). *Arabidopsis* mutants lacking all four VPE genes ($\alpha\beta\gamma\delta vpe$) are insensitive to cell death induced by the fungal toxin Fumonisin B1 (FB1) (51). Of the single mutants, only γvpe shows a delayed FB1-induced cell death, which suggests that *VPE* genes act redundantly and that γVPE makes the largest contribution to FB1-induced PCD in leaves (51). VPE proteases act on caspase substrates and are inhibited by caspase inhibitors, which indicates that VPEs are the plant functional orthologs of animal caspases (38, 51, 65, 71). The mechanism of how VPEs act in PCD is unknown, but their location, and therefore probably their signaling role, is distinct from that of animal caspases. VPEs may activate vacuolar enzymes, which may trigger the collapse of the vacuolar membrane, resulting in the disintegration of cellular structures by released hydrolytic enzymes.

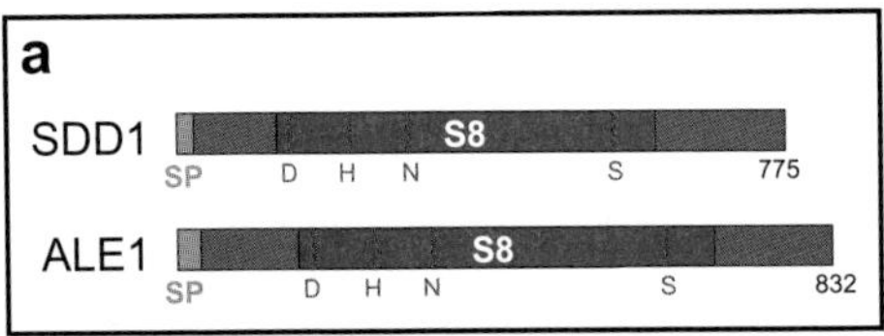

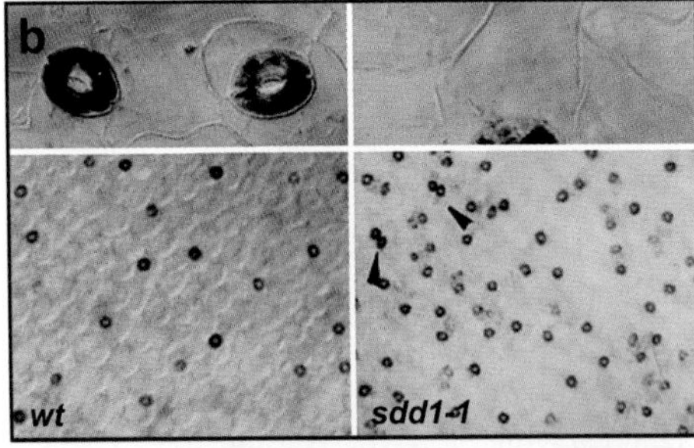

Figure 7

SDD1 and ALE1 (*a*) Domains of stomatal density and distribution 1 (SDD1) and abnormal leaf shape 1 (ALE1) proteins. SP, signal peptide (*orange*); S8, protease domain (*red*); D, H, N, S, catalytic residues Asp, His, and Ser (*purple*). (*b*) *sdd1–1* mutants have fourfold more stomata and stomata clusters than wild-type. Reprinted with permission from Reference 9, Copyright 2000, Cold Spring Harbor Laboratory Press. (*c*) 16-day-old seedlings of *ale1–1* have fused cotyledons that lack a cuticle (*arrow*). Reprinted from Reference 88 with permission from the Company of Biologists.

SERINE PROTEASES

Serine proteases use the active site Ser as a nucleophile. The catalytic mechanism is very similar to that of cysteine proteases, and some serine proteases are even evolutionarily related to cysteine proteases. With more than 200 members, serine proteases are the largest class of proteolytic enzymes in plants. Plant serine proteases are divided into 14 families. These families belong to 9 clans that are evolutionarily unrelated to each other. Families S8, S9, S10, and S33 are the largest serine protease families in plants, with each containing approximately 60 members. Biological functions for serine proteases have been described for some of the subtilases (SDD1 and ALE1; family S8, clan SB), carboxypeptidases (BRS1 and SNG1/2; family S10, clan SC), and plastid-localized members of the S1, S26, and S14 families (DegPs, Plsp1, and ClpPs; **Table 1**).

Subtilisin-Like Proteases SDD1 and ALE1

Subtilases (family S8, clan SB) contain a catalytic triad in the order Asp, His, Ser, and are folded as a seven-stranded β-sheet, sandwiched between two layers of helices. Subtilases are encoded as preproproteins and are usually secreted and processed at both the N and C terminus (68) (**Figure 7*a***). Most subtilases are endopeptidases. Some subtilases are expected to have a broad substrate range, others are considered to be specific prohormone convertases. The *Arabidopsis* genome encodes approximately 70 subtilases, which can be divided into three subfamilies (8). A biological role is known for only two *Arabidopsis* subtilases (see below). However, no macroscopic phenotypes were observed for

Table 6 Subtilisin-like proteases SDD1 (stomatal density and distribution 1) and ALE1 (abnormal leaf shape 1)

Gene name	*SDD1*	*ALE1*
Described alleles	*sdd1–1* (9)	*ale1–1*, *ale1–2* (88)
Knockout phenotype	More stomata, also in clusters (9)	Embryo lacks cuticle (88)
Knockdown phenotype	Not reported	Not reported
Overexpression phenotype	2–3-fold decrease in stomata (95)	Not reported
Endogenous expression	Only in guard mother cells (95)	Only in endosperm, not in seedling (88)
Subcellular localization	Secreted (predicted) truncated SDD1-GFP in the plasma membrane (95)	Secreted (predicted)
Genetic interactors	Overexpression phenotype depends on receptor-like protein TMM (too many mouths) (95)	Acts independently of receptor-like kinases ACR4 (*Arabidopsis thaliana* homolog of crinkly 4) and ALE2 (Abnormal leaf shape 2) (88, 97)
Proteolytic activity	Not reported	Not reported
Putative mechanism	Could release signals from developing stomata to suppress the development of neighboring stomata (95)	Could activate signals or enzymes from the endosperm to stimulate cuticle formation on the embryo surface (88)

knockout lines of 55 other subtilases, which indicates that these proteases act redundantly or have condition-specific roles (68).

SDD1. Stomatal density and distribution 1 (SDD1) (**Table 6**) specifically regulates the position of stomata development within the epidermis. The *sdd1–1* mutant was identified in a forward genetic screen for mutants with an altered stomatal density and distribution (9). The number of stomata in *sdd1–1* mutants is two- to fourfold higher than wild-type in all aerial organs except for the cotyledons (**Figure 7*b***). Many stomata are also clustered and almost every epidermal cell is in contact with at least one guard cell. No other morphological alterations are observed in *sdd1–1* mutant plants, consistent with the specific expression of the SDD1 gene: Transcripts are only detectable in guard mother cells during guard cell development (95). The *SDD1* gene encodes an S8 subtilisin-like serine protease (9) (**Figure 7*a***). The SDD1 protein is expected to be secreted, but localization studies with SDD1-GFP fusion proteins failed because subtilases are proteolytically processed at both the N and C terminus. A GFP fusion with a truncated SDD1 localizes to the plasma membrane, but it is unknown if this truncated fusion protein complements the *sdd1–1* phenotype (95). Overexpression of SDD1 results in a two- to threefold reduction in stomatal density in wild-type plants, and is accompanied by the formation of stomata that are arrested before the division into the two guard cells (95). *SDD1* overexpression does not change the increased number of stomata caused by a mutation in receptor-like protein TMM (too many mouths), which indicates that SDD1 acts upstream of TMM in the same signaling pathway (95). Although SDD1 remains to be investigated biochemically, the data are consistent with the model that SDD1 is localized at the plasma membrane of developing stomata mother cells and generates signals that move to neighboring cells to prevent the formation of nearby stomata, either by inhibiting the development of stomata or by promoting differentiation into epidermal cells (95). TMM may act as a receptor of this signal (95).

ALE1. Abnormal leaf shape 1 (ALE1) (**Table 6**) is responsible for cuticle development during embryogenesis. *ale1* mutants were identified during a forward genetic screen because they have an obvious phenotype: *ale1* seedlings die within three days after germination in open air but they survive at high relative humidity, which suggests that the lethality is caused by water loss (88). Mutant *ale1* plants produce small, crinkled cotyledons and leaves that are often fused to each other (**Figure 7*c***). Once beyond the seedling stage, *ale1* mutants develop normally. Electron microscopy reveals that no cuticle is formed on *ale1* embryos, and that the endosperm remains attached to the embryo tissue (88). The lack of a cuticle in *ale1* mutant embryos explains the crinkled and fused cotyledons and excessive water loss, which causes seedling lethality. Interestingly, the *ALE1* gene is expressed only in the endosperm and not in the embryo or the seedling, which suggests that the endosperm plays a role in the formation of the cuticle of the embryo (88). The *ALE1* gene encodes a S8 subtilisin-like serine protease (88) (**Figure 7*a***). The biochemical properties and subcellular location of the ALE1 protein remain to be characterized, but ALE1 is predicted to be secreted and proteolytically active (88). *ale1* phenotypes are similar to phenotypes caused by mutations in the receptor-like kinases ACR4 and ALE2. However, *acr4* and *ale2* mutant alleles act synergistically with *ale1*, which indicates that ALE1 has a different mode of action (89, 97). The data suggest that the ALE1 protein is secreted by the endosperm and promotes cuticle formation on the embryo, e.g., by proteolytically activating enzymes involved in cuticle deposition (88).

Figure 8

SNG1 and BRS1 (*a*) Domains of sinapoylglucose accumulator 1 (SNG1) and brassinosteroid insensitive 1 suppressor 1 (BRS1) proteins. SP, signal peptide (*orange*); LP, linker peptide (*green*); S10, protease domain (*red*); S, D, H catalytic residues Ser, Asp, His (*purple*). (*b*) *sng1* mutants are less fluorescent than wild-type under UV light because they do not accumulate the UV protectant compound sinapoylmalate. Reprinted from Reference 52 with permission of copyright holder, American Society of Plant Biologists. (*c*) *BRS1* overexpression suppresses the dwarfing caused by the *bri1-5* allele. Reprinted with permission from Reference 54, Copyright 2001, National Academy of Sciences, U. S. A.

Carboxypeptidase-Like Proteases SNG1/2 and BRS1

Serine carboxypeptidase protease-like proteins (SCPLs; family S10, clan SC) contain a catalytic triad in the primary sequence order Ser, Asp, His and fold as an α/β hydrolase, which is common to many other hydrolytic enzymes. SCPLs are distinct from other serine proteases in that they are active only at acidic pH. SCPLs are produced as preproproteases and often accumulate in the vacuole (**Figure 8*a***). Posttranslational removal of an internal linker peptide results in a disulfide-linked heterocomplex of A- and B-chains (**Figure 8*a***). There are nearly 60 SCPLs in the *Arabidopsis* genome, divided into different major subfamilies (32). Biological functions have been described for three SCPLs that belong to two different subfamilies. These proteins display a striking variety not only in phenotypes, but also especially in the reactions they catalyze.

Table 7 Carboxypeptidase-like proteins SNG1/2 (sinapoylglucose accumulator 1/2) and BRS1 [brassinosteroid insensitive 1 (BRI1) suppressor 1]

Gene name	*SNG1; SNG2*	*BRS1*
Described alleles	*sng1–1…6* (52, 57) *sng2* (82)	*brs1–1* (54)
Knockout phenotype	*sng1*: less fluorescence of leaves under UV (52)	No phenotype (54)
Knockdown phenotype	Not reported	Not reported
Overexpression phenotype	Not reported	Suppression of *bri1–5* phenotype (54)
Endogenous expression	*SNG1*: in all organs (32) *SNG2*: in siliques only (32)	Ubiquitous, overlaps with *BRI1* expression (106)
Subcellular localization	Vacuolar (predicted)	Secreted (predicted) BRS1-GFP is in the cell wall (106)
Genetic interactors	Not reported	Suppresses phenotypes only of weak *bri1* alleles, not of strong *bri1* alleles or *er* (*erecta*) and *clv1* (*clavata 1*) mutants (54)
Proteolytic activity	No carboxypeptidase activity observed for either SNG1 (52) or SNG2 (81, 82)	Cleaves basic and hydrophobic synthetic dipeptides (106)
Putative mechanism	Catalyzes the transacylation of sinypolyesters via the use of sinapoylglucose as donor and malate (SNG1) or choline (SNG2) as acceptor (52, 82)	Could remove proteins that block brassinosteroid (BR) perception or activate proteins required for BR perception (106)

SNG1 and SNG2. Sinapoylglucose accumulator 1 and 2 (SNG1 and SNG2) (**Table 7**) are SCPLs that act as acyltransferases in the biosynthesis of sinapoyl esters, which provide UV-B protection (52, 57, 82). Leaves of *Arabidopsis sng1* mutants are less fluorescent under UV light, lack sinapoylmalate, and accumulate the donor molecule, sinapoylglucose (52, 57) (**Figure 8*b***). Similarly, seeds of *sng2* mutants lack sinypoylcholine and accumulate choline (81). The identification of the proteins encoded by *SNG1* and *SNG2* was surprising. Heterologous expression of the SNG1 and SNG2 proteins demonstrated that they catalyze the acyltransferase reaction but lack carboxypeptidase activity (52, 81, 82). SNG1 and SNG2 belong to a plant-specific clade of SCPL proteins that also includes 19 other *Arabidopsis* SCPLs and a tomato glucose acyltransferase (53), but not BRS1 (see below) (32). This suggests that this clade of SCPLs contains more acyltransferases that may contribute to the diversity of secondary metabolites in plants (32).

BRS1. Bri1 suppressor 1 (BRS1) (**Table 7**) contributes to the perception of brassinosteroid (BR) growth hormone, although phenotypes are observed only by overexpression analysis in a *bri1* mutant background. Receptor-like kinase BRI1 (BR insensitive 1) is essential for the perception of BR, and reduced BR perception in *bri1* mutants leads to a dwarfed phenotype. BRS1 was identified from an activation tagging screen for suppressors of *bri1–5*, a weak mutant allele of *BRI1* (54) (**Figure 8*c***). Overexpression of *BRS1* leads to suppression of the dwarf phenotype of *bri1–5* mutant plants, but not of kinase-dead mutant *bri1* alleles (54). The phenotype is specific because BRS1 overexpression does not cause phenotypes in wild-type plants and can not suppress phenotypes caused by mutations in the receptor-like kinases *clavata-1* (*CLV1*) and *erecta* (*ER*) (54). No phenotypes are observed in *brs1* knockout lines, which indicates that BRS1 homologs act redundantly (54). Overexpression of a catalytic mutant of BRS1 could not suppress the *bri1–5* phenotype, which indicates that catalytic activity is required for BRS1 function (54). BRS1 was characterized biochemically after purification from *Arabidopsis* plants overexpressing BRS1 (106). As with other S10 enzymes, BRS1 activation involves the posttranslational removal of a linker peptide, which results in A- and B-chains that remain linked through disulfide bridges. This activation step requires BRS1 activity because active site BRS1 mutants accumulate as proproteins. Active BRS1 can cleave synthetic dipeptides in vitro, which is significant because other S10 family members, such as SNG1 (see above), act as acyltransferases, rather than proteases. A role for endogenous *BRS1* in wild-type plants remains to be shown, but its expression pattern is ubiquitous and overlaps with that of *BRI1*, and BRS1-GFP fusion proteins are detected in the cell wall, which is different from most SCPLs (106). These details and the genetic data are consistent with the model that BRS1 acts upstream of BRI1 in BR signaling, either by activating proteins that assist in BR perception, or by removing proteins that block the BR binding site.

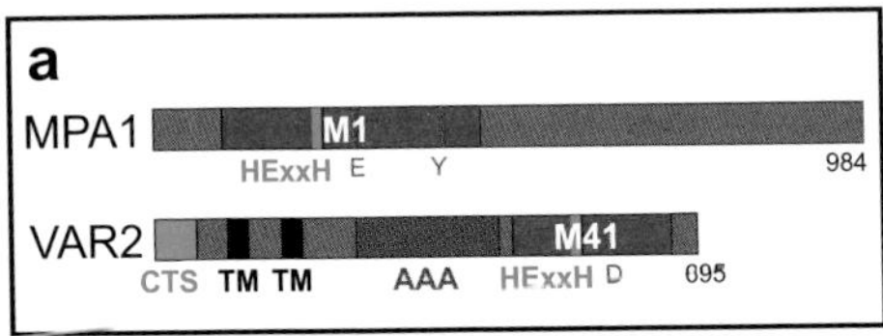

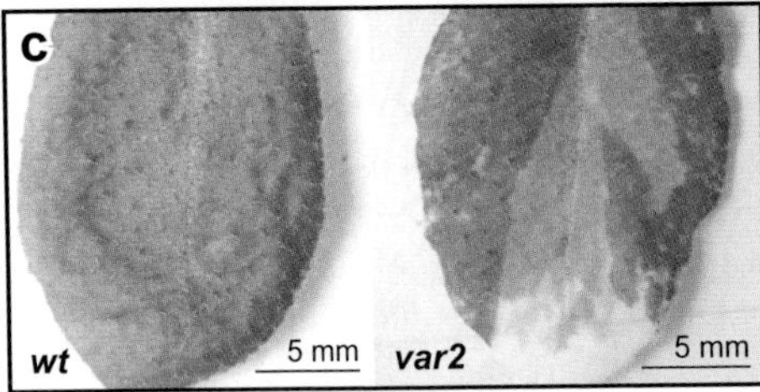

Figure 9

MPA1 and VAR1/2 (*a*) Domains of meiotic prophase aminopeptidase 1 (MPA1) and yellow variegated 1 (VAR1) proteins. CTS, chloroplast targeting sequence (*green*); TM, transmembrane domain (*black*); AAA, ATP-binding cassette (*purple*); M1/M41, protease domain (*red*); E, Y, D, catalytic residues Glu, Tyr, and Asp (*purple*); HExxH, zinc-binding motif (*green*). (*b*) The top panel shows that *mpa1* mutants have nonviable pollen (*green*). The bottom panel shows that during meiosis (diakinesis, metaphase I, anaphase I), chromosomes do not pair during metaphase I in the *mpa1* mutants, which leads to unequal division of the chromosomes. Reprinted from Reference 78 with permission from the American Society of Plant Biologists. (*c*) *var2* mutant lacks developed chloroplasts in the white sectors. Reprinted from Reference 47 with permission from the American Society of Plant Biologists.

METALLOPROTEASES

Metalloproteases contain catalytic metal ions that activate water for nucleophilic attack while stabilizing the oxyanion hole. Plant genomes encode approximately 100 metalloproteases that belong to 19 families. These families are diverse and are divided over 11 clans that are evolutionarily unrelated. Plant metalloprotease families usually contain fewer than 20 members. Metalloproteases are involved in nodulation, plastid differentiation, thermotolerance, regulation of root and shoot meristem size, sensitivity to auxin conjugates, and meiosis (**Table 1**). Four of these proteases are discussed below.

Clan MA Metalloproteases MPA1 and VAR1/2

Clan MA metalloproteases are united by the presence of a HExxH motif in which the two His (H) residues are ligands of a single zinc ion, and the Glu (E) provides a catalytic function (**Figure 9*a***). These proteases are folded as a bundle of helices and a β-sheet, and the active site is between two helices. In plants, clan MA contains six protease families. Members of the M1 family are mostly aminopeptidases, whereas family M41 members act progressively from both the N and C terminus. M41 proteases share homology with the

Table 8 Clan MA metalloproteases MPA1 (meiotic prophase aminopeptidase 1) and VAR1/2 (yellow variegated 1/2)

Gene name	*MPA1*	*VAR2*
Described alleles	*mpa1* (78)	*var2–1...8* (18, 19, 60, 87)
Knockout phenotype	Impaired meiosis, reduced fertility, suppressed recombination (78)	Variegation: white sectors in all tissues, except cotyledons (19, 60)
Knockdown phenotype	Not reported	Not reported
Overexpression phenotype	Not reported	No phenotype (103)
Endogenous expression	Reproductive and vegetative tissues (78)	All green tissues (102)
Subcellular localization	Cytoplasm and nucleus (78)	Thylakoid membrane (18)
Genetic interactors	Not reported	*var2* phenotype is suppressed by *fug1*; *sco1*; *cplc2* and overexpression of *FtsH8* (61, 66, 102)
Proteolytic activity	Not reported	Not reported
Putative mechanism	May regulate complex assembly and disassembly required for chromosome pairing during prophase I of meiosis (78)	Dual: removes photodamaged D1 protein from photosystem II (3) and regulates thylakoid formation during chloroplast biogenesis (18)

well-studied FtsH protease of *Escherichia coli*. FtsH proteases are membrane-bound, contain two transmembrane domains, and show ATP-dependent proteolytic activity.

MPA1. Meiotic prophase aminopeptidase 1 (MPA1) (**Table 8**) is essential for chromosome pairing and recombination during meiosis. *mpa1* mutants were identified from a forward genetic screen for mutants with reduced fertility (78). Siliques of *mpa1* mutants are smaller and contain only two or three seeds. A large proportion of *mpa1* pollen is not viable, smaller than wild-type, and deformed. Cytological analysis reveals that meiosis is impaired in both male and female gametogenesis (78). Homologous chromosomes fail to pair at the end of prophase I and the chromosomes separate unequally between the daughter cells (**Figure 9*b***). Homologous recombination is significantly repressed and only a few nuclei contain the proper five chromosomes by the end of anaphase II. *MPA1* encodes a metalloprotease of a M1 subfamily that is sensitive to the antibiotic purimycin and the noncompetitive fluorescent inhibitor DAMPAQ-22. Adding these inhibitors to wild-type plants can phenocopy the *mpa1* phenotype (78). Detailed immunolocalization studies with meiotic marker proteins indicate that the window of MPA1 activity occurs at an early stage in the recombination pathway, soon after the RecA homolog RAD51 is loaded onto the chromatin, but before loading of the mismatch repair protein MSH4 (78). These data indicate that MPA1 may be required for the assembly or disassembly of protein complexes that contain RAD51 or MSH4. MPA1 is also expressed in vegetative tissue, but its function there is unknown because *mpa1* plants grow normally.

VAR2. Yellow variegated 2 (VAR2) (**Table 8**) is crucial for chloroplast biogenesis and repair of photosystem II (PSII). Variegation is an obvious phenotype because parts of the green tissues appear white (**Figure 9*c***). Instead of chloroplasts, white tissues of *var2* mutants contain undifferentiated plastids that lack the typical thylakoids (19, 87). Plastids in dark-grown *var2* seedlings (etioplasts) resemble those in wild-type, but fail to differentiate in the light (18). The white sectors are initially yellow and are found in all green organs of the plant (leaves, stems, and siliques), except the cotyledons (19, 60). Eight *var2* alleles have been described, each displays different degrees of variegation (18, 19, 77, 87). *VAR2* is a nuclear gene that encodes an ATP-dependent FtsH metalloprotease (18, 87) (**Figure 9*a***).

Variegation: patchiness of pigmentation of leaves and other organs

VAR2 proteins accumulate in the thylakoid membrane with the domains for ATP binding and proteolysis facing the stroma (18).

Thylakoids: disc-shaped membrane vesicles in chloroplast stroma that carry the photosynthetic apparatus

Variegation in *var2* mutants also depends on VAR2 homologs. VAR2 (FtsH2) is one of 12 FtsH proteases encoded by the *Arabidopsis* genome (77, 102). The closest homolog of VAR2 is FtsH8. Although *ftsh8* mutants do not have a phenotype (77), *FtsH8* overexpression can suppress the *var2* phenotype (102) and the *var2/ftsh8* double mutant is completely white and can only survive on sugar-containing medium (104). These results suggest that VAR2 and FtsH8 act redundantly and support the hypothesis that FtsH8 compensates for the lack of VAR2 in the green sectors of *var2* mutant plants (102). Sector formation could arise from clonal propagation of cells that contain malfunctioning proplastids early during leaf development (102). VAR1 (FtsH5) is one of the other chloroplastic FtsH proteases, and *var1* mutant plants display a less severe variegation compared with *var2* (60). Similar to *var2*, the *var1* phenotype can be suppressed by overexpression of its closest homolog, *FtsH1* (103), and *var1/ftsh1* double mutants are completely white (104). VAR1 and VAR2 proteins form heterocomplexes that become unstable if one of the complex partners is missing (77, 102).

Apart from its role in chloroplast biogenesis, VAR2 is also essential for the repair of photosystem II by removal of the photodamaged D1 protein (3). However, hampered repair of photosystem II is probably not the cause of nonfunctional plastids in white sectors because these plastids are underdeveloped and not a result of photobleaching (47). This result suggests that VAR2 plays a role in chloroplast biogenesis, perhaps in the regulation of the formation of thylakoids by the accumulation of VAR2-containing complexes during chloroplast development.

a
AMP1 M28 TM HDE DH TRF 705
EGY1 M50 CTS HExxH 8xTM 548

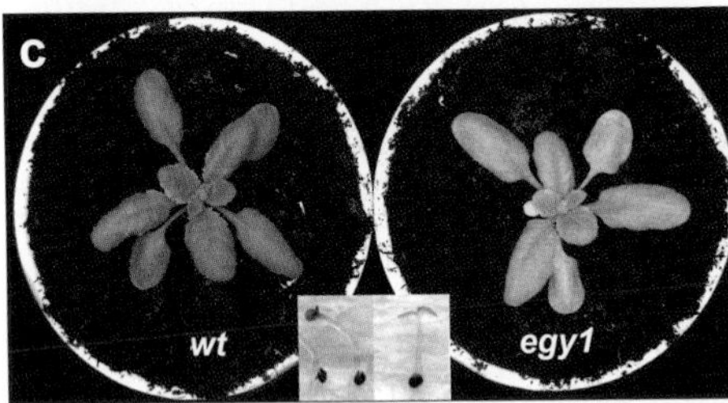

Figure 10

AMP1 and EGY1 (*a*) Domains of altered meristem program 1 (AMP1) and ethylene-dependent gravitropism-deficient yellow-green 1 (EGY1) proteins. CTS, chloroplast targeting sequence (*green*); TM, transmembrane domain (*black*); TRF, TATA binding protein–related factors (TRF) dimer motif (*dark blue*); M28/M50, protease domain (*red*); E, catalytic residue Glu (*purple*); HExxH, H, D, zinc-ion binding residues (*green*). (*b*) *amp1* mutants display an enlarged shoot apical meristem that generates more organs. Reprinted with permission from Reference 22, Copyright 1997, National Academy of Sciences, U. S. A. (*c*) *egy1* mutants display yellowish leaves with underdeveloped plastids and a hampered shoot gravitropism (*inset*). Pictures kindly provided by Dr. N. Li (Hong Kong University of Science and Technology, Hong Kong, China).

Metalloproteases AMP1 and EGY1

Two more metalloproteases are discussed here: AMP1 (family M28, clan MH) and EGY1 (family M50, clan MM). These clans are not related to each other evolutionarily or structurally. Family M28 of clan MH contains proteases that are folded as a six-stranded β-sheet surrounded by helices; the active site contains two cocatalytic zinc ions (**Figure 10*a***). Family M50 of clan MM contains proteases that are membrane-bound and contain a HExxH motif that probably binds a single zinc ion (**Figure 10*a***). The catalytic site may be in the membrane because it is part

Table 9 Metalloproteases AMP1 (altered meristem program 1) and EGY1 (ethylene-dependent gravitropism-deficient yellow-green 1)

Gene name	*AMP1*	*EGY1*
Described alleles	*amp1-1…7; pt; hpt; cop2* (14, 22, 44, 75)	*egy1-1..3* (15)
Knockout phenotype	Polycotyly, more leaves, larger shoot apical meristem (14, 22, 44, 62)	Less chlorophyl, no gravitropism, fewer seeds (15)
Knockdown phenotype	Not reported	Not reported
Overexpression phenotype	Not reported	Not reported
Endogenous expression	Throughout the plant (39)	Throughout the plant, lower in roots (15)
Subcellular localization	Unknown	Chloroplast membrane (EGY1-GFP) (15)
Genetic interactors	Independent from *clv1* and *clv3* (*clavata 1* and *3*) (62); suppressor of monopterous (*mp*) (94)	Not reported
Proteolytic activity	Not reported	Degrades β-casein in vitro (15)
Putative mechanism	May release peptides that promote differentiation or inactivate peptides that suppress differentiation (39)	May regulate the assembly and maintenance of photosystem II complexes (15)

of a predicted transmembrane domain, but so far no tertiary structure is available to confirm this topology.

AMP1. Altered meristem program 1 (AMP1) (**Table 9**) restricts the size of the shoot apical meristem by promoting differentiation. *AMP1* has many names because it was identified from many forward genetic screens and has a series of obvious phenotypes: *amp1* seedlings grow in the dark as though they are growing in the light [hence *cop2*, *constitutive photomorphogenesis* (14, 41)], frequently have more than two cotyledons [hence *hpt*, *hauptling* (44)], and generate leaves in whorls of three instead of one by one [hence *pt*, *primordia timing* (22)] (**Figure 10*b***). A reduced apical dominance also makes *amp1* mutant plants bushier, the rate of leaf formation is doubled, and the plants flower earlier (14, 22, 62). The *amp1* mutation causes male and female semisterility, which results in shorter siliques and fewer seeds (14, 62). The earliest *amp1* phenotype during embryogenesis appears at the second division of the zygote. The basal cell normally divides transversely to generate the suspensor, but in *amp1* mutant embryos the cells in the apical region of the suspensor undergo a series of vertical divisions to generate cells that become incorporated into an oversized shoot apical meristem (SAM) (22, 94). The SAM stays large throughout development and causes the initiation of mutiple organs. This phenotype suggests that in wild-type plants AMP1 promotes differentiation, which keeps the SAM small (94). Mutant *amp1* plants produce more cytokinin, probably as a result of the increased SAM size (14, 22, 39, 62). A larger SAM also occurs in *clavata* (*clv*) mutants. However, *amp1/clv1* and *amp1/clv3* double mutants show additive effects on SAM size, which indicates that AMP1 acts independently of the CLV1/3 pathway (62). AMP1 interacts genetically with MONOPTEROUS (MP), an auxin-response factor that acts with the Aux/IAA family in transcriptional regulation (94). Phenotypes of *mp* mutants are the opposite of *amp1* mutant phenotypes, and are suppressed in *amp1/mp* double mutants (94). This suggests that in wild-type plants, MP counteracts AMP1 by carving out meristematic niches by locally overcoming the differentiation-promoting activity of AMP1 (94). The data suggest that AMP1 releases signaling peptides that promote differentiation at the SAM border or inactivates signaling proteins that suppress differentiation (39, 94). Molecular details of these signaling pathways remain to be investigated.

Shoot apical meristem (SAM): population of dividing cells at the tip of the shoot axis

Gravitropic response: growth in relation to gravity

Grana: stack of thylakoids in chloroplasts

Amyloplast: colorless starch-forming plastid

EGY1. Ethylene-dependent gravitropism-deficient yellow-green 1 (EGY1) (**Table 9**) is a chloroplast intermembrane metalloprotease, essential for plastid development and shoot gravitropism. *egy1* mutants were identified from a genetic screen for mutants that were both pigmentation deficient and defective in ethylene-stimulated hypocotyl gravitropic responses (15). Instead of normal chloroplasts, *egy1* mutants contain plastids that have fewer stromal thylakoids, no grana and fewer starch grains. The *egy1* mutants also accumulate significantly fewer chlorophyll a/b binding (CAB) proteins, which are part of photosystem II antennae in the thylakoid membrane (15). Hampered photosynthesis explains the reduced growth rate, lower seed number, and the yellowish color (**Figure 10*c***). However, the absence of the shoot gravitropism response in *egy1* mutants is unexplained, although chloroplasts in the endodermis of *egy1* mutants may not differentiate into amyloplasts, which are the plastids required for the gravitropic response (15). EGY1 contains eight transmembrane helices and resides in the membrane of chloroplasts where it may regulate the maintenance and assembly of PSII complexes by intermembrane proteolysis. This is consistent with the accumulation of the EGY1 protein in chloroplasts in response to light (15). Interestingly, although EGY1 and VAR2 probably both act on the maintenance of photosystem II, their roles are likely different given the differences in phenotypes.

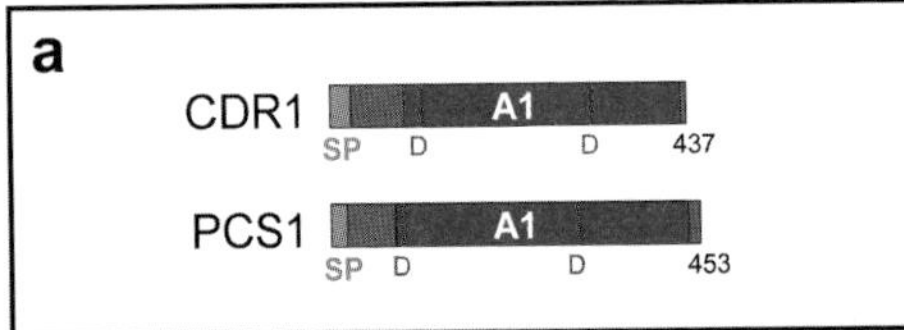

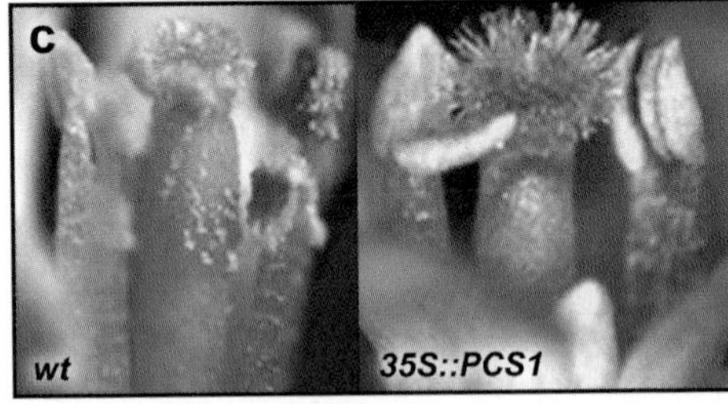

Figure 11

CDR1 and PCS1 (*a*) Domains of constitutive disease resistance 1 (CDR1) and promotion of cell survival 1 (PCS1) proteins. SP, signal peptide (*orange*); A1, protease domain (*red*); D, catalytic residue Asp (*purple*). (*b*) *CDR1*-overexpressing plants are semidwarfed and show enhanced disease resistance to infections with *Pseudomonas* bacteria. Reprinted from Reference 98 with permission from Macmillan Publishers Ltd. (*c*) *PCS1* overexpression prevents pollen release from anthers because programmed cell death is blocked in specific anther cell types. Reprinted from Reference 34 with permission from Macmillan Publishers Ltd.

ASPARTIC PROTEASES

Aspartic proteases contain two aspartic residues, which support a water molecule that acts as the nucleophile during proteolysis. Only three families of aspartic proteases exist in plants, but these families are so large that aspartic proteases make up the second-largest protease class in plants. Biological roles for aspartic proteases are only known for two pepsin-like proteases in family A1 of clan AA.

Pepsin-Like Proteases CDR1 and PCS1

Pepsin-like proteases (family A1, clan AA) are endopeptidases that are most active at acidic pH. The enzymes are produced as preproproteases and are often secreted from cells as inactive, glycosylated enzymes that activate autocatalytically at acidic pH (**Figure 11*a***). The three-dimensional structure reveals traces of ancient gene duplication: Pepsin-like proteases comprise two highly homologous lobes, each contains a homologous catalytic aspartate residue that forms the active site between the two lobes (69). The *Arabidopsis* genome encodes approximately 70 pepsin-like proteases, which can be divided into five subfamilies (8). CDR1 and PCS1 are typical pepsin-like proteases, with very different biological roles.

CDR1. Constitutive disease resistance 1 (CDR1) (**Table 10**) acts in disease resistance signaling. CDR1 was identified by activation tagging (98). *CDR1* overexpression suppresses disease caused by virulent strains of the pathogenic bacterium *Pseudomonas syringae* (**Figure 11*b***). This reduced susceptibility is explained by a constitutive upregulation of defense responses in *CDR1*-overexpressing plants, including microlesions, high levels of reactive oxygen intermediates (ROIs) and salicylic acid (SA), and constitutive expression of pathogenesis-related (PR) genes (86, 98). The constitutive defense response explains why *CDR1*-overexpressing plants are smaller and their leaves are darker and curled compared with wild-type (**Figure 11*b***). None of these phenotypes occurs when *CDR1* overexpressing plants also express the bacterial *NahG* gene, which encodes an enzyme that converts SA into cathechol. This result indicates that SA is required for *CDR1*-induced responses (98). CDR1-knockout lines are not available, but antisense *CDR1* lines are more susceptible to virulent *Pseudomonas* strains, which indicates that endogenous CDR1 also acts in defense responses (98). Active site mutants of CDR1 could not trigger resistance when overexpressed, which indicates that CDR1 protease activity is required for CDR1 function (98). The CDR1 protein displays proteolytic activity and accumulates in the extracellular space of plants during pathogen attack (86, 98). CDR1 activity may release small peptides in the apoplast that can systemically induce *PR* gene expression (98). Thus, CDR1 activity may lead to the generation of an endogenous extracellular elicitor that could act as a mobile signal for the induction of systemic acquired resistance (SAR).

Pathogenesis-related genes (PR genes): genes that are upregulated during pathogen infection

Systemic acquired resistance (SAR): activation of defense in uninfected parts of a plant

PCS1. Promotion of cell survival (PCS1) (**Table 10**) is an endoplasmic reticulum (ER)-resident aspartic protease that prevents

Table 10 Pepsin-like proteases CDR1 (constitutive disease resistance 1) and PCS1 (promotion of cell survival 1)

Gene name	*CDR1*	*PCS1*
Described alleles	Unknown	*pcs1* (34)
Knockout phenotype	Not reported	Degeneration of pollen and abortion of ovules and embryos (34)
Knockdown phenotype	Enhanced susceptibility to infection with *Pseudomonas* bacteria (98)	Not reported
Overexpression phenotype	Semidwarfing; constitutive disease resistance (86, 98)	Blocks programmed cell death in anther dehiscence (34)
Endogenous expression	Ubiquitous and slightly upregulated during pathogen infection (98)	Only in gametophytes and developing seeds (34)
Subcellular localization	Secreted (predicted) CDR1-GFP is in the cell wall and endoplasmic reticulum, and CDR1 is in the apoplast (86, 98)	Endoplasmatic reticulum (EndoH sensitive; PCS1-GFP) (34)
Genetic interactors	CDR1 overexpression phenotypes are absent in salicylic acid (SA)-deficient *NahG* lines (98)	Not reported
Proteolytic activity	Cleaves bovine serum albumin in vitro (86, 98)	Cleaves casein in vitro (34)
Putative mechanism	Could generate endogenous extracellular peptides that act as mobile signals for systemic acquired resistance (86, 98)	May release survival factors or inactivate death signals (34)

cell death during gametogenesis and embryogenesis. When knockout lines for aspartic proteases were investigated, homozygous *pcs1* plants could not be obtained (34). Further investigation revealed that a third of the pollen and ovules from heterozygous *pcs1/+* plants are degenerated, and the embryos die before the torpedo stage (34). Consistent with the observed phenotypes, *PCS1* gene expression is specific to developing gametophytes and developing seeds (34). However, when ectopically overexpressed, *PCS1* blocks PCD in the anther, which prevents the release of pollen because stobium and septum cells in the anther cell wall do not undergo PCD (34) (**Figure 11*c***). Biochemical studies show that PCS1 has proteolytic activity, but how this activity contributes to its function remains to be demonstrated. Intriguingly, deglycosylation experiments and experiments with GFP-fusion proteins demonstrated that PCS1 is localized to the ER (34). The phenotypes can be explained by a role for PCS1 in the prevention of cell death in certain cell types. PCS1 is likely involved in the proteolytic release of survival factors or the inactivation of death signals.

CONCLUSIONS

The biological roles of plant proteases are strikingly diverse (**Figure 12**). Protease functions have been identified for different stages in the life of a plant: meiosis (MPA1); gametophyte survival (PCS1); suspensor formation (mcII-Pa); embryo cuticle deposition (ALE1); seed coat formation (δVPE); meristem size (AMP1); epidermal cell fate (DEK1); stomata development (SDD1); chloroplast development (VAR2); plastid development (EGY1); growth (BRS1); UV

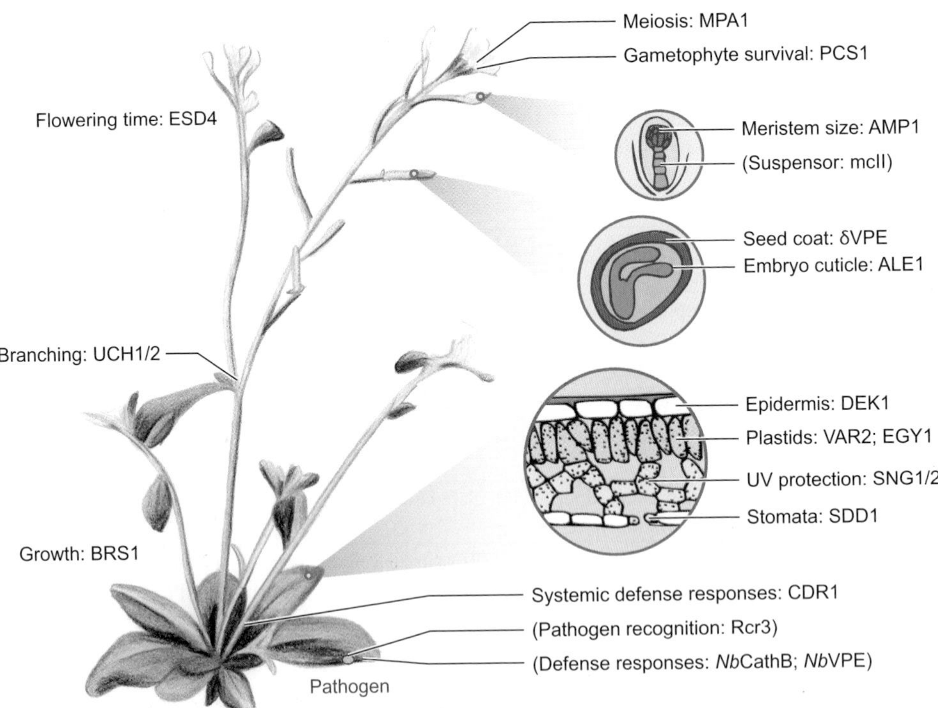

Figure 12

Summary of the biological roles of the discussed proteases. Proteases that were not studied in *Arabidopsis* are shown in parentheses.

protection (SNG1); pathogen recognition (Rcr3); defense responses (*Nb*CathB, *Nb*VPE, γVPE); systemic defense responses (CDR1); flowering time (ESD4); and branching (UCH1/2).

Proteases are crucial for plants. Protease mutations are frequently lethal (e.g., *dek1*, *ale1*, and *pcs1*), and many result in severe fitness-reducing phenotypes (e.g., *esd4*, *var2*, *egy1*, and *mpa1*), whereas some proteases act redundantly (e.g., *VAR2*, *VPEs*, *BRS1*, and *UCH1/2*), and are lethal when both genes are mutated (e.g., VAR2/FtsH8). The redundancy and lethality associated with protease mutants limit the opportunities offered by forward and reverse genetics.

The biochemical roles and subcellular locations of proteases are often conserved within the clans. Clan CA/CE, for example, contains conjugating enzymes, and clans SB and AA contain secreted proteases. However, there are only weak correlations between biological function and evolutionary relatedness within protease clans. Clan CD, for example, contains proteases that regulate PCD, and CA clan proteases are often involved in pathogen-induced hypersensitive cell death. For most clans, however, biological functions are very different, e.g., BRS1 and SNG1/2 (clan SB), MPA1 and VAR2 (clan MA), and CDR1 and PCS1 (clan AA). These differences indicate that these protease families did not arise from the evolution of new biological processes, but were recruited from existing protease families during evolution.

Proteases are found at different subcellular locations (**Figure 13**). Of the 17 discussed proteases, six are secreted into the apoplast (Rcr3, *Nb*CathB, ALE1, SDD1, BRS1, CDR1), two are in the vacuole (VPEs, SNG1/2), two are in the chloroplast (VAR2, EGY1), one resides in the ER (PCS1), four are cytoplasmic/nuclear in localization (UCH1/2, ESD4, MPA1, mcII-Pa), and two have unknown subcellular localizations (AMP1, DEK1). Transmembrane domains are found in three of the proteases (DEK1,

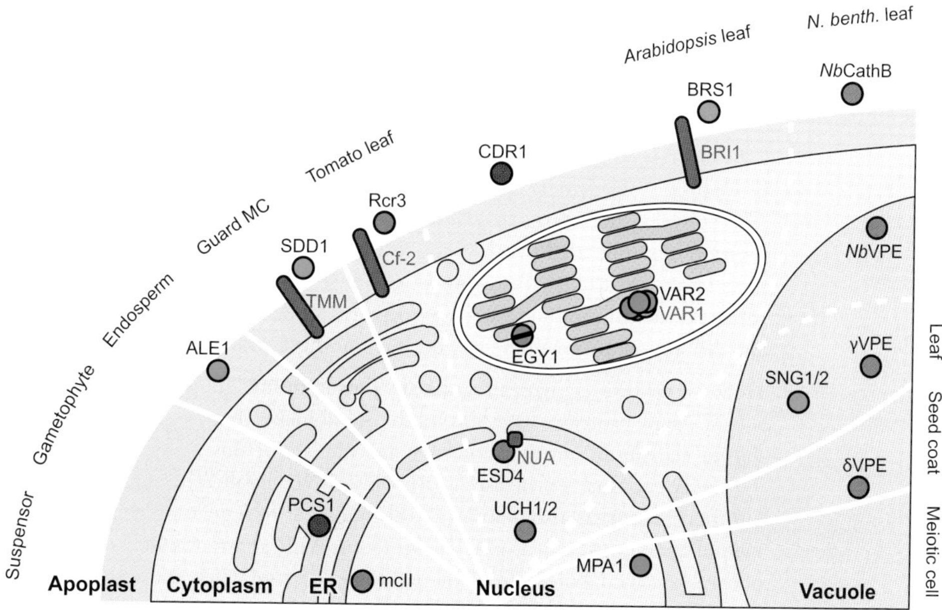

Figure 13

Summary of the subcellular locations of proteases and their interactors, as summarized in this review.

VAR2, and EGYI), and the others are soluble or associated with membranes.

No biologically relevant substrate has been identified for any of the proteases described so far. However, some proteases do not act through their substrates (e.g., Rcr3), or act by catalyzing nonproteolytic reactions (e.g., SNG1/2). The absence of identified substrates for the other proteases is the major bottleneck for research because it hampers further progress in understanding the molecular basis of how these proteases function.

We know about other proteins that are required for the function of only a few proteases, although the molecular details of these interactions are not yet known. Functions of secreted proteases frequently depend on receptor-like proteins: BRS1 enhances signaling through BRI1, SDD1 signals through TMM, and Rcr3 inactivation by Avr2 is monitored by Cf-2. In contrast, VAR2 and ESD4 physically interact with VAR1 and NUA, respectively; these interactions are essential for their function.

FUTURE ISSUES

Proteases are crucial in plants, but this field has only just started to unfold. There are phenotypic data for many proteases, but there is still little understanding of their molecular mechanisms. More than 500 proteases remain to be functionally characterized. A daunting task lies ahead to understand the molecular mechanisms of these proteases. The challenge is summarized in the following issues:

1. Where are the proteases localized? This question has already been answered for most proteases, most often via the use of GFP fusion proteins, but for some proteases, like DEK1 and AMP1, this issue remains to be addressed. This task can be challenging because many proteases are processed, which makes it difficult to generate stable GFP-fusion proteins, as described for SDD1.
2. What are the substrates? This question is the hardest to resolve but also the most important. Proteases can cleave many proteins in vitro, but the biologically relevant target substrate is determined not only by substrate specificity, but also by its colocalization with the protease, in both time and space. If there is one major biologically relevant substrate to be cleaved, then this substrate might be identified through forward genetic approaches for suppressors of protease mutant phenotypes. Alternatively, characterization of the protease cleavage specificity and the subcellular location might be used to select and test candidate proteins on the basis of their predicted colocalization, expression, and putative cleavage sites. Other approaches for substrate identification are yeast two-hybrid screening, immobilized protein arrays, and differential proteomics (79), but each of these approaches has its limitations.
3. How are protease activities regulated? This is an intriguing question, but hardly resolved. Many proteases have autoinhibitory domains that are proteolytically removed during activation, but the molecular mechanism of this activation is often unclear. The activity of many proteases is probably also controlled by endogenous inhibitors, but their identity is also unknown. Another layer of regulation comes from environmental conditions such as pH, calcium ions, ATP, and redox status. These issues are poorly described, but are fundamental to understand when and where the protease is active. Fluorescent activity-based probes and substrates are useful tools to image the space and time of protease activities (5), but their potential remains to be exploited.

4. How do proteases contribute to the phenotype? This bigger picture requires knowledge of not only the identity of the substrate, but also of other components that are part of the network in which the protease functions, such as receptors and transcription factors. Putting all this knowledge together should provide a systems biology model that explains how the protease is incorporated into the network that leads to the phenotype.
5. What is the biological function of the remaining >500 proteases? As described above, protease functions differ tremendously, even within families of related proteases. This makes it difficult to predict the biological function of a protease. Reverse genetics, via the use of RNAi approaches, T-DNA lines, or overexpression, may reveal phenotypes. This approach, however, may not be successful if the protease acts redundantly with family members. Pharmacological approaches can offer another approach to annotate functions to proteases. This approach also allows a choice of time point, dosage, and specificity of chemical interference.

DISCLOSURE STATEMENT

The author is not aware of any biases that might be perceived as affecting the objectivity of this review.

ACKNOWLEDGMENTS

I am extremely grateful to Dr. Réka Tóth, Dr. Monika Kalde, Dr. Nabil Elrouby, Dr. Farnusch Kaschani, and the members of the Plant Chemetics lab for critically reading the manuscript and providing helpful suggestions. I would like to thank Dr. Vierstra, Dr. Li, Dr. Elrouby, Dr. Ingham, Dr. Gilroy, and Dr. Bozhkov for kindly providing pictures and suggestions.

LITERATURE CITED

1. Ahn JW, Kim M, Lim JH, Kim GT, Pai HS. 2004. Phytocalpain controls the proliferation and differentiation fates of cells in plant organ development. *Plant J.* 38:969–81
2. Avrova AO, Taleb N, Rokka VM, Heilbronn J, Hein I, et al. 2004. Potato oxysterol binding protein and cathepsin B are rapidly up-regulated in independent defence pathways that distinguish *R* gene-mediated and field resistances to *Phytophthora infestans*. *Mol. Plant Pathol.* 5:45–56
3. Bailey S, Thompson E, Nixon PJ, Horton P, Mullineaux CW, et al. 2002. A critical role for the VAR2 FtsH homologue or *Arabidopsis thaliana* in the photosystem II repair cycle in vivo. *J. Biol. Chem.* 277:2006–11
4. Bartel B, Fink GR. 1995. *ILR1*, an aminohydrolase that releases active indole-3-acetic acid from conjugates. *Science* 268:1745–48
5. Baruch A, Jeffery DA, Bogyo M. 2004. Enzyme activity–it's all about image. *Trends Cell Biol.* 14:29–35
6. Becraft PW, Asuncion-Crabb Y. 2000. Positional cues specify and maintain aleurone cell fate in maize endosperm. *Development* 127:4039–48
7. Becraft PW, Li K, Dey N, Asuncion-Crabb Y. 2002. The maize *dek1* gene functions in embryonic pattern formation and cell fate specification. *Development* 129:5217–25

8. Beers EP, Jones AM, Dickerman AW. 2004. The S8 serine, C1A cysteine and A1 aspartic protease families in *Arabidopsis*. *Phytochemistry* 65:43–58
9. Berger D, Altmann T. 2000. A subtilisin-like serine protease involved in the regulation of stomatal density and distribution in *Arabidopsis thaliana*. *Genes Dev.* 14:1119–31
10. Bölter B, Nada A, Fulgosi H, Soll J. 2006. A chloroplastic inner envelope membrane protease is essential for plant development. *FEBS Lett.* 580:789–94
11. Bozhkov PV, Filonova LH, Suarez MF, Helmersson A, Smertenko AP, et al. 2004. VEIDase is a principal caspase-like activity involved in plant programmed cell death and essential for embryonic pattern formation. *Cell Death Differ.* 11:175–83
12. Bozhkov PV, Suarez MF, Filonova LH, Daniel G, Zamyatnin AA Jr, et al. 2005. Cysteine protease mcII-Pa executes programmed cell death during plant embryogenesis. *Proc. Natl. Acad. Sci. USA* 102:14463–68
13. Casamitjana-Martínez E, Hofhuis HF, Xu J, Liu CM, Heidstra R, Scheres B. 2003. Root-specific *CLE19* overexpression and the *sol1/2* suppressors implicate a CLV-like pathway in the control of *Arabidopsis* root meristem maintenance. *Curr. Biol.* 13:1435–41
14. Chaudhurry AM, Letham S, Craig S, Dennis ES. 1993. *amp1*–a mutant with high cytokinin levels and altered embryonic pattern, faster vegetative growth, constitutive photomorphogenesis and precocious flowering. *Plant J.* 4:907–16
15. Chen G, Bi YR, Li N. 2005. *EGY1* encodes a membrane-associated and ATP-independent metalloprotease that is required for chloroplast development. *Plant J.* 41:364–75
16. Chen J, Burke JJ, Velten J, Xin Z. 2006. FtsH11 protease plays a critical role in *Arabidopsis* thermotolerance. *Plant J.* 48:73–84
17. Chen JM, Rawlings ND, Stevens RAE, Barrett AJ. 1998. Identification of the active site of legumain links it to caspases, clostripain and gingipains in a new clan of cysteine endopeptidases. *FEBS Lett.* 441:361–65
18. Chen M, Choi YD, Voytas DF, Rodermel S. 2000. Mutations in the *Arabidopsis VAR2* locus cause leaf variegation due to the loss of a chloroplast FtsH protease. *Plant J.* 22:303–13
19. Chen M, Jensen M, Rodermel S. 1999. The *yellow variegated* mutant of *Arabidopsis* is plastid autonomous and delayed in chloroplast biogenesis. *J. Heredity* 90:207–14
20. Colby T, Matthäi A, Boeckelmann A, Stuible HP. 2006. SUMO-conjugating and SUMO-deconjugating enzymes from *Arabidopsis*. *Plant Physiol.* 142:318–32
21. Combier JP, Vernié T, de Billy F, El Yahyaoui F, Mathis R, Gamas P. 2007. The *Mt*MMPL1 early nodulin is a novel member of the matrix metalloendoproteinase family with a role in *Medicago truncatula* infection by *Sinorhizobium meliloti*. *Plant Physiol.* 144:703–16
22. Conway LJ, Poethig RS. 1997. Mutations of *Arabidopsis thaliana* that transform leaves into cotyledons. *Proc. Natl. Acad. Sci. USA* 94:10209–14
23. Davies RT, Goetz DH, Lasswell J, Anderson MN, Bartel B. 1999. *IAR3* encodes an auxin conjugate hydrolase from *Arabidopsis*. *Plant Cell* 11:365–76
24. Dixon MS, Golstein C, Thomas CM, van Der Biezen EA, Jones JDG. 2000. Genetic complexity of pathogen perception by plants: the example of *Rcr3*, a tomato gene required specifically by Cf-2. *Proc. Natl. Acad. Sci. USA* 97:8807–14
25. Dixon MS, Jones DA, Keddie JS, Thomas CM, Harrison K, Jones JD. 1996. The tomato *Cf-2* disease resistance locus comprises two functional genes encoding leucine-rich repeat proteins. *Cell* 84:451–59
26. Doelling JH, Soyler-Orgretim G, Phillips AR, Otegui MS, Chandler JS, et al. 2007. The ubiquitin-specific protease subfamily UBP3 and UBP4 is essential for pollen development in *Arabidopsis thaliana*. *Plant Physiol.* In press

27. Doelling JH, Yan N, Kurepa J, Walker J, Vierstra RD. 2001. The ubiquitin-specific protease UBP14 is essential for early embryo development in *Arabidopsis thaliana*. *Plant J.* 27:393–405
28. Downes B, Vierstra RD. 2005. Post-translational regulation in plants employing a diverse set of polypeptide tags. *Biochem. Soc. Trans.* 33:393–99
29. Drenth J, Jansoniu J, Koekoek R, Swen HM, Wolters BG. 1968. Structure of papain. *Nature* 218:929–32
30. Dunn BM. 2001. Determination of protease mechanism. In *Proteolytic Enzymes: A Practical Approach*, ed. R Beynon, JS Bond, pp. 77–104. Oxford: Univ. Press. 2nd ed.
31. Eason JR, Ryan DJ, Watson LM, Hedderley D, Christey MC, et al. 2005. Suppression of the cysteine protease, aleurain, delays floret senescence in *Brassica oleracea*. *Plant Mol. Biol.* 57:645–57
32. Fraser CM, Rider LW, Chapple C. 2005. An expression and bioinformatics analysis of the *Arabidopsis* serine carboxypeptidase-like gene family. *Plant Physiol.* 138:1136–48
33. García-Lorenzo M, Sjödin A, Jansson S, Funk C. 2006. Protease gene families in *Populus* and *Arabidopsis*. *BMC Plant Biol.* 6:30
34. Ge X, Dietriech C, Matsuno M, Li G, Berg G, et al. 2005. An *Arabidopsis* aspartic protease functions as an anti-cell-death component in reproduction and embryogenesis. *EMBO Rep.* 6:282–88
35. Gilroy E, Hein I, van der Hoorn RAL, Boevink P, Venter E, et al. 2007. Involvement of cathepsin B in the plant disease resistance hypersensitive response. *Plant J.* 53:1–13
36. Golldack D, Popova OV, Dietz KJ. 2002. Mutation of the matrix metalloproteinase At2-MMP inhibits growth and causes late flowering and early senescence in *Arabidopsis*. *J. Biol. Chem.* 277:5541–47
37. Hara-Nishimura I, Hatsugai N, Nakaune S, Kuroyanagi M, Nishimura M. 2005. Vacuolar processing enzyme: an executor of plant cell death. *Curr. Opin. Plant Biol.* 8:404–8
38. Hatsugai N, Kuroyanagi M, Nishimura M, Hara-Nishimura I. 2006. A cellular suicide strategy of plants: vacuole-mediated cell death. *Apoptosis* 11:905–11
39. Helliwell CA, Chin-Atkins AN, Wilson IW, Chapple R, Dennis ES, Chaudhury A. 2001. The *Arabidopsis AMP1* gene encodes a putative glutamate carboxypeptidase. *Plant Cell* 13:2115–25
40. Hosfield CM, Elce JS, Davies PL, Jia Z. 1999. Crystal structure of calpain reveals the structural basis of Ca^{2+}-dependent protease activity and a novel mode of enzyme activation. *EMBO J.* 18:6880–89
41. Hou Y, Von Arnim AG, Deng XW. 1993. A new class of *Arabidopsis* constitutive photomorphogenic genes involved in regulating cotyledon development. *Plant Cell* 5:329–39
42. Inoue K, Baldwin AJ, Shipman RL, Matsui K, Theg SM, Ohme-Takagi M. 2005. Complete maturation of the plasmid protein translocation channel requires a type I signal peptidase. *J. Cell Biol.* 171:425–30
43. Johnson KL, Degnan KA, Walker JR, Ingram GC. 2005. AtDEK1 is essential for specification of embryonic epidermal cell fate. *Plant J.* 44:114–27
44. Jürgens G, Mayer U, Torres Ruiz R, Berleth T, Misera S. 1991. Genetic analysis of pattern formation in the *Arabidopsis* embryo. *Development* 1(Suppl.):27–38
45. Hatsugai N, Kuroyanagi M, Yamada K, Meshi T, Tsuda S, et al. 2004. A plant vacuolar protease, VPE, mediates virus-induced hypersensitive cell death. *Science* 305:855–58
46. Kapri-Pardes E, Naveh L, Adam Z. 2007. The thylakoid lumen protease Deg1 is involved in the repair of photosystem II from photoinhibition in *Arabidopsis*. *Plant Cell* 19:1039–47
47. Kato Y, Miura E, Matsushima R, Sakamoto W. 2007. White leaf sectors in *yellow variegated2* are formed by viable cells with undifferentiated plastids. *Plant Physiol.* 144:952–60

48. Kinoshita T, Yamada K, Hiraiwa N, Kondo M, Nishimura M, Hara-Nishimura I. 1999. Vacuolar processing enzyme is up-regulated in the lytic vacuoles of vegetative tissues during senescence and under various stressed conditions. *Plant J.* 19:43–53
49. Krüger J, Thomas CM, Golstein C, Dixon MS, Smoker M, et al. 2002. A tomato cysteine protease required for Cf-2-dependent disease resistance and suppression of autonecrosis. *Science* 296:744–47
50. Kuroda H, Maliga P. 2003. The plastid *clpP1* protease gene is essential for plant development. *Nature* 425:86–89
51. Kuroyanagi M, Yamada K, Hatsugai N, Kondo M, Nishimura M, Hara-Nishimura I. 2005. Vacuolar processing enzyme is essential for mycotoxin-induced cell death in *Arabidopsis thaliana*. *J. Biol. Chem.* 280:32914–20
52. Lehfeldt C, Shirley AM, Meyer K, Ruegger MO, Cusumano JC, et al. 2000. Cloning of the *SNG1* gene of *Arabidopsis* reveals a role for a serine carboxypeptidase-like protein as an acyltransferase in secondary metabolism. *Plant Cell* 12:1295–306
53. Li AX, Steffens JC. 2000. An acyltransferase catalysing the formation of diacylglucose is a serine carboxypeptidase-like protein. *Proc. Natl. Acad. Sci. USA* 97:6902–7
54. Li J, Lease KA, Tax FE, Walker JC. 2001. BRS1, a serine carboxypeptidase, regulates BRI1 signaling in *Arabidopsis thaliana*. *Proc. Natl. Acad. Sci. USA* 98:5916–21
55. Lid SE, Gruis D, Jung R, Lorentzen JA, Ananiev E, et al. 2002. The *defective kernel 1* (*dek1*) gene required for aleurone cell development in the endosperm of maize grains encodes a membrane protein of the calpain gene superfamily. *Proc. Natl. Acad. Sci. USA* 99:5460–65
56. Lid SE, Olsen L, Nestestog R, Aukerman M, Brown RC, et al. 2005. Mutation in the *Arabidopsis thaliana DEK1* calpain gene perturbs endosperm and embryo development while overexpression affects organ development globally. *Planta* 221:339–51
57. Lorenzen M, Racicot V, Strack D, Chapple C. 1996. Sinapic acid ester metabolism in wild type and a sinapoylglucose-accumulating mutant of *Arabidopsis*. *Plant Physiol.* 112:1625–30
58. Luderer R, Takken FLW, de Wit PJGM, Joosten MHAJ. 2002. *Cladosporium fulvum* overcomes *Cf-2*-mediated resistance by producing truncated AVR2 elicitor proteins. *Mol. Microbiol.* 45:875–84
59. Martin MN, Saladores PH, Lambert E, Hudson AO, Leustek T. 2007. Localisation of members of the γ-glutamyl transpeptidase family identifies sites of glutathione and glutathione S-conjugate hydrolysis. *Plant Physiol.* 144:1715–32
60. Martinez-Zapater JM. 1993. Genetic analysis of variegated mutants in *Arabidopsis*. *J. Hered.* 84:138–40
61. Miura E, Kato Y, Matsushima R, Albrecht V, Laalami S, Sakamoto W. 2007. The balance between protein synthesis and degradation in chloroplasts determines leaf variegation in *Arabidopsis yellow variegated* mutants. *Plant Cell* 19:1313–28
62. Mordhorst AP, Voerman KJ, Hartog MV, Meijer EA, van Went J, et al. 1998. Somatic embryogenesis in *Arabidopsis thaliana* is facilitated by mutations in genes repressing meristematic cell divisions. *Genetics* 149:549–63
63. Mossessova E, Lima CD. 2000. Ulp1-SUMO crystal structure and genetic analysis reveal conserved interactions and a regulatory element essential for cell growth in yeast. *Mol. Cell* 5:865–76
64. Murtas G, Reeves PH, Fu YF, Bancroft I, Dean C, Coupland G. 2003. A nuclear protease required for flowering-time regulation in *Arabidopsis* reduces the abundance of SMALL UBIQUITIN-RELATED MODIFIER conjugates. *Plant Cell* 15:2308–19

65. Nakaune S, Yamada K, Kondo M, Kato T, Tabata S, et al. 2005. A vacuolar processing enzyme, δVPE, is involved in seed coat formation at the early stage of seed development. *Plant Cell* 17:876–87

66. Park S, Rodermel SR. 2004. Mutations in ClpC2/Hsp100 suppress the requirement for FtsH in thylakoid membrane biogenesis. *Proc. Natl. Acad. Sci. USA* 101:12765–70

67. Pechan T, Ye L, Chang Y, Mitra A, Lin L, et al. 2000. A unique 33-kD cysteine proteinase accumulates in response to larval feeding in maize genotypes resistant to fall armyworm and other Lepidoptera. *Plant Cell* 12:1031–40

68. Rautergarten C, Steinhauser D, Büssis D, Stintzi A, Schaller A, et al. 2005. Inferring hypothesis on functional relationships of genes: analysis of the *Arabidopsis thaliana* subtilase gene family. *PLoS Comput. Biol.* 1:297–312

69. Rawlings ND, Morton FR, Barrett AJ. 2006. MEROPS: the peptidase database. *Nucleic Acids Res.* 34:D270–72

70. Reeves PH, Murtas G, Dash S, Coupland G. 2002. *Early in short days 4*, a mutation in *Arabidopsis* that causes early flowering and reduces the mRNA abundance of the floral repressor *FLC*. *Development* 129:5349–61

71. Rojo E, Martin R, Carter C, Zouhar J, Pan S, et al. 2004. VPEγ exhibits a caspase-like activity that contributes to defense against pathogens. *Curr. Biol.* 14:1897–906

72. Rooney HCE, van't Klooster JW, van der Hoorn RAL, Joosten MHAJ, Jones JDG, de Wit PJGM. 2005. Cladosporium Avr2 inhibits tomato Rcr3 protease required for Cf-2-dependent disease resistance. *Science* 308:1783–86

73. Rupinder SK, Gurpreet AK, Manjeet S. 2007. Cell suicide and caspases. *Vascular Pharmacol.* 46:383–93

74. Saez ME, Ramirez-Lorca R, Moron FJ, Ruiz A. 2006. The therapeutic potential of the calpain family: new aspects. *Drug Discov. Today* 11:917–23

75. Saibo NJM, Vriezen WH, De Grauwe L, Azmi A, Prinsen E, Van der Straeten D. 2007. A comparative analysis of the *Arabidopsis ampi1–1* and a novel weak *amp1* allele reveals new functions of the AMP1 protein. *Planta* 225:831–42

76. Sakamoto W, Tamura T, Hanba-Tomita Y, Sodmergen, Murata M. 2002. The *VAR1* locus of *Arabidopsis* encodes a chloroplastic FtsH and is responsible for leaf variegation in the mutant alleles. *Genes Cells* 7:769–80

77. Sakamoto W, Yaltsman A, Adam Z, Takahashi Y. 2003. Coordinated regulation and complex formation of YELLOW VARIEGATED1 and YELLOW VARIEGATED2, chloroplastic FtsH metalloproteases involved in the repair cycle of photosystem II in *Arabidopsis* thylakoid membranes. *Plant Cell* 15:2843–55

78. Sanchez-Moran E, Jones GH, Franklin CH, Santos JL. 2004. A puromycin-sensitive aminopeptidase is essential for meiosis in *Arabidopsis thaliana*. *Plant Cell* 16:2895–909

79. Schilling O, Overall CM. 2007. Proteomic discovery of protease substrates. *Curr. Opin. Chem. Biol.* 11:36–45

80. Shen G, Yan J, Pasapula V, Luo J, He C, et al. 2007. The chloroplast protease subunit ClpP4 is a substrate of the E3 ligase AtCHIP and plays an important role in chloroplast function. *Plant J.* 49:228–37

81. Shirley AM, Chapple C. 2003. Biochemical characterisation of sinapoylglucose:choline sinapoyltransferase, a serine carboxypeptidase-like protein that functions as an acyltransferase in plant secondary metabolism. *J. Biol. Chem.* 278:19870–77

82. Shirley AM, McMichael CM, Chapple C. 2001. The *sng2* mutant of *Arabidopsis* is defective in the gene encoding the serine carboxypeptidase-like protein sinapoylglucose:choline sinapoyltransferase. *Plant J.* 28:83–94

83. Sjögren LLE, Stanne TM, Zheng B, Sutinen S, Clarke AK. 2006. Structural and functional insights into the chloroplast ATP-dependent Clp protease in *Arabidopsis*. *Plant Cell* 18:2635–49
84. Suarez MF, Filonova LH, Smertenko A, Savenkov EI, Clapham DH, et al. 2004. Metacaspase-dependent programmed cell death is essential for plant embryogenesis. *Curr. Biol.* 14:R338–40
85. Sun X, Peng L, Guo J, Chi W, Ma J, et al. 2007. Formation of Deg5 and Deg8 complexes and their involvement in the degradation of photodamaged photosystem II reaction center D1 protein in *Arabidopsis*. *Plant Cell* 19:1347–61
86. Suzuki H, Xia Y, Cameron R, Shadle G, Blount J, et al. 2003. Signals for local and systemic responses of plants to pathogen attack. *J. Exp. Bot.* 55:169–79
87. Takechi K, Sodmergen, Murata M, Motoyoshi F, Sakamoto W. 2000. The *YELLOW VARIEGATED (VAR2)* locus encodes a homologue of FtsH, an ATP dependent protease in *Arabidopsis*. *Plant Cell Physiol.* 41:1334–46
88. Tanaka H, Onouchi H, Kondo M, Hara-Nishimura I, Nishimura M, et al. 2001. A subtilisin-like serine protease is required for epidermal surface formation in *Arabidopsis* embryos and juvenile plants. *Development* 128:4681–89
89. Tanaka H, Watanabe M, Sasabe M, Hiroe T, Tanaka T, et al. 2007. Novel receptor-like kinase ALE2 controls shoot development by specifying epidermis in *Arabidopsis*. *Development* 134:1643–52
90. Taylor MAJ, Baker KC, Briggs GS, Connerton IF, Cummings NJ, et al. 1995. Recombinant proregions from papain and papaya proteinase IV are selective high affinity inhibitors of the mature papaya enzymes. *Protein Eng.* 8:59–62
91. van der Biezen EA, Jones JDG. 1998. Plant disease resistance proteins and the gene-for-gene concept. *Trends Biochem. Sci.* 23:454–56
92. van der Hoorn RAL, de Wit PJGM, Joosten MHAJ. 2002. Balancing selection favors guarding resistance proteins. *Trends Plant Sci.* 7:67–71
93. van der Hoorn RAL, Jones JDG. 2004. The plant proteolytic machinery and its role in defense. *Curr. Opin. Plant Biol.* 7:400–7
94. Vidaurre DP, Ploense S, Krogan NT, Berleth T. 2007. *AMP1* and *MP* antagonistically regulate embryo and meristem development in *Arabidopsis*. *Development* 134:2561–67
95. Von Groll U, Berger D, Altmann T. 2002. The subtilisin-like serine protease SDD1 mediates cell-to-cell signaling during *Arabidopsis* stomatal development. *Plant Cell* 14:1527–39
96. Wang C, Barry JK, Min Z, Tordsen G, Rao AG, Olsen OA. 2003. The calpain domain of the maize DEK1 protein contains the conserved catalytic triad and functions as a cysteine protease. *J. Biol. Chem.* 278:34467–74
97. Watanabe M, Tanaka H, Watanabe D, Machida C, Machida Y. 2004. The ACR4 receptor-like kinase is required for surface formation of epidermis-related tissues in *Arabidopsis thaliana*. *Plant J.* 39:298–308
98. Xia Y, Suzuki H, Borevitz J, Blount J, Guo Z, et al. 2004. An extracellular aspartic protease functions in *Arabidopsis* disease resistance signaling. *EMBO J.* 23:980–88
99. Xu XM, Rose A, Muthuswamy S, Heong SY, Venkatakrishnan S, et al. 2007. NUCLEAR PORE ANCHOR, the *Arabidopsis* homolog of Tpr/Mlp2/Megator, is involved in mRNA export and SUMO homeostasis and affects diverse aspects of plant development. *Plant Cell.* 19:1537–48
100. Yan N, Doelling JH, Falbel TG, Durski AM, Vierstra RD. 2000. The ubiquitin-specific protease family from *Arabidopsis*. AtUBP1 and 2 are required for the resistance to the amino acid analog canavanine. *Plant Physiol.* 124:1828–43

101. Yang P, Smalle J, Lee S, Yan N, Emborg TJ, Vierstra RD. 2007. Ubiquitin C-terminal hydrolases 1 and 2 affect shoot architecture in *Arabidopsis*. *Plant J.* 51:441–57
102. Yu F, Park S, Rodermel SR. 2004. The *Arabidopsis FtsH* metalloprotease gene family: interchangeability of subunits in chloroplast oligomeric complexes. *Plant J.* 37:864–76
103. Yu F, Park S, Rodermel SR. 2005. Functional redundancy of AtFtsH metalloproteases in thylakoid membrane complexes. *Plant Physiol.* 138:1957–66
104. Zaltsman A, Oir N, Adam Z. 2005. Two types of FtsH protease subunits are required for chloroplast biogenesis and photosystem II repair in *Arabidopsis*. *Plant Cell* 17:2782–90
105. Zheng B, MacDonald TM, Sutinen S, Hurry V, Clarke AK. 2006. A nuclear-encoded ClpP subunit of the chloroplast ATP-dependent Clp protease is essential for early development in *Arabidopsis thaliana*. *Planta* 224:1101–15
106. Zhou A, Li J. 2005. *Arabidopsis* BRS1 is a secreted and active serine carboxypeptidase. *J. Biol. Chem.* 280:35554–61

Gibberellin Metabolism and its Regulation

Shinjiro Yamaguchi

RIKEN Plant Science Center, Yokohama, Japan; email: shinjiro@postman.riken.jp

Annu. Rev. Plant Biol. 2008. 59:225–51

The *Annual Review of Plant Biology* is online at plant.annualreviews.org

This article's doi:
10.1146/annurev.arplant.59.032607.092804

1543-5008/08/0602-0225$20.00

Key Words

biosynthesis, cytochrome P450 monooxygenase, deactivation, 2-oxoglutarate–dependent dioxygenase, plant hormones, terpene synthases

Abstract

Bioactive gibberellins (GAs) are diterpene plant hormones that are biosynthesized through complex pathways and control diverse aspects of growth and development. Biochemical, genetic, and genomic approaches have led to the identification of the majority of the genes that encode GA biosynthesis and deactivation enzymes. Recent studies have highlighted the occurrence of previously unrecognized deactivation mechanisms. It is now clear that both GA biosynthesis and deactivation pathways are tightly regulated by developmental, hormonal, and environmental signals, consistent with the role of GAs as key growth regulators. In some cases, the molecular mechanisms for fine-tuning the hormone levels are beginning to be uncovered. In this review, I summarize our current understanding of the GA biosynthesis and deactivation pathways in plants and fungi, and discuss how GA concentrations in plant tissues are regulated during development and in response to environmental stimuli.

Contents

INTRODUCTION

Biologically active gibberellins (bioactive GAs) control diverse aspects of plant growth and development, including seed germination, stem elongation, leaf expansion, and flower and seed development. Among more than a hundred GAs identified from plants (**http://www.plant-hormones.info/gibberellin_nomenclature.htm**) (61), only a small number of them, such as GA_1 and GA_4, are thought to function as bioactive hormones. Therefore, many nonbioactive GAs exist in plants as precursors for the bioactive forms or deactivated metabolites. The concentrations of bioactive GAs in a given plant tissue are determined by the rates of their synthesis and deactivation. In this review, I refer to biosynthesis as the production of bioactive hormones from their precursors, deactivation as the conversion of bioactive forms or their precursors into inactive (or less active) forms, and metabolism as both biosynthesis and deactivation.

GA: gibberellin

The GA metabolism pathway in plants has been studied for a long time, and a number of genes encoding the metabolism enzymes have been identified. Genes encoding these enzymes have been identified through conventional enzyme purification from rich sources of GA enzymes, functional screening of a cDNA expression library, or molecular genetic approaches using dwarf mutants defective in GA biosynthesis (for reviews, see References 28, 29, 99, and 128). More recently, the availability of genomics tools in model plant species has accelerated the identification of additional genes involved in the GA metabolism pathway. However, our list of GA metabolism genes is likely still incomplete, and genes encoding enzymes with unexpected functions in GA metabolism have just recently been recognized (117, 140). In addition, genes encoding some expected GA metabolism enzymes, such as those involved in GA conjugation, have not been discovered yet. In this review, I outline our current understanding of the GA metabolism pathways, enzymes, and genes in plants, and discuss how GA concentrations are regulated during plant development under varying environmental conditions in selected systems. I also describe GA biosynthesis in fungi to discuss how the GA pathway has evolved in different kingdoms.

THE GIBBERELLIN METABOLISM PATHWAY

Bioactive Gibberellins

The major bioactive GAs, including GA_1, GA_3, GA_4, and GA_7, commonly have a hydroxyl group on C-3β, a carboxyl group on C-6, and a lactone between C-4 and C-10 (**Figure 1**). The 3β-hydroxyl group may be replaced by other functionalities at C-2 and C-3 to act as bioactive forms, as in GA_5 and GA_6 (**Figure 1**). GA_1 has been identified frequently in a variety of plant species (61), implying that it acts as a widespread bioactive hormone. However, GA_4 also exists in most species, and is thought to be the major bioactive GA in *Arabidopsis thaliana* and some Cucurbitaceae members. The relative roles of GA_1 versus GA_4 (and GA_3 versus GA_7) still remain to be clarified through the identification of genes encoding GA 13-oxidase (GA13ox) and mutants without this enzyme activity. The recent identification of a soluble GA receptor, GIBBERELLIN INSENSITIVE DWARF 1 (GID1), from rice (*Oryza sativa*) and its homologs in *Arabidopsis* has illustrated that these structural requirements for bioactive GAs are reflected in their affinity for receptor GID1, as well as their ability to form a complex consisting of GID1, GA, and the DELLA protein (which is a repressor of GA signaling and degraded upon interaction with the GID1-GA complex) in yeast (65, 113, 115, 137). Intriguingly, GA_4, but not GA_1, is the most favored GA for the rice GID1 in terms of the ability to replace the binding of 16,17-dihydroGA_4 to GID1 in vitro (113), the complex formation in yeast, and the degradation of the DELLA protein in seedlings and calli (114), whereas GA_1 is the major bioactive form in vegetative tissues of rice.

Gibberellin Biosynthesis

GAs are biosynthesized from geranylgeranyl diphosphate (GGDP), a common C_{20} precursor for diterpenoids (**Figure 1**). Three different classes of enzymes are required for the biosynthesis of bioactive GAs from GGDP in plants: terpene synthases (TPSs), cytochrome P450 monooxygenases (P450s), and 2-oxoglutarate–dependent dioxygenases (2ODDs) (**Figure 2**). Recent work with isotope-labeled precursors showed that the methylerythritol phosphate pathway in the plastid provides the majority of the isoprene units to GAs in *Arabidopsis* seedlings, whereas there is a minor contribution from the cytosolic mevalonate pathway (46).

Two TPSs, *ent*-copalyl diphosphate synthase (CPS) and *ent*-kaurene synthase (KS), are involved in the conversion of GGDP to the tetracyclic hydrocarbon intermediate *ent*-kaurene (**Figure 1**). Both CPS and KS are located in the plastids (1, 33, 103, 104). *ent*-Kaurene is then converted to GA_{12} by two P450s. *ent*-Kaurene oxidase (KO) [designated as CYP701A according to the P450 nomenclature (**http://drnelson.utmem.edu/CytochromeP450.html**)] (67) catalyzes the sequential oxidation on C-19 to produce *ent*-kaurenoic acid, which is subsequently converted to GA_{12} by another P450, *ent*-kaurenoic acid oxidase (KAO) (CYP88A) (67). Experiments using fusion enzymes with green fluorescent protein suggest that KO is located in the outer membrane of the plastid, whereas KAO is present in the endoplasmic reticulum (33).

GA_{12} is converted to GA_4, a bioactive form, through oxidations on C-20 and C-3 by GA 20-oxidase (GA20ox) and GA 3-oxidase (GA3ox), respectively, both of which are soluble 2ODDs (**Figure 1**). GA20ox catalyzes the sequential oxidation of C-20, including the loss of C-20 as CO_2 and the formation of γ-lactone. Thus, GA20ox is responsible for the production of C_{19}-GAs using C_{20}-GAs as substrates. The introduction of a 3β-hydroxyl group converts inactive precursors ($GA_{9,20}$) into bioactive GAs. Some GA3ox enzymes possess minor catalytic activity to synthesize GA_3 and GA_6 from GA_{20} via GA_5 (6, 41, 100) (**Figure 1**). Although the subcellular localization of these 2ODDs has not been demonstrated experimentally, they are assumed to be cytosolic enzymes because of the lack of any apparent targeting sequence (**Figure 2**). GA_{12} is also a substrate for GA13ox for the production of GA_{53}, which is a precursor for GA_1 in the 13-hydroxylated pathway. To clarify the biological relevance of 13-hydroxylation,

GIBBERELLIN INSENSITIVE DWARF 1 (GID1): a soluble GA receptor that interacts directly with the DELLA protein in a GA-dependent manner

DELLA proteins: members of the GRAS protein family that repress GA responses; degraded by the 26S-proteasome upon interaction with the GID1-GA complex

GGDP: geranylgeranyl diphosphate

TPS: terpene synthase

Cytochrome P450 monooxygenase (P450): heme-containing enzyme that catalyzes oxidation reactions of a broad range of organic compounds

2-oxoglutarate–dependent dioxygenase (2ODD): soluble enzyme that catalyzes oxidation reactions of various organic compounds using 2-oxoglutarate as a cosubstrate

CPS: *ent*-copalyl diphosphate synthase

KS: *ent*-kaurene synthase

KO: *ent*-kaurene oxidase

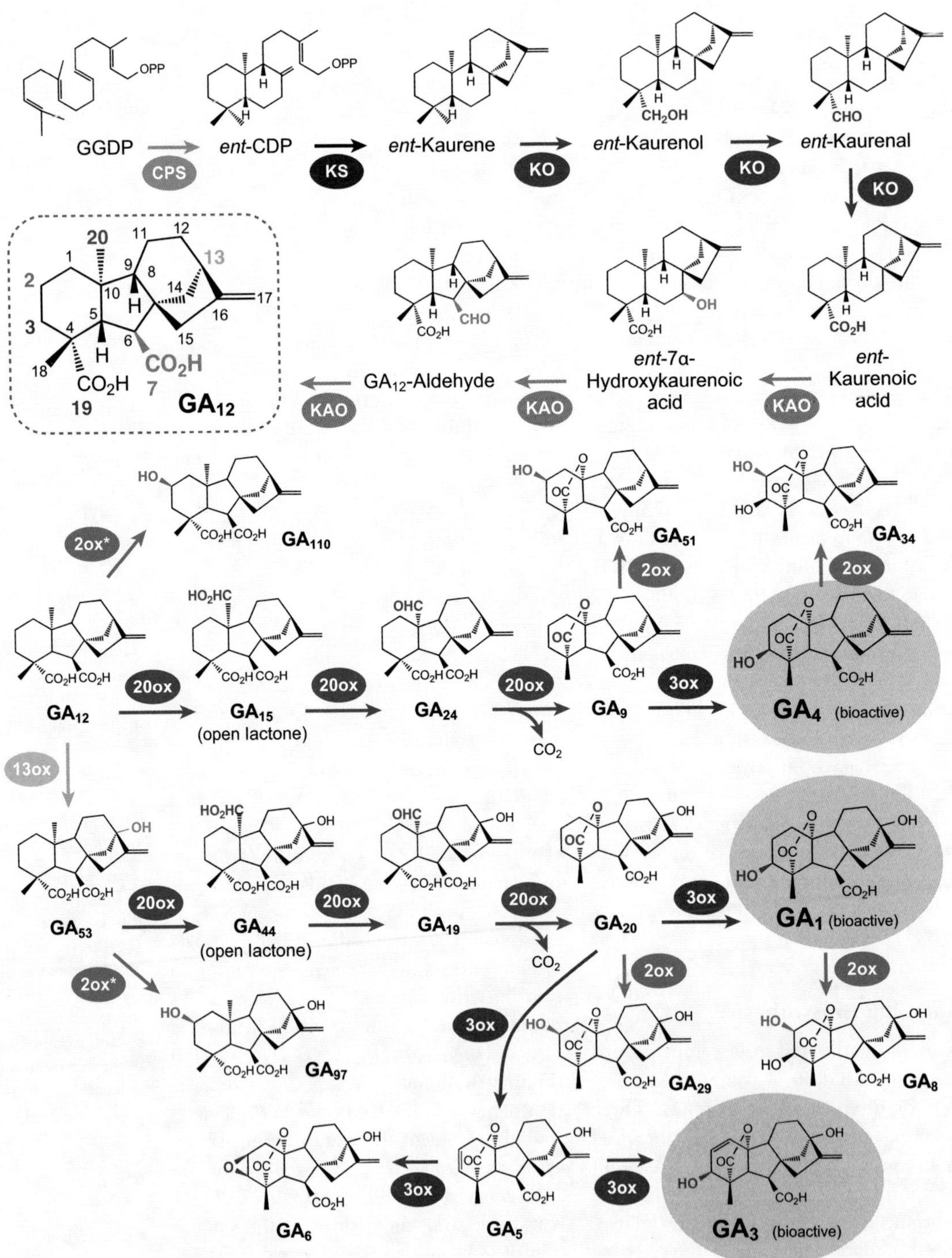

GGDP
CPS
ent-CDP
KS
ent-Kaurene
KO
ent-Kaurenol
KO
ent-Kaurenal
KO
ent-Kaurenoic acid
KAO
ent-7α-Hydroxykaurenoic acid
KAO
GA12-Aldehyde
KAO
GA12
GA110
2ox*
GA15 (open lactone)
20ox
GA24
20ox
GA9
20ox
CO2
3ox
GA4 (bioactive)
GA51
2ox
GA34
2ox
13ox
GA53
20ox
GA44 (open lactone)
20ox
GA19
20ox
GA20
CO2
3ox
GA1 (bioactive)
2ox*
GA97
2ox
GA29
2ox
GA8
3ox
GA6
3ox
GA5
3ox
GA3 (bioactive)

it will be necessary to identify genes encoding GA13ox(s). Recombinant TaGA3ox2 protein (a GA3ox from wheat) exhibits a weak GA13ox activity, in addition to GA3ox activity, in vitro, although its contribution to the overall production of 13-hydroxylated GAs in plants is likely to be small (6).

Gibberellin Deactivation

Deactivation is important for effective regulation of the concentrations of bioactive hormones in plants. GAs are metabolically deactivated in several different ways. The best-characterized deactivation reaction is 2β-hydroxylation catalyzed by a class of 2ODDs, GA 2-oxidases (GA2oxs) (**Figures 1** and **2**). Initially identified GA2oxs use C_{19}-GAs as substrates, including bioactive GAs and their immediate precursors, GA_9 and GA_{20} (106), and they belong to class I or II on the basis of the phylogenetic relationships (58). Recently, a new type of GA2ox that accepts only C_{20}-GAs was reported (58, 93). These enzymes are categorized into class III, and are likely to play a role in depleting pools of precursor GAs (such as GA_{12} and GA_{53}) that are otherwise converted to bioactive forms (**Figure 1**).

Recent work on a recessive tall rice mutant, *elongated uppermost internode* (*eui*), revealed a new GA deactivation mechanism (140). EUI is a P450 designated as CYP714D1 (67) that epoxidizes the 16,17-double bond of non13-hydroxylated GAs, including GA_4, GA_9, and GA_{12} (**Figure 3**). In the upper internodes of rice, EUI/CYP714D1 should be the principal GA deactivation enzyme, because *eui* mutants accumulate bioactive GAs at extremely high levels (140). 16α,17-dihydrodiols, hydrated products of the 16α,17-epoxides either in vivo or during purification (**Figure 3**), are detected in transgenic rice plants that overexpress the *EUI* gene. Thus, the discovery of this enzyme explains the occurrence of GA 16,17-dihydrodiols in many plant species (140). These results suggest that 16α,17-epoxidation of GAs may be a general deactivation mechanism. More recent work has shown that *Arabidopsis GAMT1* and *GAMT2* encode enzymes (gibberellin methyltransferases) that catalyze methylation of the C-6 carboxyl group of GAs using S-adenosine-L-methionine as a methyl donor (117) (**Figure 3**). GAMT1 and GAMT2 utilize a variety of GAs, including bioactive GAs and their precursors, as substrates in vitro, and produce the corresponding methyl esters. Ectopic expression of *GAMT1* or *GAMT2* in *Arabidopsis*, tobacco (*Nicotiana tabacum*), and petunia (*Petunia hybrida*) results in dwarfed plants with GA-deficiency. Both GAMT1 and GAMT2 are predominantly expressed in developing and germinating seeds during *Arabidopsis* development. In the loss-of-function *gamt1 gamt2* double mutant, the levels of bioactive GAs in developing seeds are significantly elevated, and the double mutant seeds are more resistant to a GA biosynthesis inhibitor during germination relative to wild-type seeds (117). These results suggest that the *GAMT* genes play a role in deactivating GAs in *Arabidopsis* seeds. Whether methylation of GAs is a common deactivation reaction in other plant species has yet to be investigated.

KAO: *ent*-kaurenoic acid oxidase

Figure 1

The gibberellin (GA) biosynthesis pathways and deactivation by GA 2-oxidase in plants. Bioactive GAs found in a wide variety of plant species (*highlighted grey*) are shown. As discussed in the text, GA_5 and GA_6 may also function as bioactive hormones. In each metabolic reaction, the modification is highlighted in color. GA_7 (13-nonhydroxy GA_3) is biosynthesized from GA_9 in a similar pathway to the synthesis of GA_3 from GA_{20}, but is not shown in this figure. 2ox, GA 2-oxidase (Class I and II); 2ox*, GA 2-oxidase (Class III); 3ox, GA 3-oxidase; 13ox, GA 13-oxidase; 20ox, GA 20-oxidase; GGDP, geranylgeranyl diphosphate; *ent*-CDP, *ent*-copalyl diphosphate; CPS, *ent*-copalyl diphosphate synthase; KS, *ent*-kaurene synthase; KO, *ent*-kaurene oxidase; KAO, *ent*-kaurenoic acid oxidase.

Arabidopsis thaliana
Enzyme *Gene* [*Locus*] AGI code (Reference)

Oryza sativa
Enzyme *Gene* [*Locus*] RAP locus (Reference)

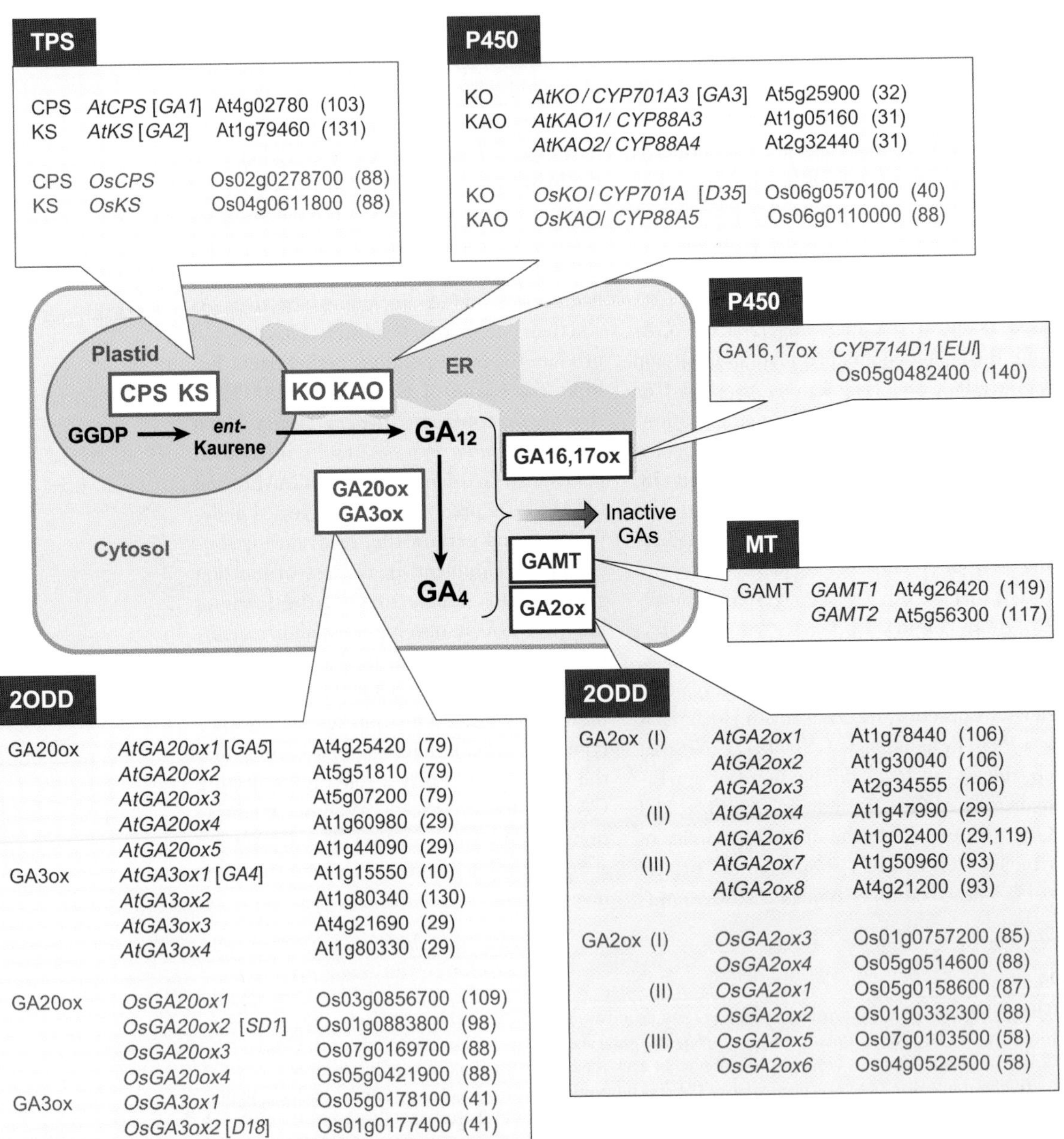

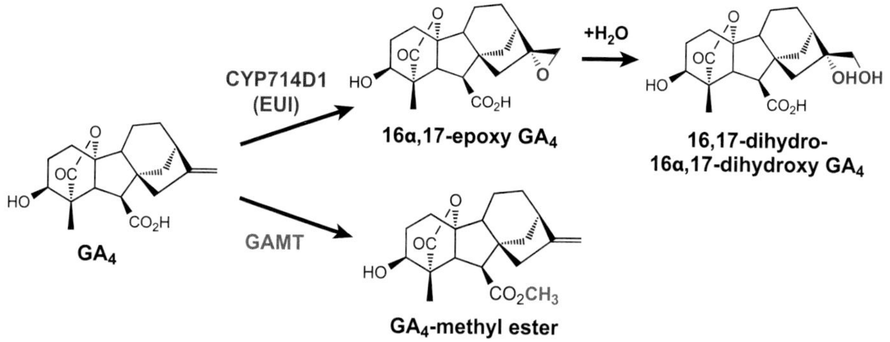

Figure 3

Gibberellins are deactivated by ELONGATED UPPERMOST INTERNODE (EUI) through 16α,17-epoxidation and by gibberellin methyltransferases (GAMTs) through methylation.

GAs can be converted into conjugates in plants (91, 92). Conjugation of GAs to glucose occurs either through a hydroxyl group of GA to give a GA-*O*-glucosyl ether or via the 6-carboxyl group to give a GA-glucosyl ester. Although the formation of these GA conjugates may also serve to deactivate GAs, it remains unclear whether GA conjugations play any regulatory role in the control of bioactive GA levels. The identification of genes encoding GA-glycosyl transferases and the resulting reverse genetic studies will clarify their role in plants.

The identification of the majority of GA metabolism enzymes has provided a clearer view as to the mechanism by which a large variety of GAs are produced in plants. Because of the multifunctionality of several enzymes in the pathway, only six enzymes are required for the 12-step conversion of GGDP to GA_4. In addition, many GA-modifying enzymes, including the 2ODDs, 16α,17-epoxidase (EUI/CYP714D1), and GAMTs, accept multiple GAs as substrates. The promiscuous nature of these enzymes creates a number of branches in the pathway and contributes to the production of diverse GAs by a relatively small number of enzymes.

GIBBERELLIN METABOLISM GENES

In both *Arabidopsis* and rice, the enzymes that catalyze the early steps of GA biosynthesis are encoded by one or two genes (**Figure 2**). In *Arabidopsis*, CPS, KS, and KO are each encoded by a single gene, and the null alleles of these genes (*ga1*, *ga2*, and *ga3*) result in severe GA-deficient dwarves (55). Interestingly, the rice genome contains two genes that encode a functional CPS (75, 81, 88), but only one of them is likely to participate in GA biosynthesis, whereas the second one is involved in the biosynthesis of diterpene phytoalexins. Additional CPS-like enzymes (OsCyc1 and OsCyc2) function as *syn*-copalyl diphosphate (CDP) synthases in the biosynthesis of

CDP: copalyl diphosphate

Figure 2

Predicted subcellular localization of gibberellin (GA) metabolism enzymes and the identities of GA metabolism genes in *Arabidopsis* (*red*) and rice (*blue*) (10, 29, 31, 32, 40, 41, 58, 79, 85, 87, 88, 93, 98, 103, 106, 109, 117, 119, 130, 131, 140). For the rice genes, identifiers from the Rice Annotation Project (RAP; **http://rapdb.lab.nig.ac.jp/**) are used. AGI, *Arabidopsis* Genome Initiative; TPS, terpene synthase; CPS, *ent*-copalyl diphosphate synthase; KS, *ent*-kaurene synthase; P450, cytochrome P450 monooxygenase; KO, *ent*-kaurene oxidase; KAO, *ent*-kaurenoic acid oxidase; MT, methyltransferase; GAMT, gibberellin methyltransferase; ER, endoplasmic reticulum; GGDP, geranylgeranyl diphosphate; 2ODD, 2-oxoglutarate–dependent dioxygenase; GA2ox, GA3ox, GA16, 17ox, GA20ox, GA oxidases. Tan-Ginbozu and Waito-C are semi-dwarf cultivars carrying the *d35* and *d18* mutant alleles, respectively (40, 41).

phytoalexins (75, 125). Genetic studies indicate that KS and KO in GA biosynthesis are also encoded by single genes, although multiple KS-like and KO-like sequences exist in the genome (88).

In comparison with the early biosynthesis enzymes, the 2ODDs that catalyze the late steps in the pathway are each encoded by multigene families. Accumulating evidence indicates that members in each of these 2ODD families are differentially regulated by developmental and environmental cues, and that they are the primary sites for the regulation of bioactive GA levels. For example, reverse genetic analysis indicates that, of the four genes encoding GA3ox in *Arabidopsis*, *AtGA3ox1* and *AtGA3ox2* play distinct as well as overlapping roles in vegetative development, but they are dispensable for reproductive development (64). Also, there is evidence that *AtGA3ox1* and *AtGA3ox2* are differentially regulated by environmental signals during seed germination (130, 134). The key role of the 2ODDs in determining bioactive GA levels is also supported by the results of overexpression studies. Increased expression of a *GA20ox* gene in transgenic *Arabidopsis* plants causes an increase in GA levels and GA-overdose phenotypes (11, 36). In contrast, although overexpression of *AtCPS* in *Arabidopsis* is effective in increasing the accumulation of *ent*-kaurene, *ent*-kaurenoic acid, and GA_{12}, it does not affect the levels of bioactive GAs or the phenotype (17). The regulation of bioactive GA levels, mainly through the 2ODDs, is summarized in the following sections.

DEVELOPMENTAL REGULATION

Sites of Gibberellin Biosynthesis

The precise sites of GA biosynthesis and response must be determined to understand how this hormone controls plant growth and development. *AtCPS* (*GA1*)-*GUS* (where *GUS* is the reporter gene, β-glucuronidase) is expressed mainly in rapidly growing tissues during *Arabidopsis* development, suggesting that its expression correlates with the sites of GA response (97). This result is consistent with the occurrence of *ent*-kaurene synthesis activity in proplastids of growing tissues in wheat (1). *Nty*, a *GA3ox* gene in tobacco, is expressed in actively dividing and elongating cells, including the rib meristem, developing anthers, and root tips (39). In rice, *OsGA20ox2* and *OsGA3ox2*, as well as *SLR1*, which encodes a DELLA protein, are expressed in rapidly elongating or dividing tissues (44). Altogether, these results suggest that, in many cases, bioactive GAs are produced at the site of their action.

During the postgerminative growth of cereal grains, GAs are synthesized in the embryo and then transported to the aleurone cells, where α-amylase gene expression is induced for the hydrolysis of endosperm starch. Kaneko and coworkers (44, 45) found two distinct spatial expression patterns of GA biosynthesis genes among *OsGA20ox1*, *OsGA20ox2*, *OsGA3ox1*, and *OsGA3ox2* in rice. Transcripts of *OsGA20ox1* and *OsGA3ox1* are detectable only in the epithelium of the scutellum, whereas *OsGA20ox2* and *OsGA3ox2* are also expressed in the growing shoots, as well as in the epithelium. Genetic evidence from the *d18* mutant (defective in *OsGA3ox2*) (**Figure 2**) proves that *OsGA3ox2* is essential, whereas *OsGA3ox1* is not sufficient, for the production of bioactive GAs for α-amylase induction (45). None of these GA biosynthesis genes are expressed in the aleurone, whereas expression of the *SLR1* transcript is detectable (44). These results support the premise that the cereal aleurone is a non-GA producing tissue that responds to GAs transported from the embryo. Therefore, in these cases, GAs likely function as a paracrine signal. In germinating *Arabidopsis* seeds, transcripts of *AtGA3ox1* and *AtGA3ox2* are present predominantly in the cortex and endodermis of embryonic axes, illustrating that these are the major sites of GA biosynthesis (129). However, in situ hybridization analysis of three GA-upregulated transcripts indicates that GA-dependent transcriptional events are not restricted to the sites of bioactive GA synthesis (69). These results suggest the movement of bioactive GAs, or a GA signal, during the induction of *Arabidopsis* seed germination.

Studies in several plant species suggest that the tapetum of anthers is one of the major sites of bioactive GA synthesis during flower development (39, 44). Weiss and colleagues (120) proposed that the anthers might be a source of GAs for other flower organs in petunia, because emasculation of anthers causes reduced growth of the corolla, which can be rescued by GA treatment. In rice, expression of GA biosynthesis genes in flowers is restricted to the tapetum cells in anthers, whereas GA-signaling genes are expressed in additional organs, supporting the potential role of anthers in providing GAs to other floral organs (44). Interestingly, the tapetum is another major site of expression of the epithelium-specific genes, *OsGA20ox1* and *OsGA3ox1*, implying the role of these genes in the production of GAs that function as a paracrine (or an endocrine) signal (44). In *Arabidopsis* flowers, the expression of all four *AtGA3ox* genes (**Figure 2**) is restricted to stamens and flower receptacles, whereas bioactive GAs are required for petal growth as well (55), suggesting that GAs originating from other floral organs (possibly stamens) are responsible for petal growth (J. Hu, M.G. Mitchum & T-p. Sun, unpublished data).

In most *Arabidopsis* tissues, expression of an early GA biosynthesis gene, *AtCPS*, overlaps with expression of at least one of the *AtGA3ox* genes (64). However, the early and late stages of the GA biosynthesis pathway may occur in separate cell types. In germinating *Arabidopsis* seeds, expression of the early GA biosynthesis gene, *AtCPS*, is localized to the provasculature, whereas transcripts of *AtKO*, *AtGA3ox1*, and *AtGA3ox2* are mainly present in the cortical and endodermal cell layers (129). Thus, the synthesis of bioactive GAs in this system would require an intercellular movement of a pathway intermediate, possibly *ent*-kaurene, within the embryonic axis. A recent finding that *ent*-kaurene (C_{20} hydrocarbon) is readily released into the atmosphere from plants suggests the facility of transporting this compound from the plastid to other sites of the plant (76). In addition, *Arabidopsis ent*-kaurene–deficient mutants efficiently take up and metabolize *ent*-kaurene from the headspace into GAs, implying that this hydrocarbon intermediate may be transported to the site of metabolism efficiently. A possible physical separation of early and late GA biosynthetic steps is also seen in *Arabidopsis* roots: The *AtGA3ox1* and *AtGA3ox2* genes are expressed in similar cell types along the vasculature of nondividing, nonelongating regions of roots (64), but *AtCPS* expression is absent in these cells (97). Determining the biological significance of the possible separations of early and late steps requires further studies.

Homeodomain Proteins in Meristem Function

KNOTTED1-like homeobox (KNOX) proteins: key regulators in the establishment of meristem identity and leaf morphology

Recent studies have linked the homeodomain proteins to GA metabolism and highlighted the role of bioactive GAs in promoting the shift from meristem identity to organ differentiation. KNOTTED1-like homeobox (KNOX) proteins are key regulators in the establishment of meristem identity and leaf morphology. Ectopic expression of *KNOX* genes from several plant species results in dwarfism and a reduction in endogenous GA levels (56, 105). Sakamoto and coworkers (86) discovered that a tobacco KNOX protein, NTH15, represses GA biosynthesis by suppressing *GA20ox* expression through direct binding to its first intron. Importantly, *KNOX* genes are expressed in the corpus of the shoot apical meristem (SAM) in tobacco and *Arabidopsis*, thereby *GA20ox* expression is excluded in this region (**Figure 4*a***). Conversely, the absence of *KNOX* expression at the flanks of the SAM and the subapical region permits GA biosynthesis in these tissues (26, 86). These results suggest that

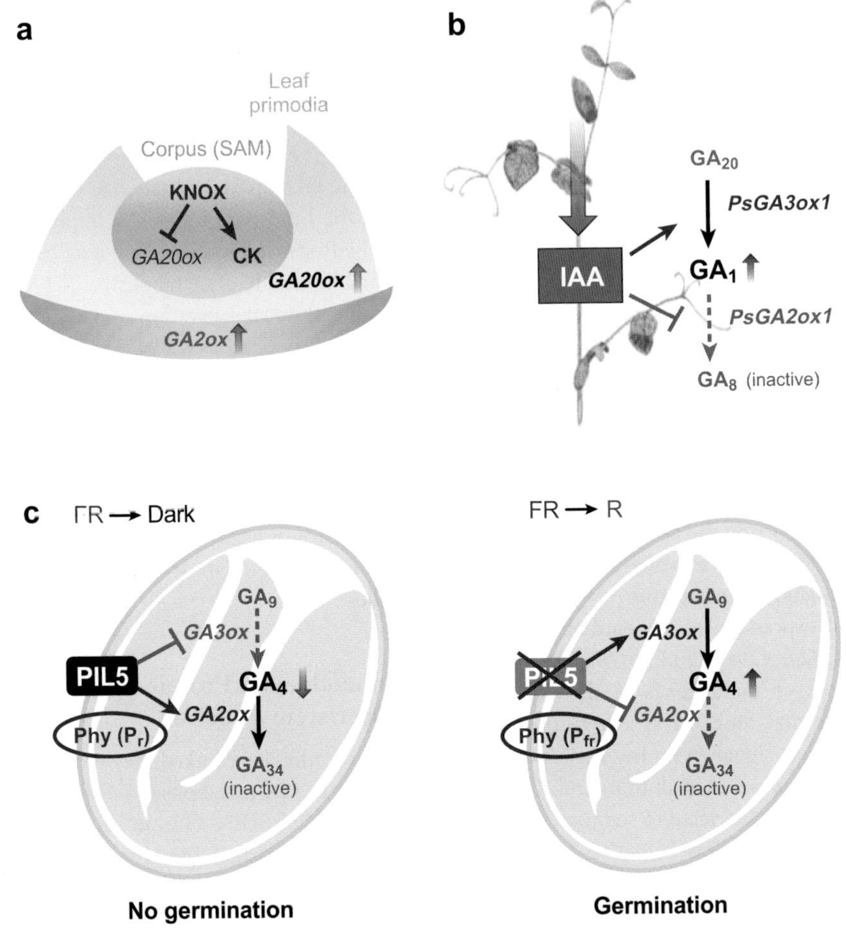

Figure 4

Developmental, hormonal, and environmental regulation of the gibberellin (GA) metabolism pathway. (*a*) Summary of the roles of KNOTTED1-like homeobox (KNOX) proteins in the control of hormonal balance in shoot apices (26, 43, 86, 89). KNOX proteins suppress GA biosynthesis (*GA20ox* expression) and activate cytokinin (CK) synthesis in the corpus of the shoot apical meristem (SAM) (*orange*). Without KNOX expression, suppression of *GA20ox* expression is alleviated in leaf primodia (*green*). The expression of GA deactivation genes (*GA2ox*) at the base of the meristem (*blue*) may assist the establishment of a low-GA regime in the SAM. (*b*) Auxin regulation of bioactive GA levels (73, 84). In pea internodes, indole-3-acetic acid (IAA) upregulates *PsGA3ox1* and downregulates *PsGA2ox1*. PsGA2ox1 also catalyzes 2-oxidation of GA_{20} to produce GA_{29}, but for simplification this reaction is not shown here. (*c*) Phytochrome-regulation of GA metabolism in *Arabidopsis* seeds (71, 94, 130, 135). In the absence of active phytochrome, PHYTOCHROME-INTERACTING FACTOR 3–LIKE 5 (PIL5) suppresses *GA3ox* expression and activates *GA2ox* expression. Once phytochrome is activated by red (R) light (P_{fr}), the PIL5 protein is degraded. This allows for the upregulation of *GA3ox* genes and causes the downregulation of *GA2ox* expression. As a consequence, GA_4 levels are elevated and germination is stimulated. *GA3ox* signifies *AtGA3ox1* and *AtGA3ox2*; *GA2ox* signifies *AtGA2ox2*. AtGA2ox2 also catalyzes 2-oxidation of GA_9 to produce GA_{51}, but for simplification this reaction is not shown here. FR, far-red; Phy, phytochrome.

KNOX proteins maintain the indeterminate state of corpus cells in part by suppressing GA biosynthesis. In *Arabidopsis*, the KNOX protein SHOOTMERISTEMLESS (STM) upregulates expression of the GA deactivation genes, *AtGA2ox4* and *AtGA2ox6*, at the base of the meristem, similar to the ring-shaped localization pattern of the *OsGA2ox1* transcript that accumulates around the vegetative shoot apex (87). This expression would also contribute to the establishment of a low-GA regime by KNOX proteins (43) (**Figure 4*a***). Recent studies have demonstrated that KNOX proteins also activate cytokinin (CK) biosynthesis through the upregulation of *IPT* genes (encoding isopentenyltransferase) and that CK plays a role in the induction of *GA2ox* gene expression (43, 89, 136) (**Figure 4*a***). Taken together, these results suggest that KNOX proteins act as orchestrators to control the balance of CK and GA in the SAM and promote meristem identity.

The homeotic gene *AGAMOUS* (*AG*) is expressed after flower induction, terminates meristem activity, and promotes development of floral organs. Microarray analysis has shown that AG elevates expression of *AtGA3ox1*, which may cause an increase in GA levels in the floral meristem and promote the shift from meristem identity to differentiation (24). AG binds to the promoter of *AtGA3ox1* both in vitro and in vivo, indicating that this gene is directly regulated by AG.

Regulators of Seed Development

Bioactive GAs and abscisic acid (ABA) act antagonistically to control seed development and germination. The levels of GA and ABA are negatively correlated during seed development (7, 121), thus there should be a mechanism that tightly regulates the balance between these hormones. LEAFY COTYLEDON 2 (LEC2) and FUSCA 3 (FUS3) are *Arabidopsis* B3 transcription factors, and both are essential for seed maturation processes. Curaba and colleagues (13) found that the levels of bioactive GAs are elevated in immature seeds of the *fus3* and *lec2* mutants, in part through ectopic activation of *AtGA3ox2* gene expression. Furthermore, FUS3 binds directly to two RY elements in the promoter of *AtGA3ox2* in vitro. Studies by Gazzarrini and coworkers (22) show that a transient induction of *FUS3* expression results in an increase in ABA content and repression of the GA biosynthesis genes, *AtGA3ox1* and *AtGA20ox1*. These results indicate that FUS3 functions as a positive and negative regulator of ABA and GA levels, respectively. Moreover, FUS3 protein levels are regulated positively by ABA and negatively by GA, suggesting that these regulatory loops may play a role in the establishment of GA-ABA balance in the seed (22).

AGAMOUS-LIKE 15 (AGL15) is a member of the MADS [named for MCM1, AGAMOUS, DEFICIENS, and serum response factor (SRF)] domain family and accumulates during embryo development in *Arabidopsis*. *AtGA2ox6*, involved in GA deactivation, has been identified as a direct target of AGL15 in vivo by chromatin immunoprecipitation (ChIP) analysis, and this gene is activated in seeds that overexpress *AGL15* (119). These results indicate that AGL15 plays a role in lowering GA content during embryogenesis through upregulation of a GA-deactivation gene.

CK: cytokinin

Chromatin immunoprecipitation (ChIP): a useful method to detect direct binding of a transcription factor to DNA in vivo

HORMONAL REGULATION

Gibberellin Homeostasis

The levels of bioactive GAs in plants are maintained via feedback and feedforward regulation of GA metabolism (29, 72). Transcript analysis shows that GA signaling is mainly targeted to 2ODDs in the GA metabolism pathway to establish homeostasis; e.g., expression of the *Arabidopsis* GA biosynthesis genes, *AtGA20ox1* and *AtGA3ox1*, is highly elevated in a GA-deficient background, whereas these genes are downregulated after application of bioactive GAs (10, 63, 79, 127, 130). In contrast, expression of the GA deactivation

IAA: indole-3-acetic acid

genes, *AtGA2ox1* and *AtGA2ox2*, is upregulated upon GA treatment (106). Although the molecular mechanisms underlying this homeostatic regulation have yet to be elucidated, the central GA signaling components are clearly required for this response, including the soluble GA receptor GID1, the DELLA proteins, and the F-box proteins SLEEPY 1 (SLY1) (*Arabidopsis*)/GID2 (rice) (for reviews, see References 102 and 115). For example, in the rice *gid1* and *gid2* mutants, expression of the *OsGA20ox2* (*SD1*) gene is upregulated and the levels of bioactive GA_1 are highly elevated (90, 113). Conversely, a DELLA loss-of-function mutant of *Arabidopsis* has reduced levels of *AtGA3ox1* transcripts even in a GA-deficient mutant background (15, 50).

REPRESSION OF SHOOT GROWTH (RSG) is a tobacco transcriptional activator that contains a basic leucine zipper domain and binds to the promoter of the *Arabidopsis AtKO* gene (20). A dominant negative version of RSG thus represses *AtKO* expression and causes dwarfism in tobacco. In addition, the feedback regulation of *GA20ox* expression is impaired in transgenic plants expressing the dominant negative RSG (38). 14-3-3 proteins interact with RSG and suppress its function by sequestering it in the cytoplasm (37). Importantly, RSG is translocated into the nucleus in response to a reduction in GA levels (38). These results suggest that RSG is negatively modulated by GAs via binding to 14-3-3 proteins and might be involved in the feedback regulation of *GA20ox* expression. The possible role of RSG in GA homeostasis appears to be restricted to *GA20ox*, because it does not affect the feedback regulation of the *GA3ox* gene (38).

Recently, additional components that might act in GA homeostasis have been identified. AT-hook protein of GA feedback regulation (AGF1) is an AT-hook protein that binds to the 43-bp *cis*-element for GA negative feedback response in the *AtGA3ox1* promoter (63). How AGF1 mediates the GA signal remains unclear, because GA does not affect the *AGF1* transcript levels or the nuclear localization of AGF1-GFP. Interestingly, this *cis*-element appears to be absent in the promoter of *AtGA20ox1*, suggesting that the GA signal may regulate *AtGA3ox1* and *AtGA20ox1* transcription by different mechanisms. YABBY1 (OsYAB1) may be a mediator of GA homeostasis downstream of the DELLA protein in rice, because its expression is dependent on the DELLA protein and overexpression of *OsYAB1* results in a semidwarf phenotype and a decrease in GA_1 levels, which might be caused by downregulation of the *OsGA3ox2* gene and upregulation of the *OsGA2ox3* gene (14). In *OsYAB1*-cosuppression plants, the GA-dependent repression of *OsGA3ox2* expression is impaired, suggesting a role for OsYAB1 as a mediator of feedback inhibition. In addition, OsYAB1 binds to a GA-responsive element in the *OsGA3ox2* promoter in vitro (14).

Regulation by Other Hormones

Multiple hormones are often involved in the regulation of a given biological process. Therefore, how different hormones cooperatively regulate a common developmental process has been an important question. Here, our recent understanding on the regulation of GA metabolism by other hormones is summarized.

Both bioactive GAs and auxin positively regulate stem elongation. In pea (*Pisum sativum*), the auxin indole-3-acetic acid (IAA) is essential for the maintenance of GA_1 levels in elongating internodes (84). Decapitation (removal of the apical bud, the source of auxin) dramatically reduces the level of endogenous GA_1 in elongating internodes, and application of IAA to the decapitated plants completely reverses these effects. The IAA induction of GA_1 levels is correlated with an increase in *PsGA3ox1* transcript abundance and a decrease in *PsGA2ox1* transcript levels (73) (**Figure 4*b***). A similar auxin-GA interaction occurs in stems of tobacco plants as well (123).

In barley, auxin from the developing inflorescence plays a role in stem elongation by upregulating GA 3-oxidation and downregulating GA 2-oxidation (122). Collectively, these results suggest that auxin regulation of GA metabolism in stems is a general mechanism. In pea, auxin-regulation of GA biosynthesis is also evident during fruit development (68). Growth of young pea fruit (pericarp) is dependent on the presence of developing seeds. In the absence of seeds, treatment with GA or the auxin 4-chloroindole-3-acetic acid (4-chloro-IAA) is effective in promoting the growth of pericarps (77, 116). In developing pericarps, expression of *PsGA3ox1* and *PsGA20ox1* is induced by 4-chloro-IAA, which is provided by the seeds. Taken together, these results support the hypothesis that auxin regulation of GA biosynthesis plays a role in the coordination of growth control between different organs/tissues. In these cases, auxin functions as a mobile signal that modulates the synthesis of other growth hormones, GAs. Frigerio and colleagues (19) found that auxin treatment upregulates expression of several *AtGA20ox* and *AtGA2ox* genes in *Arabidopsis* seedlings. Studies using various auxin-response mutants revealed that the Aux/IAA- and ARF-dependent signaling pathways are involved in these transcriptional changes, whereas they are independent of the feedback regulation mediated by DELLA proteins. Partial alleviation of the phenotype of several gain-of-function mutants of *Aux/IAA* genes by GA application suggests that changes in GA metabolism (GA-deficiency) mediate part of auxin action during *Arabidopsis* seedling development (19).

The role of brassinosteroid (BR) as a regulator of GA metabolism is less clear. In an *Arabidopsis* BR-deficient mutant, *AtGA20ox1*, mRNA accumulation is elevated after application of 24-*epi*-brassinolide, an active BR (9). However, how the induction of *AtGA20ox1* expression by BR affects endogenous GA metabolism is unclear. On the basis of the effect of BR on bioactive GA levels, Jager and coworkers (42) concluded that the BR growth response in pea is not mediated by changes in bioactive GA content.

Previous studies have suggested that ethylene may increase the level of GAs during internode elongation of deepwater rice upon submergence (35). Recently, ethylene was shown to delay *Arabidopsis* flowering by reducing bioactive GA levels (2). *Arabidopsis* plants grown in the presence of the ethylene precursor 1-aminocyclopropane-1-carboxylic acid, or in an ethylene-rich atmosphere, flower late. In addition, the *ctr1-1* loss-of-function mutation, which confers constitutive ethylene responses, causes later flowering, especially in short-day photoperiods. All these ethylene-stimulated late flowering phenotypes are rescued by exogenous GA treatment. The levels of GA_1 and GA_4 are substantially reduced in the *ctr1-1* mutant, suggesting that the ethylene signal is initially targeted to the GA metabolism pathway, and then to DELLA proteins as a consequence of altered GA content. In the *ctr1-1* mutant, transcript abundance of *AtGA3ox1* and *AtGA20ox1* genes is elevated, presumably through the negative feedback mechanism caused by the decreased bioactive GA levels. Further studies are required to clarify how the *ctr1-1* mutation alters bioactive GA levels.

Antagonistic effects of ABA and GA on seed germination have been well documented. However, evidence as to whether the endogenous GA levels are regulated by ABA, or vice versa, remains inconclusive. Recently, Seo and coworkers (94) found that GA_4 levels in dark-imbibed *Arabidopsis* seeds (after inactivation of phytochrome by a far-red light pulse) are elevated in the ABA-deficient *aba2-2* mutant. This is correlated with an increase in *AtGA3ox1* and *AtGA3ox2* transcript abundance in *aba2-2* mutant seeds relative to wild-type seeds. Furthermore, activation of GA biosynthesis genes in the *aba2-2* mutant is also observed during seed development. These results indicate that ABA plays a role in the suppression of GA biosynthesis in both imbibed and developing *Arabidopsis* seeds (94).

ENVIRONMENTAL REGULATION

Light Regulation

As detailed below, bioactive GAs function as key mediators between the perception of environmental signals and the resulting growth responses. Light is one of the major environmental factors that affects plant growth and development. Among light-dependent processes, current evidence indicates that changes in GA concentrations are, at least in part, responsible for light-regulated seed germination, photomorphogenesis during de-etiolation, and photoperiod regulation of stem elongation and flowering.

Seed germination is under phytochrome control in some small-seeded plants, such as lettuce (*Lactuca sativa*), tomato (*Solanum lycopersicum*), and *Arabidopsis* (95). In *Arabidopsis*, phytochrome B (phyB) is responsible for the low fluence response shortly after the onset of imbibition and stimulates germination in response to red (R) light in a far-red (FR) light–reversible manner (96). Unlike phyB, phyA accumulates during dark-imbibition and promotes germination by sensing very low fluence light in a wide range of wavelengths. In both phyA- and phyB-dependent germination conditions, light treatments that activate phytochromes elevate expression of *AtGA3ox1* and *AtGA3ox2*, whereas *AtGA2ox2* expression is suppressed; these changes in gene expression result in an increase in GA_4 levels in the seeds (71, 94, 130, 135) (**Figure 4*c***). PHYTOCHROME-INTERACTING FACTOR 3-LIKE 5 (PIL5), a light-liable basic helix-loop-helix (bHLH) protein, is a negative regulator of phytochrome-dependent seed germination, and is involved in both phyA- and phyB-mediated regulation of GA metabolism genes (71) (**Figure 4*c***). ChIP analysis showed that PIL5 does not bind to the promoters of *AtGA3ox1*, *AtGA3ox2*, or *AtGA2ox2* genes, suggesting that an additional component or components are required for phytochrome regulation of GA metabolism genes in *Arabidopsis* seeds (70). In contrast, the same study showed that PIL5 binds directly to the promoters of *REPRESSOR OF GA1-3* (*RGA*) and *GIBBERELLIC ACID INSENSITIVE* (*GAI*), both of which encode DELLA proteins, and regulates GA responsiveness. Besides regulating GA metabolism, PIL5 is involved in phytochrome regulation of ABA metabolism (70), which illustrates a role of PIL5 in balancing GA and ABA levels during light-dependent seed germination. In lettuce seeds, R light induces expression of the *LsGA3ox1* gene and suppresses *LsGA2ox2* expression, whereas a subsequent FR light treatment cancels the effect of R light, under a light regime similar to the phyB-dependent germination condition (66, 108). Thus, the phytochrome signal is commonly targeted to *GA3ox* and *GA2ox* genes to alter bioactive GA content in lettuce and *Arabidopsis* seeds.

Although active phytochrome positively regulates GA biosynthesis and response during seed germination, this relationship is reversed during photomorphogenesis of etiolated seedlings after irradiation. In dark-grown pea seedlings, GA_1 levels decrease significantly after exposure to white light (4, 23, 74). The reduction of GA_1 levels occurs within 4 h of exposure to R, blue, or FR light, and is mediated redundantly by phyA and cryptochrome 1 (cry1), but not phyB (18, 82). The reduction in GA_1 levels is correlated with downregulation of *PsGA3ox1* gene expression and upregulation of *PsGA2ox2* expression (18, 82). A similar role of cryptochromes (cry1 and cry2) in response to blue light was recently shown during de-etiolation of *Arabidopsis* seedlings; blue light downregulates expression of *AtGA20ox1* and *AtGA3ox1* genes, whereas it induces *AtGA2ox1* expression (139). These transcriptional changes correlate with a cry-dependent transient decrease in GA_4 levels after exposure to blue light. These studies in pea and *Arabidopsis* suggest a general role of blue light in regulating bioactive GA levels during de-etiolation. This hormonal change is likely to contribute, at least in part, to a rapid inhibition of stem elongation (and maybe other processes as well) during the establishment of photomorphogenesis. This hypothesis is supported by the essential role of GA in the repression of photomorphogenesis, as revealed by studies using GA-deficient mutants of *Arabidopsis* and pea (5). CPS activity is inhibited by the substrate GGDP and Mg^{2+} synergistically in vitro (49, 80). Thus, GGDP and Mg^{2+} may inhibit CPS activity to limit GA biosynthesis during de-etiolation, because the levels of GGDP in plastids presumably increase for the production of photosynthetic pigments and light also induces increases in plastid Mg^{2+} levels (80). However, the physiological significance of this posttranslational mechanism requires further study, because the actual GGDP concentrations in plastids are unknown.

Extensive studies have established that photoperiodic control of stem elongation in long day (LD) rosette plants is mediated by GAs (for a review, see Reference 21). Spinach (*Spinacia oleracea*) is an LD rosette plant in which exposure of short day (SD)-grown plants to FR-rich LD triggers stem elongation and subsequent floral development. This LD-induced stem elongation is inhibited by the application of GA biosynthesis inhibitors and this effect is reversed by GA_3 treatment (138). Transfer of spinach plants from SD to LD results in elevated levels of C_{19}-GAs, which is primarily attributable to upregulation of *SoGA20ox1* transcript levels (57, 59, 124). Recent work has shown that this transcriptional change is reflected in elevated accumulation of SoGA20ox1 protein in LD (59). When ^{14}C-GA_{53} is fed to spinach plants, more ^{14}C-GA_{53} is metabolized to ^{14}C-GA_{97} by 2β-hydroxylation (**Figure 1**) in SD than in LD, and more ^{14}C-GA_{20} is formed in LD than SD (58). These observations are consistent with strong upregulation of GA20ox activity in LD, although there is little change in the transcript levels of *SoGA2ox3*, which controls the conversion of GA_{53} to GA_{97} (58). Likewise, in *Arabidopsis*, an increase in the levels of bioactive GAs by LD treatments is, at least in part, attributed to increased expression of *AtGA20ox1*, whereas expression of *AtGA3ox1* is not under photoperiodic control (126). Petiole elongation of SD-grown *Arabidopsis* plants is enhanced by FR-rich LD treatment or a brief end-of-day FR exposure in SD. This response involves regulation of *AtGA20ox2* expression and, to a lesser extent, *AtGA20ox1* expression via phyB or related phytochrome(s) (34). Accordingly, stimulation of petiole elongation by end-of-day FR treatment is reduced in *AtGA20ox2* knockdown transgenic plants.

The grass *Lolium temulentum* flowers in response to a single LD treatment and has been utilized for studies on GA-induced flowering (51). Interestingly, GA_5 and GA_6 (**Figure 1**) are more effective in inducing flowering than GA_1 or GA_4, both of which are active in inducing stem elongation in *L. temulentum*. Evidence suggests that GA_5 and GA_6 are synthesized in the leaf upon exposure to LD and transported to the shoot apex to induce floral initiation (52–54). A twofold increase in the levels of GA_5 and GA_6 occurs in the shoot apex following an LD exposure, and this increase is preceded by a rapid increase in GA_5 content and a drastic increase in the levels of *LtGA20ox1* mRNA in the leaf after the LD treatment. GA_1 and GA_4 do not reach the shoot apex, presumably because of deactivation by GA2ox; the corresponding gene in rice (*OsGA2ox1*) is strongly expressed at the base of the vegetative shoot apex (**Figure 4*a***), but the expression disappears after transition to the reproductive phase (87). In contrast, GA_5 and GA_6 are resistant to deactivation by GA2ox, so logically, these compounds may act as floral stimuli. In a related species, *Lolium perenne*, both vernalization and LD are required for flower initiation. In this species, exposure to two LDs upregulates expression of the *LpGA20ox1* gene and causes an increase in some GAs in the leaf and young shoot tissues, regardless of the vernalization status (60). Thus, GA biosynthesis is regulated by the photoperiodic signal, whereas it is independent of vernalization in *L. perenne*.

In *Arabidopsis*, flower initiation under SD conditions requires GA biosynthesis. The flower meristem identity gene *LEAFY* (*LFY*) is a key component downstream of the GA signal (8). Unlike in *L. temulentum*, in *Arabidopsis* GA_4 increases drastically in abundance shortly before floral transition in the shoot apex, and functions as the major bioactive GA for the induction of *LFY* expression in the shoot apex (16). This GA_4 increase might be due to transport of GAs from other tissues, because the expression of the known GA metabolism genes in the shoot apex does not correlate with the acute increase in GA_4 content in this tissue. After application of deuterium-labeled GA_4 to a single leaf, the labeled GA_4 is detectable at the shoot apex (16). This suggests that endogenous GA_4 made in the leaf may be transported to the shoot apex to induce flowering, although further studies are necessary to verify this hypothesis.

Temperature Regulation

Exposure of imbibed seeds to cold temperature (cold stratification) accelerates the release from seed dormancy and induces germination in many plant species. In dark-imbibed after-ripened *Arabidopsis* seeds, cold treatment stimulates the expression of the GA biosynthesis genes, *AtGA3ox1* and *AtGA20ox2*, whereas the GA deactivation gene *AtGA2ox2* is down-regulated (134). Consistent with these results, the levels of bioactive GAs are significantly increased by cold treatment. Microarray analysis showed that approximately a quarter of cold-responsive genes correspond to GA-regulated genes, suggesting an important role for GA in mediating the cold temperature signal in *Arabidopsis* seeds (134). Recent work showed that SPATULA (SPT), a bHLH transcription factor closely related to PIL5, acts as a light-stable repressor of seed germination and controls responses to cold stratification in part through regulating the *AtGA3ox* genes (78). To a lesser extent, SPT also plays a role in phytochrome-dependent responses to light in seeds.

Plants monitor day and night temperatures and alter their growth and development accordingly. The ability of plants to detect the diurnal temperature change is referred to as thermoperiodism. In pea, a day/night temperature combination of 13°C/21°C significantly reduces stem elongation as compared with 21°C/13°C (and 17°C/17°C), and this response is correlated with a decrease in GA_1 levels (101). In addition, *PsGA2ox2* transcript abundance increases significantly in 13°C/21°C conditions compared with 21°C/13°C, suggesting that a higher rate of GA deactivation is involved in the thermoperiodic response in pea. Furthermore, a constitutive GA-response mutant, *la cry*^{s}, shows no or very poor thermoperiodic response in stem elongation (25, 101). This supports the interpretation that GA_1 acts as a mediator of the thermoperiodic response.

Stress Responses

Upon exposure to stresses, plants reduce their growth rate. An intimate relationship has been suggested to exist between GA levels and the acquisition of stress protection in barley (*Hordeum vulgare*) (118). Evidence has emerged that the GA metabolism pathway is altered in response to abiotic stresses. Overexpression of *DWARF AND DELAYED FLOWERING 1* (*DDF1*) causes a reduction in GA_4 content and dwarfism in *Arabidopsis* (62). *DDF1* encodes an AP2 transcription factor that is closely related to the dehydration responsive element–binding proteins (DREBs) involved in stress responses, and *DDF1* expression is strongly induced by high-salinity stress. In addition, transgenic plants overexpressing *DDF1*, as well as a GA-deficient *ga1-3* mutant, exhibit a higher survival rate under high-salinity conditions, whereas exogenous GA treatment reduces the survival rate (62). Similarly, there is a correlation between the survival of salt toxicity and the function of DELLA proteins (3). These results suggest that the salt-inducible *DDF1* gene is involved in growth responses under high salinity conditions in part through altering GA levels. In fact, salt-treated *Arabidopsis* plants contain reduced levels of bioactive GAs (3), supporting the idea that salt slows growth by modulating the GA metabolism pathway. Recent work has shown that *AtGA2ox7*, which encodes a GA2ox that specifically deactivates C_{20}-GAs (**Figures 1** and **2**), is a target of DDF1, suggesting that salt decreases bioactive GA levels through elevated deactivation (H. Magome, S. Yamaguchi, K. Oda, unpublished data).

EVOLUTION OF GIBBERELLIN BIOSYNTHESIS: FUNGI AND LOWER PLANTS

Gibberellin Biosynthesis in Fungi

GAs were first isolated as metabolites of a fungal rice pathogen, *Gibberella fujikuroi*. GAs also occur in other fungi and bacteria (61). Recent identifications of genes encoding GA biosynthesis enzymes from *G. fujikuroi* and a species of *Phaeosphaeria* revealed remarkable differences in GA biosynthesis pathways and enzymes between plants and fungi.

In plants, two separate terpene cyclases (CPS and KS) are involved in the synthesis of *ent*-kaurene from GGDP (**Figure 1**), whereas in fungi these two reactions are catalyzed by a single bifunctional enzyme (CPS/KS) (48, 107, 110) (**Figure 5**). In *G. fujikuroi*, multifunctional P450s, P450-4 and P450-1, play a similar role to that of KOs (CYP701As) and KAOs (CYP88As) in plants, respectively (83). However, despite their similar catalytic activities, the fungal P450s are not closely related to

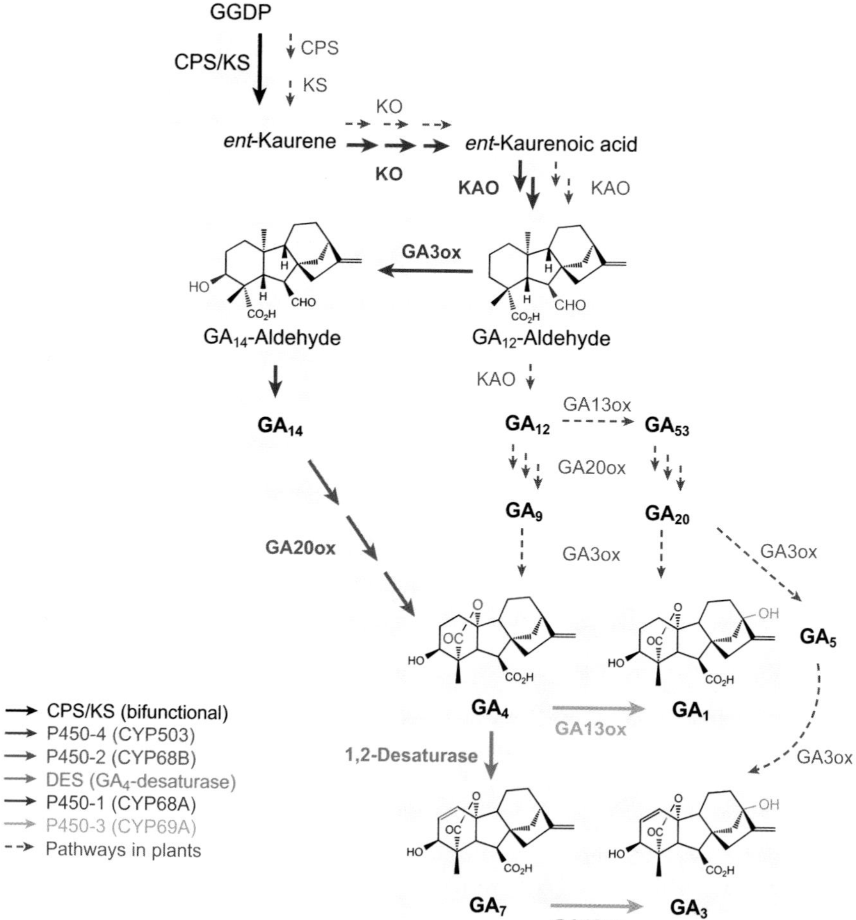

Figure 5

Comparison of the major gibberellin (GA) biosynthesis pathways in the fungus *Gibberella fujikuroi* and plants. The fungal biosynthesis route is highlighted in yellow. The plant pathways are indicated by dashed gray arrows. GGDP, geranylgeranyl diphosphate; CPS, *ent*-copalyl diphosphate synthase; KS, *ent*-kaurene synthase; KO, *ent*-kaurene oxidase; KAO, *ent*-kaurenoic acid oxidase; GA3ox, GA 3-oxidase; GA20ox, GA 20-oxidase; GA13ox, GA 13-oxidase.

the plant enzymes in amino acid sequence. Remarkably, P450-1 has 3β-hydroxylase activity in addition to KAO activity and produces GA_{14} (**Figure 5**). Thus, 3β-hydroxylation is catalyzed by a P450 at an early step of the pathway in *G. fujikuroi*, in contrast to plant GA3oxs that are soluble 2ODDs and act at the final step to produce bioactive GAs (**Figure 1**). GA_{14} is converted to GA_4 by another P450, P450-2 (112). Thus, GA 20 oxidation in *G. fujikuroi* is also catalyzed by a P450, unlike the case with plant GA20oxs. GA_4 is then converted to GA_7 by GA_4-desaturase and finally to GA_3 by P450-3 through 13-hydroxylation (111) (**Figure 5**). Notably, these GA biosynthesis genes are clustered on a single chromosome in fungi, whereas they are randomly located on multiple chromosomes in plants (30, 47). Taken together, these substantial differences in genes and enzymes suggest that plants and fungi have evolved their complex GA biosynthesis pathways independently.

Gibberellin Biosynthesis in Lower Plants

The moss *Physcomitrella patens* is a model organism of bryophytes (12). Some plant hormones, including auxin, cytokinin, and abscisic acid, are biosynthesized and function as growth regulators in *P. patens*. However, whether GAs act as growth regulators in mosses was unknown. Recently, a cDNA clone encoding *ent*-kaurene synthase was identified from *P. patens*, which indicates the occurrence of at least an early GA intermediate in the moss (27). Curiously, *P. patens* *ent*-kaurene synthase is a bifunctional enzyme with both CPS and KS activity, as is the case of fungal CPS/KSs discussed above (**Figure 5**). Both GA_1 and GA_4 were identified in sporophytes of some tree fern species (132, 133). In addition, the lycophytes *Selaginella moellendorffii* and *Selaginella kraussiana* (members of the oldest lineages of vascular plants) possess functional GID1 and DELLA homologs that are capable of forming a complex with GA (137). However, such functional GID1/DELLA proteins are not found in *P. patens*, suggesting that GA-stimulated GID1-DELLA interactions presumably arose in the land plant lineage after the bryophyte divergence (115, 137). Given these observations, it is important to assess the biological relevance of *ent*-kaurene biosynthesis in *P. patens* through reverse genetics.

SUMMARY POINTS

1. The majority of the genes encoding enzymes in the gibberellin (GA) metabolism pathway have now been identified in model plant species.
2. New GA deactivation enzymes have recently been discovered, including C_{20}-GA–specific GA 2-oxidase (class III), 16α,17-epoxidase (EUI/CYP714D1), and GA methyltransferases (GAMTs). These findings indicate the diversity of deactivation mechanisms and emphasize the presence of a number of branches in the GA metabolism pathway.
3. Some transcription factors that directly regulate GA metabolism genes have been identified. In addition, transcriptional regulators that coordinate the balance of two hormones (GA and another hormone) have been discovered, including KNOTTED1-like homeobox (KNOX) proteins, PHYTOCHROME-INTERACTING FACTOR 3-LIKE 5 (PIL5), and FUSCA3 (FUS3).
4. There is now compelling evidence that bioactive GAs act as key mediators in growth responses to environmental cues, such as light and temperature.

5. Profound differences in the GA pathways and enzymes between *Arabidopsis* and the fungus *Gibberella fujikuroi* clearly indicate that higher plants and fungi have evolved the GA pathway independently.

FUTURE ISSUES

1. The identification of additional enzymes, such as GA 13-oxidase and GA-conjugating enzymes, will be necessary to understand the whole picture of the GA metabolism pathway.
2. In many cases, GA biosynthesis and deactivation genes are reciprocally regulated by a common signal (**Figure 4**). Elucidation of the molecular mechanisms underlying this transcriptional regulation will be important to learn how hormone concentrations are effectively altered by the signal.
3. To better understand the regulation of the GA metabolism pathway, clarification of the localization of various GAs at finer spatial resolution in plants is necessary. Because GAs exist in plant tissues at extremely low levels, this will require improvements in GA analytical systems.
4. Although GAs are thought to act occasionally like paracrine signals do, it is not known how GAs move in plants. It will be an important challenge to elucidate the molecular mechanisms of GA movement/transport.

DISCLOSURE STATEMENT

The author is not aware of any biases that might be perceived as affecting the objectivity of this review.

ACKNOWLEDGMENTS

MEXT of Japan supported work in the author's lab.

LITERATURE CITED

1. Aach H, Bode H, Robinson DG, Graebe JE. 1997. *ent*-Kaurene synthetase is located in proplastids of meristematic shoot tissues. *Planta* 202:211–19
2. **Achard P, Baghour M, Chapple A, Hedden P, Van Der Straeten D, et al. 2007. The plant stress hormone ethylene controls floral transition via DELLA-dependent regulation of floral meristem-identity genes. *Proc. Natl. Acad. Sci. USA* 104:6484–89**

2. The first report to illustrate ethylene regulation of gibberellin metabolism in flowering.

3. Achard P, Cheng H, De Grauwe L, Decat J, Schoutteten H, et al. 2006. Integration of plant responses to environmentally activated phytohormonal signals. *Science* 311:91–94
4. Ait-Ali T, Frances S, Weller JL, Reid JB, Kendrick RE, Kamiya Y. 1999. Regulation of gibberellin 20-oxidase and gibberellin 3β-hydroxylase transcript accumulation during de-etiolation of pea seedlings. *Plant Physiol.* 121:783–91

5. Alabadí D, Gil J, Blázquez MA, García-Martínez JL. 2004. Gibberellins repress photomorphogenesis in darkness. *Plant Physiol.* 134:1050–57
6. Appleford NE, Evans DJ, Lenton JR, Gaskin P, Croker SJ, et al. 2006. Function and transcript analysis of gibberellin-biosynthetic enzymes in wheat. *Planta* 223:568–82
7. Batge SL, Ross JJ, Reid JB. 1999. Abscisic acid levels in seeds of the gibberellin-deficient mutant *lh-2* of pea (*Pisum sativum*). *Physiol. Plant.* 105:485–90
8. Blázquez MA, Weigel D. 2000. Integration of floral inductive signals in *Arabidopsis*. *Nature* 404:889–92
9. Bouquin T, Meier C, Foster R, Nielsen ME, Mundy J. 2001. Control of specific gene expression by gibberellin and brassinosteroid. *Plant Physiol.* 127:450–58
10. Chiang HH, Hwang I, Goodman HM. 1995. Isolation of the *Arabidopsis GA4* locus. *Plant Cell* 7:195–201
11. Coles JP, Phillips AL, Croker SJ, Garcia-Lepe R, Lewis MJ, Hedden P. 1999. Modification of gibberellin production and plant development in *Arabidopsis* by sense and antisense expression of gibberellin 20-oxidase genes. *Plant J.* 17:547–56
12. Cove D, Bezanilla M, Harries P, Quatrano R. 2006. Mosses as model systems for the study of metabolism and development. *Annu. Rev. Plant Biol.* 57:497–520
13. Curaba J, Moritz T, Blervaque R, Parcy F, Raz V, et al. 2004. *AtGA3ox2*, a key gene responsible for bioactive gibberellin biosynthesis, is regulated during embryogenesis by LEAFY COTYLEDON2 and FUSCA3 in *Arabidopsis*. *Plant Physiol.* 136:3660–69
14. Dai M, Zhao Y, Ma Q, Hu Y, Hedden P, et al. 2007. The rice *YABBY1* gene is involved in the feedback regulation of gibberellin metabolism. *Plant Physiol.* 144:121–33
15. Dill A, Sun T. 2001. Synergistic derepression of gibberellin signaling by removing RGA and GAI function in *Arabidopsis thaliana*. *Genetics* 159:777–85
16. Eriksson S, Bohlenius H, Moritz T, Nilsson O. 2006. GA_4 is the active gibberellin in the regulation of *LEAFY* transcription and *Arabidopsis* floral initiation. *Plant Cell* 18:2172–81
17. Fleet CM, Yamaguchi S, Hanada A, Kawaide H, David CJ, et al. 2003. Overexpression of *AtCPS* and *AtKS* in *Arabidopsis* confers increased *ent*-kaurene production but no increase in bioactive gibberellins. *Plant Physiol.* 132:830–39
18. Foo EJ, Platten D, Weller JL, Reid JB. 2006. PhyA and cry1 act redundantly to regulate gibberellin levels during de-etiolation in blue light. *Physiol. Plant.* 127:149–56
19. Frigerio M, Alabadí D, Pérez-Gómez J, Garcia-Cárcel L, Phillips AL, et al. 2006. Transcriptional regulation of gibberellin metabolism genes by auxin signaling in *Arabidopsis*. *Plant Physiol.* 142:553–63
20. Fukazawa J, Sakai T, Ishida S, Yamaguchi I, Kamiya Y, Takahashi Y. 2000. Repression of shoot growth, a bZIP transcriptional activator, regulates cell elongation by controlling the level of gibberellins. *Plant Cell* 12:901–15
21. García-Martínez JL, Gil J. 2002. Light regulation of gibberellin biosynthesis and mode of action. *J. Plant Growth Regul.* 20:354–68
22. Gazzarrini S, Tsuchiya Y, Lumba S, Okamoto M, McCourt P. 2004. The transcription factor FUSCA3 controls developmental timing in *Arabidopsis* through the hormones gibberellin and abscisic acid. *Dev. Cell* 7:373–85
23. Gil J, García-Martínez JL. 2000. Light regulation of gibberellin A(1) content and expression of genes coding for GA 20-oxidase and GA 3-hydroxylase in etiolated pea seedlings. *Physiol. Plant* 180:223–29
24. Gómez-Mena C, de Folter S, Costa MM, Angenent GC, Sablowski R. 2005. Transcriptional program controlled by the floral homeotic gene *AGAMOUS* during early organogenesis. *Development* 132:429–38

25. Grindal G, Ernstsen A, Reid JB, Junttila O, Lindgård B, Moe R. 1998. Endogenous gibberellin A_1 levels control thermoperiodic stem elongation in *Pisum sativum*. *Physiol. Plant* 102:523–31
26. Hay A, Kaur H, Phillips A, Hedden P, Hake S, Tsiantis M. 2002. The gibberellin pathway mediates KNOTTED1-type homeobox function in plants with different body plans. *Curr. Biol.* 12:1557–65
27. Hayashi K, Kawaide H, Notomi M, Sakigi Y, Matsuo A, Nozaki H. 2006. Identification and functional analysis of bifunctional *ent*-kaurene synthase from the moss *Physcomitrella patens*. *FEBS Lett.* 580:6175–81
28. Hedden P, Kamiya Y. 1997. Gibberellin biosynthesis: Enzymes, genes and their regulation. *Annu. Rev. Plant Physiol. Plant Mol. Biol.* 48:431–60
29. Hedden P, Phillips AL. 2000. Gibberellin metabolism: new insights revealed by the genes. *Trends Plant Sci.* 5:523–30
30. Hedden P, Phillips AL, Rojas MC, Carrera E, Tudzynski B. 2002. Gibberellin biosynthesis in plants and fungi: A case of convergent evolution? *J. Plant Growth Regul.* 20:319–31
31. Helliwell CA, Chandler PM, Poole A, Dennis ES, Peacock WJ. 2001. The CYP88A cytochrome P450, *ent*-kaurenoic acid oxidase, catalyzes three steps of the gibberellin biosynthesis pathway. *Proc. Natl. Acad. Sci. USA* 98:2065–70
32. Helliwell CA, Sheldon CC, Olive MR, Walker AR, Zeevaart JA, et al. 1998. Cloning of the *Arabidopsis ent*-kaurene oxidase gene *GA3*. *Proc. Natl. Acad. Sci. USA* 95:9019–24
33. Helliwell CA, Sullivan JA, Mould RM, Gray JC, Peacock WJ, Dennis ES. 2001. A plastid envelope location of *Arabidopsis ent*-kaurene oxidase links the plastid and endoplasmic reticulum steps of the gibberellin biosynthesis pathway. *Plant J.* 28:201–8
34. Hisamatsu T, King RW, Helliwell CA, Koshioka M. 2005. The involvement of gibberellin 20-oxidase genes in phytochrome-regulated petiole elongation of *Arabidopsis*. *Plant Physiol.* 138:1106–16
35. Hoffmann-Benning S, Kende H. 1992. On the role of abscisic acid and gibberellin in the regulation of growth in rice. *Plant Physiol.* 99:1156–61
36. Huang S, Raman AS, Ream JE, Fujiwara H, Cerny RE, Brown SM. 1998. Overexpression of 20-oxidase confers a gibberellin-overproduction phenotype in *Arabidopsis*. *Plant Physiol.* 118:773–81
37. Igarashi D, Ishida S, Fukazawa J, Takahashi Y. 2001. 14–3–3 proteins regulate intracellular localization of the bZIP transcriptional activator RSG. *Plant Cell* 13:2483–97
38. Ishida S, Fukazawa J, Yuasa T, Takahashi Y. 2004. Involvement of 14–3–3 signaling protein binding in the functional regulation of the transcriptional activator REPRESSION OF SHOOT GROWTH by gibberellins. *Plant Cell* 16:2641–51
39. Itoh H, Tanaka-Ueguchi M, Kawaide H, Chen XB, Kamiya Y, Matsuoka M. 1999. The gene encoding tobacco gibberellin 3 β-hydroxylase is expressed at the site of GA action during stem elongation and flower organ development. *Plant J.* 20:15–24
40. Itoh H, Tatsumi T, Sakamoto T, Otomo K, Toyomasu T, et al. 2004. A rice semi-dwarf gene, *Tan-Ginbozu* (*D35*), encodes the gibberellin biosynthesis enzyme, *ent*-kaurene oxidase. *Plant Mol. Biol.* 54:533–47
41. Itoh H, Ueguchi-Tanaka M, Sentoku N, Kitano H, Matsuoka M, Kobayashi M. 2001. Cloning and functional analysis of two gibberellin 3 β-hydroxylase genes that are differently expressed during the growth of rice. *Proc. Natl. Acad. Sci. USA* 98:8909–14
42. Jager CE, Symons GM, Ross JJ, Smith JJ, Reid JB. 2005. The brassinosteroid growth response in pea is not mediated by changes in gibberellin content. *Planta* 221:141–48

43. Demonstrates that the KNOX protein controls the balance of gibberellin and cytokinin in shoot apices.

43. **Jasinski S, Piazza P, Craft J, Hay A, Woolley L, et al. 2005. KNOX action in *Arabidopsis* is mediated by coordinate regulation of cytokinin and gibberellin activities. *Curr. Biol.* 15:1560–65**
44. Kaneko M, Itoh H, Inukai Y, Sakamoto T, Ueguchi-Tanaka M, et al. 2003. Where do gibberellin biosynthesis and gibberellin signaling occur in rice plants? *Plant J.* 35:104–15
45. Kaneko M, Itoh H, Ueguchi-Tanaka M, Ashikari M, Matsuoka M. 2002. The α-amylase induction in endosperm during rice seed germination is caused by gibberellin synthesized in epithelium. *Plant Physiol.* 128:1264–70
46. Kasahara H, Hanada A, Kuzuyama T, Takagi M, Kamiya Y, Yamaguchi S. 2002. Contribution of the mevalonate and methylerythritol phosphate pathways to the biosynthesis of gibberellins in *Arabidopsis*. *J. Biol. Chem.* 277:45188–94
47. Kawaide H. 2006. Biochemical and molecular analyses of gibberellin biosynthesis in fungi. *Biosci. Biotechnol. Biochem.* 70:583–90
48. Kawaide H, Imai R, Sassa T, Kamiya Y. 1997. *ent*-kaurene synthase from the fungus *Phaeosphaeria* sp. L487—cDNA isolation, characterization, and bacterial expression of a bifunctional diterpene cyclase in fungal gibberellin biosynthesis. *J. Biol. Chem.* 272:21706–12
49. Kawaide H, Sassa T, Kamiya Y. 2000. Functional analysis of the two interacting cyclase domains in *ent*-kaurene synthase from the fungus *Phaeosphaeria* sp L487 and a comparison with cyclases from higher plants. *J. Biol. Chem.* 275:2276–80
50. King KE, Moritz T, Harberd NP. 2001. Gibberellins are not required for normal stem growth in *Arabidopsis thaliana* in the absence of *GAI* and *RGA*. *Genetics* 159:767–76
51. King RW, Evans LT. 2003. Gibberellins and flowering of grasses and cereals: prizing open the lid of the "florigen" black box. *Annu. Rev. Plant Biol.* 54:307–28
52. King RW, Evans LT, Mander LN, Moritz T, Pharis RP, Twitchin B. 2003. Synthesis of gibberellin GA_6 and its role in flowering of *Lolium temulentum*. *Phytochemistry* 62:77–82
53. King RW, Moritz T, Evans LT, Junttila O, Herlt AJ. 2001. Long-day induction of flowering in *Lolium temulentum* involves sequential increases in specific gibberellins at the shoot apex. *Plant Physiol.* 127:624–32
54. King RW, Moritz T, Evans LT, Martin J, Andersen CH, et al. 2006. Regulation of flowering in the long-day grass *Lolium temulentum* by gibberellins and the *FLOWERING LOCUS T* gene. *Plant Physiol.* 141:498–507
55. Koornneef M, van der Veen JH. 1980. Induction and analysis of gibberellin-sensitive mutants in *Arabidopsis thaliana* (L.) Heynh. *Theor. Appl. Genet.* 58:257–63
56. Kusaba S, Kano-Murakami Y, Matsuoka M, Tamaoki M, Sakamoto T, et al. 1998. Alteration of hormone levels in transgenic tobacco plants overexpressing the rice homeobox gene *OSH1*. *Plant Physiol.* 116:471–76
57. Lee DJ, Zeevaart JA. 2002. Differential regulation of RNA levels of gibberellin dioxygenases by photoperiod in spinach. *Plant Physiol.* 130:2085–94
58. Lee DJ, Zeevaart JA. 2005. Molecular cloning of GA 2-oxidase3 from spinach and its ectopic expression in *Nicotiana sylvestris*. *Plant Physiol.* 138:243–54
59. Lee DJ, Zeevaart JA. 2007. Regulation of gibberellin 20-oxidase1 expression in spinach by photoperiod. *Planta* 226:35–44
60. Macmillan CP, Blundell CA, King RW. 2005. Flowering of the grass *Lolium perenne*: effects of vernalization and long days on gibberellin biosynthesis and signaling. *Plant Physiol.* 138:1794–806
61. MacMillan J. 2002. Occurrence of gibberellins in vascular plants, fungi, and bacteria. *J. Plant Growth Regul.* 20:387–442

62. Magome H, Yamaguchi S, Hanada A, Kamiya Y, Oda K. 2004. *dwarf and delayed-flowering 1*, a novel *Arabidopsis* mutant deficient in gibberellin biosynthesis because of overexpression of a putative AP2 transcription factor. *Plant J.* 37:720–29
63. Matsushita A, Furumoto T, Ishida S, Takahashi Y. 2007. AGF1, an AT-hook protein, is necessary for the negative feedback of *AtGA3ox1* encoding GA 3-oxidase. *Plant Physiol.* 143:1152–62
64. Mitchum MG, Yamaguchi S, Hanada A, Kuwahara A, Yoshioka Y, et al. 2006. Distinct and overlapping roles of two gibberellin 3-oxidases in *Arabidopsis* development. *Plant J.* 45:804–18
65. Nakajima M, Shimada A, Takashi Y, Kim YC, Park SH, et al. 2006. Identification and characterization of *Arabidopsis* gibberellin receptors. *Plant J.* 46:880–89
66. Nakaminami K, Sawada Y, Suzuki M, Kenmoku H, Kawaide H, et al. 2003. Deactivation of gibberellin by 2-oxidation during germination of photoblastic lettuce seeds. *Biosci. Biotechnol. Biochem.* 67:1551–58
67. Nelson DR, Schuler MA, Paquette SM, Werck-Reichhart D, Bak S. 2004. Comparative genomics of rice and *Arabidopsis*. Analysis of 727 cytochrome P450 genes and pseudogenes from a monocot and a dicot. *Plant Physiol.* 135:756–72
68. Ngo P, Ozga JA, Reinecke DM. 2002. Specificity of auxin regulation of gibberellin 20-oxidase gene expression in pea pericarp. *Plant Mol. Biol.* 49:439–48
69. Ogawa M, Hanada A, Yamauchi Y, Kuwahara A, Kamiya Y, Yamaguchi S. 2003. Gibberellin biosynthesis and response during *Arabidopsis* seed germination. *Plant Cell* 15:1591–604
70. Oh E, Yamaguchi S, Hu J, Yusuke J, Jung B, et al. 2007. PIL5, a phytochrome-interacting bHLH protein, regulates gibberellin responsiveness by binding directly to the *GAI* and *RGA* promoters in *Arabidopsis* seeds. *Plant Cell* 19:1192–208
71. **Oh E, Yamaguchi S, Kamiya Y, Bae G, Chung WI, Choi G. 2006. Light activates the degradation of PIL5 protein to promote seed germination through gibberellin in *Arabidopsis*. *Plant J.* 47:124–39**

71. The first identification of a regulator that links phytochrome and gibberellin levels in germinating seeds.

72. Olszewski N, Sun TP, Gubler F. 2002. Gibberellin signaling: biosynthesis, catabolism, and response pathways. *Plant Cell* 14(Suppl.):S61–80
73. O'Neill DP, Ross JJ. 2002. Auxin regulation of the gibberellin pathway in pea. *Plant Physiol.* 130:1974–82
74. O'Neill DP, Ross JJ, Reid JB. 2000. Changes in gibberellin A(1) levels and response during de-etiolation of pea seedlings. *Plant Physiol.* 124:805–12
75. Otomo K, Kenmoku H, Oikawa H, Konig WA, Toshima H, et al. 2004. Biological functions of *ent*- and *syn*-copalyl diphosphate synthases in rice: key enzymes for the branch point of gibberellin and phytoalexin biosynthesis. *Plant J.* 39:886–93
76. Otsuka M, Kenmoku H, Ogawa M, Okada K, Mitsuhashi W, et al. 2004. Emission of *ent*-kaurene, a diterpenoid hydrocarbon precursor for gibberellins, into the headspace from plants. *Plant Cell Physiol.* 45:1129–38
77. Ozga JA, van Huizen R, Reinecke DM. 2002. Hormone and seed-specific regulation of pea fruit growth. *Plant Physiol.* 128:1379–89
78. **Penfield S, Josse EM, Kannangara R, Gilday AD, Halliday KJ, Graham IA. 2005. Cold and light control seed germination through the bHLH transcription factor SPATULA. *Curr. Biol.* 15:1998–2006**

78. The first identification of a regulator that mediates temperature-regulation of gibberellin metabolism during cold stratification.

79. Phillips AL, Ward DA, Uknes S, Appleford NE, Lange T, et al. 1995. Isolation and expression of three gibberellin 20-oxidase cDNA clones from *Arabidopsis*. *Plant Physiol.* 108:1049–57

80. Prisic S, Peters RJ. 2007. Synergistic substrate inhibition of *ent*-copalyl diphosphate synthase: a potential feed-forward inhibition mechanism limiting gibberellin metabolism. *Plant Physiol.* 144:445–54
81. Prisic S, Xu M, Wilderman PR, Peters RJ. 2004. Rice contains two disparate *ent*-copalyl diphosphate synthases with distinct metabolic functions. *Plant Physiol.* 136:4228–36
82. Reid JB, Botwright NA, Smith JJ, O'Neill DP, Kerckhoffs LH. 2002. Control of gibberellin levels and gene expression during de-etiolation in pea. *Plant Physiol.* 128:734–41
83. Rojas MC, Hedden P, Gaskin P, Tudzynski B. 2001. The *P450-1* gene of *Gibberella fujikuroi* encodes a multifunctional enzyme in gibberellin biosynthesis. *Proc. Natl. Acad. Sci. USA* 98:5838–43
84. Ross JJ, O'Neill DP, Smith JJ, Kerckhoffs LH, Elliott RC. 2000. Evidence that auxin promotes gibberellin A_1 biosynthesis in pea. *Plant J.* 21:547–52
85. Sakai M, Sakamoto T, Saito T, Matsuoka M, Tanaka H, Kobayashi M. 2003. Expression of novel rice gibberellin 2-oxidase gene is under homeostatic regulation by biologically active gibberellins. *J. Plant Res.* 116:161–64
86. **Sakamoto T, Kamiya N, Ueguchi-Tanaka M, Iwahori S, Matsuoka M. 2001. KNOX homeodomain protein directly suppresses the expression of a gibberellin biosynthetic gene in the tobacco shoot apical meristem. *Genes Dev.* 15:581–90**

86. The first paper to demonstrate the role of KNOX proteins in suppressing gibberllin synthesis in the shoot apical meristem.

87. Sakamoto T, Kobayashi M, Itoh H, Tagiri A, Kayano T, et al. 2001. Expression of a gibberellin 2-oxidase gene around the shoot apex is related to phase transition in rice. *Plant Physiol.* 125:1508–16
88. Sakamoto T, Miura K, Itoh H, Tatsumi T, Ueguchi-Tanaka M, et al. 2004. An overview of gibberellin metabolism enzyme genes and their related mutants in rice. *Plant Physiol.* 134:1642–53
89. Sakamoto T, Sakakibara H, Kojima M, Yamamoto Y, Nagasaki H, et al. 2006. Ectopic expression of KNOTTED1-like homeobox protein induces expression of cytokinin biosynthesis genes in rice. *Plant Physiol.* 142:54–62
90. Sasaki A, Itoh H, Gomi K, Ueguchi-Tanaka M, Ishiyama K, et al. 2003. Accumulation of phosphorylated repressor for gibberellin signaling in an F-box mutant. *Science* 299:1896–98
91. Schneider G, Jensen E, Spray CR, Phinney BO. 1992. Hydrolysis and reconjugation of gibberellin A_{20} glucosyl ester by seedlings of *Zea mays* L. *Proc. Natl. Acad. Sci. USA* 89:8045–48
92. Schneider G, Schliemann W. 1994. Gibberellin conjugates–an overview. *Plant Growth Regul.* 15:247–60
93. **Schomburg FM, Bizzell CM, Lee DJ, Zeevaart JA, Amasino RM. 2003. Overexpression of a novel class of gibberellin 2-oxidases decreases gibberellin levels and creates dwarf plants. *Plant Cell* 15:151–63**

93. Identification of a new class of GA 2-oxidases that specifically use C_{20}-GAs as substrates.

94. Seo M, Hanada A, Kuwahara A, Endo A, Okamoto M, et al. 2006. Regulation of hormone metabolism in *Arabidopsis* seeds: phytochrome regulation of abscisic acid metabolism and abscisic acid regulation of gibberellin metabolism. *Plant J.* 48:354–66
95. Shinomura T. 1997. Phytochrome regulation of seed germination. *J. Plant Res.* 110:151–61
96. Shinomura T, Nagatani A, Hanzawa H, Kubota M, Watanabe M, Furuya M. 1996. Action spectra for phytochrome A- and B-specific photoinduction of seed germination in *Arabidopsis thaliana*. *Proc. Natl. Acad. Sci. USA* 93:8129–33
97. Silverstone AL, Chang C, Krol E, Sun TP. 1997. Developmental regulation of the gibberellin biosynthetic gene *GA1* in *Arabidopsis thaliana*. *Plant J.* 12:9–19

98. Spielmeyer W, Ellis MH, Chandler PM. 2002. *Semidwarf (sd-1)*, "green revolution" rice, contains a defective gibberellin 20-oxidase gene. *Proc. Natl. Acad. Sci. USA* 99:9043–48
99. Sponsel VM, Hedden P. 2004. Gibberellin biosynthesis and inactivation. In *Plant Hormones: Biosynthesis, Signal Transduction, Action!*, ed. PJ Davies, pp. 63–94. Dordrecht: Kluwer Acad.
100. Spray CR, Kobayashi M, Suzuki Y, Phinney BO, Gaskin P, MacMillan J. 1996. The *dwarf-1 (dt)* mutant of *Zea mays* blocks three steps in the gibberellin-biosynthetic pathway. *Proc. Natl. Acad. Sci. USA* 93:10515–18
101. Stavang JA, Lindgård B, Erntsen A, Lid SE, Moe R, Olsen JE. 2005. Thermoperiodic stem elongation involves transcriptional regulation of gibberellin deactivation in pea. *Plant Physiol.* 138:2344–53
102. Sun TP, Gubler F. 2004. Molecular mechanism of gibberellin signaling in plants. *Annu. Rev. Plant Biol.* 55:197–223
103. Sun TP, Kamiya Y. 1994. The *Arabidopsis GA1* locus encodes the cyclase *ent*-kaurene synthetase A of gibberellin biosynthesis. *Plant Cell* 6:1509–18
104. Sun TP, Kamiya Y. 1997. Regulation and cellular localization of *ent*-kaurene synthesis. *Physiol. Plant.* 101:701–8
105. Tanaka-Ueguchi M, Itoh H, Oyama N, Koshioka M, Matsuoka M. 1998. Over-expression of a tobacco homeobox gene, *NTH15*, decreases the expression of a gibberellin biosynthetic gene encoding GA 20-oxidase. *Plant J.* 15:391–400
106. Thomas SG, Phillips AL, Hedden P. 1999. Molecular cloning and functional expression of gibberellin 2-oxidases, multifunctional enzymes involved in gibberellin deactivation. *Proc. Natl. Acad. Sci. USA* 96:4698–703
107. Toyomasu T, Kawaide H, Ishizaki A, Shinoda S, Otsuka M, et al. 2000. Cloning of a full-length cDNA encoding *ent*-kaurene synthase from *Gibberella fujikuroi*: functional analysis of a bifunctional diterpene cyclase. *Biosci. Biotechnol. Biochem.* 64:660–64
108. Toyomasu T, Kawaide H, Mitsuhashi W, Inoue Y, Kamiya Y. 1998. Phytochrome regulates gibberellin biosynthesis during germination of photoblastic lettuce seeds. *Plant Physiol.* 118:1517–23
109. Toyomasu T, Kawaide H, Sekimoto H, von Numers C, Phillips AL, et al. 1997. Cloning and characterization of a cDNA encoding gibberellin 20-oxidase from rice (*Oryza sativa*) seedlings. *Physiol. Plantarum.* 99:111–18
110. Tudzynski B, Kawaide H, Kamiya Y. 1998. Gibberellin biosynthesis in *Gibberella fujikuroi*: cloning and characterization of the copalyl diphosphate synthase gene. *Curr. Genet.* 34:234–40
111. Tudzynski B, Mihlan M, Rojas MC, Linnemannstons P, Gaskin P, Hedden P. 2003. Characterization of the final two genes of the gibberellin biosynthesis gene cluster of *Gibberella fujikuroi*: *des* and *P450-3* encode GA_4 desaturase and the 13-hydroxylase, respectively. *J. Biol. Chem.* 278:28635–43
112. Tudzynski B, Rojas MC, Gaskin P, Hedden P. 2002. The gibberellin 20-oxidase of *Gibberella fujikuroi* is a multifunctional monooxygenase. *J. Biol. Chem.* 277:21246–53
113. Ueguchi-Tanaka M, Ashikari M, Nakajima M, Itoh H, Katoh E, et al. 2005. *GIBBERELLIN INSENSITIVE DWARF1* encodes a soluble receptor for gibberellin. *Nature* 437:693–98
114. Ueguchi-Tanaka M, Nakajima M, Katoh E, Ohmiya H, Asano K, et al. 2007. Molecular interactions of a soluble gibberellin receptor, GID1, with a rice DELLA protein, SLR1, and gibberellin. *Plant Cell* 19:2140–55
115. Ueguchi-Tanaka M, Nakajima M, Motoyuki A, Matsuoka M. 2007. Gibberellin receptor and its role in gibberellin signaling in plants. *Annu. Rev. Plant Biol.* 58:183–98

113. The first identification of a gibberellin receptor.

116. Van Huizen R, Ozga JA, Reinecke DM. 1997. Seed and hormonal regulation of gibberellin 20-oxidase expression in pea pericarp. *Plant Physiol.* 115:123–28

117. Varbanova M, Yamaguchi S, Yang Y, McKelvey K, Hanada A, et al. 2007. Methylation of gibberellins by *Arabidopsis* GAMT1 and GAMT2. *Plant Cell* 19:32–45

117. Reports the discovery of enzymes that deactivate gibberellins through methylation.

118. Vettakkorumakankav NN, Falk D, Saxena P, Fletcher RA. 1999. A crucial role for gibberellins in stress protection of plants. *Plant Biol.* 40:542–48

119. Wang H, Caruso LV, Downie AB, Perry SE. 2004. The embryo MADS domain protein AGAMOUS-like 15 directly regulates expression of a gene encoding an enzyme involved in gibberellin metabolism. *Plant Cell* 16:1206–19

120. Weiss D, Van Der Luit A, Knegt E, Vermeer E, Mol J, Kooter JM. 1995. Identification of endogenous gibberellins in petunia flowers (Induction of anthocyanin biosynthetic gene expression and the antagonistic effect of abscisic acid). *Plant Physiol.* 107:695–702

121. White CN, Proebsting WM, Hedden P, Rivin CJ. 2000. Gibberellins and seed development in maize. I. Evidence that gibberellin/abscisic acid balance governs germination vs maturation pathways. *Plant Physiol.* 122:1081–88

122. Wolbang CM, Chandler PM, Smith JJ, Ross JJ. 2004. Auxin from the developing inflorescence is required for the biosynthesis of active gibberellins in barley stems. *Plant Physiol.* 134:769–76

123. Wolbang CM, Ross JJ. 2001. Auxin promotes gibberellin biosynthesis in decapitated tobacco plants. *Planta* 214:153–57

124. Wu K, Li L, Gage DA, Zeevaart JA. 1996. Molecular cloning and photoperiod-regulated expression of gibberellin 20-oxidase from the long-day plant spinach. *Plant Physiol.* 110:547–54

125. Xu M, Hillwig ML, Prisic S, Coates RM, Peters RJ. 2004. Functional identification of rice *syn*-copalyl diphosphate synthase and its role in initiating biosynthesis of diterpenoid phytoalexin/allelopathic natural products. *Plant J.* 39:309–18

126. Xu YL, Gage DA, Zeevaart JA. 1997. Gibberellins and stem growth in *Arabidopsis thaliana*. Effects of photoperiod on expression of the *GA4* and *GA5* loci. *Plant Physiol.* 114:1471–76

127. Xu YL, Li L, Gage DA, Zeevaart JA. 1999. Feedback regulation of *GA5* expression and metabolic engineering of gibberellin levels in *Arabidopsis*. *Plant Cell* 11:927–36

128. Yamaguchi S, Kamiya Y. 2000. Gibberellin biosynthesis: its regulation by endogenous and environmental signals. *Plant Cell Physiol.* 41:251–57

129. Yamaguchi S, Kamiya Y, Sun T. 2001. Distinct cell-specific expression patterns of early and late gibberellin biosynthetic genes during *Arabidopsis* seed germination. *Plant J.* 28:443–53

130. Yamaguchi S, Smith MW, Brown RG, Kamiya Y, Sun T. 1998. Phytochrome regulation and differential expression of gibberellin 3β-hydroxylase genes in germinating *Arabidopsis* seeds. *Plant Cell* 10:2115–26

131. Yamaguchi S, Sun T, Kawaide H, Kamiya Y. 1998. The *GA2* locus of *Arabidopsis thaliana* encodes *ent*-kaurene synthase of gibberellin biosynthesis. *Plant Physiol.* 116:1271–78

132. Yamane H, Fujioka S, Spray CR, Phinney BO, MacMillan J, et al. 1988. Endogenous gibberellins from sporophytes of two tree ferns, *Cibotium glaucum* and *Dicksonia antarctica*. *Plant Physiol.* 86:857–62

133. Yamane H, Yamaguchi I, Kobayashi M, Takahashi M, Sato Y, et al. 1985. Identification of ten gibberellins from sporophytes of the tree fern, *Cyathea australis*. *Plant Physiol.* 78:899–903

134. Yamauchi Y, Ogawa M, Kuwahara A, Hanada A, Kamiya Y, Yamaguchi S. 2004. Activation of gibberellin biosynthesis and response pathways by low temperature during imbibition of *Arabidopsis thaliana* seeds. *Plant Cell* 16:367–78

134. The first report to show conclusive evidence that cold stratification activates the gibberellin biosynthesis pathway.

135. Yamauchi Y, Takeda-Kamiya N, Hanada A, Ogawa M, Kuwahara A, et al. 2007. Contribution of gibberellin deactivation by AtGA2ox2 to the suppression of germination of dark-imbibed *Arabidopsis thaliana* seeds. *Plant Cell Physiol.* 48:555–61
136. Yanai O, Shani E, Dolezal K, Tarkowski P, Sablowski R, et al. 2005. *Arabidopsis* KNOXI proteins activate cytokinin biosynthesis. *Curr. Biol.* 15:1566–71
137. Yasumura Y, Crumpton-Taylor M, Fuentes S, Harberd NP. 2007. Step-by-step acquisition of the gibberellin-DELLA growth-regulatory mechanism during land-plant evolution. *Curr. Biol.* 17:1225–30
138. Zeevaart JA, Gage DA, Talon M. 1993. Gibberellin A_1 is required for stem elongation in spinach. *Proc. Natl. Acad. Sci. USA* 90:7401–5
139. Zhao X, Yu X, Foo E, Symons GM, Lopez J, et al. 2007. A study of gibberellin homeostasis and cryptochrome-mediated blue light inhibition of hypocotyl elongation. *Plant Physiol.* 145:106–18
140. Zhu Y, Nomura T, Xu Y, Zhang Y, Peng Y, et al. 2006. *ELONGATED UPPERMOST INTERNODE* encodes a cytochrome P450 monooxygenase that epoxidizes gibberellins in a novel deactivation reaction in rice. *Plant Cell* 18:442–56

140. Reports the discovery of EUI/CYP714D1 as a gibberellin deactivation enzyme that catalyzes 16,17-epoxidation.

RELATED RESOURCES

Blázquez MA, Leon J. 2006. Reproductive development. In *Plant Hormone Signaling. Annual Plant Reviews*, ed. P Hedden, SG Thomas, 24:293–310. Oxford: Blackwell

Ross JJ, Symons GM, Abas L, Reid JB, Luschnig C. 2006. Hormone distribution and transport. In *Plant Hormone Signaling. Annual Plant Reviews*, ed. P Hedden, SG Thomas, 24:257–91. Oxford: Blackwell

Thomas SG, Hedden P. 2006. Gibberellin metabolsim and signal transduction. In *Plant Hormone Signaling. Annual Plant Reviews*, ed. P Hedden, SG Thomas, 24:147–84. Oxford: Blackwell

Molecular Basis of Plant Architecture

Yonghong Wang and Jiayang Li

Institute of Genetics and Developmental Biology, Chinese Academy of Sciences, Beijing 100101, China; email: yhwang@genetics.ac.cn, jyli@genetics.ac.cn

Annu. Rev. Plant Biol. 2008. 59:253–79

The *Annual Review of Plant Biology* is online at plant.annualreviews.org

This article's doi:
10.1146/annurev.arplant.59.032607.092902

1543-5008/08/0602-0253$20.00

Key Words

branching, inflorescence, phytohormone, plant height, shoot apical meristem, stem cell

Abstract

Higher plants display a variety of architectures that are defined by the degree of branching, internodal elongation, and shoot determinancy. Studies on the model plants of *Arabidopsis thaliana* and tomato and on crop plants such as rice and maize have greatly strengthened our understanding on the molecular genetic bases of plant architecture, one of the hottest areas in plant developmental biology. The identification of mutants that are defective in plant architecture and characterization of the corresponding and related genes will eventually enable us to elucidate the molecular mechanisms underlying plant architecture. The achievements made so far in studying plant architecture have already allowed us to pave a way for optimizing the plant architecture of crops by molecular design and improving grain productivity.

Contents

INTRODUCTION

Higher plants establish a great diversity of aesthetically pleasing structures, consistent with the conventional concept of architecture related to buildings, implicating both art and science and specifying both form and function. Although plant architecture is to some extent influenced by environmental factors such as light, temperature, humidity, nutrition, and plant density, plant architecture is determined mainly by the plant's genetic program. Therefore, plant architecture is the best means to identify a plant species (**Figure 1**).

Studies of plant architecture and its influences on human existence are steeped in a long history. Extensive research on plant architecture has been focused on the fundamental questions, such as how a plant maintains the activity of its shoot apical meristem (SAM) and initiates the axillary meristems (AMs), when AMs begin to grow to generate branches, when the SAM starts to produce the inflorescence meristems and then floral organs, and when shoots begin to elongate and stop (166). These questions have been addressed mainly by using both the dicotyledonous plants *Arabidopsis*, *Antirrhinum*, petunia, pea, and tomato, and the monocotyledonous plants maize and rice, strengthening our comprehension of the molecular regulatory mechanisms of plant architecture.

Crop plants with desirable architecture are able to produce much higher grain yields, as in the case of the "Green Revolution" in which grain yields have been significantly increased by growing lodging-resistant semidwarf varieties of wheat and rice (116). Therefore, understanding the mechanism that underlies plant architecture will not only address the fundamental issues in plant science but also facilitate the breeding of high-yield crops.

SAM: shoot apical meristem

AM: axillary meristem

This review aims to provide broad coverage of our latest understanding of the aerial architecture of higher plants and its potential applications to genetically modified (GM) crops.

MOLECULAR EVENTS CONTROLLING SHOOT APICAL MERISTEM ACTIVITY

Shoot Apical Meristem: The Ultimate Source of Plant Aerial Organs

The embryogenesis of higher plants establishes the plant body plan, including the SAM and root apical meristem (RAM), which determine the architecture of the aerial and underground parts of a plant, respectively. The SAM generates all above-ground components of a plant, including leaves, stems, and axillary branches, under the dynamic balance of indeterminate growth and differentiation. Because of the significance and complexity of the SAM in plant development, the maintenance and differentiation of the SAM in postembryonic development have drawn the interest of biologists for centuries.

In *Arabidopsis*, the SAM contains a pool of pluripotent stem cells, which are organized into three cell layers, L1 to L3, according to the orientation of cell divisions, and are further identified as three zones (28): the central zone (CZ), peripheral zone (PZ), and rib zone (RZ), respectively, according to their positions and functions (**Figure 2*a***). The L1 and L2 generate the epidermis and subepidermis of shoots, leaves, and flowers, and the L3 generates the internal tissues (144). The overlapped region of L3 and the CZ acts as an organizing center (OC) that specifies the overlying neighboring cells as stem cells (**Figure 2*a***). The main activities of the SAM throughout plant development are to maintain the pluripotent stem cells and to form lateral organs and stems, by which the diverse architecture of different plant species is established.

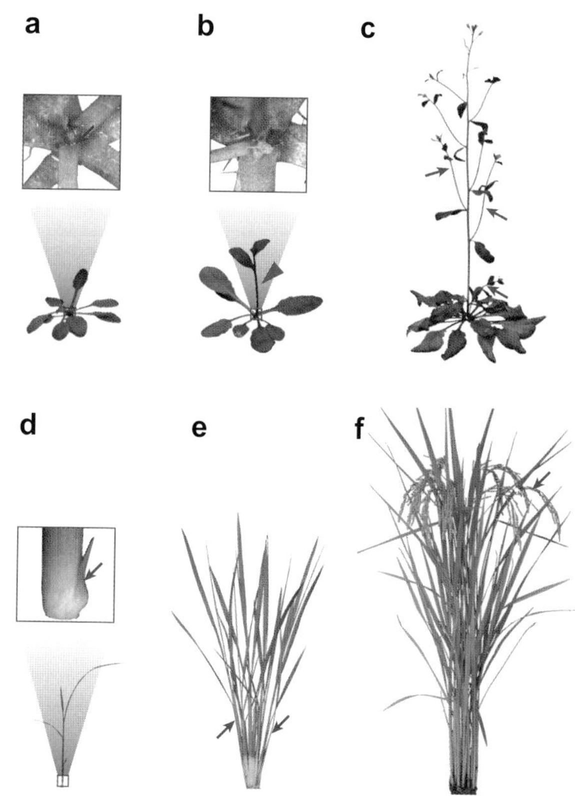

Figure 1

Plant architecture of model plants *Arabidopsis* and rice. (*a–c*) Schematic of the plant architecture of *Arabidopsis*. (*a*) At the seedling stage, no visible axillary bud can be observed in the axil of a leaf, as indicated by the red arrow in the upper panel, which is a magnification of the indicated region in the lower panel. (*b*) Transition from the vegetative stage to the reproductive stage promotes elongation of the inflorescence stem (bolting) and the outgrowth of axillary buds. The red arrow (*upper panel*) indicates a visible axillary bud in the axil of a leaf and the arrowhead (*lower panel*) indicates the elongating inflorescence stem. The upper panel is a magnification of the indicated region in the lower panel. (*c*) The continued outgrowth of the axillary buds gives rise to branches (*red arrows*). (*d–f*) Schematic of the plant architecture of rice. (*d*) At the seedling stage, a tiller bud (*red arrow*) can be observed in the axil of a leaf in the upper panel, which is a closed-view image of the indicated region in the lower panel after the leaf is removed to expose the tiller bud. (*e*) Tiller buds develop into tillers (*red arrows*). (*f*) A mature rice plant with panicle-bearing tillers (*red arrow*).

CLV-WUS Feedback Loop: A Key Factor That Affects the Dynamic Maintenance of Shoot Apical Meristems

Studies on *Arabidopsis* have revealed a CLV-WUS (for a list of gene and enzyme

GM: genetically modified

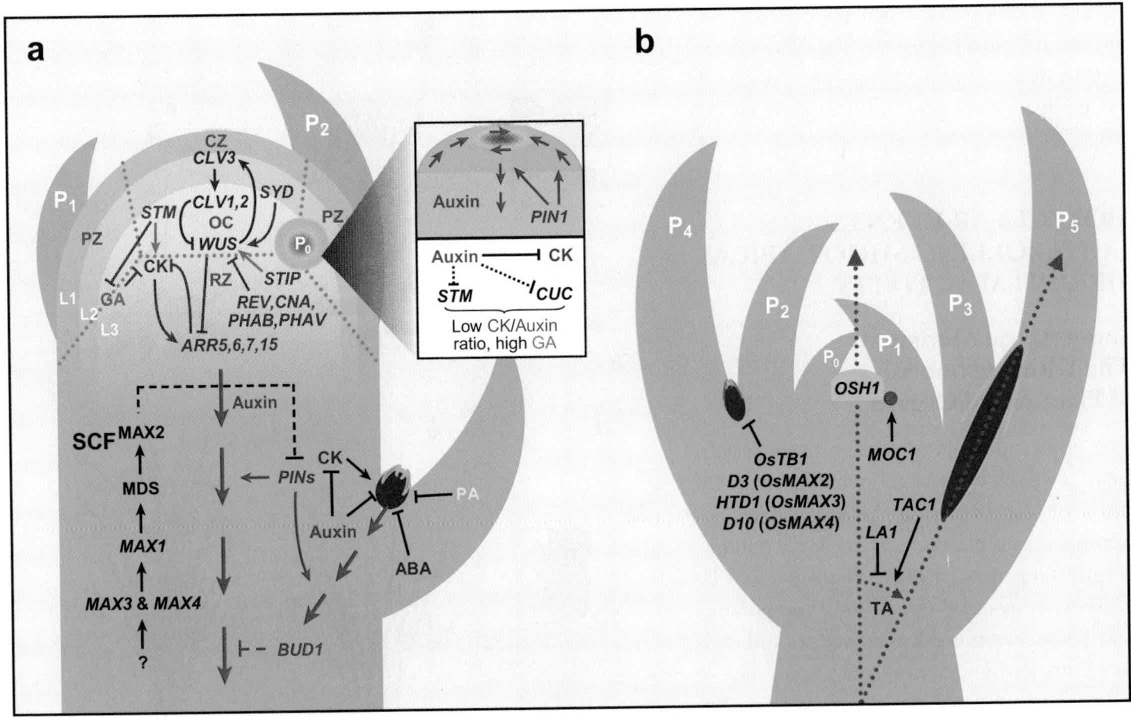

Figure 2

Pathways and elements controlling shoot apical meristem (SAM) activities and the initiation and outgrowth of axillary meristems (AMs). (*a*) Schematic of pathways and elements controlling SAM activities and the initiation and outgrowth of AMs in *Arabidopsis*. L1–L3 cell layers and developmental zones are also shown. Brown arrows indicate the CLV-WUS feedback loop. Red arrows indicate the auxin flow and its related pathway. Black arrows represent the more axillary branching (MAX)-dependent signal (MDS) pathway. Pink characters represent cytokinin (CK)-related regulators. The blue region denotes the axillary bud. (*b*) Genes controlling rice SAM activities, the initiation and outgrowth of tiller buds, and the tillering angle. Red and blue regions denote the AM and tiller buds, respectively. ABA, abscisic acid; *ARR*, *Arabidopsis response regulator*; *BUD1*, *Bushy and Dwarf1*; *CLV1–3*, *CLAVATA1–3*; *CNA*, *CORONA*; *CUC*, *CUP-SHAPED COTYLEDON*; CZ, central zone; *D3*, *Dwarf3*; *D10*, *Dwarf10*; GA, gibberellin; *HTD1*, *High-tillering Dwarf1*; *LA1*, *LAZY1*; *MOC1*, *MONOCULM1*; OC, organizing center; *OSH1*, *rice Homeobox1*; *OsTB1*, *Oryza sativa TEOSINTE BRANCHED1*; P0–P5, leaf primordial; *PIN*, *PIN-FORMED*; PZ, peripheral zone; *PHAB*, *PHABULOSA*; *PHAV*, *PHAVOLUTA*; SCF, Skp1-Cul1/Cdc53-F-box; *STM*, *SHOOTMERISTEMLESS*; *SYD*, *SPLAYED*; TA, tiller angle; *TAC1*, *Tiller Angle Control 1*; PA, polyamines; *REV*, *REVOLUTA*; RZ, rib zone; *WUS*, *WUSCHEL*.

abbreviations, see **Table 1**) feedback loop that plays a central role in maintaining SAM activities (**Figure 2*a***). The feedback loop involves leucine-rich repeat (LRR) receptor kinases, peptide ligands, and small metabolite intermediates, which set up a bridge for communication between differentiated and undifferentiated cells. Within this loop, *CLV1*, *CLV2*, and *CLV3* determine the population of stem cells in both shoot and inflorescence meristems. Plants carrying mutations in the *CLV* loci accumulate undifferentiated cells, giving rise to SAMs of enlarged size and overproduced floral meristems (32, 34, 35). *CLV1* encodes a LRR Ser/Thr kinase (36); CLV2 is a receptor-like protein resembling CLV1 with a short cytoplasmic tail but lacks a kinase domain (68); and *CLV3* encodes a 96–amino acid predicted extracellular protein that can move

CZ: central zone

PZ: peripheral zone

OC: organizing center

LRR: leucine-rich repeat

Table 1 Abbreviations of genes and enzymes

AG: *AGAMOUS*	**DAD**: *DECREASED APICAL DOMINANCE*	**MOC1**: *MONOCULM 1*
AHK: *Arabidopsis histidine kinase*	**D11**: *Dwarf11*	**NAM**: *NO APICAL MERISTEM*
ASK1: *Arabidopsis SKP1-LIKE1*	**D8**: *Dwarf 8*	**Os20ox2**: GA 20-oxidase
AtCUL1: *Arabidopsis cullin*	**d2**: *Dwarf2*, also known as *ebisu dwarf*	**PHAB**: *PHABULOSA*
AP: *APETALA*	**EUI**: *ELONGATED UPPERMOST INTERNODE*	**PHAV**: *PHAVOLUTA*
ARR: *Arabidopsis response regulator*	**FEA2**: *FASCIATED EAR2*	**PIN**: *PIN-FORMED*
Ba1: *Barren stalk1*	**FON**: *FLORAL ORGAN NUMBER*	**RMS**: *RAMOSOUS*
BES1: *Bri1-EMS-suppressor 1*	**FLO**: *FLORICAULA*	**RA**: *Ramous*
BIN2: *BR-INSENSITIVE 2*	**FZP**: *FRIZZY PANICLE*	**RAM1**: *Reduced β-amylase 1*
BAK1: LRR-RLK BRI1-ASSOCIATED RECEPTOR KINASE1	**GAI**: *Gibberellin-insensitive*	**REV**: *REVOLUTA*
BKI1: BRI1 kinase inhibitor 1	**GID**: *GIBBERELLIN-INSENSITIVE DWARF*	**RHT**: *Reduced height-1*
Bl: *Blind*	**IPT**: isopentenyl transferase	**Sd1**: *Semi-dwarf 1*
BRI1: BRASSINOSTEROID-INSENSITIVE1	**KN1**: *KNOTTED-1*	**SLR1**: *Slender1*
Br2: *Branchytic 2*	**KTN1**: ATPase katanin-like protein	**STIP**: *STIMPY*
BP: *BREVIPEDICELLUS*	**LA**: *LAZY*	**STM**: *SHOOTMERISTEMLESS*
BZR1: *Brassinazole-resistant 1*	**LAS**: *LATERAL SUPPRESSOR*	**SPA**: *SMALL PANICLE*
CNA: *CORONA*	**LAX**: *LAX PANICLE*	**Spk(t)**: *Spreading type of kasalath*
CCD: carotenoid cleavage deoxygenase	**LFY**: *LEAFY*	**SYD**: *SPLAYED*
CKX: cytokinin oxidase	**LOB**: *LATERAL ORGAN BOUNDARY DOMAIN*	**TAC1**: *Tiller Angle Control 1*
CLV: *CLAVATA*	**LOG**: *LONELY GUY*	**TD1**: *THICK TASSEL DWARF1*
CUC: *CUP-SHAPED COTYLEDON*	**Ls**: *Lateral suppressor*	**WUS**: *WUSCHEL*
CycD3: *CyclinD3*	**MAX**: *MORE AXILLARY BRANCHING*	

between cells (47). Genetic studies have provided strong evidence that these three *CLV* genes function in a common signaling pathway to maintain the balance between the CZ and PZ (35). It has been proposed that CLV1 and CLV2 form a heteromeric complex, in which CLV1 is stabilized by CLV2 (160). CLV3 has been proposed to act as a ligand to activate the CLV1-CLV2 receptor complex (47, 160). However, there is no molecular evidence to show a direct interaction between CLV3 and the CLV1-CLV2 complex in vivo.

WUS acts as a homeodomain-type transcription factor responsible for stem cell identity in the SAM (83, 96). In agreement with its function of maintaining the stem cell pool, *WUS* is expressed specifically in the OC cells (13) and the *wus* mutant displays ectopic primordium initiation with larger and more vacuolated meristem cells at shoot apices compared with the wild type (83). In the proposed feedback loop model, WUS may indirectly activate the expression of the signaling peptide CLV3 in stem cells, which in turn represses *WUS* transcription through the CLV1 receptor kinase signaling pathway (26, 87, 125, 134). Nevertheless, the molecular players directing the activation of CLV3 by WUS and the repression of WUS by CLV3 have yet to be substantiated.

Beyond the CLV-WUS feedback regulatory loop, WUS appears to be a central player that integrates the regulatory information from several pathways to govern SAM activities. Another positive regulator of SAM maintenance is *STM*, which encodes a homeodomain protein of the KN1 family. It has been shown that *STM* acts as an antagonist of *CLV* but synergistically sustains the balance of stem cell regeneration and differentiation (33, 44, 51, 86, 93). The HD-ZIPIII genes *CNA*, *PHAB*, and *PHAV* also control *WUS* and thus the meristem size (119, 173). A SNF2 chromatin-remodeling ATPase, SYD, controls the expression of *WUS* by directly binding to its proximal promoter region (81). Another reported positive regulator of *WUS* is *STIP*, which encodes a protein of the same family as WUS and is required to maintain the *WUS* expression in the SAM (177). Consistent with its central position, the *WUS* promoter contains distinct regulatory regions that control tissue specificity and levels of transcription in a combinatorial manner (13). Interestingly, a 57-bp regulatory region of the WUS promoter has been found responsible for controlling the boundaries of WUS transcription in the shoot stem cells, within which the two adjacent short sequence motifs RE1 and RE2 are essential for WUS functions (13).

Cytokinins and Shoot Apical Meristem Maintenance

Phytohormones have been regarded as indispensable players in plant development. Among them, cytokinins are plant-specific hormones that regulate cell division and are the best known hormones involved in maintaining meristem activity (124). It is reported that the constitutive expression of *CycD3* in transgenic *Arabidopsis* plants induces and maintains cell division when the plants are deprived of exogenous cytokinins (124); the overexpression of *CKX* genes decreases the endogenous cytokinin content in tobacco plants, producing stunted shoots with smaller apical meristems accompanied by a prolonged plastochrone and leaf cell production (171). The primary functions of *AHK* genes, and those of endogenous cytokinins, are triggering cell division and maintenance of the meristematic competence of cells to prevent subsequent differentiation until a sufficient number of cells has accumulated during organogenesis (107). All the above studies imply that cytokinins are involved in both maintaining the cell division cycle and promoting the transition of stem cells from the undifferentiated state to differentiation.

The direct evidence that cytokinins are involved in maintaining SAM activity comes from the experiments that revealed the relationship between cytokinins and the homeobox gene *STM*. Earlier observations that the shoot meristems overproducing cytokinins showed a similar phenotype to that of the transgenic plants overexpressing *KNAT1* or *KN1* suggested that cytokinins and homeobox genes may be involved in regulating SAM function in the same pathway and that cytokinins may act upstream of *KNAT1* and *STM* (126). Recently, two independent laboratories presented further evidence to clarify the relationship between cytokinins and the homeobox genes (67, 180), drawing an identical conclusion that the upregulated expression of *STM* will significantly induce the expression of cytokinin biosynthesis genes *AtIPT5* and *AtIPT7*, which ultimately elevate the cytokinin content. Furthermore, induction of either *STM* or *BP* will trigger the cytokinin response pathway through the primary response gene *ARR5* (67, 180). Therefore, application of cytokinins or expression of *IPT* driven by the *STM* promoter can rescue the *stm* mutant phenotype.

Cytokinin also controls the SAM size by participating in the CLV-WUS loop. WUS can directly repress the transcription of *ARR5*, *ARR6*, *ARR7*, and *ARR15*, negative regulators in the cytokinin signaling pathway (65). These findings suggest that *ARR* genes might negatively influence meristem size and that their repression by WUS might be necessary for the proper function of meristems (85). Consistent with this hypothesis is the observation that overexpression of an active form of *ARR7* produces an aborting SAM in *Arabidopsis* (85). Conversely, a loss-of-function mutation in a maize ARR homolog has an enlarged SAM (53).

INITIATION OF SHOOT AXILLARY MERISTEMS AND DEVELOPMENT OF LATERAL ORGANS

Axillary meristems are major determinants of plant architecture. A key component of architectural variation is the degree and pattern of shoot lateral organs, by which man can distinguish kinds of plants in the natural world even without advanced technologies or knowledge. The initiation of an AM at a certain position involves changes in cell proliferation and growth, accompanied by drastic and concerted modifications in gene expression profiles and hormonal actions (**Figure 2*a***).

Although the pattern of lateral organs is flexible, to some extent, in response to environmental conditions, it is essentially determined by the genetic background. Therefore, so far, a number of mutants defective in lateral organ patterns have been found in nature or generated by mutagens or T-DNA insertion. These mutants can be classified into three classes on the basis of whether they affect meristem initiation, meristem outgrowth, or both (137, 169). By cloning and performing functional analyses of the genes responsible for the altered phenotypes, the molecular mechanisms involved in controlling shoot branching have emerged over the past decade.

Auxin and Axillary Meristem Initiation

Auxin has a broad effect on plant development, particularly on AM initiation and development. Various AMs for leaves, branches, and flowers are derived from the PZ of the vegetative or reproductive SAMs. Although the CLV-WUS loop sustains the dynamic balance of SAM activities, there should be some other molecules that determine the position and timing of a primodium. Auxin has been proposed as an essential regulator in this process based on a series of studies on auxin transport and distribution. Auxin is mainly transported along the shoot-root axis from cell to cell in a polar manner, namely polar auxin transport (PAT), which requires both influx and efflux carriers (139). In *Arabidopsis*, auxin carriers, especially the efflux carriers, have been identified and well characterized; eight members of the PIN protein family have been demonstrated to facilitate auxin efflux (118). PIN1, the most well-characterized auxin efflux carrier, mediates auxin distribution and thus triggers AM initiation (14). In a vegetative SAM, PIN1 localizes in the epidermis, the vasculature of developing leaf primordia, and the L1 and L2 layers of the SAM (122) (**Figure 2*a***). When a new primordium initiates, the *DR5* promoter–driven green fluorescent protein (GFP) signals, which reflect the in vivo auxin level, show a gradient distribution with a maximum at the primordial tip and the *PIN1* promoter–driven GFP signals emerge in the outer cell layer with a polarity pointing toward the primordial tip (14). In addition, the loss-of-function *pin1* mutant is unable to form lateral organs but the defect can be reversed by exogenous application of auxin (109, 121). This is also the case when the L1 layer is destroyed by microsurgical removal (120). These data suggest an auxin patterning model where the initiation of lateral organ primordia is induced by a local auxin maximum accumulated in the PZ of the SAM and the subsequent primodium initiates at the site most distant to the preexisting primordium because the established primordia act as a sink to deplete auxin accumulation within surrounding cells (14, 46, 121, 122).

PAT: polar auxin transport

Activity and Dormancy of Axillary Meristems

Branches of higher plants originate from the AMs of shoots. Formation of a branch generally comprises two distinct steps: the initiation of a new AM and its subsequent growth and development. However, after initiation, an AM can arrest its growth and form a dormant bud. The dormant buds will release their outgrowth upon sensing a permissible environmental or developmental signal, through which the plant sustains its species-specific shoot system development.

SCF: Skp1-Cul1/Cdc53-F-box

In many plant species, axillary buds become dormant owing to the inhibiting effects of the primary shoot apex on the outgrowth of AMs, a phenomenon known as apical dominance. Auxin was first regarded as a direct controller in this process (158). However, auxin has been found incapable of accumulation in the inhibited AMs, suggesting an indirect suppression effect of auxin on AM outgrowth (22, 101). Cytokinins have been proposed as a second messenger that mediates the action of auxin in controlling apical dominance. Cytokinins are synthesized in roots and transported through xylem into axillary buds to break the dormancy of arrested buds, whereas auxin modulates the cytokinin concentration, thus repressing AM outgrowth (12, 37, 108, 112). Recently, polyamines have been found to play regulatory roles in controlling the outgrowth of axillary buds (52). In addition, abscisic acid (ABA) was also proposed to act as an inhibitor for axillary bud growth (30), although no further evidence has been reported (**Figure 2*a***).

Recent studies on a number of shoot branching mutants, including *max* in *Arabidopsis* (21, 145, 146), *rms* in pea (16), and *dad* in petunia (106, 140), have revealed the existence of an additional second messenger of auxin involved in controlling AM outgrowth. Molecular cloning of these genes and grafting analyses of the related mutants have presented a rough figure of a carotenoid-derived long-range signaling pathway, which is represented by *Arabidopsis MAX* genes as shown in **Figure 2*a***. *MAX1* encodes a cytochrome P450–type enzyme (23) and *MAX3* and *MAX4* encode carotenoid cleavage deoxygenate (CCD)-family proteins CCD7 and CCD8, respectively (21, 141, 146). In an in vitro assay system, the recombinant MAX3/CCD7 protein can specifically catalyze the 9–10 cleavage of β-carotene to produce 10′-apo-β-carotenal (C27) and β-ionone (C13), whereas the Max4/CCD8-expressed protein is able to catalyze a secondary cleavage of the 10′-apo-β-carotenal at the 13–14 position to produce 13-apo-β-carotenone (C18) (136). These enzymatic reactions may occur in plastids, where β-carotenoid is biosynthesized and accumulated (21). Furthermore, a series of reciprocal grafting experiments between *max* mutants has suggested that MAX1 to MAX4 may function in a common signaling pathway, in which MAX1 acts downstream of MAX3 and MAX4. Unlike MAX1, MAX3, and MAX4, which are involved in the biosynthesis of an acropetally mobile signal, MAX2 acts only in the shoot and is responsible for perceiving the signal (23). The molecular characteristics of MAX2 are consistent with its role in the MAX pathway. MAX2 is a member of the F-box LRR family, which interacts with the core Skp1-Cul1/Cdc53-F-box (SCF) subunits ASK1 and AtCUL1 in vivo (145, 146). After perceiving the signal derived from β-carotenoid, MAX2 will degrade some transcriptional factor proteins (145). However, the signaling from plastid to nucleus and the targets of MAX2 still remain to be identified.

All the evidence obtained so far demonstrates that MAX-dependent branching signals are not attributed to any known phytohormone. However, MAX-dependent branching signals have been proposed to function within a network of the classical hormones, for example, auxin and cytokinins. Recent evidence indicates that the *MAX* genes act as negative regulators of PAT (11, 15, 84). Consistently, some other PAT defective mutants, for example *bud1*, also display a phenotype of more branches (41).

Although the outgrowth behaviors between dicotyledonous and monocotyledonous AMs are apparently different (57, 58, 92) (**Figure 1**), they appear to share a conserved MAX-involved carotenoid-derived branching signal pathway, because orthologs/homologs of MAX2 to MAX4 have also been identified in rice (9, 66, 186) (**Figure 2*b***). Plants deficient in MAX2, MAX3, or MAX4 in rice give rise to more tillers (branches), indicating their similar functions in suppressing branch development in monocotyledonous plants (9, 66, 186). Several homologs of MAX1 have been found in the rice genome. However, which one is the MAX1 ortholog remains to be determined.

Transcriptional Factors That Determine Primodium Formation

Although the SAM maintains its activities, a subset of information termed the positional signal carves the domains that potentially form the later organs. It is still controversial whether the AMs originate from the boundary of the SAM (de novo formation) or detached from the SAM (detached meristems).

Maintenance of meristem formation competence and the subsequent initiation of AMs are regulated by a set of transcription factors including *REV*, *Ls/LAS/MOC1*, *Bl/RAM1*, *LAX1/Ba1*, and *CUC1-CUC3/CUP/NAM*. *REV* is a member of the *Arabidopsis* HD-ZIPIII subfamily of the HD-ZIP genes (110). *Ls*, *LAS*, and *MOC1* are plant-specific GRAS proteins (56, 91, 135), *Bl/RAM1* belongs to the R2R3-type MYB family (71, 103, 133), *LAX/Ba1* belongs to the helix-loop-helix (bHLH) group of proteins (50, 75), and *CUC1-CUC3/CUPs/NAMs* encode putative transcription factors containing the NAC domain (6, 7, 142, 152, 164). Recent studies have shown that *RAX1* functions to specify the axillary stem cells by regulating *CUC2* expression in a central axillary domain that anticipates the position of AMs (71). The *CUC* genes promote the expression of *STM*, a central determinant of meristem identity (42, 61, 152, 164). Sequence homology suggests that *CUC1* and *CUC2* mRNAs might be regulated by *miR164* (123). In fact, their expression levels are increased in an *Arabidopsis* background with an impaired miRNA pathway (70, 162). *CUC1* and *CUC2*, but not *CUC3*, were subsequently confirmed to be the targets of *miR164* in planta, which confines the expansion of the boundary domain of meristems by *miR164*-guided degradation of *CUC1* and *CUC2* mRNAs (82). It will be fascinating to identify more targets that activate these transcription factors and decipher the entire signaling pathway in the initiation of AMs in the future.

bHLH: basic helix-loop-helix

Control of the Branching Angle of Rice

The number of branches is an essential determinant of plant architecture. However, for monocotyledonous crops, the angle between the shoot branches and the main culm, termed the tiller angle in grass species, is also an important agronomic trait that should be considered. Several abnormal tiller angle mutants in crops have been reported, including *lazy* in maize (111), *lazy* (*la/la1*) (69, 153) and *spk*(*t*) (95) in rice, and *serpentine* in barley (147), among which the rice *la1* mutant has been intensively studied for decades (1–5, 54, 69, 90, 179). Enormous efforts have been made to understand the mechanism underlying the *la1* phenotype, but the corresponding gene *LA1* was isolated only recently (89). Molecular genetic analysis revealed that LA1 is a novel grass-specific protein that acts as a negative regulator in PAT. Loss-of-function mutations of *LA1* enhance PAT greatly and thus alter the endogenous IAA distribution in shoots, leading to the tiller-spreading phenotype of rice plants. LA1 bears both transmembrane and nuclear localization signal (NLS) functional domains, indicating that it may perform its function via an as yet undefined shuttling mechanism between the plasma membrane and the nucleus (89). Interestingly, unlike other auxin transport–defective mutants that exhibit multiple phenotypes, the mutations in the *la1* mutant affect mainly the angles of tillers. This is most likely due to the specific expression site of *LA1*, where the local auxin distribution is altered and by which the asymmetric cell elongation is disrupted. In addition to tiller angle, LA1 appears to be relevant to leaf angle (89), implying that the regulation of lateral organ angle mediated by LA1 may be common for both branching and leaf formation.

Another rice tiller angle–related gene, *TAC1*, was also isolated recently by a map-based cloning approach (183). *TAC1*, containing four introns with three in the coding region and the fourth in the 3′ untranslated region, encodes a 259-amino-acid protein, serving as a positive regulator of rice tiller angle.

LA1 and *TAC1* are the only two genes identified to date that are involved in regulating the tiller angle in monocotyledonous plants. However, their biochemical functions and signaling pathways remain to be elucidated because they are both novel proteins without any functional annotation. Identification of their interacting partners and mutant suppressors will give us further insight into the mechanisms that underlie the tiller angle of monocotyledonous crops (**Figure 2*b***).

INFLORESCENCE

Inflorescence Structures of Model Plants: *Arabidopsis*, Rice, and Maize

Higher plants display a broad range of inflorescence architecture that contributes not only to plant architecture but also to the reproductive success of plants, affecting both natural beauty and yield potential. **Figure 3** illustrates the inflorescence structures of *Arabidopsis*, rice, and maize, which are viewed as the best genetic model systems for understanding the molecular mechanisms underlying the initiation and development of inflorescences. The *Arabidopsis* inflorescence produces floral meristems directly from the inflorescence meristem with indeterminate growth habit without generating lateral

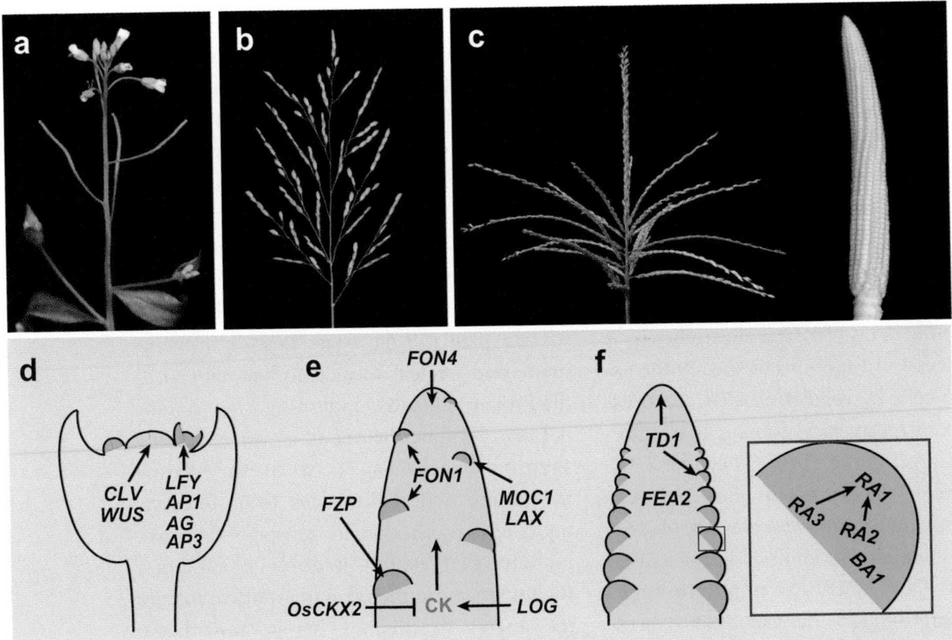

Figure 3

Inflorescences and their key regulatory genes in *Arabidopsis*, rice, and maize. (*a*) *Arabidopsis* inflorescence. (*b*) Rice panicle. (*c*) Maize tassel (*left*) and ear (*right*). (*d*) Key genes controlling the *Arabidopsis* inflorescence architecture. (*e*) Key genes controlling the rice panicle architecture. (*f*) Key genes controlling the maize inflorescence architecture. *AG*, *AGAMOUS*; *AP*, *APETALA*; *BA1*, *Barren Stalk1*; CK, cytokinin; *CKX2*, *Cytokinin Oxidase2*; *CLV*, *CLAVATA*; *FEA2*, *FASCIATED EAR2*; *FON*, *FLORAL ORGAN NUMBER*; *FZP*, *FRIZZY PANICLE*; *LAX*, *LAX PANICLE*; *LFY*, *LEAFY*; *LOG*, *LONELY GUY*; *MOC1*, *MONOCULM1*; *RA*, *Ramous*; *TD1*, *THICK TASSEL DWARF1*; *WUS*, *WUSCHEL*.

branches (**Figure 3*a***). In contrast, the rice (**Figure 3*b***) and maize (**Figure 3*c***) inflorescences generate branch and spikelet meristems before producing floral meristems in a determinate pattern. Theoretically, any tiller has the potential to produce a panicle by transitioning from a vegetative SAM into a reproductive SAM. However, in reality, not all the tillers can bear panicles because some tillers, especially the higher-order tillers, are incapable of producing panicles owing to unfavorable conditions. In agriculture, tillers that produce panicles are termed effective tillers, and they contribute to the grain yield. Compared with *Arabidopsis* and rice, maize inflorescences are more complicated. Maize has two types of inflorescences with very different architectures: the male inflorescence "tassel" and the female inflorescence "ear." The tassel consists of long branches at its base and a central spike that bears shorter branches containing spikelet pairs (**Figure 3*c***). The ears are positioned laterally, contain only short branches, and produce the seeds of maize.

As described above, *Arabidopsis* and grass have very different inflorescence architecture, implying that they should be, at least to some extent, controlled by distinct regulatory pathways or a similar pathway with different genes. In fact, increasing evidence from comparative studies shows that some genes that control the inflorescence architecture in *Arabidopsis* and in grasses are not orthologous (72).

Inflorescence Branching

During the phase transition from a vegetative SAM to a reproductive SAM, a vegetative meristem is first converted into an inflorescence meristem either indeterminately (as in *Arabidopsis*) or determinately (as in rice), and then the inflorescence meristem produces floral meristems on its flanks in a species-specific manner.

In *Arabidopsis*, after the growth stage transition, the primary inflorescence stem rapidly elongates (bolting). First, the AM gives rise to a shoot that has both vegetative and reproductive characteristics, including cauline leaves, axillary buds, and branches from the axils of leaves. Subsequently, the SAM generates multiple floral meristems, each of which differentiates a flower at the tip and a pedicel at the base, while the SAM itself maintains its indeterminate state.

Because of its importance in agriculture, much attention has been given to studying grass inflorescence architecture, and significant progress has been made in dissecting the regulators that control inflorescences of rice and maize and their potential in grain production. Grass inflorescence architecture is largely determined by inflorescence branches, from which the spikelet meristems initiate.

In rice, the inflorescence meristem itself produces several primary and secondary (and sometimes tertiary) branch meristems termed rachis-branch meristems, which further give rise to spikelet meristems. Several genes have been reported to be involved in the initiation and growth of rachis-branch meristems (**Figure 3*e***). *FZP* acts as a positive regulator of floral meristem identity to suppress the formation of AMs of rice spikelets (76). The *LAX* gene, which encodes a putative transcriptional regulator that contains a bHLH domain, has been identified as a regulator controlling the rachis-branch meristem initiation and/or maintenance during rice reproductive development (75). The phenotypic analysis of the double mutant of *lax* and *spa*, another panicle branching mutant, suggested that *LAX* may function redundantly with *SPA* in an overlapped genetic pathway during the development of rice AMs (75). Interestingly, *SPA* was later proved to be *MOC1*, an essential controller of rice tiller bud formation and development (91). Consistently, the *moc1* mutant also displays defects of panicle morphology, indicating the involvement of *MOC1* in the formation of both vegetative and reproductive AMs, similar to its ortholog *Ls* in tomato (135). The dissection of the components of the MOC1-, FZP- and LAX1-mediated regulatory pathways will facilitate understanding of the mechanism that controls the formation and development of rice tillers and panicles. Additionally, the latest reports show that cytokinins are functionally relevant to the panicle pattern of rice. The rice cytokinin oxidase, *OsCKX2*, regulates the development of inflorescence meristems by affecting the cytokinin contents in the rice vascular system of developing culms, suggesting the important role of cytokinin in forming the inflorescence architecture (10). Recently, a novel cytokinin-activating enzyme, which is encoded by *LOG*, was found to convert the inactive cytokinin nucleotides to the active free-base forms and affect panicle morphology (80).

In maize, there are many well-characterized mutants that enable us to look into the molecular regulatory mechanisms determining the formation of inflorescences. The normal tassel is generated at the upmost position of a maize plant, and consists of long branches at the base of a main spike and extremely short branches at the upper part, i.e., spikelet pairs (97). In contrast, a normal maize ear is produced laterally from the axil of a leaf, and only contains very short branches that ultimately produce seeds. Identification and characterization of three classical maize *ramous* (*ra* means branch in Latin) mutants *ra1*, *ra2*, and *ra3* reveal a ramous regulatory pathway controlling the above process. Molecular cloning and characterization of the three corresponding genes have shed light on the molecular mechanism regulating maize inflorescence branching (**Figure 3*f***). *RA1* encodes a zinc-finger transcription factor of the EPF class, which is exclusively expressed at the primordial base of short branches (163). Because a long branch grows in an indeterminate growth manner and a short branch (i.e., spikelet pair) in a determinate manner, *RA1* is regarded as a key factor directing the meristem identity transition from indeterminate to determinate. Consistent with its function, the loss-of-function mutant *ra1* is unable to terminate appropriately, leading to the production of more long and intermediate branches in both tassels and ears compared with wild-type maize (163). *RA2* encodes a plant-specific LOB transcription factor expressed in the primordia of inflorescence AMs of both long and short branches (24). The loss-of-function *ra2* mutant has a similar phenotype to that of *ra1*. The cross examination of transcripts of *RA1* and *RA2* in *ra2* and *ra1* reveals that *RA1* functions downstream of *RA2*. As a result, the *ra1ra2* double mutant resembles the phenotype of *ra2*, providing genetic evidence that *RA2* is required for the expression of *RA1* and both *RA1* and *RA2* act in the same genetic pathway (24, 163). However, unlike RA1 and RA2, which are transcription factors, *RA3* encodes a trehalose 6-phosphate phosphatase and is expressed in cells subtending the AMs in the inflorescence (132). Genetic analysis of *ra1*, *ra2*, and *ra3* indicates that RA3 also acts upstream of RA1 but in a different pathway from RA2 (**Figure 3*f***). Taken together, RA1, RA2, and RA3 coordinate to regulate meristem identity and determinancy in the maize inflorescence.

Floral Organs

In addition to the inflorescence branch system, the position, the form, and the number of floral organs also contribute to the appearance of flowering plants, and confine the plant architecture to a large extent. The constructs of floral organs are distinct among species. In dicotyledonous plants such as *Arabidopsis*, the floral organs include four sepals, four petals, six stamens, and one carpel. In monocotyledonous plants such as rice, the floral organs consist of one lemma, one palea, two lodicules, six stamens, and one gynoecium with two pistils.

From investigation of mutants displaying abnormal flowers in *Arabidopsis* and *Antirrhinum*, a few key genes have been shown to play pivotal roles in setting up floral identity. The *LFY/FLO* gene is a switch to gain floral identity (170), and its orthologs have been identified in a broad range of species (19, 27, 29, 43, 73, 98, 99, 102, 138). According to the current model, LFY directly activates *AP1* by binding to its promoter (172) and promotes the transition from inflorescence to floral meristem. *LFY* is also expressed before the homeotic genes *AG* and *AP3*, which specify organ identity within the flower (170). Under the short-day condition, the gradual increase in *LFY* transcripts can be observed in the young leaf primordia until the time of floral initiation (17, 18) (**Figure 3*d***). This process appears to be caused by the sharp increase in the gibberellin $(GA)_4$ level (45).

As described above, the CLV-WUS regulatory loop controls meristem size throughout the development of *Arabidopsis*. More importantly, increasing evidence has shown that the CLV pathway for regulating meristem size is functionally conserved in both monocotyledonous and dicotyledonous species, and contributes largely to the inflorescence architecture. For example, *FEA2* is an ortholog of *CLV2* in maize. Loss-of-function mutants of *FEA2* show severe overproliferation of the ear inflorescence meristems and display a modest effect on the floral meristem size and floral organ number (151). *TD1* encodes a putative ortholog of the *Arabidopsis* CLV1 protein (20). Mutation of *TD1* affects the formation of both male and female inflorescences, resulting in fasciated ears with excess kernels, higher spikelet density in the tassel, and abnormal stamen number (20). A CLV1 ortholog, FON1, has also been identified in rice (149), and mutations in *FON1* cause enlargement of floral meristems and thus an increase in all types of floral organ number. Additionally, rice *FON4* is a putative CLV3 ortholog, and acts in the vegetative SAM as well as in the inflorescence and floral meristems (31). All these findings suggest that a pathway similar to the CLV signaling system that regulates meristem maintenance in *Arabidopsis* may be conserved in the grass family, although the detailed components have not yet been identified.

PLANT HEIGHT

Plant height, mainly confined by stem elongation, is not only a decisive factor that affects plant architecture but also an important agronomic trait that contributes to crop yield. Although stem elongation can be visible in both *Arabidopsis* and rice after the start-up of reproductive growth, there are important differences between the two species. The rice stem consists of hollow internodes and jointed nodes, which are usually called culm, and to a large extent the stem contributes to the plant height (**Figure 4*a***). The developmental transition from the vegetative to the reproductive stage induces internode elongation. The elongated internodes in rice are derived from the vegetative SAM, and the uppermost four or five internodes elongate in response to the growth and development of intercalary meristems in the internodes when the transition begins, whereas the internodes in *Arabidopsis* are derived from the reproductive SAM, and all internodes can elongate (**Figure 4*b***).

GA: gibberellin

BR: brassinosteroid

In varieties with a semiDwarf phenotype, grain yield increases at the expense of straw biomass and their plant bodies are more resistant to lodging associated with wind and rain. Numerous dwarf mutants of crops, especially of rice and wheat, have been identified and characterized because of their agronomic importance. The rice dwarf mutants have been categorized into six groups on the basis of the elongation patterns of their upper four or five internodes (178). Based on extensive studies on mutants with dwarf phenotypes, two plant hormones, GA and brassinosteroid (BR), are regarded as major factors that determine plant height.

Regulation by Gibberellins

Gibberellins are a large family of tetracyclic diterpenoid plant hormones that play important roles in multiple plant growth and developmental progresses, especially in stem elongation (63, 150). Gibberellin-related mutants have been widely collected and extensively

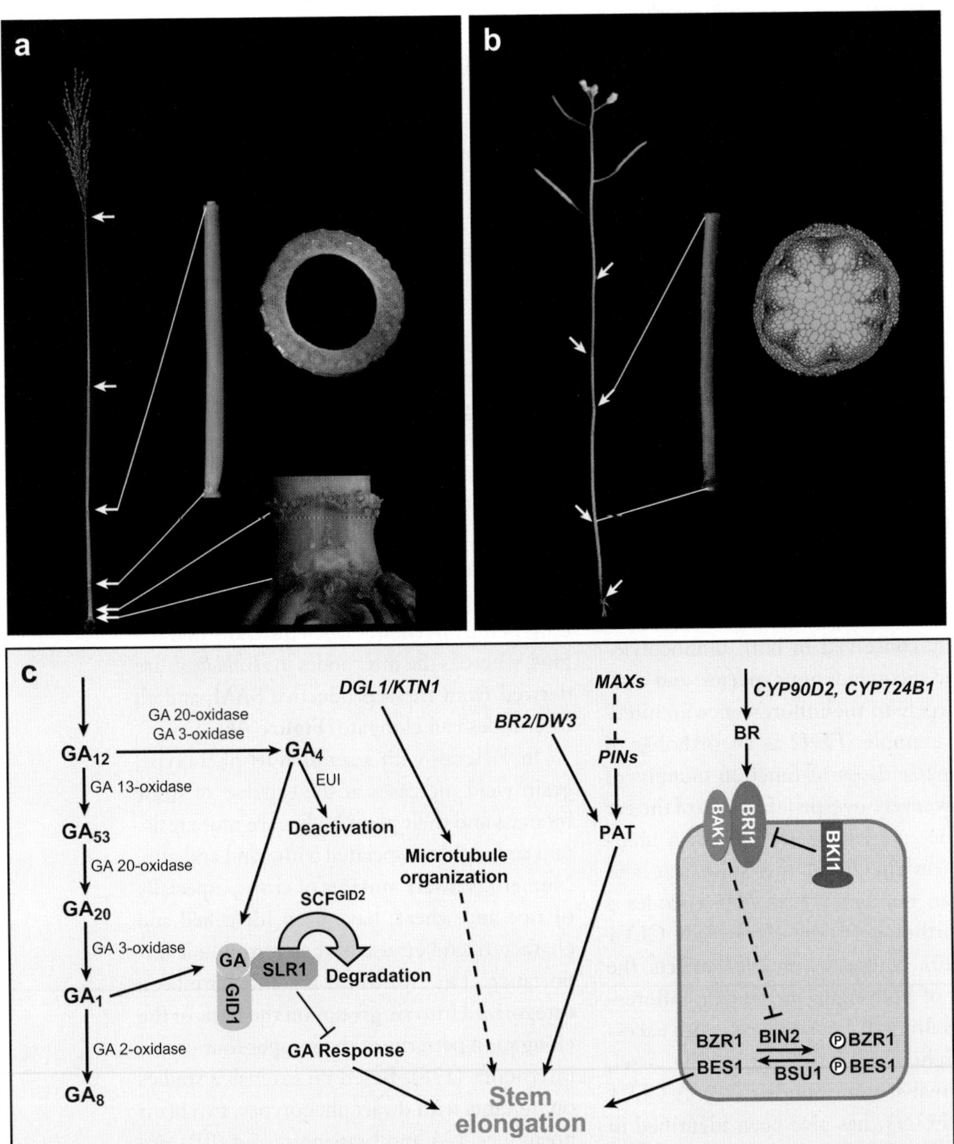

Figure 4

Stem elongation and molecular regulatory pathways in *Arabidopsis* and rice. (*a*) Schematic of the rice culm (*left*) and internode (*middle*) with its cross section (*right*) showing the cellular structure. (*b*) Schematic of the stem (*left*) and internode (*middle*) with its cross section (*right*) showing the cellular structure in *Arabidopsis*. (*c*) Proposed gibberellin (GA)-, brassinosteroids (BR)-, auxin-, and skeleton-mediated pathways that regulate stem elongation. BAK1, LRR-RLK BRI1-ASSOCIATED RECEPTOR KINASE1; BES1, Bri1-EMS-suppressor 1; BKI1, BRI1 kinase inhibitor 1; BIN2, BR-INSENSITIVE 2; BR2, *Branchytic 2*; BRI1, BRASSINOSTEROID-INSENSITIVE1; BSU1, BRI1 suppressor 1; BZR1, *Brassinazole-resistant 1*; *DW3*, *Dwarf3*; *DGL1*, *Dwarf and Gladius Leaf1*; *EUI*, *ELONGATED UPPERMOST INTERNODE*; *GID*, *GIBBERELLIN-INSENSITIVE DWARF*; *KTN1*, *ATPase katanin-like protein*; *MAX*, *More Axillary Branching*; *SLR1*, *Slender1*; PAT, polar auxin transport; *PIN*, *PIN-FORMED*; SCF, Skp1-Cul1/Cdc53-F-box.

studied in several species such as *Arabidopsis* and rice; these mutants exhibit typical phenotypes of dark green leaves and dwarfism attributable to reduced stem elongation (79, 115, 128, 148, 155).

Based on recent progress in the analysis of dwarf mutants and the molecular characterization of their corresponding genes, both signaling and biosynthesis of GAs have been shown to participate in regulating plant height. The semidominant *gai* mutation of *Arabidopsis* affects GA perception and its subsequent signal transduction (78, 114, 154, 174, 175). GAI is a negative GA-response regulator in *Arabidopsis* (113), and its orthologs in wheat (*Rht*) (49) and maize (*D8*) (59, 176) are the "Green Revolution" genes that have greatly enhanced grain yields since the 1960s. *SLR1*, the ortholog of *GAI* in rice, was also identified by characterizing a rice mutant showing a slender phenotype (157). These plant height–regulating genes share a conserved DELLA domain that is important for GA detection in the GA signaling pathway (116). Recently, characterization of a GA-insensitive dwarf mutant *gid2* in rice revealed that *GID2* encodes a putative F-box subunit of an SCF E_3 ubiquitin ligase and binds to SLR1 in a GA-dependent manner, indicating that GID2 is a positive regulator of SLR1 degradation through the SCF^{GID2} proteasome pathway (55). Moreover, molecular characterization of a rice GA-insensitive dwarf mutant *gid1* has shown that the binding of bioactive GA to GID1 promotes the interaction between GID1 and SLR1, which in turn activates the degradation of SLR1 through the SCF^{GID2} E_3 ubiquitin ligase pathway (55, 161). These findings suggest that GID1 may function as a GA receptor (161). However, the other factors in the pathway and the functions of DELLA proteins still remain elusive.

The semidwarf Green Revolution rice *sd1* results from a deficiency in the *GA 20-oxidase* gene (*Os20ox2*) of the GA biosynthetic pathway (100, 127, 131, 143). Consistent with the loss-of-function of *Os20ox2* in *sd1* plants, they show an elevated GA_{53} content and a reduced amount of GA_{20} and GA_1 (143). In addition, *eui*, a rice mutant that shows a high potential for producing hybrid rice by eliminating the panicle enclosure of male sterile cultivars, is defective in GA biosynthesis (94, 181, 185). *EUI* encodes a cytochrome P450 that is expressed mainly in the divisional zones of internodes and deactivates the bioactive GA_4 through a 16α,17-dihydroxylation reaction. Mutations in *EUI* result in extremely elevated levels of GA_4 and GA_1, which promote cell elongation of the uppermost internodes (185).

Regulation by Brassinosteroids

Brassinosteroids are natural plant growth–promoting compounds with a structure similar to animal steroid hormones, and they have significant effects on plant growth and development at an extremely low concentration (38, 40). Perception and transduction of the BR signal require a membrane-localized LRR receptor-like kinase (RLK), which is encoded in *Arabidopsis* by *BRI1* (39, 117, 159, 167), and a second BAK1 that interacts with BRI1 (88, 105), as well as their downstream factors BRI1 kinase inhibitor 1 (BKI1), BIN2, BES1, and BZR1 (60, 165, 168, 182, 184). Plants defective in either signaling or biosynthesis of BRs give rise to a typical dwarf phenotype with other abnormal morphologies, including malformed leaves with twisted and stiff blades.

A BRI1 ortholog has also been identified in rice, which is the first evidence that confirms the role of BRs in stem elongation of monocotyledonous plants (178), suggesting that dicotyledonous and monocotyledonous plants may share a conserved mechanism to perceive the BR signal. In addition, a classic rice dwarf mutant *d2*, known as *ebisu* dwarf and showing a similar phenotype to the BR-insensitive mutant *d61* (178), has been characterized as a BR-deficient mutant (62). *D2* encodes a new member of the P450 family, CYP90D2, which is highly homologous to a BR biosynthetic enzyme that catalyzes the reactions from 6-deoxoteasterone to

3-dehydro-6-deoxoteasterone and from teasterone to 3-dehydroteasterone. Recently, a new cytochrome P450, CYP724B1, was isolated in rice and characterized as a homolog of the enzyme involved in the BR biosynthetic pathway (156). The loss-of-function mutation of this enzyme results in dwarfism in the rice *d11* mutant. In *Arabidopsis*, mutants defective in the BR biosynthetic pathway also become severe dwarfs (48). Therefore, it appears that dicotyledonous and monocotyledonous plants may very likely share the conserved molecular events in modifying plant height through the BR biosynthetic and signaling pathways, although the detailed mechanisms have not been clarified so far.

Regulation by Other Factors

In addition to the involvement of GAs and BRs in regulating plant height, other factors, for example, PAT and microtubule organization (77, 104), have emerged to further our understanding of plant height control. Loss of function of a multidrug resistant (MDR) transporter that is involved in PAT leads to reduced plant height in maize *br2* or sorghum *dwarf1-dwarf3* mutants (104). Taken together with the findings that all the *max* mutants of both *Arabidopsis* and rice display not only more axillary branches but also dwarfism, and that the MAX signaling pathway is involved in PAT, we therefore expect that PAT may be a general regulatory mechanism underlying plant height, although more direct evidence needs to be identified in the future.

Plant height may also be affected by disorganization of the plant skeletal system. Studies on the rice dwarf mutant *dgl1* have revealed that the mutation in *dgl1* results in a defective ATPase katanin-like protein (KTN1), which causes an aberrant katanin-mediated microtubule organization (77). It has been found that a KTN1 loss-of-function mutant in *Arabidopsis* also has a dwarf phenotype (25). KTN1 has also been suggested to cross talk with the GA biosynthetic pathway, although their relationship is supposed to be indirect (25, 77).

PLANT ARCHITECTURE AND MOLECULAR DESIGN

The ability to produce more food in the same acreage is crucial to feeding an increasing world population and also important for curbing deforestation and dedicating more land to biofuels. Molecular design refers to pyramiding one or more genes into a plant for modifying one or more target traits via biotechnology.

Rice is one of the most important staples and feeds more than half of the world's population, and therefore rice attracts tremendous attention in crop breeding. Conventional breeding has been playing an essential role in rice cultivar innovation for centuries. However, compared with the current population explosion and crop land reduction, progress is rather slow owing to several barriers such as the time-consuming cross/selection process and limited appropriate selection for desired genotypes.

Crop plant architecture determines planting density in the field and thus influences, to a large degree, the light harvest, disease resistance, and lodging. Therefore, rice plant architecture is regarded as one of the most important factors that affect rice yield (74). Scientists from the International Rice Research Institute have proposed a model of the ideal rice plant architecture, which should have a low tiller number (9–10 tillers for transplanted conditions); a high number of productive tillers; 200–250 grains per panicle; dark-green, thick, and erect leaves; and vigorous and deep root systems. An outstanding example is the Green Revolution, the innovation of semidwarf wheat and rice cultivars that has improved crop production immensely since 1960.

Elucidation of the molecular mechanisms underlying rice plant architecture will provide a solid basis for modifying the plant architecture of rice and other crops as well. The available genome sequences and mature techniques for genetic manipulation will facilitate and eventually allow plant breeders to modify and design elite cultivars that have ideal plant architecture, improved quality, efficient use of nutrients, and strong resistance to pests and diseases. Recent transgenic studies showed that some genes affecting plant architecture have potential applications in genetically engineering the ideal plant architecture of crops. For example, the Green Revolution rice *sd1* cultivars are GA biosynthesis mutants (100, 131, 143), indicating that plant height can be manipulated through modifying the GA biosynthesis or signaling pathway at the molecular level (129). In addition, over- or underexpression of *EUI* in rice results in dwarf or *eui*-like transgenic plants (185), and the gai protein is used in a switchable expression system in which the *gai* gene can be induced by ethanol to inhibit growth at the various stages in *AlcA:gai* transgenic plants (8), demonstrating the possibility that the *gai* gene can be used to confer the dwarf phenotype in a wide range of crop species. Moreover, molecular and biochemical studies have shown that simultaneous defects in CYP90B2/OsDWARF4 and CYP724B1/D11 in the BR biosynthetic pathway lead to erect rice leaves and more grain production under dense planting even without extra fertilizer (130). By altering the expression levels of *OsCKX2*, it is possible to either increase or decrease grain number in rice (10). The tiller number or the tiller angle of rice can be manipulated by altering the expression level of *MOC1* or *LA1* and *TAC1* (89, 91, 183). All these achievements indicate that agronomically important plant architecture traits can be improved at the molecular level through biotechnology. We are sure that crop design via biotechnology will create new elite varieties with ideal plant architecture in the future. However, unlike GM cotton and maize that are mainly for industrial and feed uses, GM rice will be the first commercial staple crop in the world. Studies assessing productivity and health effects of insect-resistant GM rice varieties have provided positive evidence that farmers will benefit from adopting the GM rice with higher crop yields and reduced use of pesticides, as well as improved health (64), although public concerns regarding human health and environmental impacts of the GM rice are still high.

CONCLUSIONS AND PERSPECTIVES

Tremendous progress has been achieved over the past decade in understanding the molecular mechanisms that underlie the formation of plant architecture. Dissection of plant architecture with plant morphological mutants has enabled plant scientists to look into every aspect affecting plant architecture, for example, SAM maintenance and differentiation, the initiation of AMs, the formation and outgrowth of axillary buds, the elongation of stems, and the number or angle of branches (tillers). As summarized and commented in this review, a series of mutants defective in plant architecture of dicotyledonous and monocotyledonous plants has been generated and identified, and several key genes have been cloned and functionally characterized. More importantly, the molecular mechanisms that govern each particular aspect that collectively specializes a particular type of plant architecture are being elucidated, among which the signaling pathways that regulate plant height and control the maintenance and differentiation of the SAM have been well studied. However, generally speaking, our current understanding of how a particular plant specializes its architecture is still very limited, and studies on plant architecture will continue to be the primary interest in plant developmental biology. The following are very likely to be the major breakthroughs in the next decades:

1. Generation and identification of more mutants, especially suppressors of the mutants involved in the initiation of AMs and outgrowth of axillary buds,

cloning and functional characterization of the corresponding genes, and elucidation of their signaling pathways.

2. Establishment of an integrated network that regulates plant architecture by studying the cross talk of the signaling pathways that affect each individual feature.
3. Elucidation of the roles and interactions of phytohormones that regulate plant architecture, especially the key hormones such as auxin, cytokinin, GA, and BR.
4. Molecular design of crops to breed new elite varieties with ideal plant architecture to increase agricultural production.

DISCLOSURE STATEMENT

The authors are not aware of any biases that might be perceived as affecting the objectivity of this review.

ACKNOWLEDGMENTS

We thank Mr. Hao Lin for assistance in preparing figures. We apologize to colleagues whose work is not cited in this review owing to space limitations. This work is supported by grants from the National Science Foundation of China (30330040, 30221002), the Ministry of Science and Technology of China (2005CB120801), and the Chinese Academy of Sciences.

LITERATURE CITED

1. Abe K, Takahashi H, Hatakeda K, Suge H. 1994. Gravitropic curvature and auxin content in *lazy-kamenoo* rice. *Biol. Sci. Space* 8:160–61
2. Abe K, Takahashi H, Suge H. 1994. Graviresponding sites in shoots of normal and "lazy" rice seedlings. *Physiol. Plant* 92:371–74
3. Abe K, Takahashi H, Suge H. 1994. Localization of cells containing sedimented amyloplasts in the shoots of normal and lazy rice seedlings. *Biol. Sci. Space* 8:221–25
4. Abe K, Takahashi H, Suge H. 1996. Lazy gene (*la*) responsible for both an agravitropism of seedlings and lazy habit of tiller growth in rice (*Oryza sativa* L.). *J. Plant Res.* 109:381–86
5. Abe K, Takahashi H, Suge H. 1998. Gravimorphism in rice and barley: promotion of leaf elongation by vertical inversion in agravitropically growing plants. *J. Plant Res.* 111:523–30
6. Aida M, Ishida T, Fukaki H, Fujisawa H, Tasaka M. 1997. Genes involved in organ separation in *Arabidopsis*: an analysis of the *cup-shaped cotyledon* mutant. *Plant Cell* 9:841–57
7. Aida M, Ishida T, Tasaka M. 1999. Shoot apical meristem and cotyledon formation during *Arabidopsis* embryogenesis: interaction among the *CUP-SHAPED COTYLEDON* and *SHOOT MERISTEMLESS* genes. *Development* 126:1563–70
8. Ait-ali T, Rands C, Harberd NP. 2003. Flexible control of plant architecture and yield via switchable expression of *Arabidopsis gai*. *Plant Biotechnol. J.* 1:337–43
9. Arite T, Iwata H, Ohshima K, Maekawa M, Nakajima M, et al. 2007. *DWARF10*, an *RMS1/MAX4/DAD1* ortholog, controls lateral bud outgrowth in rice. *Plant J.* 51:1019–1029
10. Ashikari M, Sakakibara H, Lin S, Yamamoto T, Takashi T, et al. 2005. Cytokinin oxidase regulates rice grain production. *Science* 309:741–45

11. Bainbridge K, Sorefan K, Ward S, Leyser O. 2005. Hormonally controlled expression of the *Arabidopsis MAX4* shoot branching regulatory gene. *Plant J.* 44:569–80
12. Bangerth F. 1994. Response of cytokinin concentration in the xylem exudate of bean (*Phaseolus vulgaris L.*) plants to decapitation and auxin treatment and relationship to apical dominance. *Planta* 194:439–42
13. Baurle I, Laux T. 2005. Regulation of *WUSCHEL* transcription in the stem cell niche of the *Arabidopsis* shoot meristem. *Plant Cell* 17:2271–80
14. Benkova E, Michniewicz M, Sauer M, Teichmann T, Seifertova D, et al. 2003. Local, efflux-dependent auxin gradients as a common module for plant organ formation. *Cell* 115:591–602
15. Bennett T, Sieberer T, Willett B, Booker J, Luschnig C, Leyser O. 2006. The *Arabidopsis MAX* pathway controls shoot branching by regulating auxin transport. *Curr. Biol.* 16:553–63
16. Beveridge CA, Symons GM, Turnbull CG. 2000. Auxin inhibition of decapitation-induced branching is dependent on graft-transmissible signals regulated by genes *Rms1* and *Rms2*. *Plant Physiol.* 123:689–98
17. Blázquez MA, Green R, Nilsson O, Sussman MR, Weigel D. 1998. Gibberellins promote flowering of *Arabidopsis* by activating the *LEAFY* promoter. *Plant Cell* 10:791–800
18. Blázquez MA, Soowal LN, Lee I, Weigel D. 1997. *LEAFY* expression and flower initiation in *Arabidopsis*. *Development* 124:3835–44
19. Bomblies K, Wang RL, Ambrose BA, Schmidt RJ, Meeley RB, Doebley J. 2003. Duplicate *FLORICAULA/LEAFY* homologs *zfl1* and *zfl2* control inflorescence architecture and flower patterning in maize. *Development* 130:2385–95
20. Bommert P, Lunde C, Nardmann J, Vollbrecht E, Running M, et al. 2005. *thick tassel dwarf1* encodes a putative maize ortholog of the *Arabidopsis CLAVATA1* leucine-rich repeat receptor-like kinase. *Development* 132:1235–45
21. Booker J, Auldridge M, Wills S, McCarty D, Klee H, Leyser O. 2004. MAX3/CCD7 is a carotenoid cleavage dioxygenase required for the synthesis of a novel plant signaling molecule. *Curr. Biol.* 14:1232–38
22. Booker J, Chatfield S, Leyser O. 2003. Auxin acts in xylem-associated or medullary cells to mediate apical dominance. *Plant Cell* 15:495–507
23. Booker J, Sieberer T, Wright W, Williamson L, Willett B, et al. 2005. *MAX1* encodes a cytochrome P450 family member that acts downstream of *MAX3/4* to produce a carotenoid-derived branch-inhibiting hormone. *Dev. Cell* 8:443–49
24. Bortiri E, Chuck G, Vollbrecht E, Rocheford T, Martienssen R, Hake S. 2006. *ramosa2* encodes a LATERAL ORGAN BOUNDARY domain protein that determines the fate of stem cells in branch meristems of maize. *Plant Cell* 18:574–85
25. Bouquin T, Mattsson O, Naested H, Foster R, Mundy J. 2003. The *Arabidopsis lue1* mutant defines a katanin p60 ortholog involved in hormonal control of microtubule orientation during cell growth. *J. Cell Sci.* 116:791–801
26. Brand U, Fletcher JC, Hobe M, Meyerowitz EM, Simon R. 2000. Dependence of stem cell fate in *Arabidopsis* on a feedback loop regulated by *CLV3* activity. *Science* 289:617–19
27. Busch A, Gleissberg S. 2003. *EcFLO*, a *FLORICAULA*-like gene from *Eschscholzia californica* is expressed during organogenesis at the vegetative shoot apex. *Planta* 217:841–48
28. Carles CC, Fletcher JC. 2003. Shoot apical meristem maintenance: the art of a dynamic balance. *Trends Plant Sci.* 8:394–401

29. Carmona MJ, Cubas P, Martínez-Zapater JM. 2002. *VFL*, the grapevine *FLORICAULA/LEAFY* ortholog, is expressed in meristematic regions independently of their fate. *Plant Physiol.* 130:68–77
30. Chatfield SP, Stirnberg P, Forde BG, Leyser O. 2000. The hormonal regulation of axillary bud growth in *Arabidopsis*. *Plant J.* 24:159–69
31. Chu H, Qian Q, Liang W, Yin C, Tan H, et al. 2006. The floral organ number4 gene encoding a putative ortholog of *Arabidopsis CLAVATA3* regulates apical meristem size in rice. *Plant Physiol.* 142:1039–52
32. Clark SE. 1997. Organ formation at the vegetative shoot meristem. *Plant Cell* 9:1067–76
33. Clark SE, Jacobsen SE, Levin JZ, Meyerowitz EM. 1996. The *CLAVATA* and *SHOOT MERISTEMLESS* loci competitively regulate meristem activity in *Arabidopsis*. *Development* 122:1567–75
34. Clark SE, Running MP, Meyerowitz EM. 1993. *CLAVATA1*, a regulator of meristem and flower development in *Arabidopsis*. *Development* 119:397–418
35. Clark SE, Running MP, Meyerowitz EM. 1995. *CLAVATA3* is a specific regulator of shoot and floral meristem development affecting the same processes as *CLAVATA1*. *Development* 121:2057–67
36. Clark SE, Williams RW, Meyerowitz EM. 1997. The *CLAVATA1* gene encodes a putative receptor kinase that controls shoot and floral meristem size in *Arabidopsis*. *Cell* 89:575–85
37. Cline MG. 1991. Apical dominance. *Bot. Rev.* 57:318–58
38. Clouse SD. 1996. Molecular genetic studies confirm the role of brassinosteroids in plant growth and development. *Plant J.* 10:1–8
39. Clouse SD. 2002. Brassinosteroid signal transduction: clarifying the pathway from ligand perception to gene expression. *Mol. Cell* 10:973–82
40. Clouse SD, Sasse JM. 1998. BRASSINOSTEROIDS: essential regulators of plant growth and development. *Annu. Rev. Plant Physiol. Plant Mol. Biol.* 49:427–51
41. Dai Y, Wang H, Li B, Huang J, Liu X, et al. 2006. Increased expression of MAP KINASE KINASE7 causes deficiency in polar auxin transport and leads to plant architectural abnormality in *Arabidopsis*. *Plant Cell* 18:308–20
42. Daimon Y, Takabe K, Tasaka M. 2003. The *CUP-SHAPED COTYLEDON* genes promote adventitious shoot formation on calli. *Plant Cell Physiol.* 44:113–21
43. Dornelas MC, Rodriguez AP. 2005. The rubber tree (*Hevea brasiliensis* Muell. Arg.) homologue of the *LEAFY/FLORICAULA* gene is preferentially expressed in both male and female floral meristems. *J. Exp. Bot.* 56:1965–74
44. Endrizzi K, Moussian B, Haecker A, Levin JZ, Laux T. 1996. The *SHOOT MERISTEMLESS* gene is required for maintenance of undifferentiated cells in *Arabidopsis* shoot and floral meristems and acts at a different regulatory level than the meristem genes *WUSCHEL* and *ZWILLE*. *Plant J.* 10:967–79
45. Eriksson S, Böhlenius H, Moritz T, Nilsson O. 2006. GA4 is the active gibberellin in the regulation of *LEAFY* transcription and *Arabidopsis* floral initiation. *Plant Cell* 18:2172–81
46. Fleming AJ. 2005. Formation of primordia and phyllotaxy. *Curr. Opin. Plant Biol.* 8:53–58
47. Fletcher JC, Brand U, Running MP, Simon R, Meyerowitz EM. 1999. Signaling of cell fate decisions by *CLAVATA3* in *Arabidopsis* shoot meristems. *Science* 283:1911–14
48. Fujioka S, Yokota T. 2003. Biosynthesis and metabolism of brassinosteroids. *Annu. Rev. Plant Biol.* 54:137–64
49. Gale MD, Law CN, Marshall GA, Worland AJ. 1975. The genetic control of gibberellic acid insensitivity and coleoptile length in a "dwarf" wheat. *Heredity* 34:393–99
50. Gallavotti A, Zhao Q, Kyozuka J, Meeley RB, Ritter MK, et al. 2004. The role of *barren stalk1* in the architecture of maize. *Nature* 432:630–35

51. Gallois JL, Woodward C, Reddy GV, Sablowski R. 2002. Combined *SHOOT MERISTEMLESS* and *WUSCHEL* trigger ectopic organogenesis in *Arabidopsis*. *Development* 129:3207–17
52. Ge C, Cui X, Wang Y, Hu Y, Fu Z, et al. 2006. *BUD2*, encoding an S-adenosylmethionine decarboxylase, is required for *Arabidopsis* growth and development. *Cell Res.* 16:446–56
53. Giulini A, Wang J, Jackson D. 2004. Control of phyllotaxy by the cytokinin-inducible response regulator homologue *ABPHYL1*. *Nature* 430:1031–34
54. Godbole H, Takahashi H, Hertel R. 1999. The *lazy* mutation in rice affects a step between statoliths and gravity-induced lateral auxin transport. *Plant Biol.* 1:379–81
55. Gomi K, Sasaki A, Itoh H, Ueguchi-Tanaka M, Ashikari M, et al. 2004. GID2, an F-box subunit of the SCF E3 complex, specifically interacts with phosphorylated SLR1 protein and regulates the gibberellin-dependent degradation of SLR1 in rice. *Plant J.* 37:626–34
56. Greb T, Clarenz O, Schafer E, Muller D, Herrero R, et al. 2003. Molecular analysis of the *LATERAL SUPPRESSOR* gene in *Arabidopsis* reveals a conserved control mechanism for axillary meristem formation. *Genes Dev.* 17:1175–87
57. Gribic V, Bleecker AB. 1996. An altered body plan is conferred on *Arabidopsis* plants carrying dominant alleles of two genes. *Development* 122:2395–403
58. Hanada K. 1993. Tillers. In *Science of the Rice Plant.* Vol. 1: *Morphology*, ed. T Matsuo, K Hoshikawa, pp. 222–59. Tokyo: Food Agric. Policy Res. Cent.
59. Harberd NP, Freeling M. 1989. Genetics of dominant gibberellin-insensitive dwarfism in maize. *Genetics* 121:827–38
60. He JX, Gendron JM, Yang Y, Li J, Wang ZY. 2002. The GSK3-like kinase BIN2 phosphorylates and destabilizes BZR1, a positive regulator of the brassinosteroid signaling pathway in *Arabidopsis*. *Proc. Natl. Acad. Sci. USA* 99:10185–90
61. Hibara K, Takada S, Tasaka M. 2003. *CUC1* gene activates the expression of SAM-related genes to induce adventitious shoot formation. *Plant J.* 36:687–96
62. Hong Z, Ueguchi-Tanaka M, Umemura K, Uozu S, Fujioka S, et al. 2003. A rice brassinosteroid-deficient mutant, *ebisu dwarf* (*d2*), is caused by a loss of function of a new member of cytochrome P450. *Plant Cell* 15:2900–10
63. Hooley R. 1994. Gibberellins: perception, transduction and responses. *Plant Mol. Biol.* 26:1529–55
64. Huang J, Hu R, Rozelle S, Pray C. 2005. Insect-resistant GM rice in farmers' fields: assessing productivity and health effects in China. *Science* 308:688–90
65. Hwang I, Sheen J. 2001. Two-component circuitry in *Arabidopsis* cytokinin signal transduction. *Nature* 413:383–89
66. Ishikawa S, Maekawa M, Arite T, Onishi K, Takamure I, Kyozuka J. 2005. Suppression of tiller bud activity in tillering dwarf mutants of rice. *Plant Cell Physiol.* 46:79–86
67. Jasinski S, Piazza P, Craft J, Hay A, Woolley L, et al. 2005. KNOX action in *Arabidopsis* is mediated by coordinate regulation of cytokinin and gibberellin activities. *Curr. Biol.* 15:1560–65
68. Jeong S, Trotochaud AE, Clark SE. 1999. The *Arabidopsis CLAVATA2* gene encodes a receptor-like protein required for the stability of the CLAVATA1 receptor-like kinase. *Plant Cell* 11:1925–34
69. Jones JW, Acair CR. 1938. A "lazy" mutation in rice. *J. Hered.* 28:315–18
70. Kasschau KD, Xie Z, Allen E, Llave C, Chapman EJ, et al. 2003. P1/HC-Pro, a viral suppressor of RNA silencing, interferes with *Arabidopsis* development and miRNA function. *Dev. Cell* 4:205–17

71. Keller T, Abbott J, Moritz T, Doerner P. 2006. *Arabidopsis REGULATOR OF AXILLARY MERISTEMS1* controls a leaf axil stem cell niche and modulates vegetative development. *Plant Cell* 18:598–611
72. Kellogg EA. 2007. Floral displays: genetic control of grass inflorescences. *Curr. Opin. Plant Biol.* 10:26–31
73. Kelly AJ, Bonnlander MB, Meeks-Wagner DR. 1995. *NFL*, the tobacco homolog of *FLORICAULA* and *LEAFY*, is transcriptionally expressed in both vegetative and floral meristems. *Plant Cell* 7:225–34
74. Khush G. 2003. Productivity improvements in rice. *Nutr. Rev.* 61:S114–16
75. Komatsu K, Maekawa M, Ujiie S, Satake Y, Furutani I, et al. 2003. *LAX* and *SPA*: major regulators of shoot branching in rice. *Proc. Natl. Acad. Sci. USA* 100:11765–70
76. Komatsu M, Chujo A, Nagato Y, Shimamoto K, Kyozuka J. 2003. *FRIZZY PANICLE* is required to prevent the formation of axillary meristems and to establish floral meristem identity in rice spikelets. *Development* 130:3841–50
77. Komorisono M, Ueguchi-Tanaka M, Aichi I, Hasegawa Y, Ashikari M, et al. 2005. Analysis of the rice mutant *dwarf and gladius leaf 1*. Aberrant katanin-mediated microtubule organization causes up-regulation of gibberellin biosynthetic genes independently of gibberellin signaling. *Plant Physiol.* 138:1982–93
78. Koornneef M, Hanhart CJ, Elgersma A, van Loenen-Martinet EP, van Rign L, Zeevaart JAD. 1985. A gibberellin insensitive mutant of *Arabidopsis thaliana*. *Physiol. Plant* 65:33–39
79. Koornneef M, van der Veen JH. 1980. Induction and analysis of gibberellin sensitive mutants in *Arabidopsis thaliana* (L.) Hehyn. *Theor. Appl. Genet.* 58:257–63
80. Kurakawa T, Ueda N, Maekawa M, Kobayashi K, Kojima M, et al. 2007. Direct control of shoot meristem activity by a cytokinin-activating enzyme. *Nature* 445:652–55
81. Kwon CS, Chen C, Wagner D. 2005. *WUSCHEL* is a primary target for transcriptional regulation by SPLAYED in dynamic control of stem cell fate in *Arabidopsis*. *Genes Dev.* 19:992–1003
82. Laufs P, Peaucelle A, Morin H, Traas J. 2004. MicroRNA regulation of the *CUC* genes is required for boundary size control in *Arabidopsis* meristems. *Development* 131:4311–22
83. Laux T, Mayer KF, Berger J, Jürgens G. 1996. The *WUSCHEL* gene is required for shoot and floral meristem integrity in *Arabidopsis*. *Development* 122:87–96
84. Lazar G, Goodman HM. 2006. *MAX1*, a regulator of the flavonoid pathway, controls vegetative axillary bud outgrowth in *Arabidopsis*. *Proc. Natl. Acad. Sci. USA* 103:472–76
85. Leibfried A, To JP, Busch W, Stehling S, Kehle A, et al. 2005. WUSCHEL controls meristem function by direct regulation of cytokinin-inducible response regulators. *Nature* 438:1172–75
86. Lenhard M, Jürgens G, Laux T. 2002. The *WUSCHEL* and *SHOOTMERISTEMLESS* genes fulfil complementary roles in *Arabidopsis* shoot meristem regulation. *Development* 129:3195–206
87. Lenhard M, Laux T. 2003. Stem cell homeostasis in the *Arabidopsis* shoot meristem is regulated by intercellular movement of *CLAVATA3* and its sequestration by *CLAVATA1*. *Development* 130:3163–73
88. Li J, Wen J, Lease KA, Doke JT, Tax FE, Walker JC. 2002. BAK1, an *Arabidopsis* LRR receptor-like protein kinase, interacts with BRI1 and modulates brassinosteroid signaling. *Cell* 110:213–22
89. Li P, Wang Y, Qian Q, Fu Z, Wang M, et al. 2007. *LAZY1* controls rice shoot gravitropism through regulating polar auxin transport. *Cell Res.* 17:402–10
90. Li P, Zeng D, Liu X, Xu D, Gu D, et al. 2003. Mapping and characterization of a tiller-spreading mutant *lazy-2* in rice. *Chin. Sci. Bull.* 48:2715–17

91. Li X, Qian Q, Fu Z, Wang Y, Xiong G, et al. 2003. Control of tillering in rice. *Nature* 422:618–21
92. Li Y. 1979. *Morphology and Anatomy of Grass Family Crops*, pp. 138–42. Shanghai: Shanghai Sci. Technol. Press
93. Long JA, Moan EI, Medford JI, Barton MK. 1996. A member of the KNOTTED class of homeodomain proteins encoded by the *STM* gene of *Arabidopsis*. *Nature* 379:66–69
94. Luo A, Qian Q, Yin H, Liu X, Yin C, et al. 2006. *EUI1*, encoding a putative cytochrome P450 monooxygenase, regulates internode elongation by modulating gibberellin responses in rice. *Plant Cell Physiol.* 47:181–91
95. Maiyata M, Komori T, Yamamoto T, Ueda T, Yano M, Nitta N. 2005. Fine scale and physical mapping of *Spk*(t) controlling spreading stub in rice. *Breed. Sci.* 55:237–39
96. Mayer KF, Schoof H, Haecker A, Lenhard M, Jürgens G, Laux T. 1998. Role of *WUSCHEL* in regulating stem cell fate in the *Arabidopsis* shoot meristem. *Cell* 95:805–15
97. McSteen P, Laudencia-Chingcuanco D, Colasanti J. 2000. A floret by any other name: control of meristem identity in maize. *Trends Plant Sci.* 5:61–66
98. Mellerowicz EJ, Horgan K, Walden A, Coker A, Walter C. 1998. *PRFLL*—a *Pinus radiata* homologue of *FLORICAULA* and *LEAFY* is expressed in buds containing vegetative shoot and undifferentiated male cone primordia. *Planta* 206:619–29
99. Molinero-Rosales N, Jamilena M, Zurita S, Gomez P, Capel J, Lozano R. 1999. *FALSIFLORA*, the tomato orthologue of *FLORICAULA* and *LEAFY*, controls flowering time and floral meristem identity. *Plant J.* 20:685–93
100. Monna L, Kitazawa N, Yoshino R, Suzuki J, Masuda H, et al. 2002. Positional cloning of rice semidwarfing gene, *sd-1*: rice "green revolution gene" encodes a mutant enzyme involved in gibberellin synthesis. *DNA Res.* 9:11–17
101. Morris DA. 1977. Transport of exogenous auxin in two-branched pea seedlings. *Planta* 136:91–96
102. Mouradov A, Glassick T, Hamdorf B, Murphy L, Fowler B, et al. 1998. *NEEDLY*, a *Pinus radiata* ortholog of *FLORICAULA/LEAFY* genes, expressed in both reproductive and vegetative meristems. *Proc. Natl. Acad. Sci. USA* 95:6537–42
103. Müller D, Schmitz G, Theres K. 2006. *Blind* homologous *R2R3 Myb* genes control the pattern of lateral meristem initiation in *Arabidopsis*. *Plant Cell* 18:586–97
104. Multani DS, Briggs SP, Chamberlin MA, Blakeslee JJ, Murphy AS, Johal GS. 2003. Loss of an MDR transporter in compact stalks of maize *br2* and sorghum *dw3* mutants. *Science* 302:81–84
105. Nam KH, Li J. 2002. BRI1/BAK1, a receptor kinase pair mediating brassinosteroid signaling. *Cell* 110:203–12
106. Napoli C. 1996. Highly branched phenotype of the *Petunia dad1–1* mutant is reversed by grafting. *Plant Physiol.* 111:27–37
107. Nishimura C, Ohashi Y, Sato S, Kato T, Tabata S, Ueguchi C. 2004. Histidine kinase homologs that act as cytokinin receptors possess overlapping functions in the regulation of shoot and root growth in *Arabidopsis*. *Plant Cell* 16:1365–77
108. Nordstrom A, Tarkowski P, Tarkowska D, Norbaek R, Astot C, et al. 2004. Auxin regulation of cytokinin biosynthesis in *Arabidopsis thaliana*: a factor of potential importance for auxin-cytokinin-regulated development. *Proc. Natl. Acad. Sci. USA* 101:8039–44
109. Okada K, Ueda J, Komaki MK, Bell CJ, Shimura Y. 1991. Requirement of the auxin polar transport system in early stages of *Arabidopsis* floral bud formation. *Plant Cell* 3:677–84
110. Otsuga D, DeGuzman B, Prigge MJ, Drews GN, Clark SE. 2001. REVOLUTA regulates meristem initiation at lateral positions. *Plant J.* 25:223–36

111. Overbeek JV. 1936. “Lazy”, an a-geotropic form of maize. *J. Heredity* 27:93–96
112. Palni LMS, Burch L, Horgan R. 1988. The effect of auxin concentration on cytokinin stability and metabolism. *Planta* 174:231–34
113. Peng J, Carol P, Richards DE, King KE, Cowling RJ, et al. 1997. The *Arabidopsis GAI* gene defines a signaling pathway that negatively regulates gibberellin responses. *Genes Dev.* 11:3194–205
114. Peng J, Harberd NP. 1993. Derivative alleles of the *Arabidopsis* gibberellin-insensitive (*gai*) mutation confer a wild-type phenotype. *Plant Cell* 5:351–60
115. Peng J, Harberd NP. 1997. Gibberellin deficiency and response mutations suppress the stem elongation phenotype of phytochrome-deficient mutants of *Arabidopsis*. *Plant Physiol.* 113:1051–58
116. Peng J, Richards DE, Hartley NM, Murphy GP, Devos KM, et al. 1999. ‘Green revolution’ genes encode mutant gibberellin response modulators. *Nature* 400:256–61
117. Peng P, Li J. 2003. Brassinosteroid signal transduction: a mix of conservation and novelty. *J. Plant Growth Regul.* 22:298–312
118. Petrásek J, Mravec J, Bouchard R, Blakeslee JJ, Abas M, et al. 2006. PIN proteins perform a rate-limiting function in cellular auxin efflux. *Science* 312:914–18
119. Prigge MJ, Otsuga D, Alonso JM, Ecker JR, Drews GN, Clark SE. 2005. Class III homeodomain-leucine zipper gene family members have overlapping, antagonistic, and distinct roles in *Arabidopsis* development. *Plant Cell* 17:61–76
120. Reinhardt D, Frenz M, Mandel T, Kuhlemeier C. 2003. Microsurgical and laser ablation analysis of interactions between the zones and layers of the tomato shoot apical meristem. *Development* 130:4073–83
121. Reinhardt D, Mandel T, Kuhlemeier C. 2000. Auxin regulates the initiation and radial position of plant lateral organs. *Plant Cell* 12:507–18
122. Reinhardt D, Pesce ER, Stieger P, Mandel T, Baltensperger K, et al. 2003. Regulation of phyllotaxis by polar auxin transport. *Nature* 426:255–60
123. Rhoades MW, Reinhart BJ, Lim LP, Burge CB, Bartel B, Bartel DP. 2002. Prediction of plant microRNA targets. *Cell* 110:513–20
124. Riou-Khamlichi C, Huntley R, Jacqmard A, Murray JA. 1999. Cytokinin activation of *Arabidopsis* cell division through a D-type cyclin. *Science* 283:1541–44
125. Rojo E, Sharma VK, Kovaleva V, Raikhel NV, Fletcher JC. 2002. CLV3 is localized to the extracellular space, where it activates the *Arabidopsis* CLAVATA stem cell signaling pathway. *Plant Cell* 14:969–77
126. Rupp HM, Frank M, Werner T, Strnad M, Schmülling T. 1999. Increased steady state mRNA levels of the *STM* and *KNAT1* homeobox genes in cytokinin overproducing *Arabidopsis thaliana* indicate a role for cytokinins in the shoot apical meristem. *Plant J.* 18:557–63
127. Sakamoto T, Kobayashi M, Itoh H, Tagiri A, Kayano T, et al. 2001. Expression of a gibberellin 2-oxidase gene around the shoot apex is related to phase transition in rice. *Plant Physiol.* 125:1508–16
128. Sakamoto T, Miura K, Itoh H, Tatsumi T, Ueguchi-Tanaka M, et al. 2004. An overview of gibberellin metabolism enzyme genes and their related mutants in rice. *Plant Physiol.* 134:1642–53
129. Sakamoto T, Morinaka Y, Ishiyama K, Kobayashi M, Itoh H, et al. 2003. Genetic manipulation of gibberellin metabolism in transgenic rice. *Nat. Biotechnol.* 21:909–13
130. Sakamoto T, Morinaka Y, Ohnishi T, Sunohara H, Fujioka S, et al. 2006. Erect leaves caused by brassinosteroid deficiency increase biomass production and grain yield in rice. *Nat. Biotechnol.* 24:105–9

131. Sasaki A, Ashikari M, Ueguchi-Tanaka M, Itoh H, Nishimura A, et al. 2002. Green revolution: a mutant gibberellin-synthesis gene in rice. *Nature* 416:701–2
132. Satoh-Nagasawa N, Nagasawa N, Malcomber S, Sakai H, Jackson D. 2006. A trehalose metabolic enzyme controls inflorescence architecture in maize. *Nature* 441:227–30
133. Schmitz G, Tillmann E, Carriero F, Fiore C, Cellini F, Theres K. 2002. The tomato *Blind* gene encodes a MYB transcription factor that controls the formation of lateral meristems. *Proc. Natl. Acad. Sci. USA* 99:1064–69
134. Schoof H, Lenhard M, Haecker A, Mayer KF, Jürgens G, Laux T. 2000. The stem cell population of *Arabidopsis* shoot meristems is maintained by a regulatory loop between the *CLAVATA* and *WUSCHEL* genes. *Cell* 100:635–44
135. Schumacher K, Schmitt T, Rossberg M, Schmitz G, Theres K. 1999. The *Lateral suppressor* (*Ls*) gene of tomato encodes a new member of the VHIID protein family. *Proc. Natl. Acad. Sci. USA* 96:290–95
136. Schwartz SH, Qin X, Loewen MC. 2004. The biochemical characterization of two carotenoid cleavage enzymes from *Arabidopsis* indicates that a carotenoid-derived compound inhibits lateral branching. *J. Biol. Chem.* 279:46940–45
137. Shimizu-Sato S, Mori H. 2001. Control of outgrowth and dormancy in axillary buds. *Plant Physiol.* 127:1405–13
138. Shitsukawa N, Takagishi A, Ikari C, Takumi S, Murai K. 2006. *WFL*, a wheat *FLORICAULA/LEAFY* ortholog, is associated with spikelet formation as lateral branch of the inflorescence meristem. *Genes Genet. Syst.* 81:13–20
139. Sieberer T, Leyser O. 2006. Plant science: auxin transport, but in which direction? *Science* 312:858–60
140. Snowden KC, Napoli C. 2003. A quantitative study and lateral branching in petunia. *Funct. Plant Biol.* 30:987–94
141. Sorefan K, Booker J, Haurogné K, Goussot M, Bainbridge K, et al. 2003. *MAX4* and *RMS1* are orthologous dioxygenase-like genes that regulate shoot branching in *Arabidopsis* and pea. *Genes Dev.* 17:1469–74
142. Souer E, van Houwelingen A, Kloos D, Mol J, Koes R. 1996. The *no apical meristem* gene of Petunia is required for pattern formation in embryos and flowers and is expressed at meristem and primordia boundaries. *Cell* 85:159–70
143. Spielmeyer W, Ellis MH, Chandler PM. 2002. Semidwarf (*sd-1*), "green revolution" rice, contains a defective gibberellin 20-oxidase gene. *Proc. Natl. Acad. Sci. USA* 99:9043–48
144. Stewart R, Dermen H. 1970. Determination of number and mitotic activity of shoot apical initial cells by analysis of mericlinal chimeras. *Am. J. Bot.* 57:816–26
145. Stirnberg P, Furner IJ, Ottoline Leyser HM. 2007. MAX2 participates in an SCF complex which acts locally at the node to suppress shoot branching. *Plant J.* 50:80–94
146. Stirnberg P, van De Sande K, Leyser HM. 2002. *MAX1* and *MAX2* control shoot lateral branching in *Arabidopsis*. *Development* 129:1131–41
147. Suge H, Turkan I. 1991. Can plants normally produce seeds under microgravity in space? *Jpn. J. Crop Sci.* 60:427–33
148. Sun TP, Kamiya Y. 1994. The *Arabidopsis GA1* locus encodes the cyclase ent-kaurene synthetase A of gibberellin biosynthesis. *Plant Cell* 6:1509–18
149. Suzaki T, Sato M, Ashikari M, Miyoshi M, Nagato Y, Hirano HY. 2004. The gene *FLORAL ORGAN NUMBER1* regulates floral meristem size in rice and encodes a leucine-rich repeat receptor kinase orthologous to *Arabidopsis CLAVATA1*. *Development* 131:5649–57
150. Swain SM, Olszewski NE. 1996. Genetic analysis of gibberellin signal transduction. *Plant Physiol.* 112:11–17

151. Taguchi-Shiobara F, Yuan Z, Hake S, Jackson D. 2001. The *fasciated ear2* gene encodes a leucine-rich repeat receptor-like protein that regulates shoot meristem proliferation in maize. *Genes Dev.* 15:2755–66
152. Takada S, Hibara K, Ishida T, Tasaka M. 2001. The *CUP-SHAPED COTYLEDON1* gene of *Arabidopsis* regulates shoot apical meristem formation. *Development* 128:1127–35
153. Takahashi M. 1963. Linkage groups and gene schemes of some striking morphological characters in Japanese rice. In *Symp. Genet. Cytogenet. Int. Rice Inst.*, pp. 215–36. Amesterdam: Elsevier
154. Talon M, Koornneef M, Zeevaart JA. 1990. Accumulation of C19-gibberellins in the gibberellin-insensitive dwarf mutant *gai* of *Arabidopsis thaliana* (L.) Hehyn. *Planta* 182:501–5
155. Talon M, Koornneef M, Zeevaart JA. 1990. Endogenous gibberellins in *Arabidopsis thaliana* and possible steps blocked in the biosynthetic pathways of the semidwarf *ga4* and *ga5* mutants. *Proc. Natl. Acad. Sci. USA* 87:7983–87
156. Tanabe S, Ashikari M, Fujioka S, Takatsuto S, Yoshida S, et al. 2005. A novel cytochrome P450 is implicated in brassinosteroid biosynthesis via the characterization of a rice dwarf mutant, *dwarf11*, with reduced seed length. *Plant Cell* 17:776–90
157. Tanaka R, Ikeda M, Funatsuki K, Yukioka H, Katoh K, Konno H. 2001. Molecular cloning and in situ hybridization of alpha-L-arabinofuranosidase from carrot cells. *Physiol. Plant* 113:392–99
158. Thimann KV, Skoog F. 1934. On the inhibition of bud development and other functions of growth substance in *Vicia faba*. *Proc. R. Soc. London Ser. B* 114:317–39
159. Thummel CS, Chory J. 2002. Steroid signaling in plants and insects–common themes, different pathways. *Genes Dev.* 16:3113–29
160. Trotochaud AE, Hao T, Wu G, Yang Z, Clark SE. 1999. The CLAVATA1 receptor-like kinase requires CLAVATA3 for its assembly into a signaling complex that includes KAPP and a Rho-related protein. *Plant Cell* 11:393–406
161. Ueguchi-Tanaka M, Ashikari M, Nakajima M, Itoh H, Katoh E, et al. 2005. *GIBBERELLIN INSENSITIVE DWARF1* encodes a soluble receptor for gibberellin. *Nature* 437:693–98
162. Vazquez F, Gasciolli V, Crete P, Vaucheret H. 2004. The nuclear dsRNA binding protein HYL1 is required for microRNA accumulation and plant development, but not posttranscriptional transgene silencing. *Curr. Biol.* 14:346–51
163. Vollbrecht E, Springer PS, Goh L, Buckler ES 4th, Martienssen R. 2005. Architecture of floral branch systems in maize and related grasses. *Nature* 436:1119–26
164. Vroemen CW, Mordhorst AP, Albrecht C, Kwaaitaal MA, de Vries SC. 2003. The *CUP-SHAPED COTYLEDON3* gene is required for boundary and shoot meristem formation in *Arabidopsis*. *Plant Cell* 15:1563–77
165. Wang X, Chory J. 2006. Brassinosteroids regulate dissociation of BKI1, a negative regulator of BRI1 signaling, from the plasma membrane. *Science* 313:1118–22
166. Wang Y, Li J. 2006. Genes controlling plant architecture. *Curr. Opin. Biotechnol.* 17:123–29
167. Wang ZY, He JX. 2004. Brassinosteroid signal transduction–choices of signals and receptors. *Trends Plant Sci.* 9:91–96
168. Wang ZY, Nakano T, Gendron J, He J, Chen M, et al. 2002. Nuclear-localized BZR1 mediates brassinosteroid-induced growth and feedback suppression of brassinosteroid biosynthesis. *Dev. Cell* 2:505–13
169. Ward SP, Leyser O. 2004. Shoot branching. *Curr. Opin. Plant Biol.* 7:73–78

170. Weigel D, Alvarez J, Smyth DR, Yanofsky MF, Meyerowitz EM. 1992. *LEAFY* controls floral meristem identity in *Arabidopsis*. *Cell* 69:843–59
171. Werner T, Motyka V, Strnad M, Schmülling T. 2001. Regulation of plant growth by cytokinin. *Proc. Natl. Acad. Sci. USA* 98:10487–92
172. William DA, Su Y, Smith MR, Lu M, Baldwin DA, Wagner D. 2004. Genomic identification of direct target genes of LEAFY. *Proc. Natl. Acad. Sci. USA* 101:1775–80
173. Williams L, Grigg SP, Xie M, Christensen S, Fletcher JC. 2005. Regulation of *Arabidopsis* shoot apical meristem and lateral organ formation by microRNA miR166g and its AtHD-ZIP target genes. *Development* 132:3657–68
174. Wilson RN, Heckman JW, Somerville CR. 1992. Gibberellin is required for flowering in *Arabidopsis thaliana* under short days. *Plant Physiol.* 100:403–8
175. Wilson RN, Somerville CR. 1995. Phenotypic suppression of the gibberellin-insensitive mutant (*gai*) of *Arabidopsis*. *Plant Physiol.* 108:495–502
176. Winkler RG, Freeling M. 1994. Analysis of the autonomy of maize *dwarf 1* action in genetic mosaics. *J. Hered.* 85:377–80
177. Wu X, Dabi T, Weigel D. 2005. Requirement of homeobox gene *STIMPY/WOX9* for *Arabidopsis* meristem growth and maintenance. *Curr. Biol.* 15:436–40
178. Yamamuro C, Ihara Y, Wu X, Noguchi T, Fujioka S, et al. 2000. Loss of function of a rice *brassinosteroid insensitive1* homolog prevents internode elongation and bending of the lamina joint. *Plant Cell* 12:1591–606
179. Yamazaki Y. 1985. Lazy-rice gotten up with tryptophan. *Bot. Mag.* 98:193–98
180. Yanai O, Shani E, Dolezal K, Tarkowski P, Sablowski R, et al. 2005. *Arabidopsis* KNOXI proteins activate cytokinin biosynthesis. *Curr. Biol.* 15:1566–71
181. Yang RC. 2005. Genetic evaluation and breeding utilization of rice eui-germplasm. *Eng. Sci.* 7:26–30
182. Yin Y, Wang ZY, Mora-Garcia S, Li J, Yoshida S, et al. 2002. BES1 accumulates in the nucleus in response to brassinosteroids to regulate gene expression and promote stem elongation. *Cell* 109:181–91
183. Yu B, Lin Z, Li H, Li X, Li J, et al. 2007. *TAC1*, a major quantitative trait locus controlling tiller angle in rice. *Plant J.* 52:891–98
184. Zhao J, Peng P, Schmitz RJ, Decker AD, Tax FE, Li J. 2002. Two putative BIN2 substrates are nuclear components of brassinosteroid signaling. *Plant Physiol.* 130:1221–29
185. Zhu Y, Nomura T, Xu Y, Zhang Y, Peng Y, et al. 2006. *ELONGATED UPPERMOST INTERNODE* encodes a cytochrome P450 monooxygenase that epoxidizes gibberellins in a novel deactivation reaction in rice. *Plant Cell* 18:442–56
186. Zou J, Zhang S, Zhang W, Li G, Chen Z, et al. 2006. The rice *HIGH-TILLERING DWARF1* encoding an ortholog of *Arabidopsis MAX3* is required for negative regulation of the outgrowth of axillary buds. *Plant J.* 48:687–98

Decoding of Light Signals by Plant Phytochromes and Their Interacting Proteins

Gabyong Bae and Giltsu Choi

Department of Biological Sciences, Korea Advanced Institute of Science and Technology, Daejeon 305-701, Korea; email: gchoi@kaist.ac.kr

Annu. Rev. Plant Biol. 2008. 59:281–311

The *Annual Review of Plant Biology* is online at plant.annualreviews.org

This article's doi:
10.1146/annurev.arplant.59.032607.092859

1543-5008/08/0602-0281$20.00

Key Words

phytochrome-interacting protein, protein degradation, photosensory, light signaling, PIF3, PIL5

Abstract

Phytochromes are red/far-red light photoreceptors that convert the information contained in external light into biological signals. The decoding process starts with the perception of red light, which occurs through photoisomerization of a chromophore located within the phytochrome, leading to structural changes that include the disruption of intramolecular interactions between the N- and C-terminal domains of the phytochrome. This disruption exposes surfaces required for interactions with other proteins. In contrast, the perception of far-red light reverses the photoisomerization, restores the intramolecular interaction, and closes the interacting surfaces. Light information represented by the concentration of opened interacting surfaces is converted into biological signals through the modulating activity of interacting proteins. This review summarizes plant phytochromes, phytochrome-interacting proteins, and signal transmission from phytochromes to their interacting proteins.

Contents

INTRODUCTION

Although light is ubiquitous, the light in a given locale may vary in terms of its wavelength, irradiance, direction, and periodicity (114). Plants acquire energy solely from light, and plant survival depends on the availability of external light. Therefore, it is not surprising that plants are equipped with sophisticated photoreceptor systems capable of monitoring external light conditions and continuously make light-specific adjustments to physiological and developmental processes (75). Because the absorption spectra of chlorophyll molecules cover blue and red light, plants have evolved to detect these spectra. At least four different types of photoreceptors have been identified in *Arabidopsis*, including the three classical photoreceptors (phytochromes, cryptochromes, and phototropins) and a newly recognized set of blue light photoreceptors (zeitlupes), F-box proteins containing a light, oxygen, and voltage (LOV) domain and kelch repeats. These different photoreceptors play shared but distinct roles in the induction of light responses upon the perception of blue or red/far-red light. Among these photoreceptors, the phytochromes, which are red and far-red light photoreceptors, are encoded by five different genes (*PHYA* to *PHYE*) in *Arabidopsis*, and are responsible for regulating various red light responses, including seed germination, seedling photomorphogenesis, shade avoidance, flowering, and many other adaptive responses (20). This review focuses on how light signals are perceived by phytochromes and their interacting proteins. A brief summary of other photoreceptors and relevant references can be found in the **Supplemental Material**. Follow the **Supplemental Material** link from the Annual Reviews home page at **http://www.annualreviews.org**.

PLANT PHYTOCHROMES

Perception of Light by Plant Phytochromes

Since the seminal work by Borthwick and coworkers (10) on the role of red/far-red light on lettuce seed germination, phytochromes have been the protein of interest among plant scientists. Plant phytochromes are dimeric proteins typically consisting of two identical apoproteins covalently linked with phytochromobilin, a linear tetrapyrrole bilin compound that acts as a chromophore

(51, 63, 113). The ability of a given phytochrome to absorb red and far-red light stems from its bound phytochromobilin, which undergoes a reversible photoisomerization at the C15-C16 double bond in response to red light (666 nm) and far-red light (730 nm) (1). After initial assembly of the phytochrome, the phytochromobilin assumes the C15-*Z,anti* conformation and is ready to absorb red light. This form of phytochrome is called the Pr form and is considered the biologically inactive form. Upon the absorption of red light, the C15-*Z,anti* conformation is converted to the C15-*E,anti* conformation. This form of the phytochrome is called Pfr. The Pfr form interacts with other proteins either in the cytosol or inside the nucleus (after translocation into the nucleus) and regulates their functions to induce light responses. A more detailed description of a proposed photoconversion process can be found in a recent review by Rockwell and colleagues (100). The conversion between Pr and Pfr by red and far-red light is reversible, allowing the phytochrome to act as a switch that is turned on by red light and turned off by far-red light (9).

The Phytochrome Gene Family

The plant phytochromes are encoded by a small gene family in most plant species; there are five *PHY* genes (*PHYA* to *PHYE*) in *Arabidopsis*, three *PHY* genes (*PHYA* to *PHYC*) in rice, four *PHY* genes (*PHYP1*, *PHYP2*, *PHYN*, and *PHYO*) in *Pinus*, and three *PHY* genes (*PHYP*, *PHYN*, and *PHYO*) in *Ginkgo*. Phylogenetic analysis has shown that an ancestral phytochrome bifurcated before the divergence of seed plants (75). Thus, all phytochromes found in modern plant species can be classified into two groups, namely the PHYA branch (including PHYA, PHYC, PHYN, and PHYO) and the PHYB branch (including PHYB, PHYD, PHYE, and PHYP). However, the phylogenetic dichotomy of plant phytochromes is not directly correlated with their molecular properties and functions.

The various phytochromes show similar but different molecular properties. First, PHYA is light labile, whereas all the other phytochromes are light stable (1, 36, 124). Owing to this difference in light stability, PHYA is the predominant phytochrome in etiolated seedlings, whereas PHYB and the others predominate in light-grown plants. Curiously, the stability of PHYC is dramatically decreased in *phyB* mutants in both *Arabidopsis* and rice, suggesting that PHYB controls the activity of PHYC in these species by regulating its stability (79, 121). Second, *Arabidopsis* PHYA dimerizes only with itself, whereas all the other *Arabidopsis* PHYs can form dimers with each other (106). The functional significance of heterodimerization is not yet fully understood.

The various phytochromes differ largely with respect to their spectral specificities. For the majority of light responses in *Arabidopsis*, PHYA is responsible for the very low fluence response (VLFR) and the far-red high irradiance response (FR-HIR) (23, 81, 112, 138), whereas the other phytochromes are responsible for the red/far-red reversible low fluence response (LFR) (97, 98). However, PHYA can mediate red light signaling under very high irradiance red light and during dark-to-light transitions (32, 122), whereas PHYE can mediate FR-HIR for seed germination (39). In rice, FR-HIR is mediated by both PHYA and PHYC, whereas LFR is mediated by both PHYA and PHYB (121).

The various phytochromes play overlapping but distinct roles. In rice, all three phytochromes promote de-etiolation and delay flowering in long-day (LD) conditions, whereas in short-day (SD) conditions PHYB delays flowering and PHYA promotes flowering, especially in the absence of PHYB (121). In *Arabidopsis*, both PHYA and PHYB promote seed germination and de-etiolation in response to far-red (FR) and red (R) light, respectively. PHYB inhibits shade avoidance responses under a high ratio of R:FR light, whereas PHYA inhibits excessive shade avoidance responses under a low ratio of R:FR light;

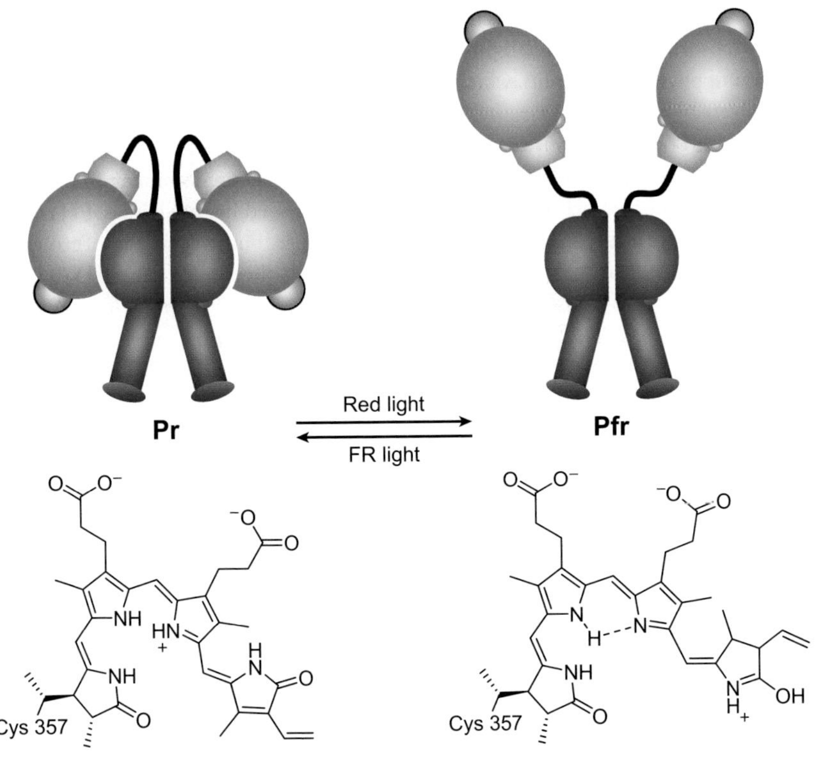

Figure 1

The photoisomerization of phytochromobilin and the accompanying structural change in phytochrome. Pr, C15-*Z*,*anti* conformation; Pfr, C15-*E*,*anti* conformation; FR light, far-red light.

PHYA promotes flowering, whereas PHYB delays flowering (34, 97). In *Arabidopsis*, the three other phytochromes also have overlapping but distinct functions. PHYC promotes seedling de-etiolation and primary leaf expansion in response to red light and delays flowering (4, 33, 79). Similarly, PHYD and PHYE promote seedling de-etiolation and suppress shade avoidance responses (3, 27, 28). Curiously, for seed germination, PHYE can promote seed germination under both LFR and FR-HIR conditions (39). The functional differences among the *Arabidopsis* phytochromes are partly due to their intrinsic properties (107). When PHYB, PHYD, and PHYE are overexpressed in the *phyB* mutant under control of the *PHYB* promoter, all three phytochromes rescue the seedling and leaf morphology phenotypes of the *phyB* mutant either partially (PHYD and PHYE) or fully (PHYB). In contrast, PHYB and PHYE rescue the flowering phenotype, but PHYD does not. Taken together, the characterizations of various phytochromes from the same or different species indicate that phytochromes share similar functions but have diverged to adopt various roles irrespective of their phylogenetic origins.

Functional Domains of Plant Phytochromes

All plant phytochromes can be divided into an N-terminal photosensory domain and a C-terminal dimerization domain. The N-terminal photosensory domain may be further divided into four consecutive subdomains called P1, P2/PAS, P3/GAF, and P4/PHY (named sequentially from the N terminus), whereas the C-terminal domain may be divided into two subdomains, the PAS-A and PAS-B domains and the histidine kinase–related domain (HKRD) (139) (**Figure 2**). The PAS domain is named after three proteins in which it occurs: Per (period circadian protein), Arn (Ah receptor nuclear translocator protein), and Sim (single-minded protein). The HKRD lacks a critical histidine residue, and thus may be an evolutionary remnant rather than an active histidine kinase (10). Among the N-terminal subdomains, the P1 domain is uniquely present in plant phytochromes, whereas the P2/PAS, P3/GAF, and P4/PHY domains are also found in phytochrome-like proteins of various origins. Among the C-terminal subdomains, the PAS-A and PAS-B domains are unique to plant phytochromes, whereas HKRDs are also found in phytochrome-like proteins.

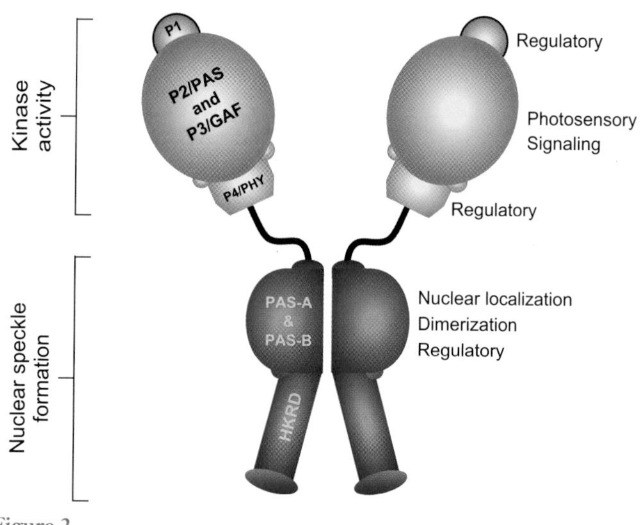

Figure 2

Domain structures of phytochrome and their associated functions. PAS, Per (period circadian protein) Arn (Ah receptor nuclear translocator protein), and Sim (single-minded protein); PHY, phytochrome; HKRD, histidine kinase–related domain; GAF, cGMP-stimulated phosphodiesterase, *Anabena* adenylate cyclases, and *Escherichia coli* FhlA.

The P1 domain is not essential for the function of PHYB. Deletion of amino acids 1–57 of *Arabidopsis* PHYB yields a protein with full activity (131). Even proteins with a deletion of the N-terminal 103 amino acids retain the ability to inhibit hypocotyl elongation in red light, although to a reduced degree (131) (**Figure 3**). In contrast, the function of the P1 domain is more complicated in PHYA. Deletion of amino acids 25–33 or 50–62 from oat PHYA destabilizes the Pfr conformation in vitro and severely reduces the activity of the protein when expressed in tobacco (17). In contrast, deletion of amino acids 6–12 of oat PHYA confers hypersensitivity to far-red light in both tobacco and *Arabidopsis* (12). However, an *Arabidopsis* PHYA protein harboring the same deletion mediates normal VLFR, but not FR-HIR, when expressed under the native PHYA promoter in *Arabidopsis* (125). These findings seem to suggest that the P1 domains of different PHYA proteins play varied roles in different plant species. This complex role of the P1 domain may suggest that its regulatory role evolved after the divergence of these species. Biochemically, serine 7 of oat PHYA is phosphorylated by unidentified kinases, whereas serine 17 of the same protein is autophosphorylated (67). The dephosphorylation of these serine residues by PHYTOCHROME-ASSOCIATED PHOSPHATASE 5 (PAPP5) stabilizes PHYA in *Arabidopsis* (101). The stabilizing effect of dephosphorylation is further supported by the hypersensitivity of oat PHYA proteins with alanines substituted in place of these serines (116). However, because deletion of the same region from *Arabidopsis* PHYA destabilizes rather than stabilizes the protein, the precise role of these phosphorylation events warrants careful investigation. Collectively, the existing data suggest that the P1 domain of PHYA regulates the stability of both the phytochrome and its Pfr conformation, but the specific roles of this domain are variable across different phytochromes and plant species.

In contrast, the P2/PAS and P3/GAF domains form a core photosensory domain and are conserved in most phytochromes and phytochrome-related proteins. These domains contain bilin lyase activity, which is responsible for ligating the chromophore to a cysteine residue either in the P2/PAS domain

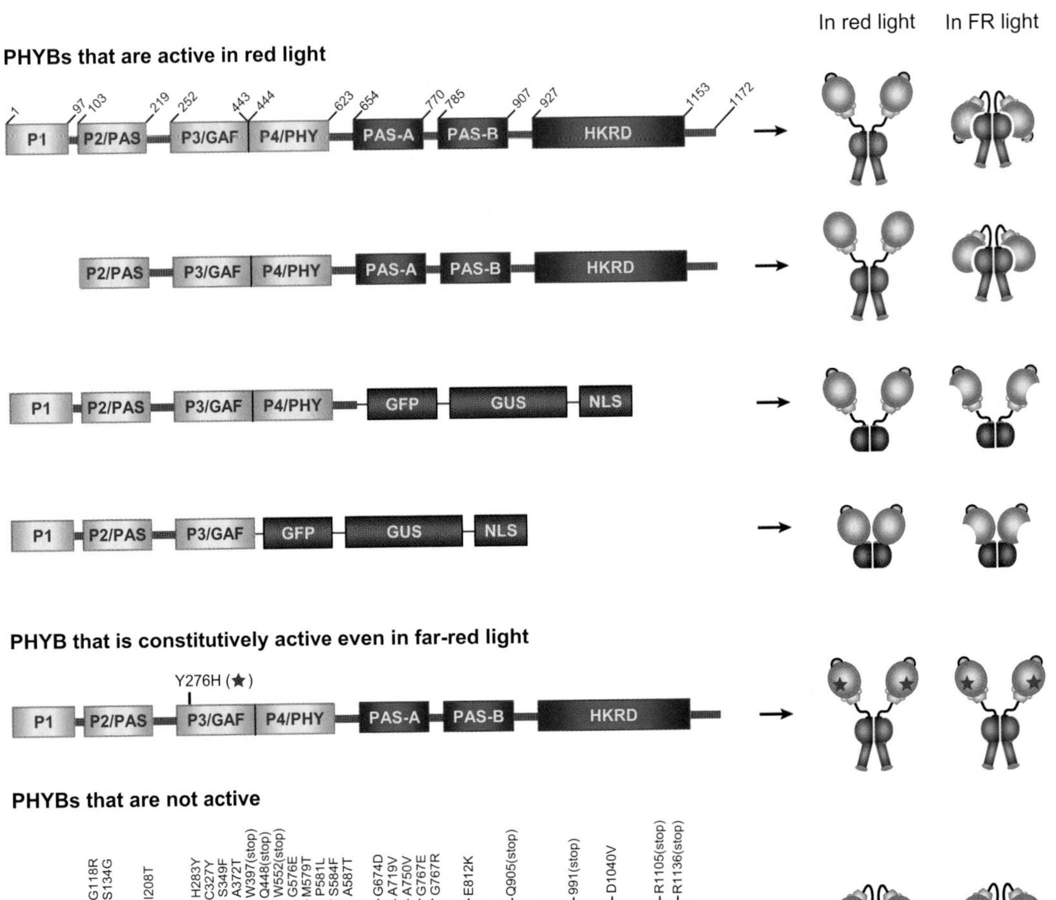

Figure 3

Phytochrome B mutants and their hypothetical conformations in red and far-red light. PHY, phytochrome; PAS, Per (period circadian protein), Arn (Ah receptor nuclear translocator protein), and Sim (single-minded protein); GAF, cGMP-stimulated phosphodiesterase, *Anabena* adenylate cyclases and *Escherichia coli* FhlA; HKRD, histidine kinase–related domain; GFP, green fluorescent protein; GUS, β-glucuronidase; NLS, nuclear localization signal; FR, far-red.

(in bacteriophytochromes) or in the P3/GAF domain (in plant phytochromes) (64, 66, 139). Accordingly, many point mutations in these domains affect either chromophore assembly or the spectral properties of the mutant proteins (**Figure 3**). Further functional separation of the two domains has proven difficult, however, because deletion of either domain impairs chromophore incorporation, resulting in a grossly nonfunctional protein. The crystal structure of the *Deinococcus* bacteriophytochrome shows that the two domains are tightly linked not only by the peptide backbone of the protein, but also by a trefoil knot (133, 134). The functional significance of this knot is unknown, but many loss-of-function missense mutations in these domains map to the knot region, suggesting that the knot formed between the P2/PAS and P3/GAF domains plays an important functional role.

A recent analysis of another mutation in the P3/GAF domain suggests that this domain plays a critical role in light signaling (117). Substitution of PHYB tyrosine 276 with histidine (Y276H) causes the loss of red light–induced photoisomerization, meaning that the mutant PHYB^{Y276H} behaves like the Pr form (at least from the spectral standpoint). However, when the mutant protein is overexpressed in *Arabidopsis*, the chromophore-assembled PHYB^{Y276H} is localized in the nucleus and is constitutively active, yielding constitutive photomorphogenic phenotypes even in the dark (**Figure 3**). Consistent with the mutant's loss of photoisomerization ability, the constitutive photomorphogenic phenotypes are not reversed by far-red light. A similar mutation in PHYA (PHYA^{Y242H}) is less active than PHYB^{Y276H}, but still yields constitutively photomorphogenic phenotypes in the dark. Taken together, these results indicate that the P2/PAS and P3/GAF domains play critical roles in both photosensing and light signaling (**Figure 2**). The constitutively active status of PHYB^{Y276H} and PHYA^{Y242H} further suggests that structural changes, rather than photoisomerization per se, are critically important for signaling.

The P4/PHY domain, which is conserved in all phytochromes and their related proteins, is necessary for fine tuning phytochrome activity. Deletion of the P4/PHY domain increases the dark reversion rate (i.e., the instability of the Pfr conformation) and causes a blue shift in absorption by both Pr and Pfr (90). Three missense mutations found in the P4/PHY domain are especially informative. First, an *Arabidopsis* PHYB harboring a missense mutation (G564E) is hyperactive, due at least in part to its decreased dark reversion rate (62). Second, a natural variation of PHYA (M548T; identified from the Lm-2 accession) shows a significant reduction in PHYA activity, a 6-nm blue shift for Pfr absorption, and reduced kinase activity (72). Third, a missense PHYB mutation (A587T) disrupts the nuclear localization of PHYB (15). Collectively, these data suggest that the P4/PHY domain is necessary for fine tuning the stability of the Pfr conformation and ensuring proper spectral properties, nuclear localization, and kinase activity.

A truncated PHYB comprising the N-terminal 651 amino acids of PHYB (including the P1, P2/PAS, P3/GAF, and P4/PHY domains) is functional when fused to a dimerization motif provided by β-glucuronidase (GUS) and the SV40 nuclear localization signal (NLS) (N651G-GUS-NLS) (99) (**Figure 3**). The activity of N651G-GUS-NLS is higher than wild-type activity, indicating that the N-terminal domain has all the activities necessary for phytochrome function except for the dimerization and nuclear localization activities. The higher activity of N651G-GUS-NLS compared with the full-length PHYB further implies that the C-terminal domain has a negative regulatory function. A truncated PHYB comprising the N-terminal 450 amino acids of PHYB is also functional when fused to GUS and the SV40 nuclear localization signal (N450G-GUS-NLS, including P1, P2/PAS, and P3/GAF), but shows an increased dark reversion rate owing to the lack of the P4/PHY domain (90) (**Figure 3**). Owing to its increased dark reversion rate, N450G-GUS-NLS becomes less active following exposure to red pulses with longer intermittent periods. Because the P1 domain of PHYB is dispensable (as discussed above), P2/PAS and P3/GAF are the minimal domains necessary for PHYB activity (90).

Unlike fusions involving the N-terminal domain of PHYB, fusion of the N-terminal domain of PHYA to GUS and NLS (PHYA-65-GFP-GUS-NLS) causes weak but constitutive photomorphogenic phenotypes, including shorter hypocotyls and cotyledon opening in the dark (74). PHYA-65-GFP-GUS-NLS shows an effective VLFR, but no FR-HIR. This suggests that, unlike the N-terminal domain of PHYB, the N-terminal domain of PHYA is sufficient for VLFR, but not for FR-HIR. Why the N-terminal domains of PHYA and PHYB behave differently remains unclear, but this result is consistent with the differences observed between PHYB^{Y276H} and PHYA^{Y242H} (117).

Although the N-terminal domains of phytochromes contain the essential photochemical and photobiological activities, the C-terminal domain also plays important roles for the proper function of the intact proteins, as indicated by the phenotypes described for numerous nonsense and missense mutations in the C-terminal domain (99, 140). The two most obvious functional motifs in the C-terminal domain are a dimerization motif and a nuclear localization signal (**Figure 2**). The dimerization domain has been roughly mapped to a region that includes parts of the PAS-A and PAS-B domains (30, 51). However, bacterial phytochromes without PAS-A and PAS-B domains still dimerize (65), suggesting that the HKRD may also contribute to the dimerization of intact phytochromes. The nuclear localization signal has been roughly mapped to a region that also includes parts of the PAS-A and PAS-B domains. The GFP-fused C-terminal domain of PHYB constitutively localizes to the nucleus and constitutively forms nuclear speckles, bright fluorescent spots in the nucleus that can also be seen in light-activated GFP-fused full-length phytohcromes (103, 126). A region that includes the PAS-A and PAS-B domains (amino acids 594–917) showed robust nuclear localization when fused to YFP (16). However, this region is not sufficient for the formation of nuclear speckles, suggesting that the formation of nuclear speckles requires both the PAS-A, PAS-B, and the HKRD domains. A few loss-of-function missense mutations found in the PAS domain also failed to show nuclear localization (G674D, A719V, and G767R of PHYB), further supporting the notion that the two PAS domains are important for proper nuclear localization (16, 76). Collectively, these data show that the PAS-A and PAS-B domains of PHYB are necessary for dimerization and nuclear localization, whereas PAS-A, PAS-B, and the HKRD domains are necessary for nuclear speckle formation. Unlike the PHYB C-terminal domain, the C-terminal domain of PHYA provides the dimerization motif but not the nuclear localization signal, which is provided instead by its interacting proteins, FHY1 (FAR-RED ELONGATED HYPOCOTYL 1) and FHL (FHY1-LIKE) (40, 41).

Finally, at least one domain must be responsible for the serine/threonine kinase activity that governs phytochrome autophosphorylation and phytochrome-directed phosphorylation of other proteins, such as PHYTOCHROME-INTERACTING FACTOR 3 (PIF3) (55, 147). The functional significance of this kinase activity remains unknown, but it may play a key role in signaling. HKRD was initially suggested to be a kinase domain because of its relatedness to bacterial histidine kinase. Deletion analysis, however, shows that the N-terminal domain has full kinase activity toward itself and PIF3, indicating that the kinase domain resides in the N-terminal domain (J. Kim, unpublished data) (**Figure 2**). Future work will be required to determine the exact location and functional significance of the kinase domain.

Light-Induced Structural Changes in Plant Phytochromes

Several lines of evidence indicate that the conversion between Pr and Pfr is accompanied by protein structural changes. Circular dichroism (CD) analysis shows that the α-helix content increases by 5% when Pr is converted to Pfr (22). Diffusion coefficient measurements show that the surface for intermolecular hydrogen bonding increases markedly during the conversion to Pfr (31). More directly, probing with tryptophan-modifying 2-hydroxy-5-nitrobenzyl bromide (HNB-Br) shows that two tryptophan residues (W773 and W777) in the C-terminal domain of oat PHYA are modified preferentially in the Pfr form; probing with cysteine-modifying iodoacetamide shows that a cysteine residue (C311) in the N-terminal domain of oat PHYA is also selectively modified in the Pfr form (68, 136). These findings indicate that the Pr to Pfr conversion is accompanied by exposure of the N-terminal P3/GAF domain

(C311) and the C-terminal PAS-A and PAS-B domains (W773 and W777). The simultaneous exposure of these relatively distant amino acids in response to red light may indicate the presence of light-dependent intramolecular interactions between these two regions. Indeed, yeast two-hybrid experiments and in vitro binding assays show that the N-terminal domain (227–651) and the C-terminal domain (594–917) of PHYB interact with each other in the dark, but dissociate upon irradiation with red light (16) (**Figure 1**). Although the chemical probing experiments involved oat PHYA and the intramolecular binding experiments involved *Arabidopsis* PHYB, the two data sets are consistent in supporting the notion that red light induces structural changes that lead to the dissociation and subsequent opening of the P3/GAF domain and the PAS-A and PAS-B domains (**Figure 1**).

Dissociation of the N- and C-terminal domains may expose the nuclear localization signal, but it does not confer phytochrome activity per se. When the N-terminal domain of PHYB or PHYA is fused to a dimerization motif and a nuclear localization motif, the chimeric photoreceptor is constitutively localized to the nucleus. Unlike $PHYB^{Y276H}$, however, N651G-GUS-NLS (or N450G-GUS-NLS) is not constitutively active, but rather requires red light for activation (76, 90, 117) (**Figure 3**). This suggests that photoisomerization causes structural changes that not only expose the C-terminal NLS, but also change the N-terminal domain in some way to allow signaling. Interestingly, some phytochrome-interacting proteins preferentially bind to the Pfr form (see **Supplemental Table 1** in **Supplemental Material**), suggesting that the structural changes associated with photoisomerization may also provide the interacting surfaces for partner proteins.

Nuclear Translocation of Plant Phytochromes

The presumed structural changes required to generate the Pfr form, including exposure of the P3/GAF, PAS-A, and PAS-B domains, initiate signaling events that induce various light responses in plants. These signaling events could occur in the cytosol for the regulation of various light responses, such as cytoplasmic motility and chloroplast movement, or the light-dependent structural changes could induce translocation of the Pfr form into the nucleus, where it could initiate other signaling events. The C-terminal domain of PHYB constitutively localizes to the nucleus irrespective of light conditions and forms nuclear speckles (126), whereas full-length PHYA or PHYB localize to the nucleus and form nuclear speckles upon light irradiation (58, 141). In the absence of light, the nuclear localization activity of the C-terminal domain is blocked by the N-terminal P3/GAF and P4/PHY domains, as indicated by the observation that a truncated PHYB protein lacking the P1 and P2/PAS domains still shows light-dependent nuclear localization (16). Because these N- and C-terminal regions interact with each other in the dark, and amino acids in these regions are exposed upon the perception of red light, structural changes in these regions likely cause the translocation of phytochromes into the nucleus.

Detailed analysis of such nuclear translocation indicates, however, that the various phytochromes behave differently in response to different light spectra. For example, PHYB-GFP moves into the nucleus and forms nuclear speckles (also called nuclear bodies) in response to red light but not far-red light (58). However, nuclear speckle formation is not strictly dependent on light. Analysis of PHYB localization in seedlings grown under light/dark cycles reveals that the number of PHYB nuclear speckles increases at dawn in anticipation of incoming light, suggesting that nuclear translocation or nuclear speckle formation is regulated not only by light, but also by circadian rhythm (57, 141). Unlike PHYB-GFP, PHYA-GFP moves into the nucleus and forms nuclear speckles in response to both white/red and far-red light (58). Under white/red light, however, PHYA is rapidly degraded, meaning that the PHYA-GFP signal decreases under red light and PHYA-GFP nuclear speckles persist in the long-term only under far-red light. The nuclear localization behavior of PHYA-GFP is consistent with the functional properties of PHYA, which is activated by all spectra of light including far-red light. In contrast, PHYC, PHYD, and PHYE fusions to GFP constitutively localize to the nucleus in light/dark grown seedlings, but their nuclear speckle formations are either light-dependent (PHYC-GFP and PHYE-GFP) or light-independent (PHYD-GFP) (57). As with PHYB-GFP, other PHY-GFPs (except for PHYD-GFP) show increased nuclear speckle formation at dawn in anticipation of incoming light. Consistent with these differences among the various PHYs, their nuclear localization kinetics also differ. PHYA-GFP signals are apparent after 15 min of light irradiation, whereas the PHYB-GFP signal appears after 2 h. These complex patterns of nuclear localization and speckle formation by different phytochromes suggest that light-dependent structural changes might not be identical among the various phytochromes. Alternatively, translocation and speckle formation may be regulated not only by light-induced structural changes, but also by other specific factors.

The precise nature of the above-described nuclear speckle is unknown, but speckle sizes and numbers may vary. In animal cells, similar nuclear speckles are associated with transcription, RNA processing, and protein degradation (37). In *Arabidopsis*, nuclear speckles are formed by a few other light signaling-related proteins, including cryptochromes, CONSTITUTIVE PHOTOMORPHOGENIC 1 (COP1), and PIF3, suggesting that at least a part of the light signaling process occurs in nuclear speckles (7, 60, 130). However, whether speckle formation is a prerequisite for phytochrome function is unclear. Many missense mutants fail to form speckles, including the loss-of-function mutations E777K and G788E of PHYA and A776V and E838K of PHYB, suggesting that nuclear speckle formation may be associated with phytochrome function (15, 145). In contrast, no speckles are formed by N651G-GUS-NLS and N450G-GUS-NLS fusion proteins, which are more active than full-length PHYB, or by PHYA-65-GFP-GUS-NLS, which is functional for VLFR (74, 76, 90). Similarly, the C-terminal domain of PHYB, which does not affect PHYB-mediated light signaling, still forms nuclear speckles (126). Thus, future identification of protein components associated with the PHY-based speckles will be necessary to help determine the precise function of nuclear speckles.

LIGHT INFORMATION PERCEIVED BY PLANT PHYTOCHROMES

Wavelength and Irradiance Information

Light information is consistent in wavelength, irradiance, direction, and periodicity. Among these values, wavelength and irradiance information is represented by the concentration of the biologically active Pfr form available in a given plant cell. This property can be more easily understood by calculating the change of Pfr concentration at the photoequilibrium state. The concentration of Pfr in vivo can be expressed as the following (see **Supplemental Material** for the kinetics calculation):

$$Pfr = \frac{\sum_\lambda \varepsilon_{r\lambda}\phi_{r\lambda}I_\lambda}{\sum_\lambda \varepsilon_{r\lambda}\phi_{r\lambda}I_\lambda + \sum_\lambda \varepsilon_{f\lambda}\phi_{f\lambda}I_\lambda + k_d + k_r} Pt \quad (1)$$

where Pr and Pfr indicate the concentrations of the Pr and Pfr forms, P_t is the concentration of total phytochrome ($Pr + Pfr$), $\varepsilon_{r\lambda}$ and $\varepsilon_{f\lambda}$ are the extinction coefficients of Pr and Pfr, respectively, for a given wavelength λ, $\phi_{r\lambda}$ and $\phi_{f\lambda}$ are the quantum yields of the Pr-to-Pfr and Pfr-to-Pr conversions, respectively, for a given wavelength λ, I_λ is the irradiance of light for a given wavelength λ,

k_d is the rate constant for Pfr protein degradation, and k_r is the rate constant for dark reversion.

Equation 1 indicates that the concentration of Pfr is the function of total phytochrome concentration (P_t), wavelength (λ), and irradiance (I). First, the concentration of Pfr is linearly proportional to P_t in a given cell, indicating that plants that contain higher amounts of total phytochromes have correspondingly higher amounts of Pfr under a given light condition. This explains why phytochrome overexpression causes stronger light responses in transgenic plants compared with wild-type plants under the same light conditions (11, 132). Second, the extinction coefficients and quantum yields vary depending on the wavelength, meaning that the concentration of Pfr varies by wavelength even under identical light irradiance and total phytochrome amounts. Owing to these varying extinction coefficients and quantum yields, phytochromes can extract wavelength information from light and convert it into the concentration of biologically active Pfr in a cell. Third, the concentration of Pfr is a rational function with irradiance as a variable, indicating that the concentration of Pfr increases with increasing irradiance. However, the concentration of Pfr does not increase linearly; instead, the value approaches an asymptotic value, which explains why the light response reaches a plateau as light irradiance increases. *Pt* also varies depending on irradiance in some plant species, meaning that the exact relationship between Pfr concentration and irradiance is more complicated in planta. Nevertheless, this simplified kinetic calculation shows how phytochromes convert wavelength and irradiance information into a concentration of the biologically active Pfr form.

Directional Light Information

Plants perceive information regarding light direction and adjust their physiological and developmental processes accordingly (137). Phototropism and chloroplast movement are two well-known examples of such responses. Blue light is the major light spectrum that provides directional information to plants. Among the blue light photoreceptors, phototropins are responsible for recognizing blue light directional information (18, 56). Directional information of red light has also been implicated in phototropism and chloroplast movement. Most research regarding the perception of red light directional information has been carried out in ferns and filamentous alga, which perceive red light directional information through neochromes rather than canonical phytochromes (52, 119). In *Physcomitrella*, however, a canonical phytochrome perceives the directional information of red light and regulates chloroplast movement (78). Other reports show that red light–induced root phototropism is impaired in *Arabidopsis phyA* and *phyB* mutants (21, 59), and the FR-induced negative shoot phototropism is defective in the cucumber *phyB* mutant (*lh*) (70), suggesting that canonical phytochromes can perceive light directional information in plants.

However, we do not yet fully understand how phytochromes perceive red light directional information. Because chlorophylls contained within chloroplasts strongly absorb red and blue light, phytochromes located behind chloroplasts are less likely to be converted to Pfr. Direct measurement shows that the irradiance of red light drops to 15% of the initial value within the first half of the palisade cells in *Medicago sativa* leaves (128), suggesting that a Pfr concentration gradient may be formed along the light directional axis, even in a single palisade cell. At the tissue level, the absorption of red light by the chloroplasts of outer layer cells could greatly reduce the red light irradiance that reaches inner layer cells. Therefore, red light directional information is converted into a Pfr concentration gradient among cells, which in turn generates gradients of both nuclear and cytoplasmic light signaling events along the axis of light. Further research is warranted to determine whether the formation of a Pfr concentration gradient within a cell or among cells has any physiological significance in higher plants.

Photoperiod Information

Plants perceive photoperiod information through phytochromes, cryptochromes, and zeitlupes, and regulate various physiological and developmental processes accordingly. Flowering is one of the best-studied photoperiod-regulated developmental processes. Molecular analysis of photoperiodic flowering responses in model species suggests that the external coincidence between a circadian phase and light is used for photoperiod perception (45). In *Arabidopsis*, two floral integrator genes, *FLOWERING LOCUS T* (*FT*) and *SUPPRESSOR OF CONSTANS* (*CO*) *1* (*SOC1*), integrate various flowering signals from the autonomous, gibberellin, photoperiod, and vernalization pathways (94). CO, a B-box zinc finger protein, plays a critical role in translating photoreceptor-perceived light signals into expression of the *FT* and *SOC1* genes. The expression of *CO* is under control of the circadian rhythm; expression reaches a broad peak between 12:00 hours and dawn in LD conditions (118). Day length has a mild but significant impact on the expression pattern of *CO*. In SD conditions, the expression peak at 12:00 hours disappears. This earlier expression peak of *CO* is induced by the targeted degradation of CDF1 by FKF1 in the presence of blue light; the expression of FKF1 is in turn regulated by a circadian clock (46, 47, 82). Therefore, the earlier *CO* expression peak in the LD condition is the product of coincidence between external light and the afternoon phase of the circadian clock.

The protein stability of CO is also regulated by light. CO is destabilized by the action of PHYB in the morning, stabilized by PHYA and CRYs in the afternoon, and destabilized by the SUPPRESSOR OF PHYA proteins (SPA1, SPA3, and SPA4) in the night (69, 127). This transcriptional and posttranscriptional regulation produces a peak of CO protein levels in the late afternoon only under LD conditions when external light and the dusk phase coincide, but not under SD conditions. In response to the differential accumulation of CO protein in LD and SD, *FT* is expressed at high levels only in LD, resulting in flowering of *Arabidopsis*. A similar external coincidence between circadian clock and external light is proposed to regulate photoperiodic flowering responses not only in other LD plants such as *Populus* (8), but also in SD plants such as rice (38, 48). In rice, the external coincidence between the circadian clock and light represses *Hd6*, the rice homolog of *FT*, inhibiting flowering under LD conditions. It will be interesting to determine if any of the rice zeitlupes also participate in the perception of photoperiod information.

PHYTOCHROME-INTERACTING PROTEINS

Phytochromes convert perceived light information into absolute concentrations and/or concentration gradients of the Pfr form, leading to the regulation of various physiological and developmental processes in plants. How is the concentration of the Pfr form translated into other biological signals? Because phytochromes do not possess any known biochemical activities other than serine/threonine kinase activity, phytochromes are believed to regulate their downstream processes by interacting with other proteins. Consistent with this notion, phytochrome-interacting proteins have been identified by several different approaches. The most widely used approach is yeast two-hybrid screening; the C-terminal domain is typically used as a bait, but the N-terminal domain or the full-length phytochrome are also sometimes used. Once a putative interacting protein is identified by screening or other methods such as targeted testing, the interaction between phytochromes and the candidate interacting proteins is generally confirmed by an in vitro binding assay, in vivo pull-down assay, or in vivo colocalization test. The functional significances of many interacting proteins have been further confirmed by genetic analysis. To date, more than 20 phytochrome-interacting proteins have been reported in the literature (see **Supplemental Table 1** in the **Supplemental Material** for the identities and functions of all phytochrome-interacting proteins). Here we focus on a few representative interacting proteins and use them to delineate how phytochrome-perceived light information is transmitted to downstream components.

Phytochrome-Interacting Proteins That Regulate the Nuclear Localization of Phytochromes

Some phytochrome-interacting proteins are needed for the nuclear/cytoplasmic partitioning of phytochromes. In eukaryotes, proteins larger than ~40 kD must be actively transported into or out of the nucleus through nuclear pore complexes, with the help of transport proteins such as importins and exportins (115). Because phytochrome dimers are approximately 240 kD in size, they require interacting proteins for their nuclear localization. Among the identified phytochrome-interacting proteins, FHY1 and FHL, which interact with PHYA but not with PHYB and promote the translocation of PHYA to the nucleus, fit the definition of this class of phytochrome-interacting proteins (**Figure 4**).

The history of FHY1 essentially parallels the history of the molecular genetic analysis of PHYA signaling in *Arabidopsis*. The *fhy1* mutant was the first *Arabidopsis* PHYA signaling mutant isolated; *fhy1* was first reported in 1993 together with *fhy2* (*phyA* mutant) and *fhy3* (138). *fhy1* mutant plants contain a normal amount of PHYA, but are partially defective in far-red-induced de-etiolation processes (FR-HIR) (138). Numerous light responses are affected in the *fhy1* mutant, including seed germination (50), hypocotyl elongation under a low R/FR ratio (50), far-red–induced inhibition of greening (5), induction of the *CHALCONE SYNTHASE* (*CHS*) gene (6), functional interactions between PHYA- and PHYB signaling (13), and the far-red-induced phase shift (146). In contrast, a few processes remain unaffected in these mutants, including flowering under low R/FR and extended short day conditions (50) and induction of the *CHLOROPHYLL a/b BINDING PROTEIN* (*CAB*) gene (6). These phenotypes indicate that FHY1 is responsible for mediating a branch of PHYA signaling. Microarray analysis of *fhy1*, however, shows that all genes affected by the *phyA* mutation are also affected by the *fhy1* mutation, but to a lesser degree (135). This result suggests that the incompleteness of the phenotypic defects in the *fhy1* mutant is likely due to redundancy. More recently, researchers identified an *FHY1* homolog called *FHL*; the double loss-of-function mutant (*fhy1 fhl*) is indistinguishable from the *phyA* mutant, indicating that PHYA requires FHY1 and FHL for complete function (150).

FHY1 and *FHL* encode 202-amino-acid and 181-amino-acid proteins, respectively, both of which contain a NLS and a nuclear exclusion signal (NES) at their N termini and a septin-related domain (SRD) at their C termini (26, 150). In vitro binding assays show that the two proteins are capable of both homo- and heterodimerization through their C-terminal domains (150). The NLS and SRD are functionally important, because the removal of those domains disrupts the function of FHY1 (149).

FHY1 and FHL are required for the nuclear localization of PHYA-GFP; this nuclear localization is significantly reduced in the *fhy1* mutant and is virtually absent in *fhy1 FHL* RNA interference (RNAi) lines under both high irradiance response (HIR) and VLFR conditions (40, 41). The nuclear localization of PHYB, however, is not affected in these mutants, indicating that FHY1 and FHL are needed for the nuclear localization of PHYA, but not PHYB. The role of FHY1 in the nuclear localization of PHYA is associated with its ability to interact with the

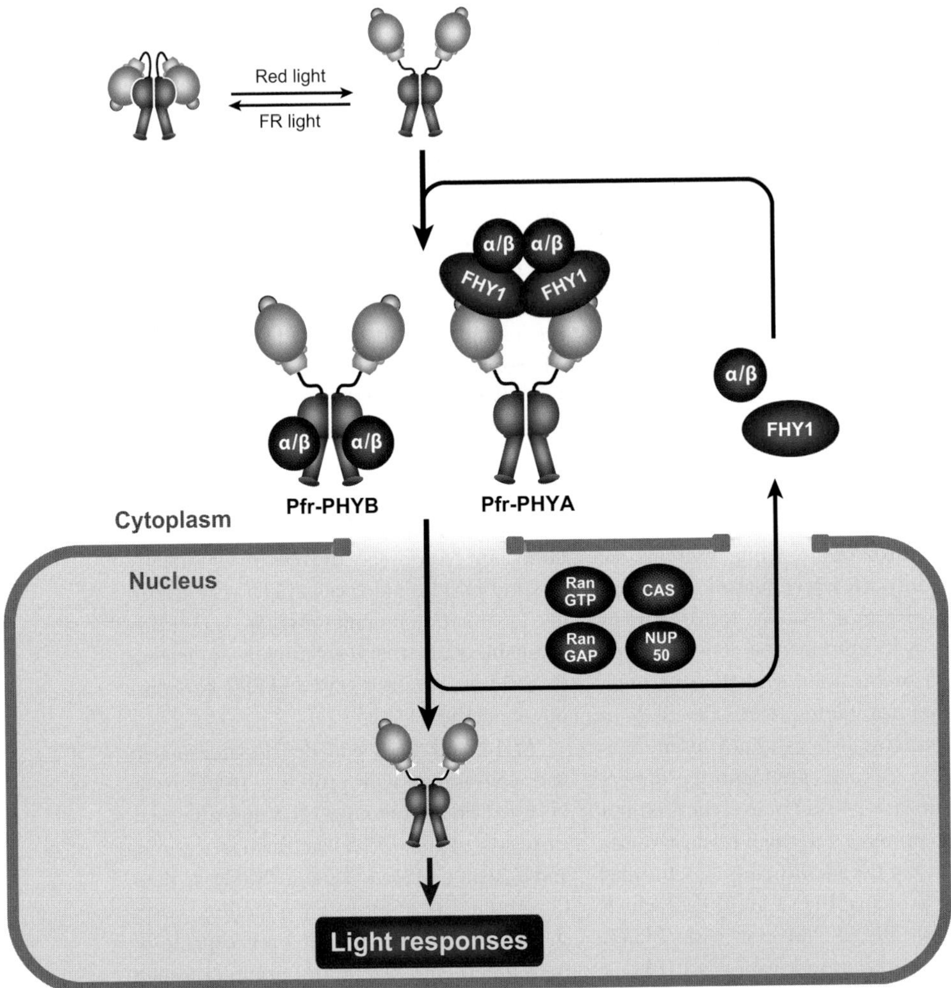

Figure 4

Regulation of phytochrome nuclear localization by two phytochrome-interacting proteins, FAR-RED ELONGATED HYPOCOTYL 1 (FHY1) and FHY1-LIKE (FHL). The involvement of importins (α/β) and other general components [RanGTP, nucleoporin 50 (NUP50), cellular apoptosis susceptibility (CAS), and RanGAP] has not been proven yet. FHL is not shown in the figure. FR, far-red; Pfr, C15-*E,anti* conformation of phytochrome.

Pfr form of this phytochrome. The interaction between the Pfr form of PHYA and FHY1/FHL occurs through the N-terminal domain of PHYA (amino acids 1–406) and the SRD of FHY1/FHL, as shown by yeast two-hybrid screening and in vitro binding assays (40). The interaction is further corroborated by the colocalization of YFP-FHY1/FHL and PHYA-CFP in nuclear speckles.

These findings indicate that the following sequence of events occurs in the nuclear translocation of PHYA (**Figure 4**): absorption of light by phytochromobilin → photoisomerization and accompanying structural changes that expose the N-terminal domain → binding of FHY1/FHL to the exposed N-terminal domain → translocation of the PHYA-FHY1/FHL complex into the nucleus via the NLS of FHY1/FHL → formation of nuclear speckles. As noted, the above-described sequence holds true only for PHYA, because the nuclear translocation of PHYB does not require the function of FHY1 and FHL (41). However, photoisomerization also likely exposes the N- and C-terminal domains of PHYB (16). Because the exposed C-terminal domain of PHYB contains a functional NLS (16, 103), the Pfr form of PHYB might be functionally equivalent to the PHYA-FHY1/FHL complex.

A few additional results indicate the need for further functional characterization of FHY1 and FHL. First, YFP-FHY1 and YFP-FHL both form nuclear speckles with PHYA-CFP in a manner that suggests the formation of stable, not temporary, complexes inside the nucleus (41). If FHY1 and FHL merely act to carry PHYA into the nucleus, they should dissociate from PHYA in the nucleus and return to the cytosol for another round of translocation. Second, PHYA promotes the degradation of the FHY1 protein through the 26S proteasome (109). This degradation could be a part of a negative feedback loop, but additional studies are required to examine why PHYA would help to degrade its carrier. Overexpression of constitutively nuclear-localized PHYA in the *fhy1 fhl* double mutant will be informative as to whether the function of FHY1/FHL is limited to the translocation of PHYA into the nucleus.

Phytochrome-Interacting Proteins That Modulate the Output Activity of Phytochromes

Some phytochrome-interacting proteins modulate the signaling output of phytochromes under a given light condition (**Figure 5**). Because the Pfr form is the biologically active form, some proteins are expected to interact with the Pfr form and regulate its output activity by either altering the concentration of Pfr or modulating its ability to transmit signals to downstream components. The phytochrome output activity can also be modulated either by altering its affinity for its downstream component or by changing its transmitting activity. Functionally, the expression levels or activities of these interacting proteins in a given plant cell will determine the signal output by phytochromes, allowing phytochrome signaling to be fine tuned in accordance with the plant's developmental and physiological status.

ARR4, which binds to PHYB and stabilizes the Pfr form, was the first identified phytochrome-interacting protein that modulates the output activity of phytochromes (120). *Arabidopsis* contains 10 type-A *Arabidopsis* response regulators (ARRs), which act as negative regulators of cytokinin signaling (123). Inspired by the histidine kinase activity of cyanobacterial phytochrome (CphI) (148), ARR4 was selected as a candidate for a signaling protein because the ARR4 protein is accumulated by red light in a PHYB-dependent manner. ARR4 binds to the N-terminal end of PHYB (amino acids 1–137), as proven by in vitro binding assays, in vivo coimmunoprecipitation analysis, and yeast two-hybrid experiments. The binding of ARR4 inhibits the dark reversion of PHYB in both yeast and plants. An aspartate residue of ARR4 is phosphorylated by cytokinin receptors. Interestingly, a mutated ARR4 (ARR^{D95N}) cannot inhibit dark reversion (77), suggesting that the ability to inhibit dark reversion is dependent on the phosphorylation of an aspartate residue. Consistent with their molecular characteristics, overexpression of ARR4 but not ARR^{D95N} is associated with shorter hypocotyl length under red light. Taken together, these studies show that ARR4 binds to the Pfr form of PHYB and increases its output activity by inhibiting the dark reversion rate of PHYB.

A few other interacting proteins that modulate phytochrome output activity have been identified (**Figure 5**). COP1 binds to PHYA and decreases PHYA output activity by decreasing the total PHYA concentration (P_t) (104). PAPP5 binds to both PHYA

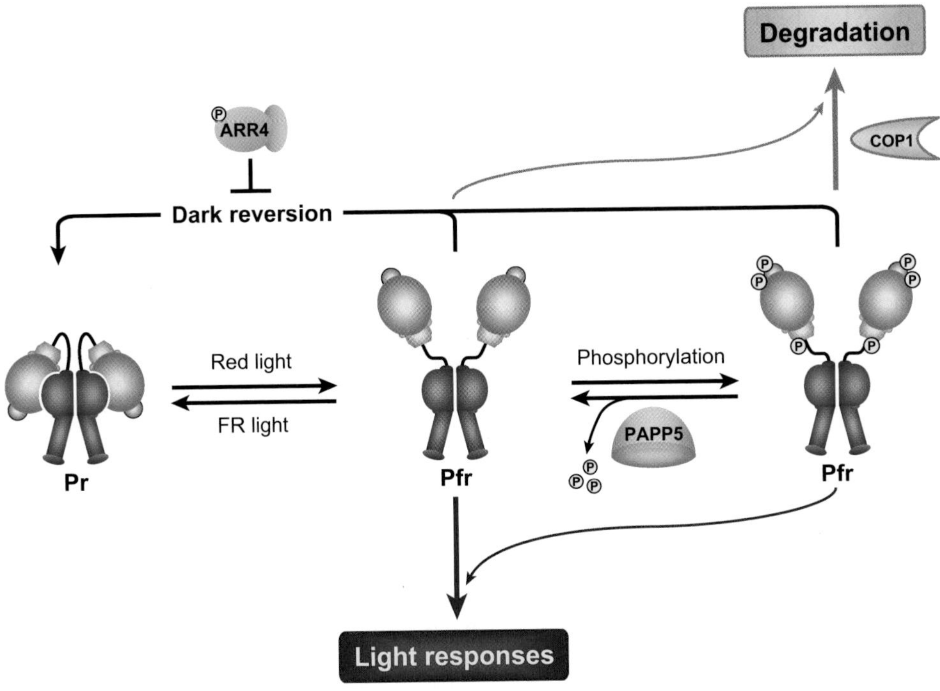

Figure 5

Modulation of phytochrome (PHY) output activity by three representative phytochrome-interacting proteins, *ARABIDOPSIS* RESPONSE REGULATOR 4 (ARR4), CONSTITUTIVE PHOTOMORPHOGENIC 1 (COP1), and PHYTOCHROME ASSOCIATED PHOSPHATASE 5 (PAPP5). ARR4 specifically inhibits the dark reversion of PHYB, whereas COP1 ubiquitinates the Pfr form of PHYA. Whether the Pfr form (C15-*E,anti* conformation) of PHYB is also ubiquitinated by COP1 is unknown. FR, far-red; Pr, C15-*Z,anti* conformation of PHY.

and PHYB and preferentially dephosphorylates the Pfr form (101). The dephosphorylation of phytochromes by PAPP5 increases their affinity for the interacting proteins nucleoside diphosphate kinase 2 (NDPK2) and PIF3, increases the stability of PHYA, and increases the stability of the Pfr form, suggesting that PAPP5 is a versatile regulator that enhances phytochrome output activity.

Phytochrome-Interacting Proteins Whose Activities are Modulated by Phytochromes

Some phytochrome-interacting proteins directly regulate the light responses, allowing the phytochromes to indirectly regulate various light responses by binding to these proteins and modulating their activities. This class of interacting proteins includes basic helix-loop-helix transcription factors such as PIF3 and PIF3-like 5 (PIL5), as well as other proteins such as COP1 (**Figure 6**).

PIF3 was the first phytochrome-interacting protein to be identified, and its characterization provides a framework for understanding how phytochromes regulate their downstream components. PIF3 was originally identified by yeast two-hybrid screening that used the C-terminal domain (amino acids 645–1210) of PHYB as bait (83). The binding between PIF3 and phytochromes (PHYA and PHYB) was further confirmed by numerous in vitro binding

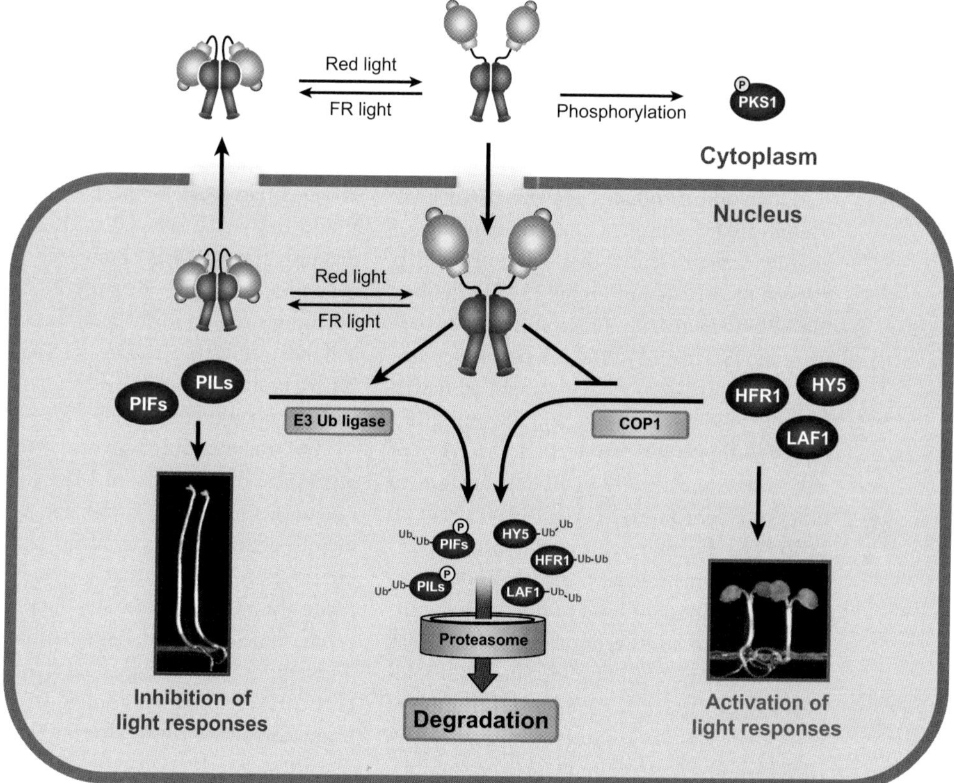

Figure 6

Activation of light responses by phytochromes (PHY) and their interacting proteins. Light responses are repressed in the dark, because negative components such as phytochrome-interacting factors (PIFs)/PIF3-like proteins (PILs) inhibit light responses, whereas positive components such as LONG HYPOCOTYL IN FAR-RED 1 (HFR1), LONG HYPOCOTYL 5 (HY5), and LONG AFTER FAR-RED LIGHT 1 (LAF1) are degraded by the nuclear-localized CONSTITUTIVE PHOTOMORPHOGENIC 1 (COP1). Upon irradiation, the Pfr forms (C15-*E,anti* conformation) of phytochromes initiate cytosolic light responses by binding cytosolic interacting proteins such as PHYTOCHROME KINASE SUBSTRATE (PKS1) or enter the nucleus with (PHYA) or without (PHYB) the help of FAR-RED ELONGATED HYPOCOTYL 1 (FHY1) or FHY1-LIKE (FHL). In the nucleus, the Pfr forms activate the degradation of PIFs/PILs through an unidentified E3 ubiquitin (Ub) ligase and inhibit COP1 by excluding it from the nucleus. Owing to decreasing levels of negative components and increasing levels of positive components, light responses are initiated. FR, far-red.

assays and in vivo colocalization analysis (7, 73, 151). Although PIF3 was identified using the C-terminal domain of PHYB, the mapping of the interacting domains shows that PIF3-PHYB binding is not confined to the C-terminal domain of PHYB. In vitro binding assays and yeast two-hybrid analysis supplemented with chromophore show that both the PHYB C-terminal domain alone and the N-terminal domain alone are sufficient for PIF3 binding (84, 110, 151). However, the exact location of this binding activity remains unclear. Deletion of the N-terminal 90 amino acids and the C-terminal 50 amino acids of PHYB virtually eliminates the interaction (151). Loss-of-function missense mutations in the PAS-A and PAS-B domain of PHYB (A776V, G793R, and E838K) also inhibit the interaction between PIF3 and PHYB (83, 84). Taken together, the results suggest that although N- and C-terminal fragments of PHYB can bind to PIF3 individually, overall structural integrity of PHYB is required for proper binding.

The binding domains of PIF3 also display complicated features. Updated mapping of binding domains shows that a part of the PIL domain of PIF3 (amino acids 13–59), dubbed the APB (for active phytochrome binding motif; amino acids 27–39), but not the putative PAS domain, is necessary and sufficient for the binding between PHYB and PIF3 (53). Binding assays show that the APB of PIF3 binds specifically to PHYB but not to other phytochromes (PHYA, PHYC, PHYD, or PHYE). Further yeast two-hybrid experiments supplemented with chromophore show that PHYA does not bind to the APB, but instead binds to another motif called the APA (for active PHYA binding motif; amino acids 193–210 of PIF3) (2). Alanine substitution of two phenylalanine residues within the APA (F203A and F209A) eliminates the binding. It should be noted that the APA motif contining two phenylalanines is not present in other PIF/PIL proteins except for a distantly related amino acid sequence found in PIL5, suggesting that the APA motif and the functionality of its two phenylalanine residues could be specific to PIF3. Thus, although both PHYA and PHYB bind to PIF3, the precise interacting domains or motifs have not yet been clearly resolved.

The functional significance of this binding is the degradation of PIF3. Red light irradiation causes rapid degradation of PIF3, as shown by the disappearance of both endogenous PIF3 and overexpressed PIF3 tagged with GFP or myc upon irradiation with red or far-red light (7, 95). PHYA is responsible for the rapid degradation of PIF3 in response to far-red light, whereas PHYA, PHYB, and PHYD are responsible for this degradation in response to red light. The degradation of PIF3 is partly associated with the nuclear speckles seen in GFP-tagged phytochromes, as shown by the rapid colocalization of PHY-YFP and PIF3-CFP and the subsequent disappearance of the PIF3-CFP signal upon irradiation. Early nuclear speckle formation (2 min after the red pulse) by PHYB is disrupted in the *pif3* mutant *photocurrent 1* (*poc1*); however, late nuclear speckle formation (6 h after a red pulse) is not disrupted, indicating that only the early PHYB nuclear speckles are dependent on PIF3. Because N651G-GUS-NLS does not form nuclear speckles (76), it will be interesting to see if N651G-GUS-NLS can still activate the degradation of PIF3 without forming nuclear speckles.

Treatment with 26S proteasome inhibitors blocks the degradation of PIF3 following irradiation (95). Because the 26S proteasome mainly degrades ubiquitinated proteins, this observation suggests that phytochromes activate the ubquitination and subsequent 26S proteasome-mediated degradation of PIF3. This hypothesis is supported by the appearance of very high molecular weight PIF3-immunoreactive bands after light irradiation, and these bands cross-react with an antiubiquitin antibody. Similar to PIF3, a few other phytochrome-interacting bHLH proteins, including PIL2/PIF6, PIF4, PIL5/PIF1, and PIL6/PIF5, are also degraded through the 26S proteasome by light (85, 89, 108), indicating that phytochromes activate degradation of PIFs/PILs by promoting ubiquitination.

The molecular mechanisms by which phytochromes activate the degradation of PIF3 are not clearly understood. The light-mediated activation of phytochromes causes the rapid appearance of higher molecular weight PIF3 bands (2 min after red pulse) in sodium dodecyl sulfate (SDS) gels (2). These band shifts are abolished in the *phyA phyB* double mutant, which also shows significantly reduced PIF3 degradation. Similarly, deletion of the phytochrome-binding motifs of PIF3 abrogates both the band shifts and the degradation, suggesting that the band shifts are correlated with PIF3 degradation. Phosphatase treatment causes the shifted bands to disappear, suggesting that the band shift is caused by phosphorylation. The experimental evidence present in the literature, however, makes it difficult to distinguish whether the phosphatase treatment converts the shifted bands to the lower band versus selectively degrading the shifted bands. In addition, the shifted bands are not a single molecular weight band, but rather form a multiple band continuum (95). Within 30 minutes after light treatment, PIF3 can be detected as a high molecular weight smear, suggesting that the band shift is not a single event. The initial small band shift may be caused by phosphorylation and the later higher molecular weight bands could be caused by other modifications, such as ubiquitination. Because phytochromes can phosphorylate PIF3 in vitro, it is tempting to postulate that activated phytochromes bind and phosphorylate PIF3, which may then be ubiquitinated by an E3 ubiquitin (Ub) ligase, leading to degradation by the 26S proteasome. Future characterization of the various shifted bands will help clarify the sequence of molecular events that leads to degradation of PIF3.

Irrespective of the underlying molecular mechanism, the degradation of PIF3 and other PIFs/PILs by light likely inhibits the function of PIFs/PILs. PIF3 acts as a negative component in both PHYA- and PHYB-mediated seedling de-etiolation processes such as hook opening, whereas it selectively acts as a negative component in PHYB-mediated inhibition of hypocotyl elongation (54). In adult plants, overexpression of PIF3 causes elongated petioles, pale green leaves, and early flowering, which is also observed in the *phyB* mutant. Two potential exceptions are anthocyanin biosynthesis under far-red light and chloroplast development during the dark-light transition. PIF3 positively regulates anthocyanin biosynthesis under far-red light by directly binding to the promoters of anthocyanin biosynthetic genes via G-box elements, and activating their transcription in the presence of HY5 (LONG HYPOCOTYL 5), a basic leucine zipper (bZIP) transcription factor (111). However, because the level of PIF3 protein in continuous far-red light is similar to that in the dark, it is difficult to infer the precise functional relationship between PIF3 and phytochromes during the expression of anthocyanin biosynthetic genes. In chloroplast development, PIF3 is suggested to act as a positive component, especially when etiolated seedlings are transferred to light (80). More careful examination, however, indicates that the seemingly retarded chloroplast development in the *pif3* mutant is due to light-induced bleaching rather than retarded chloroplast development (G. Choi, unpublished data). Thus, PIF3 inhibits all tested light responses in the dark and phytochromes release this inhibition by removing PIF3. Other PIFs/PILs that are degraded by light also mainly act to inhibit light responses in the dark (35, 43, 44, 87). Consistent with their roles in the dark, a *pif3 pif4 pil5 pil6* quadruple mutant is constitutively photomorphogenic even in the dark (G. Choi, unpublished data). Collectively, the apparently negative roles played by the PIFs/PILs suggest that phytochromes induce light responses by degrading negative light signaling components such as PIF3 (**Figure 6**).

Phytochromes also bind to COP1, a master repressor of photomorphogenesis, and negatively regulate COP1 activity in the light (142). The *cop1* mutant was identified as a constitutively photomorphogenetic mutant together with other *cop/de-etiolated* (*det*)/*fusca* (*fus*) mutants (24). Molecular characterization shows that *COP1* encodes a protein with a N-terminal RING finger domain followed by a coiled-coil motif and a WD-40 repeat domain (25). COP1 acts as an E3 Ub ligase that ubiquitinates at least three positive light-signaling transcription factors, HY5, LAF1 (LONG AFTER FAR-RED LIGHT 1), and HFR1 (LONG HYPOCOTYL IN FAR-RED 1) (49, 102, 105, 144). Because phytochromes inhibit COP1 activity partially by excluding COP1 from the nucleus (91, 129), three positive light signaling transcription factors are selectively degraded in the dark and accumulated in the light (29, 42, 93, 105, 144). Apparently, COP1 ubiquitinates and degrades these factors in conjunction with other COP/DET/FUS proteins which are components of the CDD complex (consisting of COP10, DET1, and DDB1) or the COP9 signalosome (CSN) complex (consisting of CSN1 to CSN8) and other RING finger proteins, such as SPA1 (14, 102, 143). The inhibition of COP1 activity by phytochromes and the subsequent accumulation of positive light signaling transcription factors play important roles in the induction of light responses in the light (29, 49, 92, 105). Microarray analysis shows that COP1-regulated genes largely overlap with light-regulated genes (71), further suggesting that COP1 is a master repressor of photomorphogenesis and phytochromes promote photomorphogenesis partly by inhibiting COP1 activity. Thus, phytochromes induce light responses partly by removing negative light signaling transcription factors such as PIFs/PILs through protein degradation and partly by accumulating positive light signaling transcription factors such as HFR1, HY5, and LAF1 by nuclear exclusion of COP1 (**Figure 6**).

THE FLOW OF LIGHT INFORMATION DURING SEED GERMINATION

The overall flow of light information through phytochromes and their interacting proteins to the final light responses can be better exemplified by the regulation of PIL5 (also known as PIF1 and bHLH015) by phytochromes during seed germination (**Figure 7**). Phytochromes promote seed germination partly by increasing bioactive gibberellic acid (GA) levels in seeds (61, 86). The increased GA levels are caused by transcriptional activation of GA biosynthetic genes and transcriptional repression of GA catabolic genes (86). Because phytochromes are not transcription factors per se, it was expected that some phytochrome-interacting proteins may mediate light signaling to modulate GA biosynthesis. PIL5 serves this role.

PIL5 negatively regulates seed germination by inhibiting GA biosynthesis and GA signaling while simultaneously activating abscisic acid (ABA) biosynthesis. PIL5 inhibits GA biosynthesis by repressing two GA synthetic genes (*GA3ox1* and *GA3ox2*) and activating a GA catabolic gene (*GA2ox2*), resulting in lower GA levels in seeds (89, 96). Similarly, PIL5 activates ABA biosynthesis by activating ABA biosynthetic genes (*ABA1*, *NCED6*, and *NCED9*) and repressing an ABA catabolic gene (*CYP707A2*), increasing the ABA levels in seeds (88). In addition, PIL5 also activates the expression of two DELLA genes [*GIBBERELLIC ACID INSENSITIVE* (*GAI*) and *REPRESSOR OF GA 1-3* (*RGA*)], which are key negative GA signaling components (88). Chromatin immunoprecipitation analysis shows that of all the PIL5-regulated genes, PIL5 binds directly to the promoters of only the two DELLA genes, *GAI* and *RGA*, suggesting that PIL5 regulates *GAI* and *RGA* directly, whereas it regulates other biosynthetic genes indirectly. Owing to decreased GA levels, increased DELLA protein levels, and increased ABA levels, seeds do not germinate in the dark.

Phytochromes promote seed germination by inhibiting PIL5 activity. The expression levels of all the abovementioned genes are regulated oppositely by phytochromes in seeds, and this regulation is not present in the *pil5* mutant, suggesting that phytochromes regulate these genes by inhibiting PIL5 activity (88). How do phytochromes inhibit PIL5 activity? Upon light irradiation, the Pfr forms of both PHYA and PHYB enter the nucleus, bind to PIL5, and activate its degradation by the 26S proteasome (43, 87, 89, 108). The effect of PIL5 degradation by phytochromes can be seen in the regulation of PIL5 direct target genes (88). The expression levels of *GAI* and *RGA* genes are high in the

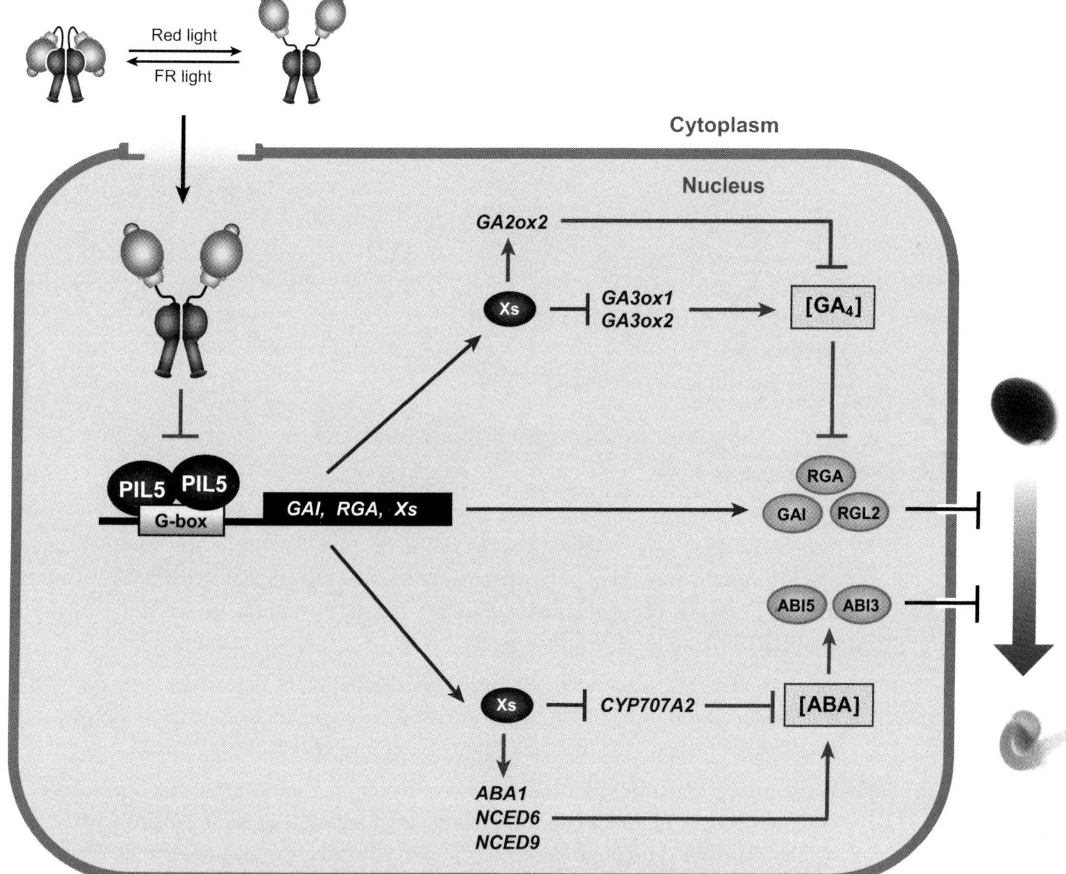

Figure 7

The flow of light information during seed germination. In the dark, PHYTOCHROME-INTERACTING FACTOR 3 (PIF3)-LIKE 5 (PIL5) activates the expression of *GIBBERELLIC ACID INSENSITIVE* (*GAI*), *REPRESSOR OF GA 1-3* (*RGA*), and other unknown factors (*Xs*), by binding directly to their promoters through G-box elements. The unknown factors repress gibberellic acid (GA) biosynthetic and abscisic acid (ABA) catabolic genes and activate GA catabolic and ABA biosynthetic genes, resulting in decreased GA levels and increased ABA levels. The decrease in GA levels further stabilizes GAI and RGA proteins, leading to the suppression of GA responses. The increase in ABA increases the levels of ABA insensitive 3 (ABI3) and ABI5, leading to the activation of ABA responses. Upon light irradiation, the Pfr form of phytochrome (C15-*E,anti* conformation) binds PIL5 and activates the degradation of PIL5. The decreased level of PIL5 translates to decreased levels of GAI, RGA, and X factors, resulting in increased GA levels and decreased ABA levels. Owing to changes in hormone levels and signaling components, seeds start to germinate. Red lines signify events occurring at the protein level, blue lines show events occurring at the transcriptional level, and green lines show events occurring via enzyme activities. RGL, RGA-like. Adapted from Reference 88.

dark; upon light irradiation, PIL5 is rapidly degraded and consequently the expression levels of *GAI* and *RGA* genes decrease. Degradation of PIL5 is further accompanied by altered expressions of GA and ABA biosynthetic genes resulting in increased GA levels and decreased ABA levels. Owing to increased GA levels, decreased DELLA protein levels, and ABA levels, seeds start to germinate in the light.

Taken together, the overall flow of light information during seed germination can be summarized as follows:

1. Light causes the photoisomerization of phytochromobilin.
2. Photoisomerization causes structural changes in phytochromes.
3. Light information is represented by the concentration of Pfr.
4. Pfr enters the nucleus either alone (PHYB) or with the help of FHY1/FHL (PHYA).
5. In the nucleus, Pfr removes PIL5 by initiating its degradation, thus the concentration of Pfr is translated into the level of PIL5.
6. The level of PIL5 is translated into the levels of two plant hormones, GA and ABA, and levels of their signaling components.
7. In response to changing hormonal levels and levels of signaling components, seeds germinate.

FUTURE ISSUES

1. Which biochemical/molecular activities of phytochromes are sufficient to induce light responses? This issue is closely associated with the question of how phytochromes activate the degradation of phytochrome interacting factors (PIFs)/PIF3-like proteins (PILs). Does this occur through kinase activity, or do phytochromes act as adaptor molecules linking the PIFs/PILs to the protein degradation machinery?
2. How are PIFs/PILs degraded? Because the degradation of PIFs/PILs is an important mechanism through which light information is converted to biological signals, it is essential to elucidate the molecular mechanism of PIF/PIL degradation.
3. What are the functional relationships between phytochrome-interacting proteins and other genetically identified light signaling components? Light information processed by phytochromes and phytochrome-interacting proteins must go through a plethora of genetic networks to induce the final responses. Can we define a specific genetic network for each light response?

DISCLOSURE STATEMENT

The authors are not aware of any biases that might be perceived as affecting the objectivity of this review.

ACKNOWLEDGMENTS

We thank lab members for critical reading of the manuscript. Our work is partially supported by the Korea Science and Engineering Foundation (R0A-2007-000-20024-0, PF06302–03, M10601000088).

LITERATURE CITED

1. Abe H, Yamamoto K, Nagatani A, Furuya M. 1985. Characterization of green tissue-specific phytochrome isolated immunologically from pea seedlings. *Plant Cell Physiol.* 26:1387–99

2. Al-Sady B, Ni W, Kircher S, Schäfer E, Quail PH. 2006. Photoactivated phytochrome induces rapid PIF3 phosphorylation prior to proteasome-mediated degradation. *Mol. Cell* 23:439–46
3. Aukerman MJ, Hirschfeld M, Wester L, Weaver M, Clack T, et al. 1997. A deletion in the *PHYD* gene of the *Arabidopsis* Wassilewskija ecotype defines a role for phytochrome D in red/far-red light sensing. *Plant Cell* 9:1317–26
4. Balasubramanian S, Sureshkumar S, Agrawal M, Michael TP, Wessinger C, et al. 2006. The *PHYTOCHROME C* photoreceptor gene mediates natural variation in flowering and growth responses of *Arabidopsis thaliana*. *Nat. Genet.* 38:711–15
5. Barnes SA, Nishizawa NK, Quaggio RB, Whitelam GC, Chua NH. 1996. Far-red light blocks greening of *Arabidopsis* seedlings via a phytochrome A-mediated change in plastid development. *Plant Cell* 8:601–15
6. Barnes SA, Quaggio RB, Whitelam GC, Chua NH. 1996. fhy1 defines a branch point in phytochrome A signal transduction pathways for gene expression. *Plant J.* 10:1155–61
7. Bauer D, Viczian A, Kircher S, Nobis T, Nitschke R, et al. 2004. Constitutive photomorphogenesis 1 and multiple photoreceptors control degradation of phytochrome interacting factor 3, a transcription factor required for light signaling in *Arabidopsis*. *Plant Cell* 16:1433–45
8. Bohlenius H, Huang T, Charbonnel-Campaa L, Brunner AM, Jansson S, et al. 2006. CO/FT regulatory module controls timing of flowering and seasonal growth cessation in trees. *Science* 312:1040–43
9. Borthwick HA, Hendricks SB, Parker MW, Toole EH, Toole VK. 1952. A reversible photoreaction controlling seed germination. *Proc. Natl. Acad. Sci. USA* 38:662–63
10. Boylan M, Quail PH. 1996. Are the phytochromes protein kinase? *Protoplasma* 195:12–17
11. Boylan MT, Quail PH. 1991. Phytochrome A overexpression inhibits hypocotyl elongation in transgenic *Arabidopsis*. *Proc. Natl. Acad. Sci. USA* 88:10806–10
12. Casal JJ, Davis SJ, Kirchenbauer D, Viczian A, Yanovsky MJ, et al. 2002. The serine-rich N-terminal domain of oat phytochrome A helps regulate light responses and subnuclear localization of the photoreceptor. *Plant Physiol.* 129:1127–37
13. Cerdan PD, Yanovsky MJ, Reymundo FC, Nagatani A, Staneloni RJ, et al. 1999. Regulation of phytochrome B signaling by phytochrome A and FHY1 in *Arabidopsis thaliana*. *Plant J.* 18:499–507
14. Chen H, Shen Y, Tang X, Yu L, Wang J, et al. 2006. *Arabidopsis* CULLIN4 forms an E3 ubiquitin ligase with RBX1 and the CDD complex in mediating light control of development. *Plant Cell* 18:1991–2004
15. Chen M, Schwab R, Chory J. 2003. Characterization of the requirements for localization of phytochrome B to nuclear bodies. *Proc. Natl. Acad. Sci. USA* 100:14493–98
16. Chen M, Tao Y, Lim J, Shaw A, Chory J. 2005. Regulation of phytochrome B nuclear localization through light-dependent unmasking of nuclear-localization signals. *Curr. Biol.* 15:637–42
17. Cherry JR, Hondred D, Walker JM, Vierstra RD. 1992. Phytochrome requires the 6-kDa N-terminal domain for full biological activity. *Proc. Natl. Acad. Sci. USA* 89:5039–43
18. Christie JM. 2007. Phototropin blue-light receptors. *Annu. Rev. Plant Biol.* 58:21–45
19. Christie JM, Reymond P, Powell GK, Bernasconi P, Raibekas AA, et al. 1998. *Arabidopsis* NPH1: a flavoprotein with the properties of a photoreceptor for phototropism. *Science* 282:1698–701

20. Clack T, Mathews S, Sharrock RA. 1994. The phytochrome apoprotein family in *Arabidopsis* is encoded by five genes: the sequences and expression of *PHYD* and *PHYE*. *Plant. Mol. Biol.* 25:413–27
21. Correll MJ, Kiss JZ. 2005. The roles of phytochromes in elongation and gravitropism of roots. *Plant Cell Physiol.* 46:317–23
22. Deforce L, Tokutomi S, Song PS. 1994. Phototransformation of pea phytochrome A induces an increase in α-helical folding of the apoprotein: comparison with a monocot phytochrome A and CD analysis by different methods. *Biochemistry* 33:4918–22
23. Dehesh K, Franci C, Parks BM, Seeley KA, Short TW, et al. 1993. *Arabidopsis* HY8 locus encodes phytochrome A. *Plant Cell* 5:1081–88
24. Deng XW, Caspar T, Quail PH. 1991. *cop1*: a regulatory locus involved in light-controlled development and gene expression in *Arabidopsis*. *Genes Dev.* 5:1172–82
25. Deng XW, Matsui M, Wei N, Wagner D, Chu AM, et al. 1992. *COP1*, an *Arabidopsis* regulatory gene, encodes a protein with both a zinc-binding motif and a G β homologous domain. *Cell* 71:791–801
26. Desnos T, Puente P, Whitelam GC, Harberd NP. 2001. FHY1: a phytochrome A-specific signal transducer. *Genes Dev.* 15:2980–90
27. Devlin PF, Patel SR, Whitelam GC. 1998. Phytochrome E influences internode elongation and flowering time in *Arabidopsis*. *Plant Cell* 10:1479–87
28. Devlin PF, Robson PR, Patel SR, Goosey L, Sharrock RA, Whitelam GC. 1999. Phytochrome D acts in the shade-avoidance syndrome in *Arabidopsis* by controlling elongation growth and flowering time. *Plant Physiol.* 119:909–15
29. Duek PD, Elmer MV, van Oosten VR, Fankhauser C. 2004. The degradation of HFR1, a putative bHLH class transcription factor involved in light signaling, is regulated by phosphorylation and requires COP1. *Curr. Biol.* 14:2296–301
30. Edgerton MD, Jones AM. 1992. Localization of protein-protein interactions between subunits of phytochrome. *Plant Cell* 4:161–71
31. Eitoku T, Zarate X, Kozhukh GV, Kim JI, Song PS, Terazima M. 2006. Time-resolved detection of conformational changes in oat phytochrome A: time-dependent diffusion. *Biophys. J.* 91:3797–804
32. Franklin KA, Allen T, Whitelam GC. 2007. Phytochrome A is an irradiance-dependent red light sensor. *Plant J.* 50:108–17
33. Franklin KA, Davis SJ, Stoddart WM, Vierstra RD, Whitelam GC. 2003. Mutant analyses define multiple roles for phytochrome C in *Arabidopsis* photomorphogenesis. *Plant Cell* 15:1981–89
34. Franklin KA, Whitelam G. 2007. Red:far-red ratio perception and shade avoidance. In *Light and Plant Development*, ed. G Whitelam, K Halliday, pp. 211–34. Oxford: Blackwell
35. Fujimori T, Yamashino T, Kato T, Mizuno T. 2004. Circadian-controlled basic/helix-loop-helix factor, PIL6, implicated in light-signal transduction in *Arabidopsis thaliana*. *Plant Cell Physiol.* 45:1078–86
36. Furuya M. 1989. Molecular properties and biogenesis of phytochrome I and II. *Adv. Biophys.* 25:133–67
37. Handwerger KE, Gall JG. 2006. Subnuclear organelles: new insights into form and function. *Trends Cell Biol.* 16:19–26
38. Hayama R, Yokoi S, Tamaki S, Yano M, Shimamoto K. 2003. Adaptation of photoperiodic control pathways produces short-day flowering in rice. *Nature* 422:719–22
39. Hennig L, Stoddart WM, Dieterle M, Whitelam GC, Schafer E. 2002. Phytochrome E controls light-induced germination of *Arabidopsis*. *Plant Physiol.* 128:194–200

40. Hiltbrunner A, Tscheuschler A, Viczian A, Kunkel T, Kircher S, Schafer E. 2006. FHY1 and FHL act together to mediate nuclear accumulation of the phytochrome A photoreceptor. *Plant Cell Physiol.* 47:1023–34
41. Hiltbrunner A, Viczian A, Bury E, Tscheuschler A, Kircher S, et al. 2005. Nuclear accumulation of the phytochrome A photoreceptor requires FHY1. *Curr. Biol.* 15:2125–30
42. Holm M, Ma LG, Qu LJ, Deng XW. 2002. Two interacting bZIP proteins are direct targets of COP1-mediated control of light-dependent gene expression in *Arabidopsis*. *Genes Dev.* 16:1247–59
43. Huq E, Al-Sady B, Hudson M, Kim C, Apel K, Quail PH. 2004. Phytochrome-interacting factor 1 is a critical bHLH regulator of chlorophyll biosynthesis. *Science* 305:1937–41
44. Huq E, Quail PH. 2002. PIF4, a phytochrome-interacting bHLH factor, functions as a negative regulator of phytochrome B signaling in *Arabidopsis*. *EMBO J.* 21:2441–50
45. Imaizumi T, Kay SA. 2006. Photoperiodic control of flowering: not only by coincidence. *Trends Plant Sci.* 11:550–58
46. Imaizumi T, Schultz TF, Harmon FG, Ho LA, Kay SA. 2005. FKF1 F-box protein mediates cyclic degradation of a repressor of CONSTANS in *Arabidopsis*. *Science* 309:293–97
47. Imaizumi T, Tran HG, Swartz TE, Briggs WR, Kay SA. 2003. FKF1 is essential for photoperiodic-specific light signalling in *Arabidopsis*. *Nature* 426:302–6
48. Izawa T, Oikawa T, Sugiyama N, Tanisaka T, Yano M, Shimamoto K. 2002. Phytochrome mediates the external light signal to repress FT orthologs in photoperiodic flowering of rice. *Genes Dev.* 16:2006–20
49. Jang IC, Yang JY, Seo HS, Chua NH. 2005. HFR1 is targeted by COP1 E3 ligase for post-translational proteolysis during phytochrome A signaling. *Genes Dev.* 19:593–602
50. Johnson E, Bradley M, Harberd NP, Whitelam GC. 1994. Photoresponses of light-grown *phyA* mutants of *Arabidopsis* (phytochrome A is required for the perception of daylength extensions). *Plant Physiol.* 105:141–49
51. Jones AM, Quail PH. 1986. Quaternary structure of 124-kDa phytochrome from *Avena sativa* L. *Biochemistry* 25:2987–95
52. Kawai H, Kanegae T, Christensen S, Kiyosue T, Sato Y, et al. 2003. Responses of ferns to red light are mediated by an unconventional photoreceptor. *Nature* 421:287–90
53. Khanna R, Huq E, Kikis EA, Al-Sady B, Lanzatella C, Quail PH. 2004. A novel molecular recognition motif necessary for targeting photoactivated phytochrome signaling to specific basic helix-loop-helix transcription factors. *Plant Cell* 16:3033–44
54. Kim J, Yi H, Choi G, Shin B, Song PS, Choi G. 2003. Functional characterization of phytochrome interacting factor 3 in phytochrome-mediated light signal transduction. *Plant Cell* 15:2399–407
55. Kim JI, Shen Y, Han YJ, Park JE, Kirchenbauer D, et al. 2004. Phytochrome phosphorylation modulates light signaling by influencing the protein-protein interaction. *Plant Cell* 16:2629–40
56. Kimura M, Kagawa T. 2006. Phototropin and light-signaling in phototropism. *Curr. Opin. Plant Biol.* 9:503–8
57. Kircher S, Gil P, Kozma-Bognar L, Fejes E, Speth V, et al. 2002. Nucleocytoplasmic partitioning of the plant photoreceptors phytochrome A, B, C, D, and E is regulated differentially by light and exhibits a diurnal rhythm. *Plant Cell* 14:1541–55
58. Kircher S, Kozma-Bognar L, Kim L, Adam E, Harter K, et al. 1999. Light quality-dependent nuclear import of the plant photoreceptors phytochrome A and B. *Plant Cell* 11:1445–56

59. Kiss JZ, Mullen JL, Correll MJ, Hangarter RP. 2003. Phytochromes A and B mediate red-light-induced positive phototropism in roots. *Plant Physiol.* 131:1411–17
60. Kleiner O, Kircher S, Harter K, Batschauer A. 1999. Nuclear localization of the *Arabidopsis* blue light receptor cryptochrome 2. *Plant J.* 19:289–96
61. Koornneef M, van der Veen JH. 1980. Induction and analysis of gibberellin sensitive mutants in *Arabidopsis thaliana*. *Theor. Appl. Genet* 58:257–63
62. Kretsch T, Poppe C, Schäfer E. 2000. A new type of mutation in the plant photoreceptor phytochrome B causes loss of photoreversibility and an extremely enhanced light sensitivity. *Plant J.* 22:177–86
63. Lagarias JC, Mercurio FM. 1985. Structure function studies on phytochrome. Identification of light-induced conformational changes in 124-kDa Avena phytochrome in vitro. *J. Biol. Chem.* 260:2415–23
64. Lamparter T, Carrascal M, Michael N, Martinez E, Rottwinkel G, Abian J. 2004. The biliverdin chromophore binds covalently to a conserved cysteine residue in the N-terminus of *Agrobacterium* phytochrome Agp1. *Biochemistry* 43:3659–69
65. Lamparter T, Esteban B, Hughes J. 2001. Phytochrome Cph1 from the cyanobacterium *Synechocystis* PCC6803. Purification, assembly, and quaternary structure. *Eur. J. Biochem.* 268:4720–30
66. Lamparter T, Mittmann F, Gartner W, Borner T, Hartmann E, Hughes J. 1997. Characterization of recombinant phytochrome from the cyanobacterium *Synechocystis*. *Proc. Natl. Acad. Sci. USA* 94:11792–97
67. Lapko VN, Jiang XY, Smith DL, Song PS. 1997. Posttranslational modification of oat phytochrome A: phosphorylation of a specific serine in a multiple serine cluster. *Biochemistry* 36:10595–99
68. Lapko VN, Jiang XY, Smith DL, Song PS. 1998. Surface topography of phytochrome A deduced from specific chemical modification with iodoacetamide. *Biochemistry* 37:12526–35
69. Laubinger S, Marchal V, Le Gourrierec J, Wenkel S, Adrian J, et al. 2006. *Arabidopsis* SPA proteins regulate photoperiodic flowering and interact with the floral inducer CONSTANS to regulate its stability. *Development* 133:3213–22
70. Lopez-Juez E, Nagatani A, Tomizawa K, Deak M, Kern R, et al. 1992. The cucumber long hypocotyl mutant lacks a light-stable PHYB-like phytochrome. *Plant Cell* 4:241–51
71. Ma L, Gao Y, Qu L, Chen Z, Li J, et al. 2002. Genomic evidence for COP1 as a repressor of light-regulated gene expression and development in *Arabidopsis*. *Plant Cell* 14:2383–98
72. Maloof JN, Borevitz JO, Dabi T, Lutes J, Nehring RB, et al. 2001. Natural variation in light sensitivity of *Arabidopsis*. *Nat. Genet.* 29:441–46
73. Martínez-Garcia JF, Huq E, Quail PH. 2000. Direct targeting of light signals to a promoter element-bound transcription factor. *Science* 288:859–63
74. Mateos JL, Luppi JP, Ogorodnikova OB, Sineshchekov VA, Yanovsky MJ, et al. 2006. Functional and biochemical analysis of the N-terminal domain of phytochrome A. *J. Biol. Chem.* 281:34421–29
75. Mathews S. 2006. Phytochrome-mediated development in land plants: red light sensing evolves to meet the challenges of changing light environments. *Mol. Ecol.* 15:3483–503
76. Matsushita T, Mochizuki N, Nagatani A. 2003. Dimers of the N-terminal domain of phytochrome B are functional in the nucleus. *Nature* 424:571–74
77. Mira-Rodado V, Sweere U, Grefen C, Kunkel T, Fejes E, et al. 2007. Functional cross-talk between two-component and phytochrome B signal transduction in *Arabidopsis*. *J. Exp. Bot.* 58:2595–607

78. Mittmann F, Brucker G, Zeidler M, Repp A, Abts T, et al. 2004. Targeted knockout in *Physcomitrella* reveals direct actions of phytochrome in the cytoplasm. *Proc. Natl. Acad. Sci. USA* 101:13939–44
79. Monte E, Alonso JM, Ecker JR, Zhang Y, Li X, et al. 2003. Isolation and characterization of phyC mutants in *Arabidopsis* reveals complex crosstalk between phytochrome signaling pathways. *Plant Cell* 15:1962–80
80. Monte E, Tepperman JM, Al-Sady B, Kaczorowski KA, Alonso JM, et al. 2004. The phytochrome-interacting transcription factor, PIF3, acts early, selectively, and positively in light-induced chloroplast development. *Proc. Natl. Acad. Sci. USA* 101:16091–98
81. Nagatani A, Reed JW, Chory J. 1993. Isolation and initial characterization of *Arabidopsis* mutants that are deficient in phytochrome A. *Plant Physiol.* 102:269–77
82. Nelson DC, Lasswell J, Rogg LE, Cohen MA, Bartel B. 2000. *FKF1*, a clock-controlled gene that regulates the transition to flowering in *Arabidopsis*. *Cell* 101:331–40
83. Ni M, Tepperman JM, Quail PH. 1998. PIF3, a phytochrome-interacting factor necessary for normal photoinduced signal transduction, is a novel basic helix-loop-helix protein. *Cell* 95:657–67
84. Ni M, Tepperman JM, Quail PH. 1999. Binding of phytochrome B to its nuclear signalling partner PIF3 is reversibly induced by light. *Nature* 400:781–84
85. Nozue K, Covington MF, Duek PD, Lorrain S, Fankhauser C, et al. 2007. Rhythmic growth explained by coincidence between internal and external cues. *Nature* 448:358–61
86. Ogawa M, Hanada A, Yamauchi Y, Kuwahara A, Kamiya Y, Yamaguchi S. 2003. Gibberellin biosynthesis and response during *Arabidopsis* seed germination. *Plant Cell* 15:1591–604
87. Oh E, Kim J, Park E, Kim JI, Kang C, Choi G. 2004. PIL5, a phytochrome-interacting basic helix-loop-helix protein, is a key negative regulator of seed germination in *Arabidopsis thaliana*. *Plant Cell* 16:3045–58
88. Oh E, Yamaguchi S, Hu J, Yusuke J, Jung B, et al. 2007. PIL5, a phytochrome-interacting bHLH protein, regulates gibberellin responsiveness by binding directly to the *GAI* and *RGA* promoters in *Arabidopsis* seeds. *Plant Cell* 19:1192–208
89. Oh E, Yamaguchi S, Kamiya Y, Bae G, Chung WI, Choi G. 2006. Light activates the degradation of PIL5 protein to promote seed germination through gibberellin in *Arabidopsis*. *Plant J.* 47:124–39
90. Oka Y, Matsushita T, Mochizuki N, Suzuki T, Tokutomi S, Nagatani A. 2004. Functional analysis of a 450-amino acid N-terminal fragment of phytochrome B in *Arabidopsis*. *Plant Cell* 16:2104–16
91. Osterlund MT, Deng XW. 1998. Multiple photoreceptors mediate the light-induced reduction of GUS-COP1 from *Arabidopsis* hypocotyl nuclei. *Plant J.* 16:201–8
92. Osterlund MT, Hardtke CS, Wei N, Deng XW. 2000. Targeted destabilization of HY5 during light-regulated development of *Arabidopsis*. *Nature* 405:462–66
93. Osterlund MT, Wei N, Deng XW. 2000. The roles of photoreceptor systems and the COP1-targeted destabilization of HY5 in light control of *Arabidopsis* seedling development. *Plant Physiol.* 124:1520–24
94. Parcy F. 2005. Flowering: a time for integration. *Int. J. Dev. Biol.* 49:585–93
95. Park E, Kim J, Lee Y, Shin J, Oh E, et al. 2004. Degradation of phytochrome interacting factor 3 in phytochrome-mediated light signaling. *Plant Cell Physiol.* 45:968–75
96. Penfield S, Josse EM, Kannangara R, Gilday AD, Halliday KJ, Graham IA. 2005. Cold and light control seed germination through the bHLH transcription factor SPATULA. *Curr. Biol.* 15:1998–2006

97. Reed JW, Nagatani A, Elich TD, Fagan M, Chory J. 1994. Phytochrome A and phytochrome B have overlapping but distinct functions in *Arabidopsis* development. *Plant Physiol.* 104:1139–49
98. Reed JW, Nagpal P, Poole DS, Furuya M, Chory J. 1993. Mutations in the gene for the red/far-red light receptor phytochrome B alter cell elongation and physiological responses throughout *Arabidopsis* development. *Plant Cell* 5:147–57
99. Rockwell NC, Lagarias JC. 2006. The structure of phytochrome: a picture is worth a thousand spectra. *Plant Cell* 18:4–14
100. Rockwell NC, Su YS, Lagarias JC. 2006. Phytochrome structure and signaling mechanisms. *Annu. Rev. Plant Biol.* 57:837–58
101. Ryu JS, Kim JI, Kunkel T, Kim BC, Cho DS, et al. 2005. Phytochrome-specific type 5 phosphatase controls light signal flux by enhancing phytochrome stability and affinity for a signal transducer. *Cell* 120:395–406
102. Saijo Y, Sullivan JA, Wang H, Yang J, Shen Y, et al. 2003. The COP1-SPA1 interaction defines a critical step in phytochrome A-mediated regulation of HY5 activity. *Genes Dev.* 17:2642–47
103. Sakamoto K, Nagatani A. 1996. Nuclear localization activity of phytochrome B. *Plant J.* 10:859–68
104. Seo HS, Watanabe E, Tokutomi S, Nagatani A, Chua NH. 2004. Photoreceptor ubiquitination by COP1 E3 ligase desensitizes phytochrome A signaling. *Genes Dev.* 18:617–22
105. Seo HS, Yang JY, Ishikawa M, Bolle C, Ballesteros ML, Chua NH. 2003. LAF1 ubiquitination by COP1 controls photomorphogenesis and is stimulated by SPA1. *Nature* 423:995–99
106. Sharrock RA, Clack T. 2004. Heterodimerization of type II phytochromes in *Arabidopsis*. *Proc. Natl. Acad. Sci. USA* 101:11500–5
107. Sharrock RA, Clack T, Goosey L. 2003. Differential activities of the *Arabidopsis* phyB/D/E phytochromes in complementing phyB mutant phenotypes. *Plant Mol. Biol.* 52:135–42
108. Shen H, Moon J, Huq E. 2005. PIF1 is regulated by light-mediated degradation through the ubiquitin-26S proteasome pathway to optimize photomorphogenesis of seedlings in *Arabidopsis*. *Plant J.* 44:1023–35
109. Shen Y, Feng S, Ma L, Lin R, Qu LJ, et al. 2005. *Arabidopsis* FHY1 protein stability is regulated by light via phytochrome A and 26S proteasome. *Plant Physiol.* 139:1234–43
110. Shimizu-Sato S, Huq E, Tepperman JM, Quail PH. 2002. A light-switchable gene promoter system. *Nat. Biotechnol.* 20:1041–44
111. Shin J, Park E, Choi G. 2007. PIF3 regulates anthocyanin biosynthesis in an HY5-dependent manner with both factors directly binding anthocyanin biosynthetic gene promoters in *Arabidopsis*. *Plant J.* 49:981–94
112. Shinomura T, Nagatani A, Hanzawa H, Kubota M, Watanabe M, Furuya M. 1996. Action spectra for phytochrome A- and B-specific photoinduction of seed germination in *Arabidopsis thaliana*. *Proc. Natl. Acad. Sci. USA* 93:8129–33
113. Siegelman HW, Turner BC, Hendricks SB. 1966. The chromophore of phytochrome. *Plant Physiol.* 41:1289–92
114. Smith H. 1983. The natural radiation environment: limitations on the biology of photoreceptors. Phytochrome as a case study. *Symp. Soc. Exp. Biol.* 36:1–18
115. Stewart M. 2007. Molecular mechanism of the nuclear protein import cycle. *Nat. Rev. Mol. Cell Biol.* 8:195–208

116. Stockhaus J, Nagatani A, Halfter U, Kay S, Furuya M, Chua NH. 1992. Serine-to-alanine substitutions at the amino-terminal region of phytochrome A result in an increase in biological activity. *Genes Dev.* 6:2364–72
117. Su YS, Lagarias JC. 2007. Light-independent phytochrome signaling mediated by dominant GAF domain tyrosine mutants of *Arabidopsis* phytochromes in transgenic plants. *Plant Cell.* 19:2124–39
118. Suarez-Lopez P, Wheatley K, Robson F, Onouchi H, Valverde F, Coupland G. 2001. CONSTANS mediates between the circadian clock and the control of flowering in *Arabidopsis*. *Nature* 410:1116–20
119. Suetsugu N, Mittmann F, Wagner G, Hughes J, Wada M. 2005. A chimeric photoreceptor gene, *NEOCHROME*, has arisen twice during plant evolution. *Proc. Natl. Acad. Sci. USA* 102:13705–9
120. Sweere U, Eichenberg K, Lohrmann J, Mira-Rodado V, Baurle I, et al. 2001. Interaction of the response regulator ARR4 with phytochrome B in modulating red light signaling. *Science* 294:1108–11
121. Takano M, Inagaki N, Xie X, Yuzurihara N, Hihara F, et al. 2005. Distinct and cooperative functions of phytochromes A, B, and C in the control of de-etiolation and flowering in rice. *Plant Cell* 17:3311–25
122. Tepperman JM, Hwang YS, Quail PH. 2006. phyA dominates in transduction of red-light signals to rapidly responding genes at the initiation of *Arabidopsis* seedling de-etiolation. *Plant J.* 48:728–42
123. To JP, Haberer G, Ferreira FJ, Deruere J, Mason MG, et al. 2004. Type-A *Arabidopsis* response regulators are partially redundant negative regulators of cytokinin signaling. *Plant Cell* 16:658–71
124. Tokuhisa JG, Daniels SM, Quail PH. 1985. Phytochrome in green tissue: spectral and immunochemical evidence for two distinct molecular species of phytochrome in light-grown *Avena* sativa L. *Planta* 164:321–32
125. Trupkin SA, Debrieux D, Hiltbrunner A, Fankhauser C, Casal JJ. 2007. The serine-rich N-terminal region of *Arabidopsis* phytochrome A is required for protein stability. *Plant Mol. Biol.* 63:669–78
126. Usami T, Matsushita T, Oka Y, Mochizuki N, Nagatani A. 2007. Roles for the N- and C-terminal domains of phytochrome B in interactions between phytochrome B and cryptochrome signaling cascades. *Plant Cell Physiol.* 48:424–33
127. Valverde F, Mouradov A, Soppe W, Ravenscroft D, Samach A, Coupland G. 2004. Photoreceptor regulation of CONSTANS protein in photoperiodic flowering. *Science* 303:1003–6
128. Vogelmann TC, Bornman JF, Josserand S. 1989. Photosynthetic light gradients and spectral regime within leaves of *Medicago sativa*. *Philos. Trans. R. Soc. London Ser. B* 323:411–21
129. von Arnim AG, Deng XW. 1994. Light inactivation of *Arabidopsis* photomorphogenic repressor COP1 involves a cell-specific regulation of its nucleocytoplasmic partitioning. *Cell* 79:1035–45
130. von Arnim AG, Deng XW, Stacey MG. 1998. Cloning vectors for the expression of green fluorescent protein fusion proteins in transgenic plants. *Gene* 221:35–43
131. Wagner D, Koloszvari M, Quail PH. 1996. Two small spatially distinct regions of phytochrome B are required for efficient signaling rates. *Plant Cell* 8:859–71
132. Wagner D, Tepperman JM, Quail PH. 1991. Overexpression of phytochrome B induces a short hypocotyl phenotype in transgenic *Arabidopsis*. *Plant Cell* 3:1275–88

133. Wagner JR, Brunzelle JS, Forest KT, Vierstra RD. 2005. A light-sensing knot revealed by the structure of the chromophore-binding domain of phytochrome. *Nature* 438:325–31

134. Wagner JR, Zhang J, Brunzelle JS, Vierstra RD, Forest KT. 2007. High resolution structure of *Deinococcus* bacteriophytochrome yields new insights into phytochrome architecture and evolution. *J. Biol. Chem.* 282:12298–309

135. Wang H, Ma L, Habashi J, Li J, Zhao H, Deng XW. 2002. Analysis of far-red light-regulated genome expression profiles of phytochrome A pathway mutants in *Arabidopsis*. *Plant J.* 32:723–33

136. Wells TA, Nakazawa M, Manabe K, Song PS. 1994. A conformational change associated with the phototransformation of *Pisum* phytochrome A as probed by fluorescence quenching. *Biochemistry* 33:708–12

137. Whippo CW, Hangarter RP. 2006. Phototropism: bending towards enlightenment. *Plant Cell* 18:1110–19

138. Whitelam GC, Johnson E, Peng J, Carol P, Anderson ML, et al. 1993. Phytochrome A null mutants of *Arabidopsis* display a wild-type phenotype in white light. *Plant Cell* 5:757–68

139. Wu SH, Lagarias JC. 2000. Defining the bilin lyase domain: lessons from the extended phytochrome superfamily. *Biochemistry* 39:13487–95

140. Xu Y, Parks BM, Short TW, Quail PH. 1995. Missense mutations define a restricted segment in the C-terminal domain of phytochrome A critical to its regulatory activity. *Plant Cell* 7:1433–43

141. Yamaguchi R, Nakamura M, Mochizuki N, Kay SA, Nagatani A. 1999. Light-dependent translocation of a phytochrome B-GFP fusion protein to the nucleus in transgenic *Arabidopsis*. *J. Cell Biol.* 145:437–45

142. Yang HQ, Tang RH, Cashmore AR. 2001. The signaling mechanism of *Arabidopsis* CRY1 involves direct interaction with COP1. *Plant Cell* 13:2573–87

143. Yang J, Lin R, Hoecker U, Liu B, Xu L, Wang H. 2005. Repression of light signaling by *Arabidopsis* SPA1 involves post-translational regulation of HFR1 protein accumulation. *Plant J.* 43:131–41

144. Yang J, Lin R, Sullivan J, Hoecker U, Liu B, et al. 2005. Light regulates COP1-mediated degradation of HFR1, a transcription factor essential for light signaling in *Arabidopsis*. *Plant Cell* 17:804–21

145. Yanovsky MJ, Luppi JP, Kirchbauer D, Ogorodnikova OB, Sineshchekov VA, et al. 2002. Missense mutation in the PAS2 domain of phytochrome A impairs subnuclear localization and a subset of responses. *Plant Cell* 14:1591–603

146. Yanovsky MJ, Mazzella MA, Whitelam GC, Casal JJ. 2001. Resetting of the circadian clock by phytochromes and cryptochromes in *Arabidopsis*. *J. Biol. Rhythms* 16:523–30

147. Yeh KC, Lagarias JC. 1998. Eukaryotic phytochromes: light-regulated serine/threonine protein kinases with histidine kinase ancestry. *Proc. Natl. Acad. Sci. USA* 95:13976–81

148. Yeh KC, Wu SH, Murphy JT, Lagarias JC. 1997. A cyanobacterial phytochrome two-component light sensory system. *Science* 277:1505–8

149. Zeidler M, Zhou Q, Sarda X, Yau CP, Chua NH. 2004. The nuclear localization signal and the C-terminal region of FHY1 are required for transmission of phytochrome A signals. *Plant J.* 40:355–65

150. Zhou Q, Hare PD, Yang SW, Zeidler M, Huang LF, Chua NH. 2005. FHL is required for full phytochrome A signaling and shares overlapping functions with FHY1. *Plant J.* 43:356–70
151. Zhu Y, Tepperman JM, Fairchild CD, Quail PH. 2000. Phytochrome B binds with greater apparent affinity than phytochrome A to the basic helix-loop-helix factor PIF3 in a reaction requiring the PAS domain of PIF3. *Proc. Natl. Acad. Sci. USA* 97:13419–24

Flooding Stress: Acclimations and Genetic Diversity

J. Bailey-Serres[1,*] and L.A.C.J. Voesenek[2,*]

[1]Center for Plant Cell Biology, University of California, Riverside, California 92521; email: serres@ucr.edu

[2]Plant Ecophysiology, Institute of Environmental Biology, Utrecht University, NL-3584 CA Utrecht, The Netherlands

Annu. Rev. Plant Biol. 2008. 59:313–39

The *Annual Review of Plant Biology* is online at plant.annualreviews.org

This article's doi:
10.1146/annurev.arplant.59.032607.092752

1543-5008/08/0602-0313$20.00

*Both authors contributed equally to this paper.

Key Words

aerenchyma, anoxia, response strategy, hypoxia, reactive oxygen species, submergence

Abstract

Flooding is an environmental stress for many natural and man-made ecosystems worldwide. Genetic diversity in the plant response to flooding includes alterations in architecture, metabolism, and elongation growth associated with a low O_2 escape strategy and an antithetical quiescence scheme that allows endurance of prolonged submergence. Flooding is frequently accompanied with a reduction of cellular O_2 content that is particularly severe when photosynthesis is limited or absent. This necessitates the production of ATP and regeneration of NAD^+ through anaerobic respiration. The examination of gene regulation and function in model systems provides insight into low-O_2-sensing mechanisms and metabolic adjustments associated with controlled use of carbohydrate and ATP. At the developmental level, plants can escape the low-O_2 stress caused by flooding through multifaceted alterations in cellular and organ structure that promote access to and diffusion of O_2. These processes are driven by phytohormones, including ethylene, gibberellin, and abscisic acid. This exploration of natural variation in strategies that improve O_2 and carbohydrate status during flooding provides valuable resources for the improvement of crop endurance of an environmental adversity that is enhanced by global warming.

Contents

INTRODUCTION

Partial to complete flooding is detrimental for most terrestrial plants because it hampers growth and can result in premature death. Some plant species have a remarkable capacity to endure these conditions, and certain species can even grow vigorously in response to flooding. This interspecific variation has a strong impact on species abundance and distribution in flood-prone ecosystems worldwide (12, 31, 122, 138, 150, 151). Furthermore, flooding has a severe negative influence on the productivity of arable farmland because most crops are not selected to cope with flooding stress (121). The Intergovernmental Panel on Climate Change (IPCC) (**http://www.ipcc.ch**) reported that the anthropogenically induced change of world climate increases the frequency of heavy precipitation and tropical cyclone activity. This is likely to engender more frequent flooding events in river flood plains and arable farmland, particularly affecting the world's poorest farmers (1).

Hypoxia (e.g., <20.9% and >0% O_2 at 20°C): characterized by increased anaerobic metabolism, increased ATP production via glycolysis owing to limited availability of O_2 for oxidative phosphorylation, and increased NAD^+ regeneration via lactate and ethanolic fermentation. Cellular ATP content is reduced

The observation that some plant species can cope with flooding stress and others cannot imposes the question of why a flooded environment is detrimental. The adversity is largely due to the dramatically reduced gas exchange between plants and their aerial environment during partial to complete submergence. Gases such as O_2, CO_2, and ethylene diffuse very slowly in water (46). Because of this tremendous barrier for gas diffusion, the cellular O_2 level can decline to concentrations that restrict aerobic respiration (39, 46). Depending on the tissue and light conditions, the cellular CO_2 level either increases in shoots in the dark and roots (47) or decreases in shoots in the light (83). The endogenous concentration of the gaseous plant hormone ethylene increases in tissues surrounded by water (59, 148). This accumulation activates adaptive signal transduction pathways, whereas similar concentrations hamper normal growth in many terrestrial plants (93). Furthermore, complete submergence decreases light intensity, dampening photosynthesis (141). A third major change in the flooded environment is the reduction of oxidized soil components to toxic concentrations (12). In summary, flooding is a compound stress in which the decline in molecular O_2 and thus the restriction of ATP synthesis and carbohydrate resources have major consequences for growth and survival. However, O_2 depletion is not the only active stress component, and often its impact is restricted to nonphotosynthesizing organs (84).

O_2 shortage (hypoxia/anoxia) is not restricted to flooding stress. It is a frequent metabolic status of cells during normal development, particularly in tissues with high cell density, a high O_2 demand, and/or restricted O_2 entry, such as meristems, seeds, fruits, and storage organs (43). Fundamental insight into the low O_2–sensing mechanism, downstream signal transduction, and metabolic alterations that promote survival is key to increased crop production in flood-prone environments and has wider implications for biologists (3, 43). Most studies on flooding stress have focused on relatively flood-tolerant species from genera such as *Oryza*, *Rumex*, and *Echinochloa*. Single species studies are valuable for an understanding of the regulation of various acclimations but less meaningful in an ecological perspective. Here genetic diversity in acclimations to flooding stress is discussed side by side with the molecular regulation of low-O_2 responses and flooding tolerance. Ultimately we aim to shed light on the genes, proteins, and processes controlling these phenotypes.

GENETIC DIVERSITY OF STRATEGIES TO SURVIVE FLOODING

Not all species in flood-prone environments are flood tolerant. Some species avoid flooding by completing their life cycle between two subsequent flood events, whereas flooding periods are survived by dormant life stages [e.g., *Chenopodium rubrum* thrives in frequently flooded environments by timing its growth between floods and producing seeds that survive flooding (134)]. Established plants also use avoidance strategies through the development of anatomical and morphological traits. This amelioration response, here called the low oxygen escape syndrome (LOES) (**Figure 1**), facilitates the survival of submerged organs. Upon complete submergence several species from flood-prone environments have the capacity to stimulate the elongation rate of petioles, stems, or leaves. This fast elongation can restore contact between leaves and air but can also result in plant death if energy reserves are depleted before emergence. Concomitant with high elongation rates, the leaves also develop a thinner overall morphology, develop thinner cell walls and cuticles, and reorient

Anoxia (e.g., 0% O_2 at 20°C): characterized by anaerobic metabolism, NAD^+ regeneration via lactate and ethanolic fermentation, and ATP production solely via glycolysis (2–4 mol ATP per mole hexose). Cellular ATP content is low, and ADP content is elevated

LOES: low-oxygen escape syndrome

Drained	Submerged	Trait
Low	High	Shoot elongation
Low	High	Aerenchyma
High	Low	Leaf thickness
Around intercellular spaces	Toward epidermis	Chloroplast position

Figure 1

Various species display the low-oxygen escape syndrome (LOES) when submerged. The syndrome includes enhanced elongation of internodes and petioles, the formation of aerenchyma in these organs (air spaces indicated by *arrows* labeled *a*), and increased gas exchange with the water layer through reduced leaf thickness and chloroplasts that lie directed toward the epidermis (indicated by *arrows* labeled *b*). Photographs are courtesy of Ronald Pierik, Liesje Mommer, Mieke Wolters-Arts, and Ankie Ammerlaan.

chloroplasts toward the leaf surface. These traits reduce the resistance for diffusion of CO_2 and O_2, facilitating inward diffusion and thereby improving underwater photosynthesis and aerobic metabolism (82, 83). Thus, the LOES improves the aeration of the plant, which is further enhanced by the relatively low resistance for internal gas diffusion owing to a system of interconnected gas conduits called aerenchyma, a property typical of many wetland plants (24, 33). These conduits are constitutive, induced in existing tissues (roots, petioles, stems) (33) or formed during the development of adventitious roots that arise from the root shoot junction or stem nodes (115, 142). In specialized cases the longitudinal diffusion of O_2 to the root apex is further enhanced by the development of a barrier to radial oxygen loss to minimize escape of O_2 to the surrounding environment (24, 25).

Sub1: *Submergence1* polygenic locus of rice; determines submergence tolerance

Oxygen deficiency/deprivation: the natural and experimental conditions in which cellular oxygen content is reduced but metabolic status is not determined

mtETC: mitochondrial electron transport chain

ROS: reactive oxygen species

LOES is costly and will only be selected for in environments where the cost is outweighed by benefits such as improved O_2 and carbohydrate status, both contributing to a higher fitness (120). The flooding regime is an important determinant for selection in favor of or against LOES. A study on the distribution of species in the Rhine floodplains confirmed this hypothesis. Here LOES occurs predominantly in species from habitats characterized by prolonged, but relatively shallow, flooding events (150). However, the benefits of LOES do not outweigh the costs when the floods are too deep or ephemeral. These regimes favor a quiescence strategy characterized by limited underwater growth and conservation of energy and carbohydrates (39, 91). This strategy is a true tolerance mechanism, driven by adjustment of metabolism. With respect to low-O_2 stress, this includes the downregulation of respiration and limited stimulation of fermentation to create a positive energy budget when organ hypoxia starts (43, 148). The *SUB1A* gene of the polygenic rice (*Oryza sativa* L.) *Submergence1* (*Sub1*) locus was shown to confer submergence tolerance through a 'quiescence' strategy in which cell elongation and carbohydrate metabolism is repressed (41, 91, 159) (**Figure 2**). *SUB1A*, encodes an ethylene-responsive element (ERF) domain–containing transcription factor (41). The lack of *SUB1A-1* or the presence of a slightly modified allele is associated with reduced submergence tolerance and the induction of the LOES. This example demonstrates that environment-driven selection on a single locus can significantly alter survival strategy.

ACCLIMATION TO FLOODING AT THE CELLULAR LEVEL

Overview of Cellular Adjustments to Oxygen Deprivation

During flooding, the onset of O_2 deprivation is rapid in the dark and in nonphotosynthetic cells. The reduced availability of O_2 as the final electron acceptor in the mitochondrial electron transport chain (mtETC) mediates a rapid reduction of the cellular ATP:ADP ratio and adenylate energy charge (AEC) ([ATP + 0.5 ADP]/[ATP+ADP+AMP]) (46). Cells cope with this energy crisis by relying primarily on glycolysis and fermentation to generate ATP and regenerate NAD^+, respectively. Whether a LOES or a quiescence response to flooding is activated, cellular acclimation to transient O_2 deprivation requires tight regulation of ATP production and consumption, limited acidification of the cytosol, and amelioration of reactive oxygen species (ROS) produced either as O_2 levels fall during flooding or upon reoxygenation after withdrawal of the flood water.

O_2 concentration is 20.95% at 20°C in air but ranges from 1 to 7% in the core of well-aerated roots, stems, tubers, and developing seeds (14, 44, 46, 107, 136, 137). Within a root, O_2 levels and consumption vary zonally; the highly metabolically active meristematic cells are in a continuous state of deficiency. Upon flooding, the ~10,000-fold-slower diffusion of O_2 in water rapidly limits its availability for mitochondrial respiration. This deprivation is progressively more severe as

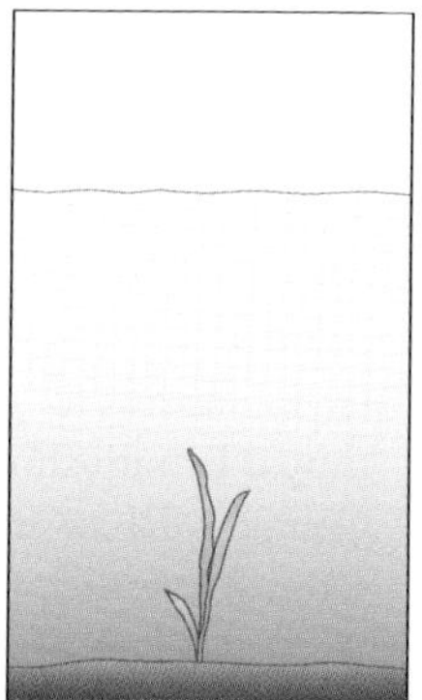
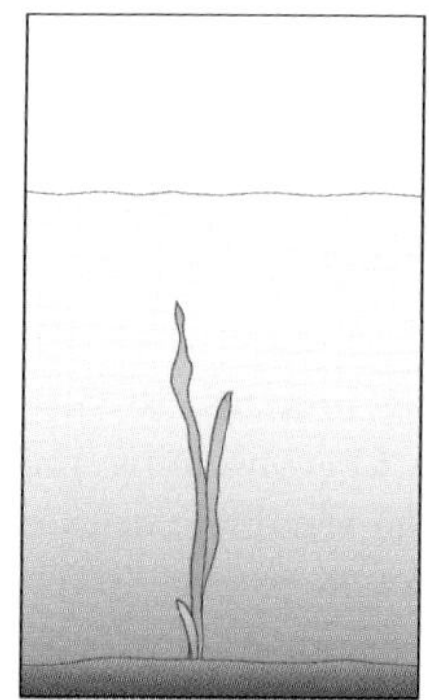
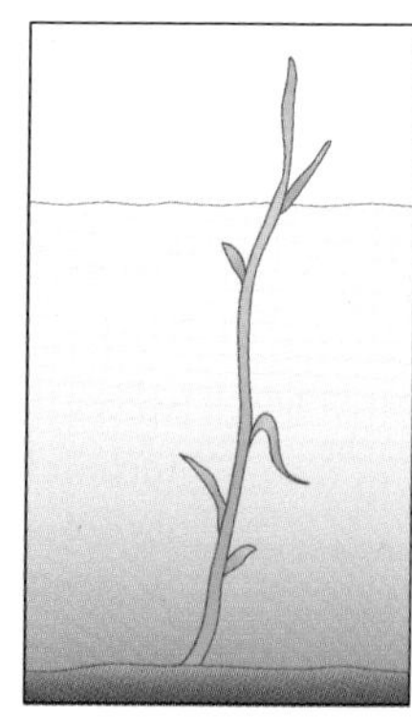

	Lowland Rice		Deepwater Rice
	Tolerant	**Intolerant**	
Strategy	**Quiescence**	**LOES**	**LOES**
Sub1 haplotype	*SUB1A-1, SUB1B, SUB1C*	*SUB1B, SUB1C* or *SUB1A-2, SUB1B, SUB1C*	*SUB1B, SUB1C* or *SUB1A-2, SUB1B, SUB1C*
Carbohydrate consumption	Limited by *SUB1A-1*	High	High
Fermentation capacity	High	Moderate	N.D.
GA response	Inhibited by *SUB1A-1*	Promoted by *SUB1C*	High

Figure 2

Rice responds via different strategies to submergence. Flood-tolerant rice varieties invoke a quiescence strategy that is governed by the polygenic *Submergence1* (*Sub1*) locus that encodes two or three ethylene-responsive factor proteins (41, 159). *SUB1A* is induced by ethylene under submergence and negatively regulates *SUB1C* mRNA levels. Flood-intolerant varieties avoid submergence via the low oxygen escape syndrome (LOES). To this end *SUB1C* expression is promoted by gibberellic acid (GA) and is associated with rapid depletion of carbohydrate reserves and enhanced elongation of leaves and internodes. The LOES is unsuccessful when flooding is ephemeral and deep. Deepwater rice varieties survive flooding via a LOES, as long as the rise in depth is sufficiently gradual to allow aerial tissue to escape submergence (61). N.D., not determined.

distance from the source increases and tissue porosity decreases. For example, the cortex of nonaerenchymatous maize (*Zea mays* L.) roots exposed to 10% O_2 becomes hypoxic, whereas the internal stele becomes anoxic. Even the apex of aerenchymatous roots encounters severe O_2 deprivation (46). In dense storage organs such as potato (*Solanum tuberosum L.*) tubers and developing plant seeds, exposure to 8% O_2 significantly reduces the endogenous O_2 level. However, the decrease in cellular O_2 is strikingly nonlinear from the exterior to the interior of the organ; cells at the interior of the tuber or endosperm maintain a hypoxic state (44, 136). This has led to the suggestion that an active mechanism may allow cells to avoid anoxia (43). Such a mechanism may include proactive limitation in the consumption of both ATP and O_2. The low K_m for cytochrome *c* oxidase (COX) [140 nM (~0.013%) O_2] should ensure that the activity of COX continues as long as O_2 is available (31, 46). However, a mechanism that inhibits the mtETC at or upstream of COX or inhibits

O_2 consumption by other enzymes may allow cells to sustain hypoxia and avoid death.

Normoxia (e.g., 20.9% O_2 at 20°C): characterized by aerobic metabolism, NAD^+ regeneration primarily via the mitochondrial electron transport chain, and ATP production via mitochondrial oxidative phsophorylation (30–36 mol ATP per mol hexose consumed); cellular ATP content is normal

Low-Oxygen Sensing

In animals the perception of O_2 deficit involves O_2-binding proteins, ROS, and mitochondria. The O_2-consuming prolyl hydroxylases (PHDs) are direct sensors of O_2 availability. Under normoxia, PHDs target the proteosomal degradation of hypoxia inducible factor 1α (HIF1α), a subunit of a heterodimeric transcription factor that regulates acclimation to hypoxia (51). The concomitant drop in PHD activity stimulates an elevation in HIF1α as O_2 declines. A paradox is that the production of ROS at the mitochondrial ubiquinone:cytochrome *c* reductase complex (Complex III) is necessary to initiate O_2 deficit responses (7, 51).

There is limited understanding of the mechanisms by which plant cells sense and initiate signaling in response to O_2 deficit (3, 39, 43). Plants lack a HIF1α ortholog, although PHD mRNAs are strongly induced by O_2 deficit in *Arabidopsis thaliana* and rice (67, 146). Furthermore, significant increases in mRNAs encoding enzymes involved in ROS signaling and amelioration (16, 63, 67, 70, 71) and evidence of ROS production have been reported in several species upon transfer to low O_2 conditions. A challenge in monitoring ROS production during O_2 deficit is that ROS are produced readily upon reoxygenation. However, ethane, a product of membrane peroxidation by ROS, evolves from submerged rice seedlings in a closed system as levels of O_2 fall to as low as 1% (112), providing evidence that ROS form as O_2 levels decline. Blokhina and colleagues (11) demonstrated that in response to anoxia, H_2O_2 accumulates to higher levels in the apoplast of root meristems of hypoxic wheat (*Triticum aestivum*) than in the more anoxia-tolerant rhizomes of *Iris pseudacorus*. In *Arabidopsis* seedlings, H_2O_2 levels increase in response to O_2 deprivation in a ROP GTPase–dependent manner (6). Genotypes that limit ROP signaling under hypoxia display lower levels of H_2O_2 accumulation and altered gene regulation in stressed seedlings. Indications that mitochondria are crucial to low-O_2 sensing in plants comes from the release of Ca^{2+} from mitochondria of cultured maize cells within minutes of transfer to anoxia (127). This release may be activated by mitochondrial ROS production at Complex III of the mtETC (99). A rapid spike in cytosolic Ca^{2+} was also observed in the cotyledons of *Arabidopsis* seedlings upon transfer to anoxia and again at higher amplitude upon reoxygenation (119). These Ca^{2+} transients are required for alterations in gene expression that enhance ethanolic fermentation and ATP management during the stress (3, 66, 88, 119, 126, 128). Further studies are needed to confirm whether mitochondrion-to-nucleus signaling, mediated by ROS production and Ca^{2+} release from mitochondria, contributes to reconfiguration of metabolism under low O_2. Additional players in the acclimation response may be the reduction of ATP content and decline in cytosolic pH as well as change in levels of metabolites such as sucrose and pyruvate (3, 39). mRNAs encoding mitochondrial alternative oxidase, (AOX) are strongly induced by low-O_2 stress (63, 67, 70, 71). AOX diverts ubiquinone from Complex III; if active as O_2 levels decrease, AOX would paradoxically reduce oxygen availability for COX and decrease ATP production. However, if active as O_2 levels rise upon reoxygenation, AOX may limit mitochondrial ROS production (99).

Management of the Energy Crisis

Within minutes of transfer to an O_2-depleted environment, cells reliant on external O_2 limit processes that are highly energy consumptive and alter metabolism to increase anaerobic generation of ATP by cytosolic glycolysis (31). This shift is followed by fermentation of pyruvate to the major end products, ethanol or lactate, yielding NAD^+ to sustain anaerobic metabolism (**Figure 3**). A crisis in ATP availability ensues because glycolysis is inefficient, yielding 2 to 4 mol ATP per mol hexose as compared with 30 to 36 mol ATP by the mtETC. Evaluation of gene transcripts, enzymes, and metabolites in a variety of species and genotypes demonstrated the production of minor metabolic end products that are also important for NAD^+ and $NAD(P)^+$ regeneration. Although mutant analyses with several species have demonstrated that glycolysis and fermentation are necessary for cell survival under O_2 deprivation, the enhancement of these processes is not well correlated with prolonged endurance of this stress (31, 46).

The anaerobic energy crisis necessitates a blend of optimized ATP production with limited energy consumption. ATP-demanding processes such as DNA synthesis and cell division are curtailed (46), and the production of rRNA is dramatically reduced (36). In *Arabidopsis* and other plants, low-O_2 stress markedly limits protein synthesis but maintains the initiation of translation of a subset of cellular mRNAs, many of which encode enzymes involved in anaerobic metabolism and the amelioration of ROS (16, 36). Therefore, under O_2 deprivation, a mechanism operates that sequesters untranslated mRNAs and lessens ATP expenditure, thereby allowing for the recovery of protein synthesis within minutes of reoxygenation.

Carbohydrate mobilization and sucrose catabolism. The metabolic response to O_2 deprivation is orchestrated by the availability and mobilization of carbohydrates (31, 137). In some plants and tissues, the induction of amylases by low O_2 or flooding promotes the conversion of starch to glucose (**Figure 3**). However, the mobilization of starch during O_2 deprivation is not universal. Both the tubers of potatoes and rhizomes of the flood-tolerant marsh plant *Acorus calamus* L. have considerable carbohydrate reserves, but *Acorus* rhizomes are more capable of mobilizing starch into respirable sugars under anoxia (2). This slow consumption of starch allows the rhizomes to sustain a low level of metabolism that affords survival of long periods of submergence. Seeds of rice, rice weeds (e.g., some *Echinochloa* species), and tubers of *Potamogeton pectinatus* also mobilize starch under anoxia (29, 40, 50). In rice seeds, this starch mobilization requires the depletion of soluble carbohydrates, suggesting regulation by sugar sensing (50, 72). In organs lacking starch reserves or effective starch mobilization, the exhaustion of soluble sugars prior to reoxygenation is likely to result in cell death.

Plants possess two independent routes for the catabolism of sucrose, the bidirectional UDP-dependent sucrose synthase (SUS) and the unidirectional invertase (INV) pathways (**Figure 3**). The net cost for entry into glycolysis is one mol pyrophosphate (PPi) per mol sucrose via the SUS route, if the UTP produced by UDP-glucose pyrophosphorylase (UGPPase) is utilized by fructokinase (FK) in the subsequent conversion of UDP-glucose to glucose-6P or the ATP consumed by FK is recycled by nucleoside diphosphate (NDP) kinase. By contrast, the cost via the INV pathway is two mol ATP per mol sucrose. The SUS route is positively regulated under O_2 deprivation through opposing increases in SUS and the repression of INV gene expression and enzymatic activity (10, 14, 43, 44, 64, 67). The energetic disadvantage of the INV route was confirmed by the inability of transgenic potato tubers with elevated INV activity to maintain ATP levels under 8% O_2 (14). The SUS pathway is enhanced in a variety of species by rapid increases in transcription of *SUS* mRNAs, which is most likely driven by sucrose starvation (64, 71). Other glycolytic reactions may utilize available PPi during O_2 deprivation, thereby improving the net yield of ATP per mol sucrose catabolized. The phosphorylation of fructose-6P to fructose-1,6P_2 by the bidirectional PPi-dependent phosphofructokinase (PFP) is favored over the unidirectional ATP-dependent phosphofructokinase (PFK), and a pyruvate Pi dikinase (PPDK) may substitute for cytosolic pyruvate kinase (PK) in O_2-deprived rice seedlings (95).

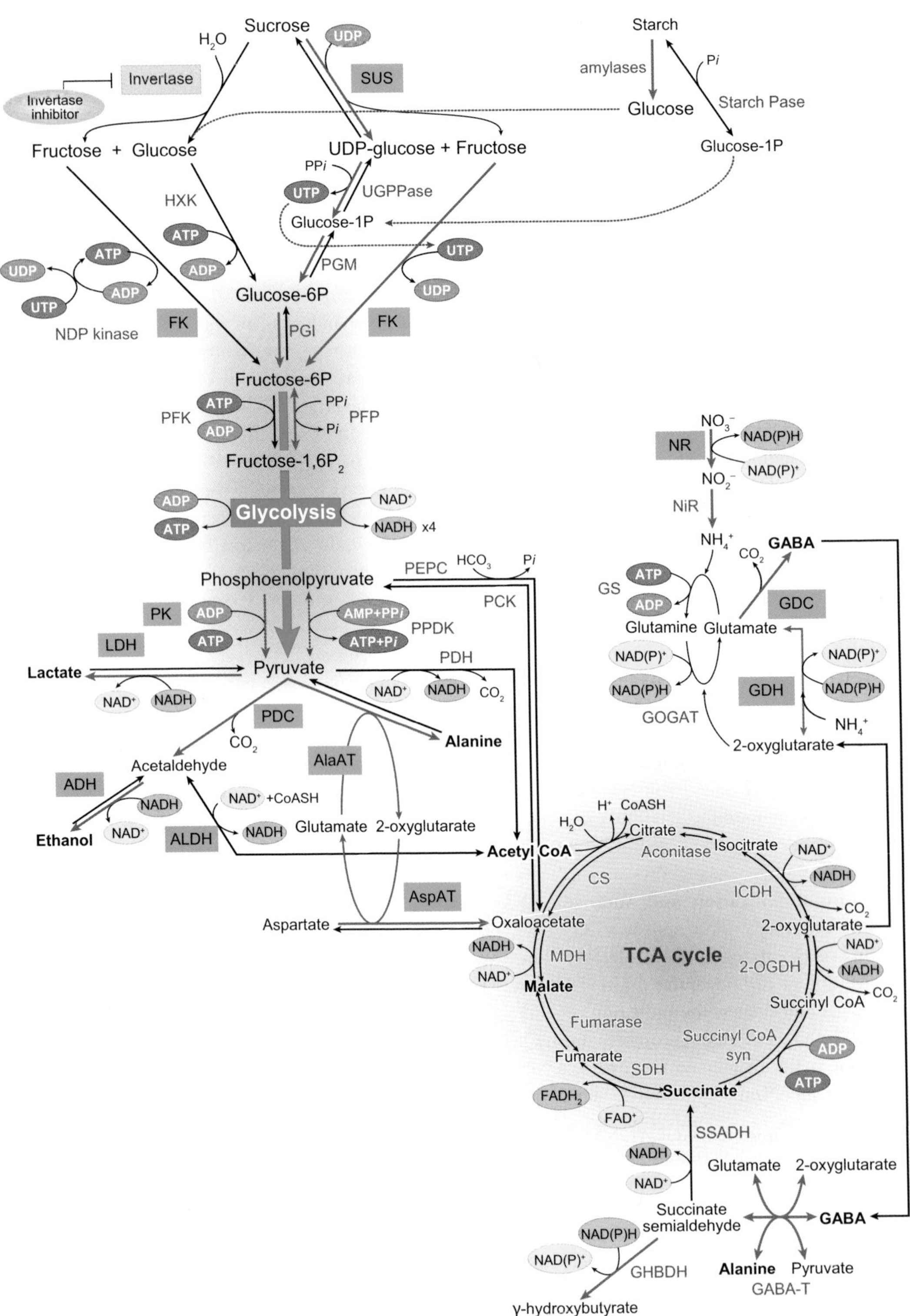

Sucrose
UDP
H_2O
SUS
Invertase
Invertase inhibitor
Starch
amylases
Pi
Glucose
Starch Pase
Glucose-1P
Fructose + Glucose
UDP-glucose + Fructose
PPi
UTP
UGPPase
HXK
Glucose-1P
ATP
ADP
UDP
ATP
ADP
UTP
PGM
UTP
UDP
Glucose-6P
NDP kinase
FK
FK
PGI
Fructose-6P
ATP
PPi
PFK
PFP
ADP
Pi
Fructose-1,6P_2
ADP
NAD$^+$
Glycolysis
ATP
NADH x4
PEPC
HCO_3
Pi
Phosphoenolpyruvate
PCK
PK
ADP
AMP+PPi
LDH
ATP
ATP+Pi
PPDK
PDH
Lactate
Pyruvate
NAD$^+$
NADH
NAD$^+$
NADH
CO_2
PDC
CO_2
Alanine
AlaAT
Acetaldehyde
ADH
NADH
NAD$^+$ +CoASH
Ethanol
NAD$^+$
ALDH
NADH
Glutamate
2-oxyglutarate
Acetyl CoA
AspAT
Aspartate
Oxaloacetate
NO_3^-
NR
NAD(P)H
NAD(P)$^+$
NO_2^-
NiR
NH_4^+
CO_2
GABA
GS
ATP
GDC
ADP
Glutamine
Glutamate
NAD(P)$^+$
NAD(P)$^+$
NAD(P)H
GDH
NAD(P)H
GOGAT
NH_4^+
2-oxyglutarate
H^+ CoASH
H_2O
Citrate
Aconitase
Isocitrate
NAD$^+$
CS
NADH
ICDH
CO_2
2-oxyglutarate
NADH
NAD$^+$
MDH
TCA cycle
2-OGDH
NADH
NAD$^+$
Malate
Succinyl CoA
CO_2
Fumarase
Succinyl CoA syn
ADP
Fumarate
SDH
ATP
$FADH_2$
Succinate
FAD$^+$
SSADH
NADH
Glutamate
2-oxyglutarate
NAD$^+$
Succinate semialdehyde
GABA
NAD(P)H
NAD(P)$^+$
GHBDH
Alanine
Pyruvate
GABA-T
γ-hydroxybutyrate

Metabolic end products. During O_2 deprivation, pyruvate decarboxylase (PDC) converts pyruvate to acetaldehyde, which is metabolized by alcohol dehydrogenase (ADH) to ethanol, with the regeneration of NAD^+ to sustain glycolysis. PDC- and ADH-deficient genotypes confirm the essentiality of ethanolic fermentation in the acclimation to flooding and low-O_2 stress (6, 31, 46, 65). In *Arabidopsis* seedlings, the level of induction of *ADH* is controlled by the activation of a ROP GTPase (5). O_2 deprivation promotes an increase in active ROP, which leads to the elevation of transcripts that encode *ADH* and *ROPGAP4*, a GTPase that inactivates ROP. In a *ropgap4* null mutant, *ADH* mRNA and ROS are significantly elevated under hypoxia, and seedling survival is reduced. This led to the proposal that a ROP rheostat controls the temporal regulation of *ADH* expression under low O_2 (3, 39).

The production of ethanol is benign owing to its rapid diffusion out of cells, whereas the intermediate acetaldehyde is toxic. Acetaldehyde dehydrogenase (ALDH) catalyzes the conversion of acetaldehyde to acetate, with the concomitant reduction of NAD^+ to NADH. A mitochondrial *ALDH* is significantly induced by anoxia in coleoptiles of rice (67, 87), but not in seedlings of *Arabidopsis* (65). ALDH activity correlates with anaerobic germination capability of *Echinochloa crus-galli* under strict anoxia (40). Under O_2-limiting conditions, ALDH consumes NAD^+ and may thereby limit glycolysis, whereas upon reoxygenation acetaldehyde converted to acetate by mitochondrial ALDH enters the tricarboxylic acid (TCA) cycle (**Figure 3**).

In addition to ethanol, lactate is produced in plant cells under O_2 deprivation. The accumulation of lactate under low-O_2 stress has garnered considerable interest (31, 35, 48, 98) ever since the demonstration that its transient appearance precedes that of ethanol in the root tips of maize seedlings (105). The pH of the cytosol of maize root tips declines from 7.5 to a new equilibrium at pH 6.8 following transfer to anoxia. It is posited that the transition from lactic to ethanolic fermentation is controlled by a pH-stat. The ~0.6 unit decrease in cytosolic pH favors the catalytic optimum of PDC and thereby limits lactate and promotes ethanol production. Anoxic ADH-deficient root tips continue to produce lactate and fail to stabilize the cytosolic pH, resulting in rapid cytosolic acidification and cell death (106). Thus, the switch from lactic to ethanolic fermentation is critical for the maintenance of cytosolic pH. An alternative proposal is that this switch, under conditions of O_2 deprivation and in aerobic cells in which ethanol is produced, is driven by a rise in pyruvate rather than the increase in lactate or reduction of cytosolic pH (130). When

Figure 3

Metabolic acclimations under O_2 deprivation. Plants have multiple routes of sucrose catabolism, ATP production, and NAD^+ and $NAD(P)^+$ regeneration. Blue arrows indicate reactions that are promoted during the stress. Metabolites indicated in bold font are major or minor end products of metabolism under hypoxia. Abbreviations are as follows: 2-OGDH, 2-oxyglutarate dehydrogenase; ADH, alcohol dehydrogenase; AlaAT, alanine aminotransferase; ALDH, acetaldehyde dehydrogenase; AspAT, aspartate aminotransferase; CoASH, coenzyme A; CS, citrate synthase; FK, fructokinase; GABA-T, GABA transaminase; GDC, glutamate decarboxylase; GDH, glutamate dehydrogenase; GHBDH, γ-aminobutyrase dehydrogenase; GOGAT, NADPH-dependent glutamine: 2-oxoglutarate aminotransferase; GS, glutamine synthase; HXK, hexokinase; ICDH, isocitrate dehydrogenase; LDH, lactate dehydrogenase; MDH, malate dehydrogenase; NDP kinase, nucleoside diphosphate kinase; NiR, nitrite reductase; NR, nitrate reductase; PCK, phosphenolpyruvate carboxylase kinase; PDC, pyruvate decarboxylase; PDH, pyruvate dehydrogenase; PEPC, phosphenolpyruvate carboxylase; PFK, ATP-dependent phosphofructokinase; PFP, PPi-dependent phosphofructokinase; PGI, phosphoglucoisomerase; PGM, phosphoglucomutase; PK, pyruvate kinase; PPDK, pyruvate Pi dikinase; SDH, succinate dehydrogenase; SSADH, succinate semialdehyde dehydrogenase; Starch Pase, starch phosphorylase; SUS, sucrose synthase; UGPPase, UDP-glucose pyrophosphorylase.

pyruvate levels increase, the low K_m of mitochondrial pyruvate dehydrogenase (PDH) and high K_m of PDC serve to limit carbon entry into the TCA cycle and promote ethanolic fermentation.

Flooding stress is likely to involve a gradual transition from normoxia to hypoxia, allowing cells to initiate processes that favor survival. Plants exposed to a period of hypoxia for 2 to 4 h prior to transfer to an anoxic environment are more capable of avoiding cell death than those that undergo an abrupt anoxic shock (31). The preexposure to 3% or 4% O_2 reduces the severity of ATP depletion, allows the synthesis of stress-induced and normal cellular proteins (19), and activates a lactate efflux mechanism (158). Lactate removal from the cytoplasm may be accomplished by the hypoxia-induced nodulin intrinsic protein (NIP2;1), which was identified in *Arabidopsis* as a plasma membrane–associated protein capable of driving lactate transport in *Xenopus* oocytes (23). Most likely, a decline in cytosolic pH of 0.2 to 0.5 units under O_2 shortfall establishes a new pH set point that influences multiple aspects of metabolism (35, 48, 95). The management of this pH decline involves ethanolic fermentation and is benefited by the availability of a lactate efflux mechanism and proton ATPase activity. However, some species or organ systems, such as the tuber shoots of *Potamogeton pectinatus*, do not show an adjustment in cytosolic pH during O_2 deprivation. The stem elongation in these shoots under anoxia results from cell expansion that occurs in the absence of an adjustment in cytosolic pH and appears to be maintained by tight constraints on ATP production and consumption (29).

Besides the major fermentation end products, lactate and pyruvate, O_2 deficiency is associated with the elevation of alanine, γ-aminobutyric acid (GABA), succinate, and occasionally malate (29, 31, 46, 113, 137, 139). Strong induction of cytosolic and mitochondrial alanine aminotransferase (AlaAT), aspartate aminotransferase, mitochondrial glutamate dehydrogenase (GDH), and mitochondrial Ca^{2+}/calmodulin-regulated glutamate decarboxylase (GDH) mRNA and/or enzymatic activity is consistent with pyruvate conversion to alanine or GABA (**Figure 3**) (63, 67, 70, 71, 100, 139). GABA may be further metabolized via the mitochondrial GABA shunt to γ-hydroxylbutyrate with the regeneration of $NAD(P)^+$ (17). Upon reoxygenation, alanine can be recycled back to pyruvate, and GABA can be converted to succinate. Amino acid oxidation may thereby minimize the decline in cytosolic pH and reduce carbon loss via ethanol or lactate. An appreciation of the relative significance of the major and minor pathways of anaerobic metabolism will require metabolite profiling and flux studies that resolve organ specific and temporal aspects of production in relationship to changes in redox and energy status.

Nitrite, nitric oxide, mitochondria, and hemoglobin. Nitrate and nitrite are also implicated in cellular adjustment to O_2 deprivation. Nitrate is assimilated and reduced to ammonia via nitrate reductase (NR) and nitrite reductase (NiR) (**Figure 3**). *NR* but not *NiR* mRNAs increase significantly in response to hypoxia/anoxia in *Arabidopsis* and rice (67, 70, 71). Even without an increase in NR levels, a reduction of cytosolic pH may increase nitrite production because of the low pH optimum of this enzyme (57). Roots of tobacco plants engineered to have reduced NR levels display several metabolic anomalies under anoxia, including higher levels of soluble hexoses and ATP, enhanced ethanol and lactate production, and increased acidification of the cytosol (125). By contrast, maize seedling roots supplied with nitrate during anoxia maintain a slightly higher cytosolic pH than do control seedlings (69). Notably, the provision of micromolar levels of nitrite to seedling roots had a similar effect on the adjustment of cytosolic pH. This unexpected benefit of low levels of nitrite is unlikely to be due to a direct effect on $NAD(P)^+$ regeneration and may indicate a role of nitrite in a regulatory mechanism that augments homeostasis under low O_2.

A plant-specific association has surfaced between nitrate/nitrite metabolism, mitochondrial ATP synthesis, and a low-O_2-induced nonsymbiotic Class 1 hemoglobin (HB). Plant mitochondria provided with micromolar levels of nitrite under anoxia have the capacity to coordinate the oxidation of NADH and NAD(P)H with low levels of ATP production (124). This nitrite-promoted process involves the evolution of nitric oxide (NO) via a pathway that requires the activity of rotenone-insensitive NAD(P)H dehydrogenases, mtETC Complex III (ubiquinone:cytochrome *c* reductase), and Complex IV (COX). In the proposed pathway (124), NAD(P)H produced during O_2 deficit is oxidized by Ca^{2+}-sensitive NAD(P)H dehydrogenases on the inner mitochondrial membrane surface, providing electrons to the ubiquinone pool. In the absence of O_2, nitrite may serve as an electron acceptor at Complex III or IV, yielding NO, which may activate signal transduction by promoting mitochondrial ROS production and Ca^{2+} release. The cytosolic HB that accumulates under O_2 deprivation, however, scavenges and detoxifies NO in planta by converting it into nitrate in an NAD(P)H-consuming reaction over a broad pH optimum (30, 57). The coupled activities of HB and cytosolic NR regenerate nitrite that may enter the mitochondrion, where it continues the cycle of NO and ATP production (94, 124). A major challenge is to confirm in planta that nitrite conversion to NO functions as a surrogate final electron acceptor. Nonetheless, the scenario is consistent with reports that overexpression of HB in several species decreases rates of ethanolic fermentation, augments ATP maintenance, and fosters NO production under hypoxia. By contrast, the inhibition of HB expression increases NAD(P)H:NAD(P)$^+$ ratios and reduces cytosolic pH (30, 56, 57, 123). Notably, NO inhibits COX activity and thereby reduces ATP production under normoxia. Might NO formed during the transition from normoxia to hypoxia be the factor that dampens O_2 consumption to avoid cellular anoxia (43)? If so, the production of NO prior to the synthesis of HB may allow the cell to transition slowly from normoxia to hypoxia, providing a segue that augments energy management.

THE LOW-OXYGEN ESCAPE SYNDROME

Enhanced Growth Leading to the Emergence of Shoots

Plants forage for limiting resources by adjusting carbon allocation and overall plant architecture such that the capture of resources is consolidated (93, 96). As O_2 and CO_2 become limiting for plants in flood-prone environments, species from widely dispersed families that share the capacity to survive in flood-intense environments initiate signaling pathways that lead to fast extension growth of shoot organs (101, 147). These leaves, when reaching the water surface, function as snorkels to facilitate the entrance of O_2 and the outward ventilation of gases such as ethylene and methane trapped in roots (24, 145). Another benefit of the emergence of leaf blades is a higher rate of carbon gain from aerial photosynthesis (82).

Fast shoot elongation under water is not restricted only to species occurring in environments with periodic floods (e.g., deepwater rice, *Rumex palustris*, *Ranunculus sceleratus*) (61, 148, 150). It persists in true aquatics that develop floating leaves or flowers [e.g., *Nymphoides peltata* (82)] and in species that germinate in anaerobic mud followed by an extension growth phase to reach better-aerated water/air layers (e.g., seedlings of *Oryza sativa*, *Potamogeton pectinatus*, *P. distinctus*) (58, 113, 129). The explored mechanism of shoot elongation in Marsh dock (*R. palustris*) and deepwater rice (92, 115, 149) can be used to shed light on the mechanistic backbone of genetic diversity in flooding-induced shoot elongation.

The shoot elongation response can occur in petioles or internodes, depending on the developmental stage or predominant growth form of the plant. Interestingly, petiole elongation in rosette plants is accompanied by hyponastic growth that changes the orientation of the petiole from prostrate to erect. This directional growth brings the leaf in such a position that enhanced petiole elongation will result in leaf blade emergence in the shortest possible time. Accordingly, petiole elongation lagged behind hyponastic growth in *R. palustris* rosettes (26).

It is generally accepted that the submergence signal for enhanced shoot elongation is the gaseous phytohormone ethylene (76, 101, 147). Ethylene is biosynthesized via an O_2-dependent pathway, and the endogenous concentration of this hormone is determined predominantly by production rate and outward diffusion. Both aspects are affected by submergence. Several biosynthetic genes [e.g., those encoding ACC synthase (ACS) and ACC oxidase (ACO)] are upregulated by submergence (102, 135, 154), whereas diffusion of ethylene to the outside environment is strongly hampered. As a result, the endogenous concentration rises to a new, higher equilibrium. Ethylene production persists in submerged shoots as O_2 continues to diffuse from the water into the shoot, guaranteeing relatively high endogenous O_2 concentrations in shoot cells even in the dark (80). Submergence or low oxygen also upregulates the expression of ethylene receptor genes, including *RpERS1* in *R. palustris* (155), *OsERL1* in deepwater rice (156), and *ETR2* in *Arabidopsis* (16, 63, 70, 72). An elevation of ethylene receptor levels following submergence is counterintuitive because these molecules are negative regulators of ethylene signaling. However, this increase would allow rapid cessation of ethylene signaling as the plants emerge from the water and vent off the accumulated ethylene.

Ethylene is the input signal for several parallel pathways required for fast elongation under water (**Figure 4**). Under fully submerged conditions the accumulated ethylene downregulates abscisic acid (ABA) levels via an inhibition of 9-*cis*-epoxycarotenoid dioxygenase (NCED) expression, a family of rate-limiting enzymes in ABA biosynthesis that belongs to the carotenoid cleavage dioxygenases, (CCDs) and via an activation of ABA breakdown to phaseic acid (9, 61, 110). The decline of the endogenous ABA concentration in *R. palustris* is required to stimulate the expression of gibberellin (GA) 3-oxidase, an enzyme that catalyzes the conversion to bioactive gibberellin (GA_1) (8), and in deepwater rice to sensitize internodes to GA (61). Downstream of GA, three sets of genes play a role in submergence-induced shoot elongation. The first group encodes proteins involved in cell wall loosening; the second, those involved in the cell cycle; and the third, those involved in starch breakdown. Additional genes with putative regulatory roles in enhanced internode elongation have been identified in flooded deepwater rice (22, 108, 117, 132, 133).

The rigid cell wall constrains the rate and direction of turgor-driven cell growth. Significant increases in acid-induced cell wall extension upon submergence were observed in rice (20), *R. palustris* (152), and *Regnellidium diphyllum* (62). This could be reversed even when *R. palustris* petioles were desubmerged, emphasizing the correlation between extensibility and submergence-induced elongation (152). Cell wall extensibility is thought to be associated with cell-wall-loosening proteins, such as expansins (EXPs) and xyloglucan endotransglycosylase/hydrolases (XTHs) (27). Submergence-induced elongation is strongly correlated with increases in mRNAs encoding expansins A (*EXPA*) and B (*EXPB*), along with EXP protein abundance and activity (21, 62, 68, 89, 152, 153). Interestingly, in some species ethylene directly regulates *EXP* expression (62, 152, 153) (**Figure 4**). In submerged *R. palustris* petioles, ethylene not only enhances *EXP* expression but also stimulates proton efflux into the apoplast (153), which is essential for EXP action.

The second group of GA-regulated genes is involved in cell cycle regulation. In very young petioles of the fringed waterlily (*Nymphoides peltata*) and the youngest

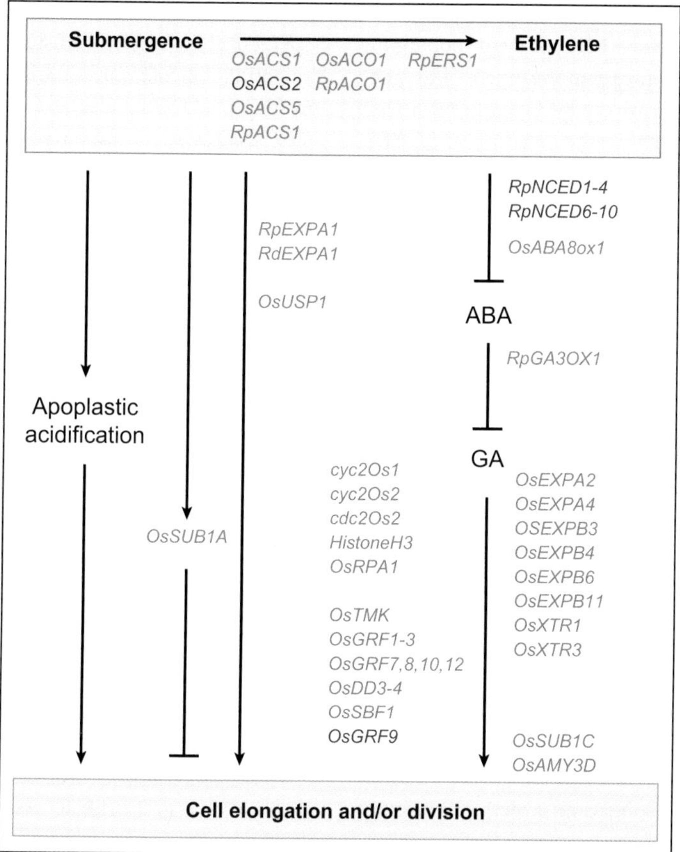

Figure 4

Schematic model of the plant processes, hormones, and genes involved in submergence-induced shoot elongation (*blue* signifies upregulated genes and *red* signifies downregulated genes). Gene abbreviations are as follows: *CYC2Os*, cyclin; *CDC2Os*, cyclin-dependent kinase; *OsACO* and *RpACO*, ACC oxidase; *OsACS* and *RpACS*, ACC synthase; *OsDD*, differentially displayed (61); *OsAMY*, amylase (41); *OsEXP*, *RdEXP*, and *RpEXP*, expansins; *OsGRF*, growth-regulating factor (22); *OsRPA*, replication protein A1; *OsSBF*, sodium/bile acid symporter family (108); *OsSUB1*, submergence1; *OsTMK*, transmembrane protein kinase (133); *OsUSP*, universal stress protein (117); *RpERS1*, ethylene receptor (155); RpNCED, 9-*cis*-epoxycarotenoid dioxygenase; *RpGA3ox*, gibberellin 3-oxidase (8); OsXTR, xyloglucan endotransglucosylase-related (27); OsABA8ox, ABA 8′-hydroxylase (110). Os indicates *Oryza sativa*, Rd indicates *Regnellidium diphyllum*, and Rp indicates *Rumex palustris*.

internode of deepwater rice, ethylene promotes not only cell elongation but also cell division. Consistent with this increase in cell division is the observed upregulation of cyclin (*CYC2Os1*, *CYC2Os2*), cyclin-dependent kinase (*CDC2Os2*), *HistoneH3*, and replication protein A1 (*OsRPA1*) (114, 115, 131).

The third group of GA-regulated genes is involved in starch breakdown. *R. palustris* plants depleted of soluble sugars and starch show a very restricted underwater elongation response (49). Carbohydrates are required to deliver energy and the building blocks for new cell wall synthesis (115, 148). The requirement of carbohydrates can be fulfilled by the translocation of photosynthates and by the degradation of starch reserves via an increase in α-amylase activity (115). Fukao and colleagues (41) reported that α-amylase gene expression (*OsAmy3D*) in leaves of submerged rice is regulated by SUB1C, an ethylene-responsive factor (ERF)-domain-containing protein of the polygenic *Sub1* locus. This gene is regulated positively by GA and negatively by a related ERF in the *Sub1* locus, *SUB1A-1*, which is present in some rice accessions. These results imply that carbohydrate levels in submerged plants are also under hormonal control.

There is considerable genetic variation between and within species in submergence-induced elongation capacity. The closely related species *Rumex acetosa* and *R. palustris* show inhibition and stimulation of petiole elongation upon exposure to ethylene, respectively. Both accumulate significant amounts of ethylene when submerged (4), but *R. acetosa* lacks ABA downregulation (9), GA upregulation (104), and increased *EXP* expression (153). However, when *R. acetosa* is exposed to elevated GA levels without enhanced ethylene or when ABA levels are reduced with fluridone in submerged plants, petiole elongation is strongly stimulated (9, 104). This demonstrates that signal transduction components required for elongation growth downstream of ABA and GA are present in this species and can be activated. It also shows that in *R. acetosa*, contrary to *R. palustris*, ethylene cannot switch on this cascade. Most likely, elements downstream of ethylene but upstream of ABA/GA explain differences in ethylene-induced elongation between *Rumex* species.

Rice cultivars also show variation in elongation capacity during submergence (28, 41, 120). The *Sub1* locus controls underwater elongation through genetic distinctions in the two to three ERF proteins it encodes (41, 159) (**Figure 2**). *SUB1A-1* is present in the *Sub1* locus only in submergence-tolerant lines and is induced by ethylene. *SUB1C* is present in all rice lines and is induced by GA. The between-cultivar variation in elongation correlates with genotypic variation and expression of ERFs of the *Sub1* locus. The slowly elongating rice varieties of *indica* rapidly and strongly induce *SUB1A-1* upon submergence, whereas all elongating *indica* and *japonica* varieties lack either the *SUB1A* gene or the *SUB1A-1* allele (159). Transformation of an elongating *japonica* variety with a *SUB1A-1* full-length cDNA under the control of the maize *Ubiquitin1* promoter resulted in a significant repression of underwater elongation (159). The expression of *SUB1A-1* coincides with repressed accumulation of transcripts for *EXPs* and reduced expression of *SUB1C* (41), suggesting that SUB1A acts upstream of GA regulation of *EXPs* and *SUB1C*.

Improvement of the Oxygen and Carbohydrate Status in Submerged Plants

At the whole-plant level, complete submergence leads to a dramatic shift in the carbon budget and energy status, potentially resulting in death. Some relief of this problem, with the leaves still submerged, is underwater photosynthesis (83). The significance of this was exposed by studies showing that light availability enhances survival under water in both flood-tolerant and intolerant species (55, 81, 86, 141) and that O_2 levels in submerged plants are affected by light intensity (90). Improved survival of submergence in the light is correlated with a higher carbohydrate status (97) and internal O_2 concentrations (80, 84, 103). However, underwater photosynthesis can be limited by low light and CO_2 availability. Consistent with these findings are studies showing that illumination can maintain sugar transport and leaf ATP content at near-normoxic levels under strict O_2 deprivation in rice and wheat leaves (85).

True aquatics develop specialized leaves characterized by an overall thin leaf and cuticle, a high degree of dissection, and epidermal cell chloroplasts. These traits reduce the diffusion barriers and shorten the diffusion pathways, thus enhancing carbon input per leaf area and unit time (111). Other strategies, developed by true aquatics to enhance carbon gain, are the utilization of HCO_3 as carbon source, C4 or CAM metabolism, or hydrosoil CO_2 consumption

(75, 83). Very little information is available about the occurrence of these last strategies in terrestrial plants from flood-prone environments.

Leaf acclimations to submergence have been characterized for *R. palustris* (82) and other amphibious species (18, 37, 157). Leaves developed under water are 20% thinner with an increased specific leaf area (SLA) (m^2 g^{-1}), indicating a large surface area relative to mass. The higher SLA is related not only to the lower leaf thickness of aquatic leaves but also to their tenfold-lower starch content. Furthermore, aquatic leaves have thinner epidermal cell walls and cuticles, and their chloroplasts lie close to the epidermis rather than toward the intercellular spaces as is typical for aerial leaves (82). These acclimations are consistent with the view that CO_2 directly enters the mesophyll cells of these leaves via diffusion through the epidermis and not via stomata and intercellular gas diffusion. This diffusion pathway under water has a much higher diffusion resistance for gases than does intercellular diffusion. Calculations for *R. palustris* indicate a 15,000-fold-higher resistance to CO_2 diffusion in leaves under submergence than when in air (81). However, the morphological and anatomical changes decrease gas diffusion resistance for CO_2 (38). In *R. palustris* these acclimations result in a dramatic reduction of the diffusion resistance between submerged leaves and leaves in air to a factor of less than 400 (81). Functional consequences of these acclimations in *R. palustris* include higher rates of net underwater assimilation and lower CO_2 compensation points (81). Similar effects are also described for amphibious species (13, 55, 140). The relatively low diffusion resistance in aquatic leaves also permits increased inward diffusion of O_2 from the water layer into the shoot. This results, in the dark, in an internal O_2 concentration of 17% in acclimated petioles of *R. palustris* when submerged in air-saturated water, whereas nonacclimated petioles reach only 9% (80).

These observations demonstrate that the water column can function as an important source of O_2 for terrestrial plants when they are exposed to submergence and that O_2 levels in leaves, stems, and petioles below the critical O_2 pressure (0.8%; 31) are rare and probably restricted to densely packed tissues or to aquatic environments that are extremely stagnant or have low O_2 levels. Although root systems will likely benefit from these shoot acclimations, O_2 pressures in the roots will still be much lower than the values mentioned here for shoots, especially at night, when there is no photosynthesis (90). It is therefore expected that even with LOES acclimations, roots will also rely on the metabolic cellular adjustments to O_2 deprivation for survival.

Plants in frequently flooded environments are expected to display these traits at a higher frequency than do those in rarely flooded areas. Consistently, *Ranunculus repens* populations in temporary lakes are characterized by constitutively dissected leaves. This morphology allows for a relatively large leaf surface and an improved gas exchange and results in relatively high rates of underwater photosynthesis. Plants from more terrestrial populations have less-dissected leaves and relatively low rates of underwater photosynthesis (73, 74). However, a comparative study of nine species, both flooding tolerant and intolerant, showed that gas exchange acclimations under water are not restricted to flood-tolerant species (84). In this study all but one species developed aquatic leaves that were thinner and had thinner outer cell walls and cuticles and a higher SLA. These responses were independent of the species' flooding tolerances. Furthermore, leaf plasticity upon submergence resulted in increased O_2 levels in all species. Therefore, between-species variation in inducible leaf acclimations in terrestrial plants, to optimize gas exchange when submerged, is not related to the variation in flooding tolerance of the species investigated (84). This conclusion hints toward a limited role of submergence signals, such as elevated ethylene, in inducing leaf acclimations that enhance gas exchange under water. Plants that are not exposed to flooding throughout their life are not expected to use these signals to switch on signaling cascades that lead to altered leaf anatomy and morphology. More likely, signals associated with changed rates of photosynthesis and/or reduced levels of carbohydrates induce these leaf acclimations. This hypothesis is consistent with observations that shade-acclimated plants with reduced rates of photosynthesis develop thinner leaves with higher SLA (78). Consistently, transgenic tobacco plants with substantially reduced Rubisco levels have reduced photosynthesis and increased SLA (34).

Improvement of Internal Gas Diffusion: Aerenchyma

Important traits for survival in flooded environments are those that reduce the resistance for diffusion of O_2 and CO_2 from the environment to the plant. Equally significant, however, is the resistance that hampers gas diffusion within organs. Fast gas diffusion can be accomplished only in a gaseous diffusion medium, over short distances, by limited loss of the gas along the diffusion path, and by restricted tortuosity of the diffusion route. These requirements are met in aerenchymatous tissue, characterized by longitudinally interconnected gas spaces in roots and shoots. Aerenchyma is either constitutively present and/or induced upon flooding (116, 144) and develops in existing tissues or concomitant with the development of new roots (32). Distinct physiological processes are at the basis of aerenchyma formation. This led to the discrimination of two aerenchyma types: (*a*) lysigenous aerenchyma formed by cell death and (*b*) schizogenous aerenchyma in which gas spaces develop through the separation of previously connected cells (23, 33, 60). A third type, termed expansigenous aerenchyma, is characterized by intercellular gas spaces that develop through cell division and cell enlargement, without cell separation or collapse/death (118). Combinations of these aerenchyma types also exist (118), and within one plant species different types can be present in different organs (32, 33).

The mechanism of schizogenous aerenchyma formation is largely unknown as compared with that of lysigenous aerenchyma. Low O_2 and elevated ethylene can induce lysigenous aerenchyma development in roots of maize in a manner that is phenotypically similar to the process promoted by flooding (32). Under flooded conditions, subambient O_2 concentrations stimulate the production of ethylene, which accumulates in roots surrounded by water and induces programmed cell death (PCD) in the cortex tissue (53). Accordingly, hypoxic roots, exposed to inhibitors of ethylene biosynthesis or action, form no gas spaces (53). Downstream components of this regulatory route include protein kinases, protein phosphatases, G proteins, Ca^{2+}, and inositol phospholipids (54). The targets of these signaling routes include proteins associated with cell wall breakdown. The activity of cellulase increases in roots upon exposure to low O_2 or ethylene (52). Furthermore, increases in pectinase and xylanase activity (15) and the induction of *XTH* mRNAs occur in diverse species in response to flooding or hypoxia (67, 70, 109).

Large data collections are available on genetic diversity in traits that contribute to the delivery of O_2 to root tips. Justin & Armstrong (60) compared 91 species from wetland, intermediate, and nonwetland habitats. Nearly all the species from nonwetland environments had low root porosities, whereas high constitutive and increased porosities upon flooding were associated with species from wetland environments. Also, other studies confirmed the strong correlation between high root porosities and occurrence in wet environments (45, 77, 143). Interestingly, a comparative study on 35 wild *Hordeum* accessions from environments that differ in flooding intensity showed that this correlation does not always exist and that aerenchyma development can be constrained by phylogeny (42).

Aerenchyma is also formed in shoot organs, providing a system of interconnected channels from leaf to root tip. In a study with 14 species divided over seven families, the aerenchyma content of petioles strongly correlated with plant survival during complete submergence. This robust correlation persisted in environmental conditions with (light) and without (dark) underwater photosynthesis (79, 84). These observations suggest that aerenchyma is important not only for survival during partial flooding but also during complete submergence. Petiole aerenchyma likely facilitates the diffusion of O_2 from shoot organs to the roots. The O_2 involved can be photosynthetically derived during the light period or obtained from the water layer by the shoot during the dark.

CONCLUSIONS AND FUTURE PERSPECTIVES

The growing understanding of the molecular basis and genetic diversity in submergence and flooding acclimations provides opportunities to breed and engineer crops tolerant of these conditions that would benefit the world's farmers. The evaluation of diversity exposes plasticity in metabolic and developmental acclimations that enable distinct strategies that increase fitness in a flooded environment. Natural variation in acclimation schemes provides opportunities for development of crops with combinations of submergence tolerance traits that are optimal at specific developmental stages and under particular flooding regimes, which vary substantially worldwide. The first example of this is the use of marker-assisted breeding to introduce the submergence-tolerance conferring *Sub1* genotype to selected rice cultivars (159), which may appreciably benefit rice production in flood-prone lands in the Third World. The further exploration of the molecular basis of genetic diversity in flooding tolerances is critical given the global climate change scenarios that predict heavy precipitation in regions of our planet.

SUMMARY POINTS

1. Evaluation of diversity exposes the remarkable plasticity in metabolic and developmental acclimations that enable increased fitness in a flooded environment.
2. Plants employing an escape strategy develop a suite of traits collectively called the low-oxygen escape syndrome (LOES).
3. A consequence of low-O_2 stress is a requirement for energy conservation that is invoked through adjustments in gene expression, carbohydrate catabolism, $NAD(P)^+$ regeneration, and ATP production.
4. Energy conservation is influenced by a low-O_2-induced nonsymbiotic hemoglobin that regulates cytosolic and mitochondrial processes, including rates of fermentation, NO, and ATP production.
5. Enhanced shoot elongation upon submergence requires the action of at least three hormones (ethylene, ABA, and GA) that regulate processes such as apoplastic acidification, cell wall loosening, cell division, and starch breakdown.
6. Anatomical and biochemical leaf acclimations upon submergence facilitate underwater photosynthesis as well as the inward diffusion of O_2 from the floodwater.
7. Aerenchyma in root and shoot tissue not only is important for survival during partial submergence but also facilitates O_2 diffusion from shoot to root while the plant is completely submerged.

FUTURE ISSUES

1. Plant species differ in their growth response to ethylene during submergence. This is far from understood but probably involves signal transduction components upstream of ABA and GA. The characterization of *SUB1A* is an important finding in this respect. More work is needed because this is probably an important selection point to differentiate survival strategies.
2. A quiescence strategy (carbohydrate conservation) in rice is associated with submergence tolerance. However, not all plants that fail to elongate under water are tolerant. The question arises as to whether cells of these plants are metabolically inactive or simply lack other aspects also needed for tolerance (e.g., the ability to manage ATP, cytosolic pH, or cellular O_2 content; protection against ROS; or aerenchyma development).
3. Characterization of the *Sub1* locus provides an opportunity to breed or engineer submergence-tolerant rice that could benefit farmers in flood-prone areas. Studies are needed to determine if submergence and salt tolerance can be combined because floodwaters can be saline.
4. The development of rice cultivars with improved underwater germination and low-O_2 escape capabilities may reduce herbicide use.

DISCLOSURE STATEMENT

The authors are not aware of any biases that might be perceived as affecting the objectivity of this review.

ACKNOWLEDGMENTS

The authors thank Ronald Pierik for his critical comments and his efforts to condense this review. Furthermore, we thank Tim Colmer, Takeshi Fukao, Robert Hill, Liesje Mommer, Angelika Mustroph, Pierdomenico Perata, and Eric Visser for comments and discussion. We regret that many publications were not cited owing to space limitations. Submergence and low-O_2 stress research in the Bailey-Serres lab is currently supported by the NSF (IBN-0420152) and USDA (06-35100-17288). Flooding research in the Voesenek lab has been continuously supported by the Netherlands Organization for Scientific Research.

LITERATURE CITED

1. Arnell N, Liu C. 2001. Climate change 2001: hydrology and water resources. In *Report Intergovernmental Panel on Climate Change*. **http://www.ipcc.ch/**
2. Arpagaus S, Braendle R. 2000. The significance of α-amylase under anoxia stress in tolerant rhizomes (*Acorus calamus* L.) and nontolerant tubers (*Solanum tuberosum* L., var. Désirée). *J. Exp. Bot.* 51:1475–77
3. Bailey-Serres J, Chang R. 2005. Sensing and signalling in response to oxygen deprivation in plants and other organisms. *Ann. Bot.* 96:507–18
4. Banga M, Slaa EJ, Blom CWPM, Voesenek LACJ. 1996. Ethylene biosynthesis and accumulation under drained and submerged conditions: a comparative study of two *Rumex* species. *Plant Physiol.* 112:229–37

5. Baxter-Burrell A, Chang R, Springer P, Bailey-Serres J. 2003. Gene and enhancer trap transposable elements reveal oxygen deprivation-regulated genes and their complex patterns of expression in *Arabidopsis*. *Ann. Bot.* 91:129–41
6. **Baxter-Burrell A, Yang Z, Springer PS, Bailey-Serres J. 2002. RopGAP4-dependent Rop GTPase rheostat control of *Arabidopsis* oxygen deprivation tolerance. *Science* 296:2026–28**
7. Bell EL, Klimova TA, Eisenbart J, Moraes CT, Murphy MP, et al. 2007. The Q_o site of the mitochondrial complex III is required for the transduction of hypoxic signaling via reactive oxygen species production. *J. Cell Biol.* 177:1029–36
8. Benschop JJ, Bou J, Peeters AJM, Wagemaker N, Gühl K, et al. 2006. Long-term submergence-induced elongation in *Rumex palustris* requires abscisic acid-dependent biosynthesis of gibberellin. *Plant Physiol.* 141:1644–52
9. Benschop JJ, Jackson MB, Gühl K, Vreeburg RAM, Croker SJ, et al. 2005. Contrasting interactions between ethylene and abscisic acid in *Rumex* species differing in submergence tolerance. *Plant J.* 44:756–68
10. Bieniawska Z, Paul Barratt DH, Garlick AP, Thole V, Kruger NJ, et al. 2007. Analysis of the sucrose synthase gene family in *Arabidopsis*. *Plant J.* 49:810–28
11. Blokhina OB, Chirkova TV, Fagerstedt KV. 2001. Anoxic stress leads to hydrogen peroxide formation in plant cells. *J. Exp Bot.* 52:1179–90
12. Blom CWPM, Voesenek LACJ. 1996. Flooding: the survival strategies of plants. *Trends Ecol. Evol.* 11:290–95
13. Boeger MRT, Poulson ME. 2003. Morphological adaptations and photosynthesis rates of amphibious *Veronica anagallis-aquatica* L. (Scrophulariaceae) under different flow regimes. *Aquat. Bot.* 75:123–35
14. Bologa KL, Fernie AR, Leisse A, Loureiro ME, Geigenberger P. 2003. A bypass of sucrose synthase leads to low internal oxygen and impaired metabolic performance in growing potato tubers. *Plant Physiol.* 132:2058–72
15. Bragina TV, Rodionova NA, Grinieva GM. 2003. Ethylene production and activation of hydrolytic enzymes during acclimation of maize seedlings to partial flooding. *Russ. J. Plant Physiol.* 50:794–98
16. Branco-Price C, Kawaguchi R, Ferreira RB, Bailey-Serres J. 2005. Genome-wide analysis of transcript abundance and translation in *Arabidopsis* seedlings subjected to oxygen deprivation. *Ann. Bot.* 96:647–60
17. Breitkreuz KE, Allan WL, Van Cauwenberghe OR, Jakobs C, Talibi D, et al. 2003. A novel γ-hydroxybutyrate dehydrogenase: identification and expression of an *Arabidopsis* cDNA and potential role under oxygen deficiency. *J. Biol. Chem.* 278:41552–56
18. Bruni NC, Young JP, Dengler NC. 1996. Leaf developmental plasticity of *Ranunculus flabellaris* in response to terrestrial and submerged environments. *Can. J. Bot.* 74:823–37
19. Chang WW, Huang L, Shen M, Webster C, Burlingame AL, Roberts JK. 2000. Patterns of protein synthesis and tolerance of anoxia in root tips of maize seedlings acclimated to a low-oxygen environment, and identification of proteins by mass spectrometry. *Plant Physiol.* 122:295–318
20. Cho HT, Kende H. 1997. Expansins and internodal growth of deepwater rice. *Plant Physiol.* 113:1145–51
21. Cho HT, Kende H. 1997. Expression of expansin genes is correlated with growth in deepwater rice. *Plant Cell* 9:1661–71

6. Identifies signal transduction pathway components that regulate ADH and ROS production under oxygen deprivation.

22. Choi D, Kim JH, Kende H. 2004. Whole genome analysis of the *OsGRF* gene family encoding plant-specific putative transcription activators in rice. *Plant Cell Physiol.* 45:897–904
23. Choi WG, Roberts DM. 2007. *Arabidopsis* NIP2;1: a major intrinsic protein transporter of lactic acid induced by anoxic stress. *J. Biol. Chem.* 282:24209–18
24. Colmer TD. 2003. Long-distance transport of gases in plants: a perspective on internal aeration and radial oxygen loss from roots. *Plant Cell Environ.* 26:17–36
25. **Colmer TD, Gibberd MR, Wiengweera A, Tinh TK. 1998. The barrier to radial oxygen loss from roots of rice (*Oryza sativa* L.) is induced by growth in stagnant solutions. *J. Exp. Bot.* 49:1431–36**

25. The first report that a barrier to radial oxygen loss can be induced in existing roots.

26. **Cox MCH, Millenaar FF, de Jong vanBerkel YEM, Peeters AJM, Voesenek LACJ. 2003. Plant movement. Submergence-induced petiole elongation in *Rumex palustris* depends on hyponastic growth. *Plant Physiol.* 132:282–91**

26. Describes the requirement of a petiole angle signal for submergence-induced petiole elongation.

27. Darley CP, Forrester AM, McQueen-Mason SJ. 2001. The molecular basis of plant cell wall extension. *Plant Mol. Biol.* 47:179–95
28. Das KK, Sarkar RK, Ismail AM. 2005. Elongation ability and nonstructural carbohydrate levels in relation to submergence tolerance in rice. *Plant Sci.* 168:131–36
29. Dixon MH, Hill SA, Jackson MB, Ratcliffe RG, Sweetlove LJ. 2006. Physiological and metabolic adaptations of *Potamogeton pectinatus* L. tubers support rapid elongation of stem tissue in the absence of oxygen. *Plant Cell Physiol.* 47:128–40
30. Dordas C, Rivoal J, Hill RD. 2003. Plant haemoglobins, nitric oxide and hypoxic stress. *Ann. Bot.* 91:173–78
31. Drew MC. 1997. Oxygen deficiency and root metabolism: injury and acclimation under hypoxia and anoxia. *Annu. Rev. Plant Physiol. Plant Mol. Biol.* 48:223–50
32. Drew MC, He CJ, Morgan PW. 2000. Programmed cell death and aerenchyma formation in roots. *Trends Plant Sci.* 5:123–27
33. Evans DE. 2004. Aerenchyma formation. *New Phytol.* 161:35–49
34. Evans JR, Von Caemmerer S, Setchell BA, Hudson GS. 1994. The relationship between CO_2 transfer conductance and leaf anatomy in transgenic tobacco with a reduced content of rubisco. *Aust. J. Plant Physiol.* 21:475–95
35. Felle HH. 2005. pH regulation in anoxic plants. *Ann. Bot.* 96:519–32
36. Fennoy SL, Nong T, Bailey-Serres J. 1998. Transcriptional and post-transcriptional processes regulate gene expression in oxygen-deprived roots of maize. *Plant J.* 15:727–35
37. Frost-Christensen H, Bolt Jorgensen L, Floto F. 2003. Species specificity of resistance to oxygen diffusion in thin cuticular membranes from amphibious plants. *Plant Cell Environ.* 26:561–69
38. Frost-Christensen H, Floto F. 2007. Resistance to CO_2 diffusion in cuticular membranes of amphibious plants and the implication for CO_2 acquisition. *Plant Cell Environ.* 30:12–18
39. Fukao T, Bailey-Serres J. 2004. Plant responses to hypoxia. Is survival a balancing act? *Trends Plant Sci.* 9:1403–9
40. Fukao T, Kennedy RA, Yamasue Y, Rumpho ME. 2003. Genetic and biochemical analysis of anaerobically-induced enzymes during seed germination of *Echinochloa crus-galli* varieties tolerant and intolerant of anoxia. *J. Exp. Bot.* 54:1421–29
41. **Fukao T, Xu K, Ronald PC, Bailey-Serres J. 2006. A variable cluster of ethylene response factor-like genes regulates metabolic and developmental acclimation responses to submergence in rice. *Plant Cell* 18:2021–34**

41. Identified physiological aspects controlled by genetic variation at the *Sub1* locus conferring distinctions between escape and quiescence survival strategies under submergence.

42. Garthwaite AJ, Von Bothmer R, Colmer TD. 2003. Diversity in root aeration traits associated with waterlogging tolerance in the genus *Hordeum*. *Funct. Plant Biol.* 30:875–89
43. Geigenberger P. 2003. Response of plant metabolism to too little oxygen. *Curr. Opin. Plant Biol.* 6:247–56
44. Geigenberger P, Fernie AR, Gibon Y, Christ M, Stitt M. 2000. Metabolic activity decreases as an adaptive response to low internal oxygen in growing potato tubers. *Biol. Chem.* 381:723–40
45. Gibberd MR, Gray JD, Cocks PS, Colmer TD. 2001. Waterlogging tolerance among a diverse range of *Trifolium* accessions is related to root porosity, lateral root formation and 'aerotropic rooting'. *Ann. Bot.* 88:579–89
46. Gibbs J, Greenway H. 2003. Review: Mechanisms of anoxia tolerance in plants. I. Growth, survival and anaerobic catabolism. *Funct. Plant Biol.* 30:1–47
47. Greenway H, Armstrong W, Colmer TD. 2006. Conditions leading to high CO_2 (>5 kPa) in waterlogged-flooded soils and possible effects on root growth and metabolism. *Ann. Bot.* 98:9–32
48. Greenway H, Gibbs J. 2003. Review: mechanisms of anoxia tolerance in plants. II. Energy requirements for maintenance and energy distribution to essential processes. *Funct. Plant Biol.* 30:999–1036
49. Groenveld HW, Voesenek LACJ. 2003. Submergence-induced petiole elongation in *Rumex palustris* is controlled by developmental stage and storage compounds. *Plant Soil* 253:115–23
50. Guglielminetti L, Yamaguchi J, Perata P, Alpi A. 1995. Amylolytic activities in cereal seeds under aerobic and anaerobic conditions. *Plant Physiol.* 109:1069–76
51. Guzy RD, Schumacker PT. 2006. Oxygen sensing by mitochondria at complex III: the paradox of increased reactive oxygen species during hypoxia. *Exp. Physiol.* 91:807–19
52. He CJ, Drew MC, Morgan PW. 1994. Induction of enzymes associated with lysigenous aerenchyma formation in roots of *Zea mays* during hypoxia or nitrogen-starvation. *Plant Physiol.* 105:861–65
53. He CJ, Finlayson SA, Drew MC, Jordan WR, Morgan PW. 1996. Ethylene biosynthesis during aerenchyma formation in roots of maize subjected to mechanical impedance and hypoxia. *Plant Physiol.* 112:1679–85
54. He CJ, Morgan PW, Drew MC. 1996. Transduction of an ethylene signal is required for cell death and lysis in the root cortex of maize during aerenchyma formation induced by hypoxia. *Plant Physiol.* 112:463–72
55. He JB, Bögemann GM, Van der Steeg HM, Rijnders JHGM, Voesenek LACJ, Blom CWPM. 1999. Survival tactics of *Ranunculus* species in river floodplains. *Oecologia* 118:1–8
56. **Hunt PW, Klok EJ, Trevaskis B, Watts RA, Ellis MH, et al. 2002. Increased level of hemoglobin 1 enhances survival of hypoxic stress and promotes early growth in *Arabidopsis thaliana*. *Proc. Natl. Acad. Sci. USA* 99:17197–202**
57. Igamberdiev AU, Hill RD. 2004. Nitrate, NO and haemoglobin in plant adaptation to hypoxia: an alternative to classic fermentation pathways. *J. Exp. Bot.* 55:2473–82
58. Ishizawa K, Murakami S, Kawakami Y, Kuramochi H. 1999. Growth and energy status of arrowhead tubers, pondweed turions and rice seedlings under anoxic conditions. *Plant Cell Environ.* 22:505–14
59. Jackson MB. 2008. Ethylene-promoted elongation: an adaptation to submergence stress. *Ann. Bot.* 101:229–48

56. A hemoglobin-like protein that is expressed in response to hypoxia confers increased tolerance to the stress.

60. Comprehensive overview of genetic diversity in aerenchyma architecture and development.

60. **Justin SHFW, Armstrong W. 1987. The anatomical characteristics of roots and plant response to soil flooding. *New Phytol.* 106:465–95**
61. Kende H, Van Der Knaap E, Cho HT. 1998. Deepwater rice: a model plant to study stem elongation. *Plant Physiol.* 118:1105–10
62. Kim JH, Cho HT, Kende H. 2000. α-Expansins in the semiaquatic ferns *Marsilea quadrifolia* and *Regnellidium diphyllum*: evolutionary aspects and physiological role in rachis elongation. *Planta* 212:85–92
63. Klok EJ, Wilson IW, Wilson D, Chapman SC, Ewing RM, et al. 2002. Expression profile analysis of the low-oxygen response in *Arabidopsis* root cultures. *Plant Cell* 14:2481–94
64. Koch K. 2004. Sucrose metabolism: regulatory mechanisms and pivotal roles in sugar sensing and plant development. *Curr. Opin. Plant Biol.* 7:235–46
65. Kürsteiner O, Dupuis I, Kuhlemeier C. 2003. The *pyruvate decarboxylase1* gene of *Arabidopsis* is required during anoxia but not other environmental stresses. *Plant Physiol.* 132:968–78
66. Kuzmin EV, Karpova OV, Elthon TE, Newton KJ. 2004. Mitochondrial respiratory deficiencies signal up-regulation of genes for heat shock proteins. *J. Biol. Chem.* 279:20672–77
67. Lasanthi-Kudahettige R, Magneschi L, Loreti E, Gonzali S, Licausi F, et al. 2007. Transcript profiling of the anoxic rice coleoptile. *Plant Physiol.* 144:218–31
68. Lee Y, Kende H. 2001. Expression of α-expansins is correlated with internodal elongation in deepwater rice. *Plant Physiol.* 127:645–54
69. Libourel IG, van Bodegom PM, Fricker MD, Ratcliffe RG. 2006. Nitrite reduces cytoplasmic acidosis under anoxia. *Plant Physiol.* 142:1710–17
70. Liu F, Vantoai T, Moy L, Bock G, Linford LD, Quackenbush J. 2005. Global transcription profiling reveals novel insights into hypoxic response in *Arabidopsis*. *Plant Physiol.* 137:1115–29
71. Loreti E, Poggi A, Novi G, Alpi A, Perata P. 2005. Genome-wide analysis of gene expression in *Arabidopsis* seedlings under anoxia. *Plant Physiol.* 137:1130–38
72. Loreti E, Yamaguchi J, Alpi A, Perata P. 2003. Sugar modulation of α-amylase genes under anoxia. *Ann. Bot.* 91:143–48
73. Lynn DE, Waldren S. 2001. Morphological variation in populations of *Ranunculus repens* from the temporary limestone lakes (turloughs) in the West of Ireland. *Ann. Bot.* 87:9–17
74. Lynn DE, Waldren S. 2002. Physiological variation in populations of *Ranunculus repens* L. (creeping buttercup) from the temporary limestone lakes (turloughs) in the west of Ireland. *Ann. Bot.* 89:707–14
75. Maberly SC, Madsen TV. 1998. Affinity for CO_2 in relation to the ability of freshwater macrophytes to use HCO_3. *Funct. Ecol.* 12:99–106
76. Malone M, Ridge I. 1983. Ethylene-induced growth and proton excretion in the aquatic plant *Nymphoides peltata*. *Planta* 157:71–73
77. McDonald MP, Galwey NW, Colmer TD. 2002. Similarity and diversity in adventitious root anatomy as related to root aeration among a range of wetland and dryland grass species. *Plant Cell Environ.* 25:441–51
78. Mommer L, De Kroon H, Pierik R, Bögemann GM, Visser EJW. 2005. A functional comparison of acclimation to shade and submergence in two terrestrial plant species. *New Phytol.* 167:197–206
79. Mommer L, Lenssen JPM, Huber H, Visser EJW, De Kroon H. 2006. Ecophysiological determinants of plant performance under flooding: a comparative study of seven plant families. *J. Ecol.* 94:1117–29

80. Mommer L, Pedersen O, Visser EJW. 2004. Acclimation of a terrestrial plant to submergence facilitates gas exchange under water. *Plant Cell Environ.* 27:1281–87
81. Mommer L, Pons TL, Visser EJW. 2006. Photosynthetic consequences of phenotypic plasticity in response to submergence: *Rumex palustris* as a case study. *J. Exp. Bot.* 57:283–90
82. Mommer L, Pons TL, Wolters-Arts M, Venema JH, Visser EJW. 2005. Submergence-induced morphological, anatomical, and biochemical responses in a terrestrial species affects gas diffusion resistance and photosynthetic performance. *Plant Physiol.* 139:497–508

82. Describes anatomical and biochemical changes upon submergence that affect underwater photosynthesis in *Rumex palustris*.

83. Mommer L, Visser EJW. 2005. Underwater photosynthesis in flooded terrestrial plants: a matter of leaf plasticity. *Ann. Bot.* 96:581–89
84. Mommer L, Wolters-Arts M, Andersen C, Visser EJW, Pedersen O. 2007. Submergence-induced leaf acclimation in terrestrial species varying in flooding tolerance. *New Phytol.* 176:337–45
85. Mustroph A, Boamfa EI, Laarhoven LJ, Harren FJ, Pörs Y, Grimm B. 2006. Organ specific analysis of the anaerobic primary metabolism in rice and wheat seedlings II: Light exposure reduces needs for fermentation and extends survival during anaerobiosis. *Planta* 225:139–52
86. Nabben RHM, Blom CWPM, Voesenek LACJ. 1999. Resistance to complete submergence in *Rumex* species with different life histories: the influence of plant size and light. *New Phytol.* 144:313–21
87. Nakazono M, Tsuji H, Li Y, Saisho D, Arimura S, Tsutsumi N, Hirai A. 2000. Expression of a gene encoding mitochondrial aldehyde dehydrogenase in rice increases under submerged conditions. *Plant Physiol.* 124:587–98
88. Nie X, Durnin DC, Igamberdiev AU, Hill RD. 2006. Cytosolic calcium is involved in the regulation of barley hemoglobin gene expression. *Planta* 223:542–49
89. Ookawara R, Satoh S, Yoshihito T, Ishizawa K. 2005. Expression of α-expansin and xyloglucan endotransglucosylase/hydrolase genes associated with shoot elongation enhanced by anoxia, ethylene and carbon dioxide in arrowhead (*Sagittaria pygmaea* Miq.) tubers. *Ann. Bot.* 96:693–702
90. Pedersen O, Vos H, Colmer TD. 2006. Oxygen dynamics during submergence in the halophytic stem succulent *Halosarcia pergranulata*. *Plant Cell Environ.* 29:1388–99
91. Perata P, Voesenek LACJ. 2007. Submergence tolerance in rice requires *Sub1A*, an ethylene-response-factor-like gene. *Trends Plant Sci.* 12:43–46
92. Pierik R, Millenaar FF, Peeters AJM, Voesenek LACJ. 2005. New perspectives in flooding research: the use of shade avoidance and *Arabidopsis thaliana*. *Ann. Bot.* 96:533–40
93. Pierik R, Tholen D, Poorter H, Visser EJW, Voesenek LACJ. 2006. The Janus face of ethylene: growth inhibition and stimulation. *Trends Plant Sci.* 11:176–83

93. Presents an integrated view on the growth-inhibitory and -stimulating effects of the gaseous plant hormone ethylene.

94. Planchet E, Jagadis Gupta K, Sonoda M, Kaiser WM. 2005. Nitric oxide emission from tobacco leaves and cell suspensions: rate limiting factors and evidence for the involvement of mitochondrial electron transport. *Plant J.* 41:732–43
95. Plaxton WC, Podesta FE. 2006. The functional organization and control of plant respiration. *Crit. Rev. Plant Sci.* 25:159–98
96. Potters G, Pasternak TP, Guisez Y, Palme KJ, Jansen MAK. 2007. Stress-induced morphogenic responses: growing out of trouble? *Trends Plant Sci.* 12:98–105
97. Ram PC, Singh BB, Singh AK, Ram P, Singh PN, et al. 2002. Submergence tolerance in rainfed lowland rice: physiological basis and prospects for cultivar improvement through marker-aided breeding. *Field Crops. Res.* 76:131–52

98. Ratcliffe RG. 1999. Intracellular pH regulation in plants under anoxia. In *Regulation of Tissue pH in Plants and Animals: A Reappraisal of Current Techniques*, ed. S Egginton, EW Taylor, JA Raven, pp. 193–213. Cambridge, UK: Cambridge Univ. Press
99. Rhoads DM, Umbach AL, Subbaiah CC, Siedow JN. 2006. Mitochondrial reactive oxygen species. Contribution to oxidative stress and interorganellar signaling. *Plant Physiol.* 141:357–66
100. Ricoult C, Echeverria LO, Cliquet JB, Limami AM. 2006. Characterization of alanine aminotransferase (AlaAT) multigene family and hypoxic response in young seedlings of the model legume *Medicago truncatula*. *J Exp. Bot.* 57:3079–89
101. Ridge I. 1987. Ethylene and growth control in amphibious plants. In *Plant Life in Aquatic and Amphibious habitats*, ed RMM Crawford, pp. 53–76. Oxford, UK: Blackwell Sci. Publ.
102. Rieu I, Cristescu SM, Harren FJM, Huibers W, Voesenek LACJ, et al. 2005. RP-ACS1, a flooding-induced 1-aminocyclopropane-1-carboxylate synthase gene of *Rumex palustris*, is involved in rhythmic ethylene production. *J. Exp. Bot.* 56:841–49
103. Rijnders JGHM, Armstrong W, Darwent MJ, Blom CWPM, Voesenek LACJ. 2000. The role of oxygen in submergence-induced petiole elongation in *Rumex palustris*: in situ measurements of oxygen in petioles of intact plants using microelectrodes. *New Phytol.* 147:479–504
104. Rijnders JGHM, Yang YY, Kamiya Y, Takahashi N, Barendse GWM, et al. 1997. Ethylene enhances gibberellin levels and petiole sensitivity in flooding-tolerant *Rumex palustris* but not in flooding-intolerant *R. acetosa*. *Planta* 20:320–25
105. Roberts JKM, Callis J, Wemmer D, Walbot V, Jardetzky O. 1984. Mechanisms of cytoplasmic pH regulation in hypoxic maize root tips and its role in survival under anoxia. *Proc. Natl. Acad. Sci. USA* 81:3368–72
106. Roberts JKM, Chang K, Webster C, Callis J, Walbot V. 1989. Dependence of ethanolic fermentation, cytoplasmic pH regulation, and viability on the activity of alcohol dehydrogenase in hypoxic maize root tips. *Plant Physiol.* 89:1275–78
107. Rolletschek H, Weschke W, Weber H, Wobus U, Borisjuk L. 2004. Energy state and its control on seed development: Starch accumulation is associated with high ATP and steep oxygen gradients within barley grains. *J. Exp. Bot.* 55:1351–59
108. Rzewuski G, Sauter M. 2002. The novel rice (*Oryza sativa* L.) gene *OsSbf1* encodes a putative member of the Na^+/bile acid symporter family. *J. Exp. Bot.* 53:1991–93
109. Saab IN, Sachs MM. 1996. A flooding-induced xyloglucan *endo*-transglycosylase homolog in maize is responsive to ethylene and associated with aerenchyma. *Plant Physiol.* 112:385–91
110. Saika H, Okamoto M, Miyoshi K, Kushiro T, Shinoda S, et al. 2007. Ethylene promotes submergence-induced expression of *OsABA8ox1*, a gene that encodes ABA 8′-hydroxylase in rice. *Plant Cell Physiol.* 48:287–98
111. Sand-Jensen K, Frost-Christensen H. 1999. Plant growth and photosynthesis in the transient zone between land and stream. *Aquat. Bot.* 63:23–35
112. Santosa IE, Ram PC, Boamfa EI, Laarhoven LJ, Reuss J, et al. 2006. Patterns of peroxidative ethane emission from submerged rice seedlings indicate that damage from reactive oxygen species takes place during submergence and is not necessarily a postanoxic phenomenon. *Planta* 226:193–202
113. Sato T, Harada T, Ishizawa K. 2002. Stimulation of glycolysis in anaerobic elongation of pondweed (*Potamogeton distinctus*) turion. *J. Exp. Bot.* 53:1847–56
114. Sauter M. 1997. Differential expression of CAK (cdc2-activating kinase)-like protein kinase, cyclins and *cdc2* genes from rice during the cell cycle and in response to gibberellin. *Plant J.* 11:181–90

115. Sauter M. 2000. Rice in deep water: "How to take heed against a sea of trouble". *Naturwissenschaften* 87:289–303
116. Sauter M, Mekhedov SL, Kende H. 1995. Gibberellin promotes histone H1 kinase activity and the expression of *cdc2* and cyclin genes during the induction of rapid growth in deepwater rice internodes. *Plant J.* 7:623–32
117. Sauter M, Rzewuski G, Marwedel T, Lorbiecke R. 2002. The novel ethylene-regulated gene *OsUsp1* from rice encodes a member of a plant protein family related to prokaryotic universal stress proteins. *J. Exp. Bot.* 53:2325–31
118. Seago JL, Marsh LC, Stevens KJ, Soukup A, Votrubova O, Enstone DE. 2005. A re-examination of the root cortex in wetland flowering plants with respect to aerenchyma. *Ann. Bot.* 96:565–79
119. Sedbrook JC, Kronebusch PJ, Borisy GG, Trewavas AJ, Masson PH. 1996. Transgenic AEQUORIN reveals organ specific cytosolic Ca2^{+} responses to anoxia in *Arabidopsis thaliana* seedlings. *Plant Physiol.* 111:243–57
120. Setter TL, Laureles EV. 1996. The beneficial effect of reduced elongation growth on submergence tolerance of rice. *J. Exp. Bot.* 47:1551–59
121. Setter TL, Waters I. 2003. Review of prospects for germplasm improvement for waterlogging tolerance in wheat, barley and oats. *Plant Soil.* 253:1–34
122. Silvertown J, Dodd ME, Gowing DJG, Mountford JO. 1999. Hydrologically defined niches reveal a basis for species richness in plant communities. *Nature* 400:61–63
123. Sowa AW, Duff SM, Guy PA, Hill RD. 1998. Altering hemoglobin levels changes energy status in maize cells under hypoxia. *Proc. Natl Acad. Sci. USA* 95:10317–21
124. Stoimenova M, Igamberdiev AU, Gupta KJ, Hill RD. 2007. Nitrite-driven anaerobic ATP synthesis in barley and rice root mitochondria. *Planta* 226:465–74
125. Stoimenova M, Libourel IGL, Ratcliffe RG, Kaiser WM. 2003. The role of nitrate reduction in the anoxic metabolism of roots II. Anoxic metabolism of tobacco roots with or without nitrate reductase activity. *Plant Soil* 253:155–67
126. Subbaiah CC, Bush DS, Sachs MM. 1994. Elevation of cytosolic calcium precedes anoxia gene expression in maize suspension-cultured cells. *Plant Cell* 6:1747–62
127. Subbaiah CC, Bush DS, Sachs MM. 1998. Mitochondrial contribution to the anoxic Ca^{2+} signal suspension cultured cells. *Plant Physiol.* 118:759–71
128. Subbaiah CC, Zhang J, Sachs MM. 1994. Involvement of intracellular calcium in anaerobic gene expression and survival of maize seedlings. *Plant Physiol.* 105:369–76
129. Summers JE, Ratcliffe RG, Jackson MB. 2000. Anoxia tolerance in the aquatic monocot *Potamogeton pectinatus*: absence of oxygen stimulates elongation in association with an unusually large Pasteur effect. *J. Exp. Bot.* 51:1413–22
130. Tadege M, Dupuis I, Kuhlemeier C. 1999. Ethanolic fermentation: new functions for an old pathway. *Trends Plant Sci.* 4:320–25
131. Van der Knaap E, Jagoueix S, Kende H. 1997. Expression of an ortholog of replication protein A1 (RPA1) is induced by gibberellin in deepwater rice. *Proc. Natl. Acad. Sci. USA* 94:9979–83
132. Van der Knaap E, Kim JH, Kende H. 2000. A novel gibberellin-induced gene from rice and its potential regulatory role in stem growth. *Plant Physiol.* 122:695–704
133. Van der Knaap E, Song WY, Ruan DL, Sauter M, Ronald PC, Kende H. 1999. Expression of a gibberellin-induced leucine-rich repeat receptor-like protein kinase in deepwater rice and its interaction with kinase-associated protein phosphatase. *Plant Physiol.* 120:559–69

120. The first paper that experimentally demonstrates that costs are associated with stimulated shoot elongation underwater.

124. Demonstrates that ATP production can be sustained under anoxia by provision of succinate and nitrite.

134. Van der Sman AJM, Blom CWPM, van de Steeg HM. 1992. Phenology and seed production in *Chenopodium rubrum*, *Rumex maritimus*, and *Rumex palustris* as related to photoperiod in river forelands. *Can. J. Bot.* 70:392–400
135. Van der Straeten D, Zhou Z, Prinsen E, Van Onckelen HA, van Montagu MC. 2001. A comparative molecular-physiological study of submergence response in lowland and deepwater rice. *Plant Physiol.* 125:955–68
136. van Dongen JT, Roeb GW, Dautzenberg M, Froehlich A, Vigeolas H, et al. 2004. Phloem import and storage metabolism are highly coordinated by the low oxygen concentrations within developing wheat seeds. *Plant Physiol.* 135:1809–21
137. van Dongen JT, Schurr U, Pfister M, Geigenberger P. 2003. Phloem metabolism and function have to cope with low internal oxygen. *Plant Physiol.* 131:1529–43
138. Van Eck WHJM, Van der Steeg HM, Blom CWPM, De Kroon H. 2004. Is tolerance to summer flooding correlated with distribution patterns in river floodplains? A comparative study of 20 terrestrial grassland species. *Oikos* 107:393–405
139. Vanlerberghe GC, Feil R, Turpin DH. 1990. Anaerobic metabolism in the N-limited green alga *Selenastrum minutum*: I. Regulation of carbon metabolism and succinate as a fermentation product. *Plant Physiol.* 94:1116–23
140. Vervuren PJA, Beurskens SMJH, Blom CWPM. 1999. Light acclimation, CO_2 response and long-term capacity of underwater photosynthesis in three terrestrial plant species. *Plant Cell Environ.* 22:959–68
141. Vervuren PJA, Blom CWPM, de Kroon H. 2003. Extreme flooding events on the Rhine and the survival and distribution of riparian plant species. *J. Ecol.* 91:135–46
142. Visser EJW, Blom CWPM, Voesenek LACJ. 1996. Flooding-induced adventitious rooting in *Rumex*: morphology and development in an ecological perspective. *Acta Bot. Neerl.* 45:17–28
143. Visser EJW, Bögemann GM, Van de Steeg HM, Pierik R, Blom CWPM. 2000. Flooding tolerance of *Carex* species in relation to field distribution and aerenchyma formation. *New Phytol.* 148:93–103
144. Visser EJW, Colmer TD, Blom CWPM, Voesenek LACJ. 2000. Changes in growth, porosity, and radial oxygen loss from adventitious roots of selected mono- and dicotyledonous wetland species with contrasting types of aerenchyma. *Plant Cell Environ.* 23:1237–45
145. Visser EJW, Nabben RHM, Blom CWPM, Voesenek LACJ. 1997. Elongation by primary lateral roots and adventitious roots during conditions of hypoxia and high ethylene concentrations. *Plant Cell Environ.* 20:647–53
146. Vlad F, Spano T, Vlad D, Daher FB, Ouelhadj A, Kalaitzis P. 2007. *Arabidopsis* prolyl 4-hydroxylases are differentially expressed in response to hypoxia, anoxia and mechanical wounding. *Physiol. Plantarium* 130:471–83
147. Voesenek LACJ, Blom CWPM. 1999. Stimulated shoot elongation: a mechanism of semiaquatic plants to avoid submergence stress. In *Plant Responses to Environmental Stress: From Phytohormones to Genome Reorganization*, ed. HR Lerner, pp. 431–48. New York: Marcel Dekker
148. Voesenek LACJ, Colmer TD, Pierik R, Millenaar FF, Peeters AJM. 2006. How plants cope with complete submergence. *New Phytol.* 170:213–26
149. Voesenek LACJ, Jackson MB, Toebes AHW, Vriezen WH, Colmer TD. 2003. Desubmergence-induced ethylene production in *Rumex palustris*: regulation and ecophysiological significance. *Plant J.* 33:341–52

150. Voesenek LACJ, Rijnders JHGM, Peeters AJM, van de Steeg HM, de Kroon H. 2004. Plant hormones regulate fast shoot elongation under water: from genes to communities. *Ecology* 85:16–27

151. Voesenek LACJ, van der Sman AJM, Harren FJM, Blom CWPM. 1992. An amalgamation between hormone physiology and plant ecology: a review on flooding resistance and ethylene. *J. Plant Growth Regul.* 11:171–88

152. Vreeburg RAM, Benschop JJ, Peeters AJM, Colmer TD, Ammerlaan AHM, et al. 2005. Ethylene regulates fast apoplastic acidification and expansin A transcription during submergence-induced petiole elongation in *Rumex palustris*. *Plant J.* 43:597–610

153. Vriezen WH, De Graaf B, Mariani C, Voesenek LACJ. 2000. Submergence induces expansin gene expression in flooding-tolerant *Rumex palustris* and not in flooding-intolerant *R. acetosa*. *Planta* 210:956–63

154. Vriezen WH, Hulzink R, Mariani C, Voesenek LACJ. 1999. 1-Aminocyclopropane-1-carboxylate oxidase activity limits ethylene biosynthesis in *Rumex palustris* during submergence. *Plant Physiol.* 121:189–95

155. Vriezen WH, van Rijn CPE, Voesenek LACJ, Mariani C. 1997. A homolog of the *Arabidopsis thaliana* ERS gene is actively regulated in *Rumex palustris* upon flooding. *Plant J.* 11:1265–71

156. Watanabe H, Saigusa M, Hase S, Hayakawa T, Satoh S. 2004. Cloning of a cDNA encoding an ETR2-like protein (Os-ERL1) from deepwater rice (*Oryza sativa* L.) and increase in its mRNA level by submergence, ethylene, and gibberellin treatments. *J. Exp. Bot.* 55:1145–48

157. Wells CL, Pigliucci M. 2000. Adapative phenotypic plasticity: the case of heterophylly in aquatic plants. *Perspect. Plant Ecol. Evol. Syst.* 3:1–18

158. Xia JH, Roberts J. 1994. Improved cytoplasmic pH regulation, increased lactate efflux, and reduced cytoplasmic lactate levels are biochemical traits expressed in root tips of whole maize seedlings acclimated to a low-oxygen environment. *Plant Physiol.* 105:651–57

159. Xu K, Xu X, Fukao T, Canlas P, Marghirang-Rodriguez R, et al. 2006. *Sub1A* is an ethylene-response-factor-like gene that confers submergence tolerance to rice. *Nature* 442:705–8

150. Discusses that submergence-induced shoot elongation is predominantly a trait associated with habitats characterized by shallow and prolonged flooding events.

159. Landmark map-based cloning of a polygenic locus that encodes a determinant of submergence tolerance in rice.

Roots, Nitrogen Transformations, and Ecosystem Services

Louise E. Jackson,[1] Martin Burger,[1] and Timothy R. Cavagnaro[2]

[1]Department of Land, Air and Water Resources, University of California, Davis, California 95616; email: lejackson@ucdavis.edu

[2]School of Biological Sciences and Australian Centre for Biodiversity, Monash University, Clayton, Victoria 3800, Australia; email: tim.cavagnaro@sci.monash.edu.au

Annu. Rev. Plant Biol. 2008. 59:341–63

The *Annual Review of Plant Biology* is online at plant.annualreviews.org

This article's doi:
10.1146/annurev.arplant.59.032607.092932

1543-5008/08/0602-0341$20.00

Key Words

ammonium, arbuscular mycorrhizae, elevated carbon dioxide concentration, nitrate, nitrogen cycle, rhizosphere

Abstract

This review considers some of the mechanistic processes that involve roots in the soil nitrogen (N) cycle, and their implications for the ecological functions that retain N within ecosystems: 1) root signaling pathways for N transport systems, and feedback inhibition, especially for NO_3^- uptake; 2) dependence on the mycorrhizal and *Rhizobium*/legume symbioses and their tradeoffs for N acquisition; 3) soil factors that influence the supply of NH_4^+ and NO_3^- to roots and soil microbes; and 4) rhizosphere processes that increase N cycling and retention, such as priming effects and interactions with the soil food web. By integrating information on these plant-microbe-soil N processes across scales and disciplinary boundaries, we propose ideas for better manipulating ecological functions and processes by which the environment provides for human needs, i.e., ecosystem services. Emphasis is placed on agricultural systems, effects of N deposition in natural ecosystems, and ecosystem responses to elevated CO_2 concentrations. This shows the need for multiscale approaches to increase human dependence on a biologically based N supply.

Contents

INTRODUCTION

Roots influence the complex set of nitrogen (N) transformations that regulate the production, flow, and loss of N in ecosystems. The linkages among root physiology, activity of soil biota, and N availability occur at various scales, affecting plant productivity, N use efficiency, and ecosystem N retention. These processes thereby contribute to the provision of ecosystem services, i.e., ecological functions and processes by which the environment provides for human needs, such as food and fiber, soil quality, reduction of greenhouse gas emissions, clean water, and aesthetic values (23). Roots and N transformations can potentially play a larger role in the provision of ecosystem services, particularly in agricultural ecosystems, although adapting to climate change may require new insights into how plant physiology and soil processes are altered by elevated CO_2. Insofar as possible in this short article, our objective is to review the physiological and ecological functions that contribute to plant-microbe-soil N cycling, to integrate information on N processes across disciplinary boundaries, and to set this information in the context of increasing the ecosystem services provided by root-soil N interactions.

Ecosystem service: ecological functions and processes by which the environment provides for human needs

Plant-microbe-soil N cycling: the exchange and transformation of N among plants, microbes, soil, water, and atmospheric N pools

High-affinity transport system (HATS): operates at low N concentrations

Low-affinity transport system (LATS): operates at high N concentrations

PLANT AND SOIL N TRANSFORMATIONS

Plant Nitrogen Uptake

Plant N acquisition relies on transport systems in the plasma membrane of root cells, root system architecture, and mechanisms that regulate the activity of N transport systems and root growth according to plants' growth requirements. External factors, such as soil ammonium (NH_4^+), nitrate (NO_3^-), organic N compounds, soil pH, light, and temperature, as well as internal factors such as carbon (C) and N metabolites, are mediated by plants to regulate N uptake.

High-affinity transport systems (HATS) in roots are able to scavenge NH_4^+ and NO_3^- from the soil at concentrations between 1 μM and 1 mM, whereas the activity of low-affinity transport systems (LATS) becomes evident when these ions are plentiful (above ~0.5 mM, a concentration exceeded at least temporarily in virtually all cropping systems). Physiological studies using ^{13}N revealed the presence of a constitutive low-capacity and inductive high-capacity HATS for NO_3^- (47), whereas the NH_4^+ transporters in rice (*Oryza sativa*) are considered to be constitutive (71).

Studies involving putative NO_3^- transporters, belonging to either of two classes of proteins encoded by the *NRT2* and *NRT1* (nitrate transporter) gene families (86), have elucidated the regulation of NO_3^- acquisition at the level of transcription. Exposure of roots to NO_3^- causes induction of HATS (iHATS) and a concurrent increase of NRT2 transcripts, whereas N metabolites, most likely glutamine, downregulate HATS (120) (**Figure 1**). The presence of NH_4^+ inhibits NO_3^- uptake (44, 46, 104). Experiments using ion-selective microelectrode techniques showed that in both rice and maize

(*Zea mays*), NO_3^- absorption is suppressed from the apex to 60 mm behind the apex when both NH_4^+ and NO_3^- are supplied (113). The mechanism underlying the immediate inhibition of NO_3^- absorption by NH_4^+ (74) remains unclear. In the longer term, products of NH_4^+ assimilation (again glutamine) may have a role as feedback inhibitors of NO_3^- uptake.

Ammonium uptake is controlled by transporters that differ in their affinity for NH_4^+, their regulation at the level of transcription, and their localization of gene expression (43, 44, 93, 109, 110). The putative NH_4^+ transporter proteins are encoded by the *AMT1* and *AMT2* (ammonium transporter) families of genes (76). In contrast to NO_3^- uptake regulation, which is governed by signals integrating the N status of the whole plant, the regulation of HATS for NH_4^+ depends mainly on the endogenous N status of the root section in contact with the external NH_4^+; in *Arabidopsis thaliana* plants little compensatory NH_4^+ absorption occurs when NH_4^+ supply to other parts of the root system is restricted (43). Increased cytosolic or high external concentrations of NH_4^+ lead to reductions in root NH_4^+ influx (43, 44, 93). Gene expression of *AtAMT1;1*, which is upregulated in response to N starvation (44), is negatively correlated with root glutamine concentrations (93).

The influx of inorganic N via LATS seems poorly regulated, with a potential considerable cost in energy to plants. In solution culture, efflux of NO_3^- and NH_4^+ increases relative to external concentrations and influx of these ions (13, 102, 121). Nitrate efflux represents a waste of energy because NO_3^- uptake is an energy dependent process (8). Yet NO_3^- uptake with LATS shows linear responses to external concentrations to as high as 50 mM (103). At high external NH_4^+ concentrations, the membrane electrochemical potentials allow for passive influx of NH_4^+, but efflux of NH_4^+, against the electrochemical gradient, is energy intensive (13). At 10 mM external concentration of NH_4^+, efflux from barley (*Hordeum vulgare*) cells constitutes up to 80%

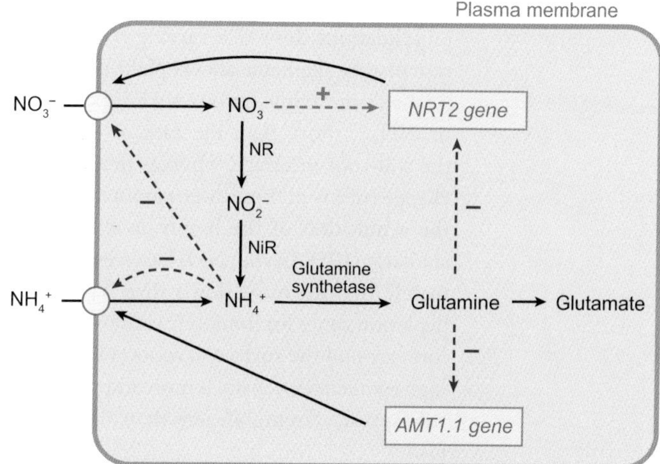

Figure 1

A model representing the proposed regulation of high-affinity transport systems (HATS) for nitrate (NO_3^-) and ammonium (NH_4^+). Glutamine represses the abundances of the putative *NRT2* and *AMT1* transcripts. Nitrate induces expression of *NRT2*. Cytosolic NH_4^+ suppresses NO_3^- and NH_4^+ uptake. Solid lines from *NRT2* and *AMT1.1* indicate transcription and translation leading to the increase of high-affinity transporters (*circles*) in the plasma membrane. Also shown are nitrate reductase (NR), nitrite (NO_2^-), nitrite reductase (NiR), glutamine synthetase, and glutamate. The diagram does not distinguish between plastidic and cytosolic nitrogen pools. Modified from Reference 48 with permission from Oxford University Press.

of primary influx. Root respiration attributed to efflux increases by 40% and is accompanied by a decline in growth. This inability to exclude NH_4^+ at the intake step seems to occur in other species that suffer NH_4^+ toxicity (83). In contrast, in rice, which is known to tolerate high levels of NH_4^+ (124), depolarization of the membrane occurs with increasing NH_4^+ provision, and the maximal NH_4^+ accumulation in the cytosol thereby decreases.

In addition to regulating uptake rates of nutrients, plants modify biomass allocation and root system architecture to optimize N capture efficiency with regard to C costs. Disproportionately more C must be allocated for the construction and maintenance of coarse roots, which grow rapidly and are relatively long-lived, than for the production of fine roots or root hairs, which are short-lived and must be replaced by new growth to maintain the same root length density (37).

Constitutive transport system: nutrient carrier system that operates regardless of prior presence of substrate

Induced transport system: nutrient carrier system that responds to exposure to specific substrate

Nutrient uptake models and their experimental validations show that varying root growth rate or root diameter affects plant capture of relatively immobile cations, such as potassium or NH_4^+, more than the rate of uptake at the soil-root interface, whereas proportional changes of any of these three parameters affect the acquisition of the highly mobile NO_3^- similarly (105). In soil, NH_4^+ moves approximately 10 times more slowly than NO_3^-, and depletion zones for immobile cations typically form around the surface of roots (115). Thus, high root length density is more important for the capture of immobile ions than mobile ions (5).

Architectural plasticity in the form of localized root proliferation to nutrient availability and root biomass allocation from roots in nutrient-poor to those in nutrient-rich patches has been widely documented (29, 45, 51). However, for single plants or monocultures, it has been difficult to demonstrate that root proliferation in an N-rich volume of soil benefits plant growth and fitness because correlations between N capture from simple N sources, such as NO_3^-, and root length densities are often weak (36, 39, 61, 117). However, root proliferation may be important in capturing N from organic sources, in interspecific competition, and in competition with microbes (58). To maximize N capture when encountering a N-rich patch, an effectively competing root system would rapidly upregulate inflow (typical measured increases are 2–3 fold) and then increase root growth (98), which takes more time; e.g., for a range of grasses this would take approximately 35 days (60, 61).

The localized lateral root elongation of N-starved *Arabidopsis* plants in response to heterogeneous availability of NO_3^- is suppressed by high levels of N metabolites (125), and the expression of *ANR1*, a putative transcription factor of lateral root growth, decreases under conditions of N sufficiency and increases under N deprivation (42). The putative dual-affinity *Arabidopsis* NO_3^- transporter encoded by NRT1.1 probably plays a role in the NO_3^- signaling pathway for lateral root colonization of NO_3^--rich patches, because neither glutamine nor NH_4^+ are able to restore lateral root growth in NRT1.1 mutants (96). To date, no NH_4^+ sensory proteins have been discovered.

Much progress has been made in elucidating the regulation of plant biomass allocation and physiological responses. This knowledge must be combined with insight about the nature of the soil colonized by roots and other organisms to better understand N economy in the environment.

Microbial Symbioses

The colonization of roots by mycorrhizal fungi provides the plant with a well-distributed and extensive absorbing system in soil, and a greater chance of encountering fertile microsites not available to roots alone. The ability of mycorrhizal fungi to access small soil pores (28) and their morphologically plastic response to localized nutrient additions (19, 114) increase the availability of N to the plant. This is of particular significance in soils of low nutrient status and for immobile nutrients, such as NH_4^+ (3, 57).

Ectomycorrhizal fungal symbionts have NH_4^+ and NO_3^- transport systems, as well as NO_3^- and nitrite (NO_2^-) reductase genes (85). For arbuscular mycorrhizae (AM) fungi, which are endosymbionts, the N uptake mechanisms are largely unknown, but NH_4^+ is preferentially used. For example, corn plants colonized by *Glomus aggregatum* take up 10 times more N from a $^{15}NH_4^+$ patch than from a $^{15}NO_3^-$ patch (112).

Under high nutrient conditions, the formation of mycorrhizal associations may become a cost to the plant, because the plant is able to satisfy its own nutrient requirements (68). According to a meta-analysis of AM and ectomycorrhizal studies, colonization generally declines in response to N fertilization (116). Nevertheless, in an organic farming system, a mycorrhiza-defective tomato mutant has slightly lower N content than the mycorrhizal wild-type (18), indicating that AM can increase N recovery in farming systems that do not use fungicides.

Ectomycorrhizal fungi can take up organic N compounds that often have slow diffusion, and thus uptake is facilitated by the greater soil access provided by hyphae (82). Mineralization of soil organic N by ectomycorrhizal fungi may be linked to the evolution of some species from saprophytes. Amino acid transporters have been identified in ectomycorrhizal fungi, and the K_m values are within the range of amino acid concentrations found in the soil (50). Genes encoding peptide and oligopeptide transporters and proteases have also been identified in ectomycorrhizae. Although AM fungi increase the recovery of N from ^{15}N-labeled decomposing plant residues in soil, it is unclear how much they rely on organic N, or the extent to which they accelerate decomposition of soil organic matter (59).

Biological N fixation, the conversion of N_2 to NH_4^+, is accomplished by both free-living and endosymbiotic prokaryotes. For the *Rhizobium*/legume endosymbiosis, N uptake from the soil is less costly to the plant than maintaining the capacity to reduce atmospheric N_2 (75). Thus, under conditions of increased soil N, e.g., fertilization and atmospheric N deposition (34), dependence upon this symbiosis decreases. Nitrate generally has a greater inhibitory effect on N_2 fixation than NH_4^+ does (55). Under N limitation, higher rates of N_2 fixation occur in N_2-fixing plants, and more N_2-fixing plant species occur in natural ecosystems (55).

N_2 fixation is influenced by many environmental and edaphic factors, but temperature and available phosphorous (P) are two of the most important ones (55, 106). Under both low temperatures (e.g., in arctic and alpine regions) and high temperatures (e.g., due to nodulation failure) N_2 fixation and nodulation are increasingly hampered and N_2 fixation can be more affected than plant growth (55). Legumes have high requirements for P, and P acquisition is enhanced by AM, dense cluster roots, and organic acid secretion to increase the availability and extraction of inorganic P, which in turn increases N-fixation capacity (73, 106). Legumes can increase the N status of neighboring plants and thus affect species distribution in grasslands (67), as well as improve the N status of subsequent crop plantings through decomposition and mineralization of N in plant material.

Soil Nitrogen Availability

The soil N cycle is driven by soil organic matter, which contains approximately 50% C and 5% N, of which typically <5% is in a labile form. Depolymerization of soil organic matter by extracellular enzymes, produced by C-limited fungi and bacteria, releases monomers, such as amino acids, which are recycled and reused through microbial metabolism, faunal grazing of microbes, and microbial death and damage that are caused by stress, such as from wet-dry or freeze-thaw cycles (99) (**Figure 2**). Root exudates, root turnover, and mycorrhizal turnover are other sources of compounds that increase the availability of labile C and N (4, 62). A key concept is that the C and N cycles are closely intertwined, and that soil C availability from root exudates and soil organic matter can drive the microbial processes that release soil N in plant-available forms.

Through mineralization, heterotrophic microbes break down organic monomers and release NH_4^+, which can be used as an energy source by ammonia-oxidizing microbes to produce NO_2^- that is usually readily converted to NO_3^- (nitrification), and also to nitric oxide (NO) and nitrous oxide (N_2O) (49) (**Figure 2**). Nitric oxide reacts with volatile organic compounds to form ozone (O_3) in the troposphere, and it is also a precursor for nitric acid deposition via atmospheric transport. Nitrous oxide is a potent greenhouse gas, and it contributes to stratospheric O_3 destruction. Denitrification takes place when heterotrophic bacteria under oxygen limitation use NO_3^- as an alternative electron acceptor to produce N_2O and N_2. The N_2:N_2O ratio

Mineralization: the breakdown of organic matter into mineral forms, such as NH_4^+

Soil organic matter: living biomass, as well as dead and chemically transformed material of biological origin in soil

Nitrification: the microbial oxidization of NH_4^+ to form NO_3^-

Denitrification: the reduction of NO_3^- under anaerobic conditions to form N_2O and N_2

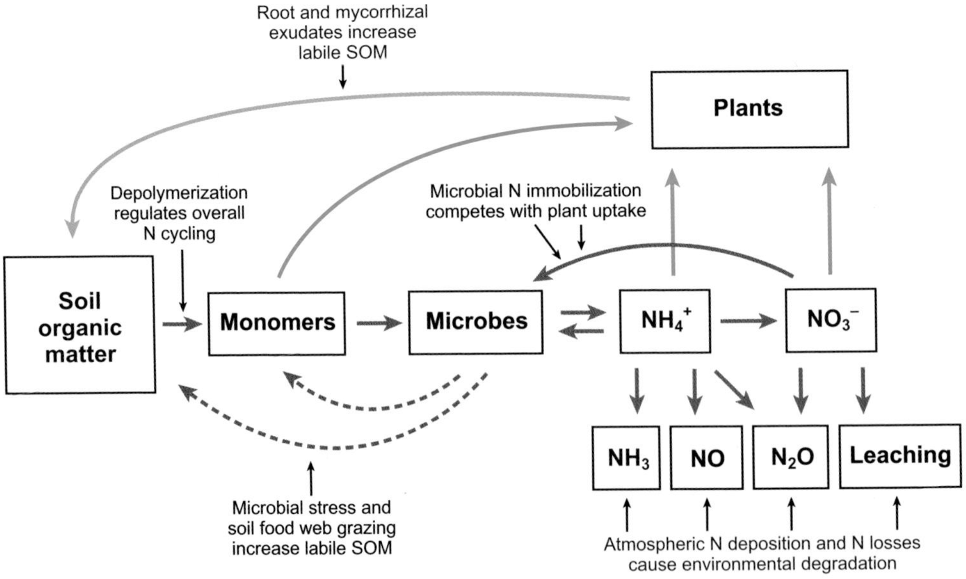

Figure 2

The soil nitrogen cycle, adapted from Schimel & Bennett (99) with permission. Mineralization refers to the microbial breakdown of organic N to form NH_4^+. Only nonsymbiotic microbial N immobilization competes with plant N uptake. Nitrification is the microbial oxidization of NH_4^+ to form NO_3^-. Denitrification is the reduction of NO_3^- under anaerobic conditions to form N_2O and N_2 gas. SOM, soil organic matter.

increases with decreasing O_2 availability, and it often decreases under high NO_3^- availability (35). Emission of ammonia (NH_3) gas begins to increase at soil pH > 8, and ultimately contributes to N deposition elsewhere in the landscape. Leaching of NO_3^-, which contaminates groundwater, occurs in conditions of high water content, especially in coarse-textured soil. Runoff carries N in various forms to surface waters. The quantity of N in terrestrial ecosystems has more than doubled owing to industrial N fixation (Haber-Bosch process) in the last century, fossil fuel combustion, and cultivation of N-fixing crops. The yearly inputs of reactive forms of N through anthropogenic activities now exceed those from natural processes, and this has intensified N cycling and increased riverine exports of N (63) and atmospheric N emissions (41).

In almost all ecosystems, plants take up mainly NH_4^+ and NO_3^-, rather than amino acids or other monomers, which apparently only play a role in extremely N-poor and cold ecosystems where N mineralization from soil organic matter is limited (100). Thus, the soil microbial processes of N mineralization and subsequent nitrification are important for the N supply to plants. Nitrification is inhibited at very low moisture, but increases with soil moisture up to –0.01 MPa, and then declines as the soil becomes saturated (107). Nitrification is more prevalent in tilled soils than in undisturbed soils (49). Mineralization is less sensitive to environmental conditions probably because so many different organisms in the soil food web are involved (see below). These processes also affect the fate of fertilizer N, some of which is taken up and metabolized by soil microbes (microbial N immobilization), and may be mineralized as the microbial biomass turns over.

Soil N availability to plants is closely tied to the labile C in the soil organic matter. For example, when plant litter with a high C:N ratio is mixed with soil, there is an initial increase in microbial N immobilization, which decreases NH_4^+ and NO_3^- availability to plants; as microbial processing proceeds, the C:N ratio decreases (11).

Plants and soil microbes compete for NH_4^+ and NO_3^-. In short-term studies (one to several days in length), microbes often take up more ^{15}N-labeled inorganic N than plants do, presumably because they have higher substrate affinities, larger surface area to volume ratios, and faster growth rates than plants (58, 99). But after a month, and for even longer time periods, plants contain an increasing proportion of the added ^{15}N, because the gradual release of microbial ^{15}N into the soil becomes available for root uptake and plants hold on to N longer than microbes (54).

The actual availability of NH_4^+ and NO_3^- is difficult to measure in soil. When rates of microbial N transformations and/or plant uptake are rapid, then NH_4^+ or NO_3^- levels can be undetectable in soil (14, 65). These pools can turn over one to several times per day. Ideally, measurements of microbial population sizes or transcripts may eventually be used as indicators of rates of N transformations in soil, and thus N availability to plants, but the current molecular methods to determine population sizes of nitrifiers and denitrifiers (24) are not yet robust enough to serve this purpose.

Rhizosphere Nitrogen Interactions

Carbon availability increases microbial and microfaunal activity in the rhizosphere, soil that exists near or is influenced by the root. Water-soluble exudates, mainly glucose, amino acids, organic acids (33), and water-insoluble materials, such as sloughed-off cells and mucilage, supply the energy for enhanced biological activity. In this region, the exchange of a diverse array of compounds takes place between roots and microflora (**Figure 3**). Some of these interactions affect N cycling among plants, rhizosphere organisms, and nonliving organic matter in soil.

Small amounts (10 $\mu g\ C\ g^{-1}$ soil) of root exudates can cause the activation of microbial biomass in a substrate-poor soil environment (**Figure 4**). Such trigger solutions lead to 2–5 times more C as CO_2 evolution than is contained as C in the exudates, and to accelerated rates of mineralization of added cellulose (27). This priming effect may occur because part of the soil microbial biomass maintains an elevated adenosine triphosphate (ATP) and adenylate energy charge ratio (AEC) to take advantage of unpredictable substrate availability, such as root exudates. Estimates of root C exudates range from 0.5–1.5% of total photosynthesis in hydroponics (33) to 5–10% in soil (69). Aboveground grazing of *Poa pratensis* promotes C root exudation, which stimulates microbial biomass activity and 7 days later results in higher soil inorganic N, plant N uptake, leaf N uptake, and photosynthesis (52). In short-term (3 h) ^{15}N isotope pool dilution experiments, the rate of average gross N mineralization is 10 times higher in rhizosphere soil of microcosms with *Avena barbata* plants compared with the rates in adjacent bulk soil (>15 mm away from the root surface) (56). The higher N production rates were attributed to enhanced N mineralization from the soil organic matter by microbes, rather than microbial biomass turnover.

Root efflux of N, mainly as amino acids, is well documented (33), and microbial products can enhance the net loss of C and N from roots (89, 90). In axenic culture, treating roots of several crop species with compounds that are released by *Pseudomonas* bacteria and *Fusarium* fungi increases the net efflux of 16 amino acids by 200% to 2600% in 3 h (89).

Rhizosphere foodweb interactions affect plant growth directly and indirectly. Root C and N efflux stimulates microbial growth. Protozoa and bacterivorous nematodes graze on microorganisms and release NH_4^+ for uptake by roots because these predators have a low C assimilation efficiency and a higher C:N ratio than the bacterial prey (20). Environmental factors, such as moisture fluctuations in the rhizosphere, may also play a role in

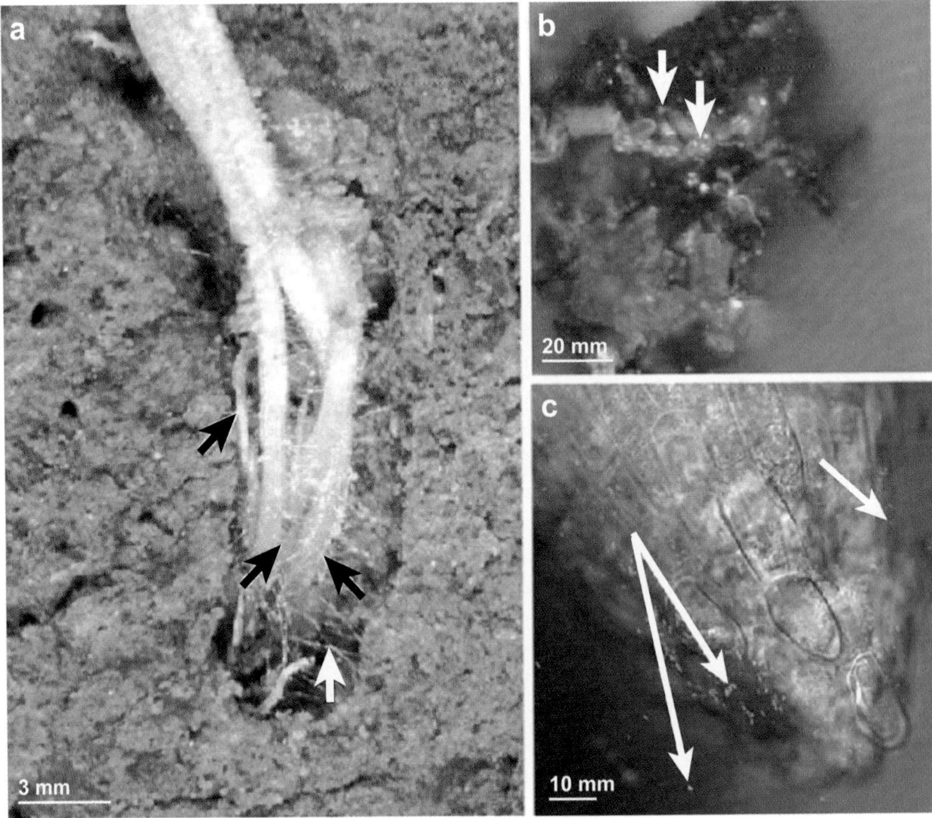

Figure 3

(*a*) Roots of canola growing into a soil pore, in close contact with each other and dead roots of wheat (*black arrows*). Root hairs (*white arrow*) extend from the canola roots to bind to soil and other living and dead remnant roots. Image credited to M.E. McCully. (*b*) Root hair of wheat associated with some dark soil organic matter, bacteria (*bright blue spots, some indicated by arrows*) and soil particles. (*c*) Tip of wheat seminal root growing on agar with *Pseudomonas* bacteria applied to the tip. Bacteria are hybridized to bacteria- and *Pseudomonas*-specific oligonucleotide probes that are conjugated to fluorescent dyes from Reference 122. Some bacteria are bound to the root cap, and others are retained in hydrated mucilage behind the tip (*white arrows*). From Reference 123 with permission from Oxford University Press.

stimulating N mineralization of soil organic matter (17). In addition to nutrient enhancement due to grazers, plant growth may also be promoted by complex mechanisms involving hormones released by rhizosphere organisms. For example, the presence of amoebae increased the size and branching of the root system of watercress seedlings (*Lepidium sativum*) and the proportion of bacteria that produced indolyl-3-acetic acid (IAA), which is known to influence root growth (9, 10) (**Figure 5**).

Some tropical pasture grasses directly influence soil N transformations through their release of nitrification inhibitors. Nitrification is suppressed by >90% in field soil under *Brachiaria humidicola* cultivation. The nitrification-inhibiting exudates, which blocked both the monooxygenase and hydroxylamino oxidoreductase pathways in *Nitrosomonas*, are more stable in a low pH (<4.5) environment and are released at three times higher rates when plants are grown with

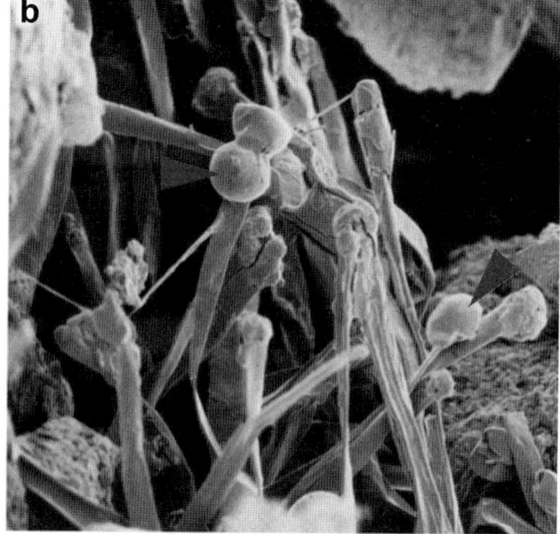

Figure 4

(*a*) The root/soil interface of a young root of buckwheat (*Fagopyron esculentum*). Root hairs extend into the rhizosphere and soil contact with the root varies. The arrowhead indicates the root epidermis. (*b*) Droplets of root exudate (*arrowheads*) on the tips of root hairs in the rhizosphere of broom corn (*Sorghum* spp.). The plant material was frozen in situ in the field with liquid N_2 and observed with a cryo-scanning electron microscope. From Reference 80, with permission.

NH_4^+, rather than with NO_3^- (111). Several crop species show detectable amounts of these compounds in root exudates.

NITROGEN PROCESS INTEGRATION

Linking plant physiological and soil microbial N processes to ecosystem N cycling and N retention is a major challenge. By integrating across scales, the aggregate set of N processes controls ecological functions. Thus, scaling up from microsite processes ultimately determines ecosystem N flows, as suggested by the following examples that attempt to set plant-microbe-soil N cycling scenarios in an ecosystem context.

1) The regulation of plant N uptake systems and of root system architecture and biomass allocation reflect that plant communities evolved in nutrient-poor environments that were also colonized by bacteria, fungi, and fauna (92). Upregulation of iHATS (48) and root elongation when N-starved plants encounter NO_3^- may allow plants to effectively compete with other plant species and with microbes for spatially and temporally heterogeneously available N. To date, components of signaling pathways regulating root elongation in response to external signals were shown only for NO_3^- (38), although root proliferation also occurs when roots of N- or P-starved plants encounter NH_4^+ or phosphate, respectively (29). So, is the NO_3^- ion one among several cues signaling the presence of a nutrient-rich patch to the plant? Although NO_3^- can rapidly be absorbed because of its mobility in soil (98), the mineralization of organic N to NH_4^+ in a patch takes more time, as does the transfer of N between microbes, microfauna, and roots. Thus, NO_3^- may be an early and reliable signal that root proliferation will be a worthwhile investment by a plant. The

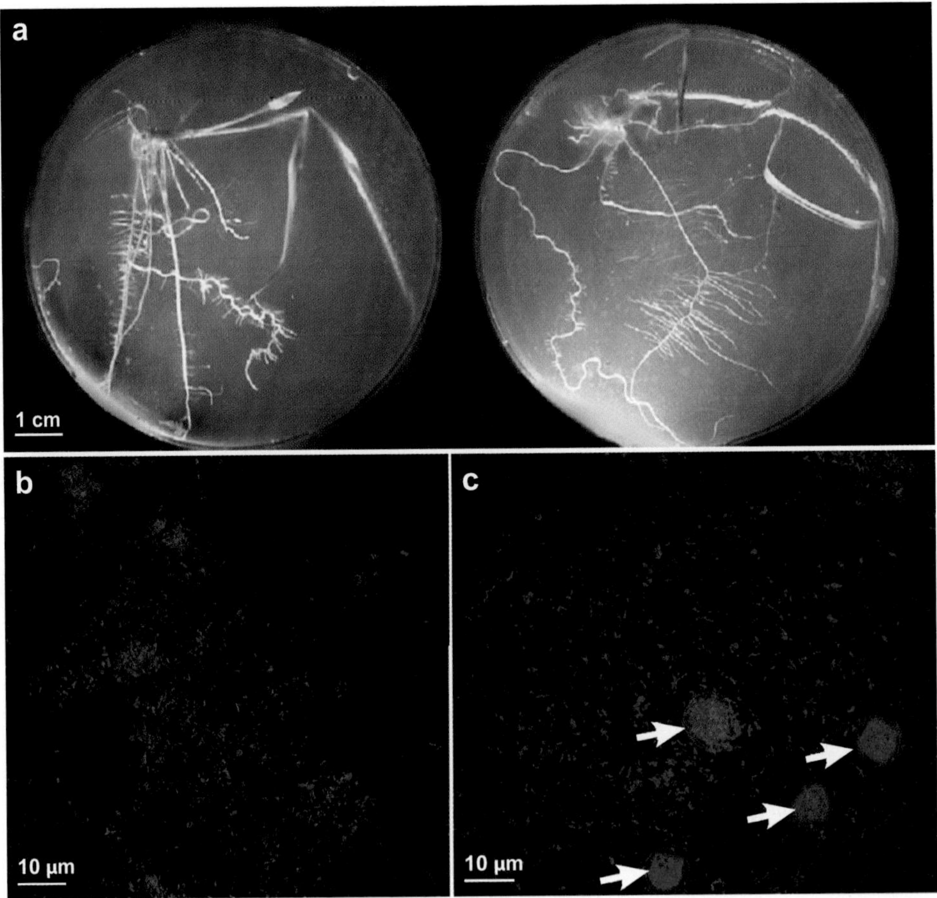

Figure 5

Protozoan effects on root architecture and bacterial communities in the rhizosphere of rice. (*a*) Root architecture of 16-day-old rice seedlings growing on agar inoculated with a diverse bacterial community in the absence (*left*) and presence (*right*) of amoebae. (*b,c*) Fluorescent in-situ hybridization of bacteria. Alpha-proteobacteria (*red*) and eubacteria (*blue*) on an agar surface near the lateral roots of plants in the absence (*b*) and presence (*c*) of amoebae. (*c*) Levels of alpha-proteobacteria decrease in the presence of amoebae. White arrows indicate red-fluoresecent amoebal cysts. From Reference 9 with permission.

role of redundant signaling pathways for the activity of transport systems or root proliferation in agricultural soils is of special interest, because these soils can have high availability of NO_3^-, and yet even in fertilized crops, 40–80% of their N is derived from mineralization of N in soil organic matter (31).

2) In addition to rhizodeposition in the form of sloughed-off cells and root turnover, a substantial amount of C and N is released by roots in soluble form (69). The exuded glucose and amino acids, which could alternatively be used for growth or seed production by plants, maintain a rhizosphere flora and fauna that in turn contributes to a consistent N supply for plants. Conversely, microorganisms benefit from high net primary productivity. Therefore, it is not surprising that in the rhizosphere, exchange of compounds that stimulate root C and N exudation or plant growth (88) has evolved. Other

Rhizodeposition: the release of soluble and insoluble material from roots

symbioses, such as mycorrhizal associations or N_2 fixation, also have important roles in ecosystem N cycling. The recent awareness of exchanges of C, N, and hormones (10) in the rhizosphere will undoubtedly create greater interest in their ecological significance and their role in N retention at the ecosystem level.

3) Diel rhythms of plant and microbial N uptake may lead to increased N cycling in soil. Plant N uptake, and the genes encoding N uptake, show a diurnal periodicity increasing to a peak level at the end of the day, with highest amplitude on high irradiance days (47). This is probably related to tissue sugar rather than transpiration levels. At night, when transpiration stops, greater moisture availability could expose rhizosphere microbes to more substrate, stimulating microbial growth (17). The efflux of NO_3^- often exceeds influx in the dark (47). Higher rhizosphere N availability at night may coincide with higher microbial C availability. Furthermore, high microbial N demand at night might stimulate the secretion of long-lived exoenzymes (i.e., extracellular enzymes) that release N from soil organic matter. Some of this N could be usurped by the plant during its peak N demand during the day. Although diel transfers have not been proven, these hypothesized mechanisms illustrate a set of processes by which plants and rhizosphere microbes may have evolved to meet their N demands, and which simultaneously could retain N in the ecosystem by recycling N that might otherwise be susceptible to loss.

Understanding the coordination of plant-microbe-soil N cycling requires a greater emphasis on in situ studies in soil, and on framing experimental designs to determine ecosystem-level outcomes. In this way, physiological and ecological functions can be understood at different scales, and then serve as a basis for evaluating ecosystem services.

ECOSYSTEM SERVICES

Services and Tradeoffs

Ecosystem processes underpin ecosystem services: Plant-microbe-soil N cycling affects a diverse set of ecosystem services that meet human needs. These include provisioning services such as food and fiber production, regulating services such as waste decomposition and enhancement of water quality, longer-term supporting services such as soil formation and nutrient cycling, and cultural services such as aesthetic and spiritual fulfillment (81). The concept of ecosystem services allows us to evaluate multiple aspects of management decisions simultaneously. Although sometimes at odds (e.g., agricultural provisioning services have often outweighed regulating and supporting services), ecosystem services can be positively interlinked. If N management can balance ecosystem N budgets by maintaining ecosystem reservoirs of stored N, such that the sink capacity of the ecosystem contributes to plant nutrient supply and to plant-microbe-soil N cycling, then the need for surplus N additions that can cause environmental degradation decreases (30).

Provisioning Services

Fertilizer is not used in 40% of the world's agroecosystems (72), due either to lack of supply or lack of access by farmers (87). Application of fertilizers to infertile soils increases provisioning services (i.e., crop productivity on marginal lands), but it is likely to shift the dominant N cycling processes from dependence on root-microbe associations to higher nitrification and LATS pathways, and produces a somewhat greater potential for environmentally harmful N loss (**Figure 6**). In contrast, when N supply and access are high, N is typically overapplied, nitrification

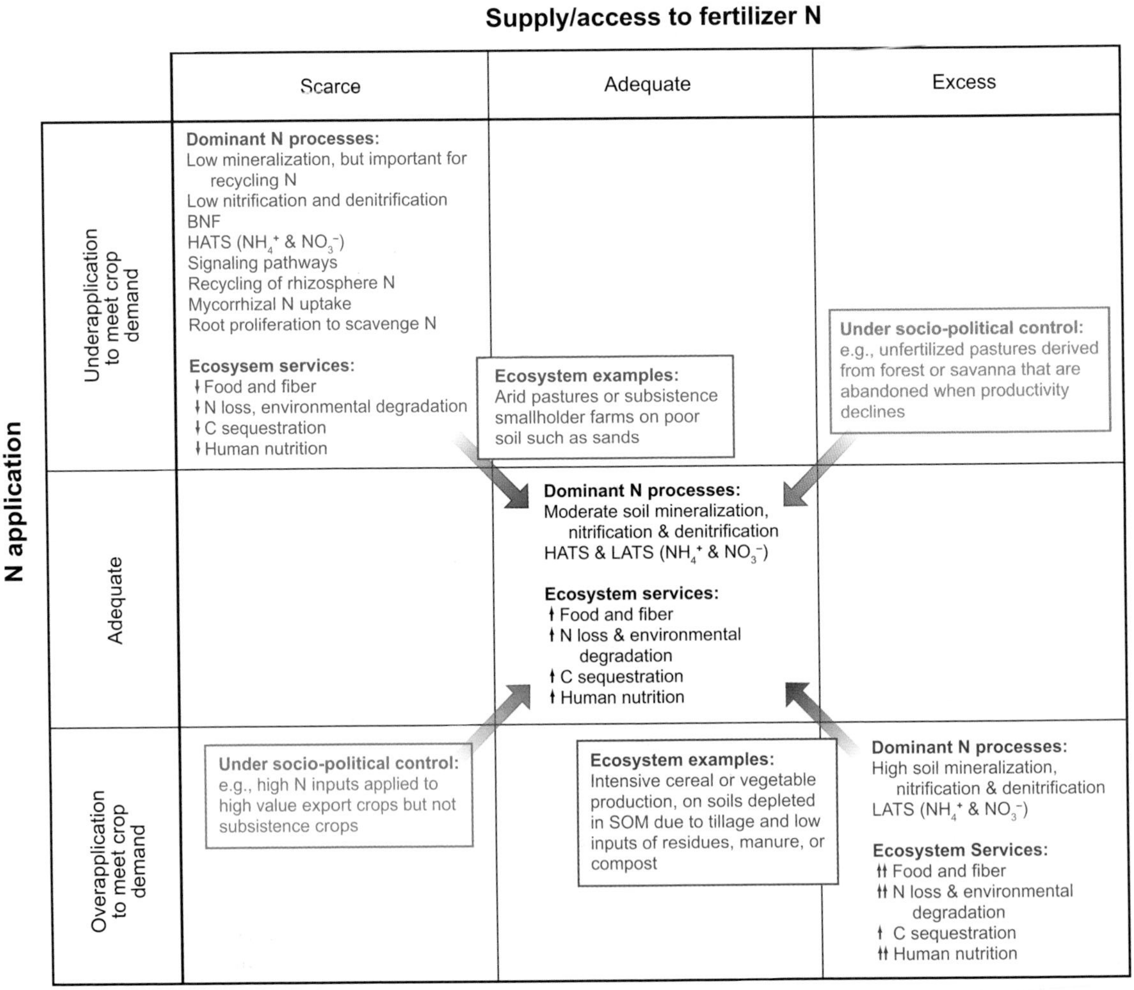

Supply/access to fertilizer N

N application

	Scarce	Adequate	Excess
Underapplication to meet crop demand	**Dominant N processes:** Low mineralization, but important for recycling N Low nitrification and denitrification BNF HATS (NH_4^+ & NO_3^-) Signaling pathways Recycling of rhizosphere N Mycorrhizal N uptake Root proliferation to scavenge N **Ecosysem services:** ↓Food and fiber ↓N loss, environmental degradation ↓C sequestration ↓Human nutrition	**Ecosystem examples:** Arid pastures or subsistence smallholder farms on poor soil such as sands	**Under socio-political control:** e.g., unfertilized pastures derived from forest or savanna that are abandoned when productivity declines
Adequate		**Dominant N processes:** Moderate soil mineralization, nitrification & denitrification HATS & LATS (NH_4^+ & NO_3^-) **Ecosystem services:** ↑Food and fiber ↑N loss & environmental degradation ↑C sequestration ↑Human nutrition	
Overapplication to meet crop demand	**Under socio-political control:** e.g., high N inputs applied to high value export crops but not subsistence crops	**Ecosystem examples:** Intensive cereal or vegetable production, on soils depleted in SOM due to tillage and low inputs of residues, manure, or compost	**Dominant N processes:** High soil mineralization, nitrification & denitrification LATS (NH_4^+ & NO_3^-) **Ecosystem Services:** ↑↑Food and fiber ↑↑N loss & environmental degradation ↑ C sequestration ↑↑Human nutrition

Figure 6

Examples of the relationships between hypothesized dominant plant/soil N processes and ecosystem services in two types of agricultural scenarios affected by the supply and access that farmers have to fertilizer N, and their decisions regarding the amount to apply. Adapted from Reference 87 with permission. The arrows show trajectories to attain optimal management. BNF, biological nitrogen fixation; HATS, high-affinity transport systems; LATS, low-affinity transport systems; SOM, soil organic matter.

is a dominant process, N cycles are open, and N losses are high. In this case, reduced fertilizer use can maintain high yields with lower N losses, and increase the provisioning services provided by plant-microbe-soil N transformations.

Most of the current agricultural emphasis on N is on fertilizer N use efficiency, largely in cereal grain production, either by optimal use of fertilizer form, rate, and method, or by matching N supply with crop demand (84). Other approaches to increase fertilizer N use efficiency are agronomic practices that reduce crop stress and crop selection for greater yield stability, and thus result in higher and more consistent recovery of applied fertilizer N from year to year. None of these approaches focus on supplying N to crops via plant-microbe-soil N processes.

If there is societal interest in developing greater dependence on plant-microbe-soil N transformations for agricultural production (e.g., to reduce the fossil fuel used for production of N fertilizer by the Haber-Bosch process), then research approaches must better integrate plant physiology and soil microbial ecology. In improving crop N efficiency (yield of grain per unit available N), selection for genotypes that differ in their regulation of N uptake, N assimilation, and N recycling from vegetative to seed organs should be carried out under a variety of environmental conditions and N availability scenarios (53). Higher root biomass allocation (97), costs of symbiosis (108), and root exudates to fuel soil microbes may reduce crop productivity. Soil microbial community composition may be critical for rhizosphere N cycling, and it can depend on cultivar traits (31). For example, shifts in ammonia-oxidizing bacterial populations increase nitrification in the rhizoplane of a modern rice cultivar, and this cultivar benefits more from the coprovision of both NH_4^+ and NO_3^- than a traditional cultivar (12). Examples exist where selection eventually benefited crops owing to plant-microbe symbiosis, e.g., more efficient *Bradyrhizobium* strains that support higher levels of biological nitrogen fixation in soybeans (*Glycine max*) (2). Some forms of organic farming systems have soil N reservoirs and mycorrhizae that adequately support crop N demand (15, 18, 31). Clearly, the time is ripe to place greater emphasis on linking microbially mediated soil N transformations, plant-microbe interactions, and plant N uptake and utilization in agroecosystems.

Regulating and Supporting Services

N budgets exist for many ecosystems, and show the stocks of N in roots and soil, the amount of various N inputs, such as biological N fixation, and the net rates of N cycling through plants and soil (16, 22, 41, 66). However, a mechanistic understanding of plant-microbe-soil N cycling is often missing, but is needed for the development of approaches that could increase regulating and supporting services, e.g., supply and mineralization of N from plant residues, C sequestration in woody plants and soil, reduced greenhouse gas emissions, and improved water quality.

One example is the deposition of N (i.e., the transfer of N from one ecosystem to another) that has affected many of the world's ecosystems and their services (81). Whereas NO_3^- pollution from agricultural runoff affects coastal, estuarine, and marine ecosystems (7), upland forests receive anthropogenic N inputs through wet and dry deposition (1). Atmospheric N deposition from urban areas now affects N cycling in natural ecosystems (34). The following examples show how an integrated understanding of plant-microbe-soil N transformations explains a decline in ecosystem services. In N-limited systems, such as evergreen and deciduous forests in the northeastern United States that have received excess N inputs (6–18-fold of background N deposition) for 15 years, most of the additional N was retained in the soil, whereas roots, foliage, and wood diminished as sinks for N, in spite of higher N concentrations in leaves and fine roots (78). Foliar N in pine (*Pinus resinosa*) needles accumulated as free amino acids, rather than as photosynthetic enzymes (6). Photosynthesis, tree growth, and fine root biomass declined, and mortality in pine stands after 15 years of N additions was 56%, but hardwood stands showed an increase in net primary productivity (6, 78). Nitrogen saturation altered chemical processes and microbially mediated processes in the soil. Mineralization of N in soil organic matter decreased, whereas gross nitrification and the production of NO increased (119) (**Figure 7**). These changes in soil N transformations were accompanied by acidification and probable cation losses, increases in NO_3^- leaching (1), and declines in soil fungal biomass and the levels of lignin-degrading enzymes (40). Microbial N immobilization did not occur to a great extent because of a lack of available C (1), and soil acidification diminished this

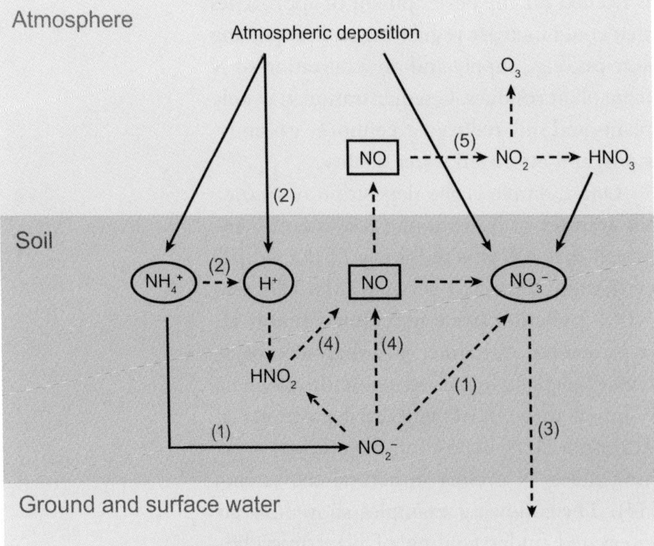

Figure 7

Illustration of the multiple influences of persistent atmospheric N deposition on pathways of N loss in forest soils, including increased (1) nitrification, (2) acidification, (3) NO_3^- availability and leaching, and (4) NO production via nitrous acid (HNO_2) decomposition and biological NO_2^- reduction. Also shown is (5) the role of NO emissions in contributing to local O_3 formation and downwind NO_3^- deposition. From Reference 118 with permission.

process further (119). This set of cascading, interrelated changes in N cycling illustrates how chronic N additions lead to ecosystem responses that depend on plant species composition, soil mineralogy, and precipitation patterns (79).

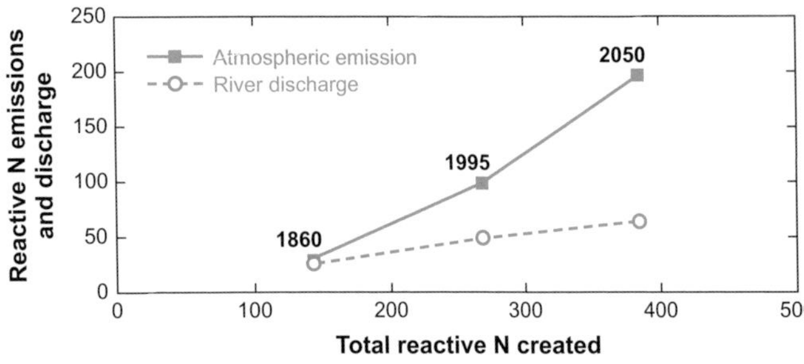

Figure 8

Reactive N creation in 1860, early 1990s, and projected in 2050 as a function of atmospheric emissions of $NO_x + NH_3$ and riverine reactive N discharge to the coastal zone (Tg N yr $^{-1}$). From Reference 41 with permission.

Land use change is another factor that reduces the regulating and supporting services provided by plant-microbe-soil N transformations in natural ecosystems. For example, between 1860 and the early 1990s, the amount of reactive N produced by natural terrestrial processes, such as biological N fixation, decreased by 15% (120 to ~107 Tg N yr^{-1}), while anthropogenic production increased ~10 fold (~15 to 156 Tg N yr^{-1}) (41) (**Figure 8**). Agricultural intensification, i.e., use of high levels of nonrenewable inputs such as inorganic fertilizers, has greatly increased productivity as well as the leakiness of N cycling. Global estimates are that ~50% of applied N fertilizer is removed by the crop, 2–5% is stored as soil N, ~25% is emitted to the atmosphere, and ~20% is discharged to aquatic systems (41). Thus, nearly 50% of N applied as fertilizer has a negative effect on regulating and supporting services that support environmental quality.

Elevated Atmospheric CO_2

Nitrogen availability will become increasingly important for ecosystem services as atmospheric CO_2 increases. Several long-term free air CO_2 enrichment (FACE) experiments in grasslands with and without N additions showed a declining stimulation of plant biomass production with time when no N was added (32, 94, 101). Across a number of types of studies, the absence of N additions, gross N mineralization, and available N are either unchanged or decline under elevated compared with ambient CO_2 conditions (26, 64, 95). These results imply that over the long term, growth stimulation of non-legumes by higher levels of CO_2 cannot be sustained without N additions.

Responses to elevated CO_2 depend on plant functional types and the form of available N. Most plants that employ the C_3 photosynthetic pathway respond to elevated CO_2 with increased rates of photosynthesis and growth, mainly because photorespiration is reduced, whereas C_4 plants show little stimulation. Biomass tissue N concentrations decline on average by 16% and 7% for C_3 and C_4 or N-fixing plants, respectively, when CO_2 concentrations are doubled (21). The decline in N, soluble protein, and Rubisco (ribulose 1,5-bisphosphate carboxylase/oxidase) concentrations, which is sometimes interpreted as a dilution effect, may also be due to a decrease in shoot NO_3^- assimilation by C_3 plants that results from suppression of photorespiration under elevated CO_2 (91). Nitrogen rhizodeposition under elevated CO_2 may also differ between C_3 and C_4 plants. More ^{15}N fed to leaves of wheat plants as $^{15}NO_3^-$ ends up in the soil, microbial biomass, and in unlabeled N receiver plants than under ambient CO_2 conditions, whereas no differences in N release are observed for corn (25). Nitrogen fixation increases under elevated CO_2, although this response is also dependent on the availability of other nutrients (26). Higher yields of effectively nodulating soybean cultivars under elevated CO_2 demonstrate the advantage of NH_4^+ availability through N_2 fixation because near-isogenic ineffectively nodulating lines have lower yields even with high N fertilization (77). Thus, N availability, as well as the proportion of soil NH_4^+ versus NO_3^-, can be expected to influence plant responses to elevated CO_2.

As atmospheric CO_2 concentrations increase, N fertilization in cropping systems will tend to increase yields and maintain grain protein levels (70), with the inherent risk of also increasing environmentally harmful N losses. Cropping systems that receive organic matter, rather than only fertilizer N inputs, and thus, show high microbial activity and continuous N mineralization-immobilization dynamics, may have fewer detrimental side-effects while still supplying adequate N in a mixture of plant-available forms.

CONCLUSIONS

Our long-range challenge is to increase the utilization of plant-microbe-soil N transformations to increase a range of ecosystem services, including provisioning, regulating, and supporting services. Optimizing food and fiber production must be balanced with concerns about N pollution that can affect public health and the preservation of natural resources. It is in the public interest to increase awareness of the need for a biologically based N supply. There is a need to foster the collaborations among plant biologists, microbiologists, ecologists, and soil scientists that will link advances in plant N physiology and soil microbial N processes with N flows and fates at the ecosystem level.

SUMMARY POINTS

1. Nitrate uptake is regulated by the whole plant N status, with glutamine acting as a putative feedback signal for the high-affinity transport system, whereas uptake of NH_4^+ via the high-affinity transport system is under localized root control. High influx of NO_3^- and NH_4^+ via low-affinity transport systems is accompanied by high efflux.
2. Higher root length density is more important for the capture of immobile (NH_4^+) than mobile (NO_3^-) ions in soil, but may improve competition for N with other plants and with soil microbes for both ions.
3. Mycorrhizal fungi increase the availability of N to the plant owing to their access to small soil pores, plastic response to localized nutrient addition, and for ectomycorrhizae, the ability to increase N mineralization from soil organic matter.

4. Labile C is an important resource in the soil because it drives microbial processes that control rates of N transformations, and thus, availability of N to plant roots. One source of labile C is root exudates and sloughed-off cells; another source is the labile C in soil organic matter.
5. Food web interactions in the rhizosphere, which increase N availability and plant growth, are controlled by plant C and N efflux or exudates that inhibit nitrification and by microbial products that promote plant growth or the release of C and N from roots.
6. The integration of plant-microbe-soil N processes requires that plant physiological processes are linked to soil microbial N processes, and are studied within the context of ecosystem N cycling and N retention. As a result, ecological functions and processes by which the environment provides for human needs (i.e., ecosystem services) can be assessed.
7. Better utilization of plant-microbe-soil N transformations can potentially increase a range of ecosystem services, including provisioning (related to food and fiber production) and regulating and supporting services (e.g., decomposition and nutrient cycling that supports water and soil quality), but will require increased public interest in the need for a biologically based N supply, especially in relation to elevated atmospheric CO_2, which will likely require greater N inputs to sustain food production.

DISCLOSURE STATEMENT

The authors are not aware of any biases that might be perceived as affecting the objectivity of this review.

ACKNOWLEDGMENTS

This review was supported by a grant from the United States Department of Agriculture NRI Soils and Soil Biology Program (2004-03329). We are grateful to Wendy Silk for her help and suggestions, and thank Laurie Drinkwater for her review of an earlier draft. Many thanks to Michael Bonkowski, Margaret McCully, and Michelle Watt for providing original versions of their images.

LITERATURE CITED

1. Aber J, McDowell W, Nadelhoffer K, Magill A, Berntson G, et al. 1998. Nitrogen saturation in temperate forest ecosystems—Hypotheses revisited. *BioScience* 48:921–34
2. Alves BJR, Boddey RM, Urquiaga S. 2003. The success of BNF in soybean in Brazil. *Plant Soil* 252:1–9
3. Ames RN, Reid CPP, Porter LK, Cambardella C. 1983. Hyphal uptake and transport on nitrogen from two ^{15}N-labelled sources by *Glomus mosseae*, a vesicular arbuscular mycorrhizal fungus. *New Phytol.* 95:381–96
4. Bais HP, Weir TL, Perry LG, Gilroy S, Vivanco JM. 2006. The role of root exudates in rhizosphere interactions with plants and other organisms. *Annu. Rev. Plant Biol.* 57:233–66

5. Barber SA, Cushman JH. 1981. Nutrient uptake model for agronomic crops. In *Modelling Wastewater Renovation for Land Treatment*, ed. IK Iksander, pp. 382–409. New York: Wiley
6. Bauer GA, Bazzaz FA, Minocha R, Long S, Magill A, et al. 2004. Effects of chronic N additions on tissue chemistry, photosynthetic capacity, and carbon sequestration potential of a red pine (*Pinus resinosa* Ait.) stand in the NE United States. *For. Ecol. Manag.* 196:173–86
7. Beman JM, Arrigo KR, Matson PA. 2005. Agricultural runoff fuels large phytoplankton blooms in vulnerable areas of the ocean. *Nature* 434:211–14
8. Bloom AJ, Sukrapanna SS, Warner RL. 1992. Root respiration associated with ammonium and nitrate absorption and assimilation by barley. *Plant Physiol.* 99:1294–301
9. Bonkowski M. 2004. Protozoa and plant growth: the microbial loop in soil revisited. *New Phytol.* 162:617–31
10. Bonkowski M, Brandt F. 2002. Do soil protozoa enhance plant growth by hormonal effects? *Soil Biol. Biochem.* 34:1709–15
11. Booth MS, Stark JM, Rastetter E. 2005. Controls on nitrogen cycling in terrestrial ecosystems: A synthetic analysis of literature data. *Ecol. Monogr.* 75:139–57
12. Briones AM, Okabe S, Umemiya Y, Ramsing NB, Reichardt W, Okuyama H. 2003. Ammonia-oxidizing bacteria on root biofilms and their possible contribution to N use efficiency of different rice cultivars. *Plant Soil* 250:335–48
13. Britto DT, Siddiqi MY, Glass ADM, Kronzucker HJ. 2001. Futile transmembrane NH_4^+ cycling: A cellular hypothesis to explain ammonium toxicity in plants. *Proc. Natl. Acad. Sci. USA* 98:4255–58
14. Burger M, Jackson LE. 2004. Plant and microbial nitrogen use and turnover: Rapid conversion of nitrate to ammonium in soil with roots. *Plant Soil* 266:289–301
15. Burger M, Jackson LE, Lundquist EJ, Louie DT, Miller RL, et al. 2005. Microbial responses and nitrous oxide emissions during wetting and drying of organically and conventionally managed soil under tomatoes. *Biol. Fertil. Soils* 42:109–18
16. Bustamante MMC, Medina E, Asner GP, Nardoto GB, Garcia-Montiel DC. 2006. Nitrogen cycling in tropical and temperate savannas. *Biogeochemistry* 79:209–37
17. Cardon ZG, Gage DJ. 2006. Resource exchange in the rhizosphere: Molecular tools and the microbial perspective. *Annu. Rev. Ecol. Evol. Syst.* 37:459–88
18. Cavagnaro TR, Jackson LE, Six J, Ferris H, Goyal S, et al. 2006. Arbuscular mycorrhizas, microbial communities, nutrient availability, and soil aggregates in organic tomato production. *Plant Soil* 282:209–25
19. Cavagnaro TR, Smith FA, Smith SE, Jakobsen I. 2005. Functional diversity in arbuscular mycorrhizas: exploitation of soil patches with different phosphate enrichment differs among fungal species. *Plant Cell Environ.* 28:642–50
20. Clarholm M. 1985. Interactions of bacteria, protozoa and plants leading to mineralization of soil nitrogen. *Soil Biol. Biochem.* 17:181–87
21. Cotrufo MF, Ineson P, Scott A. 1998. Elevated CO_2 reduces the nitrogen concentration of plant tissues. *Global Change Biol.* 4:43–54
22. Crews TE, Peoples MB. 2005. Can the synchrony of nitrogen supply and crop demand be improved in legume and fertilizer-based agroecosystems? A review. *Nutr. Cycl. Agroecosyst.* 72:101–20
23. Daily GC. 1997. *Nature's Services: Societal Dependence on Natural Ecosystems*. Washington, DC: Island Press. 392 pp.
24. Daims H, Taylor MW, Wagner M. 2006. Wastewater treatment: a model system for microbial ecology. *Trends Biotechnol.* 24:483–89

10. Proposes a hormonal feedback mechanism of root growth stimulation through preferential grazing of protozoa on specific types of bacteria.

13. Shows how barley root cells, exposed to high external concentrations of NH_4^+, engage in energy-intensive influx-efflux cycling of NH_4^+.

25. Shows that N rhizodeposition by wheat, but not by corn, increased under elevated CO_2.

27. Shows how trace amounts of soil C can activate microbial biomass.

41. Provides a review of estimates of global reactive N pools and fluxes, including biological N fixation, before and after the era of industrialization.

25. **de Graaff MA, Six J, van Kessel C. 2007. Elevated CO_2 increases nitrogen rhizodeposition and microbial immobilization of root-derived nitrogen. *New Phytol.* 173:778–86**
26. de Graaff MA, van Groenigen KJ, Six J, Hungate B, van Kessel C. 2006. Interactions between plant growth and soil nutrient cycling under elevated CO_2: a meta-analysis. *Glob. Change Biol.* 12:2077–91
27. **De Nobili M, Contin M, Mondini C, Brookes PC. 2001. Soil microbial biomass is triggered into activity by trace amounts of substrate. *Soil Biol. Biochem.* 33:1163–70**
28. Drew EA, Murray RS, Smith SE, Jakobsen I. 2004. Beyond the rhizosphere: growth and function of arbuscular mycorrhizal external hyphae in sands of varying pore sizes. *Plant Soil* 251:105–14
29. Drew MC. 1975. Comparison of effects of a localized supply of phosphate, nitrate, ammonium and potassium on growth of seminal root system, and shoot, in barley. *New Phytol.* 75:479–90
30. Drinkwater LE, Snapp SS. 2007. Nutrients in agroecosystems: Rethinking the management paradigm. *Adv. Agron.* 92:163–86
31. Drinkwater LE, Snapp SS. 2007. Understanding and managing the rhizosphere in agroecosystems. In *The Rhizosphere—An Ecological Perspective*, ed. ZG Cardon, JL Whitbeck, pp. 127–54. San Diego, CA: Elsevier
32. Dukes JS, Chiariello NR, Cleland EE, Moore LA, Shaw MR, et al. 2005. Responses of grassland production to single and multiple global environmental changes. *PloS Biol.* 3:1829–37
33. Farrar J, Hawes M, Jones D, Lindow S. 2003. How roots control the flux of carbon to the rhizosphere. *Ecology* 84:827–37
34. Fenn ME, Haeuber R, Tonnesen GS, Baron JS, Grossman-Clarke S, et al. 2003. Nitrogen emissions, deposition, and monitoring in the Western United States. *BioScience* 53:391–403
35. Firestone MK, Davidson EA. 1989. Microbiological basis of NO and N_2O production and consumption in soil. In *Exchange of Trace Gases Between Terrestrial Ecosystems and the Atmosphere*, ed. MO Andreae, DS Schimel, pp. 7–21. New York: Wiley
36. Fitter A, Williamson L, Linkohr B, Leyser O. 2002. Root system architecture determines fitness in an *Arabidopsis* mutant in competition for immobile phosphate ions but not for nitrate ions. *Proc. R. Soc. London Ser. B* 269:2017–22
37. Fitter AH. 1994. Architecture and biomass allocation as components of the plastic response of root systems to soil heterogeneity. In *Exploitation of Environmental Heterogeneity by Plants*, ed. MM Caldwell, RW Pearcy, pp. 305–23. San Diego, CA: Academic
38. Forde BG. 2002. Local and long-range signaling pathways regulating plant responses to nitrate. *Annu. Rev. Plant Biol.* 53:203–24
39. Fransen B, de Kroon H, Berendse F. 1998. Root morphological plasticity and nutrient acquisition of perennial grass species from habitats of different nutrient availability. *Oecologia* 115:351–58
40. Frey SD, Knorr M, Parrent JL, Simpson RT. 2004. Chronic nitrogen enrichment affects the structure and function of the soil microbial community in temperate hardwood and pine forests. *For. Ecol. Manag.* 196:159–71
41. **Galloway JN, Dentener FJ, Capone DG, Boyer EW, Howarth RW, et al. 2004. Nitrogen cycles: past, present, and future. *Biogeochemistry* 70:153–226**

42. Gan YB, Filleur S, Rahman A, Gotensparre S, Forde BG. 2005. Nutritional regulation of ANR1 and other root-expressed MADS-box genes in *Arabidopsis thaliana*. *Planta* 222:730–742

43. Gansel X, Munos S, Tillard P, Gojon A. 2001. Differential regulation of the NO_3^- and NH_4^+ transporter genes *AtNrt2.1* and *AtAmt1.1* in *Arabidopsis*: relation with long-distance and local controls by N status of the plant. *Plant J.* 26:143–55

44. Gazzarrini S, Lejay T, Gojon A, Ninnemann O, Frommer WB, von Wiren N. 1999. Three functional transporters for constitutive, diurnally regulated, and starvation-induced uptake of ammonium into *Arabidopsis* roots. *Plant Cell* 11:937–47

45. Gersani M, Sachs T. 1992. Development correlations between roots in heterogeneous environments. *Plant Cell Environ.* 15:463–69

46. Gessler A, Schneider S, Von Sengbusch D, Weber P, Hanemann U, et al. 1998. Field and laboratory experiments on net uptake of nitrate and ammonium by the roots of spruce (*Picea abies*) and beech (*Fagus sylvatica*) trees. *New Phytol.* 138:275–85

47. Glass ADM. 2003. Nitrogen use efficiency of crop plants: Physiological constraints upon nitrogen absorption. *Crit. Rev. Plant Sci.* 22:453–70

48. Glass ADM, Britto DT, Kaiser BN, Kinghorn JR, Kronzucker HJ, et al. 2002. The regulation of nitrate and ammonium transport systems in plants. *J. Exp. Bot.* 53:855–64

49. Gödde M, Conrad R. 2000. Influence of soil properties on the turnover of nitric oxide and nitrous oxide by nitrification and denitrification at constant temperature and moisture. *Biol. Fertil. Soils* 32:120–28

50. Graham JH, Miller RM. 2005. Mycorrhizas: gene to function. *Plant Soil* 274:70–100

51. Granato TC, Raper CD. 1989. Proliferation of maize (*Zea mays* L) roots in response to localized supply of nitrate. *J. Exp. Bot.* 40:263–75

52. Hamilton EW, Frank DA. 2001. Can plants stimulate soil microbes and their own nutrient supply? Evidence from a grazing tolerant grass. *Ecology* 82:2397–402

53. Harrison J, Brugière N, Phillipson B, Ferrario-Mery S, Becker T, et al. 2000. Manipulating the pathway of ammonia assimilation through genetic engineering and breeding: consequences to plant physiology and plant development. *Plant Soil* 221:81–93

54. Harrison KA, Bol R, Bardgett RD. 2007. Preferences for different nitrogen forms by coexisting plant species and soil microbes. *Ecology* 88:989–99

55. Hartwig UA. 1998. The regulation of symbiotic N_2 fixation: a conceptual model of N feedback from the ecosystem to the gene expression level. *Perspect. Plant Ecol. Evol. Syst.* 1:92–120

56. Herman DJ, Johnson KK, Jaeger CH, Schwartz E, Firestone MK. 2006. Root influence on nitrogen mineralization and nitrification in *Avena barbata* rhizosphere soil. *Soil Sci. Soc. Am. J.* 70:1504–11

57. Hetrick BAD. 1991. Mycorrhizas and root architecture. *Experientia* 47:355–62

58. Hodge A. 2004. The plastic plant: root responses to heterogeneous supplies of nutrients. *New Phytol.* 162:9–24

59. Hodge A, Campbell CD, Fitter AH. 2001. An arbuscular mycorrhizal fungus accelerates decomposition and acquires nitrogen directly from organic material. *Nature* 413:297–99

60. Hodge A, Robinson D, Griffiths BS, Fitter AH. 1999. Why plants bother: root proliferation results in increased nitrogen capture from an organic patch when two grasses compete. *Plant Cell Environ.* 22:811–20

61. Hodge A, Stewart J, Robinson D, Griffiths BS, Fitter AH. 1998. Root proliferation, soil fauna and plant nitrogen capture from nutrient-rich patches in soil. *New Phytol.* 139:479–94

43. Reveals a fundamental difference in the feedback regulation of NH_4^+ and NO_3^- uptake by the high-affinity transport systems of *Arabidopsis*.

47. Provides a comprehensive review of N transport systems in relation to nitrogen use efficiency of crop plants.

62. Hogberg P, Read DJ. 2006. Towards a more plant physiological perspective on soil ecology. *Trends Ecol. Evol.* 21:548–54
63. Howarth RW, Billen G, Swaney D, Townsend A, Jaworski N, et al. 1996. Regional nitrogen budgets and riverine N and P fluxes for the drainages to the North Atlantic Ocean: Natural and human influences. *Biogeochemistry* 35:75–139
64. Hu S, Chapin FS, Firestone MK, Field CB, Chiariello NR. 2001. Nitrogen limitation of microbial decomposition in a grassland under elevated CO_2. *Nature* 409:188–91
65. Jackson LE, Schimel JP, Firestone MK. 1989. Short-term partitioning of ammonium and nitrate between plants and microbes in an annual grassland. *Soil Biol. Biochem.* 21:409–16
66. Jackson RB, Mooney HA, Schulze ED. 1997. A global budget for fine root biomass, surface area, and nutrient contents. *Proc. Natl. Acad. Sci. USA* 94:7362–66
67. Jacot KA, Lüscher A, Suter M, Nösberger J, Hartwig UA. 2005. Significance of legumes for the distribution of plant species in grassland ecosystems at different altitudes in the Alps. *Plant Ecol.* 180:1–12
68. Johnson NC, Graham JH, Smith FA. 1997. Functioning of mycorrhizal associations along the mutualism-parasitism continuum. *New Phytol.* 135:575–86
69. Jones DL, Hodge A, Kuzyakov Y. 2004. Plant and mycorrhizal regulation of rhizodeposition. *New Phytol.* 163:459–80
70. Kimball BA, Morris CF, Pinter PJ, Wall GW, Hunsaker DJ, et al. 2001. Elevated CO_2, drought and soil nitrogen effects on wheat grain quality. *New Phytol.* 150:295–303
71. Kronzucker HJ, Schjoerring JK, Erner Y, Kirk GJD, Siddiqi MY, Glass ADM. 1998. Dynamic interactions between root NH_4^+ influx and long-distance N translocation in rice: Insights into feedback processes. *Plant Cell Physiol.* 39:1287–93
72. Ladha JK, Pathak H, Krupnik TJ, Six J, van Kessel C. 2005. Efficiency of fertilizer nitrogen in cereal production: Retrospects and prospects. *Adv. Agron.* 87:85–156
73. Lambers H, Shane MW, Cramer MD, Pearse SJ, Veneklaas EJ. 2006. Root structure and functioning for efficient acquisition of phosphorus: Matching morphological and physiological traits. *Ann. Bot.* 98:693–713
74. Lee RB, Purves JV, Ratcliffe RG, Saker LR. 1992. Nitrogen assimilation and the control of ammonium and nitrate absorption by maize roots. *J. Exp. Bot.* 43:1385–96
75. Lee TD, Tjoelker MG, Reich PB, Russelle MP. 2003. Contrasting growth response of an N_2-fixing and nonfixing forb to elevated CO_2: dependence on soil N supply. *Plant Soil* 255:475–86
76. Loqué D, von Wirén N. 2004. Regulatory levels for the transport of ammonium in plant roots. *J. Exp. Bot.* 55:1293–305
77. Lüscher A, Hartwig UA, Suter D, Nösberger J. 2000. Direct evidence that symbiotic N_2 fixation in fertile grassland is an important trait for a strong response of plants to elevated atmospheric CO_2. *Glob. Change Biol.* 6:655–62
78. Magill AH, Aber JD, Currie WS, Nadelhoffer KJ, Martin ME, et al. 2004. Ecosystem response to 15 years of chronic nitrogen additions at the Harvard Forest LTER, Massachusetts, USA. *For. Ecol. Manag.* 196:7–28
79. Matson PA, McDowell WH, Townsend AR, Vitousek PM. 1999. The globalization of N deposition: ecosystem consequences in tropical environments. *Biogeochemistry* 46:67–83
80. McCully M. 2005. *The rhizosphere: the key functional unit in plant/soil/microbial interactions in the field. Implications for the understanding of allelopathic effects.* (**http://www.regional.org.au/au/allelopathy/2005/index.htm**). Presented at Proc. 4th World Congr. Allelopathy, Wagga Wagga, NSW, Aust.
81. Millennium Ecosytem Assessment (MEA). 2005. *Ecosystems and human well-being: Biodiversity synthesis.* Washington, DC: World Resour. Inst.

82. Miller AJ, Cramer MD. 2004. Root nitrogen acquisition and assimilation. *Plant Soil* 274:1–36
83. Min X, Yaeesh Siddiqi M, Guy RD, Glass ADM, Kronzucker HJ. 1999. A comparative study of fluxes and compartmentation of nitrate and ammonium in early-successional tree species. *Plant Cell Environ.* 22:821–30
84. Mosier AR, Syers JK, Freney JR. 2004. Nitrogen fertilizer: an essential component of increased food, feed and fiber production. In *Agriculture and the Nitrogen Cycle*, ed. AR Mosier, JK Syers, JR Freney, pp. 3–15. Washington, DC: Island Press
85. Müller T, Avolio M, Olivi M, Benjdia M, Rikirsch E, et al. 2007. Nitrogen transport in the ectomycorrhizal association: The *Hebeloma cylindrosporum-Pinus pinaster* model. *Phytochemistry* 68:41–51
86. Orsel M, Filleur S, Fraisier V, Daniel-Vedele F. 2002. Nitrate transport in plants: which gene and which control? *J. Exp. Bot.* 53:825–33
87. Palm CA, Machado PLOA, Mahmood T, Mellillo J, Murrell ST, et al. 2004. Societal responses for addressing nitrogen fertilizer needs: balancing food production and environmental concerns. In *SCOPE 65—Agriculture and the Nitrogen Cycle: Assessing the Impacts of Fertilizer use on Food Production and the Environment*, ed. AR Mosier, JK Syers, JR Freney, pp. 71–89. Washington, DC: Island Press
88. Phillips DA, Ferris H, Cook DR, Strong DR. 2003. Molecular control points in rhizosphere food webs. *Ecology* 84:816–26
89. **Phillips DA, Fox TC, King MD, Bhuvaneswari TV, Teuber LR. 2004. Microbial products trigger amino acid exudation from plant roots. *Plant Physiol.* 136:2887–94**
90. Phillips DA, Joseph CM, Yang GP, Martinez-Romero E, Sanborn JR, Volpin H. 1999. Identification of lumichrome as a *Sinorhizobium* enhancer of alfalfa root respiration and shoot growth. *Proc. Natl. Acad. Sci. USA* 96:12275–80
91. Rachmilevitch S, Cousins AB, Bloom AJ. 2004. Nitrate assimilation in plant shoots depends on photorespiration. *Proc. Natl. Acad. Sci. USA* 101:11506–10
92. Raven JA, Edwards D. 2001. Roots: evolutionary origins and biogeochemical significance. *J. Exp. Bot.* 52:381–401
93. Rawat SR, Silim SN, Kronzucker HJ, Siddiqi MY, Glass ADM. 1999. *AtAMT1* gene expression and NH_4^+ uptake in roots of *Arabidopsis thaliana*: evidence for regulation by root glutamine levels. *Plant J.* 19:143–52
94. Reich PB, Hobbie SE, Lee T, Ellsworth DS, West JB, et al. 2006. Nitrogen limitation constrains sustainability of ecosystem response to CO_2. *Nature* 440:922–25
95. Reich PB, Hungate BA, Luo YQ. 2006. Carbon-nitrogen interactions in terrestrial ecosystems in response to rising atmospheric carbon dioxide. *Annu. Rev. Ecol. Evol. Syst.* 37:611–36
96. **Remans T, Nacry P, Pervent M, Filleur S, Diatloff E, et al. 2006. The *Arabidopsis NRT1.1* transporter participates in the signaling pathway triggering root colonization of nitrate-rich patches. *Proc. Natl. Acad. Sci. USA* 103:19206–19211**
97. Richards RA, Watt M, Rebetzke GJ. 2007. Physiological traits and cereal germplasm for sustainable agricultural systems. *Euphytica* 154:409–25
98. Robinson D, Hodge A, Griffiths BS, Fitter AH. 1999. Plant root proliferation in nitrogen-rich patches confers competitive advantage. *Proc. R. Soc. London Ser. B* 266:431–35
99. Schimel JP, Bennett J. 2004. Nitrogen mineralization: Challenges of a changing paradigm. *Ecology* 85:591–602
100. Schimel JP, Chapin FS. 1996. Tundra plant uptake of amino acid and NH_4^+ nitrogen in situ: Plants compete well for amino acid N. *Ecology* 77:2142–47

89. Demonstrates that compounds produced by bacteria and fungi can increase efflux of amino acids from roots of crop species.

96. Describes the identification of a NO_3^- transporter gene that also plays a role in sensing NO_3^- in the environment and triggering localized root proliferation.

101. Schneider MK, Lüscher A, Richter M, Aeschlimann U, Hartwig UA, et al. 2004. Ten years of free-air CO_2 enrichment altered the mobilization of N from soil in *Lolium perenne* L. swards. *Glob. Change Biol.* 10:1377–88
102. Siddiqi MY, Glass ADM, Ruth TJ. 1991. Studies of the uptake of nitrate in barley. III. Compartmentation of NO_3^-. *J. Exp. Bot.* 42:1455–63
103. Siddiqi MY, Glass ADM, Ruth TJ, Rufty TW. 1990. Studies of the uptake of nitrate in barley. I. Kinetics of $^{13}NO_3^-$ influx. *Plant Physiol.* 93:1426–32
104. Siddiqi MY, Malhotra B, Min XJ, Glass ADM. 2002. Effects of ammonium and inorganic carbon enrichment on growth and yield of a hydroponic tomato crop. *J. Plant Nutr. Soil Sci.* 165:191–97
105. Silberbush M, Barber SA. 1983. Sensitivity analysis of parameters used in simulating K-uptake with a mechanistic mathematical-model. *Agron. J.* 75:851–54
106. Sinclair TR, Vadez V. 2002. Physiological traits for crop yield improvement in low N and P environments. *Plant Soil* 245:1–15
107. Smith KA, Ball T, Conen F, Dobbie KE, Massheder J, Rey A. 2003. Exchange of greenhouse gases between soil and atmosphere: interactions of soil physical factors and biological processes. *Eur. J. Soil Sci.* 54:779–91
108. Smith SE, Read DJ. 1997. *Mycorrhizal Symbiosis*. Cambridge, UK: Academic. 605 pp.
109. Sonoda Y, Ikeda A, Saiki S, von Wiren N, Yamaya T, Yamaguchi J. 2003. Distinct expression and function of three ammonium transporter genes (*OsAMT1;1–1;3*) in rice. *Plant Cell Physiol.* 44:726–34
110. Sonoda Y, Ikeda A, Saiki S, Yamaya T, Yamaguchi J. 2003. Feedback regulation of the ammonium transporter gene family AMT1 by glutamine in rice. *Plant Cell Physiol.* 44:1396–402
111. **Subbarao GV, Ishikawa T, Ito O, Nakahara K, Wang HY, Berry WL. 2006. A bioluminescence assay to detect nitrification inhibitors released from plant roots: a case study with *Brachiaria humidicola*. *Plant Soil* 288:101–12**

111. Describes the discovery of nitrification inhibitors that are functionally stable in soil in root exudates of the tropical grass, *Brachiaria humidicola*.

112. Tanaka Y, Yano K. 2005. Nitrogen delivery to maize via mycorrhizal hyphae depends on the form of N supplied. *Plant Cell Environ.* 28:1247–54
113. Taylor AR, Bloom AJ. 1998. Ammonium, nitrate, and proton fluxes along the maize root. *Plant Cell Environ.* 21:1255–63
114. Tibbett M. 2000. Roots, foraging and the exploitation of soil nutrient patches: the role of mycorrhizal symbiosis. *Funct. Ecol.* 14:397–99
115. Tinker PB, Nye PH. 2000. *Solute Movement in the Rhizosphere*. Oxford: Oxford Univ. Press
116. Treseder KK. 2004. A meta-analysis of mycorrhizal responses to nitrogen, phosphorus, and atmospheric CO_2 in field studies. *New Phytol.* 164:347–55
117. van Vuuren MMI, Robinson D, Griffiths BS. 1996. Nutrient inflow and root proliferation during the exploitation of a temporally and spatially discrete source of nitrogen in soil. *Plant Soil* 178:185–92
118. Venterea RT, Groffman PA, Castro MS, Verchot LV, Fernandez IJ, Adams MB. 2004. Soil emissions of nitric oxide in two forest watersheds subjected to elevated N inputs. *For. Ecol. Manag.* 196:335–49
119. Venterea RT, Groffman PM, Verchot LV, Magill AH, Aber JD. 2004. Gross nitrogen process rates in temperate forest soils exhibiting symptoms of nitrogen saturation. *For. Ecol. Manag.* 196:129–42
120. Vidmar JJ, Zhuo D, Siddiqi MY, Schjoerring JK, Touraine B, Glass ADM. 2000. Regulation of high-affinity nitrate transporter genes and high-affinity nitrate influx by nitrogen pools in roots of barley. *Plant Physiol.* 123:307–18

121. Wang MY, Siddiqi MY, Ruth TJ, Glass ADM. 1993. Ammonium uptake by rice roots. II. Kinetics of $^{13}NH_4^+$ influx across the plasmalemma. *Plant Physiol.* 103:1259–67
122. Watt M, Hugenholtz P, White R, Vinall K. 2006. Numbers and locations of native bacteria on field-grown wheat roots quantified by fluorescence in situ hybridization (FISH). *Environ. Microbiol.* 8:871–84
123. Watt M, Silk WK, Passioura JB. 2006. Rates of root and organism growth, soil conditions, and temporal and spatial development of the rhizosphere. *Ann. Bot.* 97:839–55
124. Yu T-R. 1985. Soil and plants. In *Physical Chemistry of Paddy Soils*, ed. T-R Yu, pp. 197–217. Beijing, China: Science
125. Zhang HM, Jennings A, Barlow PW, Forde BG. 1999. Dual pathways for regulation of root branching by nitrate. *Proc. Natl. Acad. Sci. USA* 96:6529–34

A Genetic Regulatory Network in the Development of Trichomes and Root Hairs

Tetsuya Ishida,[1] Tetsuya Kurata,[1,*] Kiyotaka Okada,[2] and Takuji Wada[1]

[1]Plant Science Center, RIKEN, Yokohama, Kanagawa 230-0045, Japan; email: tishida@psc.riken.jp; tekurata@nibb.ac.jp; twada@psc.riken.jp

[2]National Institute for Basic Biology, Myodaiji, Okazaki, Aichi 444-8585, Japan; email: kiyo@nibb.ac.jp

Annu. Rev. Plant Biol. 2008. 59:365–86

The *Annual Review of Plant Biology* is online at plant.annualreviews.org

This article's doi:
10.1146/annurev.arplant.59.032607.092949

1543-5008/08/0602-0365$20.00

*Current address: Hasebe Reprogramming Evolution Project, ERATO, Japan Science and Technology Agency, Okazaki 444-8585, Japan

Key Words

cell differentiation, endoreduplication, tip growth

Abstract

Trichomes and root hairs differentiate from epidermal cells in the aerial tissues and roots, respectively. Because trichomes and root hairs are easily accessible, particularly in the model plant *Arabidopsis*, their development has become a well-studied model of cell differentiation and growth. Molecular genetic analyses using *Arabidopsis* mutants have demonstrated that the differentiation of trichomes and root hair/hairless cells is regulated by similar molecular mechanisms. Transcriptional complexes regulate differentiation into trichome cells and root hairless cells, and formation of the transcriptional complexes is inhibited in neighboring cells. Control of cell growth after fate determination has also been analyzed using *Arabidopsis* mutants. The progression of endoreduplication cycles, reorientation of microtubules, and organization of the actin cytoskeleton play important roles in trichome growth. Various cellular components such as ion channels, the actin cytoskeleton, microtubules and cell wall materials, and intracellular signal transduction act to establish and maintain root hair tip growth.

Contents

INTRODUCTION

Trichomes and root hairs are fine structures that differentiate from epidermal cells in the aerial parts of plants or from root epidermal cells, respectively. Trichomes can have a variety of morphologies, and are thought to perform a number of functions in various species (131). Trichomes may be unicellular or multicellular, branched or unbranched, and secretory-glandular or nonglandular. They may help resist insect herbivory by projecting a physical or chemical barrier beyond the surface of the plant. They may also provide some shade to protect plants from UV irradiation or to reduce transpiration. Cotton fibers are trichomes of cotton ovules, which may have aided in precultivation seed dispersal (131).

Root hairs provide the ability to absorb nutrients and water, interact with microorganisms, and physically anchor the plant to the soil. The distribution of root hairs varies by plant species, and can be affected by growth conditions (31). A survey of root epidermal patterning in different species demonstrated that there are three types of hair cell differentiation (31). In the first type, root epidermal cells can produce hair cells in any position. In the second type, hair cells develop from smaller cells derived from an asymmetric cell division. In the third type, described by Cormack (27, 28), cell files are arranged longitudinally such that hair-forming hair cell files alternate with hairless cell files.

In *Arabidopsis*, much progress has recently been made in understanding the development of trichomes and root hairs. Leaf trichomes are unicellular, dendritic, and nonglandular. Trichome development starts near the distal end of the maturing leaf and proceeds basipetally (50). Trichomes are regularly spaced and are rarely formed adjacent to one another, suggesting that some mechanism regulates trichome spacing (50) (**Figure 1*a***).

Arabidopsis roots have type 3 hair cell patterning. Epidermal cells that are positioned in a cleft between two underlying cortical cells develop as hair (H) cells. Other epidermal cells located over the outer periclinal wall of a single cortical cell are referred to as N (non-hair) cells because they form hairless cells (11, 27, 32) (**Figure 2*a***). This review focuses on what has recently been learned about the developmental mechanisms of root hairs and trichomes in *Arabidopsis* using genetic, molecular, and pharmacological approaches.

CELL FATE DETERMINATION

Transcriptional Complex Formation and Inhibition

A number of genes involved in trichome formation and root epidermis cell fate determination have been identified from forward genetics experiments. *TRANSPARENT TESTA GLABRA1* (*TTG1*), *GLABRA3* (*GL3*), *ENHANCER OF GLABRA3* (*EGL3*), which is a paralog of *GL3*, and *GLABRA2* (*GL2*) regulate trichome initiation and hairless cell differentiation (12, 42, 50, 71, 91, 141). *GLABRA1* (*GL1*) promotes trichome initiation, and *WEREWOLF* (*WER*) regulates hairless cell differentiation (50, 67). *TTG1* encodes a WD40 protein (132), *GL3/EGL3* encode basic helix-loop-helix (bHLH)-type transcription factors (12, 91), and *GL2* encodes a homeodomain/leucine zipper transcription factor (71). *GL1* and *WER* encode R2R3 Myb transcription factors, which are functionally equivalent (67, 68, 89). Mutations in these genes reduce trichome number and/or cause root hair formation in N cells (ectopic root hairs) (**Figures 1*a*** and **2*b***). *GL2* is expressed in trichomes and N cells (71). Reporter gene expression studies indicate that *WER*, *GL3*, *EGL3*, and *TTG1* act upstream of *GL2* in the root epidermis transcriptional network (12, 51, 67). In fact, *WER* is expressed in N cells and the WER protein binds the *GL2* promoter (63, 67). In addition, a yeast two-hybrid study showed that GL3/EGL3 physically interact with WER and TTG1 (12, 91, 141). These results suggest that complexes consisting of WER, GL3/EGL3, and TTG1 promote *GL2* expression to regulate hairless cell differentiation (**Figure 2*c***). The regulation of trichome formation is likely to be similar because *GL2* expression continues after *GL1* expression ends in trichomes, *GL2* is ectopically expressed in transgenic lines co-overexpressing *GL1* and the maize *R* gene (a bHLH gene), and GL1 physically interacts with GL3/EGL3 (91, 118, 141) (**Figure 1*b***).

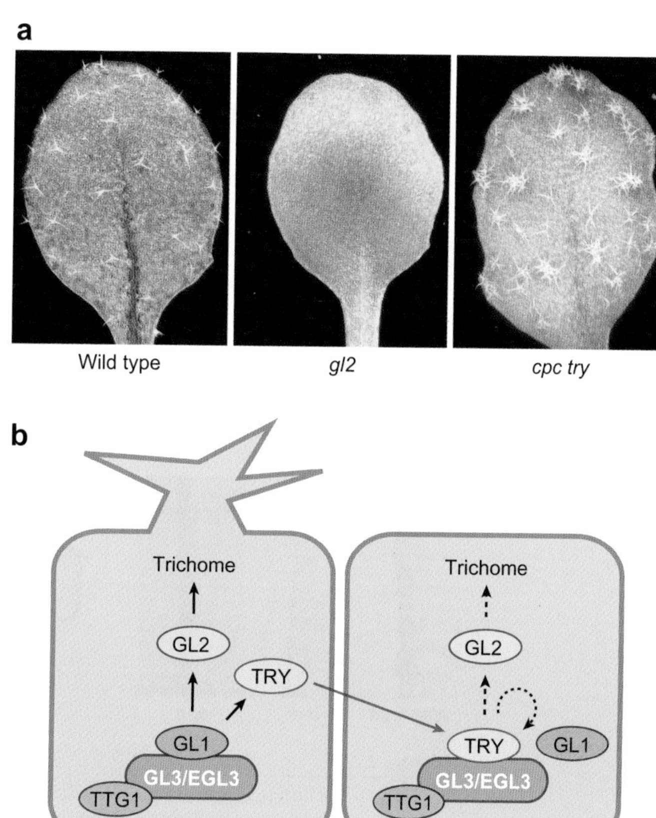

Figure 1

Trichome formation in *Arabidopsis*. (*a*) Trichome formation in wild type, *glabra 2* (*gl2*), and *caprice* (*cpc*) *triptychon* (*try*) double mutant. Trichomes are regularly spaced in the wild type. Trichomes are rarely formed in the *gl2* mutant. Clusters of trichomes are formed in the *cpc try* double mutant. (*b*) Regulatory model of trichome differentiation. The GLABRA1 (GL1)-GLABRA3 (GL3)/ENHANCER OF GLABRA3 (EGL3)-TRANSPARENT TESTA GLABRA1 (TTG1) complex promotes *GL2* and *TRY* expression. The TRY protein moves into neighboring cells where it competes with GL1 for binding to GL3/EGL3. Neither the TRY-GL3/EGL3-TTG1 complex nor dissociated GL1 can promote *GL2* or *TRY* expression. Cells expressing *GL2* differentiate into trichome cells. TRY represents R3 Myb proteins in this figure.

In contrast, expression of *CAPRICE* (*CPC*), *TRIPTYCHON* (*TRY*), *ENHANCER OF TRY AND CPC 1* (*ETC1*), or *ETC2* suppresses trichome initiation and differentiation into hairless cells in a redundant manner (59, 60, 105, 130). These genes encode R3 Myb

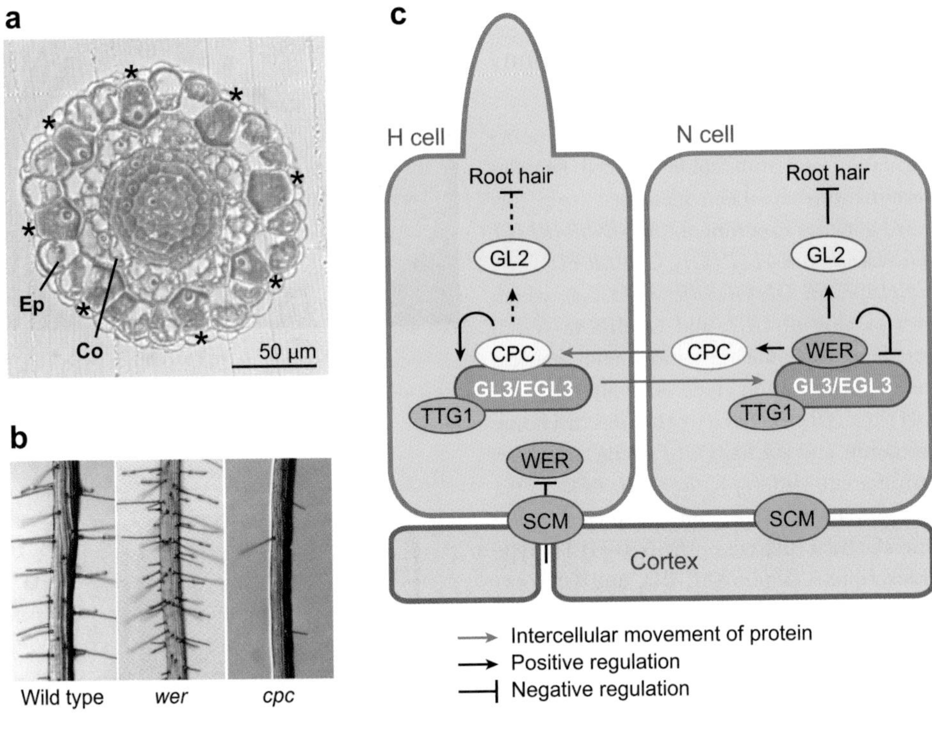

Figure 2

Epidermal cell differentiation in the *Arabidopsis* root. (*a*) Root cross section stained with toluidine blue. H cells (*) are cytoplasmically dense. Epidermis (Ep) and cortex (Co) are indicated. (*b*) Patterns of root hairs in wild type, *werewolf* (*wer*), and *caprice* (*cpc*) mutants. Hair cell files and hairless cell files are formed in the wild type. Root hairs are formed from all epidermal cells in the *wer* mutant. The number of root hairs is reduced in the *cpc* mutant. (*c*) Simple regulatory model of root epidermal cell differentiation. A positional cue from SCRAMBLED (SCM) represses *WER* expression in H cells. The WER-GLABRA3 (GL3)/ENHANCER OF GLABRA3 (EGL3)-TRANSPARENT TESTA GLABRA1 (TTG1) complex promotes *GLABRA2* (*GL2*) and *CPC* expression. The CPC protein moves into neighboring cells where it competes with WER for binding to GL3/EGL3. Neither the CPC-GL3/EGL3-TTG1 complex nor dissociated WER can promote *GL2* or *CPC* expression. GL3/EGL3 expression is positively regulated by *CPC* and negatively regulated by *WER*, *GL3*, *EGL3*, and *TTG1* (13). Cells expressing *GL2* differentiate into hairless cells.

proteins lacking the typical transcriptional activation domain (59, 60, 105, 130). Mutations in these genes cause an increase in trichome density and/or trichome clustering and reduce the number of root hairs (**Figures 1*a*** and **2*b***). R3 Myb and R2R3 Myb proteins compete for interaction with bHLH proteins, suggesting that R3 Myb proteins inhibit trichome initiation and root hairless cell differentiation by disturbing the formation of R2R3 Myb-bHLH-TTG1 complexes (35, 36) (**Figures 1*b*** and **2*c***). This could explain why *GL2* expression disappears in *35S::CPC* lines (129).

Reciprocal Cell-to-Cell Movement of Transcription Factors Determines Epidermal Cell Identity

Despite their inhibition of trichome initiation and hairless cell differentiation, R3 Myb genes are expressed in trichomes and N cells (36, 59, 60, 105, 129). For example, *cpc* mutants have fewer normally shaped root hairs in H cell files than wild-type (**Figure 2*b***), whereas *CPC* transcription is regulated by *WER*, and *CPC* mRNA can be detected in N cell files (69, 129, 130). This inconsistency raises the possibility that intercellular movement of the CPC protein causes this non–cell-autonomous action of the *CPC* gene. A transgenic approach with CPC:GFP (green fluorescent protein) fusions demonstrated that CPC is localized within the nuclei of all epidermal cells, implying that the CPC:GFP fusion protein moves from N cells to H cells within the root epidermis (129) (**Figure 2*c***). Further analysis identified the regions and amino acids required for intercellular movement, suggesting that CPC movement may proceed by targeted and regulated transport (64). An interesting point is that inhibitory effects differ among R3 Myb proteins. Mutant phenotypes indicate that the effect of TRY is local whereas that of CPC is more long ranging (105). TRY has a longer C terminus than CPC, which might be why the two proteins have different effects (36). *GL3* and *EGL3* are also non-cell-autonomous factors. GL3 and EGL3 play redundant roles in hairless cell differentiation. Experiments with promoter-GUS fusions and in situ hybridization confirmed that *GL3* and *EGL3* are preferentially expressed in H cell files (13). Experiments with a YFP translational C-terminal fusion driven by the *GL3* promoter established the localization of the GL3 protein. The GL3:YFP fusion protein accumulates in the nuclei of N cells, indicating that GL3 (and presumably EGL3) moves from H cells to N cells and regulates hairless cell differentiation (13) (**Figure 2*c***).

What is the Positional Cue Regulating Epidermal Cell Differentiation?

Although the expression of transcription factors in roots is position-dependent, knowledge about the molecular mechanisms that generate and transduce positional cues is limited. The *SCRAMBLED* (*SCM*) gene was isolated as a candidate for mediating the positional cue (66). *scm* mutants have disorganized *GL2::GUS* patterns; patchy *GL2::GUS* expression is observed in both H and N cell files. Disorganized expression patterns are also observed in *WER::GFP*, *CPC::GUS*, and *EGL3::GUS* backgrounds, suggesting that *SCM* acts upstream of these genes in cell fate determination (**Figure 2*c***). *SCM* encodes a leucine-rich repeat receptor-like kinase (LRR-RLK), which is expressed throughout all the developing tissue layers, including root epidermis (66). Because *SCM* represses *WER*, the extracellular receptor domain of SCM on H cells may detect some unknown positional signal localized between cortical cells, and then an intracellular domain may transmit its signal into the epidermal cell to establish the appropriate cell fate (i.e., hair cell or hairless cell) (65) (**Figure 2*c***). Interestingly, the intracellular kinase domain of SCM seems to have lost kinase activity (23). The SCM ligand is a future target of cell fate determination research, as is the mechanism by which SCM transduces the correct signal to the complex of transcription factors.

Leucine-rich repeat receptor-like kinase (LRR-RLK): contains a repeated motif that is rich in leucine residues in the extracellular region, one transmembrane domain, and a kinase domain in the intracellular region

Chromatin Organization and *GL2* Expression

In roots, *GL2* is transcribed in N cells but not in H cells. Costa & Shaw (29) demonstrated that the chromatin state around the *GL2* locus differs between N cells and H cells. In an elegant three-dimensional fluorescence in situ hybridization study, a *GL2* bacterial artificial chromosome (BAC) probe hybridized with the genomic region of the *GL2* locus in N cells, but not in H cells (**Figure 3**), indicating that the *GL2* locus of N cells is in an open chromatin state and can be transcribed. The chromatin state at the *GL2* locus is reorganized in the gap 1 (G1) phase of the cell cycle in response to positional information. Chromatin structure is altered by modification of core histones (39). In *Arabidopsis*, trimethylated K9 of histone H3 (H3K9me3) is a marker for the open chromatin state, and mono- and dimethylated

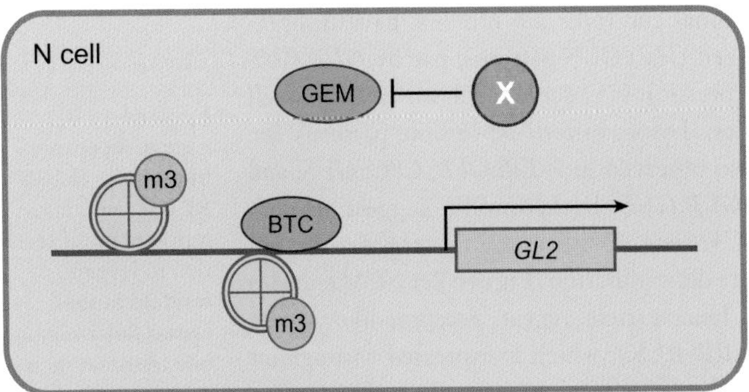

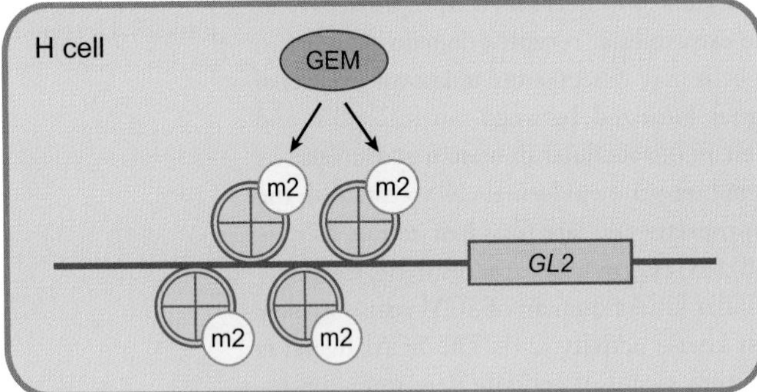

Figure 3

Hypothetical model of chromatin structure at the *GLABRA2* (*GL2*) locus, based on data from Caro and coworkers (21) and Costa & Shaw (29). In N cells, histone H3 at the *GL2* locus is trimethylated and the *GL2* locus is open in that the basal transcription complex (BTC) can bind to the promoter. GL2 EXPRESSION MODULATOR (GEM) activity on histone modification is suppressed by an unknown mechanism (X). In H cells, histone H3 at the *GL2* locus is dimethylated and the *GL2* locus is closed. GEM mediates dimethylation of histone H3 in H cells.

H3K9s (H3K9me1 and H3K9me2) indicate a closed state (**Figure 3**). Histone acetylation also causes an open chromatin state. In *gl2 expression modulator-1* (*gem-1*) mutants, root hair density is reduced and trichome density is increased, and root hair density is increased and trichome density is reduced in *GEM* overexpressors (21). *GL2* and *CPC* expression increases in *gem-1*, whereas it is reduced in *GEM* overexpressors. Physical interaction of GEM with TTG1 suggests that GEM inhibits formation of R2R3 Myb-bHLH-TTG1 complexes. *GL2* and *CPC* promoters contain both H3K9me2 and H3K9me3 methylation markers. H3K9me3 increases and H3K9me2 decreases in these promoters in the *gem-1* background, but H3K9me3 decreases and H3K9me2 increases in *GEM* overexpressors. Acetylation of histone H3 in the *GL2* and *CPC* promoters increases in *gem-1* plants. These results suggest that *GEM* controls root epidermal cell fate through both interaction with TTG1, the regulator of *GL2* and *CPC* expression, and modification of histone H3 at the *GL2* and *CPC* loci (21) (**Figure 3**).

Histone acetylation can be augmented by treatment with trichostatin A (TSA), an inhibitor of histone deacetylase (HDAC), or a mutation in the gene encoding HDAC. In roots treated with TSA, histones H3 and H4 are hyperacetylated in *GL2*, *CPC*, and *WER* loci, resulting in altered expression levels and cell-specific expression of all three genes (138). However, both treatment of roots with TSA and mutation of the *HDA18* locus, which encodes HDAC, increase root hair density and cause the plant to form ectopic root hairs. This inconsistency may indicate that an unknown mechanism mediates epidermal cell fate determination when histone acetylation occurs.

Regulation by Phytohormone Signaling

The phytohormones gibberellin (GA) and jasmonic acid increase trichome number and density, whereas salicylic acid decreases trichome number (124). However, not much is known about phytohormone signaling pathways in trichome formation. *SPINDLY* (*SPY*) encodes a repressor of GA signaling, and the *spy-5* mutant has more trichomes than wild-type, but the glabrous phenotype of *gl1-1* is epistatic to the *spy-5* phenotype, suggesting that GA signaling is upstream of *GL1* (93). In addition, *GL1* transcription is reduced in GA-deficient *ga1-3* mutants, but increases with exogenous GA application, suggesting that GA induces trichome formation through upregulation of *GL1* (93). Cytokinins also stimulate trichome formation on the inflorescence stem. The influence of cytokinins increases as the inflorescence grows (47). GA and cytokinin signals are both integrated by the C2H2 transcription factors GLABROUS INFLORESCENCE STEMS (GIS), GIS2, and ZINC FINGER PROTEIN 8 (ZFP8), and then they collectively regulate *GL1* expression (43, 44).

Ethylene and auxin promote root hair formation. Blocking ethylene perception or inhibiting ethylene synthesis reduces the number of root hairs, whereas treatment with the ethylene precursor 1-aminocyclopropane-1-carboxylic acid (ACC) results in ectopic root hairs on N cells (121). Numerous pharmacological and genetic studies have demonstrated that auxin promotes root hair formation (72, 97). Ethylene and auxin also increase the rate of hair elongation (94). Recent studies have uncovered the auxin signal transduction pathway, which makes use of the Aux/IAA family of transcriptional regulators (70). Stable dominant mutations in the *Aux/IAA* genes *AUXIN RESISTANT 3* (*AXR3*)/*IAA17*, *SOLITARY-ROOT* (*SLR*)/*IAA14*, or *AXR2*/*IAA7* reduce the number of root hairs compared with wild-type, whereas a similar dominant mutation in *SHORT HYPOCOTYL 2* (*SHY2*)/*IAA3* shows early initiation of root hairs and prolonged hair elongation, suggesting that the root hair formation stimulated by auxin is mediated by the *Aux/IAA* genes (40, 62, 82). To clarify the relationship between these hormones and cell fate determination factors *TTG1* and *GL2*, epistasis experiments and reporter gene assays have been conducted. Clearly, neither auxin nor ethylene regulate the *TTG1/GL2* pathway (73). Mutations in *ROOT HAIR DEFECTIVE 6* (*RHD6*), a downstream gene of *GL2* that encodes a bHLH transcription factor, result in a reduction of root hair density and a shift in the site of root hair emergence (72, 80). These phenotypes are similar to those of the *axr2* mutant and the ethylene-resistant *ethylene response 1* (*etr1*) mutant and are rescued by application of auxin or ACC. In addition, wild-type roots treated with an inhibitor of ethylene biosynthesis phenocopy the *rhd6* mutant phenotype. These results suggest that *RHD6* promotes root hair formation through pathways that involve auxin and ethylene (72).

Endoreduplication: a cell cycle in which DNA replication continues without mitosis or cytokinesis

REGULATION OF TRICHOME GROWTH

Cells destined to become trichomes exit the mitotic cycle and enter an endoreduplication cycle. Trichomes undergo an average of four endoreduplication cycles, reaching average nuclear DNA contents of 32C, where C equals haploid DNA content per nucleus (50, 108). Protrichome cells form branches and then expand during endoreduplication (108).

Cell Cycle Regulation in Trichomes

Some mutations affect either the shift from mitosis to endoreduplication or the number of endoreduplication cycles. The *SIAMESE* (*SIM*) gene suppresses mitotic cycling (133) (**Figure 4**). In *sim* mutants, trichomes are multicellular but their gross morphology is normal. The SIM protein has a motif similar to INHIBITOR/INTERACTOR OF CYCLIN-DEPENDENT KINASE/KIP-RELATED PROTEINS (ICK/KRP) proteins, which are inhibitors of cyclin-dependent kinases (CDKs), and interacts with D-type cyclins (CYCDs) and CDKA (25) (**Figure 4**). CYCD-CDKA complexes are typically considered to function at the G1/synthesis (S) transition (**Figure 4**). However, overexpression of a CYCD in trichomes can produce multicellular trichomes, and the *sim* mutant phenotype is rescued when *ICK1/KRP1*, a CDK inhibitor that interacts with CYCDs, is expressed in trichomes (109, 136). These observations suggest that SIM is a CDK inhibitor by virtue of its interactions with CYCD-CDKA complexes. Multicellular trichomes can also be formed when a B-type

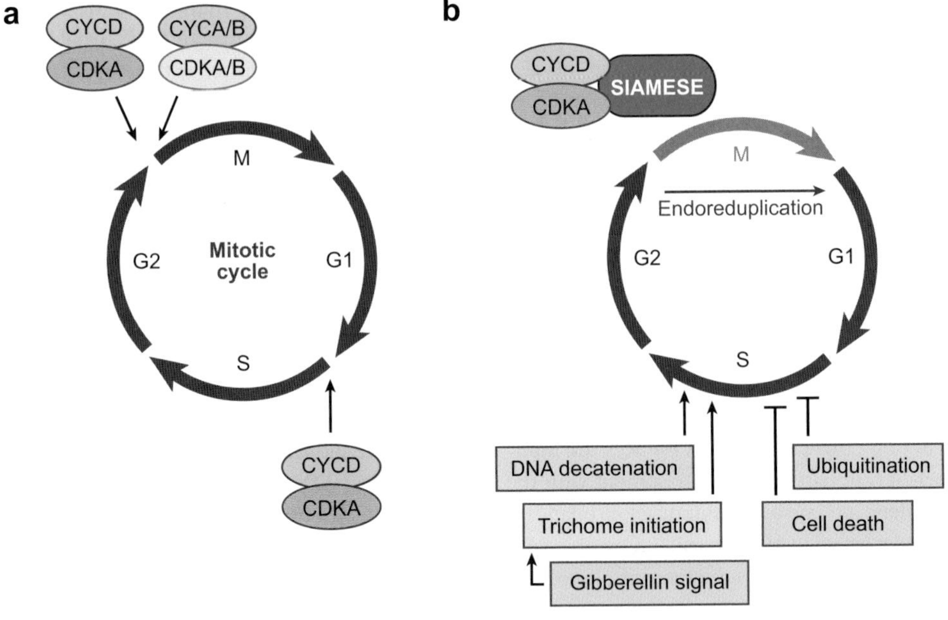

Figure 4

Regulation of the cell cycle in trichomes. The mitotic cell cycle proceeds through four phases: M (mitosis), G1 (gap 1), S (synthesis) and G2 (gap 2). (*a*) D-type cyclin-CYCLIN-DEPENDENT KINASE A (CYCD-CDKA) complexes function at the G1/S and G2/M transitions. CYCA/B-CDKA/B complexes function at the G2/M transition. (*b*) Endoreduplication cycles skip the M phase. The SIAMESE protein interacts with CYCD-CDKA complexes to repress entry into the M phase, resulting in a switch from mitotic to endoreduplication cycles. Endoreduplication cycles are also regulated by several different pathways (*green*).

cyclin (CYCB) is expressed in trichomes using the *GL2* promoter (110). Because CYCBs regulate the gap 2 (G2)/mitosis (M) transition, ectopic CYCB expression in trichomes induces a shift from endoreduplication to mitosis (**Figure 4**). *CYCB* is not expressed in wild-type trichomes, but it is expressed in *sim* trichomes, suggesting that *SIM* inhibits *CYCB* expression (110).

Cyclin: regulates cell-cycle progression with cyclin-dependent protein kinases

Ubiquitin ligase: an enzyme that attaches ubiquitin to a protein, often marking it for degradation in the proteasome

Mutations that affect the number of endoreduplication cycles lead to trichomes with supernumerary or reduced numbers of branches, possibly because of the involvement of several different molecular pathways in regulation of the number of endoreduplication cycles (**Figure 4**). *GL3* and *TRY* regulate not only trichome initiation but also endoreduplication cycles. Trichomes of *try* mutants have increased branching and an average DNA content of 64C, suggesting that one additional endoreduplication cycle occurs (119). *gl3-1* mutants have an average DNA content of 16C and reduced branching (50).

GA signaling also affects trichome branching and endoreduplication. For example, *spy-5* mutants have hyperbranched trichomes with a DNA content of 64C (92). Conversely, *ga1-3* mutants are nearly glabrous and rarely have bifurcated trichomes (93). GA signaling likely controls endoreduplication cycles via regulation of *GL1* or its homolog.

In *kaktus* (*kak*) mutants, trichomes are hyperbranched with an average DNA content of 64C (92). *KAK* encodes a member of the homologous to E6AP C terminus (HECT) ubiquitin ligase family, suggesting that ubiquitin-regulated protein degradation negatively controls trichome branching and endoreduplication (33, 34).

Two dwarf mutants, *root hairless2* (*rhl2*) and *hypocotyl6* (*hyp6*), have hypobranched trichomes and fewer endoreduplication cycles than wild-type (49, 116). *RHL2* and *HYP6* encode plant homologs of subunits of archaebacterial topoisomerase VI (topoVI). In archea, topoVI is required to disentangle chromosomes during DNA replication (decatenation) (19). Both *rhl2* and *hyp6* mutants can complete the first two rounds of endoreduplication to 8C, indicating that topoVI is required for endocycles beyond the 8C level (49, 116).

Mutations in the *CONSTITUTIVE PATHOGEN RESPONSE 5* (*CPR5*) gene mimic programmed cell death. Trichomes of *cpr5* mutants are hypobranched and are reduced in size compared with wild-type, and endoreduplication cycles are likely to stop after the second cycle is completed (56). A similar relationship between cell death and endoreduplication cycles is observed in transgenic plants expressing *ICK1/KRP1* under control of the *GL2* promoter (111). These observations indicate a pathway controls both programmed cell death and the progression of endoreduplication cycles.

Regulation of Trichome Branching

In addition to the array of genes that regulates endoreduplication cycles, many genes regulate trichome branching. Some of them are involved in microtubule (MT) function. During trichome development, cortical MTs are initially arranged transversely and shift to a longitudinal orientation when a branch is formed (74). Application of MT-interacting drugs during trichome growth results in isotropical expansion of the trichome and defective branching, whereas new branching points are initiated by transient application of taxol, an MT-stabilizing drug, to *zwichel* (*zwi*) mutants that have less-branched trichomes (74, 78). These results imply an important role for MTs in trichome branching. Mutations in genes involved in the formation of α/β-tubulin heterodimers and MTs consistently affect trichome branching. Dominant-negative mutations in both α-tubulin 4 and 6 result in unstable MTs and ultimately in the inhibition of trichome branching (2). Conversely, another mutant α-tubulin 6 allele ($TUA6^{D251A/E254A}$) makes MTs stable and results in new branch formation (1). Mutants of *KIESEL* (*KIS*), *PORCINO* (*POR*), and *KATANIN-p60* have less-branched trichomes compared with wild-type (20, 57, 58). *KIS* and *POR* encode tubulin-folding cofactors A and C, respectively, and play a role in producing assembly-competent α/β-tubulin. Katanins are known to function as MT-severing proteins. These mutant phenotypes suggest that both de novo MT synthesis and disassembly of preexisting MTs are important for branching (20, 57).

As mentioned above, *zwi* mutants have less-branched trichomes compared with wild-type. *ZWI* encodes a kinesin-like calmodulin-binding protein that binds MTs and moves in a directional manner along the MTs, suggesting the importance of transport along MTs for branching (90).

Topoisomerase: an enzyme that cuts and religates DNA to create a more relaxed DNA conformation

Microtubule (MT): a long, cylinder-like structure made from tubulin

WAVE complex: regulates the activities of the Arp2/3 complex

Regulation of Trichome Expansion

After branching, trichomes expand along the whole cell axis, not by tip growth (112). The directionality of trichome expansion depends on the actin cytoskeleton. Actin cytoskeletons are diffuse in early stages and become organized into thicker bundles aligned with the growth axis as the trichome matures (78, 120). Application of actin-interacting drugs causes aberrant organization of the bundles, similar to those of mutants classified to the *distorted* group (78, 120). *DISTORTED* genes encode subunits of the actin-related protein 2/3 (Arp2/3) and Wiskott-Aldrich syndrome protein family verprolin homologous protein (WAVE) complexes, which regulate actin polymerization (117). Organelles such as Golgi bodies or peroxisomes move along actin filaments (16, 75, 83). In *crooked*, a mutant of an Arp2/3 complex subunit, Golgi bodies accumulate and peroxisome motility is reduced in nonexpanded areas of trichomes where F-actin is densely accumulated, but Golgi

Arp2/3 complex: initiates new actin filaments on the sides of preexisting ones

ADP-ribosylation factor 1-GTPase (ARF1-GTPase): regulates vesicle formation

Mitogen-activated protein kinase (MAP kinase): one of the serine/threonine kinases

bodies and peroxisomes in expanded areas move in a manner similar to the wild-type (77). Actin filaments are also involved in membrane fusion. Wild-type trichomes have a single large vacuole, whereas both *wurm* and *distorted1*, which are mutants of the Arp2/3 complex subunits, have many small vacuoles near a large vacuole (76).

In nonplant cells, binding of Rho GTPase to a WAVE complex either activates the whole complex or releases active subcomplex, either of which binds and activates the Arp2/3 complex (18). Rho GTPase is activated by a CDM family protein (named for *Caenorhabditis elegans* CED-5, human DOCK180, and *Drosophila melanogaster* myoblast city, hypothesized to mediate cytoskeletal reorganization in response to diverse extracellular signals), which functions as a guanine nucleotide exchange factor (18, 61, 86). In *Arabidopsis*, there are 11 Rho-related GTPases (ROPs), and *SPIKE1* (*SPK1*) encodes a CDM homolog (96, 140). Detailed analysis of the WAVE-Arp2/3 pathway is necessary because contradictory data exist on the interaction between ROPs and WAVE complex subunits (8, 125).

ROOT HAIR INITIATION AND TIP GROWTH

Calcium and Potassium

In *Arabidopsis*, hair cells (trichoblasts) initiate root hair growth by causing a swelling in the hair cell at the basal position (**Figure 5*a***). Polarity is established by auxin signaling and by the appropriate trafficking of the auxin influx carrier AUX1 into the apical and basal ends of epidermal cells (46, 72) (**Figure 5*a***). ROP GTPases ROP2, ROP4, and ROP6 localize in the earliest swelling of the basal region and tip throughout hair development (53, 81). Their localization and action are regulated by ADP ribosylation factor 1 (ARF1)-GTPase, a key component of vesicle transport, which is localized in Golgi and endocytic vesicles, and by RhoGTPase GDP dissociation inhibitor (RhoGDI1), encoded by *SUPERCENTIPEDE1* (*SCN1*) (22, 139) (**Figure 5*a***). RhoGDIs are negative regulators of ROPs (140). In *scn1* mutants, ROP2 is mislocalized and supernumerary hair initiation sites are formed (22). ROP2 regulates the activity of an NADPH oxidase encoded by *ROOT HAIR DEFECTIVE 2* (*RHD2*) that plays an important role in Ca^{2+} uptake at the tip (38, 52, 137). Ca^{2+} is indispensable for root hair tip growth (106). During root hair growth, the concentration of cytoplasmic Ca^{2+} at the tip region can exceed 1 μM, which is considerably higher than the 100–200 nM found in the rest of the cell (137). Blocking Ca^{2+} channel activity causes the arrest of root hair growth, suggesting that Ca^{2+} influx is required for higher concentrations at the tip region (137). The *rhd2* mutant was identified as a short root hair mutant that is defective in Ca^{2+} uptake (107, 137). RHD2/NADPH oxidase produces reactive oxygen species (ROS) (123). ROS accumulate at higher levels in wild-type than in *rhd2*, and an NADPH oxidase inhibitor suppresses ROS production in wild-type and phenocopies the *rhd2* mutant phenotype (38). In addition, treatment with ROS causes the partial suppression of the *rhd2* phenotype and stimulates the activity of Ca^{2+} channels, suggesting that ROS produced via an NADPH oxidase-dependent process activates Ca^{2+} channels, which in turn regulate tip-focused calcium influx (38) (**Figure 5*b***). A recent study demonstrated that ROS activate the expression and activity of *Arabidopsis* serine/threonine kinase [OXIDATIVE SIGNAL-INDUCIBLE 1 (OXI1)], and *oxi1* null mutants have shorter root hairs than wild-type (99). OXI1 is required for full activation of the *Arabidopsis* mitogen-activated protein kinases (MAPKs) AtMPK3 and AtMPK6 when stimulated by treatment with ROS (99). Because AtMPK6 is an ortholog of SIMK (stress-induced MAPK), which is involved in the actin organization (described below), the regulatory target of AtMPK6 may be the cytoskeleton (**Figure 5*b***).

The role of potassium in root hair tip growth has been investigated with K^+

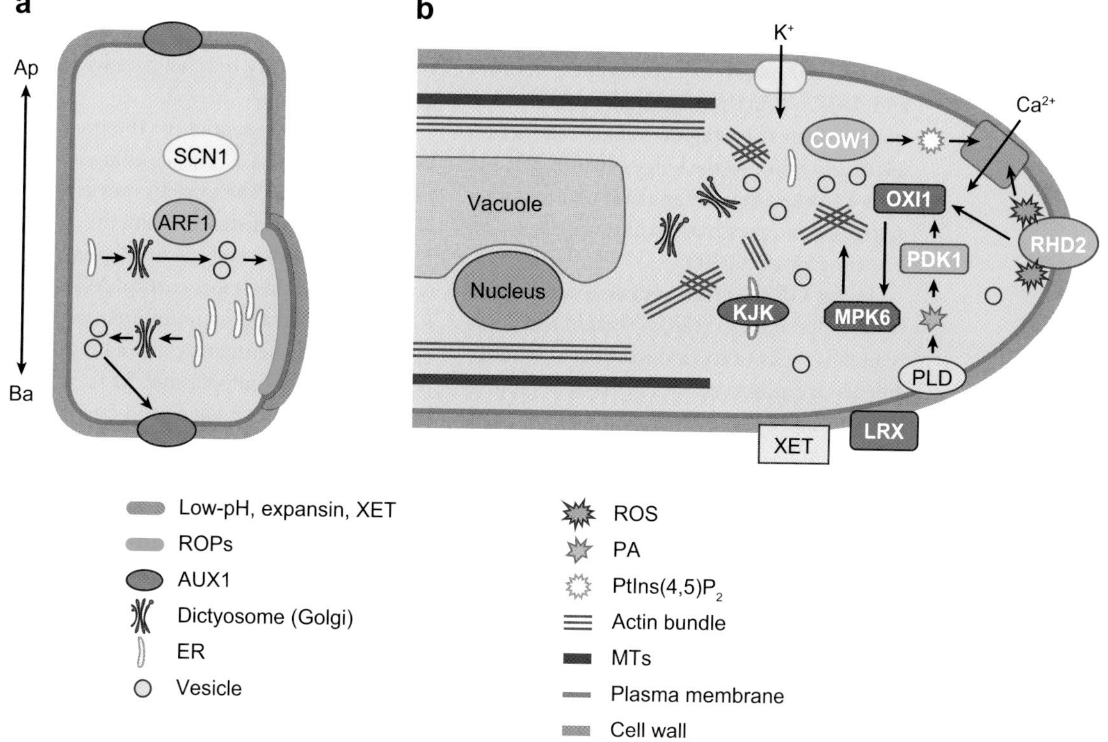

Figure 5

Initiation and tip growth of root hair. (*a*) Schematic of hair cells at the initiation stage. Swelling occurs at the basal (Ba) region. At this stage, cell wall pH in the swelling region falls, and expansin proteins are localized to the region. Specific localization of Rho-related GTPase (ROP) family members is also initiated by vesicle transport in this region. (*b*) Schematic of hair cells during tip-growth stage. Many endoplasmic reticulum (ER)- or dictyosome-derived vesicles are observed at the tip region (41). A dense mesh of actin bundles caps the tip region, and less-dense actin bundles are localized in the basal region. Microtubules (MTs) that are axially organized at the basal region participate in the direction of tip growth. A calcium gradient is generated by the activity of calcium channels that are localized in tip region plasma membranes. Potassium channels may act in this region to produce high turgor pressure. A large number of factors are involved in maintaining root hair tip growth, including factors that are involved in the organization of actin bundles or activation of calcium channels via second messengers, and others involved with the supply and restructuring of cell wall materials. XET, xyloglucan endotransglycosylase; AUX1, AUXIN RESISTANT 1; SCN1, SUPERCENTIPEDE 1; ARF1, ADP ribosylation factor 1; Ap, apical; ROS, reactive oxygen species; PA, phosphatidic acid; PtIns(4,5)P_2, phosphatidylinositol 4, 5-bisphosphate; COW1, CAN OF WORMS 1; OXI1, OXIDATIVE SIGNAL-INDUCIBLE 1; PDK1, phophoinositide-dependent kinase 1; RHD2, ROOT HAIR DEFECTIVE 2; KJK, KOJAK; MPK6, mitogen-activated protein kinase 6; PLD, phospholipase D; LRX, leucine-rich repeat/extensin protein.

transporter mutants *Arabidopsis K transporter 1* (*akt1*) and *tiny root hair 1* (*trh1*) and a biochemical blocker of K^+ transport. K^+ transporters are required for root hair tip growth and for the determination of initiation sites (30, 101) (**Figure 5*b***).

Actin Cytoskeleton and Microtubules

After basal swelling starts, the endoplasmic reticulum (ER) condenses and the pH of the cell wall falls (15, 100) (**Figure 5*a***). In this low-pH condition, wall-loosening proteins, expansins, may become active. Maize expansin accumulates in the hair cell wall at the bulge, and two *Arabidopsis* expansin genes, *AtEXP7* and *AtEXP18*, are preferentially expressed in the hair-formation region of hair-cell files (6, 24) (**Figure 5*a***). As the bulge expands, ER and actin cytoskeleton accumulate, and the actin cytoskeleton takes over maintenance of root hair tip growth (6, 100).

Using GFP-talin to visualize actin structures, a dense mesh (cap) is seen in the dome region of the root tip and less-dense actin filaments are observed at the basal region of the root hair (6) (**Figure 5*b***). Latrunculin B, an inhibitor of actin polymerization, arrests the tip growth of *Arabidopsis* and maize root hairs (6, 14). This pharmacological result was confirmed by genetic studies. Mutations in *ACTIN2* (*ACT2*), a member of the *Arabidopsis* actin family, cause a hairless or short-hair phenotype with a swollen shape (45, 84, 102). Observation of actin in the severe *act2-2D* allele mutants demonstrates that the actin filament bundles in root epidermal cells of *act2-2D* are shorter than in wild-type (84).

Several factors act as regulators of actin dynamics. Profilin (PFN) facilitates actin polymerization in vitro (115), and *PFN1* is expressed in root hairs in *Arabidopsis* (98). *PFN1*-overexpressing lines have longer root hairs than wild-type (98). Actin-interacting protein 1 (AIP1) can cap F-actin, and enhances the activity of actin depolymerizing factor (ADF) in vitro (4, 88). A recent study demonstrates that knockdown lines of *Arabidopsis* AIP1 have thicker actin bundles, abnormal actin organization, and shorter root hairs than wild-type (54). Through analysis of the stress-activated alfalfa MAP kinase SIMK, the active form of SIMK was found to induce root hair tip growth (104). This phenomenon is mediated by organization of the actin cytoskeleton because SIMK colocalizes with actin filaments, and SIMK activity is affected by actin organization (104). The Arp2/3 complex (discussed above in the trichome section) acts as an actin polymerization enhancer to create fine dendritic actin arrays. Mutants of *DISTORTED1* and *CROOKED* loci, which encode subunits of the Arp2/3 complex, have wavy root hairs under rapid tip growing conditions (76, 77).

MTs are also essential for the growth polarity of root hairs. When swelling occurs at the initiation site, the nucleus moves into the bulge at a fixed distance from the hair tip. This process is driven by actin-mediated processes (55). At this stage, cortical MTs, which form helical arrays in undifferentiated root epidermal cells, reorganize into a longitudinal position (126). Endoplasmic MTs associate primarily with the nucleus and become longitudinally oriented along the growth axis of the root hair (6, 14, 126) (**Figure 5*b***). Pharmacological treatment with oryzalin, a MT depolymerizing drug, and taxol, which stabilizes MTs, results in the production of wavy and branched hairs (14). Furthermore, transgenic plants in which one of the α-tubulin genes (*TUA6*) is suppressed produce ectopic root hairs (7). Mutations in *ECTOPIC ROOT HAIRS 3*, which encodes KATANIN-p60, cause ectopic root hair development (135). Katanins are known to sever MTs. These results suggest that radical changes in MT structures are required for both the establishment of root hair growth polarity and cell fate determination.

Phospholipid Signaling

Phospholipids are attracting attention as novel second messengers in plant cells (79, 103). Ohashi and coworkers (87) reported that the *Arabidopsis phospholipase Dζ1* (*AtPLDζ1*) gene is a direct target of GL2; GL2 normally represses the expression of this gene. Supplementation of plant growth medium with 1-butanol blocks root hair initiation in wild-type plants because 1-butanol specifically inhibits the activity of PLD (87). PLD produces the second messenger phosphatidic acid (PA), which is involved in pollen tip growth of tobacco (95). PA induces the enzymatic activity of *Arabidopsis* 3′-phophoinositide-dependent kinase 1 (AtPDK1). AGC2-1, which is an

AtPDK1-interacting protein kinase, is also activated by PA in an AtPDK1-dependent manner (5). A knockdown transformant line of *AGC2-1* has shorter root hairs than wild-type (5). These studies suggest that repression of *GL2* in root hair cells induces *AtPLDζ1*, allowing PA to accumulate, leading to the activation of AtPDK1 and AGC2-1. This cascade of biochemical regulation results in the continuous growth of root hairs (**Figure 5*b***). Because *AGC2-1* and *OXI1* (mentioned above) are the same gene (103), it can be assumed that PA and ROS cooperatively regulate tip growth.

Phosphatidylinositol transfer proteins (PITPs) also play a role in root hair tip growth (17, 127). PITPs transfer phosphatidylinositol (PtdIns) or phophatidylcholine (PtdCho) monomers between membranes (3, 26). The *can of worms 1* (*cow1*)/*atsfh1* mutant has a short root hair phenotype due to a mutation in a protein containing a Sec14p-nodulin domain (17, 48, 127). COW1/AtSFH1 localizes in discrete plasma membrane domains and in the root hair tip cytoplasm (17, 127). This localization pattern is similar to phosphatidylinositol 4, 5-bisphosphate [PtdIns(4, 5)P_2], and tip-directed PtdIns(4, 5)P_2 is absent from *cow1/atsfh1* mutants (127). Further experiments suggest that COW1/AtSFH1 regulates the polar phosphoinositide localization that focuses membrane trafficking, Ca^{2+} signaling, and thus cytoskeleton organization for hair cell tip growth (127) (**Figure 5*b***).

Cell Wall

The synthesis and rearrangement of cell wall materials are important processes for root hair tip growth. Xyloglucan endotransglycosylases (XETs) are enzymes that cleave and rejoin xyloglucan chains (85, 122). XET action is primary localized at the basal initiation site of hair cells, and then distributes approximately uniformly all over the surface of the growing root hair (128) (**Figure 5**).

Mutations in the *KOJAK* (*KJK*) gene cause the root hair to rupture soon after initiation. *KJK* encodes a cellulose synthase–like (subfamily D) protein, AtCSLD3, which is preferentially expressed in hair cells (37, 134). The KJK protein is localized in the ER, suggesting that it may function in noncellulosic wall polysaccharide synthesis (37) (**Figure 5*b***). Other evidence supports the involvement of cell wall components in root hair growth. The *rhd1* mutant has short root hairs and an epidermal bulge (107, 113). *RHD1* is one of the five ubiquitously expressed genes that encode UDP-D-glucose 4-epimerase (UGE4). UGE4 may catalyze interconversion between UDP-D-glucose and UDP-D-galactose (113). Immunocytological experiments demonstrated that *rhd1* root epidermal cell walls lack arabinosylated (1→6)-β-D-galactan and galactosylated xyloglucan (113), leading to speculation that these galactose-related cell wall polymers are required for tip growth and epidermal cell morphogenesis. Furthermore, genetic studies suggest that ethylene and auxin participate in the flux control of UDP-D-galactose into cell wall polymers (114).

There are many structural proteins in the plant cell wall. LRX1, a chimeric leucine-rich repeat/extensin protein, is specifically localized in the cell wall of hair cells (9). *lrx1* knockout mutants are characterized by aborted initiation, swelling, and/or branching root hairs (9). *LRX1* and its paralog *LRX2* synergistically participate in root hair growth (10). Thus, LRX1 and LRX2 regulate the polarized growth of hair cells via cell wall formation and assembly (9, 10) (**Figure 5*b***).

Phospholipase Dζ1: a member of a phospholipase family, which can cleave phospholipids into phosphatidic acid and base

Xyloglucan: a hemicellulosic polysaccharide with a backbone consisting of 1,4-linked α-D-glucose residues; backbone residues are occasionally branched, bearing 1,6-linked α-D-xylose residues

SUMMARY POINTS

1. GLABRA1 (GL1)-GLABRA3 (GL3)/ENHANCER OF GLABRA 3 (EGL3)-TRANSPARENT TESTA GLABRA 1 (TTG1) and WEREWOLF (WER)-GL3/EGL3-TTG1 complexes regulate *GLABRA2* (*GL2*) expression, which promotes

differentiation into trichomes and root hairless cells, respectively. R3 Myb proteins such as TRIPTYCHON (TRY) and CAPRICE (CPC) inhibit the formation of these complexes, resulting in inhibition of *GL2* expression.

2. Modification of histone H3 is likely to be involved in the chromatin structure of *GL2*. The chromatin state of *GL2* differs between root H cells and N cells.
3. Gibberellin signaling affects GL1-GL3/EGL3-TTG1 activity in trichome initiation, whereas auxin/ethylene signaling affects root hair formation after cell fate specification by *GL2* in roots.
4. Trichome development is accompanied by a progression of endoreduplication cycles, which are regulated by several different molecular pathways.
5. Reorientation of microtubules and microtubule-dependent vesicle transport and organelle delivery are important for trichome branching. Actin organization regulated by actin-related protein 2/3 (Arp2/3) and Wiskott-Aldrich syndrome protein family verprolin homologous protein (WAVE) complexes is important for directional trichome expansion and for actin-based movement of organelles.
6. During root hair elongation, several cellular components including actin bundles, microtubules, membrane-associated ion channels, endomembrane derivatives, and cell wall materials are employed via intracellular signaling pathways.

FUTURE ISSUES

1. Leaf trichomes express *GL2*, whereas root hair cells do not express *GL2*. The big question is why *GL2* has opposite effects on epidermal outgrowths of leaves and roots.
2. The regulation of intercellular movement of the CPC protein and GL3/EGL3 proteins is still a mystery, as are the mechanisms involved in preferential accumulation of CPC protein in root H cells and GL3/EGL3 proteins in N cells.
3. The factors that determine positional cues in roots are not known, and neither are the mechanisms that allow positional cues to be transduced into transcriptional regulation that ultimately determines cell fate.
4. The complex regulation of the endoreduplication cycle in trichomes by several different molecular pathways remains an important unknown.
5. There are still unidentified agents that are involved in establishing root hair tip growth, and relationships among them remain to be resolved.

DISCLOSURE STATEMENT

The authors are not aware of any biases that might be perceived as affecting the objectivity of this review.

ACKNOWLEDGMENTS

We apologize to those authors whose work could not be properly reviewed here because of space limitation. We thank Rumi Tominaga for providing photos. T.I. and T.W. are supported by the Human Frontier Science Program.

LITERATURE CITED

1. Abe T, Hashimoto T. 2005. Altered microtubule dynamics by expression of modified α-tubulin protein causes right-handed helical growth in transgenic *Arabidopsis* plants. *Plant J.* 43:191–204
2. Abe T, Thitamadee S, Hashimoto T. 2004. Microtubule defects and cell morphogenesis in the *lefty1lefty2* tubulin mutant of *Arabidopsis thaliana*. *Plant Cell Physiol.* 45:211–20
3. Allen-Baume V, Segui B, Cockcroft S. 2002. Current thoughts on the phosphatidylinositol transfer protein family. *FEBS Lett.* 531:74–80
4. Allwood EG, Anthony RG, Smertenko AP, Reichelt S, Drobak BK, et al. 2002. Regulation of the pollen-specific actin-depolymerizing factor LlADF1. *Plant Cell* 14:2915–27
5. Anthony RG, Henriques R, Helfer A, Mészáros T, Rios G, et al. 2004. A protein kinase target of a PDK1 signalling pathway is involved in root hair growth in *Arabidopsis*. *EMBO J.* 23:572–81
6. Baluska F, Salaj J, Mathur J, Braun M, Jasper F, et al. 2000. Root hair formation: F-actin-dependent tip growth is initiated by local assembly of profilin-supported F-actin meshworks accumulated within expansin-enriched bulges. *Dev. Biol.* 227:618–32
7. Bao Y, Kost B, Chua NH. 2001. Reduced expression of α-tubulin genes in *Arabidopsis thaliana* specifically affects root growth and morphology, root hair development and root gravitropism. *Plant J.* 28:145–57
8. Basu D, El-Assal Sel-D, Le J, Mallery EL, Szymanski DB. 2004. Interchangeable functions of *Arabidopsis* PIROGI and the human WAVE complex subunit SRA1 during leaf epidermal development. *Development* 131:4345–55
9. Baumberger N, Ringli C, Keller B. 2001. The chimeric leucine-rich repeat/extensin cell wall protein LRX1 is required for root hair morphogenesis in *Arabidopsis thaliana*. *Genes Dev.* 15:1128–39
10. Baumberger N, Steiner M, Ryser U, Keller B, Ringli C. 2003. Synergistic interaction of the two paralogous *Arabidopsis* genes *LRX1* and *LRX2* in cell wall formation during root hair development. *Plant J.* 35:71–81
11. Berger F, Haseloff J, Schiefelbein J, Dolan L. 1998. Positional information in root epidermis is defined during embryogenesis and acts in domains with strict boundaries. *Curr. Biol.* 8:421–30
12. Bernhardt C, Lee MM, Gonzalez A, Zhang F, Lloyd A, Schiefelbein J. 2003. The bHLH genes *GLABRA3* (*GL3*) and *ENHANCER OF GLABRA3* (*EGL3*) specify epidermal cell fate in the *Arabidopsis* root. *Development* 130:6431–39
13. **Bernhardt C, Zhao M, Gonzalez A, Lloyd A, Schiefelbein J. 2005. The bHLH genes *GL3* and *EGL3* participate in an intercellular regulatory circuit that controls cell patterning in the *Arabidopsis* root epidermis. *Development* 132:291–98**
14. Bibikova TN, Blancaflor EB, Gilroy S. 1999. Microtubules regulate tip growth and orientation in root hairs of *Arabidopsis thaliana*. *Plant J.* 17:657–65
15. Bibikova TN, Jacob T, Dahse I, Gilroy S. 1998. Localized changes in apoplastic and cytoplasmic pH are associated with root hair development in *Arabidopsis thaliana*. *Development* 125:2925–34

13. Reports that *GL3/EGL3* are transcribed in root H cells but their proteins accumulate in N cells and act to specify hairless cell fate.

16. Boevink P, Oparka K, Santa Cruz S, Martin B, Betteridge A, Hawes C. 1998. Stacks on tracks: the plant Golgi apparatus traffics on an actin/ER network. *Plant J.* 15:441–47
17. Bohme K, Li Y, Charlot F, Grierson C, Marrocco K, et al. 2004. The *Arabidopsis COW1* gene encodes a phosphatidylinositol transfer protein essential for root hair tip growth. *Plant J.* 40:686–98
18. Bompard G, Caron E. 2004. Regulation of WASP/WAVE proteins: making a long story short. *J. Cell Biol.* 166:957–62
19. Buhler C, Gadelle D, Forterre P, Wang JC, Bergerat A. 1998. Reconstitution of DNA topoisomerase VI of the thermophilic archaeon *Sulfolobus shibatae* from subunits separately overexpressed in *Escherichia coli*. *Nucleic Acids Res.* 26:5157–62
20. Burk DH, Liu B, Zhong R, Morrison WH, Ye ZH. 2001. A katanin-like protein regulates normal cell wall biosynthesis and cell elongation. *Plant Cell* 13:807–27
21. **Caro E, Castellano MM, Gutierrez C. 2007. A chromatin link that couples cell division to root epidermis patterning in *Arabidopsis*. *Nature* 447:213–17**
22. Carol RJ, Takeda S, Linstead P, Durrant MC, Kakesova H, et al. 2005. A RhoGDP dissociation inhibitor spatially regulates growth in root hair cells. *Nature* 438:1013–16
23. Chevalier D, Batoux M, Fulton L, Pfister K, Yadav RK, et al. 2005. STRUBBELIG defines a receptor kinase-mediated signaling pathway regulating organ development in *Arabidopsis*. *Proc. Natl. Acad. Sci. USA* 102:9074–79
24. Cho HT, Cosgrove DJ. 2002. Regulation of root hair initiation and expansin gene expression in *Arabidopsis*. *Plant Cell* 14:3237–53
25. **Churchman ML, Brown ML, Kato N, Kirik V, Hülskamp M, et al. 2006. SIAMESE, a plant-specific cell cycle regulator, controls endoreplication onset in *Arabidopsis thaliana*. *Plant Cell* 18:3145–57**
26. Cleves AE, McGee TP, Whitters EA, Champion KM, Aitken JR, et al. 1991. Mutations in the CDP-choline pathway for phospholipid biosynthesis bypass the requirement for an essential phospholipid transfer protein. *Cell* 64:789–800
27. Cormack RGH. 1935. Investigation on the development of root hairs. *New Phytol.* 34:30–54
28. Cormack RGH. 1947. A comparative model of developing epidermal cells in white mustard and tomato roots. *Am. J. Bot.* 34:310–14
29. **Costa S, Shaw P. 2006. Chromatin organization and cell fate switch respond to positional information in *Arabidopsis* *Nature* 439:493–96**
30. Desbrosses G, Josefsson C, Rigas S, Hatzopoulos P, Dolan L. 2003. AKT1 and TRH1 are required during root hair elongation in *Arabidopsis*. *J. Exp. Bot.* 54:781–88
31. Dolan L, Costa S. 2001. Evolution and genetics of root hair stripes in the root epidermis. *J. Exp. Bot.* 52:413–17
32. Dolan L, Duckett CM, Grierson C, Linstead P, Schneider K, et al. 1994. Clonal relationships and cell patterning in the root epidermis of *Arabidopsis*. *Development* 120:2465–74
33. Downes BP, Stupar RM, Gingerich DJ, Vierstra RD. 2003. The HECT ubiquitin-protein ligase (UPL) family in *Arabidopsis*: UPL3 has a specific role in trichome development. *Plant J.* 35:729–42
34. El Refy A, Perazza D, Zekraoui L, Valay JG, Bechtold N, et al. 2003. The *Arabidopsis KAKTUS* gene encodes a HECT protein and controls the number of endoreduplication cycles. *Mol. Genet. Genomics* 270:403–14
35. **Esch JJ, Chen M, Sanders M, Hillestad M, Ndkium S, et al. 2003. A contradictory GLABRA3 allele helps define gene interactions controlling trichome development in *Arabidopsis*. *Development* 130:5885–94**

21. Identification of *GEM*, which regulates *GL2* and *CPC* expression through the control of histone methylation and/or acetylation status of *GL2* and *CPC* promoters.

25. Reports that *SIM* encodes a plant specific CDK inhibitor that binds D-type cyclins (CYCDs) and CDKA and inhibits transition from G2 phase to mitosis.

29. Shows that chromatin organization around the *GL2* locus depends on epidermal cell position.

35. Demonstrated that TRY can prevent interaction of GL1 with GL3, suggesting that R3 Myb proteins can inhibit formation of a transcriptional complex containing R2R3 Myb and bHLH.

36. Esch JJ, Chen MA, Hillestad M, Marks MD. 2004. Comparison of *TRY* and the closely related *At1g01380* gene in controlling *Arabidopsis* trichome patterning. *Plant J.* 40:860–69
37. Favery B, Ryan E, Foreman J, Linstead P, Boudonck K, et al. 2001. *KOJAK* encodes a cellulose synthase-like protein required for root hair cell morphogenesis in *Arabidopsis*. *Genes Dev.* 15:79–89
38. **Foreman J, Demidchik V, Bothwell JH, Mylona P, Miedema H, et al. 2003. Reactive oxygen species produced by NADPH oxidase regulate plant cell growth. *Nature* 422:442–46**
39. Fuchs J, Demidov D, Houben A, Schubert I. 2006. Chromosomal histone modification patterns–from conservation to diversity. *Trends Plant Sci.* 11:199–208
40. Fukaki H, Tameda S, Masuda H, Tasaka M. 2002. Lateral root formation is blocked by a gain-of-function mutation in the *SOLITARY-ROOT/IAA14* gene of *Arabidopsis*. *Plant J.* 29:153–68
41. Galway ME, Heckman JW Jr, Schiefelbein JW. 1997. Growth and ultrastructure of *Arabidopsis* root hairs: the *rhd3* mutation alters vacuole enlargement and tip growth. *Planta* 201:209–18
42. Galway ME, Masucci JD, Lloyd AM, Walbot V, Davis RW, Schiefelbein JW. 1994. The *TTG* gene is required to specify epidermal cell fate and cell patterning in the *Arabidopsis* root. *Dev. Biol.* 166:740–54
43. Gan Y, Kumimoto R, Liu C, Ratcliffe O, Yu H, Broun P. 2006. GLABROUS INFLORESCENCE STEMS modulates the regulation by gibberellins of epidermal differentiation and shoot maturation in *Arabidopsis*. *Plant Cell* 18:1383–95
44. Gan Y, Liu C, Yu H, Broun P. 2007. Integration of cytokinin and gibberellin signalling by *Arabidopsis* transcription factors GIS, ZFP8 and GIS2 in the regulation of epidermal cell fate. *Development* 134:2073–81
45. Gilliland LU, Kandasamy MK, Pawloski LC, Meagher RB. 2002. Both vegetative and reproductive actin isovariants complement the stunted root hair phenotype of the *Arabidopsis* act2-1 mutation. *Plant Physiol.* 130:2199–209
46. Grebe M, Friml J, Swarup R, Ljung K, Sandberg G, et al. 2002. Cell polarity signaling in *Arabidopsis* involves a BFA-sensitive auxin influx pathway. *Curr. Biol.* 12:329–34
47. Greenboim-Wainberg Y, Maymon I, Borochov R, Alvarez J, Olszewski N, et al. 2005. Cross talk between gibberellin and cytokinin: the *Arabidopsis* GA response inhibitor SPINDLY plays a positive role in cytokinin signaling. *Plant Cell* 17:92–102
48. Grierson CS, Roberts K, Feldmann KA, Dolan L. 1997. The COW1 locus of Arabidopsis acts after RHD2, and in parallel with RHD3 and TIP1, to determine the shape, rate of elongation, and number of root hairs produced from each site of hair formation. *Plant Physiol.* 115:981–90
49. Hartung F, Angelis KJ, Meister A, Schubert I, Melzer M, Puchta H. 2002. An archaebacterial topoisomerase homolog not present in other eukaryotes is indispensable for cell proliferation of plants. *Curr. Biol.* 12:1787–91
50. Hülskamp M, Misra S, Jürgens G. 1994. Genetic dissection of trichome cell development in *Arabidopsis*. *Cell* 76:555–66
51. Hung CY, Lin Y, Zhang M, Pollock S, Marks MD, Schiefelbein J. 1998. A common position-dependent mechanism controls cell-type patterning and GLABRA2 regulation in the root and hypocotyl epidermis of *Arabidopsis*. *Plant Physiol.* 117:73–84
52. Jones MA, Raymond MJ, Yang Z, Smirnoff N. 2007. NADPH oxidase-dependent reactive oxygen species formation required for root hair growth depends on ROP GTPase. *J. Exp. Bot.* 58:1261–70

38. An NADPH oxidase encoded by *RHD2* generates ROS that activates Ca^{2+} channels to make $[Ca^{2+}]_c$ gradient in root hair, important for tip growth.

53. Jones MA, Shen JJ, Fu Y, Li H, Yang Z, Grierson CS. 2002. The *Arabidopsis* Rop2 GTPase is a positive regulator of both root hair initiation and tip growth. *Plant Cell* 14:763–76
54. Ketelaar T, Allwood EG, Anthony R, Voigt B, Menzel D, Hussey PJ. 2004. The actin-interacting protein AIP1 is essential for actin organization and plant development. *Curr. Biol.* 14:145–49
55. Ketelaar T, Faivre-Moskalenko C, Esseling JJ, de Ruijter NC, Grierson CS, et al. 2002. Positioning of nuclei in *Arabidopsis* root hairs: an actin-regulated process of tip growth. *Plant Cell* 14:2941–55
56. Kirik V, Bouyer D, Schobinger U, Bechtold N, Herzog M, et al. 2001. *CPR5* is involved in cell proliferation and cell death control and encodes a novel transmembrane protein. *Curr. Biol.* 11:1891–95
57. Kirik V, Grini PE, Mathur J, Klinkhammer I, Adler K, et al. 2002. The *Arabidopsis TUBULIN-FOLDING COFACTOR A* gene is involved in the control of the α/β-tubulin monomer balance. *Plant Cell* 14:2265–76
58. Kirik V, Mathur J, Grini PE, Klinkhammer I, Adler K, et al. 2002. Functional analysis of the tubulin-folding cofactor C in *Arabidopsis thaliana*. *Curr. Biol.* 12:1519–23
59. Kirik V, Simon M, Huelskamp M, Schiefelbein J. 2004. The *ENHANCER OF TRY AND CPC1* gene acts redundantly with *TRIPTYCHON* and *CAPRICE* in trichome and root hair cell patterning in *Arabidopsis*. *Dev. Biol.* 268:506–13
60. Kirik V, Simon M, Wester K, Schiefelbein J, Hülskamp M. 2004. ENHANCER of TRY and CPC 2 (ETC2) reveals redundancy in the region-specific control of trichome development of *Arabidopsis*. *Plant Mol. Biol.* 55:389–98
61. Kiyokawa E, Hashimoto Y, Kobayashi S, Sugimura H, Kurata T, Matsuda M. 1998. Activation of Rac1 by a Crk SH3-binding protein, DOCK180. *Genes Dev.* 12:3331–36
62. Knox K, Grierson CS, Leyser O. 2003. AXR3 and SHY2 interact to regulate root hair development. *Development* 130:5769–77
63. Koshino-Kimura Y, Wada T, Tachibana T, Tsugeki R, Ishiguro S, Okada K. 2005. Regulation of *CAPRICE* transcription by MYB proteins for root epidermis differentiation in *Arabidopsis*. *Plant Cell Physiol.* 46:817–26
64. **Kurata T, Ishida T, Kawabata-Awai C, Noguchi M, Hattori S, et al. 2005. Cell-to-cell movement of the CAPRICE protein in *Arabidopsis* root epidermal cell differentiation. *Development* 132:5387–98**
65. Kwak SH, Schiefelbein J. 2007. The role of the SCRAMBLED receptor-like kinase in patterning the *Arabidopsis* root epidermis. *Dev. Biol.* 302:118–31
66. **Kwak SH, Shen R, Schiefelbein J. 2005. Positional signaling mediated by a receptor-like kinase in *Arabidopsis*. *Science* 307:1111–13**
67. Lee MM, Schiefelbein J. 1999. WEREWOLF, a MYB-related protein in *Arabidopsis*, is a position-dependent regulator of epidermal cell patterning. *Cell* 99:473–83
68. Lee MM, Schiefelbein J. 2001. Developmentally distinct MYB genes encode functionally equivalent proteins in *Arabidopsis*. *Development* 128:1539–46
69. Lee MM, Schiefelbein J. 2002. Cell pattern in the *Arabidopsis* root epidermis determined by lateral inhibition with feedback. *Plant Cell* 14:611–18
70. Liscum E, Reed JW. 2002. Genetics of Aux/IAA and ARF action in plant growth and development. *Plant Mol. Biol.* 49:387–400
71. Masucci JD, Rerie WG, Foreman DR, Zhang M, Galway ME, et al. 1996. The homeobox gene *GLABRA2* is required for position-dependent cell differentiation in the root epidermis of *Arabidopsis thaliana*. *Development* 122:1253–60

64. Analysis of domains and amino acids important for intercellular movement of CPC, suggesting that CPC intercellular movement is a regulated transport.

66. Identification of SCM, which is a good candidate for transmitting extracellular positional information to the inside of epidermal cells.

72. Masucci JD, Schiefelbein JW. 1994. The *rhd6* mutation of *Arabidopsis thaliana* alters root-hair initiation through an auxin- and ethylene-associated process. *Plant Physiol.* 106:1335–46
73. Masucci JD, Schiefelbein JW. 1996. Hormones act downstream of TTG and GL2 to promote root hair outgrowth during epidermis development in the *Arabidopsis* root. *Plant Cell* 8:1505–17
74. Mathur J, Chua NH. 2000. Microtubule stabilization leads to growth reorientation in *Arabidopsis* trichomes. *Plant Cell* 12:465–77
75. Mathur J, Mathur N, Hülskamp M. 2002. Simultaneous visualization of peroxisomes and cytoskeletal elements reveals actin and not microtubule-based peroxisome motility in plants. *Plant Physiol.* 128:1031–45
76. Mathur J, Mathur N, Kernebeck B, Hülskamp M. 2003. Mutations in actin-related proteins 2 and 3 affect cell shape development in *Arabidopsis*. *Plant Cell* 15:1632–45
77. Mathur J, Mathur N, Kirik V, Kernebeck B, Srinivas BP, Hülskamp M. 2003. *Arabidopsis CROOKED* encodes for the smallest subunit of the ARP2/3 complex and controls cell shape by region specific fine F-actin formation. *Development* 130:3137–46
78. Mathur J, Spielhofer P, Kost B, Chua N. 1999. The actin cytoskeleton is required to elaborate and maintain spatial patterning during trichome cell morphogenesis in *Arabidopsis thaliana*. *Development* 126:5559–68
79. Meijer HJ, Munnik T. 2003. Phospholipid-based signaling in plants. *Annu. Rev. Plant Biol.* 54:265–306
80. Menand B, Yi K, Jouannic S, Hoffmann L, Ryan E, et al. 2007. An ancient mechanism controls the development of cells with a rooting function in land plants. *Science* 316:1477–80
81. Molendijk AJ, Bischoff F, Rajendrakumar CS, Friml J, Braun M, et al. 2001. *Arabidopsis thaliana* Rop GTPases are localized to tips of root hairs and control polar growth. *EMBO J.* 20:2779–88
82. Nagpal P, Walker LM, Young JC, Sonawala A, Timpte C, et al. 2000. *AXR2* encodes a member of the Aux/IAA protein family. *Plant Physiol.* 123:563–74
83. Nebenfuhr A, Gallagher LA, Dunahay TG, Frohlick JA, Mazurkiewicz AM, et al. 1999. Stop-and-go movements of plant Golgi stacks are mediated by the acto-myosin system. *Plant Physiol.* 121:1127–42
84. Nishimura T, Yokota E, Wada T, Shimmen T, Okada K. 2003. An *Arabidopsis ACT2* dominant-negative mutation, which disturbs F-actin polymerization, reveals its distinctive function in root development. *Plant Cell Physiol.* 44:1131–40
85. Nishitani K, Tominaga R. 1992. Endo-xyloglucan transferase, a novel class of glycosyltransferase that catalyzes transfer of a segment of xyloglucan molecule to another xyloglucan molecule. *J. Biol. Chem.* 267:21058–64
86. Nolan KM, Barrett K, Lu Y, Hu KQ, Vincent S, Settleman J. 1998. Myoblast city, the *Drosophila* homolog of DOCK180/CED-5, is required in a Rac signaling pathway utilized for multiple developmental processes. *Genes Dev.* 12:3337–42
87. Ohashi Y, Oka A, Rodrigues-Pousada R, Possenti M, Ruberti I, et al. 2003. Modulation of phospholipid signaling by GLABRA2 in root-hair pattern formation. *Science* 300:1427–30
88. Ono S. 2003. Regulation of actin filament dynamics by actin depolymerizing factor/cofilin and actin-interacting protein 1: new blades for twisted filaments. *Biochemistry* 42:13363–70
89. Oppenheimer DG, Herman PL, Sivakumaran S, Esch J, Marks MD. 1991. A *myb* gene required for leaf trichome differentiation in *Arabidopsis* is expressed in stipules. *Cell* 67:483–93

90. Oppenheimer DG, Pollock MA, Vacik J, Szymanski DB, Ericson B, et al. 1997. Essential role of a kinesin-like protein in *Arabidopsis* trichome morphogenesis. *Proc. Natl. Acad. Sci. USA* 94:6261–66
91. Payne CT, Zhang F, Lloyd AM. 2000. GL3 encodes a bHLH protein that regulates trichome development in Arabidopsis through interaction with GL1 and TTG1. *Genetics* 156:1349–62
92. Perazza D, Herzog M, Hülskamp M, Brown S, Dorne AM, Bonneville JM. 1999. Trichome cell growth in *Arabidopsis thaliana* can be derepressed by mutations in at least five genes. *Genetics* 152:461–76
93. Perazza D, Vachon G, Herzog M. 1998. Gibberellins promote trichome formation by up-regulating GLABROUS1 in Arabidopsis. *Plant Physiol.* 117:375–83
94. Pitts RJ, Cernac A, Estelle M. 1998. Auxin and ethylene promote root hair elongation in *Arabidopsis. Plant J.* 16:553–60
95. Potocký M, Eliás M, Profotová B, Novotná Z, Valentová O, Zárský V. 2003. Phosphatidic acid produced by phospholipase D is required for tobacco pollen tube growth. *Planta* 217:122–30
96. Qiu JL, Jilk R, Marks MD, Szymanski DB. 2002. The *Arabidopsis SPIKE1* gene is required for normal cell shape control and tissue development. *Plant Cell* 14:101–18
97. Rahman A, Hosokawa S, Oono Y, Amakawa T, Goto N, Tsurumi S. 2002. Auxin and ethylene response interactions during *Arabidopsis* root hair development dissected by auxin influx modulators. *Plant Physiol.* 130:1908–17
98. Ramachandran S, Christensen HE, Ishimaru Y, Dong CH, Chao-Ming W, et al. 2000. Profilin plays a role in cell elongation, cell shape maintenance, and flowering in *Arabidopsis. Plant Physiol.* 124:1637–47
99. Rentel MC, Lecourieux D, Ouaked F, Usher SL, Petersen L, et al. 2004. OXI1 kinase is necessary for oxidative burst-mediated signalling in *Arabidopsis. Nature* 427:858–61
100. Ridge RW, Uozumi Y, Plazinski J, Hurley UA, Williamson RE. 1999. Developmental transitions and dynamics of the cortical ER of *Arabidopsis* cells seen with green fluorescent protein. *Plant Cell Physiol.* 40:1253–61
101. Rigas S, Debrosses G, Haralampidis K, Vicente-Agullo F, Feldmann KA, et al. 2001. *TRH1* encodes a potassium transporter required for tip growth in *Arabidopsis* root hairs. *Plant Cell* 13:139–51
102. Ringli C, Baumberger N, Diet A, Frey B, Keller B. 2002. ACTIN2 is essential for bulge site selection and tip growth during root hair development of *Arabidopsis. Plant Physiol.* 129:1464–72
103. Samaj J, Baluska F, Menzel D. 2004. New signalling molecules regulating root hair tip growth. *Trends Plant Sci.* 9:217–20
104. Samaj J, Ovecka M, Hlavacka A, Lecourieux F, Meskiene I, et al. 2002. Involvement of the mitogen-activated protein kinase SIMK in regulation of root hair tip growth. *EMBO J.* 21:3296–306
105. Schellmann S, Schnittger A, Kirik V, Wada T, Okada K, et al. 2002. TRIPTYCHON and CAPRICE mediate lateral inhibition during trichome and root hair patterning in *Arabidopsis. EMBO J.* 21:5036–46
106. Schiefelbein JW. 1992. Calcium influx at the tip of growing root-hair cells of *Arabidopsis. Planta* 187:455–59
107. Schiefelbein JW, Somerville C. 1990. Genetic control of root hair development in *Arabidopsis thaliana. Plant Cell* 2:235–43
108. Schnittger A, Hülskamp M. 2002. Trichome morphogenesis: a cell-cycle perspective. *Philos. Trans. R. Soc. London Ser. B* 357:823–26

109. Schnittger A, Schöbinger U, Bouyer D, Weinl C, Stierhof YD, Hülskamp M. 2002. Ectopic D-type cyclin expression induces not only DNA replication but also cell division in *Arabidopsis* trichomes. *Proc. Natl. Acad. Sci. USA* 99:6410–15
110. Schnittger A, Schöbinger U, Stierhof YD, Hülskamp M. 2002. Ectopic B-type cyclin expression induces mitotic cycles in endoreduplicating *Arabidopsis* trichomes. *Curr. Biol.* 12:415–20
111. Schnittger A, Weinl C, Bouyer D, Schöbinger U, Hülskamp M. 2003. Misexpression of the cyclin-dependent kinase inhibitor ICK1/KRP1 in single-celled *Arabidopsis* trichomes reduces endoreduplication and cell size and induces cell death. *Plant Cell* 15:303–15
112. Schwab B, Mathur J, Saedler R, Schwarz H, Frey B, et al. 2003. Regulation of cell expansion by the *DISTORTED* genes in *Arabidopsis thaliana*: actin controls the spatial organization of microtubules. *Mol. Genet. Genomics* 269:350–60
113. Seifert GJ, Barber C, Wells B, Dolan L, Roberts K. 2002. Galactose biosynthesis in *Arabidopsis*: genetic evidence for substrate channeling from UDP-D-galactose into cell wall polymers. *Curr. Biol.* 12:1840–45
114. Seifert GJ, Barber C, Wells B, Roberts K. 2004. Growth regulators and the control of nucleotide sugar flux. *Plant Cell* 16:723–30
115. Sohn RH, Goldschmidt-Clermont PJ. 1994. Profilin: at the crossroads of signal transduction and the actin cytoskeleton. *BioEssays* 16:465–72
116. Sugimoto-Shirasu K, Stacey NJ, Corsar J, Roberts K, McCann MC. 2002. DNA topoisomerase VI is essential for endoreduplication in *Arabidopsis*. *Curr. Biol.* 12:1782–86
117. Szymanski DB. 2005. Breaking the WAVE complex: the point of *Arabidopsis* trichomes. *Curr. Opin. Plant Biol.* 8:103–12
118. Szymanski DB, Jilk RA, Pollock SM, Marks MD. 1998. Control of GL2 expression in *Arabidopsis* leaves and trichomes. *Development* 125:1161–71
119. Szymanski DB, Marks MD. 1998. GLABROUS1 overexpression and TRIPTYCHON alter the cell cycle and trichome cell fate in *Arabidopsis*. *Plant Cell* 10:2047–62
120. Szymanski DB, Marks MD, Wick SM. 1999. Organized F-actin is essential for normal trichome morphogenesis in *Arabidopsis*. *Plant Cell* 11:2331–47
121. Tanimoto M, Roberts K, Dolan L. 1995. Ethylene is a positive regulator of root hair development in *Arabidopsis thaliana*. *Plant J.* 8:943–48
122. Thompson JE, Fry SC. 2001. Restructuring of wall-bound xyloglucan by transglycosylation in living plant cells. *Plant J.* 26:23–34
123. Torres MA, Onouchi H, Hamada S, Machida C, Hammond-Kosack KE, Jones JD. 1998. Six *Arabidopsis thaliana* homologues of the human respiratory burst oxidase (gp91phox). *Plant J.* 14:365–70
124. Traw MB, Bergelson J. 2003. Interactive effects of jasmonic acid, salicylic acid, and gibberellin on induction of trichomes in *Arabidopsis*. *Plant Physiol.* 133:1367–75
125. Uhrig JF, Mutondo M, Zimmermann I, Deeks MJ, Machesky LM, et al. 2007. The role of *Arabidopsis SCAR* genes in ARP2-ARP3-dependent cell morphogenesis. *Development* 134:967–77
126. Van Bruaene N, Joss G, Van Oostveldt P. 2004. Reorganization and in vivo dynamics of microtubules during *Arabidopsis* root hair development. *Plant Physiol.* 136:3905–19
127. Vincent P, Chua M, Nogue F, Fairbrother A, Mekeel H, et al. 2005. A Sec14p-nodulin domain phosphatidylinositol transfer protein polarizes membrane growth of *Arabidopsis thaliana* root hairs. *J. Cell Biol.* 168:801–12
128. Vissenberg K, Fry SC, Verbelen JP. 2001. Root hair initiation is coupled to a highly localized increase of xyloglucan endotransglycosylase action in *Arabidopsis* roots. *Plant Physiol.* 127:1125–35

129. Wada T, Kurata T, Tominaga R, Koshino-Kimura Y, Tachibana T, et al. 2002. Role of a positive regulator of root hair development, CAPRICE, in *Arabidopsis* root epidermal cell differentiation. *Development* 129:5409–19

130. Wada T, Tachibana T, Shimura Y, Okada K. 1997. Epidermal cell differentiation in *Arabidopsis* determined by a Myb homolog, CPC. *Science* 277:1113–16

131. Wagner GJ, Wang E, Shepherd RW. 2004. New approaches for studying and exploiting an old protuberance, the plant trichome. *Ann. Bot.* 93:3–11

132. Walker AR, Davison PA, Bolognesi-Winfield AC, James CM, Srinivasan N, et al. 1999. The *TRANSPARENT TESTA GLABRA1* locus, which regulates trichome differentiation and anthocyanin biosynthesis in *Arabidopsis*, encodes a WD40 repeat protein. *Plant Cell* 11:1337–50

133. Walker JD, Oppenheimer DG, Concienne J, Larkin JC. 2000. *SIAMESE*, a gene controlling the endoreduplication cell cycle in *Arabidopsis thaliana* trichomes. *Development* 127:3931–40

134. Wang X, Cnops G, Vanderhaeghen R, De Block S, Van Montagu M, Van Lijsebettens M. 2001. *AtCSLD3*, a cellulose synthase-like gene important for root hair growth in Arabidopsis. *Plant Physiol.* 126:575–86

135. Webb M, Jouannic S, Foreman J, Linstead P, Dolan L. 2002. Cell specification in the *Arabidopsis* root epidermis requires the activity of ECTOPIC ROOT HAIR 3–a katanin-p60 protein. *Development* 129:123–31

136. Weinl C, Marquardt S, Kuijt SJ, Nowack MK, Jakoby MJ, et al. 2005. Novel functions of plant cyclin-dependent kinase inhibitors, ICK1/KRP1, can act noncell-autonomously and inhibit entry into mitosis. *Plant Cell* 17:1704–22

137. Wymer CL, Bibikova TN, Gilroy S. 1997. Cytoplasmic free calcium distributions during the development of root hairs of *Arabidopsis thaliana*. *Plant J.* 12:427–39

138. Xu CR, Liu C, Wang YL, Li LC, Chen WQ, et al. 2005. Histone acetylation affects expression of cellular patterning genes in the *Arabidopsis* root epidermis. *Proc. Natl. Acad. Sci. USA* 102:14469–74

139. Xu J, Scheres B. 2005. Dissection of *Arabidopsis* ADP-RIBOSYLATION FACTOR 1 function in epidermal cell polarity. *Plant Cell* 17:525–36

140. Yang Z. 2002. Small GTPases: versatile signaling switches in plants. *Plant Cell* 14(Suppl: S):375–88

141. Zhang F, Gonzalez A, Zhao M, Payne CT, Lloyd A. 2003. A network of redundant bHLH proteins functions in all TTG1-dependent pathways of *Arabidopsis*. *Development* 130:4859–69

129. *CPC* is transcribed in root N cells and CPC protein moves from N cells to H cells to specify hair cell fate.

138. Authors demonstrated that histone acetylation changes expression of *WER*, *CPC*, and *GL2* and root epidermal cell fate.

Molecular Aspects of Seed Dormancy*

Ruth Finkelstein,[1] Wendy Reeves,[1] Tohru Ariizumi,[2] and Camille Steber[2]

[1]Department of Molecular, Cellular, and Developmental Biology, University of California, Santa Barbara, California 93106-9610; email: finkelst@lifesci.ucsb.edu; reeves@lifesci.ucsb.edu

[2]United States Department of Agriculture-Agricultural Research Service and Department of Crop and Soil Science, Washington State University, Pullman, Washington 99164-6420; email: ariizumi@mail.wsu.edu, csteber@wsu.edu

Annu. Rev. Plant Biol. 2008. 59:387–415

The *Annual Review of Plant Biology* is online at plant.annualreviews.org

This article's doi:
10.1146/annurev.arplant.59.032607.092740

1543-5008/08/0602-0387$20.00

Key Words

germination, ABA, GA, after-ripening, DELLA proteins, natural variation

Abstract

Seed dormancy provides a mechanism for plants to delay germination until conditions are optimal for survival of the next generation. Dormancy release is regulated by a combination of environmental and endogenous signals with both synergistic and competing effects. Molecular studies of dormancy have correlated changes in transcriptomes, proteomes, and hormone levels with dormancy states ranging from deep primary or secondary dormancy to varying degrees of release. The balance of abscisic acid (ABA):gibberellin (GA) levels and sensitivity is a major, but not the sole, regulator of dormancy status. ABA promotes dormancy induction and maintenance, whereas GA promotes progression from release through germination; environmental signals regulate this balance by modifying the expression of biosynthetic and catabolic enzymes. Mediators of environmental and hormonal response include both positive and negative regulators, many of which are feedback-regulated to enhance or attenuate the response. The net result is a slightly heterogeneous response, thereby providing more temporal options for successful germination.

Contents

INTRODUCTION

Seed dormancy has been described as "one of the least understood phenomena in seed biology" (50) and remains confusing despite much recent progress. This confusion reflects the likelihood that dormancy is not a single phenomenon but a condition with many contributing causes. Traditionally this condition has been primarily negatively defined as a developmental state in which a viable seed fails to germinate under superficially favorable environmental conditions (e.g., adequate moisture). Seed dormancy has been further negatively categorized in terms of the requirements for release from this block, such as disruption of the seed coat (scarification), a period of dry storage (after-ripening) or moist chilling (stratification), or exposure to light. The situation is further complicated by the fact that, although germination is an all-or-nothing event for each seed, populations display variable degrees of dormancy that are reflected in the rate or percentage of germination under specific conditions. Presumably, each seed is in a state somewhere along the continuum from deeply dormant to nondormant, but it remains unclear how the tipping point between nonpermissive and permissive for germination is sensed for each seed. However, this point is of critical agronomic and ecological significance because it determines both the degree of synchronous germination in a given season and the reservoir of ungerminated viable seeds remaining in the soil until a later season, i.e., the seed bank (**Figure 1**).

Recently, genetic approaches have led to the identification of specific loci correlated with altered dormancy, and -omics approaches in many species have identified numerous transcripts and proteins correlated with dormant versus nondormant seeds. Such studies should lead toward a positive definition of dormancy. Comparative analyses should identify characteristics common to many forms of dormancy, and possibly other features unique to certain classes of dormancy. Until then, dormancy remains in the realm of

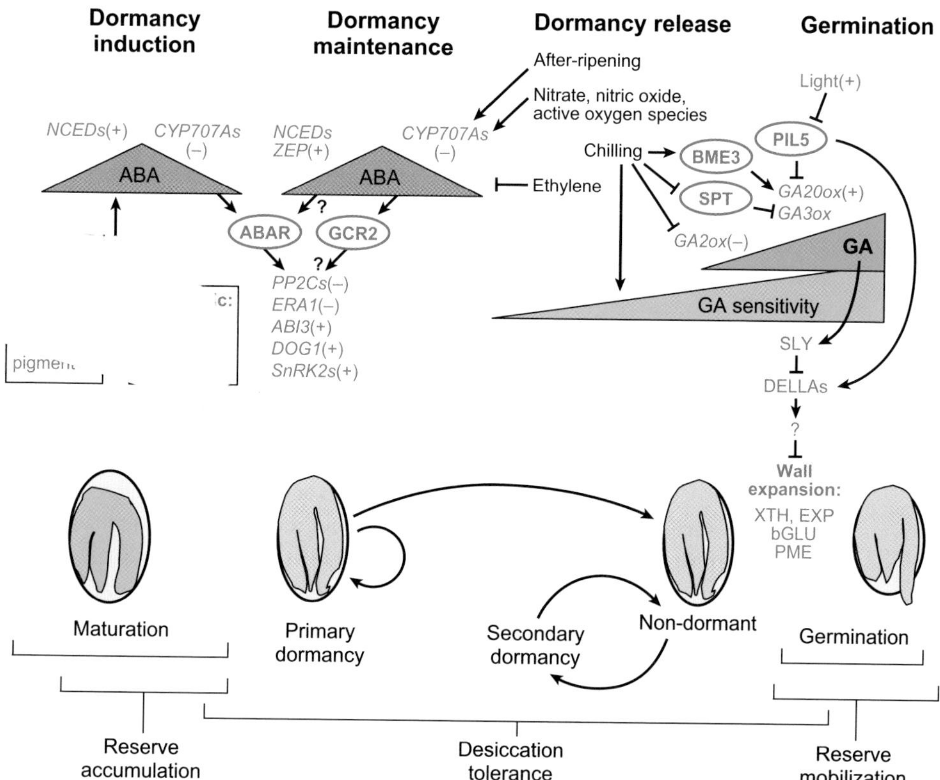

Figure 1

Time course of dormancy induction and release, including partial summary of regulatory factors. Width of abscisic acid (ABA) and gibberellin (GA) symbols represents relative hormone levels due to action of indicated biosynthetic and catabolic loci. Induction depends on combination of ABA-independent maternal and embryonic factors and ABA-dependent signaling. Release is promoted by many environmental factors, largely integrated through changes in ABA:GA signaling balance, eventually resulting in wall expansion to permit radicle emergence. Positive regulation is indicated by (+) and arrows, negative regulation by (–) and bars. NCED, 9-*cis*-epoxycarotenoid dioxygenase; CYP707A, Cytochrome P450 707A; ZEP, zeaxanthin epoxidase; NO, nitric oxide; AOS, active oxygen species; BME3, BLUE MICROPYLAR END 3; PIL5, PHYTOCHROME-INTERACTING FACTOR 3-LIKE 5; SPT, SPATULA; GA20ox, GIBBERELLIN 20 OXIDASE; GA3ox, GIBBERELLIN 3 OXIDASE; GA2ox, GIBBERELLIIN 2 OXIDASE; SLY, SLEEPY; XTH, xyloglucan endotransferase/hydrolase; EXP, expansins; bGLU, β-1,3 glucanase; PME, pectin methylesterase; DAG, DOF (DNA-binding with one zinc finger) AFFECTING GERMINATION; LEC, LEAFY COTYLEDON; FUS3, FUSCA 3; PP2C, protein phosphatase 2C; ERA, ENHANCED RESPONSE TO ABA; ABI, ABA INSENSITIVE; DOG, DELAY OF GERMINATION; SnRK, SNF1-related protein kinase; ABAR, ABA receptor; GCR, G protein–coupled receptor.

Supreme Court Justice Stewart's definition of obscenity in that it's notoriously hard to define but "[we] know it when [we] see it."

WHAT IS DORMANCY?

Seed dormancy is common in wild plants, where it may ensure the ability of a species to survive natural catastrophes, decrease competition between individuals of the same species, or prevent germination out of season. In contrast, domesticated species have been selected for fast and uniform germination, followed by rapid seedling establishment (termed stand establishment), to achieve good crop yield.

After-ripening: period of dry storage during which dormancy progressively decreases

Stratification: incubation of seeds in moist conditions to break dormancy, usually in cold to simulate overwintering

-omics: global studies of functional aspects of entire genomes, transcriptomes (all expressed transcripts in a tissue), proteomes (all expressed proteins in a tissue), etc.

Seed longevity: duration of seed viability during prolonged storage

ABA: abscisic acid

However, lack of seed dormancy is not desirable because it may cause preharvest sprouting, a serious problem in cereals including rice, wheat, barley, and maize (17), and nondormant mutants can have reduced seed longevity (36).

All types of dormancy impose a delay between seed shedding and germination, but the underlying causes may vary. This variety has been classified in terms of whether germination is inhibited owing to embryonic immaturity or physical or physiological constraints, and whether the controlling structure or substances are embryonic or in the surrounding tissues of the seed, i.e., coat-imposed (reviewed in 50). Whereas primary dormancy is acquired during seed maturation, imbibed after-ripened seeds exposed to unfavorable temperature conditions or lacking adequate light or nitrate may enter a state of secondary dormancy. Furthermore, seeds may undergo seasonal dormancy cycling if conditions are suboptimal, progressively gaining or losing dormancy until they eventually germinate or die. Although physiologically fully dormant seeds cannot germinate regardless of environmental conditions, seeds with intermediate dormancy germinate slowly or under a narrower range of light and temperature conditions (82).

Strictly defined, germination is the initial emergence of the radicle from the seed coat. This process requires that the plant embryo leave the quiescent state, mobilize stored nutrients, overcome the barrier of surrounding tissues, and resume cell elongation, cell division, and development. Dormancy may result from blocks in any of these processes. Because the forms of seed dormancy are defined on the basis of mechanisms of dormancy release, scored in terms of increased germination, it is controversial whether some of the effective signals induce dormancy release or the subsequent germination.

Dormant seeds that exhibit seed coat–imposed dormancy will germinate following damage or removal of the seed coat. Although some species require scarification or fire for dormancy release, and thus appear to show seed coat–imposed dormancy (reviewed in 82), smoke contains dormancy-breaking compounds, including nitrogen oxides (96) and a butenolide (52), suggesting that fire also stimulates germination by biochemical mechanisms.

The precise mechanisms underlying dormancy breaking by after-ripening remain elusive but have been correlated with changes in gene expression, enzyme activity, and hormone accumulation, suggesting that biological processes such as transcription and translation can occur in dry seeds (22, 49, 108). Several dormancy-breaking signals have additive or synergistic effects, suggesting that they might affect key regulators of dormancy similarly. This possibility raises several questions: What are these key regulators; do the different types of physiological dormancy reflect different underlying molecular mechanisms; and do different depths of dormancy reflect quantitative or qualitative differences? This review focuses on the balance between plant hormone signaling pathways regulating dormancy and on the molecular mechanisms by which plants control the induction and release of seed dormancy.

REGULATION OF DORMANCY BY HORMONES AND OTHER SMALL MOLECULES

Dormancy Induction and Maintenance

Potential regulators of dormancy have been identified as substances whose accumulation in seeds correlates with the depth of dormancy, and by genetic analyses of lines with different degrees of dormancy.

Abscisic Acid

Several lines of evidence have established that abscisic acid (ABA) induces dormancy during embryo maturation (reviewed in 48, 50, 51, 97, 127). ABA can inhibit germination and its accumulation correlates with the onset of dormancy. Dormancy is reduced in seeds that are ABA-deficient owing to mutations, chemical inhibition of biosynthesis, or sequestering of ABA by antibodies expressed in seeds, whereas overexpression of ABA biosynthetic enzymes leads to enhanced dormancy (110, 127). Genetic studies have shown that ABA produced by maternal tissues or supplied exogenously is not sufficient to induce dormancy (50, 51), implying that this is a form of embryo-controlled dormancy dependent on ABA synthesis in the embryo and/or endosperm.

Although ABA decreases to relatively low levels in dry dormant seeds owing to catabolism by specific ABA 8′-hydroxylases encoded by the cytochrome P450 CYP707A family (136), dormancy is maintained by renewed accumulation of ABA following imbibition of dormant seeds (2, 70, 103). Expression and genetic analyses of specific genes encoding key enzymes in ABA metabolism have identified members of the *AtNCED* (9-*cis*-epoxycarotenoid dioxygenase) family (*NCED6* and *NCED9*) that are essential for ABA synthesis in both the embryo and endosperm during dormancy induction (105). Additional studies have identified specific genes correlated with dormancy maintenance [*NCED6*, *NCED9*, and *ZEP* (zeaxanthin epoxidase)] and dormancy release via ABA catabolism (*CYP707A2*) (22, 121). Thus, seed ABA levels and the resulting dormancy are controlled by the combined action of differentially expressed enzymes involved in several steps of both synthesis and catabolism.

Dehydration and Desiccation Tolerance

The vast majority of dormant seeds are "orthodox" in that ABA induces desiccation tolerance late in seed development, permitting their survival for long periods in a dry state. In contrast, "recalcitrant" seeds are not desiccation tolerant and this is correlated with the generation of active oxygen species (AOS) and the occurrence of oxidative damage during dehydration (6, 12), leading to the suggestion that desiccation tolerance depends in part on the ability to scavenge AOS compounds by antioxidant defense systems. Most maturing seeds have increased catalase activity (6, 12) and accumulate glutathione, peroxiredoxins (79, 162), or even storage proteins serving as substrates for oxidative carbonylation (6, 93). Although glutathione production in the embryo appears to be essential for maturation (23) and overexpression of peroxiredoxins confers hypersensitivity to several germination-inhibiting stresses, peroxiredoxin levels do not correlate with depth of dormancy (80).

In addition to effects on cellular oxidation state, desiccation tolerance involves formation of an intracellular "glassy state" due to supersaturation by a combination of sugars and late embryogenesis abundant (LEA) proteins (reviewed in 12). Despite the correlation between LEA proteins and desiccation tolerance, LEA transcript levels do not appear to be correlated with dormancy (8, 49).

NCED: 9-*cis*-epoxycarotenoid dioxygenase

LEAs: late embryogenesis abundant proteins

Seed Coat Components

Genetic variation in structure and/or pigmentation of the seed coat (testa) or surrounding layers, such as the pericarp of grains, leads to altered dormancy and seed longevity in many species (44, 72, 170). The testa both protects the embryo from environmental damage and restricts its growth prior to germination. Mutations affecting pigmentation include disruption of pigment biosynthetic genes, transporters involved in compartmentation of the pigments, and transcription factors that regulate production of the biosynthetic enzymes (reviewed in 106).

Seed coat pigments are generally phenolic compounds such as flavonoids. The pigments accumulated depend on the species; red phlobaphenes are common in grains, isoflavones are common in legumes, and proanthocyanidins and flavonol glycosides are present in *Arabidopsis* (reviewed in 44). The proanthocyanidins are generally present as

GAs: gibberellins

polymers that become cross-linked to wall components by oxidation during seed maturation, resulting in thicker cell layers that provide greater mechanical restraint and reduced permeability to water, gases, and hormones. In addition, as efficient antioxidants, flavonoids can further restrict oxygen availability, thereby inhibiting metabolic processes of after-ripening and germination, e.g., oxidative degradation of ABA. Light sensing both regulates and is regulated by seed pigments. The degree of pigmentation depends on the photoperiod experienced by the maternal plant during seed set and highly pigmented seeds filter light reaching the embryo, although only UV light has been shown to be absorbed by flavonoids (187).

Flavonoids also provide protection from antimicrobial and antiherbivory functions, UV radiation, and possibly oxidative damage. Consequently, breeding programs that attempt to separate characters associated with seed color, dormancy, and longevity suggest that these characteristics may not be separable. For example, mapping of some loci affecting seed color, dormancy, and shattering characteristics of rice shows very tight linkage such that these traits are referred to as a domestication block; some of these traits may be controlled by a single locus (90). However, whereas pigmented seeds are generally more dormant, additional characters such as hormone levels or sensitivity can enhance dormancy of nonpigmented seeds (53, 60, 182).

Dormancy Release and Germination

Dormancy release is accomplished by diverse mechanisms that include complex interactions with the environment mediated by phytohormones and other small molecules, and is believed to select conditions for germination that are most conducive for plant survival. The discussion herein is restricted to the molecular mechanisms of dormancy release by gibberellins, brassinosteroids, ethylene, reactive oxygen species, and nitrogen-containing compounds such as nitrate and nitric oxide (NO).

Gibberellins

Gibberellins [e.g., gibberellic acid (GA)] are a family of 136 tetracyclic diterpenes, a small subset of which are active as plant hormones and known to stimulate seed germination in a wide range of plant species; the predominant active GA depends on the species (reviewed in 172). Gibberellins stimulate germination by inducing hydrolytic enzymes that weaken the barrier tissues such as the endosperm or seed coat, inducing mobilization of seed storage reserves, and stimulating expansion of the embryo (reviewed in 17). GA may also stimulate germination via the transition from embryonic to vegetative development, in part mediated by the chromatin remodeling factor PICKLE (PKL) (81). GA stimulation of this transition is suggested by enhancement of the *pkl* embryonic root phenotype by GA biosynthesis inhibitors, and by GA-stimulated disappearance of the embryonic identity protein FUSCA 3 (FUS3), which positively regulates ABA synthesis and negatively regulates GA synthesis (62, 81).

The role of gibberellins in dormancy release is controversial. Although GA accumulation is associated with dormancy release and/or germination, GA treatment alone does not stimulate germination in all species or in fully dormant *Arabidopsis* seeds (2, 16, 46). A decrease in ABA levels may be required before GA levels and sensitivity can increase (2, 88). However, sensitivity to both GA and light increases as after-ripening progresses in *Arabidopsis* (45) and increased GA levels mediate the dormancy-relieving effect of moist chilling in *Arabidopsis* (188). Light promotes GA synthesis, and light and GA promote the degradation of ABA in imbibing lettuce seeds (175). The accumulation of the GA biosynthetic gene *GA3ox2* (*GIBBERELLIN 3 OXIDASE*) transcript increased 40-fold in after-ripened seeds whereas the GA-deactivating enzyme *GA2ox1* (*GIBBERELLIN 2 OXIDASE*) was expressed at the highest levels in the highly dormant seeds of *Arabidopsis* ecotype Cvi (Cape Verde Islands) (49). Stratification led to increased expression of the GA biosynthesis genes *GA20ox1* (*GIBBERELLIN 20 OXIDASE*), *GA20ox2*, and *GA3ox1* and decreased expression of the GA catabolic gene *GA2ox2* (188). Taken together, GA may not trigger the onset of after-ripening, but it may be necessary though not sufficient for seed dormancy release and germination.

GA is critical for seed germination in the dicots *Arabidopsis* and tomato because mutants with defects in genes encoding GA biosynthetic enzymes fail to germinate (122, 163 and references therein). Nongermination of GA mutants is relieved by exogenous application of GA, mutations affecting ABA biosynthesis or signaling, or removal of the mechanical restraint of the testa and endosperm. Thus, GA mutants fit the classical definition of dormant, suggesting that GA synthesis is one step required to release dormancy. A dramatic increase in bioactive GA_4 level is observed just before initial radicle protrusion, consistent with the timing of GA-responsive gene induction (33, 131). GA synthesis depends on the movement of precursors within the embryo: The step catalyzed by the *Arabidopsis GA1* locus occurs in provascular tissue, but subsequent steps occur in cortex and endodermis (131). Unlike dicots, cereals do not require GA for germination. For example, mutations in the rice GA receptor *OsGID1* (*Oryza sativa GIBBERELLIN-INSENSITIVE DWARF 1*) display decreased α-amylase production, but allow germination (177), whereas loss of all three *Arabidopsis GID1* homologs blocks germination (185). This discrepancy may reflect differences in the structure, pigmentation, and composition of these seeds, or as yet undetected sources of redundancy in rice GA signaling.

Brassinosteriods

Brassinosteriods (BRs) are plant steroid hormones involved in stem elongation and leaf unfurling (reviewed in 38) that also promote seed germination. Although BR biosynthesis and signaling mutants germinate well, they are more sensitive than wild-type to ABA inhibition of seed germination, suggesting that these mutations decrease germination potential (39, 164). In *Arabidopsis*, epibrassinolide (EBR) and brassinolide (BL) application overcomes nongermination of GA biosynthetic and *sleepy 1* (*sly1*) GA signaling mutants (164), but BR and GA stimulate tobacco seed germination by different mechanisms (107). Although both BRs and GA promote endosperm rupture of nonphotodormant tobacco seeds imbibed in the dark, only GA induces the class I β-1,3 glucanase (bGLU I) activity that is critical for endosperm rupture of photodormant tobacco seeds (107). Furthermore, microarray analysis shows that both BR and GA induce the expression of cell elongation-associated genes, but these hormones induce the expression of distinct expansin family members (65). Thus, BRs may promote seed germination by directly enhancing the embryo growth potential in a GA-independent manner (107).

GA(n)ox: gibberellin (n) oxidase

GID: gibberellin-insensitive dwarf

Germination potential: likelihood of successful germination due to combination of decreased restrictive properties of tissues surrounding embryo or radicle tip, and increased ability of embryo to produce sufficient turgor to push through these tissues

Ethylene

Ethylene promotes dormancy breaking through interactions with ABA signaling. Seed of *ethylene resistant* (*etr*) *1* receptor mutants and *ethylene insensitive* (*ein*) *2*/*enhanced response to aba* (*era*) *3* mutants display increased dormancy correlated with increased sensitivity to ABA in seed germination and increased ABA synthesis (9, 33, 64). In contrast, *constitutive triple response* (*ctr*) *1* mutations and treatment of wild-type seeds with the ethylene precursor 1-aminocyclopropane-1-carboxylic acid (ACC) result in decreased sensitivity to ABA (64). The *etr1-2* mutant also overaccumulates GA, suggesting that the increased dormancy due to ABA overaccumulation is partly compensated for by increased GA accumulation. Thus, ethylene stimulation of seed germination may occur via antagonism of ABA signaling.

Nitric Oxide, Nitrate, and Active Oxygen Species

Many nitrogen-containing compounds, including NO gas, nitrite (NO_2^-), nitrate (NO_3^-), nitrogen dioxide, ammonium, azide, and cyanide, promote dormancy release and seed germination in many species, possibly as a means of sensing soil N availability (reviewed in 15). Even nitrate provided during seed development via the maternal plant leads to lower dormancy (1). Interconversion of these compounds and the lack of specificity for NO donors, scavengers, and detectors complicates analysis of their mechanism(s), but they may act as sources of NO or by similar mechanisms as NO (14, 15).

Enzymatic NO production in plants occurs primarily via nitrate reductase (NR) from nitrite and nitrate (reviewed in 15) and possibly a plant-specific nitric oxide synthase whose identity is still ambiguous (42). However, although *Arabidopsis NR1* expression is correlated with dormancy-breaking conditions (49), seeds of NR-deficient plants accumulate nitrate and have reduced dormancy (1). NO can also be produced by the oxidizing environments of glyoxysomes engaged in lipid catabolism (41), and nonenzymatic NO production may occur in the apoplast or soil where nitrite can be converted to NO at low pH (13).

These nitrogen-containing compounds may promote seed germination via effects on metabolism, oxidation state, or signaling (15). Nitrate and dormancy-relieving conditions induce the expression of some genes that encode enzymes in the pentose phosphate pathway, which may provide essential nutrients for germination (49). NO, nitrite, and nitrate may stimulate the pentose phosphate pathway, and therefore germination, by increasing oxidation of NADPH to $NADP^+$, a limiting electron acceptor. NO inhibition of catalase may lead to increased accumulation of H_2O_2 from the β-oxidation of stored fatty acids in seeds. Accumulated H_2O_2 may stimulate germination by acting as a substrate for peroxidases, leading to oxidation of NADPH to $NADP^+$ or by causing breakdown of ABA (reviewed in 6). Nitrate can also modify hormone levels by inducing the expression of enzymes that catalyze ABA deactivation (*CYP707A2*) and GA biosynthesis (*GA3ox1*) (49). In *Arabidopsis*, NO may stimulate germination by causing vacuolation and cell wall weakening of the aleurone layer (14).

PROTEINS REGULATING DORMANCY INDUCTION AND MAINTENANCE

Genetic studies have led to the identification of numerous loci that encode dormancy-regulating proteins (reviewed in 11). Mutations in many of these loci have pleiotropic effects, indicating that the specific events leading to the dormant state are only a subset of the downstream effects of these regulators. The proteins encoded by these loci include standard signaling molecules such as G proteins and G protein–coupled receptors, transcriptional regulators, and protein phosphatases or kinases regulating activity of the transcription factors via effects on phosphorylation state. Additional proteins regulate transcription factor activity, stability, or localization via other modifications. Numerous other loci display altered ABA or stress sensitivity at germination, but we focus on the relatively few that affect dormancy, as reflected in requirements for stratification or after-ripening.

Transcriptional and Posttranscriptional Regulators

A variety of mutants with major defects in seed maturation, e.g., the *Arabidopsis leafy cotyledon* class (*lec1*, *lec2 and fus3*) and *ABA-insensitive* (*abi*) *3* mutants, result in nondormancy (reviewed in 50, 51). All these loci encode transcriptional regulators, so it is tempting to suggest that some of their regulatory targets are essential to dormancy. However, because they constitute part of a regulatory hierarchy including both cross- and autoregulation (78, 173), many of their effects on maturation are likely indirect. Furthermore, because these highly pleiotropic mutants do not produce viable desiccation-tolerant seed, many of the genes misexpressed in these mutants probably reflect the failure to reach the stage of development when cues inducing dormancy begin. In this respect, the weaker *abi3* alleles provide a more promising approach toward a molecular fingerprint for dormancy because these mutants produce viable dry seeds yet are still nondormant. Although two additional classes of transcription factors, encoded by the *ABI4* and *ABI5* loci, regulate germination in response to ABA and stresses (51), they do not appear to affect dormancy significantly.

Further evidence suggesting the importance of *ABI*-like genes in dormancy regulation comes from studies of their orthologs in other dicots, cereals, and even conifers (50, 97). Although most crops have reduced dormancy compared with their wild relatives, specific cereal cultivars exhibit different degrees of dormancy, and comparison of these lines reveals some positive correlations between the depth of dormancy and high expression of the *Vp1* (*Viviparous*) genes (*ABI3* orthologs) from wild oats (95) and wheat (126), but not sorghum (26). However, wheat and barley *Vp1* genes appear to be mostly misspliced even in ancestral varieties of wheat, such that little functional protein is produced, leaving these species predisposed to preharvest sprouting (117). *ABI5* homologs are also more highly expressed in more dormant cultivars of sorghum (154). Despite these correlations, demonstration of a significant role in controlling seed dormancy would require functional evidence, e.g., coincidence with dormancy quantitative trait loci (QTL) between these cultivars or alteration of dormancy by modified expression of either gene in otherwise isogenic lines. Although transcriptional profiling studies of dormancy cycling in the highly dormant Cvi ecotype of *Arabidopsis* show a preponderance of ABA-responsive element (ABRE)-containing genes correlated with dormancy, *Arabidopsis* differs from cereals in that none of the *ABI* transcription factors are included in this set and *ABI4* actually appears in the after-ripening set (8, 22, 49). Only the basic leucine zipper domain (bZIP) *ABA-RESPONSIVE ELEMENT BINDING PROTEIN* (*AREB*) *2*/ *ABRE BINDING FACTOR* (*ABF*) *4* is enriched in dormant states (22), but mutant analyses have not tested its role in dormancy.

Unlike the highly seed-enriched expression of these *ABI* loci, the *DOF* (*DNA-binding with one zinc finger*) *AFFECTING GERMINATION* (*DAG*) *1* and *DAG2* loci encode highly similar transcription factors that are both expressed exclusively in maternal vascular tissue and have opposing effects on seed germination potential (75, 139). Double mutant analyses showed that DAG1 acts epistatically, leading to the suggestion that DAG1 activates maternal genes that promote dormancy and DAG2 represses this action, by binding to either the same *cis*-elements or the DAG1 factor. Although the specific targets of the DAG transcription factors have not yet been identified, the products of their target genes could modify characteristics of either the embryo or surrounding tissues. Whereas the DAG genes appear to be coregulated during normal growth, environmentally induced changes in their relative expression or protein accumulation might regulate seed sensitivity to germination-inducing signals such as light and GAs.

Recent studies have also provided genetic evidence for transcriptional control via effects on chromatin structure. The *REDUCED DORMANCY* (*RDO*) *4* locus (142) encodes a C3HC4 RING finger protein with homology to histone-modifying enzymes of other species (113). The mutant fails to monoubiquitinate histone H2B and the locus was consequently renamed *HISTONE MONOUBIQUITINATION* (*HUB1*). Defects in a close homolog, designated *HUB2*, also result in decreased dormancy. The single and double mutants have similar phenotypes, leading to the suggestion that these proteins

ABI: abscisic acid insensitive

Quantitative trait loci (QTL): genes that contribute quantitative variation to complex traits regulated by multiple unlinked loci

RDO: reduced dormancy

function as part of a heterotetramer, required for monoubiquitination, that is associated with actively transcribed genes. Consistent with this emphasis on transcription elongation, the *RDO2* locus encodes the transcription elongation factor S II (TFIIS) (63). TFIIS factors can enhance elongation by promoting cleavage and reactivation of nascent transcripts whose elongation is blocked under difficult conditions in yeast and mammalian cells (186). Similar blocks may occur in a drying or dry seed. However, how this control mechanism specifically targets histone modification and enhanced transcription to dormancy-related genes remains unclear.

Dormancy-related gene expression is also regulated posttranscriptionally. Early studies of potential dormancy marker genes demonstrated that transcript stability was enhanced far more than transcription rate in dormant versus after-ripened seeds (109), and transcriptional profiling demonstrated the importance of translational control during after-ripening of *Nicotiana plumbaginifolia* (18). Researchers have identified mutations resulting in increased dormancy and/or ABA hypersensitivity at germination that disrupt RNA capping [*ABA-hypersensitive* (*abh*) *1*]; miRNA biosynthesis [*hyponastic leaves* (*hyl*) *1*]; mRNA splicing, export, and degradation [*supersensitive to ABA and drought* (*sad*) *1*]; and degradation of polyadenylated RNA [*ABA hypersensitive germination* (*ahg*) *2*] (reviewed in 101, 128). Although the hypersensitivity of the mutants implies that these proteins are negative regulators of the ABA response, some of these proteins are induced by ABA or stresses (128), and therefore may participate in a negative feedback loop.

Protein Phosphatases and Kinases

Nondormant *Arabidopsis abi* mutants also include two dominant mutations in the *ABI1* and *ABI2* loci (99), which encode closely related members of the A group of the protein phosphatase 2C (PP2C) family (157). Significantly, although these mutants have greatly reduced phosphatase activity, knockout mutations in these loci result in the opposite phenotype: weak hypersensitivity to ABA and hyperdormancy (119). Recent studies of this clade of PP2Cs have demonstrated that knockout/knockdown mutants in several family members result in increased dormancy, which is most pronounced for the family members that are most highly expressed at seed maturity, i.e., *ahg1* and *ahg3*, or for double mutants (129, 191), reflecting some redundancy. A homologous PP2C from beech also negatively regulates dormancy when transferred into *Arabidopsis* (69), but one family member appears to act as a positive regulator of ABA response, mediated in part by reduction of GA levels (153). Pernas and coworkers (146) recently reported a similar ABA-hypersensitive hyperdormant phenotype for a mutant with a disrupted PP2A catalytic subunit. Expression of many of these protein phosphatases is induced by ABA, providing a negative feedback mechanism to attenuate ABA response. However, other PP2As either positively regulate (102) or have no effect on ABA response (146).

Each of these PP2Cs probably has numerous substrates, but relatively few have been identified (35). These substrates include transcription factors implicated in the drought/stress response (83), protein kinases (190), calcineurin B–like calcium sensors (77), a glutathione peroxidase (120), and fibrillin, a stress-induced photoprotective plastid protein (189). The dominant negative mutant PP2Cs fail to interact with protein kinases of the SALT OVERLY SENSITIVE (SOS) 2 family, but the mechanistic significance of this interaction remains unclear (135). The function of at least some of these PP2Cs is modified by phosphatidic acid binding (35) or H_2O_2 exposure (118). The latter provides a mechanism by which ROS production in imbibed seeds can modify transcription profiles (118). Although the specific interactions and mechanisms have not been demonstrated, this hypothesis is consistent with the recent identification of dozens of genes whose expression depends on AHG1 and/or AHG3 (129).

The activity of many of the bZIP factors is controlled by their phosphorylation states. A mitogen activated protein (MAP) kinase cascade activates ABI5 (115), possibly indirectly. Members of the calcium-dependent protein kinase (CDPK) and SNF1-related protein kinase (SnRK) families of serine-threonine protein kinases interact directly with multiple members of the AREB/ABF/ABI5-class of bZIPs in vitro, although in vivo interactions have not been demonstrated for most (29, 34, 57, 59, 98). Several of these kinases and transcription factors are differentially expressed, and the specific interactions may be partially dictated by which proteins are coexpressed. Phosphorylation of these bZIPs is correlated with their activation and, consistent with this, the SnRK2.2 and SnRK2.3 family kinases are redundant positive regulators of dormancy, ABA sensitivity of germination, and some gene expression (57). In contrast, a nonorthologous family member from rice, OSRK1/SAPK6, shows reduced sensitivity to ABA at germination (29). Additional kinases are also correlated with dormancy, but their specific substrates are unknown (19, 92). One of the best known interactions that affects germination potential is phosphorylation of the wheat bZIP factor TaABF by the SnRK PKABA1 (94), leading to both repression of GA-induced genes, including the transcription factor GA-Myb, and activation of ABA-induced genes (67, 68).

Regulation of Protein Stability and Localization

The function of some ABI transcriptional regulators is also controlled by stabilization against proteasomal degradation. ABI3 expression is high in seeds and quickly turned off in most tissues following germination (21, 140, 173), but is also targeted for destruction by the E3 ubiquitin ligase ABI3 INTERACTING PROTEIN (AIP) 2, which is expressed throughout development (195). Whether accumulation of AIP2 protein reflects AIP2 transcript levels remains unclear, but if so AIP levels are either insufficient to induce ABI3 destruction prior to germination or ABI3 synthesis exceeds destruction at this stage. However, even strong overexpression of AIP2 has relatively mild effects on ABA sensitivity, resulting in a similar phenotype to the weak allele *abi3-1*.

Although the specific ubiquitin ligase(s) involved in tagging ABI5 have not yet been definitively identified, mutations in four loci alter ABI5 stability and consequently germination kinetics: *RPN10* (161), *KEEP ON GOING* (*KEG*) (166) *SALT- AND DROUGHT-INDUCIBLE RING FINGER 1* (*SDIR1*) (196), and *ABI FIVE BINDING PROTEIN* (*AFP*) (114). Despite their effects on ABA sensitivity of germination, all these mutants are similar to *abi5* in that none have significant effects on dormancy.

Lipid modification of proteins by farnesylation can promote membrane attachment, protein stabilization, or protein-protein interactions in plants (61). *ERA1*, which encodes the β subunit of protein farnesylase, was first identified in a screen for enhanced response to ABA (hence the name, *ERA*) at germination (43), and was subsequently shown by epistasis analyses to act downstream of the ABI phosphatases but upstream of the ABI transcription factors in ABA signaling (21). *era1* mutants are highly pleiotropic, displaying hypersensitivity to ABA for multiple responses including dormancy, and defects in meristem regulation, which probably reflect ERA1's role in farnesylating multiple targets. Searches for C-terminal farnesylation targets have identified 119 potential substrates (61) including G protein γ subunits (192), suggesting ERA1 might control G protein responsiveness.

Abscisic Acid Perception

Three distinct ABA receptors have been identified in the last two years by biochemical or reverse genetic approaches (84): an RNA binding protein that regulates flowering, FLOWERING TIME CONTROL A (FCA) (152); a subunit of Mg chelatase involved in chlorophyll biosynthesis and plastid-to-nuclear retrograde communication, ABAR/CHLH/GENOMES UNCOUPLED 5 (GUN5) (158); and a G protein–coupled receptor (GCR2) (112). Only the latter two appear to regulate seed responses to ABA, and only mutations affecting ABAR have severe defects in seed development. *ABAR* knockout lines are embryonic lethal plants that lack storage proteins and lipids, but can't be readily analyzed biochemically owing to a lack of homozygotes. *ABAR* knockdown lines display ABA-resistant germination and reduced expression of *LEA* genes and the *ABI* and *MYB* transcription factors that positively regulate ABA response, but overexpress the *ABI* PP2Cs that function as negative regulators of ABA response. In this respect, the ABAR/CHLH/GUN5 receptor appears to play a central role in signaling that mediates ABA responses of seeds, but its effects on dormancy per se have not been characterized.

G protein involvement in ABA regulation of germination was first demonstrated genetically by the observation that a mutant in the sole G protein α subunit (*GPA1*) of *Arabidopsis* was hypersensitive to ABA for inhibition of germination (179), implying that GPA1 inhibits this ABA response despite the fact that it appears to promote stomatal response to ABA (138). GPA1 was subsequently shown to interact with a putative G protein–coupled receptor (GCR1) that also inhibited ABA response (40), but whose ligand was unknown. The G protein β subunit also negatively regulates ABA inhibition of germination (138). Recently, a complete signal transduction chain comprised of GCR1, GPA1, Pirin1 (an iron-containing member of the cupin superfamily), and a CCAAT box binding protein complex (nuclear factor Y) including LEC1 was described as mediating both ABA inhibition of germination and the slight induction of Lhcb (light harvesting complex/chlorophyll binding protein) expression by either blue light or ABA (184). However, whether this also reflected a change in dormancy level remained unclear. Liu and coworkers (112) recently found a second G protein–coupled receptor (GCR2) that interacts with GPA1, binds ABA, and functions as a positive regulator of ABA signaling. Mutations in GCR2 have a surprisingly mild phenotype for a receptor, leading to the suggestion that it may act redundantly with other G protein–coupled receptors present in plants. Both GCR1 and GCR2 appear to be regulators of ABA response whose interactions with the G protein complex either promote (GCR1) or repress (GCR2) its inhibitory effects on germination.

PROTEINS REGULATING DORMANCY RELEASE

Transcriptional Regulation of Gibberellin Biosynthesis by SPT, PIL5, BME3

GA synthesis is regulated developmentally and in response to environmental signals. For example, the GATA zinc finger protein BLUE MICROPYLAR END 3 (BME3) promotes expression of the GA biosynthesis genes *GA3ox1* and *GA20ox3* in the micropylar end of the seed, which stimulates breakdown of barrier tissues prior to radicle emergence; the importance of these GA biosynthesis genes is demonstrated by the delayed seed germination of *bme3* mutants (111). Changes in expression of GA biosynthetic genes in response to cold imbibition and light are regulated by two basic helix-loop-helix (bHLH) transcription factors, SPATULA (SPT) and PHYTOCHROME-INTERACTING FACTOR 3–LIKE 5 (PIL5) (132–134, 144). SPT inhibits expression of two *GA3ox* genes (*GA3ox1* and *GA3ox2*) during seed imbibition in the cold. The reduced dormancy of *spt* mutants is more pronounced in the light, suggesting SPT-mediated cross talk between light and cold regulation of dormancy. PIL5 prevents seed germination in the dark at low temperature by repressing expression of *GA3ox1* and *GA3ox2* genes, whereas it induces expression of the *GA2ox2* catabolic gene during imbibition in the dark (134, 144). PIL5 protein disappears in the light, apparently owing to phytochrome-stimulated degradation by the 26S proteasome (134). This suggests that stratification promotes germination by increasing the potential for bioactive GA accumulation. PIL5 also appears to repress GA responses by stimulating expression of the DELLA repressors of GA response, *REPRESSOR OF GA1-3* (*RGA*) and *GA-INSENSITIVE* (*GAI*), through direct binding to their promoters (133), suggesting that DELLA proteins may be involved in environmental control of seed dormancy.

The DELLA Repressors of Gibberellin Signaling and Seed Germination

DELLA proteins are negative regulators of diverse GA responses (reviewed in 169); GA stimulates germination by causing the disappearance of DELLA proteins (5, 176). The DELLA family is defined by an N-terminal DELLA domain required for GA regulation and a C-terminal GRAS [GAI (GA-INSENSITIVE), RGA (REPRESSOR OF GA 1–3), and SCARECROW] domain required for function of these putative transcription factors (145, 150). Mutations in the DELLA domain result in gain-of-function GA signaling phenotypes resembling GA deficiency, whereas loss-of-function mutations in the GRAS domain typically result in an enhanced or constitutive GA response (reviewed in 172). Although a single DELLA gene exists in rice and barley, the *Arabidopsis* genome contains five DELLA genes.

RGL (*RGA-LIKE*) *2* appears to be the major DELLA protein regulating seed germination because loss of *RGL2* function partly restores germination in GA-deficient seeds (104, 176), but single mutations in the other family members are not sufficient. However, combinations of *RGA*, *GAI*, and *RGL1* can enhance this seed germination rescue (25). *RGL2* mRNA and protein levels increase during cold imbibition, then decrease rapidly as germination approaches after transfer to 23°C (5, 7, 104). RGL2 protein disappears within 5 h of GA application to imbibing GA-deficient (*ga1-3)* seeds, long before germination occurs (176). This pattern of expression suggests that RGL2 is a potent repressor of seed germination whose repression is lifted by GA-stimulated DELLA degradation. Conversely, ABA stabilizes at least one DELLA, an RGA::GFP protein fusion (143). Recent evidence suggests that DELLA proteins promote seed dormancy through inhibition of cotyledon expansion prior to germination (143), possibly by repressing expression of hydrolytic and wall-modifying enzymes.

GA relieves DELLA repression of seed germination through proteolysis by the 26S proteasome, triggered via polyubiquitination by the SCF$^{SLY1/GID2}$ (Skp1-Cdc53/CUL-1/F-box protein, in this case SLY1/GID2) E3 ubiquitin ligase (5 and references therein). *Arabidopsis* SLY1 and rice GA-INSENSITIVE DWARF 2 (GID2) are homologous F-box subunits of an SCF E3 ubiquitin ligase that ubiquitinates DELLA proteins, thereby targeting them for destruction in the presence of GA (47, 56, 116, 156). The GA signal is received by the *GID1* GA receptor(s) (71, 87, 124, 177, 185). The GID1 protein undergoes a GA-dependent interaction with DELLA proteins, which promotes the interaction of DELLA with the F-box protein (71, 178).

DELLA function may be regulated by mechanisms other than destruction. Although rescue of *sly1* dormancy by *RGL2* mutations suggests that *sly1* dormancy is due to RGL2 overaccumulation, weak alleles and long after-ripened *sly1* seeds are able to germinate, although they retain high levels of RGL2 and RGA protein (5). This suggests that the RGL2 protein that accumulates in *sly1* mutant seeds is not fully active as a repressor of GA signaling. RGL2 may be subject to additional posttranslational regulation or germination may be regulated by parallel pathways. RGL2 is subject to phosphorylation, and phosphomimic mutations stabilize the RGL2 protein (85, 86). Mutations in the *Arabidopsis* O-linked β-N-acetylglucosamine (O-GlcNAc) transferase SPINDLY (SPY) lead to GA-independent germination and increased stability of DELLA proteins, suggesting that O-Glc-NAc modification may both activate DELLAs and stimulate their turnover (89, 159, 160). An alternative pathway mediating GA effects on dormancy release is suggested by microarray analyses demonstrating DELLA-independent GA-induced gene expression during stratification (24). Because *sly1* mutants are ABA hypersensitive, ABA catabolism may constitute one parallel pathway (167).

Role of Reserve Mobilizing Enzymes in Germination Progression

Embryos must mobilize carbon and energy sources to germinate and grow. In dicots, lipid reserves consist predominantly of triacylglycerol (TAG). During germination, TAG is hydrolyzed by lipases, and the resulting fatty acids pass into the peroxisome where β-oxidation and the glyoxylate cycle provide energy and carbon skeletons for postgerminative growth (66). Genetic studies emphasize the importance of TAG breakdown via lipid catabolism in regulating dormancy release and/or germination: Mutants defective in lipid catabolism and β-oxidation [*kat2* (ketoacyl-CoA thiolase-2) and *acx1acx2* (acyl-CoA oxidase) or *csy2csy3* (citrate synthase) double mutants] (54, 147, 148) or import of very long chain fatty acids into peroxisomes (*cts, COMATOSE*) (55, 155, 171) are deeply dormant. Although *cts* seed germination is not rescued by stratification, after-ripening, GA treatment, or *rgl2* mutations (28), removal of the seed coat rescues germination and *transparent testa glabrous* (*ttg*) mutants rescue germination upon after-ripening. However, loss of two long-chain acyl-CoA synthetases (LACS) in the *lacs6 lacs7* double mutant causes failure in TAG breakdown without blocking germination (54, 58), suggesting that breakdown of long-chain acyl-CoA esters may not be required for seed germination. After-ripening of wild-type Landsberg *erecta* (L*er*) and *cts* mutant seeds results in similar changes in gene expression (28, 54, 55), suggesting that the failure of β-oxidation in *cts* mutants may block production of a germination-promoting factor or breakdown of a germination-inhibiting factor (55).

GENETIC ANALYSES OF NATURAL VARIATION THAT AFFECTS DORMANCY

The genetic approaches described above identify regulators with either relatively minor effects on dormancy, in some cases due to redundancy, or those with such dramatic pleiotropic effects that loss of function would not be sustained in wild populations. Although some of these are candidate loci to explain natural variation resulting from more subtle changes in function or expression, studies of natural variation offer an opportunity to identify new regulators with ecological relevance in wild populations. This strategy identifies multiple QTL and their relative contribution to dormancy based on mapping and cosegregation analysis of progeny from crosses between accessions differing in dormancy characteristics. This approach has been applied to *Arabidopsis* (3, 37, 180) and a variety of crops (4, 60, 73, 76, 137, 170).

Many of the dormancy QTLs identified in *Arabidopsis* using multiple recombinant inbred lines (RILs) populations colocalize. Fourteen QTLs identified from a cross of weakly dormant L*er* and Columbia (Col) include overlaps with four from a cross between L*er* and stress-tolerant Shakdara (Sha) and seven from a cross between L*er* and the highly dormant Cvi (3, 37, 180), indicating surprisingly few loci account for much natural variation. Genetic interactions were observed between some QTLs, and several QTLs altered additional seed characteristics including longevity, sugar content, and stress tolerance.

The Ler/Cvi QTLs were introgressed into the Ler background to permit fine-mapping of individual *DELAY OF GERMINATION* (*DOG*) loci in near-isogenic lines (3). Some of these have major effects on dormancy, whereas others can be scored only under certain conditions (11).

Although several of the *Arabidopsis DOG* loci map near known seed trait loci, none have yet been colocalized and only *DOG1* has been cloned (10). This gene is expressed only in seeds, appears to be essential and specific for dormancy, and requires ABA for its action, but encodes four alternatively spliced transcripts that encode proteins of unknown function, so its mechanism of action is still unknown. Comparison of the *DOG1* locus among accessions of varying dormancy suggests that the major differences are due to altered expression levels, not specific functional differences in the coding sequence. Although four close homologs are tightly clustered on chromosome 4, none have any obvious effect on dormancy. However, only one homolog (*DOG1L4*) shows a similar expression pattern to *DOG1* (22, 123, 174), and its contributions might be masked by redundancy.

QTL mapping has been used extensively in studies of dormancy and preharvest sprouting in cereal grains. The Gramene QTL Database (**http://www.gramene.org/qtl/index.html**) lists 164 seed dormancy QTLs (qSD, qDOR, or Sdr loci) for rice, representing at least 30 loci identified in a variety of crosses among cultivars or with wild relatives (74, 91, 183). Although several of these are closely linked to loci affecting weedy characteristics such as shattering, awn length, black hull color, and red pericarp color, *qSD12* appeared unlinked and therefore presents a potentially valuable target for modifying dormancy without associated deleterious effects (74). However, no molecular information is yet available for this gene. *Sdr4* was recently cloned and analysis of insertion lines in an *Arabidopsis* homolog indicates that this gene's function in germination is conserved across monocots and dicots (168).

Additional QTLs in barley, wheat, and sorghum have been fine mapped for identification of linked markers for breeding (100) and testing for cosegregation with candidate regulators such as the orthologs of ABA signaling genes (26, 125). Although expression levels of known ABA response loci are sometimes correlated with dormancy state (95, 117, 126), no base pair changes in ABA signaling genes have yet been shown to cosegregate with the dormancy QTLs. Recent studies have tested whether the same loci regulate dormancy in cultivated and wild barley, as a means of possibly identifying loci in the wild relatives that have been lost during domestication (181). However, the molecular identities of the QTLs have not yet been identified.

DOG: delay of germination

-OMICS APPROACHES

Attempts to provide molecular fingerprints for dormancy and germination have used transcriptional profiling to compare seeds exposed to conditions resulting in different states of dormancy (18, 22, 49) and to follow the progression of germination in seeds with varying germination potential (24, 27, 28, 123, 129, 131, 149, 194). These studies have identified gene classes that are enriched in dormant versus nondormant seeds, as well as classes that are variably expressed in both states (22, 49). They have also shown that expression of these classes is more tightly correlated with the depth of dormancy than environmental conditions, suggesting that the diverse signals regulating dormancy are integrated through some common mechanisms. Profiling of germinating seeds has shown that: (*a*) major changes in gene expression occur between 1 and 3 h after imbibition of *Arabidopsis* seeds (149); (*b*) genes that are highly expressed in seeds and rapidly downregulated and/or classified as GA-repressed are enriched for ABREs in their promoters (123, 131); and (*c*) only half of the GA-regulated genes are regulated by the DELLA class repressors and these include a significant number of genes involved in responses to ABA, auxin, or ethylene (24). Surprisingly, although DELLA proteins repress GA-inducible gene expression, direct targets identified by chromatin immunoprecipitation experiments with a stabilized DELLA protein are mostly upregulated, suggesting that DELLA repression is mediated by the induction of downstream repressors (193).

Most dormancy-enriched transcripts are present in both the dry and imbibed states, and overlap significantly with ABA- and stress-regulated transcriptomes (22). Specifically, gene expression in dormant *Arabidopsis* seeds is enriched for those involved in ABA synthesis, GA catabolism, and stress response [e.g., LEAs and small heat shock proteins (sHSPs)], and repressed for translation capacity. Profiling by cDNA-amplified fragment length polymorphism (AFLP) analysis in *N. plumbaginifolia* provided a more limited view than microarray analyses, but also showed a correlation between dormancy, ABA synthesis, repression of protein synthesis, and enhanced cell rescue/defense and transport facilitation (18). The *Arabidopsis* studies also identified 30 genes that show higher expression in all dormant states than in after-ripened states, making these genes strong candidate regulators of dormancy (49). These candidates include protein kinases and phosphatases, transcription factors, and six genes of unknown function, including *DOG1*.

Despite these similarities among dormant states, the transcriptome changes significantly in seeds transitioning from primary to secondary dormancy. Genes of the metabolism and energy group showed particularly high variability, with 84 genes specific to distinct dormant states. Several transcription factors and regulators of the cell cycle and DNA processing also show increases in expression during secondary dormancy (22).

Both dormant and nondormant states differentially express many genes in the metabolism and transcription regulation classes. The state-specific expression of select transcription factors, histones, and histone-modifying enzymes suggests that a global change in chromatin structure may be associated with the dissimilar expression programs of dormant and nondormant seeds (22).

Classes of genes correlated with nondormancy include those involved in cell organization and biogenesis, proteolysis (essential for reserve mobilization), and many protein synthesis factors, such as ribosomal proteins and initiation and elongation factors (18, 22), consistent with the essential role of translation in radicle emergence during germination (151). Changes in hormone metabolism are also correlated with increased expression of specific family members required for ABA catabolism (CYP707A2) and GA synthesis (GA3ox2) (22).

Radicle emergence requires both decreased mechanical resistance of the covering tissues and increased internal force from embryo expansion. Tomato germination is correlated with GA-induced mRNA expression of enzymes involved in breakdown of the endosperm cap at the micropylar end, including the germination-specific endo-β-mannanase gene *LeMAN2* and the xyloglucan endotransglycosylase/hydrolase gene *LeXET4* (31, 130, 165). During *Arabidopsis* germination, GA induces the expression of genes involved in the induction of cell division and cell wall expansion and modification, such as xyloglucan endotransferase/hydrolases (XTH), expansins, and pectin methylesterases (131). Expansins and XTH enzymes are believed to stimulate cell elongation by loosening cell walls. *AtXTH5* (131) and *LeEXP8* (30) are both expressed prior to germination in the cortex of the embryonic axis, which suggests that they may promote cell wall expansion in the embryonic axis leading to radicle emergence. Similarly, *Arabidopsis* genes involved in cell wall modification are enriched in after-ripened states compared with dormant seeds (22).

Partial release of dormancy, by short after-ripening and imbibition under conditions that do not allow germination, affects expression of the same gene groups as full release, but the extent of upregulation and downregulation is intermediate between the levels in dormant and nondormant seeds (49), showing that the regulation of dormancy is not a simple on/off switch. Further evidence for this continuum is provided by comparisons of fresh versus after-ripened seeds, which indicated that even nondormant mutants (due to ABA deficiency or insensitivity) undergo after-ripening, reflected in changes in levels of thousands of transcripts (27). However, this study compared transcripts in 24 h imbibed seeds, so whether the observed changes truly reflect after-ripening or the rapid changes occurring upon imbibition is unclear.

In contrast to the comprehensive datasets available with microarrays, proteomic studies characterize only the most abundant proteins that differ in dormant versus nondormant seeds, i.e., only ~5% as many gene products as assayed by microarrays. However, proteomic studies reflect posttranscriptional effects and may give a more accurate view of cellular metabolic and developmental potential. During dormancy breaking in beech seeds, which requires three months of cold stratification, the translation elongation factor Tu is upregulated, as are several chaperones and energy/metabolism-related proteins. In contrast, delay of dormancy release by ABA treatment is associated with the downregulation of specific translation elongation and initiation factors (141), consistent with transcriptome studies suggesting that dormancy regulates translation capacity. However, measurements of ^{35}S-methionine incorporation indicate that protein translation occurs at similar rates in dormant and nondormant imbibed *Arabidopsis* Cvi seeds, but the identities of the de novo synthesized proteins differ significantly (32). This study also showed that although ABA prevents germination in nondormant seeds, it does not inhibit protein synthesis. Furthermore, the proteomes of truly dormant and ABA-treated nondormant seeds are significantly different, consistent with recent comparisons showing that transcriptomes of ABA-treated after-ripened seeds are more similar to those of untreated after-ripened seeds than those of dormant seeds (27). Finally, only one of the differentially regulated genes identified in *Arabidopsis* Cvi transcriptome studies showed comparable differential expression at the protein level, leaving open the possibility that (post) translational regulation plays a key role in dormancy and dormancy release.

SUMMARY POINTS

1. Potential "dormancy genes" have been identified through correlations between dormancy state and expression levels or gene function, based on mutant or quantitative trait loci (QTL) analysis. Although some potential regulators correlate in both expression and function [e.g., DELAY OF GERMINATION 1 (DOG1)], many "dormancy genes" identified by correlation are not required for dormancy per se (e.g., stress-induced genes) and some dormancy-regulating genes are not expressed in seeds [e.g., DOF (DNA-binding with one zinc finger) AFFECTING GERMINATION (DAG) 1 and 2]. Furthermore, correlations in expression are observed for factors that antagonize each other as well as for those that promote the same process.
2. QTL mapping has identified at least a dozen loci in each species analyzed that contribute to natural variation in dormancy. Classical and reverse genetic studies have identified many more loci that can modify dormancy or hormone sensitivity affecting germination.
3. Abscisic acid (ABA) is the major hormone involved in induction and maintenance of dormancy, but not all mediators of ABA response control dormancy and some

dormancy regulation is ABA-independent, e.g., that due to testa structure or pigmentation. Furthermore, ABA inhibition of germination in nondormant seeds does not phenocopy dormancy at the transcriptome or proteome level.

4. Increased gibberellin (GA) levels and sensitivity are implicated in dormancy release, and are especially important for subsequent germination and seedling growth via effects on softening of restrictive tissues and promoting reserve mobilization. DELLA repressors of GA signaling are stabilized by ABA and phosphorylation, and destabilized by O-Glc-NAc modification and GA. GA perception leads to proteasomal degradation of DELLA proteins.
5. ABA and GA levels are regulated by the balance of synthesis and catabolism due to environmentally regulated expression of specific isozymes, which sometimes requires transport of intermediates between tissues. Regulation by ethylene, brassinosteroids, reactive oxygen species, and nitric oxide or nitrate are partly mediated by effects on the ABA:GA balance, but the latter four also have independent effects.
6. Transitions between various states of dormancy are active processes that involve changes in gene expression even in dry after-ripening seeds. The expression of dormancy-associated genes correlates quantitatively with depth of dormancy.
7. Comparison of dormant versus nondormant transcriptomes and proteomes indicates regulation at multiple levels (e.g., transcript accumulation, translation, protein stability, and modifications affecting activity).

FUTURE ISSUES

1. Functional testing of the role in dormancy for loci identified as showing tightest correlations between expression and dormancy state is required.
2. Cloning of additional QTLs and comparative analyses across species to identify conserved versus novel mechanisms of dormancy regulation is necessary.
3. The timing of requirement for GA synthesis or action in after-ripening versus stratification should be clarified.
4. Researchers should distinguish between the role of ABA signaling loci in ABA response versus dormancy.

DISCLOSURE STATEMENT

The authors are not aware of any biases that might be perceived as affecting the objectivity of this review.

ACKNOWLEDGMENTS

We thank T. Lynch for critical review of the manuscript. W.R. was supported by NSF grant #IBN-0446048 to R.R.F. and T.A. was supported by USDA CSREES Grant #2005–01099 and USDA-Agricultural Research Service funds to C.M.S.

LITERATURE CITED

1. Alboresi A, Gestin C, Leydecker MT, Bedu M, Meyer C, Truong HN. 2005. Nitrate, a signal relieving seed dormancy in *Arabidopsis*. *Plant Cell Environ.* 28:500–12
2. Ali-Rachedi S, Bouinot D, Wagner MH, Bonnet M, Sotta B, et al. 2004. Changes in endogenous abscisic acid levels during dormancy release and maintenance of mature seeds: studies with the Cape Verde Islands ecotype, the dormant model of *Arabidopsis thaliana*. *Planta* 219:479–88
3. Alonso-Blanco C, Bentsink L, Hanhart CJ, Blankestijn-de Vries H, Koornneef M. 2003. Analysis of natural allelic variation at seed dormancy loci of *Arabidopsis thaliana*. *Genetics* 164:711–29
4. Argyris J, Truco MJ, Ochoa O, Knapp SJ, Still DW, et al. 2005. Quantitative trait loci associated with seed and seedling traits in *Lactuca*. *Theor. Appl. Genet.* 111:1365–76
5. Ariizumi T, Steber CM. 2007. Seed germination of GA-insensitive *sleepy1* mutants does not require RGL2 protein disappearance in *Arabidopsis*. *Plant Cell* 19:791–804
6. Bailly C. 2004. Active oxygen species and antioxidants in seed biology. *Seed Sci. Res.* 14:93–107
7. Bassel GW, Zielinska E, Mullen RT, Bewley JD. 2004. Down-regulation of DELLA genes is not essential for germination in tomato, soybean, and *Arabidopsis* seeds. *Plant Physiol.* 136:2782–89
8. Baumbusch LO, Hughes DW, Galau GA, Jakobsen KS. 2004. *LEC1*, *FUS3*, *ABI3* and *Em* expression reveals no correlation with dormancy in *Arabidopsis*. *J. Exp. Bot.* 55:77–87
9. Beaudoin N, Serizet C, Gosti F, Giraudat J. 2000. Interactions between abscisic acid and ethylene signaling cascades. *Plant Cell* 12:1103–15
10. Bentsink L, Jowett J, Hanhart CJ, Koornneef M. 2006. Cloning of *DOG1*, a quantitative trait locus controlling seed dormancy in *Arabidopsis*. *Proc. Natl. Acad. Sci. USA* 103:17042–47
11. Bentsink L, Soppe W, Koornneef M. 2007. Genetic aspects of seed dormancy. See Ref. 20, pp. 113–32
12. Berjak P. 2006. Unifying perspectives of some mechanisms basic to desiccation tolerance across life forms. *Seed Sci. Res.* 16:1–15
13. Bethke PC, Badger MR, Jones RL. 2004. Apoplastic synthesis of nitric oxide by plant tissues. *Plant Cell* 16:332–41
14. Bethke PC, Libourel IG, Aoyama N, Chung YY, Still DW, Jones RL. 2007. The *Arabidopsis* aleurone layer responds to nitric oxide, gibberellin, and abscisic acid and is sufficient and necessary for seed dormancy. *Plant Physiol.* 143:1173–88
15. Bethke PC, Libourel IG, Jones RL. 2007. Nitric oxide in seed dormancy and germination. See Ref. 20, pp. 153–75
16. Bewley JD. 1997. Seed germination and dormancy. *Plant Cell* 9:1055–66
17. Bewley JD, Black M. 1994. *Seeds: Physiology of Development and Germination*. New York: Plenum. 367 pp.
18. Bove J, Lucas P, Godin B, Oge L, Jullien M, Grappin P. 2005. Gene expression analysis by cDNA-AFLP highlights a set of new signaling networks and translational control during seed dormancy breaking in *Nicotiana plumbaginifolia*. *Plant Mol. Biol.* 57:593–612
19. Bradford KJ, Downie AB, Gee OH, Alvarado V, Yang H, Dahal P. 2003. Abscisic acid and gibberellin differentially regulate expression of genes of the SNF1-related kinase complex in tomato seeds. *Plant Physiol.* 132:1560–76
20. Bradford KJ, Nonogaki H, eds. 2007. *Seed Development, Dormancy and Germination*. Oxford: Blackwell

21. Brady S, Sarkar S, Bonetta D, McCourt P. 2003. The *ABSCISIC ACID INSENSITIVE 3* (*ABI3*) gene is modulated by farnesylation and is involved in auxin signaling and lateral root development in *Arabidopsis*. *Plant J.* 34:67–75
22. Cadman CS, Toorop PE, Hilhorst HW, Finch-Savage WE. 2006. Gene expression profiles of *Arabidopsis* Cvi seeds during dormancy cycling indicate a common underlying dormancy control mechanism. *Plant J.* 46:805–22
23. Cairns NG, Pasternak M, Wachter A, Cobbett CS, Meyer AJ. 2006. Maturation of *Arabidopsis* seeds is dependent on glutathione biosynthesis within the embryo. *Plant Physiol.* 141:446–55
24. Cao D, Cheng H, Wu W, Soo HM, Peng J. 2006. Gibberellin mobilizes distinct DELLA-dependent transcriptomes to regulate seed germination and floral development in *Arabidopsis*. *Plant Physiol.* 142:509–25
25. Cao DN, Hussain A, Cheng H, Peng JR. 2005. Loss of function of four DELLA genes leads to light- and gibberellin-independent seed germination in *Arabidopsis*. *Planta* 223:105–13
26. Carrari F, Perez-Flores L, Lijavetzky D, Enciso S, Sánchez RA, et al. 2001. Cloning and expression of a sorghum gene with homology to maize Vp1. Its potential involvement in preharvest sprouting resistance. *Plant Mol. Biol.* 45:631–40
27. Carrera E, Holman T, Medhurst A, Dietrich D, Footitt S, et al. 2007. Seed after-ripening is a discrete developmental pathway associated with specific gene networks in Arabidopsis. *Plant J.* doi:10.1111/j.1365-313X.2007.03331.x
28. Carrera E, Holman T, Medhurst A, Peer W, Schmuths H, et al. 2007. Gene expression profiling reveals defined functions of the ATP-binding cassette transporter COMATOSE late in phase II of germination. *Plant Physiol.* 143:1669–79
29. Chae MJ, Lee JS, Nam MH, Cho K, Hong JY, et al. 2007. A rice dehydration-inducible SNF1-related protein kinase 2 phosphorylates an abscisic acid responsive element-binding factor and associates with ABA signaling. *Plant Mol. Biol.* 63:151–69
30. Chen F, Dahal P, Bradford KJ. 2001. Two tomato expansin genes show divergent expression and localization in embryos during seed development and germination. *Plant Physiol.* 127:928–36
31. Chen F, Nonogaki H, Bradford KJ. 2002. A gibberellin-regulated xyloglucan endotransglycosylase gene is expressed in the endosperm cap during tomato seed germination. *J. Exp. Bot.* 53:215–23
32. Chibani K, Ali-Rachedi S, Job C, Job D, Jullien M, Grappin P. 2006. Proteomic analysis of seed dormancy in *Arabidopsis*. *Plant Physiol.* 142:1493–510
33. Chiwocha SD, Cutler AJ, Abrams SR, Ambrose SJ, Yang J, et al. 2005. The *etr1-2* mutation in *Arabidopsis thaliana* affects the abscisic acid, auxin, cytokinin and gibberellin metabolic pathways during maintenance of seed dormancy, moist-chilling and germination. *Plant J.* 42:35–48
34. Choi HI, Park HJ, Park JH, Kim S, Im MY, et al. 2005. *Arabidopsis* calcium-dependent protein kinase AtCPK32 interacts with ABF4, a transcriptional regulator of abscisic acid-responsive gene expression, and modulates its activity. *Plant Physiol.* 139:1750–61
35. Christmann A, Moes D, Himmelbach A, Yang Y, Tang Y, Grill E. 2006. Integration of abscisic acid signalling into plant responses. *Plant Biol.* 8:314–25
36. Clerkx EJM, Blankestijn-de Vries H, Ruys GJ, Groot SPC, Koornneef M. 2003. Characterization of *green seed*, an enhancer of *abi3-1* in *Arabidopsis* that affects seed longevity. *Plant Physiol.* 132:1077–84

37. Clerkx EJM, El-Lithy ME, Vierling E, Ruys GJ, Blankestijin-de Vries H, et al. 2004. Analysis of natural allelic variation of *Arabidopsis* seed germination and seed longevity traits between the accessions Landsberg *erecta* and Shakdara, using a new recombinant inbred line population. *Plant Physiol.* 135:432–43
38. Clouse S. 2001. Brassinosteroids. *Curr. Biol.* 11:R904
39. Clouse SD, Sasse JM. 1998. Brassinosteroids: Essential regulators of plant growth and development. *Annu. Rev. Plant Physiol. Plant Mol. Biol.* 49:427–51
40. Colucci G, Apone F, Alyeshmerni N, Chalmers D, Chrispeels M. 2002. *GCR1*, the putative *Arabidopsis* G protein-coupled receptor gene is cell cycle-regulated, and its overexpression abolishes seed dormancy and shortens time to flowering. *Proc. Natl. Acad. Sci. USA* 99:4736–41
41. Corpas FJ, Barroso JB, del Rio LA. 2001. Peroxisomes as a source of reactive oxygen species and nitric oxide signal molecules in plant cells. *Trends Plant Sci.* 6:145–50
42. Crawford NM, Galli M, Tischner R, Heimer YM, Okamoto M, Mack A. 2006. Response to Zemojtel et al. Plant nitric oxide synthase: back to square one. *Trends Plant Sci.* 11:526–27
43. Cutler S, Ghassemian M, Bonetta D, Cooney S, McCourt P. 1996. A protein farnesyl transferase involved in abscisic acid signal transduction in *Arabidopsis*. *Science* 273:1239–41
44. Debeaujon I, Lepiniec L, Pourcel L, Routaboul J-M. 2007. Seed coat development and dormancy. See Ref. 20, pp. 25–49
45. Derkx MPM, Karssen CM. 1993. Effects of light and temperature on seed dormancy and gibberellin-stimulated germination in *Arabidopsis thaliana*: studies with gibberellin-deficient and -insensitive mutants. *Physiol. Plant.* 89:360–68
46. Derkx MPM, Vermeer E, Karssen CM. 1994. Gibberellins in seeds of *Arabidopsis thaliana*: biological activities, identification, and effect of light and chilling on endogenous levels. *Plant Growth Regul.* 15:223–34
47. Dill A, Thomas SG, Hu J, Steber CM, Sun TP. 2004. The *Arabidopsis* F-box protein SLEEPY1 targets gibberellin signaling repressors for gibberellin-induced degradation. *Plant Cell* 16:1392–405
48. Feurtado J, Kermode A. 2007. A merging of paths: abscisic acid and hormonal cross-talk in the control of seed dormancy maintenance and alleviation. See Ref. 20, pp. 176–223
49. Finch-Savage WE, Cadman CS, Toorop PE, Lynn JR, Hilhorst HW. 2007. Seed dormancy release in *Arabidopsis* Cvi by dry after-ripening, low temperature, nitrate and light shows common quantitative patterns of gene expression directed by environmentally specific sensing. *Plant J.* 51:60–78
50. Finch-Savage WE, Leubner-Metzger G. 2006. Seed dormancy and the control of germination. *New Phytol.* 171:501–23
51. Finkelstein R, Gampala S, Rock C. 2002. Abscisic acid signaling in seeds and seedlings. *Plant Cell* 14:S15–45
52. Flematti GR, Ghisalberti EL, Dixon KW, Trengove RD. 2004. A compound from smoke that promotes seed germination. *Science* 305:977
53. Flintham JE. 2000. Different genetic components control coat-imposed and embryo-imposed dormancy in wheat. *Seed Sci. Res.* 10:43–50
54. Footitt S, Marquez J, Schmuths H, Baker A, Theodoulou FL, Holdsworth M. 2006. Analysis of the role of *COMATOSE* and peroxisomal beta-oxidation in the determination of germination potential in *Arabidopsis*. *J. Exp. Bot.* 57:2805–14
55. Footitt S, Slocombe SP, Larner V, Kurup S, Wu Y, et al. 2002. Control of germination and lipid mobilization by COMATOSE, the *Arabidopsis* homologue of human ALDP. *EMBO J.* 21:2912–22

56. Fu X, Richards DE, Fleck B, Xie D, Burton N, Harberd NP. 2004. The *Arabidopsis* mutant sleepy1^{gar2-1} protein promotes plant growth by increasing the affinity of the SCF^{SLY1} E3 ubiquitin ligase for DELLA protein substrates. *Plant Cell* 16:1406–18
57. Fujii H, Verslues PE, Zhu JK. 2007. Identification of two protein kinases required for abscisic acid regulation of seed germination, root growth, and gene expression in *Arabidopsis*. *Plant Cell* 19:485–94
58. Fulda M, Schnurr J, Abbadi A, Heinz E, Browse J. 2004. Peroxisomal Acyl-CoA synthetase activity is essential for seedling development in *Arabidopsis thaliana*. *Plant Cell* 16:394–405
59. Furihata T, Maruyama K, Fujita Y, Umezawa T, Yoshida R, et al. 2006. Abscisic acid-dependent multisite phosphorylation regulates the activity of a transcription activator AREB1. *Proc. Natl. Acad. Sci. USA* 103:1988–93
60. Gale MD, Flintham JE, Devos KM. 2002. Cereal comparative genetics and preharvest sprouting. *Euphytica* 126:21–25
61. Galichet A, Gruissem W. 2003. Protein farnesylation in plants—conserved mechanisms but different targets. *Curr. Opin. Plant Biol.* 6:530–35
62. Gazzarrini S, Tsuchiya Y, Lumba S, Okamoto M, McCourt P. 2004. The transcription factor FUSCA3 controls developmental timing in *Arabidopsis* through the hormones gibberellin and abscisic acid. *Dev. Cell* 7:373–85
63. Geyer R, Koornneef M, Soppe W. 2007. A mutation in a TFIIS transcription elongation factor causes reduced seed dormancy in *Arabidopsis*. In *2nd Int. Soc. Seed Sci. (ISSS) Workshop on Molecular Aspects of Seed Dormancy and Germination, Salamanca, Spain*
64. Ghassemian M, Nambara E, Cutler S, Kawaide H, Kamiya Y, McCourt P. 2000. Regulation of abscisic acid signaling by the ethylene response pathway in *Arabidopsis*. *Plant Cell* 12:1117–26
65. Goda H, Shimada Y, Asami T, Fujioka S, Yoshida S. 2002. Microarray analysis of brassinosteroid-regulated genes in *Arabidopsis*. *Plant Physiol.* 130:1319–34
66. Goepfert S, Poirier Y. 2007. β-oxidation in fatty acid degradation and beyond. *Curr. Opin. Plant Biol.* 10:245–51
67. Gomez-Cadenas A, Verhey SD, Holappa LD, Shen Q, Ho T-HD, Walker-Simmons MK. 1999. An abscisic acid-induced protein kinase, PKABA1, mediates abscisic acid-suppressed gene expression in barley aleurone layers. *Proc. Natl. Acad. Sci. USA* 96:1767–72
68. Gomez-Cadenas A, Zentella R, Walker-Simmons MK, Ho T-HD. 2001. Gibberellin/abscisic acid antagonism in barley aleurone cells: Site of action of the protein kinase PKABA1 in relation to gibberellin signaling molecules. *Plant Cell* 13:667–79
69. González-García MP, Rodríguez D, Nicolás C, Rodríguez PL, Nicolás G, Lorenzo O. 2003. Negative regulation of abscisic acid signaling by the *Fagus sylvatica* FsPP2C1 plays a role in seed dormancy regulation and promotion of seed germination. *Plant Physiol* 133:135–44
70. Grappin P, Bouinot D, Sotta B, Miginiac E, Jullien M. 2000. Control of seed dormancy in *Nicotiana plumbaginifolia*: Post-imbibition abscisic acid synthesis imposes dormancy maintenance. *Planta* 210:279–85
71. Griffiths J, Murase K, Rieu I, Zentella R, Zhang ZL, et al. 2006. Genetic characterization and functional analysis of the GID1 gibberellin receptors in *Arabidopsis*. *Plant Cell* 18:3399–414
72. Groos C, Gay G, Perretant MR, Gervais L, Bernard M, et al. 2002. Study of the relationship between preharvest sprouting and grain color by quantitative trait loci analysis in a white × red grain bread-wheat cross. *Theor. Appl. Genet.* 104:39–47

73. Gu XY, Kianian SF, Foley ME. 2006. Dormancy genes from weedy rice respond divergently to seed development environments. *Genetics* 172:1199–211
74. Gu XY, Kianian SF, Hareland GA, Hoffer BL, Foley ME. 2005. Genetic analysis of adaptive syndromes interrelated with seed dormancy in weedy rice (*Oryza sativa*). *Theor. Appl. Genet.* 110:1108–18
75. Gualberti G, Papi M, Bellucci L, Ricci I, Bouchez D, et al. 2002. Mutations in the Dof zinc finger genes *DAG2* and *DAG1* influence with opposite effects the germination of *Arabidopsis* seeds. *Plant Cell* 14:1253–63
76. Gubler F, Millar AA, Jacobsen JV. 2005. Dormancy release, ABA and preharvest sprouting. *Curr. Opin. Plant Biol.* 8:183–87
77. Guo Y, Xiong L, Song CP, Gong D, Halfter U, Zhu JK. 2002. A calcium sensor and its interacting protein kinase are global regulators of abscisic acid signaling in *Arabidopsis*. *Dev. Cell* 3:233–44
78. Gutierrez L, Van Wuytswinkel O, Castelain M, Bellini C. 2007. Combined networks regulating seed maturation. *Trends Plant Sci.* 12:294–300
79. Haslekås C, Stacy RA, Nygaard V, Culiánez-Macià FA, Aalen RB. 1998. The expression of a peroxiredoxin antioxidant gene, *AtPer1*, in *Arabidopsis thaliana* is seed-specific and related to dormancy. *Plant Mol. Biol.* 36:833–45
80. Haslekås C, Viken MK, Grini PE, Nygaard V, Nordgard SH, et al. 2003. Seed 1-cysteine peroxiredoxin antioxidants are not involved in dormancy, but contribute to inhibition of germination during stress. *Plant Physiol.* 133:1148–57
81. Henderson JT, Li HC, Rider SD, Mordhorst AP, Romero-Severson J, et al. 2004. PICKLE acts throughout the plant to repress expression of embryonic traits and may play a role in gibberellin-dependent responses. *Plant Physiol.* 134:995–1005
82. Hilhorst HWM. 2007. Definitions and hypotheses of seed dormancy. See Ref. 20, pp. 50–71
83. Himmelbach A, Hoffmann T, Leube M, Hohener B, Grill E. 2002. Homeodomain protein ATHB6 is a target of the protein phosphatase ABI1 and regulates hormone responses in *Arabidopsis*. *EMBO J.* 21:3029–38
84. Hirayama T, Shinozaki K. 2007. Perception and transduction of abscisic acid signals: keys to the function of the versatile plant hormone ABA. *Trends Plant Sci.* 12:343–51
85. Hussain A, Cao D, Cheng H, Wen Z, Peng J. 2005. Identification of the conserved serine/threonine residues important for gibberellin-sensitivity of *Arabidopsis* RGL2 protein. *Plant J.* 44:88–99
86. Hussain A, Cao D, Peng J. 2007. Identification of conserved tyrosine residues important for gibberellin sensitivity of *Arabidopsis* RGL2 protein. *Planta* 226:475–83
87. Iuchi S, Suzuki H, Kim YC, Iuchi A, Kuromori T, et al. 2007. Multiple loss-of-function of *Arabidopsis* gibberellin receptor AtGID1s completely shuts down a gibberellin signal. *Plant J.* 50:958–66
88. Jacobsen JV, Pearce DW, Poole AT, Pharis RP, Mander LN. 2002. Abscisic acid, phaseic acid and gibberellin contents associated with dormancy and germination in barley. *Physiol. Plant.* 115:428–41
89. Jacobsen SE, Olszewski NE. 1993. Mutations at the *SPINDLY* locus of Arabidopsis alter gibberellin signal transduction. *Plant Cell* 5:887–96
90. Ji HS, Chu SH, Jiang W, Cho YI, Hahn JH, et al. 2006. Characterization and mapping of a shattering mutant in rice that corresponds to a block of domestication genes. *Genetics* 173:995–1005

91. Jiang L, Liu SJ, Hou MY, Tang JY, Chen LM, et al. 2006. Analysis of QTLs for seed low temperature germinability and anoxia germinability in rice (*Oryza sativa* L.). *Field Crops Res.* 98:68–75
92. Jimenez JA, Rodriguez D, Lorenzo O, Nicolas G, Nicolas C. 2006. Characterization of a protein kinase (FsPK4) with an acidic domain, regulated by abscisic acid and specifically located in *Fagus sylvatica* L. seeds. *J. Plant Physiol.* 163:761–69
93. Job C, Rajjou L, Lovigny Y, Belghazi M, Job D. 2005. Patterns of protein oxidation in *Arabidopsis* seeds and during germination. *Plant Physiol.* 138:790–802
94. Johnson RR, Wagner RL, Verhey SD, Walker-Simmons MK. 2002. The abscisic acid-responsive kinase PKABA1 interacts with a seed-specific abscisic acid response element-binding factor, TaABF, and phosphorylates TaABF peptide sequences. *Plant Physiol.* 130:837–46
95. Jones HD, Peters NCB, Holdsworth MJ. 1997. Genotype and environment interact to control dormancy and differential expression of the *VIVIPAROUS 1* homologue in embryos of *Avena fatua*. *Plant J.* 12:911–20
96. Keeley JE, Fotheringham CJ. 1998. Smoke-induced seed germination in California chaparral. *Ecology* 79:2320–36
97. Kermode AR. 2005. Role of abscisic acid in seed dormancy. *J. Plant Growth Regul.* 24:319–44
98. Kobayashi Y, Murata M, Minami H, Yamamoto S, Kagaya Y, et al. 2005. Abscisic acid-activated SNRK2 protein kinases function in the gene-regulation pathway of ABA signal transduction by phosphorylating ABA response element-binding factors. *Plant J.* 44:939–49
99. Koornneef M, Reuling G, Karssen C. 1984. The isolation and characterization of abscisic acid-insensitive mutants of *Arabidopsis thaliana*. *Physiol. Plant.* 61:377–83
100. Kottearachchi NS, Uchino N, Kato K, Miura H. 2006. Increased grain dormancy in white-grained wheat by introgression of preharvest sprouting tolerance QTLs. *Euphytica* 152:421–28
101. Kuhn J, Schroeder J. 2003. Impacts of altered RNA metabolism on abscisic acid signaling. *Curr. Opin. Plant Biol.* 6:463–69
102. Kwak JM, Moon J-H, Murata Y, Kuchitsu K, Leonhardt N, et al. 2002. Disruption of a guard cell-expressed protein phosphatase 2A regulatory subunit, RCN1, confers abscisic acid insensitivity in *Arabidopsis*. *Plant Cell* 14:2849–61
103. Le Page-Degivry MT, Garello G. 1992. In situ abscisic acid synthesis: A requirement for induction of embryo dormancy in *Helianthus annuus*. *Plant Physiol.* 98:1386–90
104. Lee S, Cheng H, King KE, Wang W, He Y, et al. 2002. Gibberellin regulates *Arabidopsis* seed germination via *RGL2*, a *GAI/RGA*-like gene whose expression is up-regulated following imbibition. *Genes Dev.* 16:646–58
105. Lefebvre V, North H, Frey A, Sotta B, Seo M, et al. 2006. Functional analysis of *Arabidopsis NCED6* and *NCED9* genes indicates that ABA synthesized in the endosperm is involved in the induction of seed dormancy. *Plant J.* 45:309–19
106. Lepiniec L, Debeaujon I, Routaboul J-M, Baudry A, Pourcel L, et al. 2006. Genetics and biochemistry of seed flavonoids. *Annu. Rev. Plant Biol.* 57:405–30
107. Leubner-Metzger G. 2001. Brassinosteroids and gibberellins promote tobacco seed germination by distinct pathways. *Planta* 213:758–63
108. Leubner-Metzger G. 2005. β-1,3-Glucanase gene expression in low-hydrated seeds as a mechanism for dormancy release during tobacco after-ripening. *Plant J.* 41:133–45
109. Li B, Foley ME. 1996. Transcriptional and posttranscriptional regulation of dormancy-associated gene expression by afterripening in wild oat. *Plant Physiol.* 110:1267–73

110. Lin PC, Hwang SG, Endo A, Okamoto M, Koshiba T, Cheng WH. 2007. Ectopic expression of *ABSCISIC ACID 2/GLUCOSE INSENSITIVE 1* in *Arabidopsis* promotes seed dormancy and stress tolerance. *Plant Physiol.* 143:745–58
111. Liu PP, Koizuka N, Martin RC, Nonogaki H. 2005. The BME3 (Blue Micropylar End 3) GATA zinc finger transcription factor is a positive regulator of *Arabidopsis* seed germination. *Plant J.* 44:960–71
112. Liu X, Yue Y, Li B, Nie Y, Li W, et al. 2007. A G protein-coupled receptor is a plasma membrane receptor for the plant hormone abscisic acid. *Science* 315:1712–16
113. Liu Y, Koornneef M, Soppe WJ. 2007. The absence of histone H2B monoubiquitination in the *Arabidopsis hub1* (*rdo4*) mutant reveals a role for chromatin remodeling in seed dormancy. *Plant Cell* 19:433–44
114. Lopez-Molina L, Mongrand S, Kinoshita N, Chua N-H. 2003. AFP is a novel negative regulator of ABA signaling that promotes ABI5 protein degradation. *Genes Dev.* 17:410–18
115. Lu C, Han M-H, Guevara-Garcia A, Fedoroff N. 2002. Mitogen-activated protein kinase signaling in postgermination arrest of development by abscisic acid. *Proc. Natl. Acad. Sci. USA* 99:15812–17
116. McGinnis K, Thomas S, Soule J, Strader L, Zale J, et al. 2003. The *Arabidopsis SLEEPY1* gene encodes a putative F-box subunit of an SCF E3 ubiquitin ligase. *Plant Cell* 15:1120–30
117. McKibbin RS, Wilkinson MD, Bailey PC, Flintham JE, Andrew LM, et al. 2002. Transcripts of Vp-1 homeologues are misspliced in modern wheat and ancestral species. *Proc. Natl. Acad. Sci. USA* 99:10203–8
118. Meinhard M, Rodriguez PL, Grill E. 2002. The sensitivity of ABI2 to hydrogen peroxide links the abscisic acid-response regulator to redox signalling. *Planta* 214:775–82
119. Merlot S, Gosti F, Guerrier D, Vavasseur A, Giraudat J. 2001. The ABI1 and ABI2 protein phosphatases 2C act in a negative feedback regulatory loop of the abscisic acid signalling pathway. *Plant J.* 25:295–303
120. Miao Y, Lv D, Wang P, Wang XC, Chen J, et al. 2006. An *Arabidopsis* glutathione peroxidase functions as both a redox transducer and a scavenger in abscisic acid and drought stress responses. *Plant Cell* 18:2749–66
121. Millar AA, Jacobsen JV, Ross JJ, Helliwell CA, Poole AT, et al. 2006. Seed dormancy and ABA metabolism in *Arabidopsis* and barley: the role of ABA 8′-hydroxylase. *Plant J.* 45:942–54
122. Mitchum MG, Yamaguchi S, Hanada A, Kuwahara A, Yoshioka Y, et al. 2006. Distinct and overlapping roles of two gibberellin 3-oxidases in *Arabidopsis* development. *Plant J.* 45:804–18
123. Nakabayashi K, Okamoto M, Koshiba T, Kamiya Y, Nambara E. 2005. Genome-wide profiling of stored mRNA in *Arabidopsis thaliana* seed germination: epigenetic and genetic regulation of transcription in seed. *Plant J.* 41:697–709
124. Nakajima M, Shimada A, Takashi Y, Kim YC, Park SH, et al. 2006. Identification and characterization of *Arabidopsis* gibberellin receptors. *Plant J.* 46:880–89
125. Nakamura S, Komatsuda T, Miura H. 2007. Mapping diploid wheat homologues of *Arabidopsis* seed ABA signaling genes and QTLs for seed dormancy. *Theor. Appl. Genet.* 114:1129–39
126. Nakamura S, Toyama T. 2001. Isolation of a VP1 homologue from wheat and analysis of its expression in embryos of dormant and nondormant cultivars. *J. Exp. Bot.* 52:875–76
127. Nambara E, Marion-Poll A. 2003. ABA action and interactions in seeds. *Trends Plant Sci.* 8:213–17

128. Nishimura N, Kitahata N, Seki M, Narusaka Y, Narusaka M, et al. 2005. Analysis of *ABA hypersensitive germination2* revealed the pivotal functions of PARN in stress response in *Arabidopsis*. *Plant J.* 44:972–84
129. Nishimura N, Yoshida T, Kitahata N, Asami T, Shinozaki K, Hirayama T. 2007. *ABA-Hypersensitive Germination1* encodes a protein phosphatase 2C, an essential component of abscisic acid signaling in *Arabidopsis* seed. *Plant J.* 50:935–49
130. Nonogaki H, Gee OH, Bradford KJ. 2000. A germination-specific endo-β-mannanase gene is expressed in the micropylar endosperm cap of tomato seeds. *Plant Physiol.* 123:1235–46
131. Ogawa M, Hanada A, Yamauchi Y, Kuwahara A, Kamiya Y, Yamaguchi S. 2003. Gibberellin biosynthesis and response during *Arabidopsis* seed germination. *Plant Cell* 15:1591–604
132. Oh E, Kim J, Park E, Kim JI, Kang C, Choi G. 2004. PIL5, a phytochrome-interacting basic helix-loop-helix protein, is a key negative regulator of seed germination in *Arabidopsis thaliana*. *Plant Cell* 16:3045–58
133. Oh E, Yamaguchi S, Hu J, Yusuke J, Jung B, et al. 2007. PIL5, a phytochrome-interacting bHLH protein, regulates gibberellin responsiveness by binding directly to the *GAI* and *RGA* promoters in *Arabidopsis* seeds. *Plant Cell* 19:1192–208
134. Oh E, Yamaguchi S, Kamiya Y, Bae G, Chung WI, Choi G. 2006. Light activates the degradation of PIL5 protein to promote seed germination through gibberellin in *Arabidopsis*. *Plant J.* 47:124–39
135. Ohta M, Guo Y, Halfter U, Zhu J-K. 2003. A novel domain in the protein kinase SOS2 mediates interaction with the protein phosphatase 2C ABI2. *Proc. Natl. Acad. Sci. USA* 100:11771–76
136. Okamoto M, Kuwahara A, Seo M, Kushiro T, Asami T, et al. 2006. *CYP707A1* and *CYP707A2*, which encode abscisic acid 8′-hydroxylases, are indispensable for proper control of seed dormancy and germination in *Arabidopsis*. *Plant Physiol.* 141:97–107
137. Osa M, Kato K, Mori M, Shindo C, Torada A, Miura H. 2003. Mapping QTLs for seed dormancy and the *Vp1* homologue on chromosome 3A in wheat. *Theor. Appl. Genet.* 106:1491–96
138. Pandey S, Chen JG, Jones AM, Assmann SM. 2006. G-protein complex mutants are hypersensitive to abscisic acid regulation of germination and postgermination development. *Plant Physiol.* 141:243–56
139. Papi M, Sabatini S, Altamura MM, Hennig L, Schafer E, et al. 2002. Inactivation of the phloem-specific Dof zinc finger gene *DAG1* affects response to light and integrity of the testa of *Arabidopsis* seeds. *Plant Physiol.* 128:411–17
140. Parcy F, Valon C, Raynal M, Gaubier-Comella P, Delseny M, Giraudat J. 1994. Regulation of gene expression programs during *Arabidopsis* seed development: Roles of the *ABI3* locus and of endogenous abscisic acid. *Plant Cell* 6:1567–82
141. Pawlowski TA. 2007. Proteomics of European beech (*Fagus sylvatica* L.) seed dormancy breaking: influence of abscisic and gibberellic acids. *Proteomics* 7:2246–57
142. Peeters AJ, Blankestijn-de Vries H, Hanhart CJ, Leon-Kloosterziel KM, Zeevaart JA, Koornneef M. 2002. Characterization of mutants with reduced seed dormancy at two novel *rdo* loci and a further characterization of *rdo1* and *rdo2* in *Arabidopsis*. *Physiol. Plant.* 115:604–12
143. Penfield S, Gilday AD, Halliday KJ, Graham IA. 2006. DELLA-mediated cotyledon expansion breaks coat-imposed seed dormancy. *Curr. Biol.* 16:2366–70

144. Penfield S, Josse EM, Kannangara R, Gilday AD, Halliday KJ, Graham IA. 2005. Cold and light control seed germination through the bHLH transcription factor SPATULA. *Curr. Biol.* 15:1998–2006
145. Peng J, Richards DE, Hartley NM, Murphy GP, Devos KM, et al. 1999. 'Green revolution' genes encode mutant gibberellin response modulators. *Nature* 400:256–61
146. Pernas M, García-Casado G, Rojo E, Solano R, Sánchez-Serrano JJ. 2007. A protein phosphatase 2A catalytic subunit is a negative regulator of abscisic acid signalling. *Plant J.* 51:763–78
147. Pinfield-Wells H, Rylott EL, Gilday AD, Graham S, Job K, et al. 2005. Sucrose rescues seedling establishment but not germination of *Arabidopsis* mutants disrupted in peroxisomal fatty acid catabolism. *Plant J.* 43:861–72
148. Pracharoenwattana I, Cornah JE, Smith SM. 2005. *Arabidopsis* peroxisomal citrate synthase is required for fatty acid respiration and seed germination. *Plant Cell* 17:2037–48
149. Preston J, Tatematsu K, Kamiya Y, Nambara E. 2007. Studies on early events in response to seed imbibition in *Arabidopsis*. In *2nd Int. Soc. Seed Sci. (ISSS) Workshop on Molecular Aspects of Seed Dormancy and Germination, Salamanca, Spain*
150. Pysh LD, Wysocka-Diller JW, Camilleri C, Bouchez D, Benfey PN. 1999. The *GRAS* gene family in *Arabidopsis*: sequence characterization and basic expression analysis of the *SCARECROW-LIKE* genes. *Plant J.* 18:111–19
151. Rajjou L, Gallardo K, Debeaujon I, Vandekerckhove J, Job C, Job D. 2004. The effect of α-amanitin on the *Arabidopsis* seed proteome highlights the distinct roles of stored and neosynthesized mRNAs during germination. *Plant Physiol.* 134:1598–613
152. Razem FA, El-Kereamy A, Abrams SR, Hill RD. 2006. The RNA-binding protein FCA is an abscisic acid receptor. *Nature* 439:290–94
153. Reyes D, Rodriguez D, Gonzalez-Garcia MP, Lorenzo O, Nicolas G, et al. 2006. Overexpression of a protein phosphatase 2C from beech seeds in *Arabidopsis* shows phenotypes related to abscisic acid responses and gibberellin biosynthesis. *Plant Physiol.* 141:1414–24
154. Rodriguez M, Mendiondo G, Benech-Arnold R. 2007. ABA signaling and GA metabolism in sorghum lines with contrasting seed dormancy. In *2nd Int. Soc. Seed Sci. (ISSS) Workshop on Molecular Aspects of Seed Dormancy and Germination, Salamanca, Spain*
155. Russell L, Larner V, Kurup S, Bougourd S, Holdsworth M. 2000. The *Arabidopsis COMATOSE* locus regulates germination potential. *Development* 127:3759–67
156. Sasaki A, Itoh H, Gomi K, Ueguchi-Tanaka M, Ishiyama K, et al. 2003. Accumulation of phosphorylated repressor for gibberellin signaling in an F-box mutant. *Science* 299:1896–98
157. Schweighofer A, Hirt H, Meskiene I. 2004. Plant PP2C phosphatases: emerging functions in stress signaling. *Trends Plant Sci.* 9:236–43
158. Shen YY, Wang XF, Wu FQ, Du SY, Cao Z, et al. 2006. The Mg-chelatase H subunit is an abscisic acid receptor. *Nature* 443:823–26
159. Shimada A, Ueguchi-Tanaka M, Sakamoto T, Fujioka S, Takatsuto S, et al. 2006. The rice *SPINDLY* gene functions as a negative regulator of gibberellin signaling by controlling the suppressive function of the DELLA protein, SLR1, and modulating brassinosteroid synthesis. *Plant J.* 48:390–402
160. Silverstone AL, Tseng TS, Swain SM, Dill A, Jeong SY, et al. 2007. Functional analysis of SPINDLY in gibberellin signaling in *Arabidopsis*. *Plant Physiol.* 143:987–1000
161. Smalle J, Kurepa J, Yang P, Emborg TJ, Babiychuk E, et al. 2003. The pleiotropic role of the 26S proteasome subunit RPN10 in *Arabidopsis* growth and development supports a substrate-specific function in abscisic acid signaling. *Plant Cell* 15:965–80

162. Stacy RA, Munthe E, Steinum T, Sharma B, Aalen RB. 1996. A peroxiredoxin antioxidant is encoded by a dormancy-related gene, *Per1*, expressed during late development in the aleurone and embryo of barley grains. *Plant Mol. Biol.* 31:1205–16
163. Steber C. 2007. De-repression of seed germination by GA signaling. See Ref. 20, pp. 248–64
164. Steber C, McCourt P. 2001. A role for brassinosteroids in germination in *Arabidopsis*. *Plant Physiol.* 125:763–69
165. Still DW, Bradford KJ. 1997. Endo-β-mannanase activity from individual tomato endosperm caps and radicle tips in relation to germination rates. *Plant Physiol.* 113:21–29
166. Stone SL, Williams LA, Farmer LM, Vierstra RD, Callis J. 2006. KEEP ON GOING, a RING E3 ligase essential for *Arabidopsis* growth and development, is involved in abscisic acid signaling. *Plant Cell* 18:3415–28
167. Strader LC, Ritchie S, Soule JD, McGinnis KM, Steber CM. 2004. Recessive-interfering mutations in the gibberellin signaling gene *SLEEPY1* are rescued by overexpression of its homologue, *SNEEZY*. *Proc. Natl. Acad. Sci. USA* 101:12771–76
168. Sugimoto K, Takeuchi Y, Hirochika H, Yano M. 2007. *Map-based cloning of Sdr4, a quantitative trait locus controlling seed dormancy in rice*. Presented at Plant Anim. Genomes 15th Conf., San Diego, CA
169. Sun TP, Gubler F. 2004. Molecular mechanism of gibberellin signaling in plants. *Annu. Rev. Plant Biol.* 55:197–223
170. Sweeney MT, Thomson MJ, Pfeil BE, McCouch S. 2006. Caught red-handed: *Rc* encodes a basic helix-loop-helix protein conditioning red pericarp in rice. *Plant Cell* 18:283–94
171. Theodoulou FL, Job K, Slocombe SP, Footitt S, Holdsworth M, et al. 2005. Jasmonic acid levels are reduced in COMATOSE ATP-binding cassette transporter mutants. Implications for transport of jasmonate precursors into peroxisomes. *Plant Physiol.* 137:835–40
172. Thomas SG, Rieu I, Steber CM. 2005. Gibberellin metabolism and signaling. *Vitam. Horm.* 72:289–338
173. To A, Valon C, Savino G, Guilleminot J, Devic M, et al. 2006. A network of local and redundant gene regulation governs *Arabidopsis* seed maturation. *Plant Cell* 18:1642–51
174. Toufighi K, Brady SM, Austin R, Ly E, Provart NJ. 2005. The Botany Array Resource: e-Northerns, expression angling, and promoter analyses. *Plant J.* 43:153–63
175. Toyomasu T, Kawaide H, Mitsuhashi W, Inoue Y, Kamiya Y. 1998. Phytochrome regulates gibberellin biosynthesis during germination of photoblastic lettuce seeds. *Plant Physiol.* 118:1517–23
176. Tyler L, Thomas SG, Hu J, Dill A, Alonso JM, et al. 2004. DELLA proteins and gibberellin-regulated seed germination and floral development in *Arabidopsis*. *Plant Physiol.* 135:1008–19
177. Ueguchi-Tanaka M, Ashikari M, Nakajima M, Itoh H, Katoh E, et al. 2005. *GIBBERELLIN INSENSITIVE DWARF1* encodes a soluble receptor for gibberellin. *Nature* 437:693–98
178. Ueguchi-Tanaka M, Nakajima M, Katoh E, Ohmiya H, Asano K, et al. 2007. Molecular interactions of a soluble gibberellin receptor, GID1, with a rice DELLA protein, SLR1, and gibberellin. *Plant Cell* 19:2140–55
179. Ullah H, Chen J-G, Wang S, Jones AM. 2002. Role of a heterotrimeric G protein in regulation of *Arabidopsis* seed germination. *Plant Physiol.* 129:897–907
180. van der Schaar W, Alonso-Blanco C, Léon-Kloosterziel KM, Jansen RC, van Ooijen JW, Koornneef M. 1997. QTL analysis of seed dormancy in *Arabidopsis* using recombinant inbred lines and MQM mapping. *Heredity* 79:190–200

181. Vanhala TK, Stam P. 2006. Quantitative trait loci for seed dormancy in wild barley (*Hordeum spontaneum* c. Koch). *Genet. Res. Crop Evol.* 53:1013–19
182. Walker-Simmons M. 1987. ABA levels and sensitivity in developing wheat embryos of sprouting resistant and susceptible cultivars. *Plant Physiol.* 84:61–66
183. Wan JM, Jiang L, Tang JY, Wang CM, Hou MY, et al. 2006. Genetic dissection of the seed dormancy trait in cultivated rice (*Oryza sativa* L.). *Plant Sci.* 170:786–92
184. Warpeha KM, Upadhyay S, Yeh J, Adamiak J, Hawkins SI, et al. 2007. The GCR1, GPA1, PRN1, NF-Y signal chain mediates both blue light and abscisic acid responses in *Arabidopsis*. *Plant Physiol.* 143:1590–600
185. Willige BC, Ghosh S, Nill C, Zourelidou M, Dohmann EM, et al. 2007. The DELLA domain of GA INSENSITIVE mediates the interaction with the GA INSENSITIVE DWARF1A gibberellin receptor of *Arabidopsis*. *Plant Cell* 19:1209–20
186. Wind M, Reines D. 2000. Transcription elongation factor SII. *BioEssays* 22:327–36
187. Winkel-Shirley B. 2002. Biosynthesis of flavonoids and effects of stress. *Curr. Opin. Plant Biol.* 5:218–23
188. Yamauchi Y, Ogawa M, Kuwahara A, Hanada A, Kamiya Y, Yamaguchi S. 2004. Activation of gibberellin biosynthesis and response pathways by low temperature during imbibition of *Arabidopsis thaliana* seeds. *Plant Cell* 16:367–78
189. Yang Y, Sulpice R, Himmelbach A, Meinhard M, Christmann A, Grill E. 2006. Fibrillin expression is regulated by abscisic acid response regulators and is involved in abscisic acid-mediated photoprotection. *Proc. Natl. Acad. Sci. USA* 103:6061–66
190. Yoshida R, Umezawa T, Mizoguchi T, Takahashi S, Takahashi F, Shinozaki K. 2006. The regulatory domain of SRK2E/OST1/SnRK2.6 interacts with ABI1 and integrates abscisic acid (ABA) and osmotic stress signals controlling stomatal closure in *Arabidopsis*. *J. Biol. Chem.* 281:5310–18
191. Yoshida T, Nishimura N, Kitahata N, Kuromori T, Ito T, et al. 2006. *ABA-hypersensitive germination3* encodes a protein phosphatase 2C (AtPP2CA) that strongly regulates abscisic acid signaling during germination among *Arabidopsis* protein phosphatase 2Cs. *Plant Physiol.* 140:115–26
192. Zeng Q, Wang XJ, Running MP. 2007. Dual lipid modification of *Arabidopsis* Gγ-subunits is required for efficient plasma membrane targeting. *Plant Physiol.* 143:1119–31
193. Zentella R, Zhang Z-L, Park M, Thomas SG, Endo A, et al. 2007. Global analysis of DELLA direct targets in early gibberellin signaling in *Arabidopsis*. *Plant Cell* 19:3037–57
194. Zhang H, Sreenivasulu N, Weschke W, Stein N, Rudd S, et al. 2004. Large-scale analysis of the barley transcriptome based on expressed sequence tags. *Plant J.* 40:276–90
195. Zhang X, Garreton V, Chua N-H. 2005. The AIP2 E3 ligase acts as a novel negative regulator of ABA signaling by promoting ABI3 degradation. *Genes Dev.* 19:1532–43
196. Zhang Y, Yang C, Li Y, Zheng N, Chen H, et al. 2007. SDIR1 is a RING finger E3 ligase that positively regulates stress-responsive abscisic acid signaling in *Arabidopsis*. *Plant Cell* 6:1912–29

Trehalose Metabolism and Signaling

Matthew J. Paul, Lucia F. Primavesi, Deveraj Jhurreea, and Yuhua Zhang

Center for Crop Genetic Improvement, Rothamsted Research, Harpenden, Hertfordshire, AL5 2JQ, United Kingdom; email: matthew.paul@bbsrc.ac.uk; lucia.primavesi@bbsrc.ac.uk; deveraj.jhurreea@bbsrc.ac.uk; yuhua.zhang@bbsrc.ac.uk

Annu. Rev. Plant Biol. 2008. 59:417–41

The *Annual Review of Plant Biology* is online at plant.annualreviews.org

This article's doi:
10.1146/annurev.arplant.59.032607.092945

1543-5008/08/0602-0417$20.00

Key Words

trehalose 6-phosphate, nonreducing disaccharide, sugar signal, carbohydrate

Abstract

Trehalose metabolism and signaling is an area of emerging significance. In less than a decade our views on the importance of trehalose metabolism and its role in plants have gone through something of a revolution. An obscure curiosity has become an indispensable regulatory system. Mutant and transgenic plants of trehalose synthesis display wide-ranging and unprecedented phenotypes for the perturbation of a metabolic pathway. Molecular physiology and genomics have provided a glimpse of trehalose biology that had not been possible with conventional techniques, largely because the products of the synthetic pathway, trehalose 6-phosphate (T6P) and trehalose, are in trace abundance and difficult to measure in most plants. A consensus is emerging that T6P plays a central role in the coordination of metabolism with development. The discovery of trehalose metabolism has been one of the most exciting developments in plant metabolism and plant science in recent years. The field is fast moving and this review highlights the most recent insights.

Contents

INTRODUCTION

Nonreducing disaccharide: component hexose reducing sugars linked at the reducing ends to form sucrose (glucose plus fructose) and trehalose (two glucose units)

Sugars are fundamental to life. Their versatile chemistry is harnessed by biological systems to perform central functions. Most obviously, sugars are an immediate and transportable energy source and, when linked as polysaccharides, a longer-term energy store. Polysaccharides in the form of cellulose and chitin are also essential components of natural architecture. Beyond these roles, polysaccharides can also convey information. Sugar units can be joined in a variety of ways, with variation in ring size, linkage, and group addition, giving rise to 1.05×10^{12} possibilities (50). This structural versatility of carbohydrates provides the potential for a communication system, or glycocode (24, 30). The communication of internal and external information is a central feature of biological systems. This communication is necessary for the coordination of metabolism with development and environmental pressures and depends on sophisticated information transfer. Sugars form part of this communication system.

In this context, trehalose might seem rather unexciting at first. Trehalose consists of two glucose units linked in an α,α-1,1 configuration to yield a stable, nonreducing disaccharide. However, the biology of trehalose is special. Particularly in the last five years, understanding of the trehalose pathway in plants has gathered pace, especially in the context of the role of sugars as metabolic signals. Strong evidence shows that trehalose 6-phosphate (T6P) is a powerful and indispensable sugar signal in plants that integrates metabolism with development. There is considerable genetic proliferation of the pathway, which is under purifying selection pressure, reflecting its biological importance with likely plant-specific functions. This review concentrates on the most recent developments in trehalose biology in plants, its genetic basis, and its link to metabolism and development.

THE CENTRAL ROLE OF NONREDUCING DISACCHARIDES

Nonreducing disaccharides play a unique role in the biosphere. They provide a soluble energy source in the form of a stable molecule that can also function as a protectant compound. Nonreducing disaccharides are used as a translocated energy source by all organisms except vertebrates. Trehalose and sucrose are the two nonreducing sugars that perform this role. Their chemistry played an important part in the evolution of life. The evolution of photosynthesis, and hence oxygenation of the atmosphere and subsequent evolution of complex life forms, may have depended on the synthesis of sucrose, which is only found in photosynthetic organisms. Trehalose can be synthesized in all organisms except vertebrates. The properties of these sugars enabled life to survive, adapt, evolve, and flourish in diverse conditions.

Sucrose (β-D-fructofuranosyl α-D-glucopyranoside)

Glucose and fructose units linked in α, β-1,2 configuration

Trehalose (α-D-glucopyranosyl α-D-glucopyranoside)

Glucose units linked in α, α-1,1 configuration

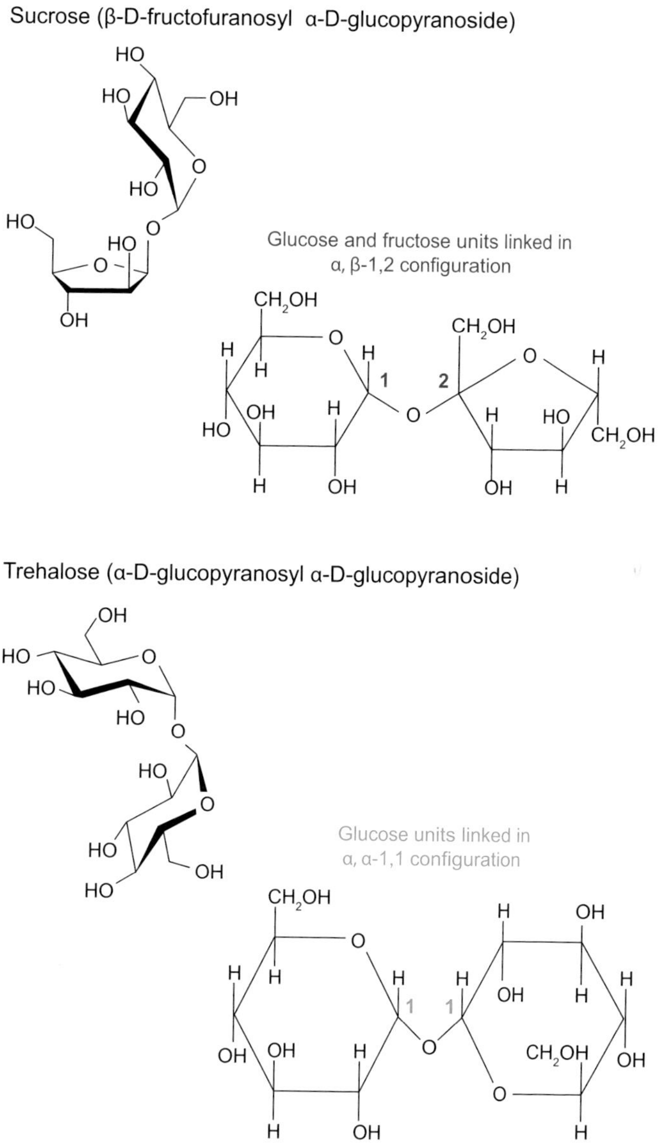

Figure 1

Structures of sucrose and trehalose presented as cyclic Haworth projections.

The component reducing sugars, glucose in the case of trehalose, glucose and fructose in the case of sucrose, are linked at their reducing ends. In naturally occurring trehalose the two glucose units are linked in a α,α-1,1 configuration. Isomers include neotrehalose, with an α,β link, and isotrehalose, which has a β,β link. In sucrose, glucose and fructose are linked in a α,β-1,2 configuration. Both configurations produce stable energy-rich molecules (**Figure 1**).

Trehalose is the main blood sugar of arthropods, fueling flight in insects. Trehalose is also found at high levels in fungi, bacteria, and archaea. Trehalose is the starting point for chitin synthesis (59), as is sucrose for cell wall polysaccharide synthesis in plants. Plants are unique in that they can synthesize both nonreducing saccharides, but sucrose performs the main role of translocated sugar in plants. Trehalose is found in millimolar amounts in only a few plants, namely specialized resurrection species, where it is thought to protect against desiccation. In the vast majority of plants trehalose is present in only trace (low micromolar or less) amounts. Conversely, sucrose is present in millimolar amounts. In the species in which they occur as circulatory sugars, trehalose and sucrose contents can fluctuate by orders of magnitude. In contrast, the other main circulatory sugar in the biosphere, glucose, the blood sugar of vertebrates, is maintained within strict limits. This is because as a reducing sugar glucose is reactive and damaging at high concentrations, as seen in diabetes, for example. In healthy humans the concentration of glucose blood sugar is typically 6–8 mM. In plants glucose levels can fluctuate, but within plant cells glucose is almost exclusively located in the vacuole (26, 34), where damaging effects can be restricted. The different chemistries of glucose, trehalose, and sucrose dictate their biology, the functions they perform, and the mechanisms that determine the concentrations of these compounds in vivo. Understanding how the metabolism of these sugars is integrated through regulatory mechanisms with the development, survival, and

Sugar signaling: precise interactions of sugars with other molecules can initiate signal transduction events that result in cellular responses such as altered gene expression and enzyme activities

growth of organisms is one of biology's key questions.

The reasons for the different distribution patterns of these circulatory sugars in the biosphere and the necessary adoption of different strategies in their internal management remain uncertain. Nevertheless, several arguments can be put forward to explain the different distributions. Sucrose is more soluble than trehalose, particularly at low temperatures, and hence may be more suited as a transport sugar in plants at phloem concentrations as high as 1 M. Sucrose can be cleaved by invertase into glucose and fructose, and by sucrose synthase into uridine diphosphoglucose (UDPG) and fructose, preserving energy as UDPG. Cell wall polysaccharides are synthesized from UDPG. A ready and continuous supply of UDPG is essential in plants for cell wall synthesis, which continues throughout the life cycle. The ability to liberate UDPG directly from sucrose to synthesize cell wall polysaccharides may be the main reason sucrose dominates in plants. Sucrose can also be directly converted into polymers of fructose, fructans, which although found in only approximately 15% of flowering plant species, are associated with some of the most evolutionarily advanced orders (e.g., Liliales, Poales, Astrales, Campanulales), which can dominate vegetation cover—grasslands, for example—particularly in regions associated with cold and drought (40). Raffinose family oligosaccharides are extensions of sucrose to which galactosyl residues are attached via galactinol made from UDP galactose converted from UDPG; unlike fructans, raffinose family oligosaccharides are ubiquitous in plants (70). Plants may accumulate protective compounds other than trehalose (sucrose, fructan, raffinose family oligosaccharides), because high trehalose concentrations are incompatible with chaperone-assisted protein refolding during stress recovery (52). Sucrose may also be favored because it is less readily available for pathogens to use. Some microbial pathogens (e.g., ectomycorrhizal fungi) lack invertase (109). It remains unclear why vertebrates have abandoned disaccharides and use glucose as blood sugar, which necessitates the adoption of regulatory mechanisms for the maintenance of glucose concentrations to within narrow limits. One possible reason why all other organisms possess a ready supply of either sucrose or trehalose is that, as already noted for plants, these organisms must synthesize large amounts of structural polysaccharides—cell wall polysaccharides and chitin—for which sucrose and trehalose, respectively, are the starting points. These compounds are synthesized continuously throughout the life of plants, fungi, and invertebrates, but not vertebrates (**Figure 2**).

TREHALOSE

Trehalose was first identified as a constituent of the ergot fungus of rye in 1832. The name trehalose was introduced in 1858 when it was found in the cocoons or "trehala" of the desert beetles of the Middle East, *Larinus nidificans* and *L. maculates*. These secretions, known by native peoples to be edible and sweet, were called "trehala manna". This may be the same manna, or food from heaven, that sustained the Israelites in the wilderness in Old Testament accounts. Trehalose has always been part of the human diet as a constituent of edible mushrooms, seafood crustacea, and baker's and brewer's yeast. As with lactose, a small percentage of people cannot digest trehalose through a genetic deficiency of trehalase, the enzyme that breaks down trehalose into two glucose units (lactase in the case of lactose). Interestingly, trehalose can serve a further function when linked to mycolic acid as a glycolipid, which is a constituent of the cell wall skeleton of *Mycobacterium* species including *M. tuberculosis* and related genera of bacteria. These glycolipids play an important part in bacterium-host interactions, the immune response, and the biology of tuberculosis (83).

Trehalose is renowned for its protective ability, stability, and low reactivity. Trehalose can withstand heating at 100°C between pH 3.5–10 for 24 h. Trehalose protects

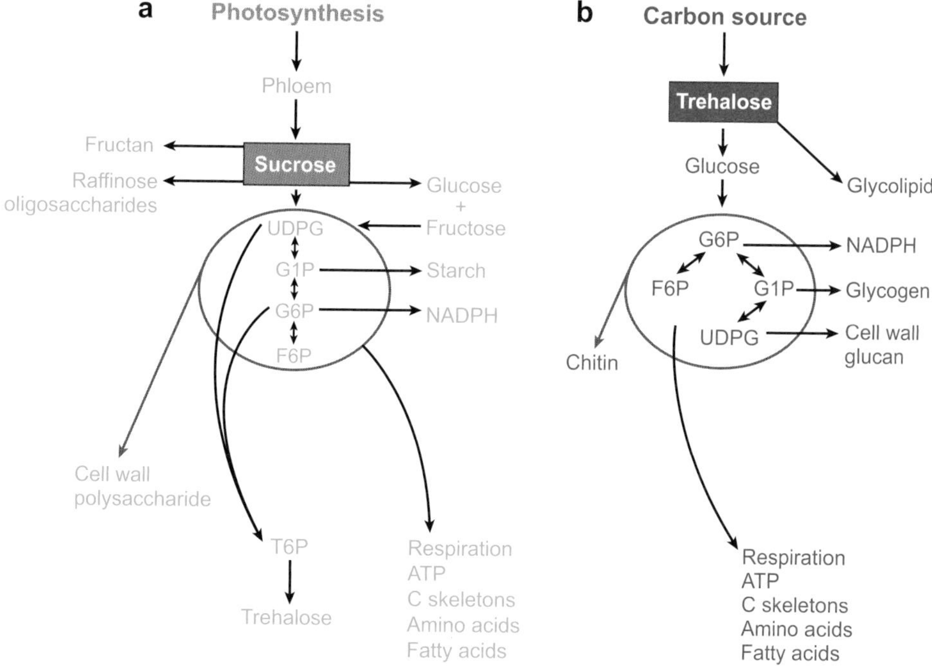

Figure 2

Centrality of the circulatory sugars; (*a*) sucrose (plants) and (*b*) trehalose (arthropods, fungi, bacteria, and archaea), from which all cellular constituents are made. Plants are the only organisms that can make both sucrose and trehalose. UDPG, uridine diphosphoglucose; G1P, glucose 1-phosphate; G6P, glucose 6-phosphate; F6P, fructose 6-phosphate; T6P, trehalose 6-phosphate; C skeletons, carbon skeletons.

proteins and membranes from denaturation by replacing water as it hydrogen bonds to polar residues. During desiccation trehalose forms an amorphous glass structure that limits molecular motion, preventing protein aggregation and free radical diffusion (19, 23, 111). The α,α-1,1 configuration is crucial for the ability of trehalose to preserve lipid bilayer structure in the absence of water (2). Even close analogs such as α,β-trehalose or sucrose do not show this property. As a nonreducing sugar trehalose shows no Maillard reaction with amino compounds and does not cause browning during cooking. Trehalose masks unpleasant tastes and odors in food and has its own sweet clean taste, with approximately half the sweetness to taste as sucrose; trehalose is an important ingredient in foodstuffs and drinks as a stabilizer and preservative of even fresh food (86). Trehalose can be used as a cryoprotectant for cells in medicine and microbiology and is a component of cosmetics. Trehalose inhibits the polyglutamine-induced protein aggregation found in Huntingdon disease in experiments conducted on a mouse model of this illness (92). This has led to the marketing of trehalose as a health food. Trehalose is a useful lead in the treatment of Huntingdon disease. Trehalose has been produced on an industrial scale only since the mid 1990s. Previously trehalose was too expensive to extract or produce commercially. A feasible method was developed via the use of an enzyme system from a soil bacterium, *Arthrobacter* sp. Q36, consisting of two novel enzymes that convert starch to trehalose via the TreY-TreZ pathway (41) (**Figure 3**).

Trehalose is widely assumed to play a similar role in vivo as its demonstrated properties in vitro. With the exception of plants, its central role as an energy source and stress response molecule in microorgansims and

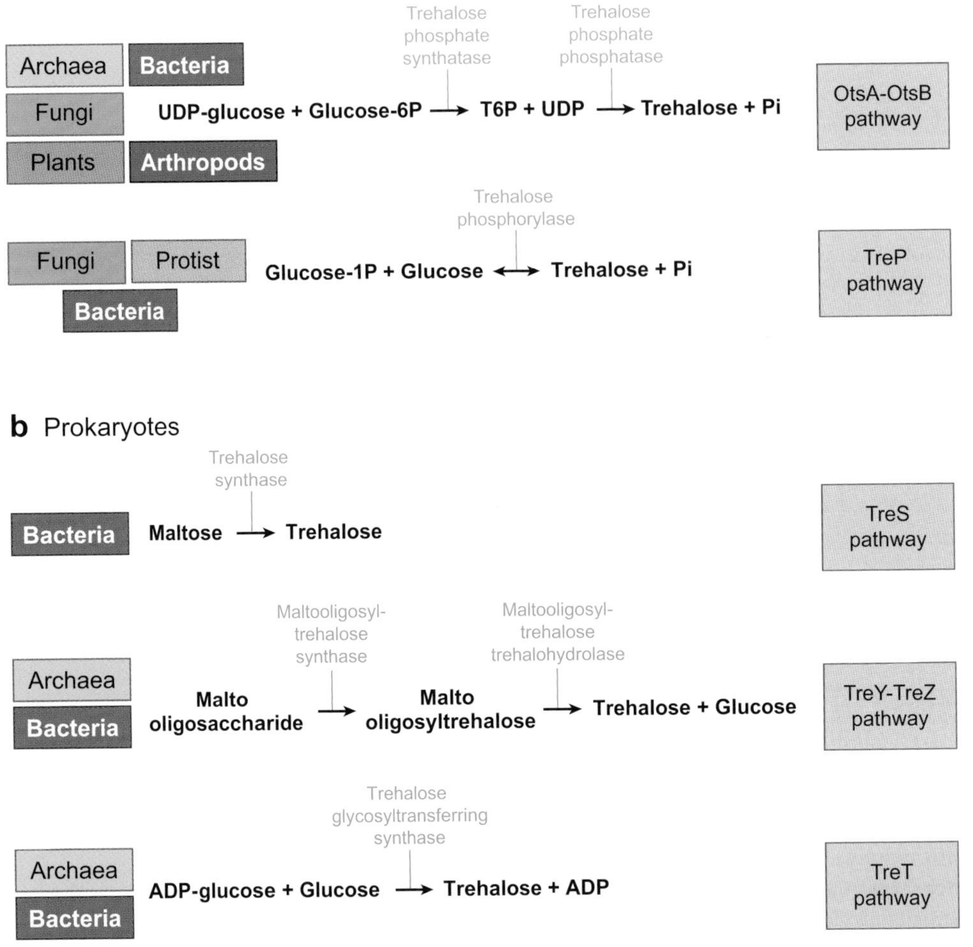

Figure 3

Known pathways of trehalose synthesis in eukaryotes (*a*) and prokaryotes (*b*). UDP, uridine diphosphate; Glucose-6P, glucose 6-phosphate; T6P, trehalose 6-phosphate; Glucose-1P, glucose 1-phosphate; ADP, adenosine triphosphate.

invertebrates and as a starting point for chitin synthesis is not in doubt. In bacteria trehalose is used as the sole carbon source, compatible osmolyte, and as part of the cell wall structure. In fungi trehalose is synthesized at the onset of reduced growth periods, which protects the cell's integrity against stress damage, and then it is rapidly mobilized during recovery and during the early germination of spores (6). The precise association of trehalose with stress has not always been clear. For example, in *Saccharomyces cerevisiae* elevated trehalose correlates with survival under desiccation, but mutant strains without trehalose phosphate synthase (TPS) are still desiccation tolerant. Trehalose is neither necessary nor sufficient to survive desiccation (79), possibly because the pathway has other, incompletely understood functions. In support of this theory, the trehalose pathway is now known to play a critical role in regulating metabolism in fungi, plants, and invertebrates including nematodes and insects (49, 87, 94). This latter role appears to be the major function in plants, where the function appears highly developed and is the driving force for the genetic diversification of the pathway.

Synthesis

There are five known naturally occurring trehalose biosynthetic routes (**Figure 3**). Interestingly, only one of these, the OtsA-OtsB pathway, involves the intermediate T6P. The OtsA-OtsB pathway is the most widespread pathway and is found in all prokaryotic and eukaryotic organisms that synthesize trehalose, and is the only pathway found in plants. TPS catalyzes the transfer of glucose from UDPG to glucose 6-phosphate (G6P) to form T6P and uridine diphosphate (UDP), and trehalose phosphate phosphatase (TPP) dephosphorylates T6P to form trehalose and inorganic phosphate. This pathway has been extensively studied in *S. cerevisiae* and *Escherichia coli*. In *S. cerevisiae* the TPS homolog, TPS1, forms a complex with the TPP homolog, TPS2, and two regulatory subunits, TPS3 and trehalose synthase long chain (TSL) (10). In *E. coli*, TPS and TPP are separate entities. A TPS that uses guanosine diphosphate glucose instead of UDPG has been described in *Streptomyces hygroscopicus* (28). The other pathway found in eukaryotes is the potentially reversible synthesis from glucose 1-phosphate (G1P) and glucose to trehalose, catalyzed by trehalose phosphorylase (TreP pathway), which is found in fungi (e.g., *Agaricus bisporus*) (106) and the protist, *Euglena gracilis* (11). The other pathways are exclusive to prokaryotes. In bacteria (e.g., *Pimelobacter*) (97), trehalose synthase isomerizes the α1-α4 bond of maltose to the α1-α1 bond of trehalose (TreS pathway). A two-step conversion from malto-oligosaccharides or α-1,4-glucans to malto-oligosyltrehalose and subsequently trehalose (TreY-TreZ pathway) (29) is found in *Arthrobacter* (57), *Rhizobium* (58), and the thermophilic archaeon, *Sulfolobus*. Finally, the TreT pathway, found in the extremeophilic archaea *Thermococcus litoralis* (76) and *Pyrococcus* (82) and the bacterium *Thermotoga maritima* (112), catalyzed by trehalose glycosyltransferring synthase, uses the substrates ADP-glucose and glucose. The presence of multiple routes for trehalose synthesis in the same organism may reflect the importance of trehalose accumulation under different stresses, which limit substrate availability selectively. For example, *Mycobacterium* has three pathways (OtsA-OtsB, TreS, and TreY-TreZ) (25). In plants the focus of the pathway may be on the synthesis of T6P rather than trehalose, which explains the exclusive presence of the OtsA-OtsB pathway. The route of trehalose breakdown by trehalase to two glucose units is universal. An additional route in which T6P is converted to glucose and G6P by trehalose 6-phosphate hydrolase exists in *E. coli* (80).

TREHALOSE PATHWAY IN PLANTS

Discovery

Early accounts of trehalose in plants were restricted to resurrection plants, for example *Selaginella* species (5) and *Myrothamnus flabellifolia* (12), and other curiosity findings such as the presence of trehalose in manna-like exudates on flowers (104). Toxic effects of feeding trehalose on the cell wall and sucrose and starch metabolism were also described (101). The lack of detection in the majority of plants led to the assumption that trehalose was of minimal relevance and that its function had died out and been replaced by sucrose. This changed in approximately 1997. First, the engineering of the trehalose pathway into plants using *E. coli* genes produced phenotypes consistent with the communication with rather than the encumbrance of endogenous signaling machinery (36). Soon after, functional genes encoding TPS and TPP were found in *Arabidopsis thaliana* (15, 102). The publication of the full genomic sequence database for *A. thaliana* confirmed the existence of a surprising abundance of genes for trehalose synthesis (52). Trehalose and

T6P were subsequently detected in *A. thaliana* (87, 103). Eastmond and colleagues (27) were the first to demonstrate the indispensability of a plant trehalose pathway gene, *AtTPS1*, which was then attributed to T6P (87). Numerous effects of altering the trehalose pathway on metabolism and development (77), possibly all due to modification of T6P content, have been reported. These include embryo (27) and leaf (69) development, cell division and cell wall synthesis (37), inflorescence architecture (84), seedling biomass (87), adult plant biomass and photosynthesis (69), sucrose utilization (87), starch metabolism (48), and tolerance of abiotic stresses, particularly drought (3, 4, 33, 46, 61, 72). These effects go beyond the results of previous genetic modifications of metabolic pathways, and would suggest an important role for this pathway in plants distinct from that of a conventional metabolic pathway. The manipulation of sucrose 6-phosphate content, for example, (22) does not give rise to any of the range of effects produced by modifying T6P, and confirms the very different functions of these nonreducing disaccharides in plants.

Genetic Basis of the Trehalose Pathway in Plants

It is interesting to compare the genes that encode the enzymes of trehalose and sucrose synthesis and breakdown in *A. thaliana*. A total of 21 genes encode enzymes putatively involved in the synthesis of trehalose (55), compared with 8 for the synthesis of sucrose (51) (**Figure 4**). Strikingly, 23 genes encode the enzymes sucrose synthase and acid and alkaline invertase, involved in the breakdown of sucrose, compared with only one gene for the breakdown of trehalose (44). These differences in gene profiles reflect the two routes of sucrose breakdown in plants, the different biological functions of sucrose and trehalose in plants, and the distinctive role of T6P.

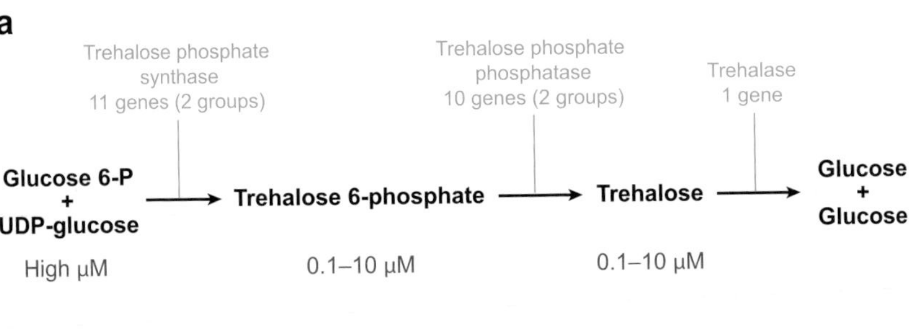

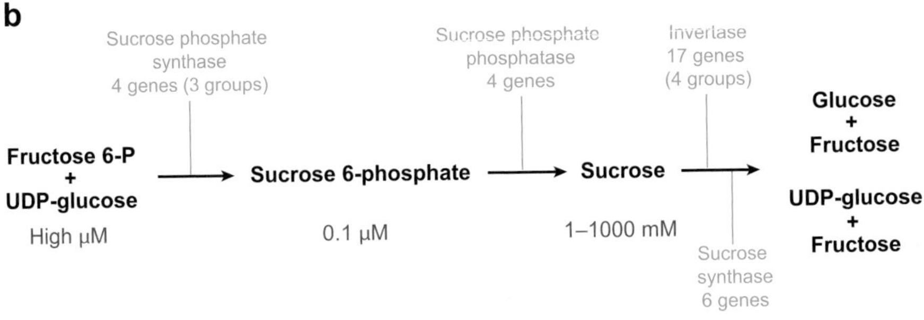

Figure 4

Arabidopsis thaliana nonreducing disaccharide synthesis and breakdown. Comparison of the trehalose (*a*) and sucrose (*b*) pathways in plants. In spite of their similarities, large differences exist in the numbers of genes that encode enzymes for each step and the relative abundances of sucrose and trehalose and their immediate precursors.

John Lunn (55) and Nelson Avonce and coworkers (8) recently conducted comprehensive phylogenetic analyses of genes encoding trehalose pathway enzymes, which cast light on the interesting evolution of trehalose biology in plants. Trehalose and its metabolism are evolutionarily ancient. All life forms are exposed to trehalose and possess trehalase to break it down to glucose. In plants, in particular, extensive proliferation of TPSs and TPPs has occurred. Plants contain two classes of *TPS* genes, two classes of *TPP* genes (although the subdivision of *TPPs* is weaker than it is for *TPSs*), and one class of *trehalase* genes. All the gene families have very ancient origins, dating back to before the divergence of the streptophyte (land plants and some algae) and chlorophyte (eukaryotic algae) lineages. *TPS* genes are most closely related to those from fungi and other eukaryotes, suggesting a eukaryotic origin, whereas *TPP* genes are most closely related to those from bacteria and may have been derived from the endosymbiotic bacterial ancestor of mitochondria.

Table 1 Trehalose pathway genes of *Arabidopsis thaliana*

Gene	Locus
Trehalose phosphate synthase	
Class I	
TPS1	At1g78580
TPS2	At1g16980
TPS3	At1g17000
TPS4	At4g27550
Class II	
TPS5	At4g17770
TPS6	At1g68020
TPS7	At1g06410
TPS8	At1g70290
TPS9	At1g23870
TPS10	At1g60140
TPS11	At2g18700
Trehalose phosphate phosphatase	
Class I	
TPP1 C	At1g22210
TPP2 D	At1g35910
TPP3 B	At1g78090
TPP4 E	At2g22190
TPP5 F	At4g12430
TPP6 G	At4g22590
TPP7 H	At4g39770
Class II	
TPP8 I	At5g10100
TPP9 A	At5g51460
TPP10 J	At5g65140
Trehalase	At4g24040

Trehalose Phosphate Synthase

TPSs fall into two distinct classes and comprise a total of 11 genes in *A. thaliana* (**Table 1**). Only one, *TPS1*, of the class I TPSs (*TPS1–4* in *A. thaliana*), shows demonstrable TPS activity (15). Class II TPSs (*AtTPS5–11*) have a synthase and a phosphatase domain, but the active sites are less well-conserved compared with class I TPS and they lack both TPS and TPP activity (39, 103). The acquisition of bacterial TPP is speculated to have driven the evolution of a new function of these TPSs (55), although the identity of this new function is unclear. One possibility is that these TPSs act as regulatory subunits of a complex with class I TPS as in yeast (10). Interestingly, Avonce and coworkers (8) conducted an analysis of the amino acid and nucleic acid composition of the TPS and TPP catalytic domains, and found that all codon substitutions in DNA sequences are synonymous at the protein level. A synonymous substitution (also called a silent substitution) is the evolutionary substitution of one base for another in a gene coding for a protein, such that the produced protein sequence is not functionally modified. Therefore, although DNA may mutate, only changes that maintain current protein function are tolerated. Both TPS and TPP proteins are under strong purifying selection. This means that natural selection acts to preserve their function and that they are not in the process of becoming pseudogenes or under strong adaptive selection. So one could propose that the acquisition of TPPs drove evolution of a new function for class II TPSs

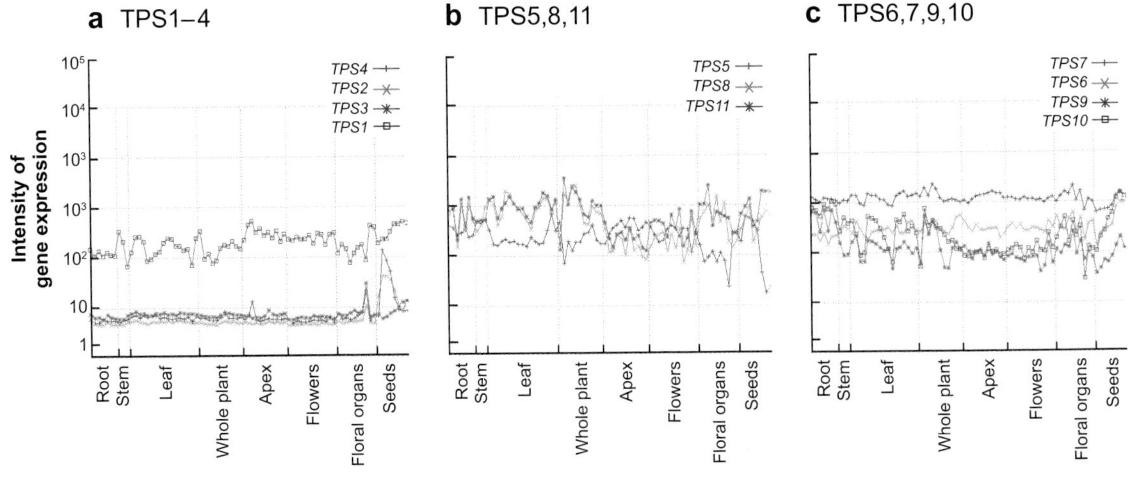

Figure 5

Expression profiles (absolute values) of trehalose pathway gene trehalose phosphate synthase in different tissues of *A. thaliana* via the use of the ATGenexpress visualization tool (from Reference 89, with permission).

that has now stabilized and is important. The expression of *TPS1* is constitutive (**Figure 5**). Of the flowering plants analyzed most have only one class I TPS gene, which has been duplicated in some species such as maize and poplar. *A. thaliana* and members of the Brassicaceae are exceptional in having four class I TPS genes (55). Interestingly, *AtTPS2–4* may serve particular functions in brassica seeds and siliques, in which these genes are specifically expressed (**Figure 5**). The function of *ATPS2–4* is distinct from *TPS1* because these genes do not compensate for mutation of *TPS1* (27). Although plant *TPS1* is catalytically active (15), a plant-specific N-terminal extension of class I TPSs is autoinhibitory and restricts activity in vivo (98); *AtTPS2–4* have lost this feature.

Class II *TPSs* are expressed throughout the plant (**Figure 5**). *TPS8* and *TPS11* have parallel expression patterns; the expression patterns of the other class II TPSs are more distinctive. The biological importance of class II TPSs is further confirmed by the observation that they are subject to a high degree of regulation, particularly by light, sugars, starvation, diurnal rhythms, and cytokinin (17, 38, 88, 95, 113). The expression of *AtTPS5* peaks at the end of the day, whereas the expression of the other genes peaks at the end of the night (13, 71). The rhythms of *TPS5* and *TPS10* are contrary. In agreement with the idea that these genes may be regulated by assimilate supply, *AtTPS5* is induced by sugars (88) and repressed by starvation, whereas the opposite is true for *AtTPS8–10* (65). Class II TPS proteins are also targets of multisite phosphorylation by sucrose nonfermenting (SNF1)-related protein kinase (SnRK1) and calcium-dependent protein kinases (35, 39). TPS5–7 bind 14-3-3 proteins when phosphorylated (39). However, the function of class II TPSs is unresolved.

Trehalose Phosphate Phosphatase

Plant TPP sequences are most closely related to those from bacteria and may have originated from the endosymbiotic ancestor of mitochondria (55). Gene structure is broadly conserved between species and two subfamilies of TPP are thought to have arisen by duplication of a common ancestor before the separation of the monocot and eudicot lineages. Further gene duplications have taken place, for example in *A. thaliana* (TPPB/D,

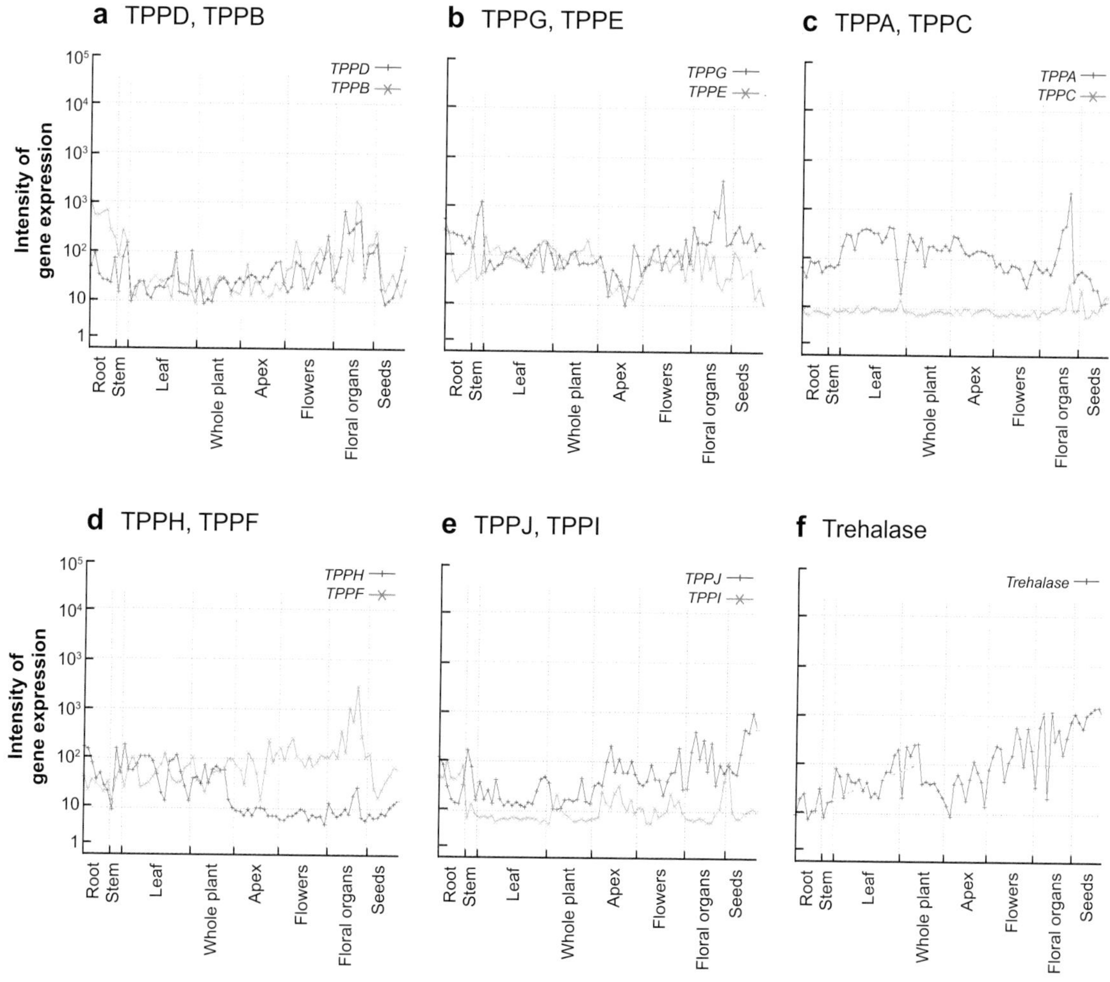

Figure 6

Gene expression profiles (absolute values) of trehalose pathway genes trehalose phosphate phosphatase and trehalase in different tissues of *Arabidopsis thaliana* via the use of the ATGenexpress visualization tool (from Reference 89, with permission).

TPPE/G, TPPF/H, and TPPI/J), which has a total of 10 TPP genes (expression patterns are depicted in **Figure 6**). Monocots have a distinct clade of TPPs, for example *RAMOSA3*. In contrast to TPSs, the function of TPPs is clearer. All plant TPPs have conserved amino acid motifs characteristic of the 2-haloacid dehalogenase superfamily of enzymes (20), and are under strong purifying selection (8). The *AtTTPA* and *AtTPPB* genes complement a yeast TPP mutant and encode active TPP enzymes (102), together with those from rice—TPP2a (75) and maize *RAMOSA* (84). Recently, a more extensive characterization of biochemical properties of rice TPP1 and TPP2 (91) showed that the enzymes have stringent substrate specificity for T6P with K_m values of 92 and 186 μM for *OsTPP1* and *OsTPP2*, respectively. This is approximately tenfold lower than the K_m found in microorganisms, whose TPPs have less substrate specificity and can also use G1P and G6P as substrates. The expression of both rice TPPs is under strong regulation by stress treatments—chilling, drought, salt, and abscisic acid—specific for each TPP. *A. thaliana* TPPs are also induced by hypoxia and nitrate (53, 105). TPPs in particular respond to stress; this response may lead to the metabolism of T6P in different cell types and tissues, although an impact of endogenous plant TPP genes on T6P levels in planta has not been proven. Some TPPs have a transit peptide, suggesting that they could be chloroplastic, although some are almost certainly cytosolic (e.g., *OsTPP1*, *OsTPP2*) (91).

Trehalase

In comparison with TPP and TPS genes, plant trehalase genes have proliferated much less. *A. thaliana* has just one trehalase gene (**Figure 6**). Overexpression of trehalase in *A. thaliana* produces no phenotype, in contrast to the strong phenotypes produced by overexpressing TPS and TPP genes. Trehalase may be required to metabolize trehalose produced during the synthesis of T6P and also trehalose encountered in plant-pathogen interactions and in symbioses with other organisms. For example, trehalase activity is particularly high in legume root nodules (64) and is strongly induced in roots and hypocotyls of *A. thaliana* infected with clubroot (18). Expression of trehalase in *A. thaliana* is most pronounced in flowers and seeds (**Figure 6**). Recently, Frison and coworkers (32) showed that trehalase is a plasma membrane–bound enzyme with its catalytic domain oriented toward the cell wall, and showed that it has extracellular activity. The implication of this finding is that the regulation of endogenous trehalose levels requires the transport of trehalose out of the cell.

FUNCTION OF THE PATHWAY

A Role in Metabolic Regulation in Yeast

A key discovery in metabolic regulation in yeast in the early 1990s showed that the trehalose synthase small subunit, *TSS1*, as well as synthesizing T6P, controls glucose influx into glycolysis. Yeast glycolysis had been classically thought to be controlled at the level of its two irreversible steps, catalyzed by phosphofructokinase (PFK) and pyruvate kinase (PK). However, increased expression of PFK and PK does not change glycolytic flux (85) and metabolic control analysis also points to sugar uptake as a major controlling step. The discovery came out of work on the molecular defect in glucose-negative mutants and separate work to clone the genes encoding the trehalose synthase complex (94). Disabled trehalose synthesis led to an inability to grow on glucose, the accumulation of glycolytic intermediates, and low ATP. Three hypotheses were proposed to explain this result. First, the TPS1 protein could have a direct regulatory function (93). Second, the phosphate recovery hypothesis proposes that trehalose synthesis diverts sugar phosphates away from glycolysis into trehalose synthesis, which recovers inorganic phosphate, preventing metabolism from stalling (42). Third, T6P could restrict sugar flux by inhibiting hexokinase activity (14). In yeast, T6P inhibition of hexokinase is not the only mechanism by which TPS1 controls the influx of glucose into glycolysis (16). Elements of each explanation could be involved in yeast species.

The Link Between Metabolism and Development in Multicellular Organisms

Researchers were surprised to discover that the basic principles of metabolic regulation by the trehalose pathway observed in yeast appear to have been built upon over the course of evolution in the more complex organisms: higher plants, fungi, and insects. In these organisms metabolism must be regulated in the context of multicellular growth and tissue and organ development. Therefore, the basic principle of metabolic regulation imparted by the trehalose pathway in yeast was likely elaborated upon and diversified in multicellular organisms. In plants, disruption of the trehalose pathway produces the same metabolite profile pattern as in yeast (87): The plants accumulate phosphorylated intermediates and show low levels of ATP when T6P levels are low, although the mechanism does not involve hexokinase because plant hexokinases are not inhibited by physiological concentrations of T6P (45). In *Drosophila*, mutations of *TPS1* are lethal (21, 22); similarly, in the nematode *Caenorhabditis elegans*, mutation of a TPP gene, *gob-1*, is lethal (49). The mutations are thought to be lethal owing to the toxic buildup of T6P, because controlled levels of T6P are required for metabolic regulation. Particularly, T6P may play a role in integrating metabolism and development in the embryonic intestine in *C. elegans* and in insects. Researchers recently found that in the multicellular plant pathogenic fungus, *Magnaporte grisea*, TPS1 plays a central role in the integration of carbon and nitrogen metabolism and in the establishment of plant disease; these roles are unrelated to the catalytic function of TPS1 (31, 108). The apparent inability of *M. grisea* Δ*tps1* to grow on glucose is not due to glycolytic misregulation, as predicted by studies in yeast, but is instead due to a role for TPS1 in the control of NADPH levels via regulation of the oxidative pentose phosphate pathway. TPS1 integrates carbon and nitrogen metabolism through G6P sensing, which regulates NADPH production and the activity of nitrate reductase. TPS1 also controls the expression of the nitrogen metabolite repressor gene, *NMR1*, and is required for the expression of virulence-associated genes.

The Link Between Metabolism and Development in Plants

In plants the major and possibly only role of the trehalose pathway, except in specialized resurrection plants, is as a central metabolic regulator. This regulatory function is performed, at least in part, by T6P (48, 55, 87). There is no evidence of other regulatory roles for plant TPS1, although other TPSs without catalytic activity (*AtTPS5–11*) may be associated with the regulatory function of the pathway as discussed above. Expression of the *E. coli otsA* gene rescues the *Attps1* mutant (87). Rescue is likely not due to a regulatory role of the TPS protein encoded by *otsA*, because the plant and bacterial proteins are quite different. However, the plant and bacterial proteins both synthesize T6P. Relative amounts of T6P are different in *A. thaliana* expressing *otsA* and *otsB* (87). This different relative amount of T6P strongly affects growth on sucrose. High T6P levels stimulate growth on sucrose compared with wild-type. Conversely, a near absence of T6P compromises the ability of the plant to utilize sugar. The amount of T6P is inversely related to the amounts of hexose phosphates and UDPG (69, 87), suggesting that T6P may regulate the amounts of these intermediates. Interestingly, T6P is not only involved in regulating the utilization of sucrose, but the amounts of T6P also respond strongly to sucrose. In a recent study, Lunn and coworkers (56) showed a 27-fold increase in T6P levels within 3 h in response to sucrose feeding. What might be the link to sucrose? In plants T6P is synthesized from G6P and UDPG, downstream products of sucrose breakdown. UDPG is produced directly via sucrose synthase; G6P is produced from glucose via invertase and hexokinase or via fructose and fructose 6-phosphate (F6P) through sucrose synthase, fructokinase, and phosphoglucose isomerase. The rapid response of T6P to sucrose feeding may be a response to an increase in the pool size of G6P and UDPG passing through a constitutively expressed TPS1. Thus, T6P levels may reflect the availability of hexose phosphates, UDPG, and sucrose, because sucrose feeds into this pool. F6P stimulates trehalose synthesis in yeast (54), and hence trehalose synthesis could reflect levels of this metabolite as well. It is interesting to note that levels of T6P, hexose phosphates, and UDPG stabilize and begin to fall 3 h after sucrose feeding (56), which supports the observation in transgenic plants that T6P may regulate this pool size. Knowledge of downstream targets of T6P would help substantiate the nature of the interaction between T6P and this pool.

UDPG and G6P are two central molecules from which all other cellular functions can be ultimately derived—respiratory energy and carbon skeletons for cellulose and cell wall polysaccharides, starch, lipids, proteins, and sucrose. UDPG assumes particular importance in plants because of cell wall synthesis. Being made from UDPG and G6P, trehalose is at the center of metabolism and plant development; however, because trehalose is not a major end product in plants it is removed from the main metabolic flux (**Figure 7**). Therefore, the synthesis of T6P and trehalose can potentially act as an effective indicator of the G6P and UDPG pool size without compromising other functions. The importance of

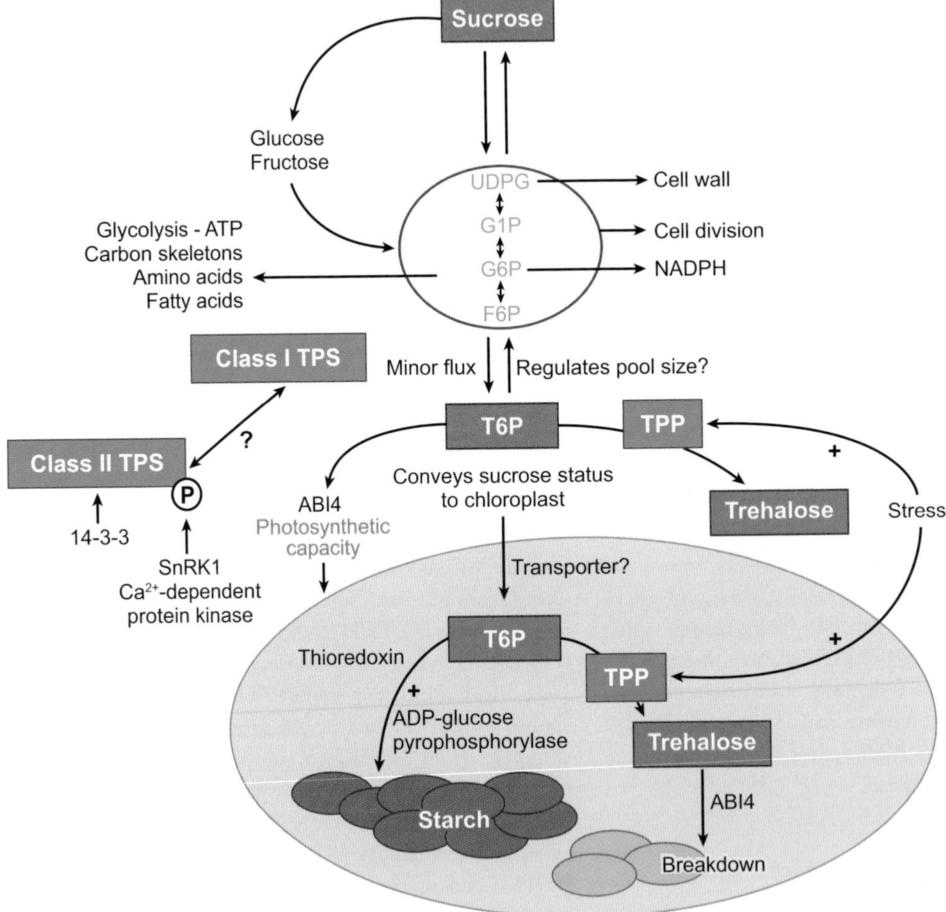

Figure 7

Overall summary of the role of the trehalose pathway in plants. Trehalose 6-phosphate (T6P) is, as a signal metabolite, in close proximity to the pool size of hexose phosphates and uridine diphosphoglucose (UDPG), which it may respond to and regulate. A variety of internal and external cues—carbon status and stress—regulate trehalose phosphate synthases (TPSs) (at the gene level and posttranslationally) and trehalose phosphate phosphatases (TPPs) (at the gene level), which may further impact T6P levels. T6P also links the cytosolic carbon status to starch synthesis in the chloroplast. G1P, glucose 1-phosphate; G6P, glucose 6-phosphate; F6P, fructose 6-phosphate; SnRK1, sucrose nonfermenting (SNF1)-related protein kinase.

this pool in determining growth was confirmed recently in a study of a recombinant inbred line of *A. thaliana* showing strong transgressive segregation for biomass, which displayed a close relationship between the size of the hexose phosphate pool (G1P, G6P, and F6P) and biomass (60). Interestingly, in the same study trehalose levels and biomass show a positive correlation, although the reason for this is not clear. As might be expected, the pool of hexose phosphates is depleted as growth increases. Studies of temperature and nitrogen effects on metabolism (43, 67) show this phenomenon clearly: The hexose phosphate pool size increases as growth decreases with low temperature and nitrogen limitation. These studies show the centrality of this metabolite pool, which links metabolism with growth and development. The dramatic effects seen in different tissues when the trehalose pathway is perturbed could arise because of the role T6P plays in linking this key pool of intermediates with growth and development. The involvement of the trehalose pathway in stress tolerance may also act, at least in part, through this pool. One framework to understand the role of T6P is as an indicator of G6P and UDPG pool size, and hence an indicator of sucrose, which feeds into this pool. Constitutive expression of TPS1 would enable T6P levels to increase under conditions of high assimilate supply and flux into this pool, but decrease under conditions of starvation and stress, which would decrease this pool size and T6P content through extensive regulation of TPPs. T6P may initiate homeostatic mechanisms that then regulate this pool size.

Starch

Starch metabolism is the closest to a direct target that has been found for T6P and starch accumulation is one of the most striking examples of metabolic regulation by the trehalose pathway. Wingler and coworkers (110) showed a strong accumulation of starch in response to trehalose feeding and transcriptional regulation of ADP-glucose pyrophosphorylase (AGPase), the key enzyme of starch synthesis. T6P activates AGPase through a thioredoxin-dependent redox activation mechanism (48). This activation mechanism operates under conditions of high sucrose, which induce high T6P levels (56, 87). This finding again supports the concept that T6P reflects conditions of high assimilate supply and in this case communicates these conditions to the chloroplast to activate starch synthesis. Interestingly, the link with starch has been extended to starch breakdown. Recent work suggests that the induction of high starch on trehalose is due to inhibited breakdown, which is due to inhibited transcription of *SEX1* and β-amylase, regulated by the transcription factor ABI4 (78). The wide range of phenotypes observed in transgenic plants with a modified trehalose pathway clearly suggests that AGPase and starch metabolism are not the only site of action of T6P, and supports an overall model in which T6P is involved in coordinating UDPG and G6P with growth and development in different tissues, including coordinating flux to starch.

Embryos

Embryo development in embryo-lethal *tps1* mutants, which have a perturbed trehalose pathway, has been analyzed in depth. This work showed that *TPS1* is required for developmental progression beyond the torpedo stage at the end of early embryogenesis (9, 27, 37). This requirement is almost certainly due to the need for T6P and can be rationalized as an impact of T6P on the coordination of metabolism with development. The torpedo stage is characterized by a transition from cell division to cell expansion and differentiation and the accumulation of storage compounds. Accompanying this transition is a change in the nature of the carbon supply, from hexoses provided by cell wall invertases to UDPG provided by sucrose synthase. The *tps1* embryos are still able to use sucrose for the synthesis of storage reserves, but this pathway is compromised as the amounts of protein and lipids decrease. Sucrose and starch accumulate in these embryos because of decreased flux into lipid and protein and as a consequence of a severe decrease in embryo growth. Cell division is also reduced in the embryos, which may be directly attributable to the perturbation of cell wall biosynthesis and the thickening of cell walls, which could delay progression through various phases of cell division. *TPS1*, through its synthesis of T6P, may regulate synthesis of the cellulose and pectin component of the cell wall. The expression of cellulose synthases and pectin-modifying enzymes is decreased in *tps1* embryos, as is the expression of enzymes involved in sucrose and starch degradation.

Leaves

TPS1 is also absolutely essential for normal vegetative growth (37, 99). Even if embryo lethality is overcome through transient expression of *AtTPS1*, germinated *tps1* mutants fail to establish and develop vegetatively (99). In transgenic plants expressing *E. coli* TPS and TPP, researchers observe large changes in vegetative development, which correlate with T6P content (66, 68, 69). In leaves, as in seedlings, there is a relationship between T6P and the pool size of hexose phosphates and UDPG, at least in the dark (69). Quite remarkably, photosynthetic capacity per unit leaf area is enhanced in transgenic plants expressing TPS. This enhancement is due to a specific increase in Rubisco activity, because of increased amounts of Rubisco protein, chlorophyll, and the light-harvesting apparatus. Expression of ABI4, a transcription factor that binds sites in the promoter region of Rubisco and CAB genes (1), is elevated where *AtTPS1* is overexpressed (7). This finding could provide a mechanistic explanation for selective changes in photosynthesis genes. In plants expressing TPP, with low T6P levels, photosynthetic capacity per unit leaf area is decreased by parallel changes in Rubisco and chlorophyll, but specific leaf area (SLA, leaf area per leaf mass) is increased. Photosynthetic capacity per unit leaf area and SLA are the means through which photosynthesis is regulated at the whole plant level. It is quite remarkable that perturbation of the trehalose pathway and particularly of one molecule, T6P, influences plant photosynthetic strategy so strongly. SLA is closely correlated with productivity (73). When taken to final harvest, plants expressing *E. coli* TPP have larger biomass than wild-type or plants expressing *E. coli* TPS, even though they have lower photosynthetic capacity, supporting the stronger link between SLA and productivity. The changes in cell wall biosynthesis and cell division seen in embryos may also occur in leaves to account for the change in final leaf size through the regulation of UDPG and hexose phosphate pools, although the full mechanistic details of how T6P imparts such strong regulation on plant photosynthesis are not yet fully understood. Photosynthesis has proved to be a trait that is difficult to breed for and engineer, probably because it is so intimately associated with leaf development and whole plant processes, although some successful strategies to target photosynthesis directly are bearing fruit in model species (47, 62). Nevertheless, targeting the trehalose pathway provides another means to alter plant photosynthesis for improved yield.

Flowering

TPS1 is also necessary for the normal transition to flowering (37, 99), probably again through provision of T6P. Ectopic expression of *TPS1* also leads to changes in inflorescence development, including increased inflorescence branching. Recently, the genetic basis of *ramosa3*, a classical mutant of maize, which causes large changes in inflorescence branching, was determined to be a TPP that metabolizes T6P (84). RAMOSA3 is part of a distinct clade of TPPs found in monocots and is expressed in discrete domains subtending axillary inflorescence meristems. Overaccumulation in T6P in these meristems may cause the large change in inflorescence phenotype. Meristems are characterized by the need to coordinate the supply of intermediates, UDPG and G6P, with cell growth and development, hence the possibility of a crucial role for T6P as in embryos and leaves.

Sugar Signals

The initial discovery that the trehalose pathway, and T6P in particular, has a powerful function in metabolic regulation is, on reflection, perhaps not surprising. T6P and trehalose are made from UDPG and G6P, so T6P and trehalose synthesis draw from a metabolite pool at the center of metabolism, but because trehalose is not a major end-product in plants, it is removed from major metabolic flux (**Figure 7**). This means that the synthesis of T6P and trehalose can act as an effective indicator of G6P and UDPG pool size without compromising any other function of the trehalose pathway. T6P is a low abundance molecule and responds rapidly to the sucrose supply (56). This rapid and large response is a consequence of as yet not fully elucidated control features (transcriptional and posttranslational control, including phosphorylation) that regulate T6P synthesis and breakdown. However, T6P synthesis mediated through constitutive *TPS1* expression likely reflects the availability of hexose phosphates, UDPG, and sucrose, which feeds into this pool. T6P therefore has all the characteristics of a signaling molecule. The role of sugars as signaling molecules has been widely documented (63, 81). In terms of metabolic signaling, it has been somewhat difficult to differentiate between sucrose and glucose as signaling molecules because sucrose can be rapidly converted into glucose. However, glucose and sucrose are clearly capable of relaying their own specific information. Glucose can signal through the conserved glucose sensor hexokinase (63) and acts a molecular signal and integrator of senescence (74). Sucrose specifically controls translation of basic leucine zipper (bZIP)-type transcription factors and hence the downstream gene targets of these transcription factors (107). The low abundance and dynamic response of T6P could potentiate specific and rapid communication of metabolic status that reflects pool sizes of G6P, UDPG, and sucrose and hence provide a different and specific kind of signaling to that of other sugars. *TPS1* expression appears to be constitutive, but other trehalose pathway enzymes are regulated developmentally and by stress, providing the basis for a regulatory system linking the hexose phosphate pool and UDPG with development and the environment.

It is worthwhile to make the comparison with fructose 2,6-bisphosphate (F26BP), a similarly low abundance regulator with a dynamic response. F26BP regulates the interconversion of F6P and fructose 1,6-bisphosphate and influences pool sizes of hexose and triose phosphates, which can regulate the flux of photosynthetic carbon to sucrose and starch in plants (90). In contrast to the modification of T6P in transgenic plants, modification of F26BP produces effects limited to the partition between sucrose and starch, with possibly even less importance in species such as wheat (96). The wide-ranging effects on growth and development caused by the modification of T6P are not observed when F26BP levels are altered. F26BP is clearly an important molecule in metabolic regulation and was an important discovery in the early 1980s (100), but unlike T6P, it is not linked with growth and development.

PERSPECTIVE

The discovery of the trehalose pathway in plants is quite a remarkable story. Less than 10 years ago this pathway was not even considered as a component of metabolic regulation. Now the trehalose pathway is known to play a central part in the coordination of metabolism with growth and development as part of a signaling network that communicates internal and external cues to coordinate these processes (**Figure 7**). One framework to understand the role of T6P is as a signal of G6P and UDPG pool size (the precursors of T6P), and hence as an indicator of sucrose, which feeds into this pool. Constitutive expression of *TPS1* would enable T6P to increase under conditions of high assimilate supply and flux into this pool, but decrease under conditions of starvation and stress, which would decrease this pool size and T6P content through extensive regulation of TPPs. T6P may be involved in metabolic homeostasis of this pool size, the effective regulation of which is necessary for the coordination of metabolism with development (particularly, for example, the supply of UDPG for cell wall synthesis). T6P further communicates the metabolite and sucrose status of the cytosol to the chloroplast, activating starch synthesis via AGPase.

SUMMARY POINTS

1. Plants are unique in that they can synthesize both of the nonreducing disaccharides found in nature, sucrose and trehalose. The sugars have divergent roles in plants; sucrose is found at high concentrations and trehalose is found in trace abundance in most species.
2. Trehalose pathway genes have proliferated in plants [2 classes of *trehalose phosphate synthases* (*TPS*), 11 genes in *A. thaliana*; 10 *A. thaliana trehalose phosphate phosphatase* (*TPP*) genes; but only 1 *trehalase* gene]. The genes are under purifying selection. The acquisition of bacterial TPP may have driven the creation of a new role for class II TPSs, which have both synthase and phosphatase domains but no demonstrated catalytic activity.
3. TPS1 (class I) synthesizes trehalose 6-phosphate (T6P), class II TPSs may have a regulatory function, and TPPs are catalytically active as phosphatases. TPS1 is constitutively expressed. Class II TPSs and TPPs are regulated transcriptionally by carbon status and stress. Class II TPSs are phosphorylated and interact with 14-3-3 proteins.
4. The wide-ranging and unprecedented impacts of altering the trehalose pathway in transgenic plants appear to link the trehalose pathway with the coordination between metabolism and development in all tissues. T6P is a potent sugar signal that putatively coordinates metabolism with development in response to carbon availability and stress. A key to its role may lie in its proximity to UDPG and hexose phosphate pools. UDPG is important in cell wall synthesis and hence cell and organ growth and development. The role of trehalose is less clear but it may regulate starch breakdown.

FUTURE ISSUES

1. Further substantiation of the hypothesis that T6P responds to and regulates UDPG and hexose phosphate pools is required to explain its role in the integration of metabolism and development.
2. T6P direct targets and the mechanism of T6P action should be identified.
3. We require a fuller understanding of the role of T6P in metabolism and development.
4. We need more information about the role of class II TPS genes (*AtTPS5–11*).

5. High-throughput methods of T6P measurement are required, as well as resolution to particular cell types.
6. The function of trehalose must be established.

DISCLOSURE STATEMENT

The authors are not aware of any biases that might be perceived as affecting the objectivity of this review.

ACKNOWLEDGMENTS

Rothamsted Research receives grant-aided support from the Biotechnology and Biological Sciences Research Council (BBSRC) of the United Kingdom. M.P. would like to thank the many generous colleagues who have enabled scientific progress to reach the current stage. In particular, M.P. would like to mention the part played by Oscar Goddijn, Klaus-Peter Krause, and Deborah Keith (Mogen International, Zeneca-Mogen, and subsequently Syngenta-Mogen) in the early stages of this research, the sharing of plant material by them and Henriette Schluepmann and Sjef Smeekens (University of Utrecht), and recent funding from the BBSRC (grants BB/C51257X/1 and BB/D006112/1). M.P. is grateful to John Lunn for a copy of a review article prior to publication and to Detlef Weigel for permission to present gene expression patterns using the ATGenexpress visualization tool from Reference 89. Gratitude is further extended to Astrid Wingler (University College London) and Till Pellny (Rothamsted Research) for reading and commenting on the manuscript.

LITERATURE CITED

1. Acevedo-Hernandez GJ, Leon P, Herrera-Estrella LR. 2005. Sugar and ABA responsiveness of a minimal RBCS light responsive unit is mediated by direct binding of ABI4. *Plant J.* 43:506–19
2. Albertorio F, Chapa VA, Chen X, Diaz AJ, Cremer PS. 2007. The α,α-(1–1) linkage of trehalose is key to anhydrobiotic preservation. *J. Am. Chem. Soc.* 129:10567–74
3. Almeida AM, Silva AB, Araújo SS, Cardoso LA, Santos DM, et al. 2007. Responses to water withdrawal of tobacco plants genetically engineered with the *AtTPS1* gene: a special reference to photosynthetic parameters. *Euphytica* 154:113–26
4. Almeida AM, Villalobos E, Araújo SS, Leyman B, van Dijck P, et al. 2005. Transformation of tobacco with an *Arabidopsis thaliana* gene involved in trehalose biosynthesis increases tolerance to several abiotic stresses. *Euphytica* 146:165–76
5. Anselmino O, Gilg E. 1913. Ueber das Vorkommen von Trehalose in *Selaginella lepidophylla. Ber. Deut. Pharm. Ges.* 23:326–30
6. Arguelles JC. 2000. Physiological roles of trehalose in bacteria and yeasts: a comparative analysis. *Arch. Microbiol.* 174:217–24
7. Avonce N, Leyman B, Mascorro-Gallardo JO, van Dijck P, Thevelein JM, Iturriaga G. 2004. The *Arabidopsis* trehalose 6-phosphtae synthase *AtTPS1* gene is a regulator of glucose, abscisic acid and stress signalling. *Plant Physiol.* 136:3649–59
8. **Avonce N, Mendoza-Vargas A, Morett E, Iturriaga G. 2006. Insights on the evolution of trehalose biosynthesis. *BMC Evol. Biol.* 6:109**

8. Concludes that natural selection is acting upon codons of TPS and TPP domains of eukaryotic proteins to preserve functionality.

9. Baud S, Graham IA. 2006. A spatiotemporal analysis of enzymatic activities associated with carbon metabolism in wild type and mutant embryos of *Arabidopsis* using in situ histochemistry. *Plant J.* 46:155–69
10. Bell W, Sun W, Hohmann S, Wera S, Reinders A, et al. 1998. Composition and functional analysis of the *Saccharomyces cerevisiae* trehalose synthase complex. *J. Biol. Chem.* 273:33311–19
11. Belocopitow E, Marechal LR. 1970. Trehalose phosphorylase from *Euglena gracilis*. *Biochim. Biophys. Acta* 198:151–54
12. Bianchi G, Gamba A, Limiroli R, Pozzi N, Elster R, et al. 1993. The unusual sugar composition in leaves of the resurrection plant *Myrothamnus flabellifolia*. *Physiol. Plant.* 87:223–26
13. Bläsing OE, Gibon Y, Gunther M, Hohne M, Morcuende R, et al. 2005. Sugars and circadian regulation make major contributions to the global regulation of diurnal gene expression in *Arabidopsis*. *Plant Cell* 17:3257–81
14. Blázquez MA, Lagunas R, Gancedo C, Gancedo JM. 1993. Trehalose 6-phosphate, a new regulator of yeast glycolysis that inhibits hexokinases. *FEBS Lett.* 329:51–54
15. Blázquez MA, Santos E, Flores C-L, Martínez-Zapater JM, Salinas J, Gancedo C. 1998. Isolation and molecular characterisation of the *Arabidopsis TPS1* gene, encoding trehalose 6-phosphate synthase. *Plant J.* 13:685–89
16. Bonini BM, van Dijck P, Thevelein JM. 2003. Uncoupling of the glucose growth defect and the deregulation of glycolysis in *Saccharomyces cerevisiae tps1* mutants expressing trehalose 6-phosphate insensitive hexokinase from *Schizosaccharomyces pombe*. *Biochim. Biophys. Acta* 1606:83–93
17. Brenner WG, Romanov GA, Kollmer I, Burkle L, Schmulling T. 2005. Immediate-early and delayed cytokinin response genes of *Arabidopsis thaliana* identified by genome-wide expression profiling reveal novel cytokinin-sensitive processes and suggest cytokinin action through transcriptional cascades. *Plant J.* 44:314–33
18. Brodmann A, Schuller A, Ludwig-Müller J, Aeschbacher RA, Wiemken A, et al. 2002. Induction of trehalase in *Arabidopsis* plants infected with the trehalose-producing pathogen *Plasmodiophora brassicae*. *Mol. Plant-Microbe Int.* 15:693–700
19. Brumfiel G. 2004. Cell biology: just add water. *Nature* 428:14–15
20. Burroughs AM, Allen KN, Dunaway-Mariano D, Aravind L. 2006. Evolutionary genomics of the HAD superfamily: understanding the structural adaptations and catalytic diversity in a superfamily of phosphoesterases and allied enzymes. *J. Mol. Biol.* 361:1003–34
21. Chen Q, Haddad GG. 2004. Role of trehalose phosphate synthase and trehalose during hypoxia: from flies to mammals. *J. Exp. Biol.* 207:3125–29
22. Chen S, Hajirezaei M, Peisker M, Tschiersch H, Sonnewald U, et al. 2005. Decreased sucrose-6-phosphate phosphatase level in transgenic tobacco inhibits photosynthesis, alters carbohydrate partitioning and reduces growth. *Planta* 221:479–92
23. Crowe JH, Carpenter JF, Crowe LM. 1998. The role of vitrification in anhydrobiosis. *Annu. Rev. Physiol.* 60:73–103
24. Davis BG. 2000. Hand in glove. *Chem. Ind.* 4:134–38
25. De Smet KAL, Weston A, Brown IN, Young DB, Robertson BD. 2000. Three pathways for trehalose biosynthesis in mycobacteria. *Microbiology* 146:199–208
26. Deuschle K, Chaudhuri B, Okumoto S, Lager I, Lalonde S, Frommer WB. 2006. Rapid metabolism of glucose detected with FRET glucose nanosensors in epidermal cells and intact roots of *Arabidopsis* RNA-silencing mutants. *Plant Cell* 18:2314–25

27. **Eastmond PJ, van Dijken AJ, Spielman M, Kerr A, Tissier AF, et al. 2002. Trehalose-6-phosphate synthase 1, which catalyses the first step in trehalose synthesis, is essential for *Arabidopsis* embryo maturation. *Plant J.* 29:223–35**

27. First paper to show the essential requirement for a trehalose pathway gene in plants.

28. Elbein AD. 1967. Carbohydrate metabolism in Streptomycetes. II. Isolation and enzymatic synthesis of trehalose. *J. Bacteriol.* 94:1520–24
29. Elbein AD, Pan YT, Pastuszak I, Carroll D. 2003. New insights on trehalose: a multifunctional molecule. *Glycobiology* 13:17–27
30. Feizi T, Chai W. 2004. Oligosaccharide microarrays to decipher the glycocode. *Nat. Mol. Cell Biol.* 5:582–88
31. Foster AJ, Jenkinson JM, Talbot NJ. 2003. Trehalose synthesis and metabolism are required at different stages of plant infection by *Magnaporthe grisea*. *EMBO J.* 22:225–35
32. Frison M, Parrou JL, Guillaumot D, Masquelier D, Francois J, et al. 2007. The *Arabidopsis thaliana* trehalase is a plasma membrane-bound enzyme with extracellular activity. *FEBS Lett.* 581:4010–16
33. Garg AK, Kim J-K, Owens TG, Ranwala AP, Do Choi Y, et al. 2002. Trehalose accumulation in rice plants confers high tolerance to different abiotic stresses. *Proc. Natl. Acad. Sci. USA* 99:15898–903
34. Gerhardt R, Stitt M, Heldt HW. 1987. Subcellular metabolite levels in spinach leaves. Regulation of sucrose synthesis during diurnal alterations in photosynthesis. *Plant Physiol.* 83:399–407
35. Glinski M, Weckwerth W. 2005. Differential multisite phosphorylation of the trehalose 6-phosphate synthase gene family in *Arabidopsis thaliana*. *Mol. Cell Proteomics* 4:1614–25
36. **Goddijn OJM, Verwoerd TC, Voogd E, Krutwagen RWHH, de Graaf PTHM, et al. 1997. Inhibition of trehalase activity enhances trehalose accumulation in transgenic plants. *Plant Physiol.* 113:181–90**

36. Landmark paper that initiated the emergence of the centrality of the trehalose pathway in plants.

37. Gomez LD, Baud S, Gilday A, Li Y, Graham I. 2006. Delayed embryo development in the *Arabidopsis* trehalose 6-phosphate synthase 1 mutant is associated with altered cell wall structure, decreased cell division and starch accumulation. *Plant J.* 46:69–84
38. Harmer SL, Hogenesch JB, Straume M, Chang HS, Han B. 2000. Orchestrated transcription of key pathways in *Arabidopsis* by the circadian clock. *Science* 290:2110–13
39. Harthill JE, Meek SEM, Morrice N, Peggie MW, Borch J, et al. 2006. Phosphorylation and 14-3-3 binding of *Arabidopsis* trehalose phosphate synthase 5 in response to 2-deoxyglucose. *Plant J.* 47:211–23
40. Hendry GAF, Wallace RK. 1993. The origin, distribution, and evolutionary significance of fructans. In *Science and Technology of Fructans*, ed. M Suzuki, NJ Chatterton, pp. 119–39. Boca Raton, FL: CRC Press
41. Higashiyama T. 2002. Novel functions and applications of trehalose. *Pure Appl. Chem.* 74:1263–69
42. Hohmann S, Neves MJ, de Koning W, Alijo R, Ramos J, Thevelein JM. 1993. The growth and signalling defects of the *ggs1 (fdp/byp1)* deletion mutant on glucose are suppressed by a deletion of the gene encoding hexokinase PII. *Curr. Genet.* 23:281–89
43. Hurry VM, Strand A, Tobiaeson M, Gardestrom P, Oquist G. 1995. Cold hardening of spring and winter wheat and rape results in differential effects on growth, carbon metabolism, and carbohydrate content. *Plant Physiol.* 109:697–706
44. Ji X, Van den Ende W, Van Laere A, Cheng S, Bennett J. 2005. Structure, evolution and expression of the two invertase families of rice. *J. Mol. Evol.* 60:615–34
45. Kandel-Kfir M, Damari-Weissler H, German MA, Gidoni D, Mett A. 2006. Two newly identified membrane-associated and plastidic tomato HXKs: characteristics, predicted structure and intracellular localisation. *Planta* 224:1341–52

46. Karim S, Aronsson H, Ericson H, Pirhonen M, Leyman B, et al. 2007. Improved drought tolerance without undesired side effects in transgenic plants producing trehalose. *Plant Mol. Biol.* 64:371–86

47. Kebeish R, Niessen M, Thiruveedhi K, Bari R, Hirsch HJ, et al. 2007. Chloroplastic photorespiratory bypass increases photosynthesis and biomass production in *Arabidopsis thaliana*. *Nat. Biotech.* 25:593–99

48. Kolbe A, Tiessen A, Schluepmann H, Paul M, Ulrich S, Geigenberger P. 2005. Trehalose 6-phosphate regulates starch synthesis via post-translational redox activation of ADP-glucose pyrophosphorylase. *Proc. Natl. Acad. Sci. USA* 102:11118–23

48. The closest work yet to the identification of a direct target site for trehalose 6-phosphate.

49. Kormish JD, McGhee JD. 2005. The *C. elegans* lethal gut-obstructed *gob-1* gene is trehalose-6-phosphate phosphatase. *Dev. Biol.* 287:35–47

50. Laine RA. 1994. Invited commentary: A calculation of the possible oligosaccharide isomers both branched and linear yields 1.05×10^{12} structures for a reducing hexasaccharide: the isomer barrier to development of single method saccharide sequencing or synthesis systems. *Glycobiology* 4:759–67

51. Langenkämper G, Fung RWM, Newcomb RD, Atkinson RG, Gardner RC, MacRae EA. 2002. Sucrose-phosphate synthase genes in plants belong to three different families. *J. Mol. Evol.* 54:322–32

52. Leyman B, van Dijck P, Thevelein JM. 2001. An unexpected plethora of trehalose biosynthesis genes in *Arabidopsis thaliana*. *Trends Plant Sci.* 6:510–13

52. First documented genomic analysis of trehalose pathway genes in plants.

53. Liu F, Van Toai T, Moy LP, Bock G, Linford LD, Quackenbush J. 2005. Global transcription profiling reveals comprehensive insights into hypoxic response in *Arabidopsis*. *Plant Physiol.* 137:1115–29

54. Londesborough J, Vuorio OE. 1993. Purification of trehalose synthase from baker's yeast. Its temperature-dependent activation by fructose 6-phosphate and inhibition by phosphate. *Eur. J. Biochem.* 216:841–48

55. Lunn JE. 2007. Gene families and evolution of trehalose metabolism in plants. *Funct. Plant Biol.* 34:550–63

55. Tremendously thorough analysis of trehalose pathway genes in plants, which shows the ancient ancestry of the trehalose pathway.

56. Lunn JE, Feil R, Hendriks JHM, Gibon Y, Morcuende R, et al. 2006. Sugar-induced increases in trehalose 6-phosphate are correlated with redox activation of ADP-glucose pyrophosphorylase and higher rates of starch synthesis in *Arabidopsis thaliana*. *Biochem J.* 397:139–48

56. Important confirmation of trehalose 6-phosphate as a sugar signal and development of technology to measure trehalose 6-phosphate.

57. Maruta K, Hattori K, Nakada T, Kubota M, Sugimoto T, Kurimoto M. 1996. Cloning and sequencing of trehalose biosynthesis genes from *Arthrobacter sp.* Q36. *Biochim. Biophys. Acta* 1289:10–13

58. Maruta K, Hattori K, Nakada T, Kubota M, Sugimoto T, Kurimoto M. 1996. Cloning and sequencing of trehalose biosynthesis genes from *Rhizobium sp.* Q36. *Biosci. Biotech. Biochem.* 60:717–20

59. Merzendorfer H, Zimoch L. 2003. Chitin metabolism in insects: structure, function and regulation of chitin synthases and chitinases. *J. Exp. Biol.* 206:4393–412

60. Meyer RC, Steinfath M, Lisec J, Becher M, Witucka-Wall H, et al. 2007. The metabolic signature related to high plant growth rate in *Arabidopsis thaliana*. *Proc. Natl. Acad. Sci. USA* 104:4759–64

61. Miranda JA, Avonce N, Suárez R, Thevelein JM, Van Dijck P, Iturriaga G. 2007. A bifunctional TPS-TPP enzyme from yeast confers tolerance to multiple and extreme abiotic-stress conditions in transgenic *Arabidopsis*. *Planta*. In press

62. Miyagawa Y, Tamoi M, Shigeoka S. 2001. Overexpression of a cyanobacterial fructose-1,6-sedoheptulose-1,7-bisphosphatase in tobacco enhances photosynthesis and growth. *Nat. Biotechnol.* 19:965–69
63. Moore B, Zhou L, Rolland F, Hall Q, Cheng WH, et al. 2003. Role of the *Arabidopsis* glucose sensor HXK1 in nutrient, light and hormonal signalling. *Science* 300:332–36
64. Müller J, Boller T, Wiemken A. 1995. Effects of validamycin A, a potent trehalase inhibitor, and phytohormones on trehalose metabolism in roots and root nodules of soybean and cowpea. *Planta* 197:362–68
65. Osuna D, Usadel B, Morcuende R, Gibon Y, Blasing OE, et al. 2007. Temporal responses of transcripts, enzyme activities and metabolites after adding sucrose to carbon-deprived *Arabidopsis* seedlings. *Plant J.* 49:463–91
66. Paul M. 2007. Trehalose 6-phosphate. *Curr. Opin. Plant Biol.* 10:303–9
67. Paul MJ, Driscoll SP. 1997. Sugar repression of photosynthesis: the role of carbohydrates in signalling nitrogen deficiency through source:sink imbalance. *Plant Cell Environ.* 20:110–16
68. Paul MJ, Pellny TK, Goddijn O. 2001. Enhancing photosynthesis with sugar signals. *Trends Plant Sci.* 6:197–200
69. Pellny TK, Ghannoum O, Conroy JP, Schluepmann H, Smeekens S, et al. 2004. Genetic modification of photosynthesis with *E. coli* genes for trehalose synthesis. *Plant Biotech. J.* 2:71–82
70. Peters S, Mundree SG, Thomson JA, Farrant JM, Keller F. 2007. Protection mechanisms in the resurrection plant *Xerophyta viscosa* (Baker): both sucrose and raffinose family oligosaccharides (RFOs) accumulate in leaves in response to water deficit. *J. Exp. Bot.* 58:1947–56
71. Piippo M, Allahverdiyeva Y, Paakkarinen V, Suoranta U-M, Battchikova N, Aro E-M. 2006. Chloroplast-mediated regulation of nuclear genes in *Arabidopsis thaliana* in the absence of light stress. *Physiol. Genomics* 25:142–52
72. Pilon-Smits EAH, Terry N, Seors T, Kim H, Zayed A, et al. 1998. Trehalose-producing transgenic tobacco plants show improved growth and performance under drought stress. *J. Plant Physiol.* 152:525–32
73. Poorter H, de Jong R. 1999. A comparison of specific leaf area, chemical composition and leaf construction costs of field plants from 15 habitats differing in productivity. *New Phytol.* 143:163–76
74. Pourtau N, Jennings R, Pelzer E, Pallas J, Wingler A. 2006. Effect of sugar-induced senescence on gene expression and implications for the regulation of senescence in *Arabidopsis*. *Planta* 224:556–68
75. Pramanik MHR, Imai R. 2005. Functional identification of a trehalose 6-phosphate phosphatase gene that is involved in transient induction of trehalose biosynthesis during chilling stress in rice. *Plant Mol. Biol.* 58:751–62
76. Qu Q, Lee SJ, Boss W. 2004. TreT, a novel trehalose glycosyltransferring synthase of the hyperthermophilic archeon *Thermococcus litoralis*. *J. Biol. Chem.* 279:47890–97
77. Ramon M, Rolland F. 2007. Plant development: introducing trehalose metabolism. *Trends Plant Sci.* 12:185–88
78. Ramon M, Rolland F, Thevelein JM, Van Dijck P, Leyman B. 2007. ABI4 mediates the effects of exogenous trehalose on *Arabidopsis* growth and starch breakdown. *Plant Mol. Biol.* 63:195–206
79. Ratnakumar S, Tunnacliffe A. 2006. Intracellular trehalose is neither necessary nor sufficient for desiccation tolerance in yeast. *FEMS Yeast Res.* 6:902–13

80. Rimmele M, Boos W. 1994. Trehalose 6-phosphate hydrolase of *Escherichia coli*. *J. Bacteriol.* 176:5654–64
81. Rolland F, Baena-Gonzalez E, Sheen J. 2006. Sugar sensing and signalling in plants: conserved and novel mechanisms. *Annu. Rev. Plant Biol.* 57:675–709
82. Ryu SI, Park CS, Cha J, Woo EJ, Lee SB. 2005. A novel trehalose-synthesising glycosyltransferase from *Pyrococcus horikoshii*: molecular cloning and characterisation. *Biochem. Biophys. Res. Commun.* 329:429–36
83. Saavedra R, Segura E, Tenorio EP, López-Marín LM. 2006. Mycobacterial trehalose-containing glycolipid with immunomodulatory activity on human $CD4^+$ and $CD8^+$ T-cells. *Microbes Infect.* 8:533–40
84. Satoh-Nagasawa N, Nagasawa N, Malcomber S, Sakai H, Jackson D. 2006. A trehalose metabolic enzyme controls inflorescence architecture in maize. *Nature* 441:227–30
85. Schaaff I, Heinisch J, Zimmermann FK. 1989. Overproduction of glycolytic enzymes in yeast. *Yeast* 5:285–90
86. Schiraldi C, Lernia ID, Rosa MD. 2002. Trehalose production: exploiting novel approaches. *Trends Biotechnol.* 20:420–25
87. **Schluepmann H, Pellny T, van Dijken A, Smeekens S, Paul MJ. 2003. Trehalose 6-phosphate is indispensable for carbohydrate utilisation and growth in *Arabidopsis thaliana*. *Proc. Natl. Acad. Sci. USA* 100:6849–54**

87. First paper to show the indispensability of trehalose 6-phosphate in plants and hence a reason for the requirement for *TPS1*.

88. Schluepmann H, van Dijken A, Aghdasi M, Wobbes B, Paul M, Smeekens S. 2004. Trehalose mediated growth inhibition of *Arabidopsis* seedlings is due to trehalose 6-phosphate accumulation. *Plant Physiol.* 135:879–90
89. Schmid M, Davison TS, Henz SR, Pape UJ, Demar M, et al. 2005. A gene expression map of *Arabidopsis thaliana* development. *Nat. Genet.* 37:501–6
90. Scott P, Lange AJ, Kruger NJ. 2000. Photosynthetic carbon metabolism in leaves of transgenic tobacco (*Nicotiana tabacum* L.) containing decreased amounts of fructose-2,6-bisphosphate. *Planta* 211:864–73
91. Shima S, Matsui H, Tahara S, Imai R. 2007. Biochemical characterisation of rice trehalose 6-phosphate phosphatases supports distinctive functions of these plant enzymes. *FEBS J.* 274:1192–201
92. Tanaka M, Machida Y, Niu S, Ikeda T, Jana NR, et al. 2004. Trehalose alleviates polyglutamine-mediated pathology in a mouse model of Huntingdon disease. *Nat. Med.* 10:148–54
93. Thevelein JM. 1992. The RAS-adenylate cyclase pathway and cell cycle control in *Saccharomyces cerevisiae*. *Antonie van Leeuwenhoek* 62:109–30
94. Thevelein JM, Hohmann S. 1995. Trehalose synthase: guard to the gate of glycolysis in yeast? *Trends Biochem. Sci.* 20:3–10
95. Thimm O, Blasing O, Gibon Y, Nagel A, Meyer S. 2004. MAPMAN: a user-driven tool to display genomics data sets onto diagrams of metabolic pathways and other biological processes. *Plant J.* 37:914–39
96. Trevanion SJ. 2002. Regulation of sucrose and starch synthesis in wheat (*Triticum aestivum* L.) leaves: role of fructose 2,6-bisphosphate. *Planta* 215:653–55
97. Tsusaki K, Nishimoto T, Nakada T, Kubota M, Chaen H, et al. 1996. Cloning and sequencing of trehalose synthase gene from *Pimelobacter sp.* R48. *Biochim. Biophys. Acta* 1290:1–3
98. Van Dijck P, Mascorro-Gallardo JO, De Bus M, Royackers K, Iturriaga G, Thevelein JM. 2002. Truncation of *Arabidopsis thaliana* and *Selaginella lepidophylla* trehalose 6-phosphate synthase (TPS) unlocks high catalytic activity and supports high trehalose levels upon expression in yeast. *Biochem. J.* 366:63–71

99. Van Dijken AJH, Schluepmann H, Smeekens SCM. 2004. *Arabidopsis* trehalose 6-phosphate synthase 1 is essential for normal vegetative growth and transition to flowering. *Plant Physiol.* 135:969–77
100. Van Schaftingen E, Hue L, Hers HG. 1980. Fructose 2,6-bisphosphate, the probable structure of the glucose- and glucagon-sensitive stimulator of phosphofructokinase. *Biochem. J.* 192:897–901
101. Veluthambi K, Mahadevan S, Maheshwari R. 1982. Trehalose toxicity in *Cuscuta reflexa*. *Plant Physiol.* 69:1247–51
102. Vogel G, Aeschbacher RA, Müller J, Boller T, Wiemken A. 1998. Trehalose 6-phosphate phosphatases from *Arabidopsis thaliana*: identification by functional complementation of the yeast *tps2* mutant. *Plant J.* 13:673–83
103. Vogel G, Fiehn O, Jean-Richard-dit-Bressel L, Boller T, Wiemken A, et al. 2001. Trehalose metabolism of *Arabidopsis*: occurrence of trehalose and molecular cloning and characterisation of trehalose 6-phosphate synthase homologues. *J. Exp. Bot.* 52:1817–26
104. Von Lippmann E. 1912. Ueber Vorkommen von Trehalose Vanillin und d-Sorbit. *Ber. Dtsch. Chem. Ges.* 45:3431–33
105. Wang R, Okamoto M, Xing X, Crawford NM. 2003. Microarray analysis of the nitrate response in *Arabidopsis* roots and shoots reveals over 1000 rapidly responding genes and new linkages to glucose, trehalose 6-phosphate, iron, and sulphate metabolism. *Plant Physiol.* 132:556–67
106. Wannet WJB, Hermans JHM, Van Der Drift C, den Camp H. 2000. HPLC detection of soluble carbohydrates involved in mannitol and trehalose metabolism in the edible mushroom *Agaricus bisporus*. *J. Agric. Food Chem.* 48:287–91
107. Wiese A, Elzinga N, Wobbes B, Smeekens S. 2004. A conserved upstream open reading frame mediates sucrose-induced repression of translation. *Plant Cell* 16:1717–29
108. Wilson RA, Jenkinson JM, Gibson RP, Littlechild JA, Wang Z-Y, Talbot NJ. 2007. TPS1 regulates the pentose phosphate pathway, nitrogen metabolism and fungal virulence. *EMBO J.* 26:3673–85
109. Wingler A. 2002. The function of trehalose biosynthesis in plants. *Phytochemistry* 60:437–40
110. Wingler A, Fritzius T, Wiemken A, Boller T, Aeschbacher A. 2000. Trehalose induces the ADP-glucose pyrophosphorylase gene and starch synthesis in *Arabidopsis*. *Plant Physiol.* 124:105–14
111. Wolkers WF, Looper SA, Fontanilla RA, Tsvetkova NM, Tablin F, Crowe JH. 2003. Temperature dependence of fluid phase endocytosis coincides with membrane properties of pig platelets. *Biochim. Biophys. Acta* 1612:154–63
112. Worning P, Jensen LJ, Nelson KE, Brunak S, Ussery DW. 2000. Structural analysis of DNA sequence: evidence for lateral gene transfer in *Thermotoga maritima*. *Nucleic Acids Res.* 28:706–9
113. Zimmerman P, Hennig L, Gruissem W. 2005. Gene expression analysis and network discovery using Genevestigator. *Trends Plant Sci.* 10:407–9

108. Provided understanding of the role of the trehalose pathway in regulating carbon and nitrogen metabolism in a plant pathogenic fungus.

Auxin: The Looping Star in Plant Development

René Benjamins and Ben Scheres

Department of Biology, Faculty of Science, Utrecht University, 3584 CH Utrecht, The Netherlands; email: R.Benjamins@uu.nl; B.Scheres@uu.nl

Annu. Rev. Plant Biol. 2008. 59:443–65

The *Annual Review of Plant Biology* is online at plant.annualreviews.org

This article's doi:
10.1146/annurev.arplant.58.032806.103805

1543-5008/08/0602-0443$20.00

Key Words

auxin transport, polarity, auxin signaling, auxin receptor

Abstract

The phytohormone auxin is a key factor in plant growth and development. Forward and reverse genetic strategies have identified important molecular components in auxin perception, signaling, and transport. These advances resulted in the identification of some of the underlying regulatory mechanisms as well as the emergence of functional frameworks for auxin action. This review focuses on the feedback loops that form an integrative part of these regulatory mechanisms.

Contents

INTRODUCTION

Auxin is probably the most investigated plant hormone and is known to be involved in virtually every aspect of plant growth and development. The exact sites of auxin biosynthesis are unknown, but the identification of molecular components of auxin biosynthesis revealed the existence of at least two separate biosynthesis pathways (6, 23, 145). The synthesized auxin is transported to specific tissues where it triggers a signaling cascade that causes developmental responses. Transport of auxin is unique because it displays directionality, which is provided through the specific subcellular localization of auxin efflux and auxin influx machineries (9). The subcellular targeting of the constituent proteins is regulated by components involved in endosomal trafficking, and also depends on the phosphorylation status of the proteins, as well as on components that determine membrane composition (38, 44, 71, 135). Auxin is perceived by auxin receptors, represented by members of the TRANSPORT INHIBITOR RESPONSE 1 (TIR1) family, which results in the proteolysis of AUXIN/INDOLE-3-ACETIC ACID (Aux/IAA) proteins, thereby releasing their inhibitory effect on AUXIN RESPONSE FACTORS (ARFs), transcription factors that regulate auxin responsive gene expression (93).

TIR1: TRANSPORT INHIBITOR RESPONSE 1

Aux/IAA: auxin/indole-3-acetic acid

Indole-3-acetic acid (IAA): the most abundant naturally occurring auxin

ARF: AUXIN RESPONSE FACTOR

This review discusses how the emerging molecular mechanisms of auxin action are beginning to suggest concrete regulatory mechanisms for plant development and behavior. First the molecular players in auxin perception and auxin distribution are discussed separately. Then we discuss that auxin action involves two intertwined regulatory loops, one transcriptional and one polarity loop. Finally, examples are presented on how this information is beginning to be integrated to yield biological understanding.

AUXIN BIOSYNTHESIS

The exact mechanisms and cellular locations of auxin biosynthesis remain relatively unknown. However, experiments that include auxin measurements, labeling studies, and analysis of candidate biosynthetic genes provide steadily growing insights into possible mechanisms and sites of auxin biosynthesis.

Two auxin biosynthesis pathways exist: One is dependent on the precursor tryptophan (Trp) and the other is Trp-independent. Cytochrome P450 can convert Trp into indole-3-acetaldoxime (IAOx), an intermediate, at least in vitro. This cytochrome P450 is expressed in young leaves and flowers, which are the suggested sites of auxin biosynthesis (72). Plants overexpressing CYP79B2, a cytochrome P450, contain elevated levels of free auxin and display auxin overproduction phenotypes, whereas double mutants in *cyp79B2cyp79B3* have reduced levels of IAA (146). The *YUCCA* gene, encoding a flavin monooxygenase, is also involved in Trp-dependent auxin biosynthesis, where it converts tryptamine into N-hydroxyl-tryptamine (125, 145). *YUCCA* genes are expressed mainly in meristems, young primordia, vascular tissues, and reproductive organs, all of which are suggested sites of auxin synthesis (23). Quadruple *yuc1yuc4yuc10yuc11* mutants do not develop a hypocotyl and root meristem, a phenotype related to defects in auxin signaling, indicating the importance of this auxin biosynthetic branch in plant development (24). Plants that overexpress *YUCCA* genes have higher endogenous auxin levels and display auxin-related phenotypes similar to mutants that overexpress the *Agrobacterium* auxin biosynthesis gene *iaaM* (23, 99, 125, 145). Subsequently, the N-hydroxyl-tryptamine is converted to IAOx, probably by a cytochrome P450 or another flavin monooxygenase. Finally, this Trp-dependent pathway should also include a tryptophan decarboxylase to convert the tryptophan into tryptamine (66).

An auxin-related mutant, *superroot* (*sur1*), overproduces auxin, probably owing to its elevated aldehyde-oxydase activity (19, 106). Aldehyde oxydases are likely involved in the last step of auxin production in which indole acetaldehyde is converted to IAA (83). The mutant contains higher levels of both free and conjugated auxin, which cause auxin-related phenotypes with a typical disintegration of the connection between the stele and cortical cells (19). *SUR1* encodes a protein with similarity to tyrosine aminotransferases and may be involved in both the Trp-dependent pathway(s) and the Trp-independent pathway. The *SUR2* gene, encoding a cytochrome P450, may also alter auxin homeostasis (6). Mutants in the *SUR2* gene contain an increased level of free auxin in almost all organs analyzed in seedlings, which is likely due to an increased conversion of IAOx to IAA (6). *WEAK ETHYLENE INSENSITIVE2/ANTHRANILATE SYNTHASE alpha 1* (*WEI2/ASA1*) and *WEAK ETHYLENE INSENSITIVE7/ANTHRANILATE SYNTHASE beta 1* (*WIE7/ASB1*), suppressors of *sur1* and *sur2* mutants, represent subunits of a rate-limiting enzyme in Trp biosynthesis, anthranilate synthase. Overexpression of *WIE2* and *WIE7* results in auxin accumulation, whereas mutants do not accumulate auxin in response to ethylene, providing a link between ethylene and auxin synthesis (111). The effect of ethylene on root development is likely to proceed via upregulation of auxin biosynthesis as well as modulation of auxin transport (102, 115).

The presence of a Trp-independent pathway is partly based on physiological data involving mainly labeling experiments. Experiments using deuterium-labeled Trp and deuterium-labeled water showed that maize seedlings do not synthesize IAA solely from Trp. Mutants in tryptophan biosynthesis, such as *trp2-1* and *trp3-1*, have increased levels of total IAA, whereas the level of free IAA is comparable to that of wild-type. Labeling experiments using the *trp2-1* mutant imply that during Trp-independent IAA biosynthesis, IAA is produced from a precursor of Trp (87).

A well-recognized caveat of auxin biosynthesis research is that several genes known to affect auxin biosynthesis may not be directly involved in the biosynthesis of auxin but may rather influence auxin levels through modifications in related pathways (144). A second complication is that most of the synthesized IAA is not present in the free, active form, but in an inactive, conjugated form (92). Free IAA comprises only approximately 1% of the total auxin pool in plants, whereas the remaining part is conjugated to amino acids and sugars (90, 92). The regulation of auxin homeostasis likely depends on the hydrolysis of auxin conjugates. Both the amide- and sugar-linked IAA conjugates can be hydrolyzed, resulting in the release of free IAA. Different amide conjugate hydrolases with their own specificity likely exist in *Arabidopsis* (7, 27). Therefore, although the availability of mutants and molecular tools has provided information on auxin biosynthesis and homeostasis, we only begin to understand how these processes affect plant growth and development.

SCF^{TIR1}: ubiquitin ligase complex consisting of a SKP1 homolog (ASK1 in *Arabidopsis*), a Cullin, and an F-box protein, in this case TIR1

F-box: protein motif that functions as a protein-protein interaction domain to link the F-box protein to the SCF complex

AUXIN SIGNALING COMPONENTS

Over the past decades several auxin-responsive genes and gene families involved in the signaling of auxin have been identified, of which the *Aux/IAAs* and *ARFs* are the best studied. We focus here on the information needed to put the molecular components in a framework. Recent reviews provide more extensive information on Aux/IAA proteins, their degradation by the SCF^{TIR1} (for SKP1, Cullin, and F-box protein, in this case TRANSPORT INHIBITOR RESPONSE 1) complex, and their interaction with ARF transcription factors (31, 49, 65, 93, 133).

Aux/IAA and ARF Proteins

The expression of most *Aux/IAAs* is rapidly upregulated by auxin; *Aux/IAAs* are primary response genes. The *Arabidopsis* genome contains 29 different *Aux/IAA* genes and the encoded proteins contain four conserved domains (49). Domain II is thought to represent the targeting sequence for ubiquitination that leads to degradation of the protein. Domain III shows resemblance to DNA-binding domains of Arc and MetJ proteins, which led to the proposition that Aux/IAA proteins function as repressors (2). However, DNA binding was never demonstrated for these proteins. Domains III and IV mediate homodimerization. Interestingly, domains III and IV are also found in ARF proteins and mediate heterodimerization between ARFs and Aux/IAAs (128).

Forward genetic screens have led to the identification of *Arabidopsis* mutants in ten different *Aux/IAA* genes, which display a range of developmental defects caused by a reduced sensitivity to auxin (39, 50, 60, 80, 97, 100, 122, 137). All the identified mutations affect a stretch of five amino acids in domain II and represent gain-of-function mutations, explaining the (semi) dominant nature of their phenotypes. Importantly, these mutations increase the half-life of the normally short-lived Aux/IAA proteins. The Aux/IAA proteins are subject to degradation by the 26S proteasome following ubiquitination mediated by the E3 ubiquitin-ligase SCF^{TIR1} (31). Domain II of the Aux/IAA proteins is sufficient for interaction with the SCF^{TIR1} complex through the F-box protein TIR1 (see below), which explains how mutations in this domain stabilize Aux/IAA proteins (21, 47, 86).

The Aux/IAA proteins are suggested to interact functionally with ARF proteins, of which there are 22 encoded in the *Arabidopsis* genome. ARFs have an N-terminal DNA-binding domain (DBD) similar to that found in the transcription factor FUSCA 3 (67). This DBD specifically binds to so-called auxin response elements (AuxREs), which are typically represented by the sequence TGTCTC; related sequences can also act as target binding sites of ARF proteins (126, 127). Whether or not the middle region (MR) of ARF proteins is Q-rich determines transcriptional activation or repression of target genes. ARF proteins with a Q-rich MR, such as ARF5, 7, 8 and 19, are suggested to be activators, whereas ARF proteins without a Q-rich MR, such as ARF1 and 2, are thought to act as repressors (124). Whether the nature of the MR solely defines an ARF protein as a repressor or activator is not known. A well-characterized interaction between an ARF and an Aux/IAA is represented by that between MONOPTEROS (MP/ARF5) and BODENLOS (BDL/IAA12). The interaction between MP and BDL is crucial with respect to embryo pattern formation (134). In general, specific pairs of Aux/IAA and ARF proteins are suggested to determine auxin-dependent developmental processes (132). The analysis of pairs of ARF and Aux/IAA proteins is necessary to substantiate this point, but this endeavor is complicated by their large numbers and by the functional redundancy of members of both families. How do Aux/IAAs and ARFs regulate auxin-responsive gene expression? A current model states that an increase in the auxin levels results in a more rapid proteolysis of Aux/IAA proteins, relieving the active repression of the auxin-responsive genes by allowing the formation of ARF dimers. However, this model does not explain the function of the ARF isoforms that presumptively act as repressors.

Although important information on Aux/IAA and ARF function is available, several questions remain. Are ARFs still attached to Aux/IAAs when these are ubiquitinated and targeted to the proteasome? Do SCF^{TIR1}, Aux/IAAs, and ARFs form a complex on DNA? Do Aux/IAAs also bind DNA and is the binding site different from the ARF binding site? What is the function of ARFs that are suggested not to be activators?

THE TIR1 FAMILY OF AUXIN RECEPTORS

In the last decades a lot of effort has gone toward finding the auxin receptor(s). Proteins able to bind auxin have been identified, but none of those is generally accepted to be the elusive auxin receptor (123).

TIR1 was initially identified in a screen for mutants resistant to auxin transport inhibitors; *TIR1* encodes an F-box protein. TIR1 provides specificity to the SCF^{TIR1} ubiquitin protein ligase by binding Aux/IAA proteins that modulate the transcriptional response to auxin (47, 93). A degron of 17 amino acids in domain II is sufficient for auxin-regulated interaction. Not surprisingly, these 17 amino acids also include the amino acids that are mutated in the stabilized gain-of-function mutants that are described above (58). If TIR1 is important for the auxin response, mediated via the breakdown of Aux/IAA proteins, then why do *tir1* mutants not display phenotypes comparable to *aux/iaa* mutants? The *Arabidopsis* genome encodes five close homologs of *TIR1*, *AFB1* to *5* (for auxin signaling F-box protein 1 to 5), of which at least *AFB1*, *2*, and *3* act redundantly. Double, triple, and quadruple mutant plants display auxin-related phenotypes; quadruple mutants in all four F-box genes resemble *mp/arf5* and *bdl/iaa12* mutants (30, 50–52).

In contrast to other eukaryotic pathways that involve SCF-regulated breakdown of proteins, no evidence was found that a modification of the target (Aux/IAA proteins) was necessary for its interaction with SCF^{TIR1}. Instead, the interaction between Aux/IAA proteins and the SCF^{TIR1} is regulated by auxin; auxin affects either TIR1 or an associated protein (58). This result indicates a different mode of action compared with other SCF ligases, which require marked targets. This different mode of action, beautiful in its simplicity, is that auxin promotes the interaction between TIR1 and Aux/IAA proteins by binding to TIR1, thereby earmarking TIR1 as an auxin receptor (29, 59). However, firm proof that TIR1 binds the auxin instead of a TIR1-associated protein was lacking (29, 59). Finally, after resolving the crystal structure of TIR1 in complex with its SKP1 homolog *Arabidopsis* Skp1-like 1 (ASK1), with and without auxin or auxin-like compounds, researchers found that TIR1 indeed binds the auxin via its leucine-rich repeat (LRR) domain (117). Binding of auxin does not induce a conformational change and therefore auxin may serve as a molecular glue to facilitate binding of the Aux/IAA substrate, possibly through enhancing the affinity; this rather important issue remains to be investigated in depth. To their surprise the crystallographers found that inositol hexakisphosphate ($InsP_6$) bound as a cofactor to a TIR1 site different from the auxin and target binding site. The exact function of this interaction is not known (117), but it could indicate a new mode of cross talk between plant signaling pathways.

Questions that are raised by these findings include the following: Do other F-box proteins also function as receptors in plants? Do F-box proteins transmit hormonal signals only or other signals/stimuli as well? Are F-box receptors unique to plants or does

Inositol hexaphosphate ($InsP_6$): ubiquitous in plants; the major storage form of phosphorus implicated in various cellular processes

F-box mediated signaling also occur in other organisms?

PIN: PIN FORMED

AUXIN TRANSPORT COMPONENTS

Polar transport of auxin mediated by carrier proteins is a unique mechanism resulting in a controlled distribution of auxin that generates higher auxin concentrations in specific cells/tissues. The chemiosmotic model for polar auxin transport as proposed by Rubery, Sheldrake, and Raven (94, 101) states that auxin, a weak acid, can freely enter the cell, but is subsequently trapped inside the cell owing to the higher pH of the cytosol compared with the apoplast. Therefore, active efflux is needed to transport auxin out of the cell. An important aspect of this model is that the specific membrane localization of the auxin efflux carrier provides directionality to auxin transport. Several of the molecular components fitting this classical model have been identified and are discussed below.

Auxin Efflux: PIN Proteins

The PIN FORMED (PIN) protein family consists of 8 members, most of which mediate auxin efflux (89, 121). The proteins are predicted to contain 6 to 10 transmembrane domains, similar to bacterial transporters (42, 68). Two important characteristics provided the first hints of their proposed function in the efflux of auxin. First, PIN proteins are expressed in auxin-transporting tissues and cells. Second, and even more importantly, they are asymmetrically localized in the plasma membranes of these cells, consistent with the direction of auxin transport (35–37, 42, 77). Functional analysis of mutants in most of the *PIN* genes strengthened the belief that these genes encode important catalysts of auxin efflux. The gene family was named after the *pin formed 1* mutant, which almost entirely lacks flowers or lateral organs along its inflorescence, a phenotype that can be copied by growing plants on auxin transport inhibitors (84). Moreover, the mutant displays severely reduced auxin transport activity in stem segments (84). PIN1 is mainly detected in stele cells of stems and roots, which are believed to be important conductors of auxin. Importantly, PIN1 localizes preferentially to the lower side of these cells, which is in accordance with the predicted direction of auxin transport (42).

The first well-studied *PIN* family member to be cloned was *ETHYLENE INSENSITIVE ROOT 1* (*EIR1*; later also termed *PIN2*, *AGR1*, or *WAV6*), named according to the specific phenotype of the corresponding *eir1-1* mutant (22, 68, 77, 129). In addition, mutants in *EIR1/PIN2* display agravitropic root growth. PIN2 is localized to the upper side of epidermal and lateral root cap cells and to the lower side of cortex cells. In elongated epidermal cells PIN2 also localizes to the inner lateral membrane. This rather specific distribution of the protein suggests that it is involved in the transport of auxin from the root tip into the elongation zone and back again via the cortex toward the root tip (1, 17, 77). The auxin in the elongation zone would mediate cell elongation, which is important in the regulation of gravitropic root curvature. The stability of the PIN2 protein is important for its function during the root gravitropic response (1, 107).

The PIN3, PIN4, and PIN7 proteins have been linked to active auxin transport as well (35–37). PIN3 is involved in the control of tropic growth responses and is expressed in the root pericycle, the columella, the hypocotyl endodermis, and the apical hook (37). PIN4 is involved in the stabilization of a local auxin maximum in the root meristem (35, 103). In line with this function, the PIN4 protein localizes in a polar manner around the auxin maximum in the root meristem (35). PIN7 is expressed from early embryogenesis onward and appears to be involved in the auxin-mediated control of embryonic axis formation (36). Functional analysis of the *PIN5*, *6*, and *8* genes has not yet been reported.

Hints toward the exact molecular function of PIN proteins came from experiments in which they represent the rate-limiting factor in the efflux of auxin as well as major determinants in providing directionality to polar auxin flow (91, 136). However, these data do not definitively demonstrate that PIN proteins are efflux carriers.

Although indications toward the exact molecular function of PIN proteins are provided, several aspects remain unclear. For example, how do PIN proteins transport auxin, or does an associated protein transport auxin? Resolving the crystal structure of PIN proteins would be a critical step in elucidating their exact molecular function.

Auxin Efflux: MDR and PGP Proteins

The PIN genes are not the only components able to mediate auxin efflux. Another class of likely auxin efflux facilitators is represented by the MULTIDRUG RESISTANCE (MDR)–p-glycoprotein (PGP) family of membrane proteins, which comprises MDR1, PGP1, PGP2, PGP4, and PGP19 (20, 46, 78, 79, 81, 82). Noh and coworkers (82) used mutant analysis to show that polar auxin transport is reduced in *mdr1* mutant plants and severely reduced in *mdr1pgp1* double mutants, suggesting a role for these MDR proteins in auxin distribution. Furthermore, MDR proteins display auxin-transporting activity when expressed in heterologous hosts (16). Recently, Blakeslee and colleagues (15) showed that PIN and PGP proteins colocalize and interact with each other. Remarkably, only PIN1 coimmunoprecipitates with PGP1 and PGP19, not PIN2, suggesting specificity of interaction. *pin2pgp1pgp19* triple mutants display synergistic interaction among these genes, indicating that PIN and PGP proteins function in distinct auxin transport pathways that partially overlap (15). The exact functional relationship between PINs and PGPs remains unclear. An interesting hypothesis is that PIN proteins act to guide the action of several MDR transporters, which may provide an alternative explanation for the capacity of PIN proteins to transport auxin in heterologous systems (91).

MDR: MULTIDRUG RESISTANCE

AUX1: AUXIN RESISTANT 1

Auxin Influx: AUX1

Before auxin can be transported out of the cell it first needs to get in. This occurs mainly via diffusion, but active auxin import also takes place. AUXIN RESISTANT 1 (AUX1) is the only well-described auxin import carrier (12, 114). Carrier-mediated auxin import has been proposed to be required for transport against a diffusion gradient or to prevent diffusion into neighboring cells, and therefore would provide an effective means to establish and maintain optimal auxin concentrations and distributions within cells and tissues (54, 95, 112). The *AUX1* gene shows similarities to plant amino acid permeases that contain 11 transmembrane domains, consistent with a role for AUX1 in cellular uptake of auxin (69, 112). Membrane-associated AUX1 expression in root cap and root epidermis cells further links the agravitropic root phenotype of *aux1* to defects in polar auxin transport (113). Differences in the sensitivity to various auxins indicated that a defect in active uptake of IAA might cause the mutant phenotypes (69, 142). Together the available data suggest a function of AUX1 to support polar auxin delivery to the root apex. Swarup and colleagues (113) performed a set of elegant experiments, involving tissue specific expression of AUX1, to demonstrate that expression of AUX1 in lateral root cap and epidermal cells is necessary for the root gravitropic response. AUX1 is capable of transporting auxin even in a heterologous system (143). As in the case of the PIN proteins, the specific localization of AUX1 and AUX1-like proteins can be anticipated to be very important for its function. A wealth of information is available on functional aspects of AUX1; however, the biochemical characterization of AUX1, as well as the crystal structure, is still lacking. These characterizations should provide important information on how

AUX1 controls auxin distribution in relation to developmental responses. The analysis of the AUX1 family members might also provide information on their role in auxin transport. An interesting aspect is how AUX1 activity is regulated during a root gravitropic response.

REGULATORY LOOPS

Given the available data on components involved in auxin perception, signaling, and transport, the existence of two regulatory loops, rather then a strictly hierarchical system, can be anticipated (**Figure 1**). The transcriptional loop involves auxin, Aux/IAA, and ARF proteins as well as SCF^{TIR1}; an associated polarity loop involves auxin, transcription factors, and PIN proteins. These loops represent extensive feedback as well as feedforward regulation.

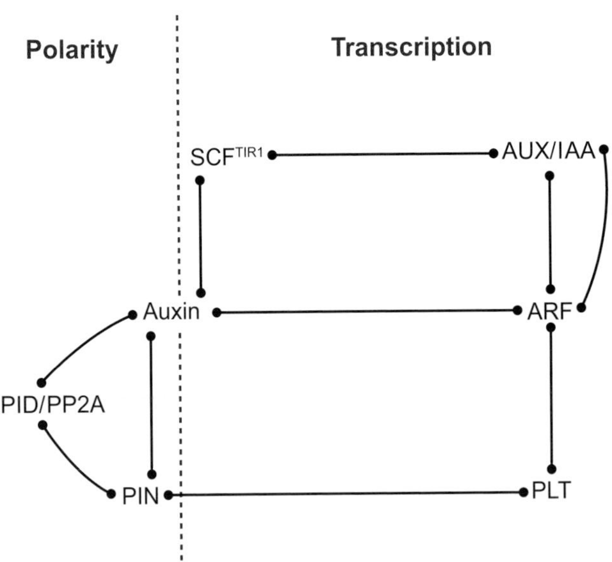

Figure 1

Schematic representation of the two intertwined regulatory loops anticipated to mediate auxin action. The transcriptional loop involves auxin, AUXIN/INDOLE-3-ACETIC ACID (Aux/IAA), and AUXIN RESPONSE FACTOR (ARF) proteins as well as SCF^{TIR1} (SKP1, Cullin, and F-box protein, in this case TRANSPORT INHIBITOR RESPONSE 1); an associated polarity loop involves auxin, kinases, phosphatases [PINOID (PID)/PROTEIN PHOSPHATASE 2A (PP2A)], transcription factors [PLETHORA (PLT)], and PIN FORMED (PIN) proteins. Connective lines indicate a regulatory interaction. The nature of the regulation is explained in **Figures 2** and **4**.

Transcriptional Loop

Auxin induces expression of Aux/IAA proteins, which in many cases reduces the sensitivity of cells toward auxin (61). This induction is mediated by ARF proteins that regulate auxin-responsive gene transcription through their interaction with specific Aux/IAA proteins (65). The auxin-dependent degradation of Aux/IAA proteins mediated by SCF^{TIR1} (TIR1 perceives auxin) releases ARF proteins to transcribe auxin-regulated genes, including the *Aux/IAA* genes (31, 47) (**Figure 2*a***). This mechanism, together with the differences in stability between Aux/IAA proteins, indicates a self-regulatory mechanism for auxin-induced gene expression (33). In the process of lateral root initiation this signaling is likely to be fine tuned by NAC1, a transcriptional activator of the NAM, ATAF, CUC family, which is targeted to the proteasome by the RING-finger protein SINA of *Arabidopsis thaliana* 5 (SINAT5)-dependent ubiquitination, thereby regulating auxin signaling (138, 139) (**Figure 2*b***).

A deeper understanding of the significance of this regulatory loop requires knowledge of (direct) targets of the ARFs as well as a functional context. Existing models for the function of Aux/IAA-ARF interactions are only generic. Current efforts are therefore directed toward generating a more specific model for certain combinations of Aux/IAAs and ARFs, because there are differences in the relative stability of Aux/IAA and evidence exists for specific functional combinations of ARF and Aux/IAA proteins (33, 132).

Several putative downstream targets of ARF transcription factors do not allow an escape from the loop: *ARF4*, *IAA5*, *IAA14*, and *IAA19* are downregulated in the *nph4arf19* double mutant, suggesting that feedforward regulation is part of the auxin signaling pathway (85). Auxin transport components were also found to be under the control of ARF proteins (85). This suggests a regulatory mechanism in which high auxin concentrations are sensed by SCF^{TIR1}, which results in breakdown of Aux/IAAs and the subsequent release of ARF transcription factors that upregulate the expression of auxin transport components, which transport auxin out of the cell. On the basis of the feedback mechanism described above, the decreasing cellular auxin content then most likely feeds back on SCF^{TIR1}, resulting in a decrease in its activity and a subsequent decrease in ARF-mediated transcription. The relative timing as well as the balance between auxin-induced expression of *Aux/IAA* genes and the auxin-mediated degradation of Aux/IAA proteins,

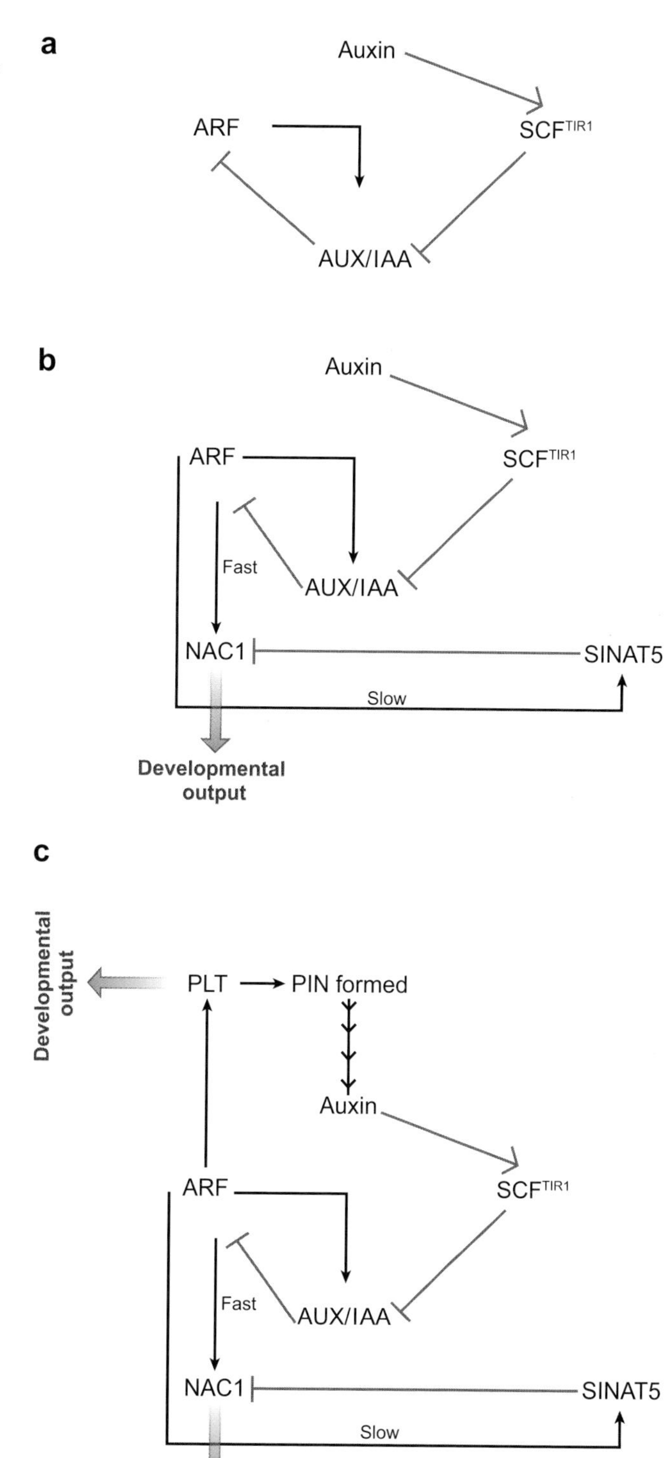

Figure 2

Schematic representation of the components involved in the transcriptional loop. (*a*) The expression of *AUXIN/INDOLE-3-ACETIC ACID* (*Aux/IAA*) genes is induced by auxin, mediated by the SCF^{TIR1} (SKP1, Cullin, and F-box protein, in this case TRANSPORT INHIBITOR RESPONSE 1) ubiquitin ligase complex and AUXIN RESPONSE FACTOR (ARF) proteins, which in turn feeds back on the sensitivity of cells toward auxin, in most cases making the cell less sensitive. ARF proteins interact with Aux/IAA proteins and together regulate the transcription of auxin-responsive genes, including *Aux/IAA* genes. (*b*) The stability of Aux/IAA proteins is dependent on the activity of the SCF^{TIR1} complex in response to changing auxin levels. High auxin levels will lead to the degradation of Aux/IAA proteins, resulting in the derepression of ARF proteins, inducing the expression of auxin-responsive genes. In case of lateral root development this regulatory loop is fine-tuned by the action of NAC1, a transcriptional activator of the NAM, ATAF, CUC family, depending on the activity of SINA of *Arabidopsis thaliana* 5 (SINAT5), a RING-finger protein with ubiquitin ligase activity, which acts downstream of TIR1. The induction of expression by auxin is faster in the case of NAC1 compared to that of SINAT5, allowing fine-tuning of the loop (139). (*c*) Transcription of *PLETHORA* (*PLT*) genes is dependent on ARF action and PLT proteins induce the expression of PIN FORMED (PIN) genes, which in turn affects cellular auxin concentrations. The NAC1 and PLT proteins mediate the developmental outputs in response to auxin. Black arrows indicate regulation at the transcriptional level. Grey lines indicate positive (*arrows*) or negative (*bars*) regulation at the protein level. Multiple arrows indicate regulation at the transport level.

PLT: PLETHORA

Quiescent center (QC): consists of four cells and acts as an organizer to keep the surrounding meristem initials/stem cells undifferentiated

PID: PINOID

at a given auxin concentration, will result in more or less auxin response (**Figure 2*b***). PLETHORA 1 (PLT1) and PLETHORA 2 (PLT2) are important transcription factors of the AP2 class that are essential for QC specification and definition of the stem cell niche in the root meristem (3). The regulation of *PLT* genes is probably mediated by ARF transcription factors because stabilization of SLR1/IAA14, which causes inhibition of ARF-mediated transcription, results in a decrease in auxin-induced *PLT* expression (3). Interestingly, the expression of *PLT* genes is auxin inducible and largely overlaps with the auxin maximum in the root (3, 103).

PLT genes are necessary for the expression of *PIN* genes in the embryonic root pole and root meristem, which can in part explain the severe mutant phenotype (17, 41).

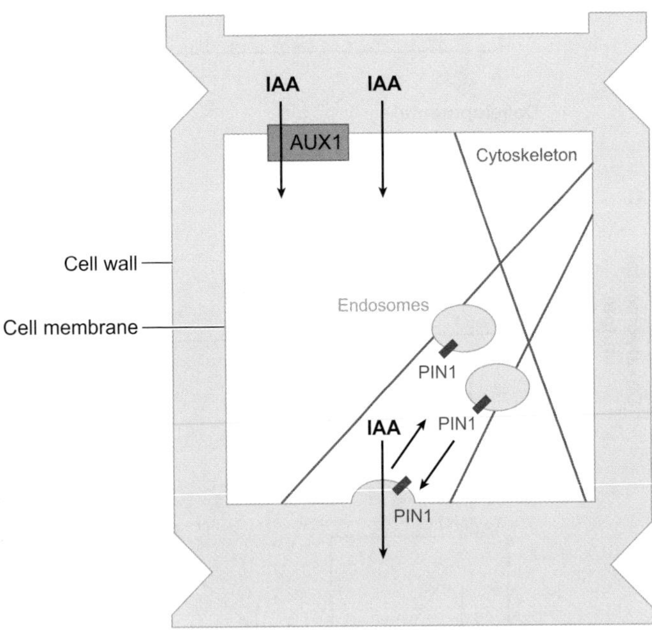

Figure 3

Model for auxin transport. Auxin enters the cell through diffusion and/or the activity of the auxin influx carrier AUXIN RESISTANT 1 (AUX1). Cellular auxin is actively transported out of the cell, mediated by the auxin efflux machinery of which PIN FORMED (PIN) proteins represent a rate-limiting factor. The polar localization of PIN proteins in the membrane provides directionality to auxin transport. Membrane targeting of PIN proteins is mediated by endosomal recycling along the cytoskeleton.

In turn the *PIN* genes are needed to position the auxin maximum in the root meristem, thereby restricting the expression of the *PLT* genes (17). This suggests that the auxin maximum is not only read out by *PLT* genes, which are themselves likely activated by ARF-dependent transcription, but also that the *PLT* genes subsequently regulate expression of at least a subset of *PIN* genes to shape auxin distribution (**Figure 2*c***).

Transcriptional and translational studies with PLT fusion proteins reveal gradients with highest expression in the stem cell area, intermediate levels in the division zone, and low levels in the elongation zone (41). Changing the expression pattern and thereby the shape of the gradient together with the detailed analysis of the different mutant combinations suggested that high PLT levels maintain stem cells, intermediate levels control cell division, and low levels are needed for cell elongation (41). Grieneisen and coworkers (48) recently presented computational evidence for an auxin gradient spanning the main root meristem, which largely overlaps with the PLT gradient. We envisage that such developmental gradients are the result of feedback interactions.

Polarity Loop: Regulation of Polar Localization

The most intriguing aspect of PIN auxin efflux facilitators and the AUX1 influx carrier that fascinated researchers for almost a decade is their polar localization (**Figure 3**).

PIN expression, as well as PIN protein stability, is regulated by auxin (1, 131) (**Figure 4*a***). An important factor affecting polar localization of PIN proteins is the protein serine/threonine kinase PINOID (PID), which was previously identified as an auxin-inducible regulator of auxin transport (10, 13, 25) (**Figure 4*b***). Plant lines overexpressing the *PID* gene under control of the 35S-promoter (*35S::PID*) reveal severe defects in gravitropism and a loss of root meristem organization in the main root tip (10). This phenotype correlates with the mislocalization of PIN proteins because both PIN2 and PIN4, important regulators of root meristem maintenance, are shifted from the upper to the lower side of cells, causing the auxin maximum to decrease, which results in the loss of meristem organization (38). In inflorescences of *pid* mutants PIN1 also displays a shift from the upper to the lower side of epidermis cells (38), explaining the phenotypic resemblance between *pin1* and *pid* mutants (13, 84). Besides PID, PROTEIN PHOSPHATASE 2A (PP2A) was also recently shown to regulate polar PIN localization (43, 71) (**Figure 4*b***). PID and PP2A partly colocalize with PIN proteins at the membrane and antagonistically act on the phosphorylation status of PIN proteins, thereby regulating the localization of PIN proteins, which is probably mediated by endosomal sorting (71).

Interestingly, Paciorek and coworkers (88) suggested that auxin controls the amount of PIN2 protein at the plasma membrane by inhibiting the endocytotic cycling of PIN2. During a root gravitropic response auxin accumulates at the new lower side of the root tip. This results in a decrease in PIN2 endocytosis at the lower side of a gravistimulated root, whereas on the upper side PIN2 is still endocytosed (1, 88). This indicates a regulatory loop in which auxin, by regulating the transcriptional loop, modulates the expression and/or activity of PID or PID-like kinases as well as phosphatases that regulate the localization of PIN proteins, thereby regulating auxin efflux (**Figure 4*b***).

Endosomal cycling plays an important role in the localization of PIN proteins. The phenotype of *gnom* mutants, showing severe pattern formation defects from early embryogenesis onward, can be partly explained by mislocalization of PIN1 (110). GNOM encodes an ADP ribosylation factor-GTP/GDP exchange factor (ARF-GEF), a regulator of vesicular trafficking that localizes to endosomes (44). GNOM-mediated endocytosis is sensitive to brefeldin A (BFA), an inhibitor of endocytosis (44). In addition to PIN1,

a

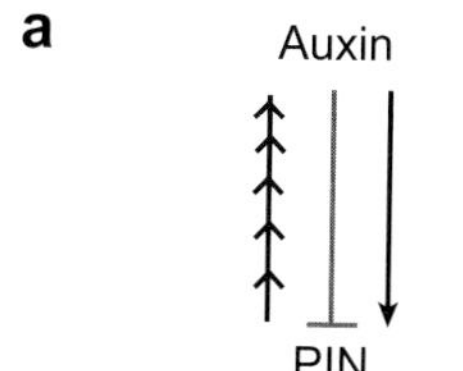

b

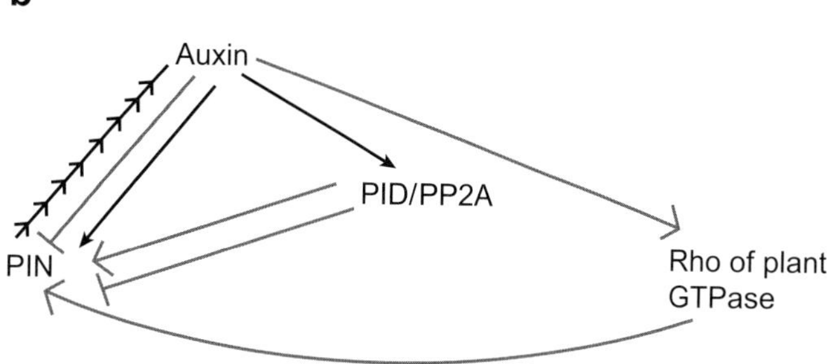

Figure 4

Schematic representation of the components involved in the polarity loop. (*a*) *PIN FORMED* (*PIN*) expression and PIN stability as well as the localization of the PIN proteins are affected by auxin. Auxin induces expression of *PIN* genes, but also destabilizes PIN proteins. Auxin action depends on its distribution, which is regulated by PIN proteins. (*b*) The activity of kinases and phosphatases, represented by PINOID (PID) and PROTEIN PHOSPHATASE 2A (PP2A), regulates the polar localization of PIN proteins. PID and PP2A antagonistically influence PIN activity. ROPs (Rho of plant GTPases) probably also regulate PIN polarity; however, their exact mode of action remains unknown. Some ROP GTPases are likely to be activated by auxin. Black arrows indicate regulation at the transcriptional level. Grey lines indicate positive (*arrows*) or negative (*bars*) regulation at the protein level. Multiple arrows indicate regulation at the transport level.

PIN7 localization is also GNOM-dependent, because GNOM is needed for the shift of PIN7 from the upper to the lower side of the suspensor cells during early embryogenesis (36). However, PIN2 cycling remains BFA-sensitive in BFA-resistant *gnom* plants, indicating the specificity of GNOM. Indeed, PIN2 localization requires different, AtSNX1-dependent endosomes (56). Nevertheless, endocytotic cycling represents a highly regulated mechanism for polar PIN localization; PID is an important regulator of this process, and possibly acts via direct phosphorylation of PIN proteins (37, 44, 45, 71, 96, 110, 141).

Furthermore, functional analysis of members of the RHO OF PLANTS (ROP) class

ROP: Rho of plant GTPase

of GTPases has shown that they can display polar membrane localization, which corroborates their suggested role in aspects of plant cell polarity (14, 64, 75). As a result these GTPases, which are in several cases involved in vesicle cycling, are also suggested to be involved in PIN localization (18, 76, 116) (**Figure 4*b***). For ROP2, which is axially localized in the root tip, Li and coworkers (64) presented evidence that it is involved in regulating polar localization of PIN2 by controlling the stability of the cytoskeleton. ROP2 localization is partly dependent on the activity of ADP RIBOSYLATION FACTOR 1 (ARF1), a GTPase of another class, which is a substrate for ARF-GEF proteins, such as GNOM (141). Another member, ROP3, is activated by auxin and overexpression of a constitutively active form results in enhanced degradation of Aux/IAA proteins (118, 119). Although connections have not been fully worked out, these data suggest links between auxin, auxin signaling, endosomal sorting, and cell polarity.

The localization of AUX1 depends on the activity of AUXIN RESISTANT 4 (AXR4), which encodes an ER-localized protein. AXR4 specifically affects trafficking of AUX1 because the localization of other membrane proteins, including PINs, is unaffected in *axr4* mutants (32). Therefore, considerable specialization exists in the trafficking systems for different polarly located proteins involved in auxin transport.

INTEGRATED ANALYSIS OF AUXIN BIOLOGY

Feedback and feedforward loops represent essential mechanisms in developmental biology and there are strong indications that such loops play a crucial role in auxin biology. Good examples are phyllotaxis, vascular patterning, and root patterning. To understand such developmental processes, computer modeling has become an appreciated tool that allows the resolution of regulatory loops by testing experimental data in silico and vice versa. This approach is beginning to provide valuable insights into the dynamics of auxin transport and its role in regulating organogenesis. In the following sections auxin transport models for three developmental systems that address regulatory loops are discussed.

Phyllotaxis

The processes and mechanisms that regulate the arrangement of organs around the shoot of a plant, called phyllotaxis, have interested plant scientists as well as mathematicians for centuries. As early as the 1400s Leonardo da Vinci postulated that proper arrangement of plant organs is crucial for plant growth and survival (26).

The importance of auxin transport in organ initiation was suggested by experiments in which plants are grown on polar auxin transport inhibitors, which strongly resemble *pin1* mutant plants. Application experiments suggested that an auxin accumulation mechanism could account for organ initiation (95). Interestingly, the PIN1 protein colocalizes with patches of high auxin; PIN1 polarizes toward new primordia (53, 95, 109). In addition, AUX1 is coexpressed with PIN1 in the epidermal layer of the shoot meristem, although AUX1 localization is less polar compared with PIN1 (95). These findings resulted in the proposition of a model in which PIN1 together with AUX1 determines the localization of auxin maxima that are important for organ primordia initiation. However, the *pin1aux1* double mutant does not significantly enhance either single mutant phenotype. The new primordia subsequently function as auxin sinks, draining auxin from the surrounding tissue and thereby preventing growth of adjacent cells. This mechanism determines the position of the next primordium, thus guaranteeing outgrowth of lateral organs in a regular phyllotactic pattern.

This model has subsequently been tested in computer simulations and is generally capable of generating realistic phyllotactic patterns (28, 57, 109). The distribution of

PIN1, although quite complex and dynamic, represents the most crucial parameter in the model (53). A pivotal issue is how PIN1 localization is regulated during primordium initiation. A variant of the principle that auxin regulates its own efflux was used as the basis of models that predict PIN1 localization during primordium initiation (57, 109). The important assumption in these models is that in a given cell of the L1 layer PIN1 is always polarly localized toward the neighboring cell that has the highest auxin concentration through a regulatory loop involving auxin and auxin transport. These models are able to generate the expected phyllotactic pattern. Moreover, these models can explain different phyllotactic patterns when parameters are changed (109).

The auxin transport fluxes that are important for initiating organ primordia are also suggested to determine later events in the differentiating primordium, such as boundary formation and organ polarity, by influencing the expression pattern of genes such as *CUC2* and *STM* (4, 40, 53, 55, 120, 130). Although the above-described modeling studies indicate that feedback between auxin accumulation and polar positioning of PIN proteins can generate phyllotaxis, the exact regulatory mechanisms by which this process is controlled remain enigmatic.

Auxin Transport and Leaf Vascular Development

The formation of continuous and ordered vascular networks in leaves has been connected to the transport of auxin. A classical model proposed by Sachs (104), also referred to as the canalization hypothesis, suggests that vasculature is formed by a feedback mechanism in which auxin transport through cells increases the capacity of these cells for polar transport of auxin, which in turn triggers their differentiation into vascular cells.

The involvement of auxin transport in *Arabidopsis* vascular patterning was first studied by pharmacological inhibition of polar auxin transport (70, 108). These studies suggested that the major source of auxin resides at the margins of the developing leaf; this hypothesis was confirmed later (5). This latter study further suggested that free auxin concentrations shift from the tip downward along the margins during the development of a leaf primordium. PIN1 is the major auxin transport component in vascular development, because it is the only family member expressed during early stages of procambium formation (105). Domains of high auxin express PIN1 and appear to predict the sites of procambium formation. A distinct PIN1 localization suggests that auxin is transported toward so-called convergence points at the leaf margin, which guide the positioning of new veins. Application experiments using auxin and auxin transport inhibitors provided an excellent correlation between the accumulation of auxin in convergence points and PIN1 expression determining the site of vein formation. This prompted Scarpella and coworkers (105) to propose the following model: Auxin is transported through the epidermis of the new primordium and accumulates at the top of the primordium; this determines the formation of a convergence point for PIN1 expression, which leads to the formation of a midvein from the top toward the base. This is remarkably similar to the relation between auxin fluxes and PIN1 expression as well as PIN1 localization as proposed for the formation of lateral roots and phyllotaxis (11, 95).

As early as the 1980s Mitchison (73, 74) produced a mathematical transport model based on a feedback mechanism in which the transport of auxin varies as a function of the flux of auxin. This model was adapted by Rolland-Lagan & Prusinkiewicz (98) by taking into account the importance of background diffusion of auxin, which can make the cells in the model more or less sensitive to small changes in auxin flux. Moreover, this model suggested that in the young primordium, vascular strand formation is sink-driven (low concentration of auxin); the sink is the base of the leaf and the source(s) is at

L1 layer: the outermost cell layer of the shoot apical meristem that gives rise to epidermal cells

the margin of the leaf. As the leaf grows new auxin sources appear in favored regions, determined by the distance to existing sources and veins, displaying a second important analogy to the process of phyllotaxis. In their model the localized auxin sources also provide an explanation for the formation of discontinuous veins, something that is observed in vesicle trafficking mutants such as *gnom* and *van3* (44, 45, 62). This observation has been controversial because it is not easily explainable by the canalization hypothesis (63). The model by Rolland-Lagan & Prusinkiewicz (98) shows that when multiple auxin sources as well as a high auxin flux from both source and sink exist in the leaf the canalization process can be stopped and discontinuous strands can be formed.

Another model included a variable that was called the auxin flux-bifurcator, which makes it possible that a given cell under specific conditions can transport auxin in two directions, fitting the data of Scarpella and coworkers (34, 105). This would allow a cell to share its auxin flux with two neighboring cells. Discontinuous veins are then readily explained by setting low values for the flux-bifurcator. An interesting issue that remains unresolved is whether and how auxin fluxes rather than concentrations could be measured in the cell.

Root Development

Auxin and auxin distribution are known to play a crucial role in the patterning and growth of roots, which represents the first case where an auxin maximum was demonstrated to be instructive for patterning (103). PIN expression is crucial to the localization of the auxin maximum, which in turn induces the expression of stem cell–specifying *PLT* genes (3, 17). Grieneisen and colleagues (48) recently used multilevel computational modeling of diffusion and permeability to demonstrate that a robust auxin maximum and auxin gradient can be maintained in the root meristem that spans the meristem and can have an instructive function in patterning and meristem zonation. A long standing hypothesis states that auxin acts as a morphogen, which would typically be present in a gradient that is instructive for cell division and growth. Because of the lack of representative experimental tools the visualization of such an auxin gradient has hitherto remained elusive. Direct auxin measurements using sorted cell populations should now validate this theoretical framework.

In the theoretical model for auxin distribution in the root, polarly localized PIN proteins are the main players—crucial and sufficient to set up the auxin maximum and gradient. This model is supported by the critical role that PINs play in root development (17). Importantly, many predictions of the model were validated experimentally or explained by previous observations. In the model, setting up the auxin maximum is fast, which is in line with earlier experimental data in which the auxin maximum is rapidly re-established after laser ablation of the QC (140). In contrast, setting up the auxin gradient is slow, providing a parsimonious explanation for why meristems slowly increase in size (8). The precise auxin gradient likely depends on auxin influx as well (112, 113).

The projected instructive auxin gradient should depend on a readout by molecular components. The family of *PLT* genes (see above), which are also present in a gradient that nicely overlaps with the anticipated auxin gradient, are good candidates for performing the readout. Taking into account the interdependence of *PIN* and *PLT* genes, this model implies the existence of a regulatory loop that sets up an auxin gradient, which is self-regulating because PLT transcription factors subsequently regulate the expression of PINs (3, 17, 48).

The theoretical model also predicted an auxin gradient inside individual cells, which possibly is instructive for the retention of PIN proteins at the membrane as well as for their polar localization, as suggested by Paciorek and coworkers (88). This intracellular auxin gradient might also regulate cell polarity in general. In this way the polarity of cells might be reinforced during their journey through the meristem. However, high auxin was reported to retain PIN proteins at the membrane, whereas in the model low intracellular auxin correlates with the position of PIN proteins at the membrane (48, 88). This raises the question, at which location does auxin act to influence PIN endocytosis?

FUTURE DIRECTIONS: WHAT IS IT LIKE TO BE A STAR?

Auxin has emerged as a star player in almost every aspect of plant development. It is exactly this pervasive role that makes auxin research so complex. How to move ahead? First, many research themes now focus on context-specific analysis of auxin signaling, response, and transport in roots, shoots, and flowers; this strategy should, in the coming years, result in a detailed picture of specific auxin responses. Second, computer modeling together with quantitative experimental data represents a powerful tool in resolving the mechanisms and connections of specific responses, including regulatory loops. To refine the current computer models, additional regulatory mechanisms and links as well as molecular players must be identified. For example, studying the transcriptional as well as translational control of *PIN* genes in relation to auxin would provide important information. Identifying direct targets of the ARF transcription factors will fill another missing link in the regulatory circuits. In addition, resolving the function and targets of the ARF proteins that are thought not to be activators will possibly uncover new regulatory mechanisms involving new molecular players.

SUMMARY POINTS

1. Auxin is involved in many aspects of plant growth and development. Many molecular components have been identified and their biological function is at least partly understood.
2. Members of the TIR1 family of proteins are able to bind auxin, and therefore represent auxin receptors for which the downstream signaling pathway is known. TIR1 proteins are involved in the regulation of the stability of AUXIN/INDOLE-3-ACETIC ACID (Aux/IAA) proteins, which are transcriptional regulators acting in concert with AUXIN RESPONSE FACTOR (ARF) proteins.
3. The currently known regulatory mechanisms stress the importance of feedback loops in auxin action. At least two such regulatory loops exist: a transcriptional loop and a polarity loop.
4. The transcriptional loop involves auxin regulation of the activity of SCF^{TIR1} (SKP1, Cullin, and F-box protein, in this case TRANSPORT INHIBITOR RESPONSE 1), thereby regulating the transcriptional activity of ARF proteins via the proteolysis rate of Aux/IAA proteins. PLETHORA (PLT) proteins directly or indirectly regulate the transcription of *PIN FORMED* (*PIN*) genes that feed back on auxin by regulating the distribution of auxin, thereby completing the loop. The relative timing and balance between auxin-mediated expression of *Aux/IAA* genes and the auxin-dependent degradation of the Aux/IAA proteins balance the auxin response and auxin transport.
5. The polarity loop involves the regulation of the subcellular localization of PIN efflux facilitators by affecting the phosphorylation status through the activity of PINOID (PID) (or PID-like) kinases and PROTEIN PHOSPHATASE 2A (PP2A) phosphatases. GTPases likely also perform a regulatory function in polarity determination.

DISCLOSURE STATEMENT

The authors are not aware of any biases that might be perceived as affecting the objectivity of this review.

ACKNOWLEDGMENTS

The authors would like to thank the members of the Scheres laboratory for suggestions and critical reading of the manuscript and Germa Elzing for artwork. R.B. is a recipient of a VENI fellowship of the Netherlands Organization for Scientific Research (NWO). Owing to space constraints we could not cite all the publications in the field and apologize to those colleagues whose relevant contributions were not mentioned here.

LITERATURE CITED

1. Abas L, Benjamins R, Malenica N, Paciorek T, Wisniewska J, et al. 2006. Intracellular trafficking and proteolysis of the *Arabidopsis* auxin-efflux facilitator PIN2 are involved in root gravitropism. *Nat. Cell Biol.* 8:249–56
2. Abel S, Oeller PW, Theologis A. 1994. Early auxin-induced genes encode short-lived nuclear proteins. *Proc. Natl. Acad. Sci. USA* 91:326–30
3. Aida M, Beis D, Heidstra R, Willemsen V, Blilou I, et al. 2004. The *PLETHORA* genes mediate patterning of the *Arabidopsis* root stem cell niche. *Cell* 119:109–20
4. Aida M, Vernoux T, Furutani M, Traas J, Tasaka M. 2002. Roles of PIN-FORMED1 and MONOPTEROS in pattern formation of the apical region of the *Arabidopsis* embryo. *Development* 129:3965–74
5. Aloni R, Schwalm K, Langhans M, Ullrich CI. 2003. Gradual shifts in sites of free-auxin production during leaf-primordium development and their role in vascular differentiation and leaf morphogenesis in *Arabidopsis*. *Planta* 216:841–53
6. Barlier I, Kowalczyk M, Marchant A, Ljung K, Bhalerao R, et al. 2000. The *SUR2* gene of *Arabidopsis thaliana* encodes the cytochrome P450 CYP83B1, a modulator of auxin homeostasis. *Proc. Natl. Acad. Sci. USA* 97:14819–24
7. Bartel B, Fink GR. 1995. ILR1, an amidohydrolase that releases active indole-3-acetic acid from conjugates. *Science* 268:1745–48
8. Beemster GT, Baskin TI. 1998. Analysis of cell division and elongation underlying the developmental acceleration of root growth in *Arabidopsis thaliana*. *Plant Physiol.* 116:1515–26
9. Benjamins R, Malenica N, Luschnig C. 2005. Regulating the regulator: the control of auxin transport. *BioEssays* 27:1246–55
10. Benjamins R, Quint A, Weijers D, Hooykaas P, Offringa R. 2001. The PINOID protein kinase regulates organ development in *Arabidopsis* by enhancing polar auxin transport. *Development* 128:4057–67
11. Benkova E, Michniewicz M, Sauer M, Teichmann T, Seifertova D, et al. 2003. Local, efflux-dependent auxin gradients as a common module for plant organ formation. *Cell* 115:591–602
12. Bennett MJ, Marchant A, Green HG, May ST, Ward SP, et al. 1996. *Arabidopsis AUX1* gene: a permease-like regulator of root gravitropism. *Science* 273:948–50
13. Bennett SRM, Alvarez J, Bossinger G, Smyth DR. 1995. Morphogenesis in pinoid mutants of *Arabidopsis thaliana*. *Plant J.* 8:505–20

14. Bischoff F, Vahlkamp L, Molendijk A, Palme K. 2000. Localization of AtROP4 and AtROP6 and interaction with the guanine nucleotide dissociation inhibitor AtRhoGDI1 from *Arabidopsis*. *Plant Mol. Biol.* 42:515–30
15. Blakeslee JJ, Bandyopadhyay A, Lee OR, Mravec J, Titapiwatanakun B, et al. 2007. Interactions among PIN-FORMED and P-glycoprotein auxin transporters in *Arabidopsis*. *Plant Cell* 19:131–47
16. Blakeslee JJ, Peer WA, Murphy AS. 2005. Auxin transport. *Curr. Opin. Plant Biol.* 8:494–500
17. Blilou I, Xu J, Wildwater M, Willemsen V, Paponov I, et al. 2005. The PIN auxin efflux facilitator network controls growth and patterning in *Arabidopsis* roots. *Nature* 433:39–44
18. Bloch D, Lavy M, Efrat Y, Efroni I, Bracha-Drori K, et al. 2005. Ectopic expression of an activated RAC in *Arabidopsis* disrupts membrane cycling. *Mol. Biol. Cell* 16:1913–27
19. Boerjan W, Cervera MT, Delarue M, Beeckman T, Dewitte W, et al. 1995. *superroot*, a recessive mutation in Arabidopsis, confers auxin overproduction. *Plant Cell* 7:1405–19
20. Brown DE, Rashotte AM, Murphy AS, Normanly J, Tague BW, et al. 2001. Flavonoids act as negative regulators of auxin transport in vivo in Arabidopsis. *Plant Physiol.* 126:524–35
21. Callis J, Vierstra RD. 2000. Protein degradation in signaling. *Curr. Opin. Plant Biol.* 3:381–86
22. Chen R, Hilson P, Sedbrook J, Rosen E, Caspar T, Masson PH. 1998. The *Arabidopsis thaliana AGRAVITROPIC 1* gene encodes a component of the polar-auxin-transport efflux carrier. *Proc. Natl. Acad. Sci. USA* 95:15112–17
23. Cheng Y, Dai X, Zhao Y. 2006. Auxin biosynthesis by the YUCCA flavin monooxygenases controls the formation of floral organs and vascular tissues in *Arabidopsis*. *Genes Dev.* 20:1790–99
24. Cheng Y, Dai X, Zhao Y. 2007. Auxin synthesized by the YUCCA flavin monooxygenases is essential for embryogenesis and leaf formation in *Arabidopsis*. *Plant Cell* 19:2430–39
25. Christensen SK, Dagenais N, Chory J, Weigel D. 2000. Regulation of auxin response by the protein kinase PINOID. *Cell* 100:469–78
26. Cook TA. 1903. *Spirals in Nature and Art: A Study of Spiral Formations Based on the Manuscripts of Leonardo da Vinci*. London: Murray
27. Davies RT, Goetz DH, Lasswell J, Anderson MN, Bartel B. 1999. *IAR3* encodes an auxin conjugate hydrolase from *Arabidopsis*. *Plant Cell* 11:365–76
28. de Reuille PB, Bohn-Courseau I, Ljung K, Morin H, Carraro N, et al. 2006. Computer simulations reveal properties of the cell-cell signaling network at the shoot apex in *Arabidopsis*. *Proc. Natl. Acad. Sci. USA* 103:1627–32
29. Dharmasiri N, Dharmasiri S, Estelle M. 2005. The F-box protein TIR1 is an auxin receptor. *Nature* 435:441–45
30. Dharmasiri N, Dharmasiri S, Weijers D, Lechner E, Yamada M, et al. 2005. Plant development is regulated by a family of auxin receptor F box proteins. *Dev. Cell* 9:109–19
31. Dharmasiri S, Estelle M. 2002. The role of regulated protein degradation in auxin response. *Plant Mol. Biol.* 49:401–9
32. Dharmasiri S, Swarup R, Mockaitis K, Dharmasiri N, Singh SK, et al. 2006. AXR4 is required for localization of the auxin influx facilitator AUX1. *Science* 312:1218–20
33. Dreher KA, Brown J, Saw RE, Callis J. 2006. The *Arabidopsis* Aux/IAA protein family has diversified in degradation and auxin responsiveness. *Plant Cell* 18:699–714
34. Feugier FG, Iwasa Y. 2006. How canalization can make loops: a new model of reticulated leaf vascular pattern formation. *J. Theor. Biol.* 243:235–44
35. Friml J, Benkova E, Blilou I, Wisniewska J, Hamann T, et al. 2002. AtPIN4 mediates sink-driven auxin gradients and root patterning in *Arabidopsis*. *Cell* 108:661–73

36. Friml J, Vieten A, Sauer M, Weijers D, Schwarz H, et al. 2003. Efflux-dependent auxin gradients establish the apical-basal axis of *Arabidopsis*. *Nature* 426:147–53
37. Friml J, Wisniewska J, Benkova E, Mendgen K, Palme K. 2002. Lateral relocation of auxin efflux regulator PIN3 mediates tropism in *Arabidopsis*. *Nature* 415:806–9
38. Friml J, Yang X, Michniewicz M, Weijers D, Quint A, et al. 2004. A PINOID-dependent binary switch in apical-basal PIN polar targeting directs auxin efflux. *Science* 306:862–65
39. Fukaki H, Tameda S, Masuda H, Tasaka M. 2002. Lateral root formation is blocked by a gain-of-function mutation in the *SOLITARY-ROOT/IAA14* gene of *Arabidopsis*. *Plant J.* 29:153–68
40. Furutani M, Vernoux T, Traas J, Kato T, Tasaka M, Aida M. 2004. PIN-FORMED1 and PINOID regulate boundary formation and cotyledon development in *Arabidopsis* embryogenesis. *Development* 131:5021–30
41. Galinha C, Hofhuis H, Luijten M, Willemsen V, Blilou I, et al. 2007. PLETHORA protein gradients as dose-dependent master regulators of *Arabidopsis* root development. *Nature* 449:1053–57
42. Galweiler L, Guan C, Muller A, Wisman E, Mendgen K, et al. 1998. Regulation of polar auxin transport by AtPIN1 in *Arabidopsis* vascular tissue. *Science* 282:2226–30
43. Garbers C, DeLong A, Deruére J, Bernasconi P, Söll D. 1996. A mutation in protein phosphatase 2A regulatory subunit A affects auxin transport in *Arabidopsis*. *EMBO J.* 15:2115–24
44. Geldner N, Anders N, Wolters H, Keicher J, Kornberger W, et al. 2003. The *Arabidopsis* GNOM ARF-GEF mediates endosomal recycling, auxin transport, and auxin-dependent plant growth. *Cell* 112:219–30
45. Geldner N, Friml J, Stierhof YD, Jürgens G, Palme K. 2001. Auxin transport inhibitors block PIN1 cycling and vesicle trafficking. *Nature* 413:425–28
46. Gil P, Dewey E, Friml J, Zhao Y, Snowden KC, et al. 2001. BIG: a calossin-like protein required for polar auxin transport in *Arabidopsis*. *Genes Dev.* 15:1985–97
47. Gray WM, Kepinski S, Rouse D, Leyser O, Estelle M. 2001. Auxin regulates SCF^{TIR1}-dependent degradation of AUX/IAA proteins. *Nature* 414:271–76
48. Grieneisen VA, Xu J, Maree AFM, Blilou I, Hogeweg P, Scheres B. 2007. Auxin transport is sufficient to generate a maximum and gradient guiding root growth. *Nature*. 449:1008–13
49. Hagen G, Guilfoyle T. 2002. Auxin-responsive gene expression: genes, promoters and regulatory factors. *Plant Mol. Biol.* 49:373–85
50. Hamann T, Benkova E, Bäurle I, Kientz M, Jürgens G. 2002. The *Arabidopsis BODENLOS* gene encodes an auxin response protein inhibiting MONOPTEROS-mediated embryo patterning. *Genes Dev.* 16:1610–15
51. Hamann T, Mayer U, Jürgens G. 1999. The auxin-insensitive *bodenlos* mutation affects primary root formation and apical-basal patterning in the *Arabidopsis* embryo. *Development* 126:1387–95
52. Hardtke CS, Berleth T. 1998. The *Arabidopsis* gene *MONOPTEROS* encodes a transcription factor mediating embryo axis formation and vascular development. *EMBO J.* 17:1405–11
53. Heisler MG, Ohno C, Das P, Sieber P, Reddy GV, et al. 2005. Patterns of auxin transport and gene expression during primordium development revealed by live imaging of the *Arabidopsis* inflorescence meristem. *Curr. Biol.* 15:1899–911
54. Hellmann H, Hobbie L, Chapman A, Dharmasiri S, Dharmasiri N, et al. 2003. *Arabidopsis AXR6* encodes CUL1 implicating SCF E3 ligases in auxin regulation of embryogenesis. *EMBO J.* 22:3314–25

55. Hibara K, Karim MR, Takada S, Taoka K, Furutani M, et al. 2006. *Arabidopsis* CUP-SHAPED COTYLEDON3 regulates postembryonic shoot meristem and organ boundary formation. *Plant Cell* 18:2946–57
56. Jaillais Y, Fobis-Loisy I, Miege C, Rollin C, Gaude T. 2006. AtSNX1 defines an endosome for auxin-carrier trafficking in *Arabidopsis*. *Nature* 443:106–9
57. Jönsson H, Heisler MG, Shapiro BE, Meyerowitz EM, Mjolsness E. 2006. An auxin-driven polarized transport model for phyllotaxis. *Proc. Natl. Acad. Sci. USA* 103:1633–38
58. Kepinski S, Leyser O. 2004. Auxin-induced SCF^{TIR1}-Aux/IAA interaction involves stable modification of the SCF^{TIR1} complex. *Proc. Natl. Acad. Sci. USA* 101:12381–86
59. Kepinski S, Leyser O. 2005. The *Arabidopsis* F-box protein TIR1 is an auxin receptor. *Nature* 435:446–51
60. Kim BC, Soh MC, Kang BJ, Furuya M, Nam HG. 1996. Two dominant photomorphogenic mutations of *Arabidopsis thaliana* identified as suppressor mutations of *hy2*. *Plant J.* 9:441–56
61. Kim J, Harter K, Theologis A. 1997. Protein-protein interactions among the Aux/IAA proteins. *Proc. Natl. Acad. Sci. USA* 94:11786–91
62. Koizumi K, Naramoto S, Sawa S, Yahara N, Ueda T, et al. 2005. VAN3 ARF-GAP-mediated vesicle transport is involved in leaf vascular network formation. *Development* 132:1699–711
63. Koizumi K, Sugiyama M, Fukuda H. 2000. A series of novel mutants of *Arabidopsis thaliana* that are defective in the formation of continuous vascular network: calling the auxin signal flow canalization hypothesis into question. *Development* 127:3197–204
64. Li L, Xu J, Xu ZH, Xue HW. 2005. Brassinosteroids stimulate plant tropisms through modulation of polar auxin transport in *Brassica* and *Arabidopsis*. *Plant Cell* 17:2738–53
65. Liscum E, Reed JW. 2002. Genetics of Aux/IAA and ARF action in plant growth and development. *Plant Mol. Biol.* 49:387–400
66. Ljung K, Hull AK, Kowalczyk M, Marchant A, Celenza J, et al. 2002. Biosynthesis, conjugation, catabolism and homeostasis of indole-3-acetic acid in *Arabidopsis thaliana*. *Plant Mol. Biol.* 49:249–72
67. Luerssen H, Kirik V, Herrmann P, Misera S. 1998. *FUSCA3* encodes a protein with a conserved VP1/AB13-like B3 domain which is of functional importance for the regulation of seed maturation in *Arabidopsis thaliana*. *Plant J.* 15:755–64
68. Luschnig C, Gaxiola RA, Grisafi P, Fink GR. 1998. EIR1, a root-specific protein involved in auxin transport, is required for gravitropism in *Arabidopsis thaliana*. *Genes Dev.* 12:2175–87
69. Marchant A, Kargul J, May ST, Muller P, Delbarre A, et al. 1999. AUX1 regulates root gravitropism in *Arabidopsis* by facilitating auxin uptake within root apical tissues. *EMBO J.* 18:2066–73
70. Mattsson J, Sung ZR, Berleth T. 1999. Responses of plant vascular systems to auxin transport inhibition. *Development* 126:2979–91
71. Michniewicz M, Zago MK, Abas L, Weijers D, Schweighofer A, et al. 2007. Antagonistic regulation of PIN phosphorylation by PP2A and PINOID directs auxin flux. *Cell* 130:1044–56
72. Mikkelsen MD, Hansen CH, Wittstock U, Halkier BA. 2000. Cytochrome P450 CYP79B2 from *Arabidopsis* catalyzes the conversion of tryptophan to indole-3-acetaldoxime, a precursor of indole glucosinolates and indole-3-acetic acid. *J. Biol. Chem.* 275:33712–17
73. Mitchison GJ. 1980. A model for vein formation in higher plants. *Proc. R. Soc. London Ser. B* 207:79–109

74. Mitchison GJ. 1981. The polar transport of auxin and vein patterns in plants. *Philos. Trans. R. Soc. London Ser. B* 295:461–71
75. Molendijk AJ, Bischoff F, Rajendrakumar CS, Friml J, Braun M, et al. 2001. *Arabidopsis thaliana* Rop GTPases are localized to tips of root hairs and control polar growth. *EMBO J.* 20:2779–88
76. Molendijk AJ, Ruperti B, Palme K. 2004. Small GTPases in vesicle trafficking. *Curr. Opin. Plant Biol.* 7:694–700
77. Muller A, Guan C, Galweiler L, Tanzler P, Huijser P, et al. 1998. *AtPIN2* defines a locus of *Arabidopsis* for root gravitropism control. *EMBO J.* 17:6903–11
78. Murphy A, Peer WA, Taiz L. 2000. Regulation of auxin transport by aminopeptidases and endogenous flavonoids. *Planta* 211:315–24
79. Murphy AS, Hoogner KR, Peer WA, Taiz L. 2002. Identification, purification, and molecular cloning of N-1-naphthylphthalmic acid-binding plasma membrane-associated aminopeptidases from *Arabidopsis. Plant Physiol.* 128:935–50
80. Nagpal P, Walker LM, Young JC, Sonawala A, Timpte C, et al. 2000. *AXR2* encodes a member of the Aux/IAA protein family. *Plant Physiol.* 123:563–74
81. Noh B, Bandyopadhyay A, Peer WA, Spalding EP, Murphy AS. 2003. Enhanced gravi- and phototropism in plant *mdr* mutants mislocalizing the auxin efflux protein PIN1. *Nature* 424:999–1002
82. Noh B, Murphy AS, Spalding EP. 2001. Multidrug resistance-like genes of *Arabidopsis* required for auxin transport and auxin-mediated development. *Plant Cell* 13:2441–54
83. Normanly J, Bartel B. 1999. Redundancy as a way of life—IAA metabolism. *Curr. Opin. Plant Biol.* 2:207–13
84. Okada K, Ueda J, Komaki MK, Bell CJ, Shimura Y. 1991. Requirement of the auxin polar transport system in early stages of *Arabidopsis* floral bud formation. *Plant Cell* 3:677–84
85. Okushima Y, Overvoorde PJ, Arima K, Alonso JM, Chan A, et al. 2005. Functional genomic analysis of the *AUXIN RESPONSE FACTOR* gene family members in *Arabidopsis thaliana*: unique and overlapping functions of *ARF7* and *ARF19*. *Plant Cell* 17:444–63
86. Ouellet F, Overvoorde PJ, Theologis A. 2001. IAA17/AXR3: biochemical insight into an auxin mutant phenotype. *Plant Cell* 13:829–41
87. Ouyang J, Shao X, Li J. 2000. Indole-3-glycerol phosphate, a branchpoint of indole-3-acetic acid biosynthesis from the tryptophan biosynthetic pathway in *Arabidopsis thaliana. Plant J.* 24:327–33
88. Paciorek T, Zazimalova E, Ruthardt N, Petrasek J, Stierhof YD, et al. 2005. Auxin inhibits endocytosis and promotes its own efflux from cells. *Nature* 435:1251–56
89. Paponov IA, Teale WD, Trebar M, Blilou I, Palme K. 2005. The PIN auxin efflux facilitators: evolutionary and functional perspectives. *Trends Plant Sci.* 10:170–77
90. Park WJ, Schafer A, Prinsen E, van Onckelen H, Kang BG, Hertel R. 2001. Auxin-induced elongation of short maize coleoptile segments is supported by 2,4-dihydroxy-7-methoxy-1,4-benzoxazin-3-one. *Planta* 213:92–100
91. Petrasek J, Mravec J, Bouchard R, Blakeslee JJ, Abas M, et al. 2006. PIN proteins perform a rate-limiting function in cellular auxin efflux. *Science* 312:914–18
92. Pollmann S, Müller A, Piotrowski M, Weiler EW. 2002. Occurrence and formation of indole-3-acetamide in *Arabidopsis thaliana. Planta* 216:155–61
93. Quint M, Gray WM. 2006. Auxin signaling. *Curr. Opin. Plant Biol.* 9:448–53
94. Raven JA. 1975. Transport of indoleacetic acid in plant cells in relation to pH and electrical potential gradients, and its significance for polar IAA transport. *New Phytol.* 74:163–72
95. Reinhardt D, Pesce ER, Stieger P, Mandel T, Baltensperger K, et al. 2003. Regulation of phyllotaxis by polar auxin transport. *Nature* 426:255–60

96. Richter S, Geldner N, Schrader J, Wolters H, Stierhof YD, et al. 2007. Functional diversification of closely related ARF-GEFs in protein secretion and recycling. *Nature* 448:488–92
97. Rogg LE, Lasswell J, Bartel B. 2001. A gain-of-function mutation in *IAA28* suppresses lateral root development. *Plant Cell* 13:465–80
98. Roland-Lagan AG, Prusinkiewicz P. 2005. Reviewing models of auxin canalization in the context of leaf vein pattern formation in Arabidopsis. *Plant J.* 44:854–65
99. Romano CP, Robson PR, Smith H, Estelle M, Klee H. 1995. Transgene-mediated auxin overproduction in *Arabidopsis*: hypocotyl elongation phenotype and interactions with the *hy6-1* hypocotyl elongation and *axr1* auxin-resistant mutants. *Plant Mol. Biol.* 27:1071–83
100. Rouse D, Mackay P, Stirnberg P, Estelle M, Leyser O. 1998. Changes in auxin response from mutations in an AUX/IAA gene. *Science* 279:1371–73
101. Rubery PH, Sheldrake AR. 1974. Carrier-mediated auxin transport. *Planta* 118:101–21
102. Ruzicka K, Ljung K, Vanneste S, Podhorská R, Beeckman T, et al. 2007. Ethylene regulates root growth through effects on auxin biosynthesis and transport-dependent auxin distribution. *Plant Cell* 19:2197–212
103. Sabatini S, Beis D, Wolkenfelt H, Murfett J, Guilfoyle T, et al. 1999. An auxin-dependent distal organizer of pattern and polarity in the *Arabidopsis* root. *Cell* 99:463–72
104. Sachs T. 1981. The control of the patterned differentiation of vascular tissues. *Adv. Bot. Res.* 9:152–62
105. Scarpella E, Marcos D, Friml J, Berleth T. 2006. Control of leaf vascular patterning by polar auxin transport. *Genes Dev.* 20:1015–27
106. Seo M, Akaba S, Oritani T, Delarue M, Bellini C, et al. 1998. Higher activity of an aldehyde oxidase in the auxin-overproducing superroot1 mutant of *Arabidopsis thaliana*. *Plant Physiol.* 116:687–93
107. Sieberer T, Seifert GJ, Hauser MT, Grisafi P, Fink GR, Luschnig C. 2000. Post-transcriptional control of the *Arabidopsis* auxin efflux carrier EIR1 requires AXR1. *Curr. Biol.* 10:1595–98
108. Sieburth LE. 1999. Auxin is required for leaf vein pattern in *Arabidopsis*. *Plant Physiol.* 121:1179–90
109. Smith RS, Guyomarc'h S, Mandel T, Reinhardt D, Kuhlemeier C, Prusinkiewicz P. 2006. A plausible model of phyllotaxis. *Proc. Natl. Acad. Sci. USA* 103:1301–6
110. Steinmann T, Geldner N, Grebe M, Mangold S, Jackson CL, et al. 1999. Coordinated polar localization of auxin efflux carrier PIN1 by GNOM ARF GEF. *Science* 286:316–18
111. Stepanova AN, Hoyt JM, Hamilton AA, Alonso JM. 2005. A link between ethylene and auxin uncovered by the characterization of two root-specific ethylene-insensitive mutants in *Arabidopsis*. *Plant Cell* 17:2230–42
112. Swarup R, Friml J, Marchant A, Ljung K, Sandberg G, et al. 2001. Localization of the auxin permease AUX1 suggests two functionally distinct hormone transport pathways operate in the *Arabidopsis* root apex. *Genes Dev.* 15:2648–53
113. Swarup R, Kramer EM, Perry P, Knox K, Leyser HM, et al. 2005. Root gravitropism requires lateral root cap and epidermal cells for transport and response to a mobile auxin signal. *Nat. Cell Biol.* 7:1057–65
114. Swarup R, Marchant A, Bennett MJ. 2000. Auxin transport: providing a sense of direction during plant development. *Biochem. Soc. Trans.* 28:481–85
115. Swarup R, Perry P, Hagenbeek D, Van Der Straeten D, Beemster GT, et al. 2007. Ethylene upregulates auxin biosynthesis in *Arabidopsis* seedlings to enhance inhibition of root cell elongation. *Plant Cell* 19:2186–96

116. Symons M, Rusk N. 2003. Control of vesicular trafficking by Rho GTPases. *Curr. Biol.* 13:R409–18
117. Tan X, Calderon-Villalobos LI, Sharon M, Zheng C, Robinson CV, et al. 2007. Mechanism of auxin perception by the TIR1 ubiquitin ligase. *Nature* 446:640–45
118. Tao LZ, Cheung AY, Nibau C, Wu HM. 2005. RAC GTPases in tobacco and *Arabidopsis* mediate auxin-induced formation of proteolytically active nuclear protein bodies that contain AUX/IAA proteins. *Plant Cell* 17:2369–83
119. Tao LZ, Cheung AY, Wu HM. 2002. Plant Rac-like GTPases are activated by auxin and mediate auxin-responsive gene expression. *Plant Cell* 14:2745–60
120. Taoka K, Yanagimoto Y, Daimon Y, Hibara K, Aida M, Tasaka M. 2004. The NAC domain mediates functional specificity of CUP-SHAPED COTYLEDON proteins. *Plant J.* 40:462–73
121. Teale WD, Paponov IA, Palme K. 2006. Auxin in action: signalling, transport and the control of plant growth and development. *Nat. Rev. Mol. Cell Biol.* 7:847–59
122. Tian Q, Reed JW. 1999. Control of auxin-regulated root development by the *Arabidopsis thaliana SHY2/IAA3* gene. *Development* 126:711–21
123. Timpte C. 2001. Auxin binding protein: curiouser and curiouser. *Trends Plant Sci.* 6:586–90
124. Tiwari SB, Hagen G, Guilfoyle T. 2003. The roles of auxin response factor domains in auxin-responsive transcription. *Plant Cell* 15:533–43
125. Tobena-Santamaria R, Bliek M, Ljung K, Sandberg G, Mol JN, et al. 2002. FLOOZY of petunia is a flavin mono-oxygenase-like protein required for the specification of leaf and flower architecture. *Genes Dev.* 16:753–63
126. Ulmasov T, Hagen G, Guilfoyle TJ. 1997. ARF1, a transcription factor that binds to auxin response elements. *Science* 276:1865–68
127. Ulmasov T, Hagen G, Guilfoyle TJ. 1999. Dimerization and DNA binding of auxin response factors. *Plant J.* 19:309–19
128. Ulmasov T, Murfett J, Hagen G, Guilfoyle TJ. 1997. Aux/IAA proteins repress expression of reporter genes containing natural and highly active synthetic auxin response elements. *Plant Cell* 9:1963–71
129. Utsuno K, Shikanai T, Yamada Y, Hashimoto T. 1998. *Agr*, an *Agravitropic* locus of *Arabidopsis thaliana*, encodes a novel membrane-protein family member. *Plant Cell Physiol.* 39:1111–18
130. Vernoux T, Kronenberger J, Grandjean O, Laufs P, Traas J. 2000. PIN-FORMED 1 regulates cell fate at the periphery of the shoot apical meristem. *Development* 127:5157–65
131. Vieten A, Vanneste S, Wisniewska J, Benkova E, Benjamins R, et al. 2005. Functional redundancy of PIN proteins is accompanied by auxin-dependent cross-regulation of PIN expression. *Development* 132:4521–31
132. Weijers D, Benkova E, Jager KE, Schlereth A, Hamann T, et al. 2005. Developmental specificity of auxin response by pairs of ARF and Aux/IAA transcriptional regulators. *EMBO J.* 24:1874–85
133. Weijers D, Jürgens G. 2004. Funneling auxin action: specificity in signal transduction. *Curr. Opin. Plant Biol.* 7:687–93
134. Weijers D, Schlereth A, Ehrismann JS, Schwank G, Kientz M, Jürgens G. 2006. Auxin triggers transient local signaling for cell specification in *Arabidopsis* embryogenesis. *Dev. Cell* 10:265–70

135. Willemsen V, Friml J, Grebe M, van den Toorn A, Palme K, Scheres B. 2003. Cell polarity and PIN protein positioning in *Arabidopsis* require STEROL METHYLTRANSFERASE1 function. *Plant Cell* 15:612–25
136. Wisniewska J, Xu J, Seifertová D, Brewer PB, Ruzicka K, et al. 2006. Polar PIN localization directs auxin flow in plants. *Science* 312:883
137. Wong LM, Abel S, Shen N, de la Foata M, Mall Y, Theologis A. 1996. Differential activation of the primary auxin response genes, *PS-IAA4/5* and *PS-IAA6*, during early plant development. *Plant J.* 9:587–99
138. Xie Q, Frugis G, Colgan D, Chua NH. 2000. *Arabidopsis* NAC1 transduces auxin signal downstream of TIR1 to promote lateral root development. *Genes Dev.* 14:3024–36
139. Xie Q, Guo HS, Dallman G, Fang S, Weissman AM, Chua NH. 2002. SINAT5 promotes ubiquitin-related degradation of NAC1 to attenuate auxin signals. *Nature* 419:167–70
140. Xu J, Hofhuis H, Heidstra R, Sauer M, Friml J, Scheres B. 2006. A molecular framework for plant regeneration. *Science* 311:385–88
141. Xu J, Scheres B. 2005. Dissection of *Arabidopsis* ADP-RIBOSYLATION FACTOR 1 function in epidermal cell polarity. *Plant Cell* 17:525–36
142. Yamamoto M, Yamamoto KT. 1998. Differential effects of 1-naphthaleneacetic acid, indole-3-acetic acid and 2,4-dichlorophenoxyacetic acid on the gravitropic response of roots in an auxin-resistant mutant of Arabidopsis, *aux1*. *Plant Cell Physiol.* 39:660–64
143. Yang Y, Hammes UZ, Taylor CG, Schachtman DP, Nielsen E. 2006. High-affinity auxin transport by the AUX1 influx carrier protein. *Curr. Biol.* 16:1123–27
144. Zazimalova E, Napier RM. 2003. Points of regulation for auxin action. *Plant Cell Rep.* 21:625–34
145. Zhao Y, Christensen SK, Fankhauser C, Cashman JR, Cohen JD, et al. 2001. A role for flavin monooxygenase-like enzymes in auxin biosynthesis. *Science* 291:306–9
146. Zhao Y, Hull AK, Gupta NR, Goss KA, Alonso J, et al. 2002. Trp-dependent auxin biosynthesis in *Arabidopsis*: involvement of cytochrome P450s CYP79B2 and CYP79B3. *Genes Dev.* 16:3100–12

Regulation of Cullin RING Ligases

Sara K. Hotton and Judy Callis

Section of Molecular and Cellular Biology, University of California, Davis, California 95616; email: skhotton@ucdavis.edu, jcallis@ucdavis.edu

Annu. Rev. Plant Biol. 2008. 59:467–89

The *Annual Review of Plant Biology* is online at plant.annualreviews.org

This article's doi:
10.1146/annurev.arplant.58.032806.104011

1543-5008/08/0602-0467$20.00

Key Words

RUB, Nedd8, rubylation, neddylation, CSN, ubiquitin

Abstract

The ubiquitin/26S proteasome pathway largely mediates selective proteolysis in the nucleus and cytosol. This pathway catalyzes covalent attachment of ubiquitin (UBQ) to substrate proteins in an E1-E2-E3 cascade. Ubiquitin E3 ligases interact with substrates to catalyze UBQ transfer from E2 to substrate. Within the E3 ligase superfamily, cullin RING ligases (CRLs) are significant in plants because they are linked to hormonal signaling, developmental programs, and environmental responses. Thus, knowledge of CRL regulation is required for a complete understanding of these processes. A major mechanism modulating CRL activity is modification of the cullin subunit by RUB (RELATED TO UBIQUITIN), a ubiquitin-like protein, and demodification by the COP9 signalosome (CSN). CULLIN-ASSOCIATED NEDD8-DISSOCIATED 1 (CAND1) interacts with CRLs, affecting both rubylation and derubylation. Described here are the pathways, regulation, and biological function of rubylation and derubylation, as well as future directions and outstanding questions.

Contents

Ubiquitin: a 76-amino-acid protein covalently attached to substrate proteins via a three-enzyme cascade

E3 ligase: interacts with the ubiquitylation target and then catalyzes transfer of ubiquitin from E2 to target

INTRODUCTION

The ubiquitin pathway is a well characterized method of protein modification in which the 76-amino-acid protein, ubiquitin (UBQ), is covalently attached to other proteins in a catalytic cascade of three enzymes (for general reviews see References 25, 41, 63, and 71) (**Figure 1*a***). The first enzyme, E1 or UBQ-activating enzyme (UBA), forms a UBQ-thioester linkage after activation of the UBQ C terminus by adenylation. Activated UBQ is then transferred to a cysteinyl residue on E2, the UBQ-conjugating enzyme (UBC), forming the second UBQ-thioester in the cascade. Finally, UBQ transfer, typically to the ε-amino group of a lysyl residue on a substrate protein, requires a third protein, or protein complex, called E3 or UBQ ligase. This final step in the attachment cascade serves as the primary substrate recognition event, and several diverse classes of E3 ligases have been identified. The E3 ligase family called the CRL, for cullin RING ligase, is discussed in more detail below. Formation of a polyubiquitin chain via lysine 48 of UBQ on a substrate typically targets it for degradation by a large multicatalytic complex called the 26S proteasome (74). Mono-, oligo-, or polyubiquitylation via alternate UBQ lysines serves other cellular functions, such as intracellular targeting, DNA repair, and other processes that are less well understood, especially in plants (36, 42, 58, 64).

CRLs constitute the largest class of E3 ligase. All CRLs contain a small RING (really interesting new gene) domain–containing protein, a cullin protein, and one or more additional cullin-specific subunit(s) that have substrate recognition and adaptor functions (**Figure 2**). The adaptor protein links the substrate recognition protein to the cullin. The same RING domain–containing protein [RING BOX 1 (RBX1) in plants and other organisms, and alternatively called regulator of cullins 1 (Roc1) or high-level expression reduces Ty3 transposition 1 (Hrt1) in mammals and yeast] binds to all cullins, with the exception of the divergent cullin (APC2) in the anaphase-promoting E3 ligase. RBX1 binds the UBQ E2 to allosterically activate the E2 for UBQ transfer and additionally functions in the rubylation pathway (see below). RBX1 also interacts directly with the C terminus of the cullin subunit, thus indirectly linking RBX1 and the E2 to the substrate.

All eukaryotes examined to date contain a small family of cullin proteins (InterPro domain IPR001373), and for most cullins, orthologous members can be identified across

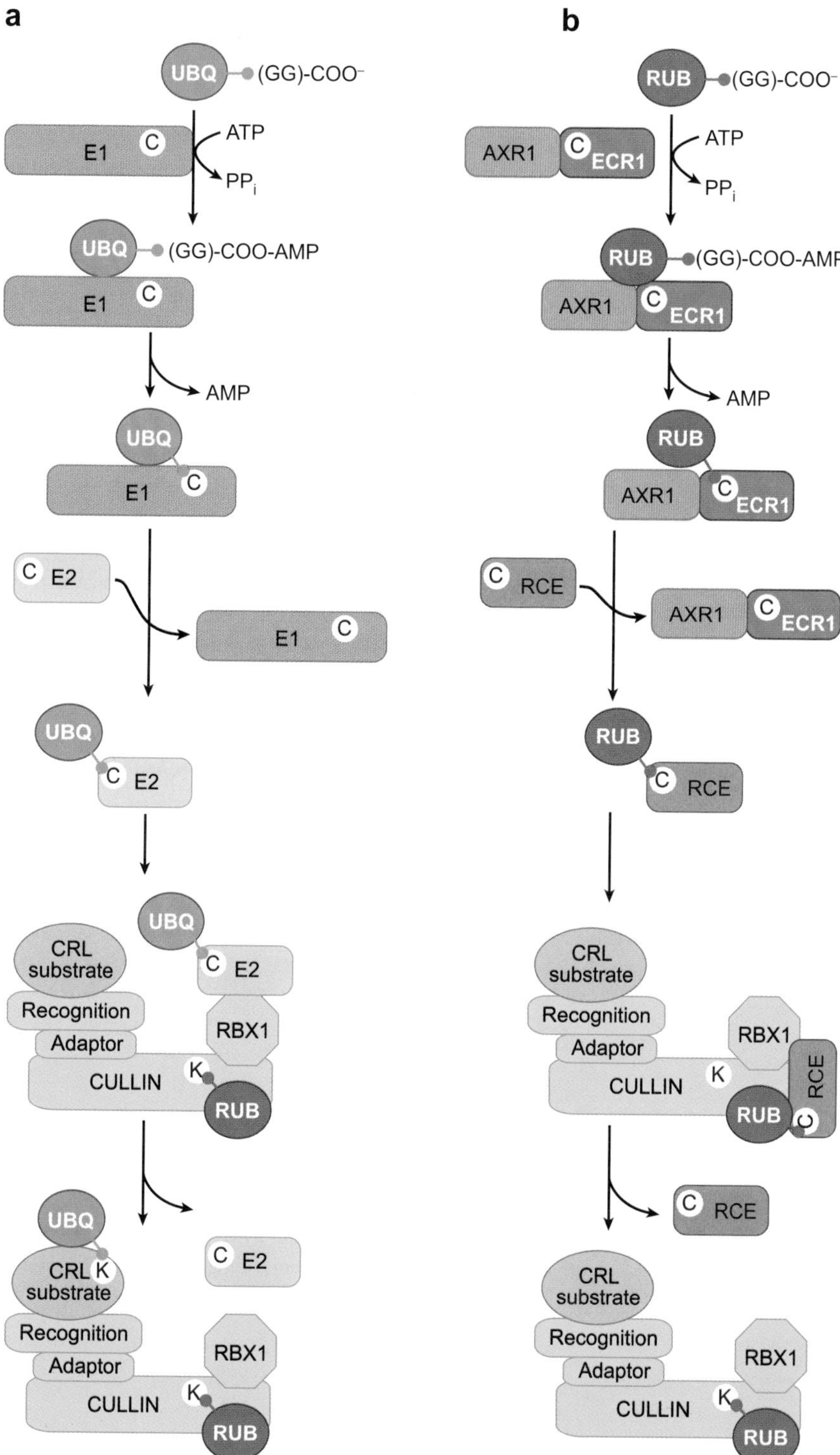

Figure 1

Comparison of (*a*) the ubiquitylation pathway to (*b*) the rubylation pathway. Unique enzymes are used for each pathway, but amino acid similarity is observed between analogous enzymes, and their mechanisms are strikingly similar. UBQ, ubiquitin; GG, C-terminal glycine-glycine; E1, ubiquitin-activating enzyme; C, cysteine; E2, ubiquitin-conjugating enzyme; CRL, cullin RING (really interesting new gene) ligase; Recognition, recognition subunit of CRL; Adaptor, adaptor subunit of CRL; K, lysine; RUB, RELATED TO UBIQUITIN; RBX1, RING BOX 1; AXR1, AUXIN RESISTANT 1; ECR1, E1 C-TERMINAL RELATED 1; RCE, RUB-CONJUGATING ENZYME.

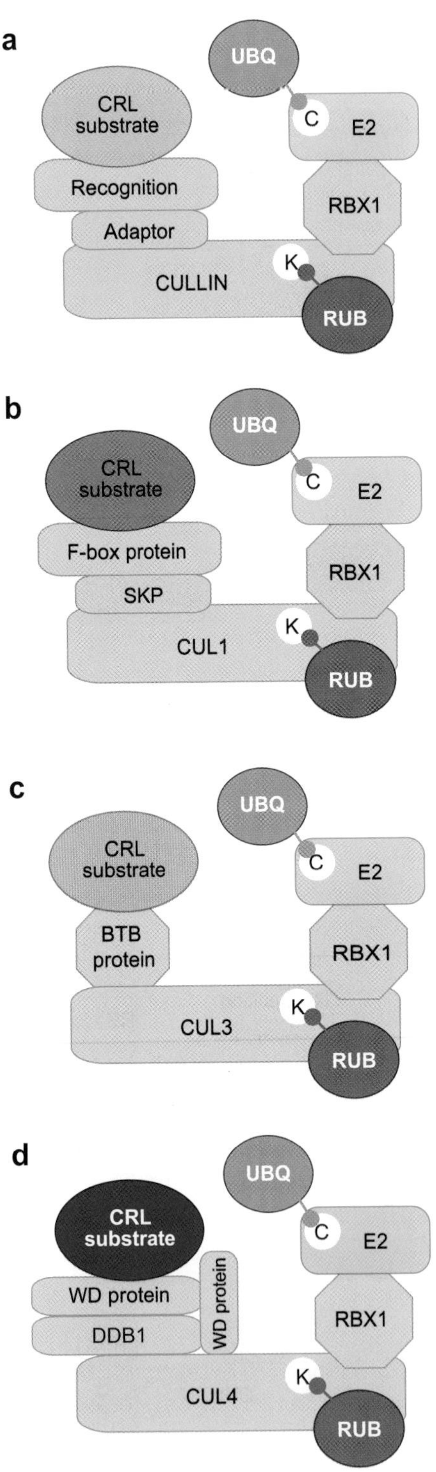

kingdoms. No *Arabidopsis thaliana* proteins functionally homologous to human cullin 2 (Cul2) or Cul5 proteins have been identified, but proteins corresponding to the other human cullins are encoded in plant genomes on the basis of sequence similarity and/or on the presence of their associated cullin-specific subunits (24, 70). The X-ray crystal structure of human Cul1 revealed its scaffold function (94). Cul1 links the substrate to be ubiquitylated to the UBQ-thioester–linked E2 by binding Rbx1 at its C-terminal globular domain and the substrate recognition and adaptor subunits at its N terminus, at the tip of an ~110 Å, elongated, slightly curved stalk. The other CRLs likely have a similar organization and interact via similar structural motifs despite sequence divergence (94).

Gene families encode substrate recognition and adaptor functions for each class of CRL; classes are named typically for their common motif (**Figure 2**). For CUL1-based CRLs, the substrate recognition subunit is an F-box protein that binds the adaptor protein SKP (S-PHASE KINASE-ASSOCIATED PROTEIN). SKP binds to both the F-box protein and CUL1. A CUL1-based ligase is typically referred to as an SCF^X for SKP-CUL1-F-box protein, with the specific F-box

Figure 2

Schematic representation of the types of cullin RING ligases (CRLs) in *Arabidopsis*, described to date. (*a*) A generic CRL. (*b–d*) Subunits of the characterized CULLIN 1 (CUL1)-, CUL3-, and CUL4- type CRLs, respectively. Recognition, recognition subunit of CRL; Adaptor, adaptor subunit of CRL; K, lysine; RUB, RELATED TO UBIQUITIN; RBX1, RING BOX 1; E2, ubiquitin-conjugating enzyme; C, cysteine; UBQ, ubiquitin; F-box, a protein interaction domain; SKP, S-PHASE KINASE-ASSOCIATED PROTEIN; BTB, broad-complex/tramtrack/bric-a-brac protein interaction domain; WD, tryptophan/aspartate-dipeptide that terminates a type of protein interaction domain; DDB1, DNA-DAMAGE BINDING 1. Different colored CRL substrates indicate unique targets for each CRL type.

protein in superscript. For CUL3-based CRLs, different domains of a BTB/POZ (BROAD-COMPLEX/TRAMTRACK/BRIC-A-BRAC/POXVIRUS AND ZINC FINGER) protein serve substrate recognition and adaptor functions (22, 24, 81). CUL3-based ligases are called BTB-CUL3-RBX1 (BCR) ligases. A DWD (DDB1-BINDING WD40 PROTEIN) or DCAF (DDB1- AND CUL4-ASSOCIATED FACTOR) protein, possibly with additional proteins, is the substrate recognition subunit of CUL4-based ligases. The adaptor protein DDB1 (DNA-DAMAGE BINDING 1) links CUL4 and DWD (2, 3, 6, 34, 38, 54).

The large number of potential substrate recognition and adaptor subunits in the proteomes of different species indicates a conserved combinatorial organization for CRLs. The same CUL-RBX1 proteins operate with different substrate recognition and adaptor proteins. This evolutionary conservation together with the substrate recognition components encoded by large gene families (e.g., ~700 F-box proteins in *Arabidopsis*) suggests that collectively they have complex and diverse roles in organisms, which is supported by genetic data. CRLs play prominent roles in plants, for example, ubiquitylating critical players in auxin, gibberellin (GA), ethylene, and jasmonic acid (JA) hormonal signaling pathways through the F-box proteins TIR1/AFB1–3 (TRANSPORT INHIBITOR RESPONSE 1/AUXIN SIGNALING F-BOX 1–3), SLY1 (SLEEPY 1), EBF1–2 (EIN3-BINDING F-BOX 1–2), and COI1(CORONATINE INSENSITIVE 1), respectively. In addition, ZEITLUPE 1 (ZTL1) and EMPFINDLICHER IM DUNKELROTEN LICHT 1 (EID1) are F-box proteins involved in light responses and circadian rhythms. ETHYLENE-OVERPRODUCER 1 (ETO1), a BTB protein, modulates ethylene synthesis through regulation of ACC synthase (80). CUL4-based CRLs repress photomorphogenesis (6). These selected examples of CRLs linked to physiological processes are representative of others that have been described and are only a small percentage of the total number predicted in *Arabidopsis* and rice (37, 47, 66, 71).

The presence of diverse substrate recognition proteins complexed with shared subunits raises questions. How is the activity of a specific CRL regulated? How is the composition of different CRLs modulated, or in other words, what are the assembly and disassembly processes? Surprisingly, some answers to these questions come from a second protein modification pathway, the related to ubiquitin (Rub) pathway. RUB attachment to and removal from cullins plays a key role in regulating CRLs. Another conserved regulator is the protein called CULLIN-ASSOCIATED NEDD8-DISSOCIATED 1 (CAND1). Equally important is the COP9 signalosome (CSN) complex and its derubylation activity. All three are discussed in detail below. Wherever possible, we review published work done in plant systems and with plant proteins and broaden the review to different model organisms in cases where experiments are lacking in plants.

Cullin RING ligase (CRL): an E3 ligase with a RING protein, RBX1 (also called Roc1 or Hrt1), a cullin protein, and different substrate recognition and adaptor subunit(s)

RBX1: RING BOX 1

F-box protein: substrate recognition subunit of the SCF-type of E3 ligase; contains the F-box domain and a distinct protein-protein interaction domain that functions in substrate recognition

SCF: a CRL that, in addition to RBX1, contains the subunits SKP, CULLIN 1, and one of many F-box proteins

CULLIN-ASSOCIATED NEDD8-DISSOCIATED 1 (CAND1): binds to unmodified CUL-RBX1 subunits of CRLs and prevents substrate recognition and adaptor subunit(s) from binding

COP9 signalosome (CSN): an eight-subunit complex with derubylating activity

THE RUB/NEDD8 UBIQUITIN-LIKE PATHWAY

The RUB/Nedd8 [RELATED TO UBIQUITIN, in plants and budding yeast (*Saccharomyces cerevisiae*), and neuronal precursor cell–expressed developmentally downregulated 8, in animals and fission yeast (*Schizosaccharomyces pombe*)] pathway, here referred to as the Rub pathway, is just one of several protein modification systems that parallels the ubiquitin pathway (reviewed in References 19, 41, and 61). Consistent with other ubiquitin-like (UBL) pathways, the Rub pathway has an analogous enzyme cascade to the UBQ E1-E2-E3 and attaches RUB/Nedd8 to a substrate protein (**Figure 1*b***). Of the UBLs, RUB/Nedd8 has the highest primary sequence identity to UBQ (~60%) and has a nearly identical structure (reviewed in References 19, 32, and 77). In addition to the similarity between the processes for covalent

Nedd8/RUB: a ubiquitin-like protein from yeast, animals, plants, and budding yeast; Nedd8 stands for neuronal precursor cell–expressed developmentally downregulated 8; RUB stands for RELATED TO UBIQUITIN

AUXIN RESISTANT 1 (AXR1): one half of the dimeric RUB-activating enzyme

E1 C-TERMINAL RELATED 1 (ECR1): one half of the dimeric RUB-activating enzyme

attachment of RUB and UBQ to proteins, homologous structures also exist for removal of the respective UBL: RUB is removed from its substrate protein by a zinc metalloprotease subunit in the CSN, whereas UBQ is detached by a homologous subunit in the lid complex of the 26S proteasome (reviewed in Reference 83).

RUBYLATION ENZYMES

A genetic screen for *Arabidopsis* seedling roots resistant to inhibitory concentrations of an auxin, 2,4-dichlorophenoxyacetic acid (2,4-D), identified multiple alleles of *AUXIN RESISTANT 1* (*AXR1*) (20, 51). Comprehensive phenotypic analyses of the severe *axr1-12* mutant indicated that mutant plants are less sensitive than wild-type to every tested physiological auxin response and show an altered morphology (20, 51, 75). *AXR1* affects additional hormonal signaling pathways. For example, *axr1* roots are slightly more resistant to the growth inhibitory effects of added cytokinin, ethylene, and *epi*-brassinolide (75, 76). Subsequent to the cloning of *AXR1*, a screen for JA resistance in seedling roots identified the cause as a defect in *AXR1*, but the sequence change in the implicated allele, *axr1-24*, could not be identified (76). The weak *axr1* allele, *axr1-3*, is also resistant to the inhibitory effect of JA on roots (68). *axr1-24* is, additionally, more resistant than wild-type to the inhibition of germination mediated by abscisic acid (ABA) (76).

Further studies identified additional signaling pathways that require *AXR1*. *axr1-3* is a strong photomorphogenic mutant when in combination with a *cop10* allele, a weak constitutive photomorphogenic (cop) mutant (68). Increases in mRNA abundance of the *COLD-RESPONSIVE* (*COR*) genes, *COR6.6* and *COR47*, are delayed in *axr1-3* (68). Dark-grown seedlings of a strong *AXR1* mutant allele, *axr1-13*, produce less ethylene than wild-type (5). Altogether these analyses point toward an expansive role for *AXR1* in multiple hormonal and developmental pathways, to include hormone synthesis and signaling, in and beyond the auxin response, as well as in responses to environmental change.

Map-based cloning was an essential but partial step toward understanding the function of *AXR1* (49). Although AXR1 bears some resemblance to the ubiquitin-activating enzyme, E1, it is approximately half the size of E1 and lacks the catalytic cysteine required for E1 activity. Thus, its function was initially unclear. Genetic and biochemical analyses in budding yeast provided the first insight into the biochemical function of AXR1. E1-like protein N-terminal region 2/ubiquitin-like protein activation 1 (Enr2p/Ula1p, hereafter referred to as Enr2p), an ortholog of AXR1, is required to produce a modified form of the protein cell division cycle 53 (Cdc53p), a cullin protein that functions in the budding yeast SCF E3 ligase (45, 50). In wild-type cells, Cdc53p is present in two electrophoretically distinct forms differing by ~6 kDa, but in an *enr2* deletion strain, only one form is seen. Curiously, *enr2Δ* strains are phenotypically indistinguishable from isogenic wild-type, but are synthetically lethal with mutations in components of the ubiquitylation pathway, notably a temperature-sensitive mutation in a gene encoding a particular E2, Cdc34p (45). These data led to the hypothesis (subsequently verified with an epitope-tagged Rub1p) that Rub1p, an 8.7-kDa protein, covalently modifies Cdc53p, slowing its migration on SDS polyacrylamide gel electrophoresis (45, 50).

Because genetic data suggested that *ENR2* was responsible for Rub1p attachment, and like AXR1, the protein resembles only the N-terminal half of the UBQ E1, proteins with similarity to the C-terminal half of E1 were identified in the predicted proteomes of budding yeast (50) and *Arabidopsis* (15). These proteins were named ubiquitin-like activating enzyme 3 (Uba3p) and E1 C-TERMINAL RELATED 1 (ECR1) in yeast and *Arabidopsis*, respectively. Characterization of the heterodimeric activating enzyme for the UBL, small ubiquitin-like modifier (SUMO), also provided insight because it has a similar organization (reviewed in Reference 32). Subsequent in vitro biochemical experiments verified that the *Arabidopsis* proteins AXR1 and ECR1 were together capable of synthesizing a RUB1-adenylate and an ECR1-thioester linkage with RUB1 (14, 15), exactly paralleling ubiquitin activation.

Continuing with a search for enzymes in addition to the AXR1-ECR1 heterodimeric RUB-activating enzyme, a RUB-specific E2 enzyme was identified, encoded by two closely related genes in *Arabidopsis*, called *RCE1* and *RCE2* (for *RUB-CONJUGATING ENZYME*) (14). The analogous RUB-specific E3-like activity was more difficult to identify. Reconstitution experiments using human or yeast proteins require the addition of Rbx1 to a reaction containing Nedd8, Nedd8 E1, Nedd8 E2 (Ubc12), and the substrate, Cul1. Only Rbx1 proteins with intact RING domains are active in rubylation: Rbx1 interaction alone with Cul1 is insufficient (39, 57). Further support for Rbx1's role in neddylation came from the demonstration of in vitro interaction of the RING-domain of Rbx1 with Ubc12 (57). Thus, Rbx1 appears to be required for both ubiquitylation of CRL substrates and rubylation of cullins. Genetic studies in *Arabidopsis* have shown, through the use of a conditional knockdown strategy, that a reduction in RBX1 results in a concomitant reduction in RUB-modified CUL1 in vivo, pointing to the importance of RBX1 in the rubylation pathway (48). Thus, the rubylation pathway in *Arabidopsis* unfolded as a protein modification pathway analogous to the ubiquitylation pathway, with AXR1/ECR1 heterodimer, RCE, and RBX1 proteins operating as RUB-specific E1-like, E2-like, and E3-like activities, respectively.

CULLIN SUBUNITS OF CRLS ARE MAJOR RUBYLATION SUBSTRATES

Although yeast Cdc53p was the first protein that was demonstrated to be rubylated, subsequent studies identified other proteins, possessing a cullin domain and an amino acid sequence of VRIMK, or a variant, that are also RUB1/Rub1p/Nedd8 substrates. Substitution of the lysine residue of VRI/VMK in human Cul2, fission yeast Pcu1, Pcu3, and Pcu4, and *Arabidopsis* CUL1 and CUL3a/b blocks rubylation; thus, the lysine is considered to be the site of modification (14, 60, 78, 81, 95). At least six human cullins can be neddylated in vitro (35), and other cullin-like proteins in *S. cerevisiae*, in addition to Cdc53p, are rubylated in vivo (46). In *Arabidopsis*, there are eleven cullin (AtCUL) proteins, but only six contain a VRIMK sequence (24, 70). AtCUL1, AtCUL3a, and AtCUL3b are rubylated in vitro and in vivo (5, 14, 22, 81). AtCUL4 exists in two electrophoretic forms in vivo, so it also likely undergoes rubylation (6, 18). The in vivo expression of the remaining *Arabidopsis* cullin proteins that possess the VRIMK site, AtCUL2 and At1g43140, is still in question, and their rubylation status is not known. In summary, all AtCUL proteins that possess the conserved VRIMK rubylation site and have been demonstrated to function in a CRL appear to be modified by RUB.

RCE: RUB-CONJUGATING ENZYME

To date, only three Nedd8 substrates are known that are not cullin proteins. The human tumor suppressor protein, p53, is neddylated in vivo; this process requires the RING UBQ E3 ligase Mdm2 (for mouse double minute 2), which is also neddylated (89). Neddylated p53 is transcriptionally less active than wild-type, whereas the function of Mdm2 neddylation is unknown. The human von Hippel Lindau protein (pVHL) functions as a substrate recognition subunit in a Cul2-type CRL and is also neddylated in vivo. Loss of pVHL neddylation results in a failure to bind to fibronectin and to promote the assembly of the fibronectin matrix, which are important for cell differentiation and monolayer organization in cell cultures (72). Homologous proteins to these noncullin neddylation substrates have not yet been identified in plants.

Do rubylated noncullin proteins exist in plants? Such a determination will require a focused proteomic analysis because cullin proteins appear to be the major rubylated species in extracts from transgenic plants that express epitope-tagged RUB proteins (5). The number of additional substrates could be small, or if there are many different RUB substrates, their individual abundance could be low, potentially making protein identification and verification problematic.

EFFECT OF RUBYLATION/ NEDDYLATION ON CRL ACTIVITY

In vitro biochemical studies that focus on the role of cullin rubylation suggest the catalytic activity of an assembled CRL is increased when modified by RUB/Nedd8, thus enhancing ubiquitylation of substrates (40, 56, 88) (**Figure 3*a***). Although such studies of plant CRLs are lacking, given the conservation among CRLs between kingdoms, we can speculate that the effects in plants may be similar, if not identical, to those revealed in mammalian and yeast studies on orthologous proteins. Studies have provided data to support several models, detailed below, that are not necessarily mutually exclusive. One is that Nedd8 increases the local concentration of a UBQ thioester-linked E2, and the other is that Nedd8 facilitates CRL dimerization; the dimer is postulated to be the more active form. **Figure 4** outlines the possible effects of cullin rubylation/neddylation on CRL activity.

Nedd8 is a Docking Site for E2

In in vitro reactions, Nedd8 modification of Cul1 increases ubiquitylation of phosphorylated IκBα (a substrate of $SCF^{\beta TrCP1}$). Concomitantly, recruitment of the UBQ E2, Ubc4, to the SCF complex is enhanced (40). On the basis of these reconstitution and pull-down experiments, Nedd8 is proposed to be an E2 docking site (40). In nuclear magnetic resonance and mutational studies, Nedd8 interacts with Ubc4, but not with the Nedd8 E2 (Ubc12) (65). Thus, Nedd8 forms a platform on the SCF complex for selective recruitment of ubiquitin-charged E2s and, in collaboration with Rbx1, upregulates E3 activity (**Figure 4*a***). Nedd8 interacts with the

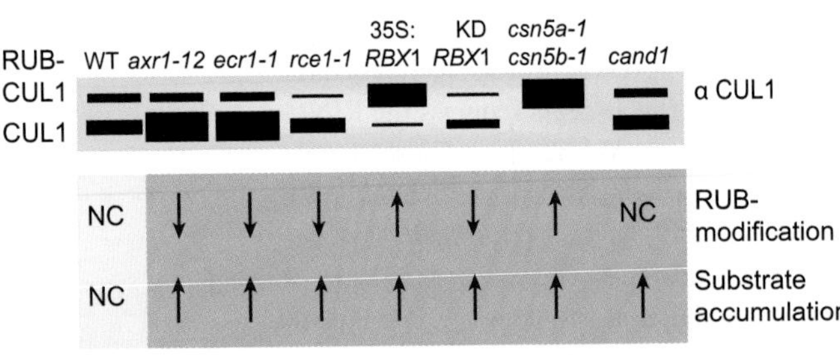

Figure 3

(*a*) Schematic of the effects of rubylation and derubylation enzymes on ubiquitylation in vitro. (*b*) Schematic of the effects of rubylation and derubylation mutants on (*top*) CUL1 abundance, (*middle*) rubylation status, and (*bottom*) substrate accumulation in *Arabidopsis*. E1, ubiquitin-activating enzyme; E2, ubiquitin-conjugating enzyme; E3, ubiquitin ligase; UBQ, ubiquitin; Nedd8, neuronal precursor cell–expressed developmentally downregulated 8 conjugation system; CSN, COP9 signalosome; RUB, RELATED TO UBIQUITIN; CUL1, CULLIN 1; WT, wild-type; *axr, auxin resistant*; *ecr, e1 c-terminal related*; *rce, rub-conjugating enzyme*; *RBX, RING BOX*; *cand, cullin-associated nedd8-dissociated*; NC, no change.

UBQ E2 through its small surface hydrophobic region around isoleucine 44 (65).

Nedd8 Mediates Dimerization of Cul3

Nedd8 activates BCR ligases by mediating the dimerization of human Cul3 (**Figure 4*b***). Fluorescence resonance energy transfer (FRET) analysis and coimmunoprecipitation of differentially tagged cullins demonstrate that Cul3 is found as a neddylated heterodimer (one neddylated, one unneddylated) in vivo (84). Additionally, FRET experiments show decreased interaction of Cul3 heterodimers when temperature-sensitive Nedd8 mutants are grown at nonpermissive temperature, suggesting that Nedd8 is required for this interaction. The heterodimer consists of Nedd8 covalently attached to one Cul3 molecule and noncovalently bound to the second Cul3 molecule. Coexpression of two distinct nonfunctional Cul3 mutants can rescue the ubiquitin ligase function of the BCR complex. Thus, in mammalian cells, Nedd8 modification promotes dimerization of Cul3 (84).

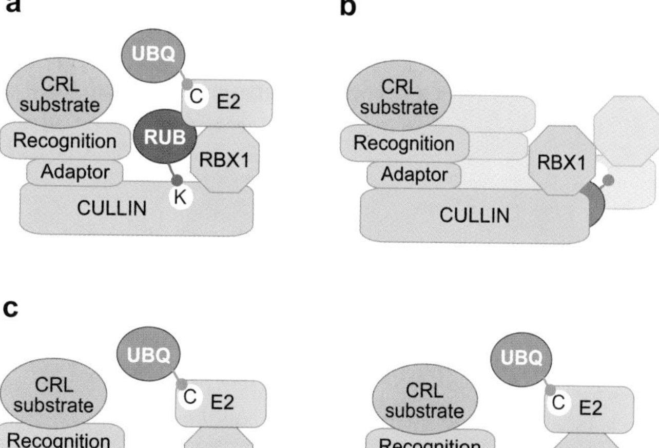

Figure 4

Models for regulation of cullin RING ligase (CRL) activity by RELATED TO UBIQUITIN (RUB) modification, based on studies done in mammalian systems. (*a*) RUB serves as an E2 docking site. (*b*) RUB facilitates cullin dimerization. (*c*) RUB may function as an allosteric effector. Recognition, recognition subunit of CRL; Adaptor, adaptor subunit of CRL; K, lysine; RBX1, RING BOX 1; E2, ubiquitin-conjugating enzyme; C, cysteine; UBQ, ubiquitin.

Additional Models

One could envision that RUB binding to a cullin within a CRL could result in a conformational change in the CRL that brings the UBQ-loaded E2 into closer proximity with its substrate (**Figure 4*c***). Another possibility is that RUB recruits yet unidentified proteins to the CRL that enhance or mediate UBQ transfer from E2 to substrate. There may be no single effect of rubylation, and multiple mechanisms could act collectively to regulate CRL activity in vivo.

THE RUB PATHWAY IS ESSENTIAL IN PLANTS

The RUB/Nedd8 family of proteins is found in all eukaryotes investigated to date, and studies have clearly established its significance in almost all organisms. The Rub pathway, both rubylation and derubylation, is essential in mammals, worms, and plants (reviewed in Reference 10). There are a few interesting exceptions to this generalization. Rubylation is essential to fission yeast (60), but loss of the derubylation activity of the CSN does not have an adverse effect (59, 95). In contrast, Rub1p is not essential in budding yeast, in which the initial genetic and biochemical analyses were performed (45, 50).

In *Arabidopsis*, single mutation in *RUB1* or *RUB2* does not result in a phenotype, likely owing to genetic redundancy, which is commonly seen in plants. Conversely, the double mutant is embryo lethal at the 2-cell stage, highlighting the plant's requirement for a functional Rub pathway (5). A double mutant of *axr1* and its paralog, *axr1-like 1* (*axl1*), is also lethal early in development, which correlates with the absence of cullin rubylation (16 and M. Bostick,

S.K. Hotton & J. Callis, unpublished observations). Loss of the CSN complex results in seedling lethality (reviewed in Reference 83). Thus, rubylation/derubylation is essential in plants, similar to other organisms. Partial loss-of-function and overexpression strategies have helped to elucidate the Rub pathway in plants.

EFFECT OF ALTERING EXPRESSION OF RUBYLATION PATHWAY COMPONENTS IN *ARABIDOPSIS*

When the activity of the rubylation pathway is decreased in vivo, CRL substrates accumulate, suggesting a positive role for RUB modification, with the caveat that this effect has been tested only for CUL1 and a few CUL1-dependent substrates in *Arabidopsis*. Loss of function *axr1* mutants accumulate proportionally less RUB-modified CUL1 than wild-type (13). The auxin/indole-3-acetic acid (Aux/IAA) protein, AXR2/IAA7, and the fusion proteins AXR3NT-GUS (β-glucuronidase fusion) and IAA1-LUC (luciferase fusion) undergo slower $SCF^{TIR1/AFB1-3}$-mediated degradation in *axr1-12* (28, 92). Overexpression of ECR1 that carries a substitution of its catalytic cysteine, C215A, results in a dominant negative (dn) phenotype; severe mutants (correlated with greater expression of dnECR1) have a phenotype similar to *axr1* mutants (13). Consistent with the *axr1* mutant phenotype, dnECR1 lines show reduced apical dominance, auxin insensitivity, and reduced fertility. dnECR1 mutants have less RUB-modified CUL1, and the CUL1 modification status of the most severe line studied is identical to *axr1-12* (13). A recessive mutant in *ECR1*, *ecr1-1*, has a missense mutation that results in a leucine to phenylalanine change at residue 217, close to the catalytic cysteine, C215. *ecr1-1* has more unmodified CUL1 and thus, proportionally less RUB-modified CUL1, as seen for dnECR1 and *axr1* plant lines, and has a phenotype similar to these plant lines. AXR3NT-GUS is stabilized in *ecr1-1* to a similar degree as the weak *axr1-3* allele (85).

A recessive mutation in the RUB E2, *RCE1*, designated *rce1-1*, has a *Ds* (*Dissociation*) insert in the promoter of *RCE1*, resulting in a dramatic reduction in *RCE1* transcripts. *rce1-1* has a phenotype similar to the severe *axr1-12* mutant plants (17). Mutants are dwarfed and bushy, auxin insensitive, and show a decreased gravitropic response. *rce1-1* mutants show a significant reduction in RUB-CUL1 and the degradation rate of AXR2/IAA7 is slowed, consistent with other rubylation mutants.

In *RBX1* dexamethasone (dex)-inducible overexpression lines, increased RBX1 protein was verified under induced conditions, but plants do not show clear phenotypic differences from wild-type (48). The rubylation status of CUL1 was not determined. Knockdown *RBX1* lines, confirmed to have reduced *RBX1* RNA and protein under dex treatment, produce small bushy plants. Knockdown *RBX1* lines have reduced levels of both unmodified and RUB-modified CUL1 and accumulate more cyclin D3. Cyclin D3 shows CRL-mediated degradation in mammalian systems, but this has not been tested in plants (48). In contrast, Gray and coworkers (27), using a different ecotype and constitutive expression, reported that the phenotype of *35S:RBX1* lines, with verified higher *RBX1* mRNA, is reminiscent of *axr1-12*, a severe *axr1* mutant with reduced auxin responsiveness and severe growth defects. As in *axr1-12*, degradation of the $SCF^{TIR1/AFB1-3}$ substrate AXR2/IAA7 is slowed in *35S:RBX1* lines. In contrast to *axr1-12* mutants, *35S:RBX1* lines have reduced levels of unmodified CUL1 and increased levels of RUB-modified CUL1. Interpretation of the results from experiments that alter RBX1 levels is not straightforward because of the dual role of RBX1 in rubylation and ubiquitylation reactions. The current data suggest that both hyper- and hyporubylation result in the accumulation of CUL1-based CRL substrates. This issue is discussed further below in the context of rubylation/derubylation cycles. **Figure 3*b*** summarizes the relationship between alterations in the Rub pathway in vivo and the accumulation of CUL1, RUB-CUL1, and CRL substrate.

DERUBYLATION

The CSN is a conserved complex that catalyzes derubylation. Surprisingly, loss-of-function mutations in *Arabidopsis* in either rubylation or derubylation result in shared phenotypes, specifically reduced auxin responsiveness, which is characterized by dwarfism, loss of apical dominance, and other pleiotropic effects. Despite opposite accumulation of RUB-modified cullins, with increased rubylation in CSN loss-of-function mutants, researchers observe CRL substrate accumulation (**Figure 3*b***). This observation is not consistent with in vitro results, where addition of CSN inhibits ubiquitylation of substrates, as diagrammed in **Figure 3*a*** (53, 90). These data have led to a model, albeit incomplete, in which cycles of RUB modification and removal are required for proper CRL function (53, 67).

The CSN Complex Removes RUB/Nedd8 from Cullins

The CSN is a multiprotein complex with eight subunits; six subunits contain a PCI (proteasome/COP9 signalosome/initiation factor 3) domain and two subunits contain an MPN (Mpr1/Pad1/N-terminal) domain. The six PCI domain–containing proteins, designated CSN1 to CSN4, CSN7, and CSN8, were originally identified genetically as repressors of photomorphogenesis in *Arabidopsis*. Null mutation in only one subunit results in the *constitutive photomorphogenic/de-etiolated/fusca* (*cop/det/fus*) phenotype, which is characterized by de-etiolation, anthocyanin accumulation, constitutive expression of light-induced genes, and early seedling lethality, owing to loss of integrity of the CSN complex. Both null and partial loss-of-function PCI-domain mutants are reviewed elsewhere (69, 83).

The *cop/det/fus* screens in *Arabidopsis* did not identify either of the MPN domain–containing CSN subunits because two genes encode CSN5, namely *CSN5a* and *CSN5b*, and two genes encode CSN6, *CSN6a* and *CSN6b*. Null T-DNA insertion alleles have recently been analyzed for *CSN5a/b* and *CSN6a/b* (30). Complete depletion of either of the two MPN members results in loss of the CSN complex and lower levels of multiple CSN components, similar to null mutation in the PCI domain subunits (30). *csn5a-1 csn5b-1* or *csn6a-1 csn6b-1* null mutants show a standard *cop/det/fus* phenotype and are thus seedling lethal.

As noted above, the CSN removes RUB/Nedd8 from CRLs (53) and appears to be the primary such activity in *Arabidopsis* seedlings because loss of the CSN complex results in completely rubylated CUL1, CUL3, and CUL4 in total extracts (30). The JAMM (Jab1/MPN/MOV34 domain metalloenzyme) motif in one subunit, CSN5, functions as a zinc metalloprotease that is specifically responsible for RUB/Nedd8 cleavage (12) (**Figure 5**).

A single null mutation in *CSN5a*, but not *CNS5b*, results in multiple developmental defects, including dwarfism and reduced apical dominance, which are characteristic of auxin signaling defects, along with alterations in RUB modification (29, 30). These phenotypes are also consistent with partial loss-of-function mutations in the PCI domain–containing subunits (reviewed in Reference 69). Previous characterization of a *CSN5* knockdown mutant showed stabilization of the SCF^{TIR1} substrate PsIAA6-LUC, suggesting that CSN positively regulates SCF activity (67). A similar effect is seen in mammalian cells (reviewed in Reference 10). For example, a conditionally silenced *csn5* mutant in human cells results in a JAMM-dependent reduction in two F-box proteins (out of seven tested), Skp2 and Fbw7, and increases accumulation of

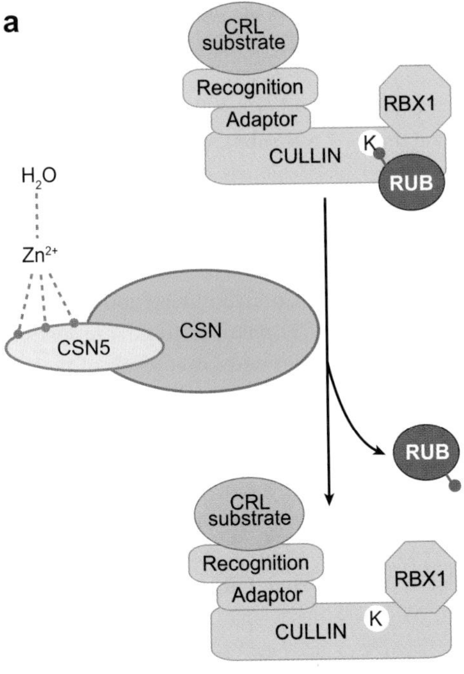

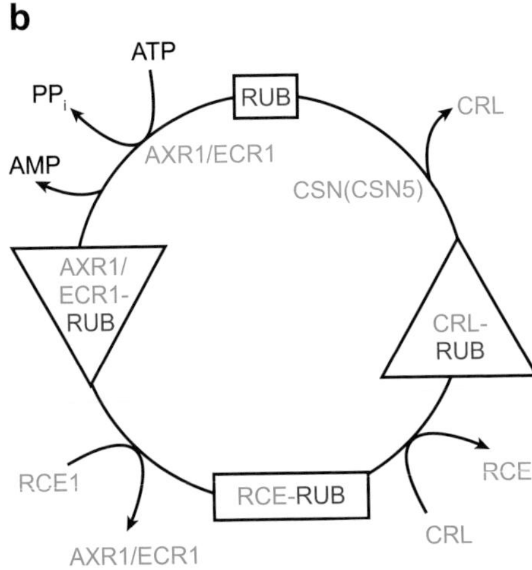

Figure 5

(*a*) Function of COP9 signalosome (CSN). (*b*) In vivo, rubylation and derubylation work to optimize cullin RING ligase (CRL) activity. Recognition, recognition subunit of CRL; Adaptor, adaptor subunit of CRL; K, lysine; RUB, RELATED TO UBIQUITIN; RBX1, RING BOX 1; AXR1, AUXIN RESISTANT 1; ECR1, E1 C-TERMINAL RELATED 1; RCE, RUB-CONJUGATING ENZYME.

the substrates of SCF^{Fbw7}, cyclin E, and c-myc (11).

Intriguingly, complete loss of CSN5 or other CSN subunits results in normal germination and embryo development; mutants then show early seedling lethality (30). In contrast, complete loss of rubylation ability, as seen in *rub1 rub2* double mutants, for example, results in early embryo lethality (5). These genetic results suggest that the requirement for rubylation/derubylation cycling is relaxed, or not absolutely required, during early embryo development and germination, and becomes more critical during seedling establishment and later in development.

EXPLAINING THE PARADOX

Using in vitro ubiquitylation reactions, researchers showed that the addition of rubylation components results in increased ubiquitylation of substrate, and the addition of CSN results in decreased ubiquitylation, suggesting a model in which RUB modification promotes and CSN inhibits CRL activity (40, 53, 56, 90) (**Figure 3*a***). Paradoxically, genetic analyses of *axr1* null mutants and *CSN5* knockdown mutants, for example, suggest both attachment and detachment of RUB/Nedd8 are essential for proper CRL function because both mutants accumulate CRL substrates (28, 67) (**Figure 3*b***).

A possible explanation for this paradox comes from the observation that neddylation results in auto-ubiquitylation and destabilization of CRL components, which results in reduced CRL activity (23, 97). In *Drosophila melanogaster* and *Neurospora crassa*, degradation of Cul1 and Cul3 increases in CSN mutants in which hyperneddylation is observed; in an *N. crassa csn2* mutant, degradation of a SCF substrate is impaired (33, 87). In mammals, Cul1 is not destabilized by neddylation; however, both substrate recognition and adaptor subunits are destabilized by neddylation, which leads to accumulation of substrates (11). Hence, hyperneddylation could lead to the same phenotype as hyponeddylation, that is, accumulation of CRL substrates. Accumulation of substrate occurs, in the former case, because the CRL has been destabilized by auto-ubiquitylation and degradation resulting in a limiting amount of ligase, whereas in the latter case, substrate accumulation occurs because the CRL is less active without RUB/Nedd8 modification.

In *Arabidopsis*, loss of derubylation in *csn5a-1 csn5b-1* and in *csn6a-1 csn6b-1* seedlings results in destabilization of CUL3, consistent with previous observations in *D. melanogaster* and *N. crassa* (30). In contrast, CUL4 is stabilized and CUL1 stability is unchanged, highlighting that more attention to this question is required in plants (30).

Another reason for the discrepancy between CSN's role in vitro and in vivo is that not all of CSN's functions are present or relevant in in vitro CRL activity assays. The CSN serves a scaffold function, interacting with other proteins, including a deubiquitylating enzyme (designated UBP12, for ubiquitin-specific protease 12), the 26S proteasome, and several kinases (31, 44, 86). UBP12 has been proposed to stabilize CRL subunits by removing covalently attached ubiquitin generated from the autocatalytic ubiquitylation activity of CRLs (82, 86, 96). UBP12 could thus promote CRL activity by preservation of the complex. In *csn* mutants, loss of the CSN complex results both in the loss of the catalytic activity housed in subunit 5 (CSN5) and in disbandment of UBP12. Both effects contribute to destabilization of the CRL, leading to the accumulation of CRL substrates.

The 26S proteasome interacts with and degrades ubiquitylated proteins (reviewed in Reference 71). Accumulation of CRL substrates could also result in mutants lacking a CSN due to loss of CSN-mediated interaction between the CRLs and the 26S proteasome. CSN-associated kinases have been shown to both increase and decrease ubiquitylation and degradation of CRL substrates (reviewed in Reference 31), so the effect of loss of CSN on their activities is more complex.

However, current data suggest that the effect of associated proteins is secondary because *CSN5* active site mutants that maintain the CSN complex but lack metalloprotease activity are unable to complement the abnormal phenotypes associated with null mutation of CSN components (12, 29, 87). Thus, deneddylation is an essential function of the CSN complex. However, these studies do not confirm that the inactive CSN can interact as efficiently as the endogenous complex with CSN-associated proteins (e.g., the CRLs). The purpose of these multidimensional CSN interactions requires further investigation.

Thus, the differences in the results from in vitro and in vivo studies likely result from the narrow focus of in vitro reactions, which reveal only the negative effect of CSN-mediated deneddylation on CRL catalytic activity. These assays do not account for the effects of CSN-interacting proteins and other regulatory mechanisms operating in vivo, such as the modulation of CRL subunit stability. Optimal CRL activity, as required in vivo, is then maintained both by upregulation and downregulation of its catalytic activity.

REQUIREMENTS FOR RUB/NEDD8 ATTACHMENT TO CULLINS

In cullin immunoblots from total protein extracts, a minor fraction of the total cullin is rubylated, which seems surprising, given the importance of this modification. Why is only a subset of total cullin rubylated at any given time, and how is the process of RUB attachment to cullins regulated? An answer to the first question is consistent with the instability of fully active (RUB/Nedd8-modified) CRLs. To maintain the pool of CRL components, only a small proportion of the total cullin is modified and active. To achieve this, the process of RUB/Nedd8 addition and/or removal must be highly regulated.

Studies show that rubylation requires the substrate recognition and adaptor subunit(s),

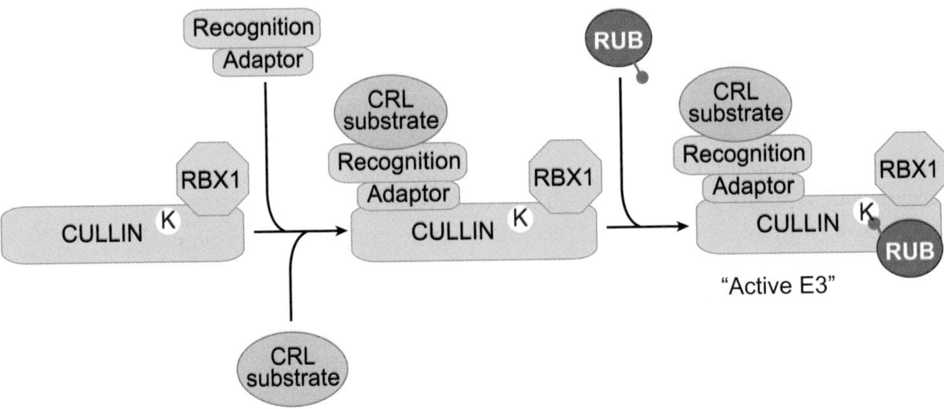

Figure 6

Order of cullin RING ligase (CRL) assembly and activation. Assembly of substrate recognition and adaptor subunit(s) on cullin (CUL)-RING BOX 1 (RBX1) backbone precedes and is required for rubylation. Substrate is also sometimes required for rubylation. K, lysine; Recognition, recognition subunit of CRL; Adaptor, adaptor subunit of CRL; RUB, RELATED TO UBIQUITIN.

in addition to the RUB/Nedd8-attachment site, and in some cases, the substrate additionally promotes the extent of RUB/Nedd8 modification (**Figure 6**). Several laboratories observed the requirement for these components using mammalian protein–based systems (4, 8, 73). Addition of an F-box protein, specifically Skp2 (along with its adaptor Skp1), and its substrate, in this case p27, enhances in vitro neddylation of Cul1 in the presence of HeLa cell extracts (4). Cotransfection of pVHL and elongin B/C, substrate recognition and adaptor subunits for Cul2-based CRLs, specifically increases Cul2 neddylation in COS cells (79).

Cotransfection of a plasmid encoding C-terminally truncated human Cul1, Cul2, Cul3, or Cul4a (lacking the Rbx1-binding and neddylation sites) with a plasmid for expression of respective full-length (FL) cullin, reduces FL-Cul neddylation (8). Presumably, by competing for substrate recognition factors and/or substrates required for FL-Cul neddylation, the truncated proteins have a dominant negative function (8). Introduction of Skp2 or pVHL without their substrate recognition domains also reduces Cul1 or Cul2 neddylation, respectively, indicating a requirement for substrate in these CRLs (8, 73). In contrast, introduction of a BTB protein, Keap1, without its substrate recognition domain, does not affect neddylation of Cul3-based CRLs (8). In summary, experimental data from mammalian cells suggest that substrate and substrate-recognition subunits promote neddylation, but the mechanism needs elucidation.

An additional enzyme, identified in budding yeast and *C. elegans* and called defective in cullin neddylation 1 (Dcn1p and DCN-1, respectively), facilitates RUB/Nedd8 transfer (43). DCN-1 interacts with Nedd8 and Rbx1 (43, 91). In *S. cerevisiae*, *dcn1*Δ mutants show less accumulation of Rub1p-modified Cdc53p compared to wild-type. Similar results are seen for neddylation of CUL-3 in *C. elegans* mutants. Addition of yeast extracts expressing GFP-Dcn1p enhances in vitro rubylation of Cdc53p to a much greater extent than extracts from *dcn1*Δ (43). DCN-1/Dcn1p may function either in a regulatory role or as part of the RUB/Nedd8 E3 ligase (43). Although genetic data clearly implicate DCN-1/Dcn1p as a player in the rubylation pathway, its exact biochemical role requires clarification and the orthologous activity in plants awaits characterization.

CAND1

Another component involved in regulating the Rub pathway, at least in animals and plants, is the ~120-kDa CAND1 protein. CAND1 normally binds to Cul1-Rbx1, blocking Skp1 (the adaptor subunit) binding and Nedd8 modification to prevent formation of an active CRL complex (26, 52, 93). Additionally, CAND1-Cul1-Rbx1 does not bind CSN, thus CAND1 could indirectly promote deneddylation by prevention of CSN binding to unmodified CRLs, leaving the CSN free to target neddylated CRLs (55). CAND1 binds other cullins, in addition to Cul1, in mammalian systems (52, 93). In vitro ubiquitylation experiments show that addition of CAND1 has a negative effect on ubiquitylation of SCF substrates, suggesting that CAND1 is a negative regulator of CRL activity (52, 93). However, loss-of-function mutation in CAND1 results in a phenotype that is similar to mutants in the Rub pathway, and thus the in vitro assays do not tell the complete story.

Four groups independently characterized *Arabidopsis* CAND1 (1, 7, 9, 21). A screen for naturally occurring variation in leaf and cotyledon venation identified a spontaneous missense mutation in *CAND1* of the *Arabidopsis* Eifel-5 accession. The missense mutation, designated *hemivenata 1-1* (*hve1-1*), has decreased venation in cotyledons and regular leaves (1). Two additional *cand1* missense mutations were identified in mutant screens; one, initially designated *eta2-1*, is an enhancer of the weak *tir1* auxin-resistance phenotype (9), and the other was recovered in a screen for resistance to sirtinol, an auxin analog (7). In addition, all four groups characterized *CAND1* T-DNA insertion mutants (1, 7, 9, 21).

cand1 mutants show characteristic reduced auxin responsiveness in the form of reduced apical dominance, increased root length and fewer lateral roots on auxin, and reduced expression of the auxin-induced reporters, BA3-GUS and DR5-GUS (1, 7, 9, 21). *cand1* mutants show alterations in responses to multiple hormones, including JA, ethylene, and ABA (7, 9, 21). Interestingly, *cand1* mutants have an unaltered RUB modification pattern of cullin (9, 21). Additionally, and similar to the rubylation mutants described above, *cand1* mutants have increased accumulation of AXR2/IAA7 protein and accumulate another protein, REPRESSOR OF GA1-3 1 (RGA1), a negative regulator of GA signaling that is ubiquitylated by SCF^{SLY1} (9, 21). CAND1 is a positive regulator of SCF on the basis of genetic studies that show accumulation of SCF substrates in *cand1* mutants (9, 21). Interestingly, Chuang and colleagues (9) suggest, on the basis of double mutant analysis of *cand1 axr1*, that displacement of CAND1 is not the primary function of RUB modification, as previously suggested (52).

There appears to be only one *CAND1* gene in *Arabidopsis*, yet germination and early seedling growth appear fairly normal under control conditions in *cand1* mutants (7, 21). A stronger phenotype becomes apparent later in vegetative and reproductive growth, when mutants phenocopy *axr1* and other Rub pathway mutants (1, 7, 9, 21). Thus, CAND1 is not an essential regulator of CRL function, but instead has a more specialized role. CAND1 can dissociate Skp1-Skp2 from Cul1-Rbx1, and likewise Skp1-Skp2 can dissociate CAND1 from Cul1-Rbx1; thus, cycling between these two CRL states may be important for maintenance of active CRLs (4, 93). The paradox of its negative activity in vitro and its positive function in vivo could be explained as follows (reviewed in Reference 10): CAND1 is a negative regulator in vitro, because its primary effect is to prevent formation of an active CRL. CAND1 has a positive role in vivo because conversion between active and inactive CRLs is important for optimal activity in vivo.

Figure 7 compiles the various components of the Rub pathway into a single model that highlights the different points of regulation in cycling between active and inactive CRLs (4, 8, 11, 12, 23, 33, 40, 53, 56, 79, 82, 87, 88, 93, 96, and 97). One caveat to this model is that it is based on research done in multiple

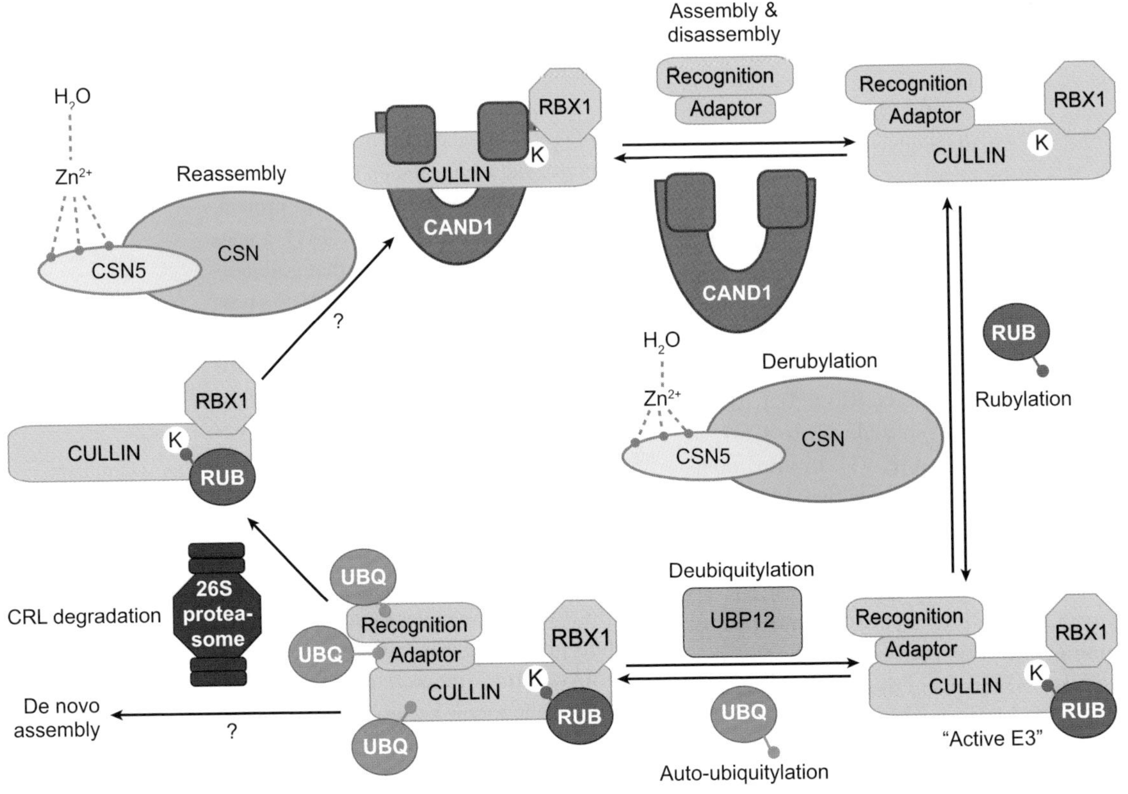

Figure 7

Model for assembly, rubylation, auto-ubiquitylation, proteolysis, and reassembly, or reverse reactions, in the regulation of cullin RING ligases (CRLs). CAND1, CULLIN-ASSOCIATED NEDD8-DISSOCIATED 1; K, lysine; RBX1, RING BOX 1; Recognition, recognition subunit of CRL; Adaptor, adaptor subunit of CRL; RUB, RELATED TO UBIQUITIN; CSN, COP9 signalosome; UBQ, ubiquitin; UBP12, UBIQUITIN-SPECIFIC PROTEASE 12.

organisms and conducted predominantly with SCF-type CRLs. Whether this model will prove to be a general model for CRL cycling, or whether only a subset of CRLs and/or organisms will adhere to such a model, remains to be determined.

BUILDING NEW CRLS

Currently unclear is whether reuse of CRL subunits occurs, and if so, to what extent. Is disassembly and reassembly a normal aspect of the production of optimal levels of active CRLs? Or, do CRLs undergo regular degradation and de novo assembly? A current model proposes that Ubp12, CSN, and CAND1 function in a disassembly process (62) (**Figure 7**). This model would allow for dynamic reuse of common subunits with new substrate recognition subunits for ubiquitylation of different substrates, giving the cell flexibility in the rapid remodeling of its proteome.

PERSPECTIVE

A currently unresolved issue regarding the relationship between phenotypic changes, cullin modification status, and substrate stability is the identification of the critical determinant. Which is significant: changes in the total cullin pool, the level of unmodified or

RUB-modified cullin, or the ratio between the two? Second, the difficulties of analyses at the level of a single cell or cell type have precluded determination of cullin modification status within specific cells, and the modification status could be different in different cell types. Thus, visualization of the cullin modification status in total extracts from entire seedlings may not accurately reflect the modification state in specific cells/cell types.

SUMMARY

Although genetic analyses of Rub pathway mutants and in vitro data support the hypothesis that RUB/Nedd8 is a positive regulator of CRL function, regulation of RUB detachment also appears to be essential. Lack or overabundance of RUB modification results in plants with multifaceted developmental defects and altered hormone signaling, suggesting that CRLs are under tight regulation and both RUB modification and removal processes play an integral role in organism homeostasis. Complete loss of either rubylation or derubylation is lethal early in development for plants; hence, our understanding of RUB function has come from the partial disruption of these processes. Regulation of CRL activity is under active investigation in multiple organisms. Although some hypotheses have been generated and are supported by experimental data, our understanding is incomplete. We can look forward to understanding why modifying the cullin subunit of CRLs is so important and so evolutionarily conserved.

SUMMARY POINTS

1. Posttranslational modification of cullin proteins by the ubiquitin-like protein RELATED TO UBIQUITIN (RUB) (in plants and budding yeast)/neuronal precursor cell–expressed developmentally downregulated 8 (Nedd8) (in fission yeast and animals) is essential in most organisms; budding yeast is the notable exception.
2. Cullin proteins are an essential subunit of the multi-subunit cullin RING E3 ligases (CRLs) of the ubiquitin system.
3. CRLs promote ubiquitylation of substrate proteins. Rubylation of the cullin subunit stimulates this activity, and derubylation by COP9 signalosome (CSN) inhibits this activity in vitro, but both processes are required for proper substrate degradation in vivo.
4. CRL activity is important in plants to regulate many hormonal, developmental, and environmental response pathways, so defects in rubylation/derubylation have strong and pleiotropic effects.
5. CRL activity is highly regulated by controlling assembly, activation, deactivation, and proteolysis of one or more of its subunits.
6. Each class of CRL may be regulated by a unique set of processes.

FUTURE ISSUES

1. The biochemical role of RUB modification is not completely resolved; experimental data support several models.
2. The relationship between RUB cycling and in vivo CRL assembly and activity, subunit stability, and complex disassembly remains to be resolved.

3. The role of CULLIN-ASSOCIATED NEDD8-DISSOCIATED 1 (CAND1) in CRL assembly and modification in vivo is unresolved.
4. Additional, yet unidentified factors are probably involved in CRL activity.

DISCLOSURE STATEMENT

The authors are not aware of any biases that might be perceived as affecting the objectivity of this review.

ACKNOWLEDGMENTS

The authors apologize to those whose work could not be cited owing to space limitations. The authors gratefully acknowledge support from the National Science Foundation (2010 Program MCB-0519970 and IBN 0212659) and the Department of Energy (DE-FG02-03ER15416) to JC and a UC Davis Steindler Fellowship and NSF Graduate Research Fellowship to SH. We thank M. Hsia, M. Wogulis, and B. White for helpful discussions.

LITERATURE CITED

1. Alonso-Peral MM, Candela H, del Pozo JC, Martinez-Laborda A, Ponce MR, Micol JL. 2006. The *HVE/CAND1* gene is required for the early patterning of leaf venation in *Arabidopsis*. *Development* 133:3755–66
2. Angers S, Li T, Yi X, MacCoss MJ, Moon RT, Zheng N. 2006. Molecular architecture and assembly of the DDB1-CUL4A ubiquitin ligase machinery. *Nature* 443:590–93
3. Bernhardt A, Lechner E, Hano P, Schade V, Dieterle M, et al. 2006. CUL4 associates with DDB1 and DET1 and its downregulation affects diverse aspects of development in *Arabidopsis thaliana*. *Plant J.* 47:591–603
4. Bornstein G, Ganoth D, Hershko A. 2006. Regulation of neddylation and deneddylation of cullin1 in SCF^{Skp2} ubiquitin ligase by F-box protein and substrate. *Proc. Natl. Acad. Sci. USA* 103:11515–20
5. Bostick M, Lochhead SR, Honda A, Palmer S, Callis J. 2004. Related to ubiquitin 1 and 2 are redundant and essential and regulate vegetative growth, auxin signaling, and ethylene production in Arabidopsis. *Plant Cell* 16:2418–32
6. Chen H, Shen Y, Tang X, Yu L, Wang J, et al. 2006. *Arabidopsis* CULLIN4 forms an E3 ubiquitin ligase with RBX1 and the CDD complex in mediating light control of development. *Plant Cell* 18:1991–2004
7. Cheng Y, Dai X, Zhao Y. 2004. AtCAND1, a HEAT-repeat protein that participates in auxin signaling in Arabidopsis. *Plant Physiol.* 135:1020–26
8. Chew EH, Hagen T. 2007. Substrate-mediated regulation of cullin neddylation. *J. Biol. Chem.* 282:17032–40
9. Chuang HW, Zhang W, Gray WM. 2004. Arabidopsis *ETA2*, an apparent ortholog of the human cullin-interacting protein CAND1, is required for auxin responses mediated by the SCF^{TIR1} ubiquitin ligase. *Plant Cell* 16:1883–97
10. Cope GA, Deshaies RJ. 2003. COP9 signalosome: a multifunctional regulator of SCF and other cullin-based ubiquitin ligases. *Cell* 114:663–71
11. Cope GA, Deshaies RJ. 2006. Targeted silencing of Jab1/Csn5 in human cells downregulates SCF activity through reduction of F-box protein levels. *BMC Biochem.* 7:1

12. Cope GA, Suh GSB, Aravind L, Schwarz SE, Zipursky SL, et al. 2002. Role of predicted metalloprotease motif of Jab1/Csn5 in cleavage of Nedd8 from Cul1. *Science* 298:608–11
13. del Pozo JC, Dharmasiri S, Hellmann H, Walker L, Gray WM, Estelle M. 2002. AXR1-ECR1-dependent conjugation of RUB1 to the Arabidopsis cullin AtCUL1 is required for auxin response. *Plant Cell* 14:421-33
14. del Pozo JC, Estelle M. 1999. The *Arabidopsis* cullin AtCUL1 is modified by the ubiquitin-related protein RUB1. *Proc. Natl. Acad. Sci. USA* 96:15342–47
15. del Pozo JC, Timpte C, Tan S, Callis J, Estelle M. 1998. The ubiquitin-related protein RUB1 and auxin response in *Arabidopsis*. *Science* 280:1760–63
16. Dharmasiri N, Dharmasiri S, Weijers D, Karunarathna N, Jurgens G, Estelle M. 2007. *AXL* and *AXR1* have redundant functions in RUB conjugation and growth and development in Arabidopsis. *Plant J.* 52:114–23
17. Dharmasiri S, Dharmasiri N, Hellmann H, Estelle M. 2003. The RUB/Nedd8 conjugation pathway is required for early development in *Arabidopsis*. *EMBO J.* 22:1762–70
18. Dohmann EMN, Kuhnle C, Schwechheimer C. 2005. Loss of the CONSTITUTIVE PHOTOMORPHOGENIC9 signalosome subunit 5 is sufficient to cause the *cop/det/fus* mutant phenotype in Arabidopsis. *Plant Cell* 17:1967–78
19. Downes B, Vierstra RD. 2005. Post-translational regulation in plants employing a diverse set of polypeptide tags. *Biochem. Soc. Trans.* 33:393–99
20. Estelle MA, Somerville C. 1987. Auxin-resistant mutants of *Arabidopsis thaliana* with an altered morphology. *Mol. Gen. Genet.* 206:200–6
21. Feng S, Shen Y, Sullivan JA, Rubio V, Xiong Y, et al. 2004. Arabidopsis CAND1, an unmodified CUL1-interacting protein, is involved in multiple developmental pathways controlled by ubiquitin/proteasome-mediated protein degradation. *Plant Cell* 16:1870–82
22. Figueroa P, Gusmaroli G, Serino G, Habashi J, Ma L, et al. 2005. Arabidopsis has two redundant cullin3 proteins that are essential for embryo development and that interact with RBX1 and BTB proteins to form multisubunit E3 ubiquitin ligase complexes in vivo. *Plant Cell* 17:1180–95
23. Galan JM, Peter M. 1999. Ubiquitin-dependent degradation of multiple F-box proteins by an autocatalytic mechanism. *Proc. Natl. Acad. Sci. USA* 96:9124–29
24. Gingerich DJ, Gagne JM, Salter DW, Hellmann H, Estelle M, et al. 2005. Cullins 3a and 3b assemble with members of the broad complex/tramtrack/bric-a-brac (BTB) protein family to form essential ubiquitin-protein ligases (E3s) in *Arabidopsis*. *J. Biol. Chem.* 280:18810–21
25. Goldberg AL. 2007. Functions of the proteasome: from protein degradation and immune surveillance to cancer therapy. *Biochem. Soc. Trans.* 35:12–17
26. Goldenberg SJ, Cascio TC, Shumway SD, Garbutt KC, Liu J, et al. 2004. Structure of the Cand1-Cul1-Roc1 complex reveals regulatory mechanisms for the assembly of the multisubunit cullin-dependent ubiquitin ligases. *Cell* 119:517–28
27. Gray WM, Hellmann H, Dharmasiri S, Estelle M. 2002. Role of the Arabidopsis RING-H2 protein RBX1 in RUB modification and SCF function. *Plant Cell* 14:2137–44
28. Gray WM, Kepinski S, Rouse D, Leyser O, Estelle M. 2001. Auxin regulates SCF^{TIR1}-dependent degradation of AUX/IAA proteins. *Nature* 414:271–76
29. Gusmaroli G, Feng S, Deng XW. 2004. The Arabidopsis CSN5A and CSN5B subunits are present in distinct COP9 signalosome complexes, and mutations in their JAMM domains exhibit differential dominant negative effects on development. *Plant Cell* 16:2984–3001
30. Gusmaroli G, Figueroa P, Serino G, Deng XW. 2007. Role of the MPN subunits in COP9 signalosome assembly and activity, and their regulatory interaction with *Arabidopsis* cullin3-based E3 ligases. *Plant Cell* 19:564–81

31. Harari-Steinberg O, Chamovitz DA. 2004. The COP9 signalosome: mediating between kinase signaling and protein degradation. *Curr. Protein Pept. Sci.* 5:185–89
32. Hay RT. 2005. SUMO: a history of modification. *Mol. Cell* 18:1–12
33. He Q, Cheng P, He Q, Liu Y. 2005. The COP9 signalosome regulates the *Neurospora* circadian clock by controlling the stability of the SCF^{FWD-1} complex. *Genes Dev.* 19:1518–31
34. He YJ, McCall CM, Hu J, Zeng Y, Xiong Y. 2006. DDB1 functions as a linker to recruit receptor WD40 proteins to CUL4-ROC1 ubiquitin ligases. *Genes Dev.* 20:2949–54
35. Hori T, Osaka F, Chiba T, Miyamoto C, Okabayashi K, et al. 1999. Covalent modification of all members of human cullin family proteins by NEDD8. *Oncogene* 18:6829–34
36. Hurley JH, Lee S, Prag G. 2006. Ubiquitin-binding domains. *Biochem. J.* 399:361–72
37. Jain M, Nijhawan A, Arora R, Agarwal P, Ray S, et al. 2007. F-box proteins in rice. Genome-wide analysis, classification, temporal and spatial gene expression during panicle and seed development, and regulation by light and abiotic stress. *Plant Physiol.* 143:1467–83
38. Jin J, Arias EE, Chen J, Harper JW, Walter JC. 2006. A family of diverse Cul4-Ddb1-interacting proteins includes Cdt2, which is required for S phase destruction of the replication factor Cdt1. *Mol. Cell* 23:709–21
39. Kamura T, Conrad MN, Yan Q, Conaway RC, Conaway JW. 1999. The Rbx1 subunit of SCF and VHL E3 ubiquitin ligase activates Rub1 modification of cullins Cdc53 and Cul2. *Genes Dev.* 13:2928–33
40. Kawakami T, Chiba T, Suzuki T, Iwai K, Yamanaka K, et al. 2001. NEDD8 recruits E2-ubiquitin to SCF E3 ligase. *EMBO J.* 20:4003–12
41. Kerscher O, Felberbaum R, Hochstrasser M. 2006. Modification of proteins by ubiquitin and ubiquitin-like proteins. *Annu. Rev. Cell Dev. Biol.* 22:159–80
42. Kirkin V, Dikic I. 2007. Role of ubiquitin- and Ubl-binding proteins and cell signaling. *Curr. Opin. Cell Biol.* 19:199–205
43. Kurz T, Ozlu N, Rudolf F, O'Rourke SM, Luke B, et al. 2005. The conserved protein DCN-1/Dcn1p is required for cullin neddylation in *C. elegans* and *S. cerevisiae*. *Nature* 435:1257–61
44. Kwok SF, Staub JM, Deng XW. 1999. Characterization of two subunits of *Arabidopsis* 19S proteasome regulatory complex and its possible interaction with the COP9 complex. *J. Mol. Biol.* 285:85–95
45. Lammer D, Mathias N, Laplaza JM, Jiang W, Lui Y, et al. 1998. Modification of yeast Cdc53p by the ubiquitin-related protein Rub1p affects function of the SCF^{Cdc4} complex. *Genes Dev.* 12:914–26
46. Laplaza JM, Bostick M, Scholes DT, Curcio MJ, Callis J. 2004. *Saccharomyces cerevisiae* ubiquitin-like protein Rub1 conjugates to cullin proteins Rtt101 and Cul3 in vivo. *Biochem. J.* 377:459–67
47. Lechner E, Achard P, Vansiri A, Potuschak T, Genschik P. 2006. F-box proteins everywhere. *Curr. Opin. Plant Biol.* 9:631-38
48. Lechner E, Xie D, Grava S, Pigaglio E, Planchais S, et al. 2002. The AtRbx1 protein is part of plant SCF complexes, and its down-regulation causes severe growth and developmental defects. *J. Biol. Chem.* 277:50069–80
49. Leyser HMO, Lincoln CA, Timpte C, Lammer D, Turner J, Estelle M. 1993. *Arabidopsis* auxin-resistance gene *AXR1* encodes a protein related to ubiquitin-activating enzyme E1. *Nature* 364:161–64
50. Liakopoulos D, Doenges G, Matuschewski K, Jentsch S. 1998. A novel protein modification pathway related to the ubiquitin system. *EMBO J.* 17:2208–14

51. Lincoln C, Britton JH, Estelle M. 1990. Growth and development of the *axr1* mutants of *Arabidopsis*. *Plant Cell* 2:1071–80
52. Liu J, Furukawa M, Matsumoto T, Xiong Y. 2002. NEDD8 modification of CUL1 dissociates p120^{CAND1}, an inhibitor of CUL1-SKP1 binding and SCF ligases. *Mol. Cell* 10:1511–18
53. Lyapina S, Cope G, Shevchenko A, Serino G, Tsuge T, et al. 2001. Promotion of NEDD8-CUL1 conjugate cleavage by COP9 signalosome. *Science* 292:1382–85
54. McCall CM, Hu J, Xiong Y. 2005. Recruiting substrates to cullin 4-dependent ubiquitin ligases by DDB1. *Cell Cycle* 4:27–29
55. Min KW, Kwon MJ, Park HS, Park Y, Yoon SK, Yoon JB. 2005. CAND1 enhances deneddylation of CUL1 by COP9 signalosome. *Biochem. Biophys. Res. Commun.* 334:867–74
56. Morimoto M, Nishida T, Honda R, Yasuda H. 2000. Modification of cullin-1 by ubiquitin-like protein Nedd8 enhances the activity of SCF^{Skp2} toward p27^{kip1}. *Biochem. Biophys. Res. Commun.* 270:1093–96
57. Morimoto M, Nishida T, Nagayama Y, Yasuda H. 2003. Nedd8-modification of Cul1 is promoted by Roc1 as a Nedd8-E3 ligase and regulates its stability. *Biochem. Biophys. Res. Commun.* 301:392–98
58. Mukhopadhyay D, Riezman H. 2007. Proteasome-independent functions of ubiquitin in endocytosis and signaling. *Science* 315:201–5
59. Mundt KE, Liu C, Carr AM. 2002. Deletion mutants in COP9/signalosome subunits in fission yeast *Schizosaccharomyces pombe* display distinct phenotypes. *Mol. Biol. Cell* 13:493–502
60. Osaka F, Saeki M, Katayama S, Aida N, Toh-E A, et al. 2000. Covalent modifier NEDD8 is essential for SCF ubiquitin-ligase in fission yeast. *EMBO J.* 19:3475–84
61. Parry G, Estelle M. 2004. Regulation of cullin-based ubiquitin ligases by the Nedd8/RUB ubiquitin-like proteins. *Semin. Cell Dev. Biol.* 15:221–29
62. Petroski MD, Deshaies RJ. 2005. Function and regulation of cullin-RING ubiquitin ligases. *Nat. Rev. Mol. Cell Biol.* 6:9–20
63. Pickart CM, Eddins MJ. 2004. Ubiquitin: structures, functions, mechanisms. *Biochim. Biophys. Acta* 1695:55–72
64. Pickart CM, Fushman D. 2004. Polyubiquitin chains: polymeric protein signals. *Curr. Opin. Chem. Biol.* 8:610–16
65. Sakata E, Yamaguchi Y, Miyauchi Y, Iwai K, Chiba T, et al. 2007. Direct interactions between NEDD8 and ubiquitin E2 conjugating enzymes upregulate cullin-based E3 ligase activity. *Nat. Struct. Mol. Biol.* 14:167–68
66. Schwechheimer C, Calderon Villalobos LI. 2004. Cullin-containing E3 ubiquitin ligases in plant development. *Curr. Opin. Plant Biol.* 7:677–86
67. Schwechheimer C, Serino G, Callis J, Crosby WL, Lyapina S, et al. 2001. Interactions of the COP9 signalosome with the E3 ubiquitin ligase SCF^{TIR1} in mediating auxin response. *Science* 292:1379–82
68. Schwechheimer C, Serino G, Deng XW. 2002. Multiple ubiquitin ligase-mediated processes require COP9 signalosome and AXR1 function. *Plant Cell* 14:2553–63
69. Serino G, Deng XW. 2003. The COP9 signalosome: regulating plant development through the control of proteolysis. *Annu. Rev. Plant Biol.* 54:165–82
70. Shen WH, Parmentier Y, Hellmann H, Lechner E, Dong A, et al. 2002. Null mutation of *AtCUL1* causes arrest in early embryogenesis in *Arabidopsis*. *Mol. Biol. Cell* 13:1916–28
71. Smalle J, Vierstra RD. 2004. The ubiquitin 26S proteasome proteolytic pathway. *Annu. Rev. Plant Biol.* 55:555–90

72. Stickle NH, Chung J, Klco JM, Hill RP, Kaelin WG Jr, Ohh M. 2004. pVHL modification by NEDD8 is required for fibronectin matrix assembly and suppression of tumor development. *Mol. Cell. Biol.* 24:3251–61
73. Sufan RI, Ohh M. 2006. Role of the NEDD8 modification of Cul2 in the sequential activation of ECV complex. *Neoplasia* 8:956–63
74. Thrower JS, Hoffman L, Rechsteiner M, Pickart CM. 2000. Recognition of the polyubiquitin proteolytic signal. *EMBO J.* 19:94–102
75. Timpte C, Lincoln C, Pickett FB, Turner J, Estelle M. 1995. The *AXR1* and *AUX1* genes of *Arabidopsis* function in separate auxin-response pathways. *Plant J.* 8:561–69
76. Tiryaki I, Staswick PE. 2002. An Arabidopsis mutant defective in jasmonate response is allelic to the auxin-signaling mutant *axr1*. *Plant Physiol.* 130:887–94
77. Ulrich HD. 2005. SUMO modification: wrestling with protein conformation. *Curr. Biol.* 15:R257–59
78. Wada H, Yeh ETH, Kamitani T. 1999. Identification of NEDD8-conjugation site in human cullin-2. *Biochem. Biophy. Res. Commun.* 257:100–5
79. Wada H, Yeh ETH, Kamitani T. 1999. The von Hippel-Lindau tumor suppressor gene product promotes, but is not essential for, NEDD8 conjugation to cullin-2. *J. Biol. Chem.* 274:36025–29
80. Wang KLC, Yoshida H, Lurin C, Ecker JR. 2004. Regulation of ethylene gas biosynthesis by the *Arabidopsis* ETO1 protein. *Nature* 428:945–50
81. Weber H, Bernhardt A, Dieterle M, Hano P, Mutlu A, et al. 2005. Arabidopsis AtCUL3a and AtCUL3b form complexes with members of the BTB/POZ-MATH protein family. *Plant Physiol.* 137:83–93
82. Wee S, Geyer RK, Toda T, Wolf DA. 2005. CSN facilitates cullin-RING ubiquitin ligase function by counteracting autocatalytic adapter instability. *Nat. Cell Biol.* 7:387–91
83. Wei N, Deng XW. 2003. The COP9 signalosome. *Annu. Rev. Cell. Dev. Biol.* 19:261–86
84. Wimuttisuk W, Singer JD. 2007. The cullin3 ubiquitin ligase functions as a Nedd8-bound heterodimer. *Mol. Biol. Cell* 18:899–909
85. Woodward AW, Ratzel SE, Woodward EE, Shamoo Y, Bartel B. 2007. Mutation of *E1-CONJUGATING ENZYME-RELATED1* decreases RELATED TO UBIQUITIN conjugation and alters auxin response and development. *Plant Physiol.* 144:976–87
86. Wu JT, Chan YR, Chien CT. 2006. Protection of cullin-RING E3 ligases by CSN-UBP12. *Trends Cell Biol.* 16:362–69
87. Wu JT, Lin HC, Hu YC, Chien CT. 2005. Neddylation and deneddylation regulate Cul1 and Cul3 protein accumulation. *Nat. Cell Biol.* 7:1014–20
88. Wu K, Chen A, Tan P, Pan ZQ. 2002. The Nedd8-conjugated ROC1-CUL1 core ubiquitin ligase utilizes Nedd8 charged surface residues for efficient polyubiquitin chain assembly catalyzed by Cdc34. *J. Biol. Chem.* 277:516–27
89. Xirodimas DP, Saville MK, Bourdon JC, Hay RT, Lane DP. 2004. Mdm2-mediated NEDD8 conjugation of p53 inhibits its transcriptional activity. *Cell* 118:83–97
90. Yang X, Menon S, Lykke-Andersen K, Tsuge T, Di X, et al. 2002. The COP9 signalosome inhibits $p27^{kip1}$ degradation and impedes G1-S phase progression via deneddylation of SCF Cul1. *Curr. Biol.* 12:667–72
91. Yang X, Zhou J, Sun L, Wei Z, Gao J, et al. 2007. Structural basis for DCN-1's function in protein neddylation. *J. Biol. Chem.* 282:24490–94
92. Zenser N, Dreher KA, Edwards SR, Callis J. 2003. Acceleration of Aux/IAA proteolysis is specific for auxin and independent of *AXR1*. *Plant J.* 35:285–94

93. Zheng J, Yang X, Harrell JM, Ryzhikov S, Shim EH, et al. 2002. CAND1 binds to unneddylated CUL1 and regulates the formation of SCF ubiquitin E3 ligase complex. *Mol. Cell* 10:1519–26
94. Zheng N, Schulman BA, Song LZ, Miller JJ, Jeffrey PD, et al. 2002. Structure of the Cul1-Rbx1-Skp1-F box^{Skp2} SCF ubiquitin ligase complex. *Nature* 416:703–9
95. Zhou C, Seibert V, Geyer R, Rhee E, Lyapina S, et al. 2001. The fission yeast COP9/signalosome is involved in cullin modification by ubiquitin-related Ned8p. *BMC Biochem.* 2:7
96. Zhou C, Wee S, Rhee E, Naumann M, Dubiel W, Wolf DA. 2003. Fission yeast COP9/signalosome suppresses cullin activity through recruitment of the deubiquitylating enzyme Ubp12p. *Mol. Cell* 11:927–38
97. Zhou P, Howley PM. 1998. Ubiquitination and degradation of the substrate recognition subunits of SCF ubiquitin-protein ligases. *Mol. Cell* 2:571–80

RELATED RESOURCES

Dye BT, Schulman BA. 2007. Structural mechanisms underlying posttranslational modification by ubiquitin-like proteins. *Annu. Rev. Biophys. Biomol. Struct.* 36:131–50

Plastid Evolution

Sven B. Gould, Ross F. Waller, and Geoffrey I. McFadden

School of Botany, University of Melbourne, Parkville VIC-3010, Australia; email: sbgould@gmail.com, rossfw@unimelb.edu.au, gim@unimelb.edu.au

Annu. Rev. Plant Biol. 2008. 59:491–517

The *Annual Review of Plant Biology* is online at plant.annualreviews.org

This article's doi: 10.1146/annurev.arplant.59.032607.092915

1543-5008/08/0602-0491$20.00

Key Words

secondary/tertiary endosymbiosis, complex plastids, protein targeting, genome evolution, intracellular gene transfer, plastid biochemistry

Abstract

The ancestors of modern cyanobacteria invented O_2-generating photosynthesis some 3.6 billion years ago. The conversion of water and CO_2 into energy-rich sugars and O_2 slowly transformed the planet, eventually creating the biosphere as we know it today. Eukaryotes didn't invent photosynthesis; they co-opted it from prokaryotes by engulfing and stably integrating a photoautotrophic prokaryote in a process known as primary endosymbiosis. After approximately a billion of years of coevolution, the eukaryotic host and its endosymbiont have achieved an extraordinary level of integration and have spawned a bewildering array of primary producers that now underpin life on land and in the water. No partnership has been more important to life on earth. Secondary endosymbioses have created additional autotrophic eukaryotic lineages that include key organisms in the marine environment. Some of these organisms have subsequently reverted to heterotrophic lifestyles, becoming significant pathogens, microscopic predators, and consumers. We review the origins, integration, and functions of the different plastid types with special emphasis on their biochemical abilities, transfer of genes to the host, and the back supply of proteins to the endosymbiont.

Contents

INTRODUCTION

In nature the counterpart of chaos is not cosmos, but evolution. The spark of life was initially a chemical one, leading to the synthesis of the first molecules. Some of these persisted and evolved in a precellular period, perhaps similar to that described in the model of the RNA world, leading to the first prokaryotic life approximately 3.5 to 4 billion years ago (48, 74). The invention of oxygenic photosynthesis by prokaryotic cyanobacteria approximately 500 million years later was the next major achievement of biological evolution. It had a major impact on the earth by enriching the atmosphere with O_2 to a level that transformed the geochemistry of the planet.

The first molecular carbon skeletons typical of cyanobacteria can be identified in strata from approximately 2.75 billion years ago (15). At the same time a novel mineral known as hematite (Fe_2O_3), which can form only in the presence of a minimum critical concentration of oxygen, began to appear. These geological indices testify to an ever-increasing concentration of atmospheric oxygen due to photosynthetic activity. Photosynthesis was also the evolutionary trigger for the sweeping diversification of O_2-dependent life. Indeed, oxygen has become critical for most living things, acting as an acceptor for the electrons released from carbon-carbon bonds that were ultimately created using energy captured by photosynthesis. Thus, a byproduct of photosynthesis (oxygen) became an essential component for the burning of the sugars produced by photosynthesis. The balance of the biosphere was born.

Nineteenth century microscopists (Sachs, Altmann, and Schimper) recognized the semi-autonomous nature and bacterial-like staining properties of chloroplasts (then known as chlorophyll bodies) and mitochondria (then known as cell granules) (4, 106), but it took another 15 years before Mereschkowsky synthesized these observations into the theory that chloroplasts are derived from cyanobacteria (81, 109). Margulis later formalized the Theory of Endosymbiosis, which posits that plastids and mitochondria of eukaryotic cells derive from bacterial endosymbionts (71).

FROM FREEDOM TO SLAVERY: OUTLINING ENDOSYMBIOTIC STEPS

As far as we know, all eukaryotes have mitochondria (or modified, anaerobic forms of mitochondria known as hydrogenosomes or mitosomes), and the establishment of this partnership is generally regarded as integral to the origin of eukaryotes (123). The acquisition of plastids by eukaryotes occurred later, after the establishment of a diversity of heterotrophic eukaryotic lineages, one of which adopted a cyanobacterium-like endosymbiont to acquire photosynthesis and become autotrophic. We refer to an initial plastid-creating endosymbiosis as the primary endosymbiosis. Secondary (or eukaryotic) endosymbiosis refers to subsequent endosymbiotic events in which the progeny of the primary endosymbiotic partnership become endosymbionts within other heterotrophic eukaryotes, thus transferring the captured cyanobacterial symbiont laterally among eukaryotes. Subsequently, the progeny of these secondary endosymbiotic partnerships have become endosymbionts in other eukaryotes, creating tertiary endosymbioses, to weave an extraordinarily complex set of endosymbiotic relationships of cells within cells within cells within cells (**Figure 1**). In this review we examine the cell biology of these endosymbiotic events and examine how the various compartments and genomes of these extraordinary chimeras cooperate as a single cell, albeit one made up of parts from multiple individual cells.

Primary Endosymbiosis

The endosymbiotic integration of a free-living, cyanobacterial-like prokaryote into a eukaryotic host produced three major autotrophic lineages: the glaucophytes, the green algae (and their descendants, the plants), and the red algae (2, 46) (**Figure 1**). Plastids in these primary endosymbionts are characterized by having two bounding membranes, which are derived from the two membranes (plasma membrane and outer membrane) of the Gram-negative cyanobacterium (17, 20). If a phagocytotic membrane surrounded the symbiont when it was first internalized by the host, it has disappeared without a trace (20). The main lines of evidence supporting homology between the outer envelope membrane and the outer membrane of a cyanobacterium are (*a*) the presence of galactolipids (52), (*b*) the presence of β-barrel proteins in both membranes (110), and (*c*) the occurrence of peptidoglycan (or rudiments of peptidoglycan synthesis machinery) beneath these membranes (117).

Phylogenetic analyses suggest that the glaucophytes were the first primary endosymbiotic lineage to diverge, some 550 mya, and that the red and green algae diverged later (75, 82, 103). Plants, which probably diverged from their green algal ancestors approximately 400 to 475 mya (36), subsequently conquered the terrestrial environment, paving the way for animals to follow them onto land. In accordance with this sequence, plastids in the glaucophytes (which are sometimes referred to as cyanelles but are definitely plastids) most resemble their cyanobacterial ancestors in that they retain a peptidoglycan, wall-like layer between the inner and outer envelope membranes (57). Additionally, the thylakoids inside the glaucophyte plastid stroma are studded with phycobilisomes that are identical to those of cyanobacteria, and the composition of the oxygen-evolving enhancer complex is also very similar to that of free-living cyanobacteria (117). Rhodophyte plastids also use phycobilins in protein-based light harvesting antenna (phycobilisomes), but their plastids have apparently lost the peptidoglycan wall (31). The green algal/plant lineage plastids are the most derived in the primary endosymbiosis lineage. Phycobilisomes were replaced by chlorophyll *b* embedded in thylakoid membranes, and a rich panoply of accessory pigments developed to capture light and protect the photosynthetic apparatus from the unfiltered terrestrial light (80).

Generally, primary plastids have undergone major modification during their tenure in the eukaryotic host; reduction of their genome's coding capacity is one of the more conspicuous attenuations. The genome of the cyanobacterium *Anabaena* sp. PCC 7120 has 5366 protein-encoding genes, and other cyanobacteria possess similar numbers of genes (53). In contrast, the most gene-rich plastid reported to date, that of the red alga *Porphyra purpurea*, encodes a paltry 251 genes (99), and the plastids of the parasitic plant *Epifagus virginiana* harbor a mere 42 genes (132). Thus, most of the original genetic material of the endosymbiont was clearly either lost or transferred to the host genome during their coevolution. Selection likely favored the initial loss of genetic material by the endosymbiont because it turned the

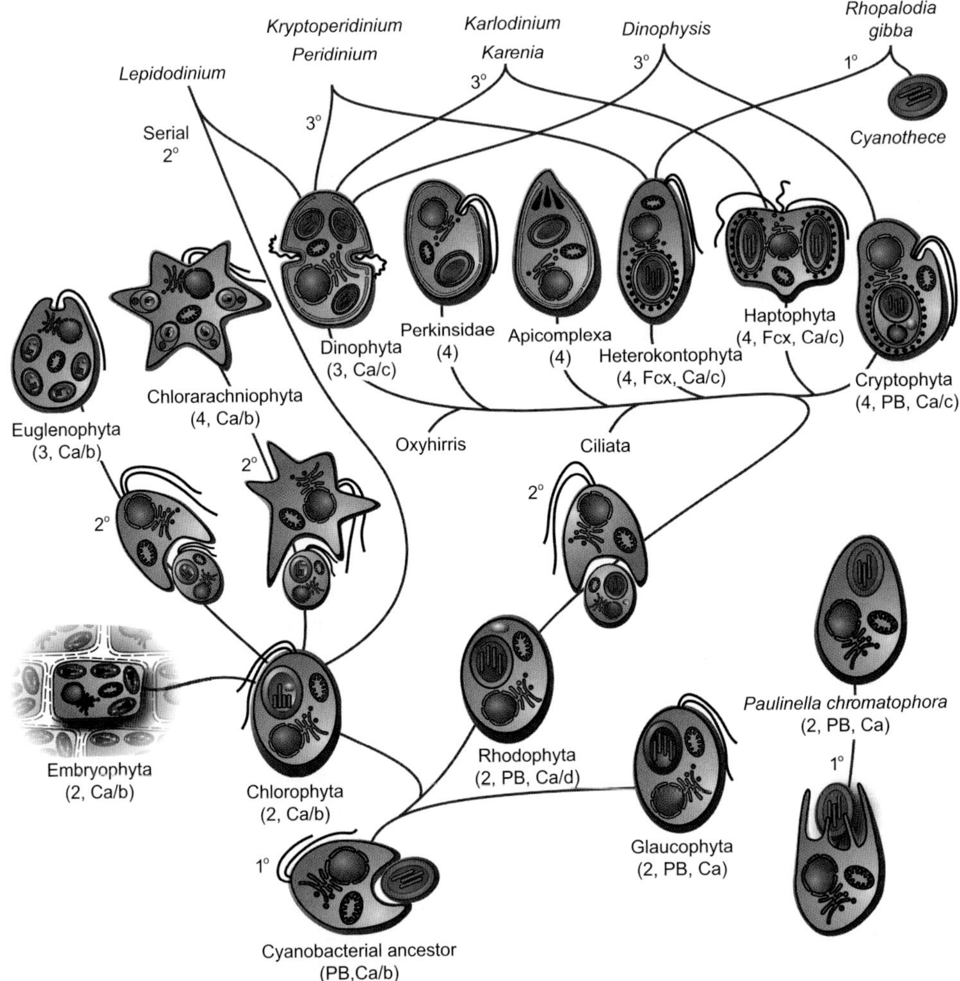

Figure 1

A schematic representation of plastid evolution. Engulfment of a cyanobacterial ancestor and subsequent reduction to a primary plastid (1°) by a eukaryotic host initially led to the formation of three lineages with primary plastids: the chlorophytes, and land plants, rhodophytes and glaucophytes. The subsequent uptake of a green or a red alga by independent hosts to form secondary endosymbioses (2°) resulted in euglenophytes, chlorarachniophytes, and the monophyletic chromalveolates. Chromalveolates, which represent the association of chromists (Heterokontophyta, Haptophyta, and Cryptophyta) and the Alveolata (Apicomplexa, Perkinsidae, Dinophyta, Ciliata), unite an extremely diverse array of protists and not all authors accept the grouping. Different Dinophyta have replaced their original secondary plastid with a green alga either by serial secondary endosymbiosis (*Lepidodinium*) or even tertiary endosymbioses (3°); e.g., *Karlodinium* harbors a tertiary plastid of haptophyte origin. The heterokontophyte *Rhopalodia gibba* engulfed a cyanobacterial *Cyanothece* species and reduced it to so-called spheroid bodies, which are not used for photosynthesis, but rather act in N_2-fixation. The plastid organelles were apparently lost in the case of the ciliates and the dinoflagellate *Oxyhirris*. A possible nascent primary endosymbiosis (1°) is represented by *Paulinella chromatophora*, although whether this endosymbiont is a true plastid organelle remains uncertain. The number of membranes surrounding the plastid and the photosynthetic pigments is shown in parentheses. PB, phycobilin proteins; Fcx, fucoxanthin; C*a*/*b*/*c*/*d*, chlorophyll *a*/*b*/*c*/*d*.

prokaryote-eukaryote consortium into an obligate symbiotic relationship. However, we now know that a concerted and ongoing transfer of genes from endosymbiont to host has radically depleted the endosymbiont's gene catalog. Much of this intracellular gene transfer was likely achieved prior to the divergence of the three primary endosymbiotic lineages because they share a similar residue of common genes (75).

This transfer of genetic material mandated the development of a mechanism to return the gene product to the organelle. We discuss this problem in detail below, but some general concepts can be outlined now. Host-encoded proteins destined for the plastid are typically translated as precursor proteins bearing an N-terminal topogenic signal that is recognized by a proteinaceous receptor, which is either soluble in the cytoplasm or bound to the outer plastid membrane. After recognition, the precursor is subsequently translocated across the plastid envelope by a suite of translocation machineries spanning the two bounding membranes. The preprotein is pulled into the plastid and the topogenic signal is proteolytically removed to yield the mature protein.

The protein import mechanism probably evolved early on in the conversion of the endosymbiont into an organelle and no doubt facilitated the relocation of genes from the endosymbiont to the host. Transferred genes would need to acquire expression and topogenic signals for the gene product to be returned to the organelle. Rhodophtye and green algal/plant plastid-protein-targeting machineries appear to be fairly similar (79); although virtually nothing is known about the translocation machinery in glaucophytes, we predict that it is also similar because these plastids have also relinquished so many of their genes to the host genome (75).

Eukaryotic Endosymbiosis

The current consensus of molecular phylogeny recognizes six eukaryotic superclusters: Opisthokonta, Amoebozoa, Plantae (Archaeplastida), Chromalveolata, Rhizaria, and Excavata (2, 54). The Plantae supercluster embraces the three lines (glaucophytes, rhodophytes, and chlorophytes) with primary endosymbiotic (two membrane) plastids and their monophyly is consistent with a common origin for their plastids (103). However, plastids also occur in the Chromalveolata, Rhizaria, and Excavata, and all these multi-membrane plastids are derived from secondary endosymbioses (**Figure 1**). These events created a variety of eukaryotic-eukaryotic chimeras referred to as meta-algae (22). Secondary or complex plastids are derived from eukaryotic, primary plastid-containing endosymbionts and have undergone reduction during their tenure in the secondary host. The degree of reduction varies; sometimes it is relatively minor, such as in the partially integrated secondary endosymbionts of *Hatena* (85), and sometimes it is extensive, such as in the case of euglenoids in the Excavata where the only trace of the eukaryotic endosymbiont is an extra (third) membrane around the plastid (130). Two important intermediate stages in the secondary endosymbiont reduction process are represented by cryptophytes and chlorarachniophytes, in which a very reduced endosymbiont nucleus, cytoplasm, and plasma membrane can still be identified. The remnant nucleus, known as the nucleomorph, is located inside the periplastidial compartment (the former endosymbiont's cytosol), and the overall topology allows us to rationalize the presence of four membranes around related plastids in chromalveolates, in which the endosymbiont nucleus has completely disappeared. Reduction forces have obviously been at work in these endosymbionts because the great majority of the endosymbiont nuclear genes have been transferred to the host nucleus and most of the cytoplasmatic features, other than a small collection of ribosomes, have been lost (27, 33).

Secondary endosymbioses introduced plastids into heterotrophic lineages, and

Nucleomorph: the former nucleus of the eukaryotic endosymbiont; lost in most secondary algae, but still present in a highly reduced form in cryptophytes and chlorarachniophytes

Chromalveolate hypothesis: monophyly of the chromists (Cryptophyta, Haptophyta and Heterokontophyta) and Alveolata (Dinophyta, Ciliata and Apicomplexa); also, the common ancestor contained a complex plastid derived from a red alga that is retained in several of these lineages

much energy has been focused on establishing how many separate times a eukaryotic symbiont has been integrated into a previously nonphotosynthetic lineage. The environmental and commercial importance of the lineages created, not to mention the importance of these events as drivers of eukaryotic diversity, make this a particularly fascinating question. The antiquity of these events and the reduction processes that have occurred in the ensuing millennia also make the question a difficult one to resolve. The most parsimonious hypothesis, put forward by Cavalier-Smith, invokes only two secondary endosymbioses: one involving a green alga leading to the Cabozoa (which unites euglenophytes and chlorarachniophytes) and one involving a red alga that created the Chromalveolata (which unites cryptophytes, haptophytes, heterokontophytes, dinoflagellates, perkinsids, apicomplexa, and the plastid-lacking ciliates) (22). Interestingly, no examples of a glaucophyte secondary endosymbiont are known. Various lines of evidence now refute the Cabozoa hypothesis (7, 10, 33, 66, 104) and it is now clear that two separate acquisitions of green algal endosymbionts created the euglenophytes and chlorarachniophytes independently. The veracity of the chromalveolate hypothesis remains uncertain, and whether or not the chromalveolates are derived from a single or multiple secondary endosymbioses of separate red algal endosymbionts is still much debated. The chromalveolate hypothesis finds some support from molecular phylogenies (44, 86), and some unusual recruitments of enzymes to the endosymbiont shared by chromalveolates also lend credence to a single secondary endosymbiotic event (9, 30, 43, 44, 88). It was argued early on that the mechanism of how proteins are targeted from the host to the complex plastid would give insight into the endosymbiont's ancestry (22), and recent insights into this process (see **Figure 2** and below) are congruent with the chromalveolate scenario. Drawn together, these different analyses support the idea of a monophyletic origin for chromalveolates from a single red

Figure 2

Models of the machineries that import nuclear-encoded plastid proteins for select primary and secondary plastids. Nuclear-encoded factors are brown, plastid-encoded factors are green, and nucleomorph-encoded factors are gray. Organisms with primary plastids (green algae, plants, and rhodophytes) share core components of the import apparatus, although land plants apparently have a more elaborate set of receptors (Toc159 and Toc64) in the outer envelope membrane (OEM) and other participating factors (Tic55 and Tic40) in the inner envelope membrane (IEM). These factors, together with Tic62, might be involved in redox-regulated import. Oep16 imports protochlorophyllide oxidoreductase A from the cytosol in *Arabidopsis* independently of the canonical Toc system. A more complicated import pathway is necessary for secondary plastids, as in the case of the cryptophytes, which are surrounded by additional membranes, namely the periplastidial membrane (PPM) and rough endoplasmatic reticulum (rER). In cryptophytes preproteins are cotranslationally inserted into the ER via the Sec61 complex and the signal peptide (SP) is cleaved by the lumenal signal peptide peptidase (SiPP). The remaining transit peptide (TP) mediates translocation across the remaining three membranes, before being cleaved by the stromal processing peptidase (StPP) inside the stroma, similar to primary plastids. Whether the secondary plastid of *P. falciparum* and chlorarachniophytes is actually located within part of the ER, as in cryptophytes and other chromists, is uncertain. Morphology obviously has a significant impact on the actual import pathway and machinery necessary. Proposed models for complex plastids are mostly inferred from genome data mining and lack experimental proof. Tic20 and Der1-2 have not yet been identified in cryptophytes (*question marks*) but genes that encode proteins believed to be targeted into the plastid are present in other chromalveolates for which full genome sequence is available. PPC, periplastidial compartment; EPM, epiplastid membrane. Topogenic signals for stromal targeting are displayed beneath the organisms' names. The F-motif, which is apparently critical for stromal targeting, occurs in plastids with red algal origin.

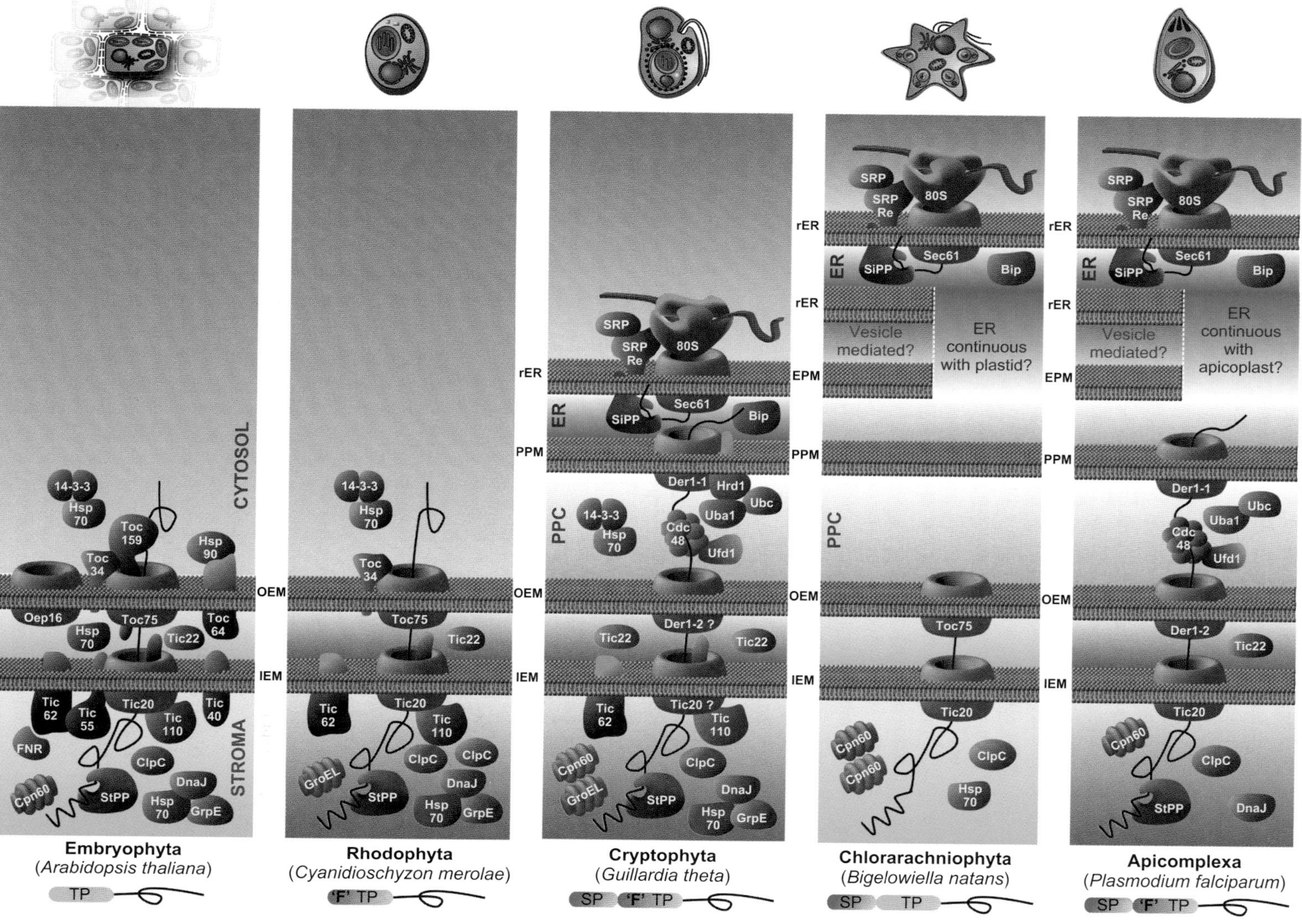

CYTOSOL
STROMA
14-3-3
Hsp 70
Toc 159
Toc 34
Hsp 90
Oep16
Toc75
Toc 64
Tic22
Tic 62
Tic 55
Tic20
Tic 110
Tic 40
FNR
ClpC
Cpn60
StPP
DnaJ
GrpE
OEM
IEM
GroEL
rER
PPM
EPM
ER
PPC
SRP
SRP Re
80S
Sec61
SiPP
Bip
Der1-1
Hrd1
Ubc
Uba1
Cdc 48
Ufd1
Der1-2 ?
Tic20 ?
Vesicle mediated?
ER continuous with plastid?
ER continuous with apicoplast?
Der1-2
Embryophyta
(Arabidopsis thaliana)
TP
Rhodophyta
(Cyanidioschyzon merolae)
'F' TP
Cryptophyta
(Guillardia theta)
SP 'F' TP
Chlorarachniophyta
(Bigelowiella natans)
SP TP
Apicomplexa
(Plasmodium falciparum)
SP 'F' TP

alga endosymbiont. However, some analyses with genes encoding cytosolic host proteins do not support the chromalveolate hypothesis (86, 120), suggesting that the spread of a single red algal endosymbiont among the chromalveolate branch may have occurred by subsequent tertiary endosymbioses. Furthermore, the clustering of genes representing Rhizaria together with the Chromalveolata in a recent report by Hackett and colleagues (40) reminds us that definite proof for the monophyletic origin of chromalveolates has not been found.

Eukaryotic endosymbiosis: all events in which the engulfed organism that was reduced to an organelle was a eukaryote

Endosymbiont metabolic replacement: replacement of an existing host-cell metabolic pathway with one acquired with the endosymbiont

One further aspect of eukaryotic endosymbiosis is tertiary, maybe even quaternary, and serial secondary endosymbiosis. Tertiary endosymbiosis is the uptake of a secondary endosymbiosis-derived alga by a eukaryote, and serial secondary endosymbiosis is the replacement of an original complex plastid with a new, primary endosymbiosis–derived alga. Select dinoflagellate algal lineages represent the best-studied cases of these higher order endosymbiotic events, and independent cases are represented by the genera *Lepidodinium*, *Kryptoperidinium*, *Karlodinium*, and *Dinophysis* (for detailed description of these unusual dinoflagellates lineages see References 39, 46, and 54) (**Figure 1**). In each case, the host dinoflagellate previously contained a secondary plastid, so these new endosymbionts represent organelle replacements. The mechanisms for organelle reduction and integration are likely the same for secondary endosymbionts; however, in cases of organelle replacement even transferred genes from the first plastid can contribute to the integration of these new recruits (49, 91).

Nature's Playground: The Evolution Continues

Plastid loss and reversion to obligate heterotrophy. A fascinating but often overlooked element of endosymbiotic theory concerns organelle reduction and loss. In a sense, all endosymbiotic organelles are products of massive reduction of the metabolic complexity and capabilities of the ancestral free-living symbiont. But there is a tendency to regard functional organelles as having reached a stable suite of core metabolic functions—in the case of plastids photosynthesis is considered the cornerstone of organellar function (see below for summary of plastid biochemical functions). Despite this mindset, an extensive number of lineages have independently advanced their plastids a further rung on the ladder of reduction by losing their photosynthetic capability (21). Parasitic plants and apicomplexan parasites such as the malaria parasites are notable examples; many other protists have also lost the ability to perform photosynthesis but retained their further reduced plastids (e.g., the euglenid *Astasia* and the dinoflagellate *Crypthecodinium*). These nonphotosynthetic plastids apparently still provide essential services to the host cells—for instance, fatty acid synthesis, isoprenoid synthesis, and heme synthesis in the case of the malaria parasites (96). Most of these additional plastid pathways have likely replaced equivalent host cell pathways that occurred in the ancestral host cell prior to plastid acquisition (endosymbiont metabolic replacement). Why a plastid pathway should replace an existing host cell pathway is unclear, although it is quite conceivable that chance has played a role in the elimination of any one of the duplicated pathways after endosymbiotic merger. In any case, fixation of the plastid copy of any essential metabolic pathway would commit a cell to plastid retention even if photosynthesis was subsequently abandoned. What, then, is the likelihood of such a cell achieving complete plastid loss?

To date, members of at least six major eukaryotic lineages may have achieved outright plastid loss: ciliates, the apicomplexan (e.g., *Cryptosporidium*), dinoflagellates (several lineages), heterokontophytes (e.g., oomycetes), trypanosomatids, and cryptophytes (*Goniomonas*). However, for several of these lineages such claims have inspired lively debate. The case for plastid loss in alveolates (i.e., ciliates, apicomplexans, and dinoflagellates) largely hinges on acceptance of the chromalveolata hypothesis, which unites alveolates with chromists (heterokontophytes, cryptophytes, and haptophytes) and proposes plastid origin in a common ancestor (22). If this hypothesis is correct, ciliates and basal lineages of apicomplexans (*Cryptosporidium* and gregarines) and dinoflagellates (e.g., *Oxyrrhis, Amoebophyra, Noctiluca*) that all lack plastids must have independently lost these organelles (1, 107, 121, 134). Challenging this scenario is the lack of strong phylogenetic evidence for the monophyly of chromalveolates host cells (40, 86, 120). Thus, an alternative explanation for plastid occurrence in alveolates is that apicomplexans and dinoflagellates independently gained their plastids, and that ciliates and the basal members of each ancestrally lacked a plastid. The dinoflagellate lineage, however, may represent an independent case for plastid loss, because several nonphotosynthetic groups are apparently scattered throughout photosynthetic dinoflagellates [according to small subunit rRNA phylogenies and plate tabulation data (107)], implying several independent losses. However, loss of photosynthesis may not always imply plastid loss, and the recent demonstration that at least one such taxon (*Crypthecodinium*) retains a nonphotosynthetic plastid indicates that plastid loss should be more closely examined in this group (108).

In contrast to the conspicuous photosynthetic members of the heterokontophytes such as kelp and diatoms, many members (e.g., thraustochytrids or oomycetes) are nonphotosynthetic (23). Oomycetes are well known plant pathogens, responsible for significant historical events such as the Irish potato famine. Most nonphotosynthetic heterokontophytes fall into basal clades (23), and therefore again the question of plastid loss hinges on whether heterokontophytes share a common plastid with other major lineages (i.e., other chromists, or indeed all chromalveolates) or whether a plastid was independently acquired within the heterokontophyte radiation. Trypanosomatids are a heterotrophic group of parasites whose sister relationship to the euglenids (many of which are photosynthetic) has inspired suggestion that these parasites also once contained a plastid but have since lost it (41). However strong evidence for secondary plastids as a recent gain in the euglenoid lineages (66), along with the rebuttal of the Cabozoa hypothesis (see above), undermines the case for plastid loss in trypanosomatids.

Perhaps the strongest case for plastid loss occurs in the Cryptophyta. Most cryptophytes are photosynthetic, although some have apparently lost photosynthesis but retain a relict plastid (113). Conversely, *Goniomonas* is a basal heterotrophic cryptophyte that apparently lacks a plastid (77). Recent phylogenies based on molecular data have strongly identified haptophytes as the sister lineage to cryptophytes (40, 86), and a gene replacement of plastid-encoded rpl36 is uniquely shared by these taxa, implying they share a common plastid (55, 101). Thus, reasonable evidence exists that the common ancestor of cryptophytes and haptophytes contained a plastid, and therefore *Goniomonas* has lost its plastid.

Although further cases of plastid loss will likely be substantiated as global phylogenies develop better resolution, a case for plastid loss in cryptophytes at least looks well supported. How then, is a eukaryote able to reverse the endosymbiotic process—particularly, how can endosymbiont metabolic replacement be reversed? Two scenarios are possible. One is that the plastid is lost relatively early in endosymbiont integration, before endosymbiont metabolic replacement occurs. Cavalier-Smith (19) has suggested that this accounts for why plastidless taxa are often basal to photosynthetic lineages; they represent the period before a cell starts to rationalize its own biochemistry and rely on elements of the symbiont's biochemistry. If the chromalveolate hypothesis is correct, then only after the major lineages diverged did the plastid become essential beyond photosynthesis, because most of the major lineages have plastidless basal members. A second scenario is that through heterotrophy a cell can satisfy its requirement for the macromolecules it had come to rely upon from the plastid. Many secondarily nonphotosynthetic groups are either predators or highly adapted parasites, with access to a rich supply of macromolecules. If this diet can satisfy the need for fatty acids, isoprenoids, and heme, for instance, a cell might be well on the way to making its plastid obsolete.

In either case, if a plastid is lost from a eukaryotic lineage, would evidence of the plastid's tenancy remain? The many hundreds to thousands of nucleus-encoded plastid genes would initially be present, but without a function these would likely degrade quite rapidly. However, any plastid genes that had come to fulfill an alternative, nonplastid-localized function would remain useful even after plastid loss. Such genes, referred to as EGT (endosymbiont gene transfers) have been estimated to represent between 10% of nucleus-encoded genes derived from the plastid in glaucophytes and 50% in plants (73, 100). This amounts to ~150 and ~2250 genes in total in the two groups, respectively. Thus, loss of a plastid could conceivably leave a conspicuous footprint if these genes remained useful in the absence of the plastid. In the oomycetes one such plastid-derived gene (*gnd*) has been hailed as evidence for the former plastid in this lineage (6). However, to form a compelling case for a former plastid we should anticipate a large collection of such genes when the annotation of oomycete genomes is complete. Conversely, ciliates have revealed no such plastid footprint; the complete sequence of *Tetrahymena thermophila* was recently investigated for just such relict plastid genes (29). It will be very interesting to undertake the same analysis for *Goniomonas* in pursuit of a better understanding of the process of plastid loss.

Symbioses in progress. In addition to full-fledged plastid organelles, numerous organisms demonstrate that endosymbiosis is a continual driving force in evolution. Here we present four interesting cases of organisms at various points of negotiation of these cellular marriage contracts.

Rhopalodia gibba is a diatom that hosts both a secondary red algal–derived plastid and a novel cyanobacterial symbiont (**Figure 1**) known as the spheroid body (32). Unlike cyanobacterial-derived plastids, which are typically photosynthetic, the spheroid body has apparently lost this ability. However, the spheroid body has retained another core cyanobacterial function, the ability to fix nitrogen, which it performs for its diatom host during the day (93). Spheroid bodies are inherited vertically from one generation to the next, and their numbers are regulated in the host cell, which implies a high level of host control over the endosymbiont. As yet no evidence for spheroid body genes in the diatom host has been found, so whether the final stage of organelle integration has been achieved in this case remains undetermined. However, the spheroid bodies have clearly suffered gene loss, and they are most likely incapable of again living outside the host (93). Nitrogen fixation is another of the innovations specific to prokaryotes, so it is noteworthy that endosymbiotic capture again has played a role in extending such fundamental capabilities to eukaryotes.

A further independent example of primary endosymbiosis is seen in the freshwater amoeba *Paulinella chromatophora*, which also hosts a cyanobacterium-like symbiont (56). In this case photosynthesis is retained, and *P. chromatophora* accordingly has converted from heterotrophy to autotrophy. The *Paulinella* endosymbiont, referred to as a cyanelle, occurs in the cytoplasm without any additional bounding membranes, and symbiont numbers are strictly regulated, again suggesting a higher level of host-symbiont interaction (133). Attempts to culture the symbiont separate from the host have thus far been unsuccessful, but analysis of the *Paulinella* cyanelle genome reveals neither obvious gene loss nor transfer of genes to the host, so it appears that there has been relatively little genetic response to this union so far (133). The *Paulinella* symbionts are thus enigmatic; however, these symbionts potentially represent a second case of primary endosymbiosis enabling photosynthetic capture. Fortunately, *Paulinella chromatophora* has symbiont-lacking sister species (*P. indentata* and *P. ovalis*), which offers the possibility of understanding how this organism can acquire a permanent prokaryotic endosymbiont in a process reminiscent of the origin of plastids.

Nascent secondary endosymbioses are also in evidence. The enigmatic flagellate *Hatena arenicola* harbors a quasi-permanent prasinophyte-like endosymbiont (related to the genus *Nephroselmis*), which exhibits substantial structural modification when within the host. Permanent integration of this photosynthetic symbiont is apparently pending because division of the symbiont is not yet coordinated with that of the host (85). Nevertheless, a degree of integration has apparently occurred, because host cell division results in one daughter cell inheriting the endosymbiont while the other daughter cell is left without a symbiont and presumably sources a new symbiont from the environment.

Perhaps one of the more startling cases of endosymbiosis in progress is the plastid theft performed by the sea slug *Elysia chlorotica*. This sea slug feeds upon algae and can salvage the plastids from their diet of *Vaucheria litorea* and maintain them, generating photosynthate that can nourish the animal for many months. The plastids, which are arrayed in specially generated diverticulae of the slug gut to be exposed to incoming light, remain transcriptionally and translationally active for up to nine months (83). Circumstantial evidence suggests that the plastids even receive proteins synthesized by the sea slug (42). If substantiated, this would implicate horizontal transfer of a gene from the alga to the sea slug, which by one definition would make this captured plastid an animal organelle. However, these plastids are unable to divide, and are not passed on from one slug generation to another, nor do they occur in the animal's germ line. In fact, stolen plastids such as these could probably never achieve permanent endosymbiont status because many essential plastid genes would have been left behind when the algal nucleus was digested. Sea slug plastids are thus examples of kleptoplastids: photosynthetic organelles stolen from another organism but not permanently acquired.

PREPROTEIN TARGETING

Intracellular gene relocation is dependent on the existence of a system to reimport the gene product back to the compartment of origin. Given the massive scale of plastid-to-nucleus gene relocation, this system must recognize and sort a large number of plastid-destined proteins from all other proteins synthesized in the cytoplasm. Elements of this system, including proteins of the import apparatus embedded in the plastid membranes and some features of plastid precursor proteins, are shared throughout phototrophic eukaryotes and reflect the common origin of primary plastids. Core elements of the system shared by red algae and green algae/plants clearly arose early, prior to the diversification of the primary endosymbiont-containing lineage (79). In plants additional elements such as extra receptors and redox-sensing components of plastid protein import clearly have arisen to optimize this system and also facilitate the biogenesis of different plastid types (e.g., amyloplasts, chromoplasts, and chloroplasts) (14). Great insight has now been achieved into the complex and sophisticated plastid protein import machinery of plants, the details of which are reviewed elsewhere (14, 38, 115). Here, we confine ourselves to a synopsis of the primary plastid import system and give more focus to the less well-understood machinery for protein import into secondary plastids with multiple bounding membranes.

Targeting to Primary Plastids

Primary plastids contain three distinct sets of membrane: the outer envelope membrane

(OEM), the inner envelope membrane (IEM), and the thylakoid membranes, which thus create three separate compartments (intermembrane space, stroma, and thylakoid lumen). Proteins can therefore be targeted to six regions within plastids: three membranes and three soluble compartments. Dedicated translocation machineries and peptide targeting information within the nuclear-encoded plastid proteins are used in concert to achieve these targeting feats (**Figure 2**).

The majority of proteins is targeted to the plastid posttranslationally, facilitated by an N-terminal transit peptide extension. This peptide leader can vary in length from approximately 20 to 150 amino acids and no primary sequence consensus or common secondary structure has been identified in the large collections of transit peptides known from different plants. General characteristics include hydrophobicity at the extreme N terminus, enrichment of hydroxylated amino acids, and a depletion in acidic residues that leads to a positive charge, particularly toward the N terminus (16, 89, 95). Some transit peptides are phosphorylated by an ATP-dependent cytosolic kinase, which leads to an interaction with a guidance complex; these peptides are then preferred for import (76). After translocation, transit peptides are cleaved off by the stromal processing peptidase, which belongs to the M16 family of metallopeptidases, releasing the mature protein into the stroma (102).

Transport of the majority of preproteins across the two envelope membranes is the job of the Toc (translocator of the outer chloroplast membrane) and Tic (translocator of the inner chloroplast membrane) machineries. These two apparatuses comprise multiple soluble and membrane-bound proteins named for their molecular masses (see **Figure 2**). Toc75 is the main translocation pore in the outer membrane (28) and together with Toc 33/34 and 159 makes up the Toc core (111, 112). Other Toc components apparently have subsidiary roles; for example, Toc64 is implicated in plastid protein recognition and delivery to the Toc pore. In plants such as *Arabidopsis* multigene families encode different (partially redundant) isoforms of Toc components and differential isoform expression probably generates import complexes tailored to particular plastid states in different tissues (12, 51). Conversely, the haploid moss *Physcomitrella patens* appears to lack these isoforms, and thus is emerging as a superior model for gene knockout studies of Toc/Tic function (47). Interestingly, in the genome of the red alga *Cyanidioschyzon merolae*, only Toc34 and Toc75 have thus far been identified (**Figure 2**), which might mean that major receptor components of the outer membrane (e.g., Toc 159 and 64) of land plant plastids are specific to this green lineage, and that red-specific Toc receptors await discovery (79).

The core of the Tic complex includes Tic20, Tic22, and Tic110 (**Figure 2**). Tic22 is a soluble protein in the intermembrane space and is thought to be the first Tic component to interact with incoming precursors (59). Either or both of the two membrane proteins Tic20 and Tic110 could be involved in pore formation but details are unclear (50, 60, 122). Tic110 also interacts with the chaperone Hsp93 (ClpC) inside the stroma (3). A similar function is proposed for Tic40, because it possesses a conserved domain known from Hsp70 cochaperones (24). Several reports suggest the other Tic components of land plants (Tic32, Tic55, and Tic62) might be involved in the redox-regulated import of preproteins (13, 61). The presence of homologs for Tic20, Tic22, Tic62, and Tic110 in the genome of the red alga *C. merolae*, combined with the apparent absence of Tic32 and 55, might suggest that the former are essential and the latter dispensable for functional plastid import (79), but experimental confirmation is needed. Finally, on the stromal side of the membrane chaperones such as GroEL and CplC interact with the Tic complex to receive the imported proteins and fold them, after cleavage of the transit peptide, to their mature conformation (125). However, some proteins require further targeting and the thylakoid membranes contain no less than three independent sets of protein translocation machineries for this purpose: the signal recognition particle–dependent (Albino3) pathway, the Tat (twin arginine translocon) pathway, and the Sec-dependent pathway. In addition, spontaneous insertion of proteins into thylakoid membranes is also known to occur, thus offering at least four alternative routes into the membrane or lumen of thylakoids (38).

Alternative, Toc/Tic-independent routes to plastids are also becoming apparent (60, 97). For instance, the outer envelope protein 16 (Oep16)—a homolog of bacterial preprotein and amino acid transporters—serves as the translocase for one plastid protein, NADPH:protochlorophyllide oxidoreductase A (98). Another noncanonical import pathway through the outer envelope membrane was recently revealed with the identification of nuclear-encoded plastid proteins possessing N-terminal signal peptides rather than the standard plastid transit peptides (94, 126). These plastid proteins traverse the endoplasmic reticulum (ER), and most likely also traverse the Golgi apparatus where they are glycosylated, and are subsequently targeted to the outer envelope membrane of the plastid (94, 126). The details of this alternate route remain mysterious.

Targeting Into and Within Secondary Plastids

Translocation of precursor proteins to secondary plastids must surmount additional obstacles in the form of extra bounding membranes, which also creates additional compartments that have their own specific proteomes. Three membranes surround dinoflagellate and euglenophyte complex plastids, whereas cryptophyte, heterokontophyte, haptophytes, apicomplexan, and chlorarachniophyte plastids are surrounded by four membranes (22). Independent origins of secondary plastids have resulted in distinct targeting solutions to these advanced trafficking needs; however, remarkably, some unifying principals have emerged. Virtually all known complex plastid preproteins encoded in the nucleus possess an N-terminal topogenic signal composed of at least two parts: a signal peptide and a transit peptide. The ubiquity of what appears to be a canonical signal peptide in complex plastid-targeted proteins is consistent with the outermost membrane being a component of the host cell's endomembrane system, apparently derived from the formative phagocytic event (22). The signal peptide mediates cotranslational import into the ER lumen, where signal peptidase removes the signal peptide to expose the transit peptide, which is responsible for targeting across the remaining membranes. An unusual elaboration of this bipartite leader occurs in the two cases of complex plastids surrounded by three membranes: dinoflagellates and euglenoids. Here an additional signal, a hydrophobic membrane anchor, is embedded in the transit peptide region of most plastid proteins (84, 87, 118). Thus, insertion of preproteins into the ER lumen in these taxa is apparently delayed; plastid preproteins are anchored to endomembranes until they are delivered to the plastid and the complete plastid import is enabled.

In heterokonts, haptophytes, and cryptophytes the outer plastid membrane is continuous with the host rough ER and thus is studded with ribosomes (18). Plastid proteins encoded in the nucleus have therefore already passed through the first of four membranes after cotranslational insertion into the ER lumen by the N-terminal signal peptide (**Figure 2**). However, in other complex plastid systems no such continuity of plastids and ER is apparent, so plastid preproteins must be delivered from the ER lumen to the outer plastid membranes [termed epiplastid membranes (EPM) in **Figure 2**], presumably by vesicular traffic (84, 118). After signal peptide cleavage, plastid proteins must be distinguished from secretory proteins; mutagenesis experiments in several complex plastid systems indicate that the transit peptide is responsible for this discrimination (34, 62, 129).

Epiplastid membrane (EPM): the outermost membrane surrounding complex plastids

Periplastidial compartment (PPC): the reduced cytosol of the engulfed alga; harbors the nucleomorph and 80S ribosomes in cryptophytes and chlorarachniophytes

Periplastidial membrane (PPM): represents the former cytoplasmic membrane of the endosymbiont and is the second outermost membrane in four-membrane-bounded plastids

The signal peptide and transit peptide thus act sequentially to mediate targeting into the stroma of complex plastids.

At least for some complex plastids, proteins are also targeted into the periplastidial compartment (PPC); these proteins also utilize a bipartite leader. The most N-terminal residue of the transit peptide is critical in dictating whether a protein travels all the way through the three innermost plastid membranes to the stroma or whether it stops in the PPC after traversing only the periplastidial membrane (35, 116). In the cryptophyte *Guillardia theta* and the heterokontophyte *Phaeodactylum tricornutum*, this +1 transit peptide residue is typically a phenylalanine for stromal proteins (in a few exceptions other aromatic amino acids fulfill this role). In the absence of this phenylalanine the preprotein accumulates in the PPC (34, 37). In other chromalveolates an aromatic amino acid–based motif (F-motif) is also a conspicuous feature of the N terminus of transit peptides, and likely plays a role in correct stromal targeting (35, 58, 90). Interestingly, this F-motif also occurs in the transit peptides of plastid-targeted proteins of glaucophytes and rhodophytes (117), which suggests that the F-motif could be an ancient targeting element for plastid import. Thus, in complex plastids the role of this F-motif has apparently been extended to discriminate between proteins that are required to be targeted fully into the plastid stroma and those that must be halted in the PPC. The corollary is that the remainder of the transit peptide is sufficient for targeting across the periplastidial membrane (PPM) (**Figure 2**). Curiously, the F-motif does not occur in transit peptides of the green algal/plant lineage, and thus this ancient targeting signal has apparently been abandoned here. This might explain the apparent need for extra receptors like Toc159 and 64 in these plastids (**Figure 2**).

The second step of protein trafficking into complex plastids (the translocation from the ER lumen into the PPC, see **Figure 2**) presumably requires a translocon in the PPM. Termed the Top translocon (22), this hypothetical membrane transporter and its intriguing evolutionary pedigree may recently have been identified. The nucleomorph of the cryptophyte *G. theta* encodes ERAD (ER-associated degradation) components, including a Der1p (degradation in the ER) membrane translocon able to complement ERAD-deficient yeast (116). Because no ER is present inside the periplastidial space, the location of this nucleomorph-encoded ERAD machinery was intriguing. Preliminary immunolocalization studies suggest that the Der1p translocon is located in the PPM of the cryptophyte's complex plastid (116), leading to speculation that it could be the long sought after Top translocon. Further credence for this hypothesis comes from the identification of an extra set of ERAD machinery (distinct from the canonical host ER ERAD machinery) that is apparently targeted to the complex plastids of other chromalveolates such as diatoms and *Plasmodium* (116). Because these plastids have lost all traces of the endosymbiont cytoplasm it is highly plausible that this ERAD machinery could localize to the periplastidial membrane and have a role in translocating transit peptide–bearing preproteins into the complex plastids. The ERAD-derived translocon is proposed to recognize the transit peptide (which might resemble an unfolded protein similar to the normal ERAD substrate) and to pull the precursor proteins out of the ER and into the periplastidial compartment (**Figure 2**).

Although the role of this ERAD apparatus in targeting proteins to complex plastids remains to be substantiated, it provides tantalizing support for the chromalveolate hypothesis. As alluded to above, solving the "protein-import problem" was a major hurdle in the establishment of secondary endosymbionts (18). The apparent co-option of a normally ER-based protein translocation system into plastid transport by cryptophytes, heterokontophytes, and Apicomplexa is suggestive of a common origin for the plastids. Similarly, use of the F-motif to discriminate between periplastidial and stromal-directed proteins by cryptophytes, diatoms, and perhaps even apicomplexa is also congruent with a common origin for their plastids.

BIOCHEMICAL PATHWAYS

The union of a heterotroph and an autotroph in an endosymbiotic partnership amalgamates two suites of metabolic pathways into a single organism (131). The driver for the union is typically believed to be the acquisition of photosynthesis by the host. Thus, both primary and secondary endosymbioses likely converted heterotrophs into phototrophs. Some serial secondary endosymbioses and tertiary endosymbioses may have simply exchanged one photoautotrophic endosymbiont for another, but in general we can frame the question in terms of heterotroph + autotroph = new autotroph. From a metabolic perspective this fusion creates interesting possibilities. Autotrophs are typically self-sufficient metabolically; some require vitamins, but in general they synthesize everything they need from scratch. Conversely, heterotrophs have access to a range of preformed macromolecules in their diet and are able to salvage various building blocks from these macromolecules and utilize them in their metabolism. Thus, as a general principle, the endosymbiosis likely introduced extra metabolic capability beyond just photosynthesis to the host's repertoire. A key challenge is to unravel which pathways were introduced into the amalgam from the endosymbiont. As discussed above, the host can become dependent on endosymbiont pathways other than photosynthesis, and this dependency can impact plastid persistence should the organism subsequently revert to a totally heterotrophic lifestyle.

What do we know about the metabolic repertoires of the original hosts and endosymbionts? For the hosts we can say very little. We have a relatively poor understanding of the nature of the host for the primary endosymbiosis, and, similarly, we are largely ignorant of the host's affinities for the three known secondary endosymbioses (euglenophytes, chlorarachniophytes, and chromalveolates). It is thus rather difficult to speculate on what kind of metabolisms these hosts could have had at the outset of the endosymbiotic relationship. However, we are in a better position to hypothesize about the metabolic repertoire of the endosymbionts. For primary endosymbiosis we can postulate that the endosymbiont had a suite of metabolic capabilities similar to those in modern-day cyanobacteria. For secondary endosymbioses we can assume that the endosymbionts had a metabolic potential similar to that in the modern representatives of red or green algae as appropriate.

Weeden (131) was the first to ponder from a metabolic perspective the consequences of fusing an endosymbiont and host. He recognized that the endosymbiont introduced novel pathways into the host and he outlined how amino acid, heme, and starch pathways were inducted into hosts via endosymbiosis. We have subsequently learned that cells have also exercised considerable creativity during these metabolic mergers, and complex amalgams of host and symbiont pathways have also been the fruits of these partnerships.

Starch Synthesis

Excess photosynthate is generally stored as glucan polymers. Plants and green algae store starch (α-1,4 glucan) in the plastid, whereas red algae store starch in the cytosol (127). On the basis of these localities of starch synthesis, red algae were assumed to utilize a host-derived glucan synthesis mechanism whereas the green algae and plants were assumed to employ a system derived from the endosymbiotic ancestor of the plastid (**Figure 3**). The starting points for each of these pathways—UDP-glucose precursors for red algae and ADP-glucose precursors for green algae and plants—also reflect the dichotomy between eukaryotic and prokaryotic glucan pathways. However, in reality both host and symbiont proteins have been recruited in starch synthesis in both red and green algae, and only

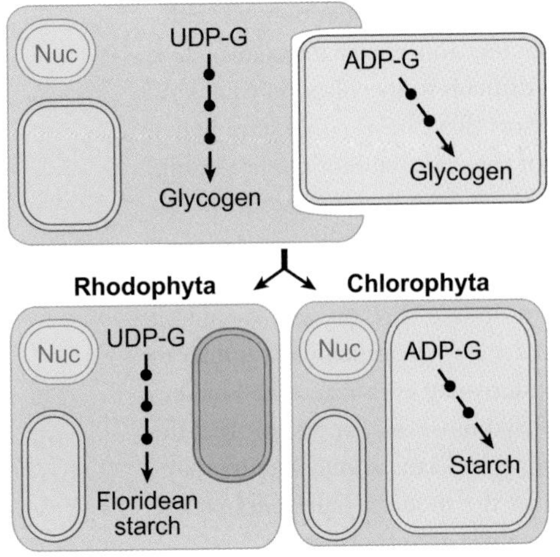

Figure 3

Schematic representation of starch synthesis before and after primary endosymbiosis. Nuc, nucleus; UDP-G, uridine-diphosphate glucose; ADP-G, adenosine-diphosphate glucose.

the localities, either cytosolic or organellar, have been derived from either host or symbiont (87). Why red algae retained the site of host glucan storage whereas green algae (and their descendants) adopted the endosymbiont storage site remains unknown (**Figure 4**).

In secondary endosymbiosis glucan storage distribution differs: Sometimes it is in the host, and sometimes it is in the endosymbiont. For instance, euglenoids store paramylon (β-1,3 glucan) in the cytosol, although their endosymbiont is thought to have been a green alga that presumably stored starch in the plastid (26, 128). Chlorarachniophytes and heterokontophytes also store β-1,3 glucans in the secondary host cytosol and have abandoned the glucan storage systems of the green and red algal endosymbionts, respectively (78). Conversely, cryptophytes store starch in the PPC (remnant endosymbiont cytoplasm), thus conserving the endosymbiont glycan storage system of the red algal endosymbiont (34). Dinoflagellates also store starch; however, rather than in a PPC, storage occurs in the host cytoplasm, implying relocation of this pathway from the red algal cytosol to that of the host (25). Thus, the storage of surplus photosynthate in either the host or endosymbiont compartments has taken a range of alternatives in both primary and secondary endosymbiotic partnerships.

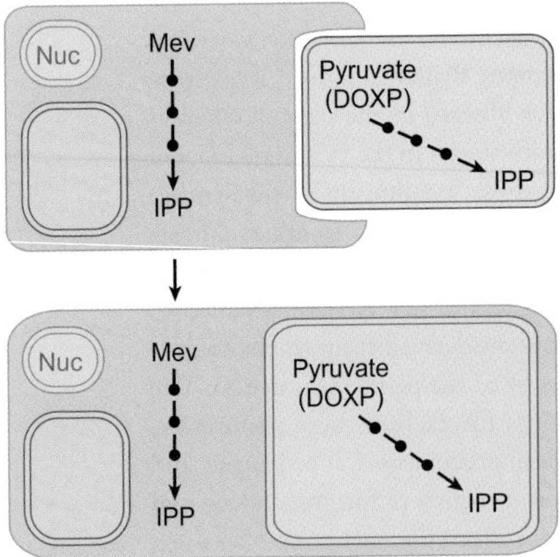

Figure 4

Schematic representation of the isopentenyl diphosphate (IPP) synthesis pathway before and after primary endosymbiosis. Mev, mevalonate; DOXP, 1-deoxy-D-xylulose 5-phosphate.

Isopentenyl Diphosphate (Isoprenoid Precursor) Synthesis

Isopentenyl diphosphate (IPP) is a building block for terpenes, sterols, carotenoids, and isoprenoids that are important components of a diverse range of cellular molecules such as chlorophylls and quinones. IPP synthesis was only recently discovered to occur in plastids (68). In plants the cytosol harbors the canonical mevalonate pathway for IPP synthesis (8), and for many years it was presumed that this was the sole source of isoprenoid precursors in plants. Given the extensive use of isoprene subunits in plants for secondary metabolites such as terpenes, chlorophylls, ubiquinol, prenylated proteins, and isopentyl tRNAs, it is sobering to reflect that a plastid-based, nonmevalonate, deoxyxylulose (DOXP) pathway for IPP synthesis was overlooked, or at least unrecognized, by plant physiologists. However, once it emerged that bacteria synthesize IPP from pyruvate and glyceraldehyde 3-phosphate and not from mevalonate like eukaryotes, it was a simple step to identify a DOXP pathway in plastids (105). Indeed, the discovery of the plastid DOXP pathway reconciled some previously incongruous precursor incorporation and inhibitor data (67). Synthesis of IPP in plastids also simplifies the delivery of these entities to isopentenylate tRNAs for plastid translation and to isoprene chains for chlorophyll production (63).

In plants, IPP synthesis occurs in both the host compartment (cytosol) and the endosymbiont compartment (plastid). The two different pathways coexist and are even integrated to an extent (65), but their differences are congruent with one (acetate/mevalonate) being derived from the host and the other (DOXP) being introduced with the cyanobacterial symbiont (**Figure 4**). Exactly why both pathways persist is not known but the requirement for products in both the host and endosymbiont compartments perhaps necessitated the retention of two pathways.

Heme Synthesis

The synthesis of the tetrapyrroles that act as temporary electron carriers in various redox reactions is reminiscent of IPP synthesis in that there are two very different pathways that begin with different substrates and utilize some, but not all, different enzymes. Many plastid-lacking eukaryotes utilize the so-called C4 or Shemin pathway, which commences by fusing succinyl-CoA and glycine to create δ-aminolevulinic acid (ALA), courtesy of aminolevulinic acid synthase (ALAS) (**Figure 5**). In animals and yeast, ALAS (114) is located in the mitochondrion and ALA is then exported to the cytosol where a series of steps convert it to coproporphinobilogen III (CPIII). CPIII is then routed back into the mitochondrion by a recently identified transporter for the last four steps to eventually produce heme (**Figure 5**).

Cyanobacteria have a different initial substrate, commencing C-5–type heme synthesis from glutamyl-tRNA rather than succinyl-CoA and glycine (5) (**Figure 5**). Glu-tRNA

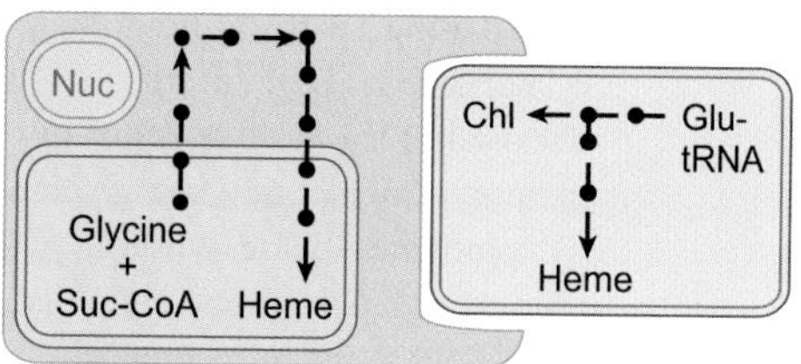

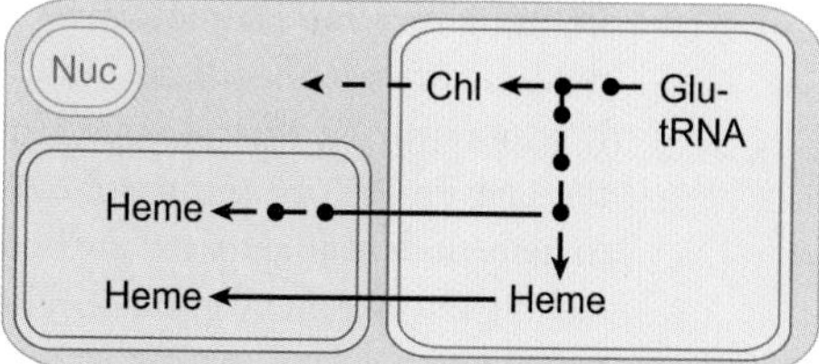

Figure 5

Schematic representation of heme synthesis before and after primary endosymbiosis. Nuc, nucleus; Glu tRNA, glutamyl tRNA; Suc-CoA, succinyl-Coenzyme A; Chl, chlorophyll.

reductase followed by Glu-SA aminomutase convert the aminoacylated tRNA to ALA. Steps from ALA to heme are then identical in cyanobacteria and the Shemin pathway, and the enzymes involved are homologous. However, in cyanobacteria the pathway forks at protoporphinobilogen IX. One branch leads to heme as per the Shemin pathway, but the other branch involves the addition of Mg^{2+} to protoporphinobilogen IX to generate chlorophyll (124).

Because the original host for primary endosymbiosis likely had aerobically respiring mitochondria, we can assume it had a Shemin pathway to generate heme for its cytochromes. The acquisition of a cyanobacterial endosymbiont almost certainly introduced the glutamyl-tRNA–based pathway into the first eukaryotic autotrophs. At the outset this organism would have had two heme synthesis pathways: a Shemin pathway in the mitochondrion/cytosol and a cyanobacterial-like C5 pathway in the endosymbiont (**Figure 5**). To carry on photosynthesis, the endosymbiont likely continued to synthesize chlorophyll from glutamyl-tRNA; indeed, plant plastids still synthesize chlorophyll entirely within the plastid using a pathway homologous to that of cyanobacteria (124). Interestingly, plants have disposed of the early portions of the Shemin pathway and do not use glycine or ALAS to commence heme synthesis (92). Rather, they export protoporphinobilogen IX from the plastid to the mitochondrion, which then performs the last two steps of heme synthesis using enzymes homologous to those of the animal/yeast Shemin pathway (**Figure 5**). It is noteworthy that plastids also complete the conversion of protoporphinobilogen IX to heme independently for the benefit of furnishing the prosthetic group for their own cytochromes.

For heme we thus see a picture of two pathways rationalized into one pathway that forks three ways: chlorophyll and heme synthesis from glutamyl-tRNA in the plastid, and heme synthesis in the mitochondrion commencing not from its original ALAS but from plastid-synthesised ALA (**Figure 5**).

Aromatic Amino Acid Synthesis

The essential amino acids are a necessary part of the animal diet because we lack a pathway to synthesize tryptophan, phenylalanine, and tyrosine. Autotrophs lack a diet and must synthesize these and all 17 other amino acids. In plants the shikimate pathway located in the plastid synthesizes the precursors for the aromatic amino acids. There are two versions of the shikimate pathway: a prokaryotic-style version, which is what occurs in the plant plastid, and a cytosolic-based version with different enzymes, as occurs in fungi (45). In plants the plastid has clearly retained its ancestral ability to synthesize tryptophan, phenylalanine, and tyrosine and supplies these amino acids to the cytosol (host) (**Figure 6**). Whether or not the original host possessed a shikimate pathway prior to primary endosymbiosis remains unclear. If it did, all traces are now lost and the plastid bears sole responsibility for this task in members of the red algae, green algae, and plants.

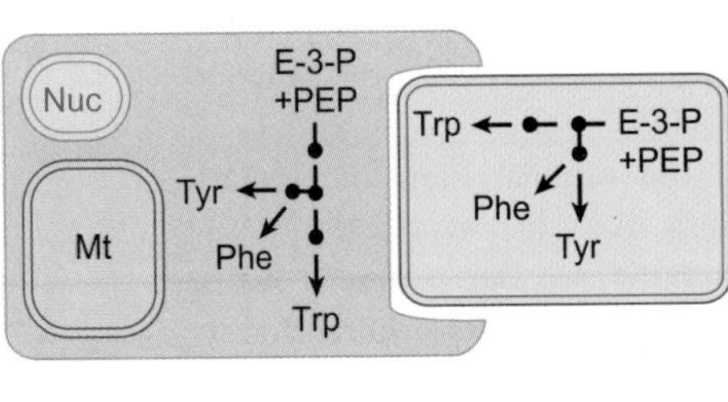

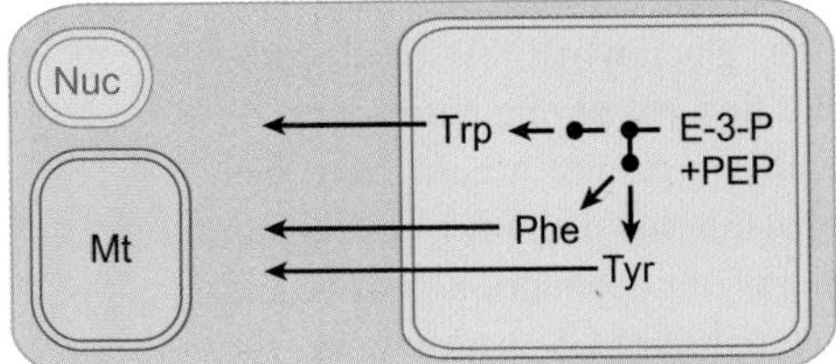

Figure 6

Schematic representation of aromatic amino acid synthesis before and after primary endosymbiosis. Nuc, nucleus; Mt, mitochondrion; E-3-P, erythrose-3-phosphate; PEP, phosphoenolpyruvate; Tyr, tyrosine; Phe, phenylalanine; Trp, tryptophan.

Fe-S Clusters

Fe-S clusters are important prosthetic groups of various metalloproteins that participate in redox reactions, sensing of iron and oxygen, and catalysis (69). The Fe atom in Fe-S clusters is able to take up an electron reversibly, thus providing the required electron carrier capacity. Fe-S–containing proteins are pervasive in life and ancient; well-known examples include the ferredoxins, NADH dehydrogenase, and Coenzyme Q. The clusters contain different numbers of iron and sulfur depending on cluster type and are coordinated into the protein through cysteinyl ligands. Synthesis and insertion or removal of Fe-S clusters into and out of proteins is managed by a number of enzymes, not all of which have been identified. At least three different systems for Fe-S cluster formation and insertion [iron sulfur cluster (ISC), nitrogen fixation (NIF), and mobilization of sulfur (Suf)] are known thus far. Plastids harbor a Suf-type Fe-S cluster formation system homologous to that of cyanobacteria (11, 119). Suf system–generated Fe-S clusters are probably incorporated into a range of plastid proteins including ferredoxin and the Rieske iron sulfur protein.

The original host of the primary plastid endosymbiont almost certainly contained an Fe-S cluster formation system, but it was probably not cytosolic. Eukaryotes all appear to form Fe-S clusters, but the initial steps are mitochondrial and typically utilize the ISC system (64). An export machinery translocates the Fe-S cluster into the cytosol where machinery exists to insert the cluster into apoproteins. This mitochondrial-based synthesis was likely obtained with the α-proteobacterial endosymbiont that gave rise to the mitochondrion (70). The host cell for primary endosymbiosis likely had this system, and indeed, plants utilize an ISC system in their mitochondria and a Suf system in the plastid (11).

SUMMARY POINTS

1. All plastids ultimately arose from a single prokaryotic endosymbiosis, where a cyanobacterium was engulfed and retained by a eukaryotic cell.
2. Eukaryotic endosymbiosis has occurred multiple times, and this process has lead to the spread of plastids throughout a great diversity of eukaryotes.
3. Further endosymbiotic events continue to occur in nature, and a wide continuum exists between temporary symbiotic relationships, stable interdependent partnerships, and those that are intimately integrated at a molecular-genetic level.
4. Pivotal to the integration of plastids was the establishment of protein delivery systems that enabled a shift of genetic control from the organelle to the host nucleus. Prokaryotic endosymbiosis required the generation of a novel protein import system, whereas eukaryotic endosymbionts have co-opted and adapted existing protein translocation systems to achieve this task for complex plastids.
5. Eukaryotes have gained numerous metabolic capabilities through endosymbiosis, including but not restricted to photosynthesis. Some of these capabilities were unique prokaryotic inventions, and have thus extended the capabilities of eukaryotes. Others represented duplications of existing host pathways, and in many cases rationalization of redundancy has generated novel chimeric pathways in eukaryotes.

FUTURE ISSUES

In recent years the broadening of genome sequencing programs has encompassed a greater diversity of plastid-bearing eukaryotes, and we are now seeing great advances in our understanding of plastids. This diversity includes the molecular integration of plastid genomes with those of the host, the mechanisms and trafficking routes of transferred gene products on their return journey to the plastid, and the metabolic integration and trade between plastids and their diverse hosts. Several key research directions now present themselves and are conceivably within greater reach than ever before. (1) Although the phylogenetic affinities between the major eukaryotic lineages are begining to slowly resolve into focus, considerable controversy continues to surround the question of how many endosymbiotic events have generated the plastid diversity observed in eukaryotes—notably with respect to the plastids of the Chromalveolates. Resolution of these issues is critical to our interpretation of evolution of the diversity we see among plastids in this group, and our understanding of the frequency and mechanisms of plastid loss. (2) Although our understanding of protein targeting to primary plastids has reached a relatively advanced state, equivalent insight into the mechanisms for targeting proteins to complex plastids lags behind. These details may be vital in tackling some of the more insidious complex plastid-bearing eukaryotes such as the apicomplexan parasites, where plastid-targeted pathways offer tantalizing possibilities as drug targets for diseases such as malaria. (3) Genomic analyses have presented some insights into the broader suite of metabolic functions of plastids beyond photosynthesis; however, little is known about delivery of the products of these pathways to the host cell, or vice versa. Although this presents one of the larger challenges to plastid researchers, the realization of this goal is necessary to provide a full appreciation of the significance of plastid gain in eukaryotes through endosymbiosis.

DISCLOSURE STATEMENT

The authors are not aware of any biases that might be perceived as affecting the objectivity of this review.

ACKNOWLEDGMENTS

G.M. is an ARC Federation Fellow and Howard Hughes International Scholar and supported by a Program Grant from the NHMRC. S.B.G. is supported by the ARC grant DP0664097.

LITERATURE CITED

1. Abrahamsen MS, Templeton TJ, Enomoto S, Abrahante JE, Zhu G, et al. 2004. Complete genome sequence of the apicomplexan, *Cryptosporidium parvum*. *Science* 304:441–45
2. Adl SM, Simpson AG, Farmer MA, Andersen RA, Anderson OR, et al. 2005. The new higher level classification of eukaryotes with emphasis on the taxonomy of protists. *J. Eukaryot. Microbiol.* 52:399–451
3. Akita M, Nielsen E, Keegstra K. 1997. Identification of protein transport complexes in the chloroplastic envelope membranes via chemical cross-linking. *J. Cell Biol.* 136:983–94
4. Altmann R. 1890. *Die Elementarorganismen und ihre Beziehungen zu den Zellen*. Leipzig: Veit
5. Andersen T, Briseid T, Nesbakken T, Ormerod J, Sirevåg R, Thorud M. 1983. Mechanisms of synthesis of 5-aminolevulinate in purple, green and blue-green bacteria. *FEMS Microbiol. Lett.* 19:303–6
6. Andersson JO, Roger AJ. 2002. A cyanobacterial gene in nonphotosynthetic protists—an early chloroplast acquisition in eukaryotes? *Curr. Biol.* 12:115–19
7. Archibald JM, Longet D, Pawlowski J, Keeling PJ. 2003. A novel polyubiquitin structure in Cercozoa and Foraminifera: evidence for a new eukaryotic supergroup. *Mol. Biol. Evol.* 20:62–66
8. Bach TJ, Boronat A, Campos N, Ferrer A, Vollack KU. 1999. Mevaloate biosynthesis in plants? *Crit. Rev. Biochem. Mol. Biol.* 34:107–22

9. Bachvaroff TR, Sanchez Puerta MV, Delwiche CF. 2005. Chlorophyll c-containing plastid relationships based on analyses of a multigene data set with all four chromalveolate lineages. *Mol. Biol. Evol.* 22:1772–82
10. Baldauf SL, Roger AJ, Wenk-Siefert I, Doolittle WF. 2000. A kingdom-level phylogeny of eukaryotes based on combined protein data. *Science* 290:972–77
11. Balk J, Lobreaux S. 2005. Biogenesis of iron-sulfur proteins in plants. *Trends Plant Sci.* 10:324–31
12. Bauer J, Chen K, Hiltbunner A, Wehrli E, Eugster M, et al. 2000. The major protein import receptor of plastids is essential for chloroplast biogenesis. *Nature* 403:203–7
13. Becker T, Hritz J, Vogel M, Caliebe A, Bukau B, et al. 2004. Toc12, a novel subunit of the intermembrane space preprotein translocon of chloroplasts. *Mol. Biol. Cell* 15:5130–44
14. Bedard J, Jarvis P. 2005. Recognition and envelope translocation of chloroplast preproteins. *J. Exp. Bot.* 56:2287–320
15. Brocks JJ, Logan GA, Buick R, Summons RE. 1999. Archean molecular fossils and the early rise of eukaryotes. *Science* 285:1033–36
16. Bruce BD. 2000. Chloroplast transit peptides: structure, function and evolution. *Trends Cell Biol.* 10:440–47
17. Cavalier-Smith T. 1982. The origins of plastids. *Biol. J. Linn. Soc.* 17:289–306
18. Cavalier-Smith T. 1986. The kingdom Chromista: origin and systematics. In *Progress in Phycological Research*, ed. FE Round, DJ Chapman, pp. 309–47. Bristol: Biopress
19. Cavalier-Smith T. 1993. The origin, losses and gains of chloroplasts. In *Origins of Plastids: Symbiogenesis, Prochlorophytes and the Origins of Chloroplasts*, ed. RA Lewin, pp. 291–348. New York: Chapman & Hall
20. Cavalier-Smith T. 2000. Membrane heredity and early chloroplast evolution. *Trends Plant Sci.* 5:174–82
21. Cavalier-Smith T. 2002. Chloroplast evolution: secondary symbiogenesis and multiple losses. *Curr. Biol.* 12:R62–64
22. Cavalier-Smith T. 2003. Genomic reduction and evolution of novel genetic membranes and protein-targeting machinery in eukaryote-eukaryote chimaeras (meta-algae). *Philos. Trans. R. Soc. London Ser. B* 358:109–33
23. Cavalier-Smith T, Chao EE. 2006. Phylogeny and megasystematics of phagotrophic heterokonts (kingdom Chromista). *J. Mol. Evol.* 62:388–420
24. Chou ML, Fitzpatrick LM, Tu SL, Budziszewski G, Potter-Lewis S, et al. 2003. Tic40, a membrane-anchored co-chaperone homolog in the chloroplast protein translocon. *EMBO J.* 22:2970–80
25. Deschamps P, Haferkamp I, Dauvillee D, Haebel S, Steup M, et al. 2006. Nature of the periplastidial pathway of starch synthesis in the cryptophyte *Guillardia theta*. *Eukaryot. Cell* 5:954–63
26. Dodge JD. 1969. The ultrastructure of *Chroomonas mesostigmatica* Butcher (Cryptophyceae). *Arch. Mikrobiol.* 69:266–80
27. Douglas S, Zauner S, Fraunholz M, Beaton M, Penny S, et al. 2001. The highly reduced genome of an enslaved algal nucleus. *Nature* 410:1091–96
28. Eckart K, Eichacker L, Sohrt K, Schleiff E, Heins L, Soll J. 2002. A Toc75-like protein import channel is abundant in chloroplasts. *EMBO Rep.* 3:557–62
29. Eisen JA, Coyne RS, Wu M, Wu D, Thiagarajan M, et al. 2006. Macronuclear genome sequence of the ciliate *Tetrahymena thermophila*, a model eukaryote. *PLoS Biol.* 4:e286
30. Fast NM, Kissinger JC, Roos DS, Keeling PJ. 2001. Nuclear-encoded, plastid-targeted genes suggest a single common origin for apicomplexan and dinoflagellate plastids. *Mol. Biol. Evol.* 18:418–26

31. Gabrielson PW, Garbary DJ, Sommerfeld MR, Townsend RA, Tyler PL. 1990. Rhodophyta. See Ref. 72, pp. 102–18
32. Geitler L. 1977. Zur Entwicklungsgeschichte der Epithemiaceen *Epithemia, Rhopalodia* und *Denticula* (Diatomophyceae) und ihre vermutlich symbiontischen Sphaeroidkoerper. *Plant Syst. Evol.* 128:295–75
33. Gilson PR, Su V, Slamovits CH, Reith ME, Keeling PJ, McFadden GI. 2006. Complete nucleotide sequence of the chlorarachniophyte nucleomorph: nature's smallest nucleus. *Proc. Natl. Acad. Sci. USA* 103:9566–71
34. Gould SB, Sommer MS, Hadfi K, Zauner S, Kroth PG, Maier UG. 2006. Protein targeting into the complex plastid of cryptophytes. *J. Mol. Evol.* 62:674–81
35. Gould SB, Sommer MS, Kroth PG, Gile GH, Keeling PJ, Maier UG. 2006. Nucleus-to-nucleus gene transfer and protein retargeting into a remnant cytoplasm of cryptophytes and diatoms. *Mol. Biol. Evol.* 23:2413–22
36. Grambast L. 1974. Phylogeny of the Charophyta. *Taxon* 23:463–81
37. Gruber A, Vugrinec S, Hempel F, Gould SB, Maier UG, Kroth PG. 2007. Protein targeting into complex diatom plastids: functional characterisation of a specific targeting motif. *Plant Mol. Biol.* 64:519–30
38. Gutensohn M, Fan E, Frielingsdorf S, Hanner P, Hou B, et al. 2006. Toc, Tic, Tat et al.: structure and function of protein transport machineries in chloroplasts. *J. Plant Physiol.* 163:333–47
39. Hackett JD, Anderson D, Erdner D, Bhattacharya D. 2004. Dinoflagellates: a remarkable evolutionary experiment. *Am. J. Bot.* 9:1523–34
40. Hackett JD, Yoon HS, Li S, Reyes-Prieto A, Rummele SE, Bhattacharya D. 2007. Phylogenomic analysis supports the monophyly of cryptophytes and haptophytes and the association of 'rhizaria' with chromalveolates. *Mol. Biol. Evol.* 24:1702–13
41. Hannaert V, Saavedra E, Duffieux F, Szikora JP, Rigden DJ, et al. 2003. Plant-like traits associated with metabolism of *Trypanosoma* parasites. *Proc. Natl. Acad. Sci. USA* 100:1067–71
42. Hanten JJ, Pierce SK. 2001. Synthesis of several light-harvesting complex I polypeptides is blocked by cycloheximide in symbiotic chloroplasts in the sea slug, *Elysia chlorotica* (Gould): a case for horizontal gene transfer between alga and animal? *Biol. Bull.* 201:34–44
43. Harper JT, Keeling PJ. 2003. Nucleus-encoded, plastid-targeted glyceraldehyde-3-phosphate dehydrogenase (GAPDH) indicates a single origin for chromalveolate plastids. *Mol. Biol. Evol.* 20:1730–35
44. Harper JT, Waanders E, Keeling PJ. 2005. On the monophyly of chromalveolates using a six-protein phylogeny of eukaryotes. *Int. J. Syst. Evol. Microbiol.* 55:487–96
45. Herrmann KM, Weaver LM. 1999. The shikimate pathway. *Annu. Rev. Plant. Physiol. Plant Mol. Biol.* 50:473–503
46. Hjorth E, Hadfi K, Gould SB, Kawach O, Sommer MS, et al. 2004. Zero, one, two, three, and perhaps four. Endosymbiosis and the gain and loss of plastids. *Endocytobiol. Cell Res.* 15:459–68
47. Hofmann NR, Theg SM. 2003. *Physcomitrella patens* as a model for the study of chloroplast protein transport: conserved machineries between vascular and non-vascular plants. *Plant Mol. Biol.* 53:621–32
48. Hughes RA, Robertson MP, Ellington AD, Levy M. 2004. The importance of prebiotic chemistry in the RNA world. *Curr. Opin. Chem. Biol.* 8:629–33

49. Ishida K, Green BR. 2002. Second- and third-hand chloroplasts in dinoflagellates: phylogeny of oxygen-evolving enhancer 1 (PsbO) protein reveals replacement of a nuclear-encoded plastid gene by that of a haptophyte tertiary endosymbiont. *Proc. Natl. Acad. Sci. USA* 99:9294–99
50. Jackson DT, Froehlich JE, Keegstra K. 1998. The hydrophilic domain of Tic110, an inner envelope membrane component of the chloroplastic protein translocation apparatus, faces the stromal compartment. *J. Biol. Chem.* 273:16583–88
51. Jarvis P, Chen LJ, Li H, Peto CA, Fankhauser C, Chory J. 1998. An *Arabidopsis* mutant defective in the plastid general protein import apparatus. *Science* 282:100–3
52. Jarvis P, Dormann P, Peto CA, Lutes J, Benning C, Chory J. 2000. Galactolipid deficiency and abnormal chloroplast development in the *Arabidopsis* MGD synthase 1 mutant. *Proc. Natl. Acad. Sci. USA* 97:8175–79
53. Kaneko T, Nakamura Y, Wolk CP, Kuritz T, Sasamoto S, et al. 2001. Complete genomic sequence of the filamentous nitrogen-fixing cyanobacterium *Anabaena sp.* strain PCC 7120. *DNA Res.* 8:205–13, 227–53
54. Keeling PJ. 2004. Diversity and evolutionary history of plastids and their hosts. *Am. J. Bot.* 91:1481–93
55. Khan H, Parks N, Kozera C, Curtis BA, Parsons BJ, et al. 2007. Plastid genome sequence of the cryptophyte alga *Rhodomonas salina* CCMP1319: Lateral transfer of putative DNA replication machinery and a test of chromist plastid phylogeny. *Mol. Biol. Evol.* 24:1832–42
56. Kies L. 1974. Electron microscopical investigations on *Paulinella chromatophora* Lauterborn, a thecamoeba containing blue-green endosymbioints (cyanelles). *Protoplasma* 80:69–89
57. Kies L, Kremer BP. 1990. Phylum glaucocystophyta. See Ref. 72, pp. 152–66
58. Kilian O, Kroth PG. 2005. Identification and characterization of a new conserved motif within the presequence of proteins targeted into complex diatom plastids. *Plant J.* 41:175–83
59. Kouranov A, Chen X, Fuks B, Schnell DJ. 1998. Tic20 and Tic22 are new components of the protein import apparatus at the chloroplast inner envelope membrane. *J. Cell Biol.* 143:991–1002
60. Kouranov A, Wang H, Schnell DJ. 1999. Tic22 is targeted to the intermembrane space of chloroplasts by a novel pathway. *J. Biol. Chem.* 274:25181–86
61. Kuchler M, Decker S, Hormann F, Soll J, Heins L. 2002. Protein import into chloroplasts involves redox-regulated proteins. *EMBO J.* 21:6136–45
62. Lang M, Apt KE, Kroth PG. 1998. Protein transport into complex diatom plastids utilizes two different targeting signals. *J. Biol. Chem.* 273:30973–78
63. Lange BM, Rujan T, Martin W, Croteau R. 2000. Isoprenoid biosynthesis: the evolution of two ancient and distinct pathways across genomes. *Proc. Natl. Acad. Sci. USA* 97:13172–77
64. Lange H, Kaut A, Kispal G, Lill R. 2000. A mitochondrial ferredoxin is essential for biogenesis of cellular iron-sulfur proteins. *Proc. Natl. Acad. Sci. USA* 97:1050–55
65. Laule O, Furholz A, Chang HS, Zhu T, Wang X, et al. 2003. Crosstalk between cytosolic and plastidial pathways of isoprenoid biosynthesis in *Arabidopsis thaliana*. *Proc. Natl. Acad. Sci. USA* 100:6866–71
66. Leander BS. 2004. Did trypanosomatid parasites have photosynthetic ancestors? *Trends Microbiol.* 12:251–58
67. Lichtenthaler HK. 1999. The 1-deoxy-D-xylulose-5-phosphate pathway of isoprenoid biosynthesis in plants. *Annu. Rev. Plant. Physiol. Plant Mol. Biol.* 50:47–65

68. Lichtenthaler HK, Schwender J, Disch A, Rohmer M. 1997. Biosynthesis of isoprenoids in higher plant chloroplasts proceeds via a mevalonate-independent pathway. *FEBS Lett.* 400:271–74
69. Lill R, Muhlenhoff U. 2005. Iron-sulfur-protein biogenesis in eukaryotes. *Trends Biochem. Sci.* 30:133–41
70. Lill R, Muhlenhoff U. 2006. Iron-sulfur protein biogenesis in eukaryotes: components and mechanisms. *Annu. Rev. Cell Dev. Biol.* 22:457–86
71. Margulis L. 1971. Symbiosis and evolution. *Sci. Am.* 225:48–57
72. Margulis L, Corliss JO, Melkonian M, Chapman DJ, eds. 1990. *Handbook of Protoctista.* Boston: Jones & Bartlett
73. Martin W, Rujan T, Richly E, Hansen A, Cornelsen S, et al. 2002. Evolutionary analysis of Arabidopsis, cyanobacterial, and chloroplast genomes reveals plastid phylogeny and thousands of cyanobacterial genes in the nucleus. *Proc. Natl. Acad. Sci. USA* 99:12246–51
74. Martin W, Russell MJ. 2003. On the origins of cells: a hypothesis for the evolutionary transitions from abiotic geochemistry to chemoautotrophic prokaryotes, and from prokaryotes to nucleated cells. *Philos. Trans. R. Soc. London Ser. B* 358:59–83
75. Martin W, Stoebe B, Goremykin V, Hansmann S, Hasegawa M, Kowallik K. 1998. Gene transfer to the nucleus and the evolution of chloroplasts. *Nature* 393:162–65
76. May T, Soll J. 2000. 14–3–3 proteins form a guidance complex with chloroplast precursor proteins in plants. *Plant Cell* 12:53–64
77. McFadden GI, Gilson PR, Hill DRA. 1994. Goniomonas—rRNA sequences indicate that this phagotrophic flagellate is a close relative of the host component of cryptomonads. *Eur. J. Phycol.* 29:29–32
78. McFadden GI, Gilson PR, Simms I. 1997. Preliminary characterization of carbohydrate stores from chlorarachniophytes (Division Chlorarachniophyta). *Phycol. Res.* 45:145–51
79. McFadden GI, van Dooren GG. 2004. Evolution: red algal genome affirms a common origin of all plastids. *Curr. Biol.* 14:R514–16
80. Melkonian M. 1990. Phylum chlorophyta. See Ref. 72, pp. 597–99
81. Mereschkowsky C. 1905. Über Natur und Ursprung der Chromatophoren im Pflanzenreiche. *Biol. Centralbl.* 25:593–604
82. Moreira D, Le Guyader H, Philippe H. 2000. The origin of red algae and the evolution of chloroplasts. *Nature* 405:69–72
83. Mujer CV, Andrews DL, Manhart JR, Pierce SK, Rumpho ME. 1996. Chloroplast genes are expressed during intracellular symbiotic association of *Vaucheria litorea* plastids with the sea slug *Elysia chlorotica*. *Proc. Natl. Acad. Sci. USA* 93:12333–38
84. Nassoury N, Cappadocia M, Morse D. 2003. Plastid ultrastructure defines the protein import pathway in dinoflagellates. *J. Cell Sci.* 116:2867–74
85. Okamoto N, Inouye I. 2006. *Hatena arenicola* gen. et sp. nov., a katablepharid undergoing probable plastid acquisition. *Protist* 157:401–19
86. Patron NJ, Inagaki Y, Keeling PJ. 2007. Multiple gene phylogenies support the monophyly of cryptomonad and haptophyte host lineages. *Curr. Biol.* 17:887–91
87. Patron NJ, Keeling PJ. 2005. Common evolutionary origin of starch biosynthesis enzymes in green and red algae. *J. Phycol.* 41:1131–41
88. Patron NJ, Rogers MB, Keeling PJ. 2004. Gene replacement of fructose-1,6-bisphosphate aldolase supports the hypothesis of a single photosynthetic ancestor of chromalveolates. *Eukaryot. Cell* 3:1169–75
89. Patron NJ, Waller RF. 2007. Transit peptide diversity and divergence: a global analysis of plastid targeting signals. *BioEssays* 29:1048–58

90. Patron NJ, Waller RF, Archibald JM, Keeling PJ. 2005. Complex protein targeting to dinoflagellate plastids. *J. Mol. Biol.* 348:1015–24
91. Patron NJ, Waller RF, Keeling PJ. 2006. A tertiary plastid uses genes from two endosymbionts. *J. Mol. Biol.* 357:1373–82
92. Porra RJ, Klein O, Wright PE. 1983. The proof by ^{13}C-NMR spectroscopy of the predominance of the C5 pathway over the Shemin pathway in chlorophyll biosynthesis in higher plants and of the formation of the methyl ester group of chlorophyll from glycine. *Eur. J. Biochem.* 130:509–16
93. Prechtl J, Kneip C, Lockhart P, Wenderoth K, Maier UG. 2004. Intracellular spheroid bodies of *Rhopalodia gibba* have nitrogen-fixing apparatus of cyanobacterial origin. *Mol. Biol. Evol.* 21:1477–81
94. Radhamony RN, Theg SM. 2006. Evidence for an ER to Golgi to chloroplast protein transport pathway. *Trends Cell Biol.* 16:385–87
95. Ralph SA, Foth BJ, Hall N, McFadden GI. 2004. Evolutionary pressures on apicoplast transit peptides. *Mol. Biol. Evol.* 21:2183–94
96. Ralph SA, van Dooren GG, Waller RF, Crawford MJ, Fraunholz M, et al. 2004. Metabolic maps and functions of the *Plasmodium falciparum* apicoplast. *Nat. Rev. Microbiol.* 2:203–16
97. Reinbothe S, Mache R, Reinbothe C. 2000. A second, substrate-dependent site of protein import into chloroplasts. *Proc. Natl. Acad. Sci. USA* 97:9795–800
98. Reinbothe S, Quigley F, Springer A, Schemenewitz A, Reinbothe C. 2004. The outer plastid envelope protein Oep16: role as precursor translocase in import of protochlorophyllide oxidoreductase A. *Proc. Natl. Acad. Sci. USA* 101:2203–8
99. Reith M, Munholland J. 1995. Complete nucleotide sequence of the *Porphyra purpurea* chloroplast genome. *Plant Mol. Biol. Rep.* 13:333–35
100. Reyes-Prieto A, Hackett JD, Soares MB, Bonaldo MF, Bhattacharya D. 2006. Cyanobacterial contribution to algal nuclear genomes is primarily limited to plastid functions. *Curr. Biol.* 16:2320–25
101. Rice DW, Palmer JD. 2006. An exceptional horizontal gene transfer in plastids: gene replacement by a distant bacterial paralog and evidence that haptophyte and cryptophyte plastids are sisters. *BMC Biol.* 4:31
102. Richter S, Lamppa GK. 1998. A chloroplast processing enzyme functions as the general stromal processing peptidase. *Proc. Natl. Acad. Sci. USA* 95:7463–68
103. Rodriguez-Ezpeleta N, Brinkmann H, Burey SC, Roure B, Burger G, et al. 2005. Monophyly of primary photosynthetic eukaryotes: green plants, red algae, and glaucophytes. *Curr. Biol.* 15:1325–30
104. Rogers MB, Gilson PR, Su V, McFadden GI, Keeling PJ. 2007. The complete chloroplast genome of the chlorarachniophyte *Bigelowiella natans*: evidence for independent origins of chlorarachniophyte and euglenid secondary endosymbionts. *Mol. Biol. Evol.* 24:54–62
105. Rohmer M. 1999. The discovery of a mevalonate-independent pathway for isoprenoid biosynthesis in bacteria, algae and higher plants. *Nat. Prod. Rep.* 16:565–74
106. Sachs J. 1882. *Vorlesungen über Pflanzen-Physiologie*. Leipzig: W. Engelmann
107. Saldarriaga JF, Taylor FJ, Keeling PJ, Cavalier-Smith T. 2001. Dinoflagellate nuclear SSU rRNA phylogeny suggests multiple plastid losses and replacements. *J. Mol. Evol.* 53:204–13
108. Sanchez Puerta MV, Lippmeier JC, Apt KE, Delwiche CF. 2007. Plastid genes in a non-photosynthetic dinoflagellate. *Protist* 158:105–17
109. Schimper AFW. 1883. Über die Entwicklung der Chlorophyllkörner und Farbkörper. *Bot. Z.* 41:105–62

110. Schleiff E, Eichacker LA, Eckart K, Becker T, Mirus O, et al. 2003. Prediction of the plant β-barrel proteome: a case study of the chloroplast outer envelope. *Protein Sci.* 12:748–59
111. Schleiff E, Jelic M, Soll J. 2003. A GTP-driven motor moves proteins across the outer envelope of chloroplasts. *Proc. Natl. Acad. Sci. USA* 100:4604–9
112. Schleiff E, Soll J, Kuchler M, Kuhlbrandt W, Harrer R. 2003. Characterization of the translocon of the outer envelope of chloroplasts. *J. Cell Biol.* 160:541–51
113. Sepenswol S. 1973. Leucoplast of the cryptomonad *Chilomonas paramecium*. *Exp. Cell Res.* 76:395–409
114. Shemin D, Russell CS. 1953. δ-Aminolevulinic acid, its role in the biosynthesis of porphyrins and purines. *J. Am. Chem. Soc.* 75:4873–74
115. Soll J, Schleiff E. 2004. Protein import into chloroplasts. *Nat. Rev. Mol. Cell Biol.* 5:198–208
116. Sommer MS, Gould SB, Lehmann P, Gruber A, Przyborski JM, Maier UG. 2007. Der1-mediated preprotein import into the periplastid compartment of chromalveolates? *Mol. Biol. Evol.* 24:918–28
117. Steiner JM, Yusa F, Pompe JA, Loffelhardt W. 2005. Homologous protein import machineries in chloroplasts and cyanelles. *Plant J.* 44:646–52
118. Sulli C, Fang Z, Muchhal U, Schwartzbach SD. 1999. Topology of *Euglena* chloroplast protein precursors within endoplasmic reticulum to Golgi to chloroplast transport vesicles. *J. Biol. Chem.* 274:457–63
119. Takahashi Y, Tokumoto U. 2002. A third bacterial system for the assembly of iron-sulfur clusters with homologs in archaea and plastids. *J. Biol. Chem.* 277:28380–83
120. Teich R, Zauner S, Baurain D, Brinkmann H, Petersen J. 2007. Origin and distribution of Calvin cycle fructose and sedoheptulose bisphosphatases in plantae and complex algae: A single secondary origin of complex red plastids and subsequent propagation via tertiary endosymbioses. *Protist* 158:263–76
121. Toso MA, Omoto CK. 2007. *Gregarina niphandrodes* may lack both a plastid genome and organelle. *J. Eukaryot. Microbiol.* 54:66–72
122. van den Wijngaard PW, Vredenberg WJ. 1999. The envelope anion channel involved in chloroplast protein import is associated with Tic110. *J. Biol. Chem.* 274:25201–4
123. van der Giezen M. 2005. Endosymbiosis: past and present. *Heredity* 95:335–36
124. Vavilin DV, Vermaas WF. 2002. Regulation of the tetrapyrrole biosynthetic pathway leading to heme and chlorophyll in plants and cyanobacteria. *Physiol. Plant* 115:9–24
125. Vierling E. 1991. The roles of heat shock proteins in plants. *Annu. Rev. Plant. Physiol. Plant Mol. Biol.* 42:579–620
126. Villarejo A, Buren S, Larsson S, Dejardin A, Monne M, et al. 2005. Evidence for a protein transported through the secretory pathway en route to the higher plant chloroplast. *Nat. Cell Biol.* 7:1224–31
127. Viola R, Nyvall P, Pedersen M. 2001. The unique features of starch metabolism in red algae. *Proc. Biol. Sci.* 268:1417–22
128. Vogel K, Barber AA. 1968. Degradation of paramylon by *Euglena gracilis*. *J. Protozool.* 15:657–62
129. Waller RF, Cowman AF, Reed MB, McFadden GI. 2000. Protein trafficking to the plastid in *Plasmodium falciparum* is via the secretory pathway. *EMBO J.* 19:1794–802
130. Walne PL, Kivic PA. 1990. Euglenida. See Ref. 72, pp. 270–87
131. Weeden NF. 1981. Genetic and biochemical implications of the endosymbiotic origin of the chloroplast. *J. Mol. Evol.* 17:133–39

132. Wolfe KH, Morden CW, Palmer J. 1992. Function and evolution of a minimal plastid genome from a nonphotosynthetic parasitic plant. *Proc. Natl. Acad. Sci. USA* 89:10648–52
133. Yoon HS, Reyes-Prieto A, Melkonian M, Bhattacharya D. 2006. Minimal plastid genome evolution in the *Paulinella* endosymbiont. *Curr. Biol.* 16:R670–72
134. Zhu G, Marchewka MJ, Keithly JS. 2000. *Cryptosporidium parvum* appears to lack a plastid genome. *Microbiology* 146(Pt. 2):315–21

Coordinating Nodule Morphogenesis with Rhizobial Infection in Legumes

Giles E.D. Oldroyd and J. Allan Downie

Departments of Disease and Stress Biology and Molecular Microbiology, John Innes Center, Norwich NR4 7UH, UK; email: giles.oldroyd@bbsrc.ac.uk; allan.downie@bbsrc.ac.uk

Annu. Rev. Plant Biol. 2008. 59:519–46

The *Annual Review of Plant Biology* is online at plant.annualreviews.org

This article's doi: 10.1146/annurev.arplant.59.032607.092839

1543-5008/08/0602-0519$20.00

Key Words

nodulation, nitrogen fixation, bacterial infection, legumes

Abstract

The formation of nitrogen-fixing nodules on legumes requires an integration of infection by rhizobia at the root epidermis and the initiation of cell division in the cortex, several cell layers away from the sites of infection. Several recent developments have added to our understanding of the signaling events in the epidermis associated with the perception of rhizobial nodulation factors and the role of plant hormones in the activation of cell division leading to nodule morphogenesis. This review focuses on the tissue-specific nature of the developmental processes associated with nodulation and the mechanisms by which these processes are coordinated during the formation of a nodule.

Contents

INTRODUCTION

The acquisition of mineral nutrients is one of the major challenges for plant survival. In particular, the availability of the macronutrients nitrogen and phosphorus often limits plant growth. Several genera of plants have overcome these nutrient limitations via symbiotic interactions with microorganisms. The most widespread symbiosis is that between plants and mycorrhizal fungi, which aid the plant in the capture of nutrients and are particularly important for the uptake of phosphate. A more specialized symbiosis is that between certain genera of plants and nitrogen-fixing bacteria; an example is the legume/rhizobial symbiosis. During this interaction the bacteria invade the plant root and are contained in intracellular compartments within a specialized organ, the nodule, where they convert molecular dinitrogen into ammonia, a form of nitrogen that is usable by the plant.

Nodulation in legumes is activated in response to rhizobial signaling molecules called nodulation (Nod) factors. Although produced by the bacteria, Nod factors behave in many regards like plant hormones: They are diffusible signals that activate diverse developmental processes in the plant. Nod factors consist of a chitin backbone with an *N*-linked fatty acid moiety attached to the nonreducing terminal sugar (**Figure 1**). Several additional modifications to this basic structure (**Figure 1**) can occur, and these modifications coupled with the length and degree of saturation of the fatty acid group differ between species of rhizobia. These species-specific modifications have important

Figure 1

Representative nodulation (Nod) factors produced by *Sinorhizobium meliloti*, *Rhizobium leguminosarum* bv. *viciae*, *Azorhizobium caulinodans* and *Mesorhizobium loti* are shown with a backbone of β 1–4-linked *N*-acetylglucosamine residues (*black*) with N-linked acyl groups (*green*) and other host-specific decorations (*red*). Each species produces multiple Nod factors; e.g., the number of glucosamine residues can be four or five, the acyl chains (1) of the Nod factors from *S. meliloti* and *R. leguminosarum* bv. *viciae* can be C18:1 instead of C16:2 and C18:4 as shown, and not all Nod factors necessarily carry all the host-specific decorations. Mutants of *S. meliloti* and *R. leguminosarum* bv. *viciae* producing Nod factors lacking the acetyl group (2) on the acylated glucosamine and carrying a C18:1 acyl group (owing to mutations affecting *nodL* and *nodFE*, respectively) are defective for infection but can induce signaling responses in legumes. The acetyl group (3) on the *R. leguminosarum* bv. *viciae* Nod factor is attached by NodX and is required for infection of peas carrying the *SYMBIOSIS2* (*SYM2*) allele from the cv. Afghanistan pea. Mutants of *A. caulinodans* lacking the fucosyl (4), arabinosyl (5), and/or carbamoyl groups are defective for root hair infection but not bacterial entry via cracks in the epidermis.

S. meliloti

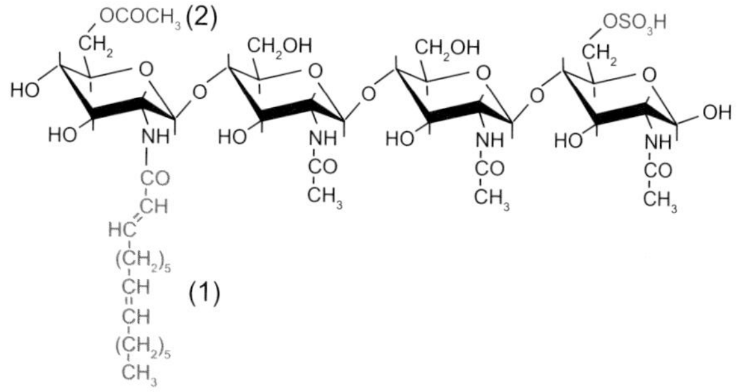

R. leguminosarum bv. *viciae*

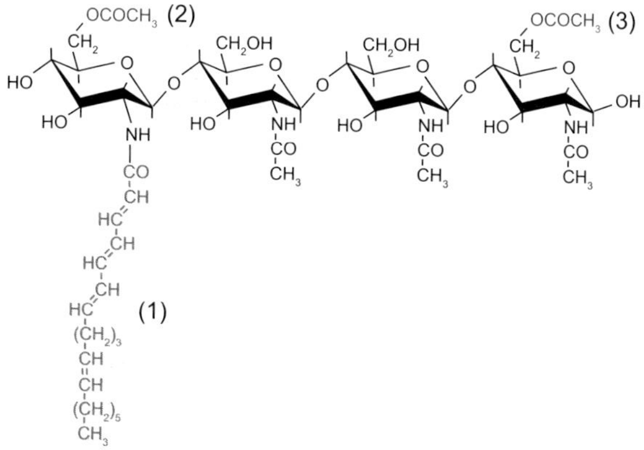

A. caulinodans

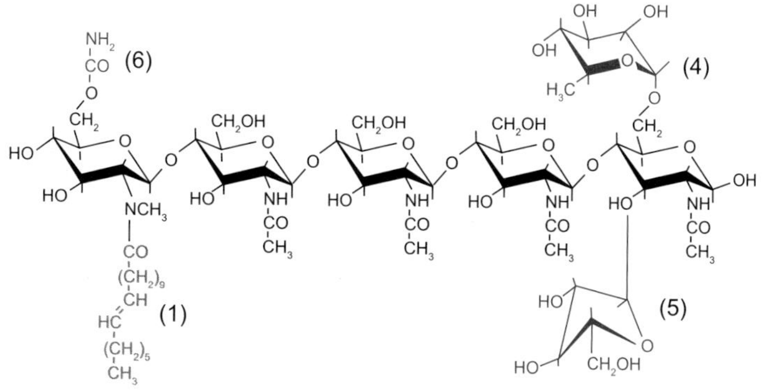

M. loti

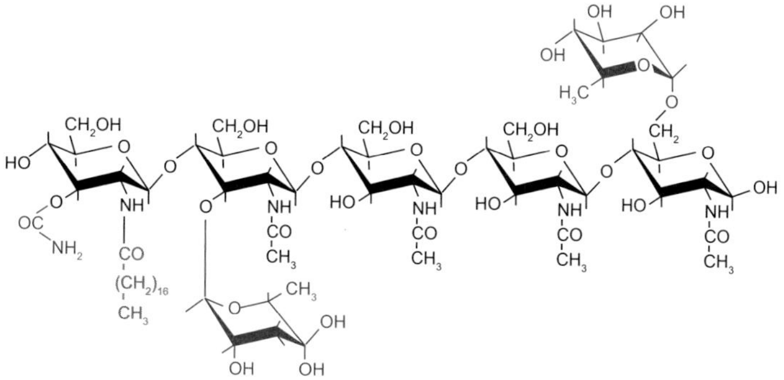

functions in defining the specificity of the interaction between the rhizobia and their plant hosts (28, 35).

Coordinated root development is a key component in the formation of a bacterially infected nodule. Bacterial infection generally occurs through root hair cells that curl around rhizobia, entrapping attached bacteria. These bacteria grow and form infection foci from which infection threads are initiated. Infection threads are unique plant-made invasive invaginations that are capable of crossing cell boundaries, allowing bacterial invasion into cortical cells (**Figure 2**). Concomitant with these epidermal responses, cortical cells below the sites of infection activate mitosis to form a nodule primordium (**Figure 2**). The infection threads grow toward the developing primordia and rhizobia are released into the inner cells in the nodule via an endocytotic-type mechanism that encapsulates the bacteria within a plant membrane. These membranes and enclosed bacteria differentiate into organelle-like structures called symbiosomes within which the differentiated bacteria (bacteroids) are responsible for nitrogen fixation.

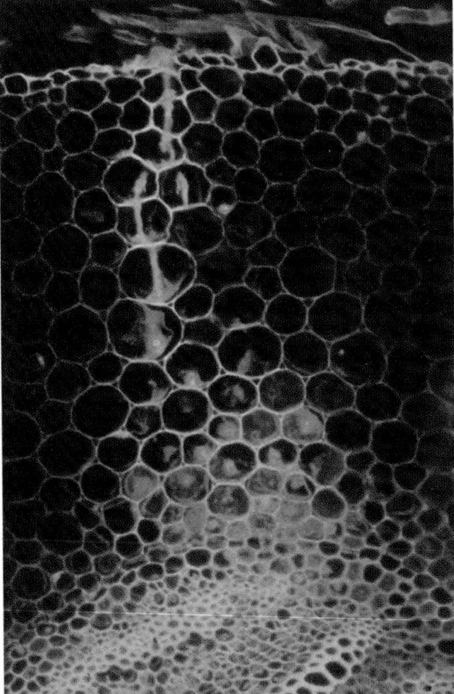

Figure 2

Infection of pea by *Rhizobium leguminosarum* bv. *viviae*. An infection thread is visible growing through the cortex. Cortical cells at the base of the infection thread show preinfection thread structures formed by an alignment of the cytosol, predicting the future path of the infection thread. Inner cortical cells below the infection site have initiated cell division to form the nodule meristem. Image from Reference 80.

Many of the advances made in the area of plant perception of Nod factor and the Nod factor signaling pathway have been reviewed by us and others (51, 67, 106, 107, 119) and so here we focus on the most recent insights into Nod factor signaling. An area that has been covered less is the mechanisms by which the epidermal and cortical responses are coordinated to allow bacterial infection and nodule initiation. To understand such coordinated plant development, it is critical to define the tissue-specific nature of Nod factor perception and to characterize the signaling components in the cortex and in the epidermis. Several advances have recently occurred in this area and the tools are now in place to allow much more detailed studies on the mechanisms that allow coordinated root development during nodulation. This review focuses on the tissue-specific nature of the responses that occur during nodulation and aims to focus the thinking in the area of coordinated root development during nodulation.

EPIDERMAL RESPONSES: PROMOTING BACTERIAL INFECTION

The root epidermis represents the first barrier that must be breached by the bacteria and in most legume/rhizobial interactions the root hair cells play a central role in facilitating bacterial infection. Because the epidermis is the first point of contact with rhizobia it must influence where, when, and how many nodules will be formed. In some legume species, particularly the more basal legumes, this

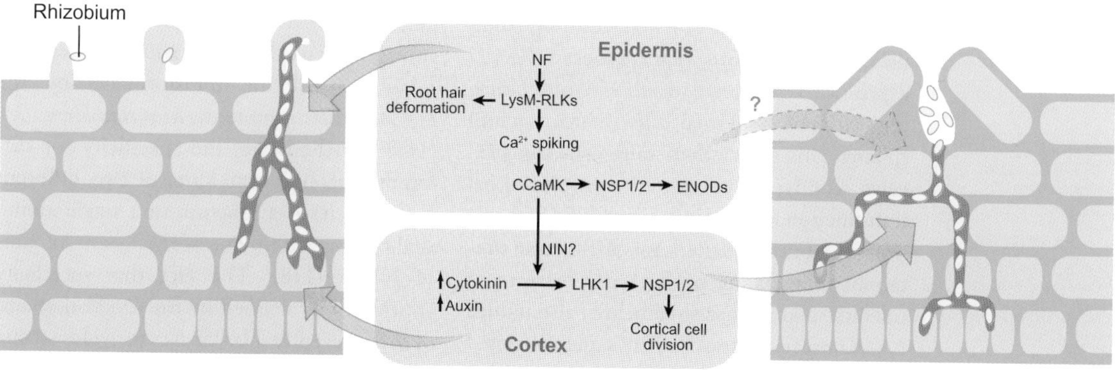

Figure 3

Coordinated root development during nodulation. Bacterial infection can occur either through root hair curls or cracks in the epidermis. Root hair invasion is initiated by bacterial adhesion to root hairs and root hair deformation that entraps the colony of bacteria. Infection threads initiate from this infection focus and allow bacterial invasion of the cortex. Concomitant with these epidermal responses, cortical cells activate cell division to form the nodule meristem. During root hair entry, epidermal responses are associated with nodulation (Nod) factor perception that leads to gene expression via a calcium spiking–dependent signaling pathway and root hair deformation via a signaling pathway independent of calcium spiking. Cortical responses are associated with increases in cytokinin and auxin; cytokinin is perceived by *Lotus* histidine kinase (LHK1). The GRAS [gibberellin insensitive (GAI), repressor of ga1-3 (RGA), SCARECROW (SCR)] proteins nodulation signaling pathway 1 (NSP1) and NSP2 are required in the epidermis downstream of calcium/calmodulin-dependent protein kinase (CCaMK) and in the cortex downstream of LHK1. CCaMK activation leads to the induction of cortical responses. During crack invasion the epidermis is breached and the bacteria gain direct access to cortical cells. Nod factor signaling is important in some species that undergo crack entry, but Nod factor–independent crack invasion also exists and may be associated with rhizobial modification of cytokinins. Abbreviations: ENODs, early nodulation genes; NIN, nodule inception, LysM-RLK, lysin motif receptor-like kinase.

epidermal barrier to bacterial infection can be overcome by rhizobial infection at points of epidermal damage, generally caused by the emergence of lateral roots. In these cases the bacteria infect these cracks and gain access to cortical cells from infection threads originating from the infected cracks (**Figure 3**). Nod factor signaling is clearly important for both modes of bacterial infection, but there are several important differences in Nod factor signaling and the mechanisms of infection between epidermal infection by bacteria and cortical infection by bacteria (**Figure 3**).

Nod Factor Perception

Fluorescent Nod factors added to plant roots accumulate in the cell walls of the root epidermis (55), apparently limiting the free flow of Nod factor through the root. Therefore, it seems unlikely that Nod factors can transverse the epidermal cell layer to directly affect cortical cells. Hence, perception of Nod factors by root-attached rhizobia is probably limited to epidermal cells. It is not surprising then that the first responses to rhizobial bacteria occur in the epidermis, with induction of early nodulation genes (*ENODs*) (60, 68, 69, 128).

Both bacterial infection and *ENOD* induction are usually restricted to a zone of the epidermis where root hairs are actively growing (68). *ENOD* induction in the epidermis is a result of Nod factor perception and signal transduction (14, 60, 109). Oscillations in cytosolic calcium, termed calcium spiking, are a component of this Nod factor signal transduction pathway (38, 155, 157) and have also been used as a measure of Nod factor signaling (97). Although Nod factor–induced *ENOD* expression is restricted to a zone of the epidermis, all root epidermal cells induce calcium spiking; this shows that some cells can perceive Nod factor and partially activate signal transduction without inducing *ENOD* expression (97). Furthermore, gain-of-function mutations in signaling proteins downstream of calcium spiking (discussed below) also induce *ENOD* expression within the same restricted zone of epidermal cells (54). This suggests that the restriction of *ENOD* induction is not due to a limitation of Nod factor–responsive cells.

Initial Nod factor perception occurs in the epidermis, but Nod factor signaling continues to be important as the bacteria invade the root cortex (12, 30, 83), and may also be important for bacterial release into cells of the nodule (61). However, the stringency of Nod factor perception is differentially important at different stages of the plant-bacterial interaction: Nod factor induction of root hair deformation, calcium spiking, and *ENOD* induction has a lower stringency for the Nod factor structure than is required for bacterial infection (5, 106, 121, 156) (**Figure 1**). This suggests differences exist in the receptors that are involved in Nod factor perception at early and later stages of the interaction, with proposed signaling and entry Nod factor receptors functioning at the different stages of the interaction.

Receptor-like kinases with *N*-acetylglucosamine–binding lysin motifs (LysM) in the extracellular domain have emerged as excellent candidates for the Nod factor receptors (6, 82, 87, 117). These proteins were initially identified by the analysis of mutants in which plant perception of Nod factors was abolished (2, 117). In *Lotus japonicus* two LysM domain receptor-like kinases, Nod-factor receptor 1 (NFR1) and NFR5, are both important for the early recognition of Nod factor, and therefore may be the signaling receptors (87, 117). The Nod factor specificity of legume/rhizobial symbiosis is determined by these LysM receptor-like kinases (118). Transferring *L. japonicus NFR1* and *NFR5* to *Medicago truncatula* enables nodulation of the transformants by the *L. japonicus* symbiont *Mesorhizobium loti* (118). Furthermore, the specificity for different rhizobial symbionts of two different *Lotus* species is a function of a single amino acid residue within one of the LysM domains of NFR5 (118). The fact that specificity appears to be defined by the LysM domains of these receptor-like kinases provides strong evidence that these are indeed the Nod factor receptors that bind Nod factor. However, formal proof of Nod factor binding has yet to be shown and more work is necessary to understand Nod factor recognition by these receptor-like kinases.

Alternative candidates for Nod factor perception were identified by defining Nod factor binding proteins. These studies revealed an extracellular apyrase, lectin nucleotide phosphohydrolase (LNP), which preferentially binds Nod factors compared with chitin oligomers (43). Significantly, Nod factor binding induced the apyrase activity (ATP hydrolysis to AMP). LNP is localized in root hair cells within the zone of growing root hairs (71), an LNP gene in soybean is induced upon rhizobial inoculation (25), and overexpression of an LNP in soybean enhances nodulation (93). These observations strongly support a role for LNPs during legume nodulation but do not reveal the function of LNP following Nod factor binding. LNPs could function in a complex with other signaling proteins, or may function in a parallel pathway, for instance regulating ATP levels during the bacterial interaction.

Nod Factor Signal Transduction

Nod factor–induced calcium spiking (38), which functions in Nod factor signal transduction, is restricted to the nuclear region (131), with calcium oscillations in the nucleoplasm and nuclear-associated cytoplasm

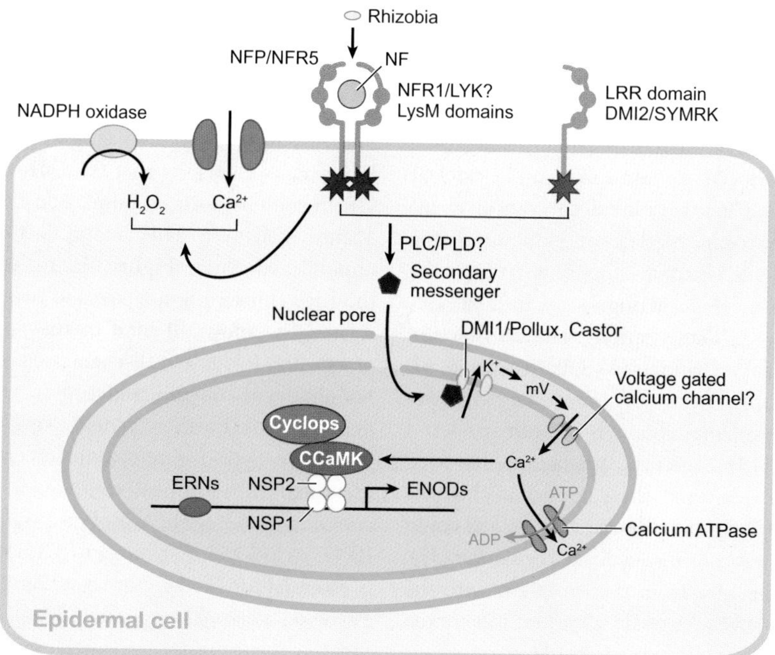

Figure 4

Nod factor signaling in the epidermis. Nodulation (Nod) factor perception involves receptor-like kinases containing lysin motifs (LysM) and a leucine-rich repeat (LRR). This perception is linked to calcium spiking in the nucleus and to changes in root hair growth that presumably involve the modification of the H_2O_2-induced calcium gradient at the tip of root hair cells. A secondary messenger is presumed to link Nod factor perception at the plasma membrane with calcium changes in the nucleus. A potassium channel on the nuclear membrane may be the target of the secondary messenger and the resultant changes in potassium may drive membrane hyperpolarization that could activate a voltage-gated calcium channel. Perception of the calcium-spiking signal involves calcium/calmodulin-dependent protein kinase (CCaMK), and the transcriptional regulators nodulation signaling pathway 1 (NSP1), NSP2, and Ets2 repressor factor (ERF) required for nodulation (ERN). Abbreviations: NFP/NFR5, Nod factor perception/Nod factor receptor; NFR1/LYK, Nod factor receptor/LysM domain-containing receptor-like kinases, DM12/SYMRK, doesn't make infections/symbiosis receptor-kinase; PLC/PLD, phospholipase C/D; NSP1 and 2, nodulation signaling pathway 1 and 2; ENOD, early nodulation genes.

(J. Sun, H. Miwa, J. A. Downie, and G. Oldroyd, unpublished data). Therefore, Nod factor perception by LysM receptor-like kinases in the plasma membrane must be linked to calcium changes in and around the nucleus. Genetic studies have revealed several components, in addition to the LysM receptor-like kinases, necessary for Nod factor induction of calcium spiking (**Figure 4**). These include a receptor-like kinase containing extracellular leucine-rich repeat domains (39, 139), two nucleoporins (72, 122), and up to two putative cation channels in the nuclear membrane (4, 37, 66, 120). Biochemical and pharmacological approaches have indicated the importance of phospholipase C (PLC), phospholipase D (PLD), and an ATP-driven calcium pump for Nod factor signaling and calcium spiking (18, 29, 40, 142).

Considering the requirement for multiple receptor-like kinases, Nod factor perception must lead to a phosphorylation cascade at the plasma membrane (161), probably causing the production of a secondary messenger such as a phospholipid (implicating PLC and PLD) (**Figure 4**). Secondary messengers can link ligand perception at the plasma membrane with calcium changes in the nucleus (7). The nuclear envelope and the nuclear-associated endoplasmic reticulum are likely the internal stores for calcium released during Nod factor–induced calcium spiking. The nuclear membrane localization of the cation channels required for Nod factor–induced calcium spiking (120) further supports a role for the nuclear envelope acting as an internal calcium store. These cation channels function as potassium channels (M. Charpentier & M. Parniske, personal communication) that can regulate calcium channels in both yeast and plants (113). Structural predictions have led to a model in which these potassium channels may be partly gated by calcium, which could provide a means for feedback regulation (37). Potassium flow from the cytoplasm into the nuclear envelope could alter the membrane polarity, opening voltage-gated calcium channels (**Figure 4**). One attraction of this model is that voltage gating on the inner nuclear membrane could coordinate the simultaneous opening of many calcium channels and this is essential for the rapid calcium spike. If this hypothesis is correct, then the potassium channels themselves could be direct targets for activation by a secondary messenger. What then is the function of the nuclear pore proteins? One possibility is that they could allow a secondary messenger into the nucleoplasm. An alternative hypothesis is that they are necessary for the localization of the potassium channels in the inner nuclear membrane; such a role for the nuclear pore in targeting inner nuclear membrane proteins has already been proposed in yeast and mammals (86).

Perception and transduction of the calcium-spiking signal is the function of a calcium- and calmodulin-dependent protein kinase (CCaMK) (78, 96) and at least three transcriptional regulators, two in the GRAS family [gibberellin insensitive (GAI), repressor of ga1-3 (RGA), SCARECROW (SCR)] (61, 70, 99, 134) and an ERF (Ets2 repressor factor) transcription factor (95). CCaMK can bind calcium directly through EF-hand domains and can also bind calcium in a complex with calmodulin (112, 144). This dual regulation of CCaMK by calcium may be essential for its ability to perceive the oscillatory calcium-spiking signal (106). Evidence is emerging that CCaMK and the GRAS proteins form a complex on DNA (A. Munoz, J. Kim, S. Hirsch, and G. Oldroyd, unpublished data) (**Figure 4**). In addition, the ERF transcription factor and two closely related homologs all bind to the promoter of *ENOD11* (3), a well-characterized early nodulin gene initially induced in the epidermis (68). Further genetic studies and yeast two-hybrid interaction screens have identified an additional component of this complex, interacting protein of DMI3 (IPD3)/Cyclops, that binds to CCaMK and is essential for Nod factor signaling (94) (M. Parniske, personal communication). Defining the mechanisms by which the calcium signal is perceived and how this activates transcription is an important area for further study.

BACTERIAL INFECTION

Rhizobial Attachment to Roots

Attachment of rhizobial bacteria to the root epidermis, predominantly root hair cells, is the first direct step in the association of the bacteria with the plant host. The specialized ability of rhizobia to attach to legume roots and root hairs in preference to other bacteria has two major advantages: It enhances rhizobial numbers in the rhizosphere and enhances the probability of specific strains being infective (47, 124). This latter point is especially important because infections are clonal events leading to relatively high numbers of bacteria growing within nodules. Even though the bacteria that differentiate into nitrogen-fixing bacteroids are unable to dedifferentiate into the free-living state, the release into the rhizosphere of rhizobia that are contained within infection threads inside the nodule represents a very substantial level of clonal growth and therefore the selection pressure for optimizing infection is very high.

Plant lectins enhance rhizobial attachment by binding to specific surface polysaccharides (26, 132); a clear interaction has recently been identified between a pea lectin and a neutral glucomannan that is located at one pole of *Rhizobium leguminosarum* bv. *viciae* (76), the symbiont of pea. Nodulation can occur in the absence of the glucomannan (76), but in mixed infections bacterial mutants lacking the glucomannan are outcompeted by wild-type bacteria (A. Williams & J.A. Downie, unpublished data). Lectins are located on root hairs, particularly near the growing tip (33). The transfer of lectins between legume species can enhance nodulation capacity, permitting nodulation by rhizobia that do not produce Nod factors optimal for that legume species (32, 63, 153). This indicates that the enhanced accumulation of rhizobia at appropriate locations can allow infection even with suboptimal Nod factor signaling. This could occur as a consequence of increasing bacterial numbers on root hair cells and thus enhancing Nod factor concentrations; Nod factors lacking the appropriate substitutions to determine specificity can induce Nod factor signaling if their concentration is high enough (110, 157).

Infection Thread Formation and Bacterial Entry

Infection of legume roots by rhizobia occurs via infection threads, which can be broadly classified as transcellular or intercellular (10). The former require significant cytoskeletal changes in plant cells to form transcellular tunnels harboring rhizobia, whereas the latter can be considered as organized lines of infecting rhizobia between cells, with an associated lignification of adjacent cell walls (9, 10). As a general point, infection via intercellular infection threads has less specificity for Nod factor structure than infection via intracellular infection threads. This distinction is particularly clear in *Sesbania rostrata*: The intracellular mode of infection is blocked with a bacterial mutant that makes Nod factors lacking the carbamoyl, arabinosyl, and fucosyl substitutions (**Figure 1**), whereas the intercellular mode of infection by such a mutant is retained, albeit at a lower efficiency than wild-type bacteria (58, 59). Significantly, many nodule primordia are initiated by the mutant bacteria, demonstrating that nodule morphogenesis can be induced with Nod factors of relatively low stringency (59).

The formation of intracellular infection threads is a key step that determines specificity in many legume interactions. This Nod factor–induced process is initiated with the inhibition of root hair growth and followed by initiation of a new growth axis (31, 150). Hence, Nod factor signaling must impact the components that normally regulate root hair growth (50) (**Figure 4**). This results in a root hair curling around the attached bacteria; on the basis of experiments with Nod factor spot inoculations (42), such curls are probably the result of directional sources of Nod factor. This root hair deformation requires the Nod factor signaling receptor (2, 117) but does not require the pathway of Nod factor signaling that involves calcium spiking, because root hair deformation occurs in legume mutants blocked for the induction of calcium spiking (42, 98). Furthermore, the Nod factor–induced cytoskeletal changes, including actin remodelling, associated with root hair deformation are initiated within 3–6 min of Nod factor application (1, 13, 41, 42), and this is generally prior to the induction of calcium spiking. Hence, Nod factor perception by root hair cells leads to at least two signaling events: one that involves calcium spiking and gives rise to gene expression changes and one that is associated with root hair deformation.

The subsequent steps of infection thread growth are highly specific and are initiated following the growth of the bacteria entrapped by the root hair curl. Bacterial proliferation in the root hair curl most likely results in the accumulation of Nod factors within the infection foci (58, 98), and this may be important to activate later events. What occurs next is essentially an inversion of root hair tip growth such that an intracellular tunnel is formed; in several respects the lumen of this tunnel is similar to an intercellular space (10). The bacteria divide at the growing infection thread tip, forming a column of bacteria. If more than one bacterial type is entrapped by the root hair curl, the process of infection thread growth tends to select out one bacterial type, resulting in a clonal infection (48, 49). The initiation of infection thread growth is a major stage for the discrimination of the appropriate bacterial species and involves a number of checkpoints: a high degree of Nod factor specificity, probably increased levels of Nod factors, and the presence of appropriate polysaccharides on the surface of the bacteria.

Rhizobial surface polysaccharides clearly play a critical role during infection and the best-understood interaction is the one between *Sinorhizobium meliloti* and *M. truncatula* (67). Most strains of *S. meliloti* produce two structurally distinct exopolysaccharides called succinoglycan and EPSII; mutants lacking both are unable to produce normal infections but mutants lacking only one are able to initiate infection (67). The active components of these polysaccharides are low-molecular-weight forms, because *S. meliloti* mutants unable to produce these forms are defective for infection (56, 77, 149). This finding points toward the possibility of polysaccharide fragments acting as signals, which fits with reports that addition of polysaccharide fragments can complement exopolysaccharide mutants (34, 77). Initiation of infection in *S. rostrata* by its symbiont *Azorhizobium caulinodans* also requires surface polysaccharides, but in this case purified lipopolysaccharides can restore infection in an *A. caulinodans* mutant with pleiotrophic alterations to diverse surface polysaccharides (92). One possible role for these surface polysaccharide signals could be to affect plant cell defense responses (24), although a positive signaling role is also possible.

Experiments with alfalfa and pea have shown that a high level of Nod factor structural specificity is required for the initiation of infection (**Figure 1**). Rhizobial mutants lacking various host-specific additions to Nod factors (**Figure 1**) could induce root hair deformation, *ENOD* induction, and calcium spiking, but infection was arrested in infection pockets within root hairs (5, 156). The arrested infections of these *S. meliloti* and *R. leguminosarum* mutants together with the lack of intracellular infection by the *S. rostrata* mutant defective for Nod factor modifications (59) have led to a model of two types of Nod factor receptors, an early signaling receptor with relatively low specificity for Nod factor structure and an entry receptor with relatively high specificity for Nod factor structure.

How do these models fit with the recently identified multiplicity of Nod factor receptor genes? Infection of a specific pea cultivar (cv. Afghanistan) carrying the *SYM2* locus was arrested if the *R. leguminosarum* bv. *viciae* strain lacked *nodX* (52), whose product is required for adding an acetyl group to the reducing sugar on Nod factor (46) (**Figure 1**). Recent work in search of the *SYM2* gene in pea led to the identification of a cluster of genes at a syntenic location in *M. trunculata* (82); these genes encode proteins closely related to the *NFR1* Nod factor receptor in *L. japonicus* (117). Silencing of two of these *M. truncatula* genes (LysM-type receptor-like kinase 3 and 4, *LYK3* and *LYK4*) resulted in blocked infection thread initiation by some strains of *S. meliloti* (82). Loss-of-function mutations in *LYK3* resulted in blocked infection initiation (133), indicating that *LYK3* encodes the entry Nod factor receptor. However, the view that there are defined signaling and entry receptors may be an oversimplification. LYK3 likely acts together with NFP (the *M. truncatula* ortholog of *NFR5* in *L. japonicus*), because in an *nfp* null mutant the LYK receptors are insufficient to allow any responses to Nod factor (2), so it is unlikely that LYK3 alone can function as a Nod factor receptor. Thus, in *M. truncatula* NFP is likely essential for initial Nod factor perception and subsequently an association between NFP and LYK3 can confer higher specificity of Nod factor perception, leading to initiation of infection. Such a model for an entry receptor has not emerged in *L. japonicus*. Indeed, the *LYK3* homolog, *NFR1*, has a clear role as a signaling Nod factor receptor (117). These differences between *L. japonicus* and *M. truncatula* could be explained by redundancy of function of *NFR1*-like genes in *M. truncatula* for early recognition and redundancy of function for *LYK3*-like genes in *L. japonicus* for entry recognition. Alternatively, a specific recognition may not be required for infection of *L. japonicus*.

Infection Thread Growth

The formation of infection threads may involve the action of phragmoplast-like structures, which are nuclear-associated structures that normally act as scaffolds for cell plate formation and subsequent cell wall deposition during cell division (10). The growth of the infection thread tube has been suggested to be analogous to what would occur if a single phragmoplast was formed and this was moved downward through the cell. Thus, a tube-like structure could be formed instead of the two cell walls that result from phragmoblast-organized cell plates (10). Hence, the genetic dissection of infection thread growth may reveal components associated with cell division.

Several legume mutants have been identified with defects in the initiation and growth of infection threads. It is not always easy to distinguish between mutants affected in cell signaling and those specifically affected in infection thread growth. For example, the *bit1* mutant of *M. truncatula* (*BIT1* encodes the ERF transcription factor, ERN1) shows a defect in infection thread initiation and growth (95). However, ERN1 functions in Nod factor signaling and plays a role in Nod factor induction of *ENOD*s in the epidermis (3, 95). Several other mutants show arrested infection thread growth. Some of these mutants, such as *lot*, *crinkle*, *sym40*, and *sym67* in *L. japonicius* (111, 125, 126, 145) and *rit1* in *M. truncatula* (138), are affected in the polar growth of cells, because in addition to their defect in infection, they have aberrant trichome and/or root hair growth. Several other mutants have been described as defective for infection thread growth, including *nip*, *lin*, and *rpg* in *M. truncatula* (75, 154) and *alb1*, *sym7*, *sym8*, *sym10*, *sym80*, *itd1*, *itd3*, and *itd4* in *L. japonicus* (74, 85, 125, 126, 160). Identification of the roles of these different genes will clearly give novel insights into the requirements for initiation of transcellular infection threads.

The apparent similarities between aspects of cell division and infection thread formation has clear implications with regard to the coordinated Nod factor induction of preinfection thread structures in epidermal cells and the induction of cortical cell divisions leading to the formation of a nodule meristem. Isolated, fully decorated Nod factors can promote the formation of preinfection thread structures and the differentiation of cortical cells into root hair cells (73, 151). In addition, isolated Nod factors can induce cortical cell divisions in *Vicia sativa*; this requires the appropriate host-specific modifications of the Nod factor structure (136). Hence, the Nod factor requirements for cortical cell responses correlate well with epidermal responses, including bacterial infection. This correlation could be due to structural specificity of Nod factors, but it is also possible that it could be related to the potency of the different Nod factor structures. For example, loss of some host-specific Nod factor modifications requires a 100-fold increase in the threshold concentration of Nod factor required to induce calcium spiking in *M. truncatula* (110). Nevertheless, a clear correlation still exists between Nod factor structural requirements for infection thread initiation and induction of cortical cell division in legumes such as *M. truncatula*, *Vicia sativa*, and pea (52, 136, 151, 156). However, once the bacteria gain entry to the cortical cells, the structural specificity for Nod factors is less stringent (52), possibly as a consequence of infection foci of bacteria producing high enough concentrations of Nod factors to overcome infection defects. However, this could also be a consequence of different stringencies of Nod-factor recognition, as proposed (59) to explain the infection phenotype of Nod factor host-specificity mutants of *A. caulinodans* that retain the ability to infect *S. rostrata* via epidermal cracks but not root hairs.

Recent analyses of legume mutants with defects in Nod factor signaling components provide insights into the subtle differences between induction of infection threads and induction of cortical cell divisions. *L. japonicus* mutants mutated in either of the nucleoporin genes *NUP85* or *NUP133* lack Nod factor–induced calcium spiking, but maintain some cortical cell divisions (72, 122). Similarly, the weak allele *symrk-14* induces nodule morphogenesis but not calcium spiking or infection thread initiation (100) (S. Kosuta, G. Morieri & K. Szczyglowski, personal communication). These data highlight that calcium spiking in the epidermis is more closely associated with the induction of infection than with cortical cell division. One way of interpreting these data is that the initiation of calcium spiking conditions cells for secondary signaling associated with the initiation of infection thread growth. Although there is certainly a good correlation between Nod factor induction of calcium spiking and initiation of infection, induction of calcium spiking is clearly not sufficient. Presumably some other events, such as recognition of exopolysaccharides (67) and/or possibly a calcium influx (98), are also necessary for the initiation of bacterial infection.

CORTICAL RESPONSES: THE MAKING OF A NODULE

The epidermis regulates bacterial infection, whereas the root cortex controls the formation of a nodule. The activation of the mitotic cell cycle in cortical cells is therefore an important step during the interaction with the bacteria, and regulators of the cell cycle play an important role during the formation of a nodule primordium (15). Several nodulins, such as *ENOD40*, play a role in cell division, and are not induced in the epidermis but are induced in the developing nodule primordia (16, 17, 22). In addition, transcription factors expressed in the nodule meristem appear to be important for meristem identity and are regulated by microRNAs (20). Hence, the developmental processes that occur in the cortex during nodulation are different from those that occur in the epidermis. The study of nodulation-defective mutants has revealed that epidermal responses and cortical responses can be separated: Bacterial infection can occur in the absence of nodule organogenesis (101), and conversely nodule organogenesis can occur in the absence of bacterial infection (54, 146–148). However, to produce a bacterially infected nodule the epidermal and cortical processes should be coordinated such that a nodule primordium occurs close to the site of bacterial infection.

Nod Factor–Independent Induction of Nodulation

The fact that nodulation can occasionally occur in the absence of rhizobia was used as the basis for a *L. japonicus* genetic screen that identified mutations in at least four loci that led to spontaneous nodulation in the absence of rhizobia (147). These studies, as well as the results of targeted mutagenesis in *M. truncatula*, revealed that mutations affecting CCaMK, which functions in Nod factor signaling, can lead to spontaneous nodulation (54, 146). These gain-of-function mutations of CCaMK (CCaMK*) autoactivate epidermal *ENOD11* induction in a pattern similar to that normally seen during bacterial infection: *ENOD11* expression occurs within epidermal cells restricted to the zone of growing root hairs and then becomes focused in clusters of cortical cells, associated with nodule primordia, that are surrounded by epidermal cells lacking *ENOD11* expression (54). Hence, activation of CCaMK is sufficient to initiate a train of developmental responses in both the epidermis and the cortex with similar timing and spatial patterning as induced by rhizobia (69).

This indicates that the coordination of these responses does not require bacterial infection, but is a train of events locked in place following the perception of Nod factor. Although CCaMK* can activate nodule organogenesis, it does not induce root hair deformation or preinfection thread structures in the absence of rhizobia (54). Hence, activation of CCaMK is associated with early epidermal responses and cortical responses to Nod factor, but additional components are necessary for the activation of processes associated with bacterial infection.

The activation of nodulation in the absence of Nod factor was further highlighted by recent work on two photosynthetic *Bradyrhizobium* species that initiate nodulation via crack entry on the legumes *Aeschynomene sensitiva* and *Aeschynomene indica*. Genome sequencing revealed that these bacteria lack genes essential for Nod factor production, suggesting that they induce nodulation in the absence of Nod factor (53). Importantly, this ability is not just a function of these two *Bradyrhizobium* spp, but also requires components in the plant. This was elegantly shown using a different *Bradyrhizobium* species that does produce Nod factor and can nodulate both *A. sensitiva* and other legume hosts. Mutation of the Nod factor synthesis genes in this strain blocked nodulation of other hosts, but did not block nodulation of *A. sensitiva* (53). This indicates that *A. sensitiva* does not require Nod factor for the activation of nodulation. This reveals that a well-accepted paradigm of the nodulation field, the essential requirement for Nod factor, is not an absolute. However, it is still fair to say that Nod factors are essential for nodulation in most legume species.

Hormones in Nodulation: The Positive Regulators

Considering the importance of hormones in plant organogenesis, it is not surprising that they play a role in nodule formation. Recent developments have surprisingly shown the absolute control that hormones have in nodule development (**Figure 5**). Auxin transport inhibitors have long been known to induce the formation of pseudonodules and the expression of *ENOD40*, a gene associated with nodule primordia (44, 64, 65, 90). Furthermore, transferring the ability to make transzeatin (a cytokinin) to rhizobia unable to make Nod factors, or even to *E. coli*, gives these bacteria the ability to activate nodulation in legumes (21). In addition, a cytokinin-responsive promoter is induced in the developing nodule meristem (84). These results indicate that modulating auxin and cytokinin levels is a key step in making a nodule.

The essential role of cytokinins in nodulation has also been highlighted by genetic studies in *L. japonicus* and *M. truncatula*. One of the *L. japonicus* spontaneous nodulation mutants carries a mutation in a *Lotus* histidine kinase (LHK1) that functions as a cytokinin receptor (148). Furthermore, loss-of-function mutations in *LHK1* (101) or RNAi-mediated downregulation of its ortholog in *M. truncatula* (57) leads to a dramatic reduction in nodule formation. *lhk1* mutants lose the ability to form nodule primordia, but are unaffected for the initiation of bacterial infection (101). However, the infection threads appear to lose directionality in their growth and instead of growing down through the cortex they spread laterally, developing highly elaborated infection structures. This not only reveals the importance of the nodule primordia in directing the growth of infection threads, but also indicates that the ability to form nodule primordia is not essential for bacterial infection. The exogenous application of cytokinins induces the expression of genes normally associated with nodule primordia (44, 90). The gain-of-function and loss-of-function mutations in *LHK1* highlight the central role that cytokinins play in nodule organogenesis in the cortex (**Figure 5**) and indicate that they do not play a role in bacterial infection in the epidermis.

In addition to auxins and cytokinins, gibberellins (GA) and brassinosteroids (BR) also

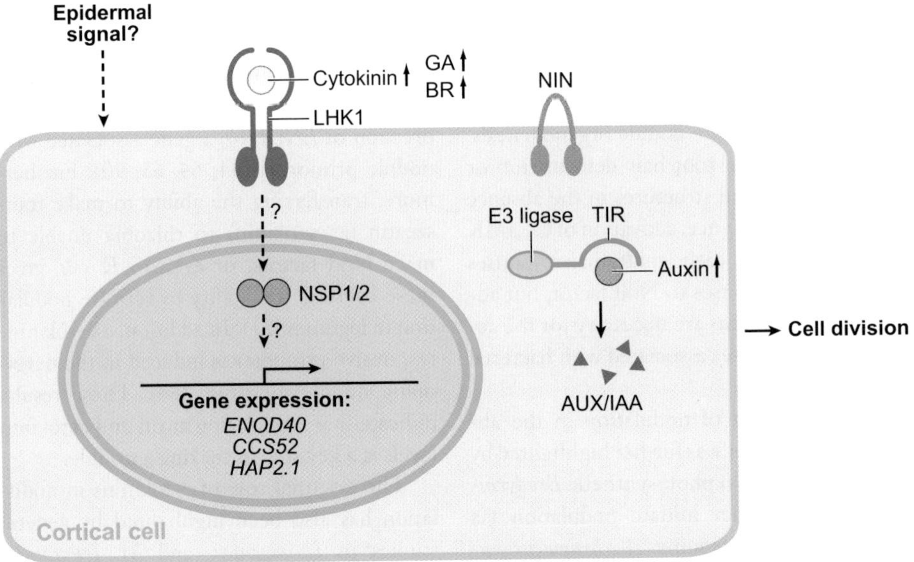

Figure 5

Nodule mersitem formation in the cortex. The induction of cortical cell division is associated with increases in auxin, cytokinin, gibberellin (GA), and brassinosteroid (BR) levels. An epidermal signal may be necessary for the induction of cortical responses and may be directly involved in the local modulation of hormone levels. The histidine kinase LHK1 is involved in cytokinin perception and its activation is sufficient to induce cortical cell division. The action of LHK1 requires the transcriptional regulators nodulation signaling pathway 1 (NSP1) and NSP2, but a direct role for these proteins downstream of LHK1 has not been validated. Nodule inception (NIN) is also necessary for cortical responses. We assume that auxin perception involving TRANSPORT INHIBITOR RESPONSE 1 (TIR1) is involved in the induction of the nodule meristem. Abbreviations: Aux/IAA, auxin/indole acetic acid; ENOD40, early nodulation gene 40; CCS52, cell cycle switch.

positively regulate nodule formation. Mutations in pea that reduce GA or BR production greatly reduce nodulation, and exogenous application of GA to the GA biosynthesis mutant rescues the mutant phenotype (45). Furthermore, GA-responsive genes are induced upon rhizobial infection and inhibitors of GA biosynthesis inhibit nodulation in *S. rostrata* (81). Taken together, this work reveals that cytokinins, auxin, GA, and BR all function in the formation of a nodule and the levels of these hormones are critical in nodule organogenesis.

How do these hormones lead to nodulation and what are the key steps during the interaction with rhizobia that set nodule organogenesis in motion? Although a role for hormones has been shown, the intricacies of hormone regulation during nodulation are not well defined. One suggestion for a mechanism for rhizobia to induce localized hormonal changes in the cortex has been the induction of localized flavonoid production (89). Flavonoids can inhibit auxin transport (91) and the increased levels of flavonoids induced by rhizobia should cause perturbations in auxin flow. The balance of auxin and cytokinin levels is central to the induction of plant organogenesis; rhizobia, perhaps through the induction of flavonoid production, can influence the balance of these hormones in the root cortex. The major source of cytokinin is the root tip, although localized cytokinin production may also occur, whereas auxin originates from the shoot tip and so cytokinin generally flows in the opposite direction to auxin (79, 123). Accumulation of auxin can affect the flow of cytokinin and so the modulation of auxin could affect the localized levels of cytokinin, which can initiate nodule formation in the cortex. Mutations in chalcone synthase, a key enzyme in flavonoid biosynthesis, cause a defect in nodule initiation (158); this could be explained as a consequence of the requirement for flavonoids to regulate auxin.

The capacity for some rhizobia to directly influence hormone levels was also inferred from the study on non-Nod factor–producing photosynthetic *Bradyrhizobium* spp. In an attempt to define how these Nod factor–defective strains induce nodulation, mutants unable to activate nodulation in *A. sensitiva* were sought. These experiments revealed that genes involved in purine biosynthesis are important for nodulation (53), and this is significant because that pathway generates precursors to cytokinins. These bacteria may induce nodulation by feeding the plant intermediates of cytokinin biosynthesis, although all the identified mutants are still able to activate nodulation, albeit at greatly reduced levels. However, this is still an attractive model supported by the plant genetics work (105) and may reveal multiple mechanisms of nodule initiation, with Nod factor activation of nodulation by the majority of rhizobia and cytokinin induction of nodulation by a subset of rhizobia (**Figure 3**). *Bradyrhizobium* spp. gain access to root tissues through cracks in the epidermis, and this direct colonization of cortical cells may be an important component in their ability to use cytokinins in place of Nod factor to activate nodulation (36).

COORDINATION OF PLANT DEVELOPMENT DURING NODULATION

Above we have highlighted the different responses that occur in the epidermis and the cortex during the formation of a nodule. These responses correlate with different signaling processes: Nod factor signal transduction in the epidermis and hormonal signaling in the cortex. Although these tissue-specific processes can be separated, they are clearly interlinked by rhizobia. The mechanisms that underpin such developmental coordination are not well defined, but there are several components that clearly play a role; the mechanisms that regulate the levels of nodulation may also be important.

Hormones in Nodulation: The Negative Regulators

The plant hormones abscissic acid (ABA), jasmonic acid (JA), ethylene, and salicylic acid all act as negative regulators to repress nodulation (108, 114, 137, 141, 143). The best-studied hormone of these is ethylene, with a wealth of genetic and physiological evidence defining its role in the regulation of nodulation. Early studies in pea indicated that modulating the levels of ethylene impacts the degree of nodulation, but it was not until the discovery of the *skl* mutant in *M. truncatula* that the full role of ethylene in the negative regulation of nodulation was revealed (114). *skl* was initially identified as a supernodulation mutant, producing approximately tenfold more nodules than a wild-type plant. The *skl* mutant is defective for perception of ethylene and it has since been shown that *SKL* encodes the *M. truncatula* homolog of *ETHYLENE INSENSITIVE 2* (*EIN2*) (V. Penmetsa & D. Cook, personal communication), a key member of the ethylene signal transduction pathway in *Arabidopsis*.

Ethylene regulates nodulation at multiple levels. Ethylene affects the sensitivity of the plant to Nod factor, directly affecting the number of root hair cells that are able to induce calcium spiking (108). This finding suggests that ethylene regulates a component of the Nod factor signal transduction pathway upstream of calcium spiking and this is sufficient to explain how ethylene could negatively regulate *ENOD* gene induction in the epidermis (108, 115). Ethylene also regulates infection thread growth, because infection threads in the *skl* mutant grow in an apparently uncontrolled fashion throughout the cortex (114), not dissimilar to infection threads in the *lhk1* mutant of *L. japonicus*. Ethylene is also implicated in defining the position of nodule initiation, opposite protoxylem poles (62). Hence, ethylene functions in the regulation of nodulation responses in the epidermis, as well as responses in the cortex.

Ethylene regulation of nodulation has further twists in other legume species. *S. rostrata* can grow in both dry and waterlogged conditions (58). In dry conditions the symbiont enters the root through root hairs, analogous to the mechanism described in *Medicago* and *Lotus*, and under these conditions ethylene acts as a negative regulator of nodulation (59). In waterlogged conditions the rhizobia enter the root through cracks generated in the epidermis from lateral root emergence. This mode of entry involves programmed cell death that leads to the formation of an infection pocket from which infection threads initiate, allowing bacterial entry into the emerging nodule primodium. In contrast to root hair entry, where ethylene is a negative regulator, crack entry requires ethylene (59). Hence, *S. rostrata* uses ethylene to control the mode of bacterial entry: In dry conditions when ethylene is easily dissipated root hair entry is promoted, whereas in waterlogged conditions, when ethylene will accumulate, crack entry is promoted.

JA decreases Nod factor–induced calcium spiking and nodulation, with a similar effect as ethylene, influencing the number of cells able to induce calcium spiking (102, 141). However, at lower concentrations, JA can regulate the frequency of calcium spiking (141). Nod factor concentration alone has no impact on the frequency of calcium spiking (38). Therefore, JA modulates the nature of Nod factor–induced calcium spiking, which the signaling ligand alone is unable to do.

Ethylene, JA, salicylic acid, and ABA are all induced in response to environmental stresses such as pathogen and herbivore attack and drought. The regulation of nodulation by these hormones likely allows the plant to balance the levels of nodulation with the overall health of the plant. Bacterial nitrogen fixation represents a significant carbon drain, and in some situations, nitrogen availability is not a critical factor limiting plant growth. In such situations the plant will redirect its resources to tackle the more severe challenges presented by the environment, and so it seems logical to link stress hormones to the regulation of nodulation. The depth to which these hormones are linked to nodulation is interesting: both the multiple levels at which they function, regulating both epidermal and cortical processes, and their ability to modulate the Nod factor signaling pathway with a subtlety of action that the signaling ligand alone is unable to achieve.

Autoregulation of Nodulation

In addition to *skl*, screens for supernodulation mutants of legumes revealed a class of mutants, *hypernodulation aberrant root formation 1* (*har1*) in *L. japonicus* (159), *nodule autoregulation receptor kinase* (*nark*) in soybean (130), and *supernumerary nodules* (*sunn*) in *M. truncatula* (115), that are considered defective in autoregulation. These mutants all show excessive nodulation coupled with reduced root growth. Grafting revealed that this mode of regulation is shoot specific, because a mutant shoot grafted onto a wild-type root imparts a mutant phenotype in the root (27, 159). Unlike *skl*, the *har1/nark/sunn* mutations do not affect the positioning of nodules relative to the xylem poles (115), and *sunn* and *har1* do not affect the ability of Nod factor to activate calcium spiking (G. Oldroyd, G. Morieri & J.A. Downie, unpublished data). However, these mutants show excessive bacterial infection as well as excessive nodule organogenesis, indicating that autoregulation can influence both epidermal and cortical responses (115, 159). *har1, nark, and sunn* are all alleles of orthologous genes, the legume homologs of *CLAVATA1* (*CLV1*) (103, 129, 130), a receptor-like kinase involved in shoot meristem identity in *Arabidopsis* (19). Although no legume genome sequence is yet complete, legumes do not appear to have another *CLV1* homolog, except for soybean, which has an *a* and *b* copy in its tetraploid genome. Hence, legumes have usurped *CLV1* into shoot regulation of nodulation, and alternative genes must fulfill the original function of *CLV1* in shoot meristem identity.

Considering the shoot-specific nature of autoregulation, there must be a shoot-derived signal produced as a function of *HAR1/NARK/SUNN* action that can regulate nodule number in the root (104). This signal has not been identified, but it could be one of the hormones already known to regulate nodulation. Such a hypothesis is supported by the mutants' short root phenotype, which is, at least in part, a function of reduced auxin flow in the roots (152). Whether this reduced auxin flow is a direct or indirect effect of these mutations remains to be shown, but the regulation of hormone movement in the roots of this shoot-specific function implicates hormones in its mode of action.

Integrating Epidermal and Cortical Responses During Nodulation

We argue above that Nod factor perception is limited to the epidermis and that the Nod factor signaling pathway that includes the induction of calcium spiking is most strongly correlated with the promotion of bacterial infection. However, the ability of CCaMK* mutations to induce nodule organogenesis in the cortex (54, 146) highlights the ability of such Nod factor signaling components to induce cortical processes that lead to nodule formation. Whether the CCaMK activation that leads to the induction of nodule organogenesis occurs in the epidermis or in the cortex remains unknown. However, cells in the cortical cell layer below the epidermis induce calcium spiking in response to external Nod factor application (97). If our assumptions are correct about the inability of Nod factor to diffuse through the root, then cortical cells should not perceive Nod factor directly. This could imply that Nod factor perception by epidermal cells could lead to the activation of calcium spiking in the cortex. Therefore, a signal that is not Nod factor would induce this signaling pathway in cortical cells (**Figure 5**). Considering the symplastic isolation of epidermal cells, such a signal would have to traverse the epidermal plasma membrane; therefore it is unlikely that this signal is calcium, because calcium levels are already far higher in the extracellular medium than they are in the cytosol. One possibility is that a wave of calcium spiking induction through the cortex, induced by an as yet unidentified signal generated as a result of Nod factor perception at the epidermis, can induce CCaMK in the cortex, leading to nodule organogenesis. Alternatively, CCaMK induction in the epidermis alone may be sufficient to set in motion a train of events leading to nodule organogenesis.

Mutations affecting the GRAS domain transcriptional regulators nodulation signaling pathway 1 (NSP1) and NSP2 abolish both Nod factor–induced *ENOD* gene induction in the epidermis (14, 109) and CCaMK*-induced spontaneous nodulation (54). These results place NSP1 and NSP2 in the Nod factor signaling pathway downstream of calcium spiking and imply a critical function in the epidermis. However, NSP1 and NSP2 also act in cortical cells downstream of LHK1 because LHK1*-induced spontaneous nodulation is abolished in *nsp1* and *nsp2* mutants (148). One interpretation of these results is to place cytokinin and LHK1 as intermediates in Nod factor signaling between CCaMK and NSP1/NSP2 (148) (**Figure 3**). However, combining CCaMK* and LHK1* creates more nodules than either mutation alone (148), suggesting an additive effect and thus implying the existence of two parallel pathways. Hence, we propose that the signaling pathway involving CCaMK is separate from the signaling pathway involving LHK1; the simplest explanation is that Nod factor induction of CCaMK leads to localized changes in cortical cytokinin levels that activate LHK1. In this model NSP1 and NSP2 have dual roles in nodulation signaling, functioning both downstream of CCaMK in the epidermis and downstream of LHK1 in the cortex. GRAS domain proteins have the capacity to move between cells and this mobility is critical for their mode of action (23). The dual requirement for NSP1 and NSP2 in both epidermal and cortical responses and the intricate linking of the CCaMK signaling pathway with the LHK1 pathway through these potentially mobile GRAS domain proteins could be a tantalizingly attractive means to coordinate the epidermal and cortical responses.

Another component with the capacity to integrate epidermal and cortical responses is *NODULE INCEPTION* (*NIN*) (8, 88, 127). Mutations in this gene abolish both bacterial infection in the epidermis and nodule initiation in the cortex. Like the *NSP* genes, *NIN* is required for both CCaMK*- and LHK1*-induced spontaneous nodulation (88, 148). However, unlike *NSP1* and *NSP2*, *NIN* does not play a role in Nod factor signaling; *nin* mutants are normal for Nod factor induction of calcium spiking and *ENOD* expression in the epidermis (88, 98). *NIN* does play a role in *ENOD* expression because *nin* mutants show an expansion in the zone of *ENOD* expression (88). However, this regulatory function may simply be the result of an absence of effective nodulation and thus an absence in the secondary suppression of Nod factor responses. Thus, *NIN* is a positive regulator of epidermal responses that lead to bacterial infection and a positive regulator of cortical responses that lead to nodule organogenesis, and yet *NIN* functions independently of Nod factor signaling. This places *NIN* in something of a no man's land with regard to nodulation signaling; it is a key regulator with an unknown mode of action. The structure of *NIN* does not provide many more clues; it is a novel protein but has apparent structural similarities to the Notch receptor (127), an integral membrane protein that undergoes cleavage, allowing the cytoplasmic domain to enter the nucleus to function as a transcription factor (11). Clearly, *NIN* plays an essential role during nodulation, but its exact function remains ambiguous. However, its dual role in both epidermal and cortical responses makes it an excellent candidate for coordinating plant development during the formation of a nodule.

In every case where nodulation is activated, discrete nodules are formed. This is true whether rhizobia promote nodulation via Nod factor or via alternative means, and is true whether nodulation is induced by *CCaMK** or *LHK1** mutants (54, 146–148), even when these mutations are expressed from constitutive promoters. Therefore, a mechanism must exist to generate discrete nodules even when the gain-of-function proteins are expressed in many if not all root cells. This control must function at a very late stage, downstream of *CCaMK* and *LHK1*. A similar statement can be made with regard to bacterial infection: Although all cells perceive and activate calcium spiking and many cells induce *ENOD* expression, only a few cells actually develop infection foci and infection threads. These limitations are not a function of ethylene or autoregulation, because mutations that abolish both of these modes of regulation generate plants with discrete nodules. Even a *sunn/skl* double mutant makes discrete nodules, albeit many more than wild-type (115). Therefore, a master regulator of this whole process must exist, one that ensures discrete nodules and specific sites of infection, even when many cells are promoted to enter the nodulation pathway. It would be surprising if these limitations to epidermal and cortical responses were unrelated. This regulatory mechanism must dictate that some epidermal cells and some cortical cells will respond to nodulation stimuli while others do not. Such a regulator could act in a manner analogous to lateral inhibition, which can produce evenly spaced hairs on the back of *Drosophila* within a field of apparently equal activation (116). The mechanism of this level of regulation for nodule formation remains an enigmatic and undefined process.

SUMMARY POINTS

1. Rhizobial nodulation (Nod) factors activate parallel concomitant responses in the root epidermis (leading to bacterial infection) and in the root cortex (leading to the formation of a nodule meristem).
2. Nod factor perception in the epidermis leads to gene expression changes that result from Nod factor signaling that involves calcium spiking; however, root hair deformation is independent of calcium spiking.
3. Different stringencies of Nod factor perception are involved at different stages of the rhizobial interaction and this structural specificity of Nod factor perception is a function of lysin motif (LysM) domain receptor-like kinases.
4. Nodulation responses in the cortex associated with the formation of the nodule meristem are driven by hormonal changes, with cytokinins playing a pivotal role. Some species of rhizobia appear to circumvent the requirement for Nod factors in nodule initiation by directly regulating cytokinin levels.
5. The coordination of epidermal and cortical responses during nodulation may be a function of an as yet undefined signal, may involve localized flavonoid accumulation that regulates hormone flow, and may also involve NODULE INCEPTION (NIN) and the GRAS [gibberellin insensitive (GAI), repressor of ga1-3 (RGA), SCARECROW (SCR)] domain proteins nodulation signaling pathway 1 (NSP1) and NSP2.

DISCLOSURE STATEMENT

The authors are not aware of any biases that might be perceived as affecting the objectivity of this review.

ACKNOWLEDGMENTS

We thank all the members of our research group for stimulating discussions that helped formulate some of the ideas expressed in this article. We also thank J. Sun, H. Miwa, A. Munoz, J. Kim, S. Hirsch, A. Williams, G. Morieri, M. Charpentier, M. Parniske, S. Kosuta, K. Szczyglowski, V. Penmetsa, and D. Cook for allowing us to mention their unpublished work and we thank K. Libbenga for permission to use the image in **Figure 2**. Our research related to this article is supported by the BBSRC via a David Phillips Fellowship (to G.E.D.O.), a grant-in-aid and responsive-mode funding (BB/EO170/1, BB/D521749/1, BB/E003850/1), and by the EU (RTN-CT-2003-505227, MRTN-CT-2006-035546). G.E.D.O. also holds a Royal Society Wolfson award and an EMBO young investigator award.

LITERATURE CITED

1. Allen NS, Bennett MN. 1996. Electro-optical imaging of F-actin and endoplasmic reticulum in living and fixed plant cells. *Scan. Microsc. Suppl.* 10:177–87
2. Amor BB, Shaw SL, Oldroyd GE, Maillet F, Penmetsa RV, et al. 2003. The *NFP* locus of *Medicago truncatula* controls an early step of Nod factor signal transduction upstream of a rapid calcium flux and root hair deformation. *Plant J.* 34:495–506

3. Andriankaja A, Boisson-Dernier A, Frances L, Sauviac L, Jauneau A, et al. 2007. AP2-ERF transcription factors mediate Nod factor-dependent *MtENOD11* activation in root hairs via a novel cis-regulatory motif. *Plant Cell* 19:2866–85
4. Ane JM, Kiss GB, Riely BK, Penmetsa RV, Oldroyd GE, et al. 2004. *Medicago truncatula* DMI1 required for bacterial and fungal symbioses in legumes. *Science* 303:1364–67
5. Ardourel M, Demont N, Debellé F, Maillet F, de Billy F, et al. 1994. *Rhizobium meliloti* lipooligosaccharide nodulation factors: different structural requirements for bacterial entry into target root hair cells and induction of plant symbiotic developmental responses. *Plant Cell* 6:1357–74
6. Arrighi JF, Barre A, Ben Amor B, Bersoult A, Soriano LC, et al. 2006. The *Medicago truncatula* lysin motif-receptor-like kinase gene family includes NFP and new nodule-expressed genes. *Plant Physiol.* 142:265–79
7. Berridge MJ. 1993. Inositol trisphosphate and calcium signalling. *Nature* 361:315–25
8. Borisov AY, Madsen LH, Tsyganov VE, Umehara Y, Voroshilova VA, et al. 2003. The *Sym35* gene required for root nodule development in pea is an ortholog of *Nin* from *Lotus japonicus*. *Plant Physiol.* 131:1009–17
9. Brewin NJ. 1991. Development of the legume root nodules. *Annu. Rev. Cell Biol.* 7:191–226
10. Brewin NJ. 2004. Plant cell wall remodelling in the *Rhizobium*-legume symbiosis. *Crit. Rev. Plant Sci.* 23:293–316
11. Brown MS, Ye J, Rawson RB, Goldstein JL. 2000. Regulated intramembrane proteolysis: a control mechanism conserved from bacteria to humans. *Cell* 100:391–98
12. Capoen W, Goormachtig S, De Rycke R, Schroeyers K, Holsters M. 2005. SrSymRK, a plant receptor essential for symbiosome formation. *Proc. Natl. Acad. Sci. USA* 102:10369–74
13. Cardenas L, Vidali L, Dominguez J, Perez H, Sanchez F, et al. 1998. Rearrangement of actin microfilaments in plant root hairs responding to *Rhizobium etli* nodulation signals. *Plant Physiol.* 116:871–77
14. Catoira R, Galera C, de Billy F, Penmetsa RV, Journet EP, et al. 2000. Four genes of *Medicago truncatula* controlling components of a Nod factor transduction pathway. *Plant Cell* 12:1647–65
15. Cebolla A, Vinardell JM, Kiss E, Olah B, Roudier F, et al. 1999. The mitotic inhibitor ccs52 is required for endoreduplication and ploidy-dependent cell enlargement in plants. *EMBO J.* 18:4476–84
16. Charon C, Johansson C, Kondorosi E, Kondorosi A, Crespi M. 1997. enod40 induces dedifferentiation and division of root cortical cells in legumes. *Proc. Natl. Acad. Sci. USA* 94:8901–6
17. Charon C, Sousa C, Crespi M, Kondorosi A. 1999. Alteration of enod40 expression modifies *Medicago truncatula* root nodule development induced by *Sinorhizobium meliloti*. *Plant Cell* 11:1953–66
18. Charron D, Pingret JL, Chabaud M, Journet EP, Barker DG. 2004. Pharmacological evidence that multiple phospholipid signaling pathways link *Rhizobium* nodulation factor perception in *Medicago truncatula* root hairs to intracellular responses, including Ca^{2+} spiking and specific *ENOD* gene expression. *Plant Physiol.* 136:3582–93
19. Clark SE, Williams RW, Meyerowitz EM. 1997. The *CLAVATA1* gene encodes a putative receptor kinase that controls shoot and floral meristem size in *Arabidopsis*. *Cell* 89:575–85
20. Combier JP, Frugier F, de Billy F, Boualem A, El-Yahyaoui F, et al. 2006. MtHAP2-1 is a key transcriptional regulator of symbiotic nodule development regulated by microRNA169 in *Medicago truncatula*. *Genes Dev.* 20:3084–88

21. Cooper JB, Long SR. 1994. Morphogenetic rescue of *Rhizobium meliloti* nodulation mutants by *trans*-zeatin secretion. *Plant Cell* 6:215–25
22. Crespi MD, Jurkevitch E, Poiret M, d'Aubenton-Carafa Y, Petrovics G, et al. 1994. *enod40*, a gene expressed during nodule organogenesis, codes for a non-translatable RNA involved in plant growth. *EMBO J.* 13:5099–107
23. Cui H, Levesque MP, Vernoux T, Jung JW, Paquette AJ, et al. 2007. An evolutionarily conserved mechanism delimiting SHR movement defines a single layer of endodermis in plants. *Science* 316:421–25
24. D'Haeze W, Holsters M. 2004. Surface polysaccharides enable bacteria to evade plant immunity. *Trends Microbiol.* 12:555–61
25. Day RB, McAlvin CB, Loh JT, Denny RL, Wood TC, et al. 2000. Differential expression of two soybean apyrases, one of which is an early nodulin. *Mol. Plant Microbe. Interact.* 13:1053–70
26. Dazzo FB, Truchet GL, Sherwood JE, Hrabak EM, Abe M, Pankratz SH. 1984. Specific phases of root hair attachment in the *Rhizobium trifolii*-clover symbiosis. *Appl. Environ. Microbiol.* 48:1140–50
27. Delves AC, Mathews A, Day DA, Carter AS, Carroll BJ, Gresshoff PM. 1986. Regulation of the soybean-*Rhizobium* nodule symbiosis by shoot and root factors. *Plant Physiol.* 82:588–90
28. Dénarié J, Debellé F, Prome J-C. 1996. *Rhizobium* lipo-chitooligosaccharide nodulation factors: Signaling molecules mediating recognition and morphogenesis. *Annu. Rev. Biochem.* 65:503–35
29. den Hartog M, Musgrave A, Munnik T. 2001. Nod factor-induced phosphatidic acid and diacylglycerol pyrophosphate formation: a role for phospholipase C and D in root hair deformation. *Plant J.* 25:55–65
30. Den Herder J, Vanhee C, De Rycke R, Corich V, Holsters M, Goormachtig S. 2007. Nod factor perception during infection thread growth fine-tunes nodulation. *Mol. Plant Microbe. Interact.* 20:129–37
31. de Ruijter NCA, Rook MB, Bisseling T, Emons AMC. 1998. Lipochito-oligosaccharides re-initiate root hair tip growth in *Vicia sativa* with high calcium and spectrin-like antigen at the tip. *Plant J.* 13:341–50
32. Diaz CL, Melchers LS, Hooykaas PJJ, Lugtenberg BJJ, Kijne JW. 1989. Root lectin as a determinant of host-plant specificity in the *Rhizobium*-legume symbiosis. *Nature* 338:579–81
33. Diaz CL, Spaink HP, Wijffelman CA, Kijne JW. 1995. Genomic requirements of *Rhizobium* for nodulation of white clover hairy roots transformed with the pea lectin gene. *Mol. Plant-Microbe. Interact.* 8:348–56
34. Djordjevic SP, Chen H, Batley M, Redmond JW, Rolfe BG. 1987. Nitrogen fixation ability of exopolysaccharide synthesis mutants of *Rhizobium sp.* strain NGR234 and *Rhizobium trifolii* is restored by the addition of homologous exopolysaccharides. *J. Bacteriol.* 169:53–60
35. Downie JA. 1998. Functions of rhizobial nodulation genes. See Spaink et al., 1998, pp. 387–402
36. Downie JA. 2007. Plant science. Infectious heresy. *Science* 316:1296–97
37. Edwards A, Heckmann AB, Yousafzai F, Duc G, Downie JA. 2007. Structural implications of mutations in the pea *SYM8* symbiosis gene, the *DMI1* ortholog, encoding a predicted ion channel. *Mol. Plant-Microbe Interact.* 20:1183–91
38. Ehrhardt DW, Wais R, Long SR. 1996. Calcium spiking in plant root hairs responding to *Rhizobium* nodulation signals. *Cell* 85:673–81

39. Endre G, Kereszt A, Kevei Z, Mihacea S, Kalo P, Kiss GB. 2002. A receptor kinase gene regulating symbiotic nodule development. *Nature* 417:962–66
40. Engstrom EM, Ehrhardt DW, Mitra RM, Long SR. 2002. Pharmacological analysis of nod factor-induced calcium spiking in *Medicago truncatula*. Evidence for the requirement of type IIA calcium pumps and phosphoinositide signaling. *Plant Physiol.* 128:1390–401
41. Esseling JJ, Emons AM. 2004. Dissection of Nod factor signalling in legumes: cell biology, mutants and pharmacological approaches. *J. Microsc.* 214:104–13
42. Esseling JJ, Lhuissier FG, Emons AM. 2003. Nod factor-induced root hair curling: continuous polar growth towards the point of nod factor application. *Plant Physiol.* 132:1982–88
43. Etzler ME, Kalsi G, Ewing NN, Roberts NJ, Day RB, Murphy JB. 1999. A nod factor binding lectin with apyrase activity from legume roots. *Proc. Natl. Acad. Sci. USA* 96:5856–61
44. Fang Y, Hirsch AM. 1998. Studying early nodulin gene ENOD40 expression and induction by nodulation factor and cytokinin in transgenic alfalfa. *Plant Physiol.* 116:53–68
45. Ferguson BJ, Ross JJ, Reid JB. 2005. Nodulation phenotypes of gibberellin and brassinosteroid mutants of pea. *Plant Physiol.* 138:2396–405
46. Firmin JL, Wilson KE, Carlson RW, Davies AE, Downie JA. 1993. Resistance to nodulation of cv. Afghanistan peas is overcome by nodX, which mediates an O-acetylation of the *Rhizobium leguminosarum* lipo-oligosaccharide nodulation factor. *Mol. Microbiol.* 10:351–60
47. Fujishige NA, Kapadia NN, De Hoff PL, Hirsch AM. 2006. Investigations of *Rhizobium* biofilm formation. *FEMS Microbiol. Ecol.* 56:195–206
48. Gage DJ. 2002. Analysis of infection thread development using Gfp- and DsRed-expressing *Sinorhizobium meliloti*. *J. Bacteriol.* 184:7042–46
49. Gage DJ. 2004. Infection and invasion of roots by symbiotic, nitrogen-fixing rhizobia during nodulation of temperate legumes. *Microbiol. Mol. Biol. Rev.* 68:280–300
50. Gapper C, Dolan L. 2006. Control of plant development by reactive oxygen species. *Plant Physiol.* 141:341–45
51. Geurts R, Fedorova E, Bisseling T. 2005. Nod factor signaling genes and their function in the early stages of *Rhizobium* infection. *Curr. Opin. Plant Biol.* 8:346–52
52. Geurts R, Heidstra R, Hadri A-E, Downie JA, Franssen H, et al. 1997. Sym2 of pea is involved in a nodulation factor-perception mechanism that controls the infection process in the epidermis. *Plant Physiol.* 115:351–59
53. Giraud E, Moulin L, Vallenet D, Barbe V, Cytryn E, et al. 2007. Legumes symbioses: absence of *Nod* genes in photosynthetic bradyrhizobia. *Science* 316:1307–12
54. Gleason C, Chaudhuri S, Yang T, Munoz A, Poovaiah BW, Oldroyd GE. 2006. Nodulation independent of rhizobia induced by a calcium-activated kinase lacking autoinhibition. *Nature* 441:1149–52
55. Goedhart J, Hink MA, Visser AJ, Bisseling T, Gadella TW Jr. 2000. In vivo fluorescence correlation microscopy (FCM) reveals accumulation and immobilization of Nod factors in root hair cell walls. *Plant J.* 21:109–19
56. González JE, Reuhs BL, Walker GC. 1996. Low molecular weight EPS II of *Rhizobium meliloti* allows nodule invasion in *Medicago sativa*. *Proc. Natl. Acad. Sci. USA* 93:8636–41
57. Gonzalez-Rizzo S, Crespi M, Frugier F. 2006. The *Medicago truncatula* CRE1 cytokinin receptor regulates lateral root development and early symbiotic interaction with *Sinorhizobium meliloti*. *Plant Cell* 18:2680–93
58. Goormachtig S, Capoen W, Holsters M. 2004. *Rhizobium* infection: lessons from the versatile nodulation behaviour of water-tolerant legumes. *Trends Plant Sci.* 9:518–22

59. Goormachtig S, Capoen W, James EK, Holsters M. 2004. Switch from intracellular to intercellular invasion during water stress-tolerant legume nodulation. *Proc. Natl. Acad. Sci. USA* 101:6303–8
60. Hadri AE, Bisseling T. 1998. Responses of the plant to Nod factors. See Ref. 135, pp. 403–16
61. Heckmann AB, Lombardo F, Miwa H, Perry JA, Bunnewell S, et al. 2006. *Lotus japonicus* nodulation requires two GRAS domain regulators, one of which is functionally conserved in a non-legume. *Plant Physiol.* 142:1739–50
62. Heidstra R, Yang WC, Yalcin Y, Peck S, Emons AM, et al. 1997. Ethylene provides positional information on cortical cell division but is not involved in Nod factor-induced root hair tip growth in *Rhizobium*-legume interaction. *Development* 124:1781–87
63. Hirsch AM. 1999. Role of lectins (and rhizobial exopolysaccharides) in legume nodulation. *Curr. Opin. Plant Biol.* 2:320–26
64. Hirsch AM, Bhuvaneswari TV, Torrey JG, Bisseling T. 1989. Early nodulin genes are induced in alfalfa root outgrowths elicited by auxin transport inhibitors. *Proc. Natl. Acad. Sci. USA* 86:1244–48
65. Hirsch AM, Fang Y. 1994. Plant hormones and nodulation: what's the connection? *Plant Mol. Biol.* 26:5–9
66. Imaizumi-Anraku H, Takeda N, Charpentier M, Perry J, Miwa H, et al. 2005. Plastid proteins crucial for symbiotic fungal and bacterial entry into plant roots. *Nature* 433:527–31
67. Jones KM, Kobayashi H, Davies BW, Taga ME, Walker GC. 2007. How rhizobial symbionts invade plants: the *Sinorhizobium-Medicago* model. *Nat. Rev. Microbiol.* 5:619–33
68. Journet EP, El-Gachtouli N, Vernoud V, de Billy F, Pichon M, et al. 2001. *Medicago truncatula ENOD11*: a novel RPRP-encoding early nodulin gene expressed during mycorrhization in arbuscule-containing cells. *Mol. Plant Microbe. Interact.* 14:737–48
69. Journet EP, Pichon M, Dedieu A, de Billy F, Truchet G, Barker DG. 1994. *Rhizobium meliloti* Nod factors elicit cell-specific transcription of the *ENOD12* gene in transgenic alfalfa. *Plant J.* 6:241–49
70. Kalo P, Gleason C, Edwards A, Marsh J, Mitra RM, et al. 2005. Nodulation signaling in legumes requires NSP2, a member of the GRAS family of transcriptional regulators. *Science* 308:1786–89
71. Kalsi G, Etzler ME. 2000. Localization of a Nod factor-binding protein in legume roots and factors influencing its distribution and expression. *Plant Physiol.* 124:1039–48
72. Kanamori N, Madsen LH, Radutoiu S, Frantescu M, Quistgaard EM, et al. 2006. A nucleoporin is required for induction of Ca^{2+} spiking in legume nodule development and essential for rhizobial and fungal symbiosis. *Proc. Natl. Acad. Sci. USA* 103:359–64
73. Karas B, Murray J, Gorzelak M, Smith A, Sato S, et al. 2005. Invasion of *Lotus japonicus* root hairless 1 by *Mesorhizobium loti* involves the nodulation factor-dependent induction of root hairs. *Plant Physiol.* 137:1331–44
74. Kawaguchi M, Imaizumi-Anraku H, Koiwa H, Niwa S, Ikuta A, et al. 2002. Root, root hair, and symbiotic mutants of the model legume *Lotus japonicus*. *Mol. Plant-Microbe. Interact.* 15:17–26
75. Kuppusamy KT, Endre G, Prabhu R, Penmetsa RV, Veereshlingam H, et al. 2004. *LIN*, a *Medicago truncatula* gene required for nodule differentiation and persistence of rhizobial infections. *Plant Physiol.* 136:3682–91
76. Laus MC, Logman TJ, Lamers GE, Van Brussel AAN, Carlson RW, Kijne JW. 2006. A novel polar surface polysaccharide from *Rhizobium leguminosarum* binds host plant lectin. *Mol. Microbiol.* 59:1704–13

77. Leigh JA, Signer ER, Walker GC. 1985. Exopolysaccharide-deficient mutants of *Rhizobium meliloti* that form ineffective nodules. *Proc. Natl. Acad. Sci. USA* 82:6231–35
78. Levy J, Bres C, Geurts R, Chalhoub B, Kulikova O, et al. 2004. A putative Ca^{2+} and calmodulin-dependent protein kinase required for bacterial and fungal symbioses. *Science* 303:1361–64
79. Leyser O. 2006. Dynamic integration of auxin transport and signalling. *Curr. Biol.* 16:R424–33
80. Libbenga KR. 1970. *Nodulatie bij Leguminosae*. PhD thesis. Leiden University.
81. Lievens S, Goormachtig S, Den Herder J, Capoen W, Mathis R, et al. 2005. Gibberellins are involved in nodulation of *Sesbania rostrata*. *Plant Physiol.* 139:1366–79
82. Limpens E, Franken C, Smit P, Willemse J, Bisseling T, Geurts R. 2003. LysM domain receptor kinases regulating rhizobial Nod factor-induced infection. *Science* 302:630–33
83. Limpens E, Mirabella R, Fedorova E, Franken C, Franssen H, et al. 2005. Formation of organelle-like N2-fixing symbiosomes in legume root nodules is controlled by DMI2. *Proc. Natl. Acad. Sci. USA* 102:10375–80
84. Lohar DP, Schaff JE, Laskey JG, Kieber JJ, Bilyeu KD, Bird DM. 2004. Cytokinins play opposite roles in lateral root formation, and nematode and *Rhizobial symbioses*. *Plant J.* 38:203–14
85. Lombardo F, Heckmann AB, Miwa H, Perry JA, Yano K, et al. 2006. Identification of symbiotically defective mutants of *Lotus japonicus* affected in infection thread growth. *Mol. Plant Microbe. Interact.* 19:1444–50
86. Lusk CP, Blobel G, King MC. 2007. Highway to the inner nuclear membrane: rules for the road. *Nat. Rev. Mol. Cell Biol.* 8:414–20
87. Madsen EB, Madsen LH, Radutoiu S, Olbryt M, Rakwalska M, et al. 2003. A receptor kinase gene of the LysM type is involved in legume perception of rhizobial signals. *Nature* 425:637–40
88. Marsh JF, Rakocevic A, Mitra RM, Brocard L, Sun J, et al. 2007. *Medicago truncatula* NIN is essential for rhizobial-independent nodule organogenesis induced by autoactive calcium/calmodulin-dependent protein kinase. *Plant Physiol.* 144:324–35
89. Mathesius U. 2001. Flavonoids induced in cells undergoing nodule organogenesis in white clover are regulators of auxin breakdown by peroxidase. *J. Exp. Bot.* 52:419–26
90. Mathesius U, Charon C, Rolfe BG, Kondorosi A, Crespi M. 2000. Temporal and spatial order of events during the induction of cortical cell divisions in white clover by *Rhizobium leguminosarum* bv. *trifolii* inoculation or localized cytokinin addition. *Mol. Plant Microbe. Interact.* 13:617–28
91. Mathesius U, Schlaman HR, Spaink HP, Sautter C, Rolfe BG, Djordjevic MA. 1998. Auxin transport inhibition precedes root nodule formation in white clover roots and is regulated by flavonoids and derivatives of chitin oligosaccharides. *Plant J.* 14:23–34
92. Mathis R, Van Gijsegem F, De Rycke R, D'Haeze W, Van Maelsaeke E, et al. 2005. Lipopolysaccharides as a communication signal for progression of legume endosymbiosis. *Proc. Natl. Acad. Sci. USA* 102:2655–60
93. McAlvin CB, Stacey G. 2005. Transgenic expression of the soybean apyrase in *Lotus japonicus* enhances nodulation. *Plant Physiol.* 137:1456–62
94. Messinese E, Mun J-H, Yeun L, Jayaraman D, Rouge P, et al. 2007. A novel nuclear protein interacts with the symbiotic DMI3 calcium and calmodulin dependent protein kinase of *Medicago truncatula*. *Mol. Plant-Microbe Interact.* 20:912–21
95. Middleton PH, Jakab J, Penmetsa RV, Starker CG, Doll J, et al. 2007. An ERF transcription factor in *Medicago truncatula* that is essential for Nod factor signal transduction. *Plant Cell* 19:1221–34

96. Mitra RM, Gleason CA, Edwards A, Hadfield J, Downie JA, et al. 2004. A Ca^{2+}/calmodulin-dependent protein kinase required for symbiotic nodule development: Gene identification by transcript-based cloning. *Proc. Natl. Acad. Sci. USA* 101:4701–5
97. Miwa H, Sun J, Oldroyd G, Downie A. 2006. Analysis of calcium spiking using a cameleon calcium sensor reveals that nodulation gene expression is regulated by calcium spike number and the developmental status of the cell. *Plant J.* 48:883–94
98. Miwa H, Sun J, Oldroyd GE, Downie JA. 2006. Analysis of Nod-factor-induced calcium signaling in root hairs of symbiotically defective mutants of *Lotus japonicus*. *Mol. Plant Microbe. Interact.* 19:914–23
99. Murakami Y, Miwa H, Imaizumi-Anraku H, Kouchi H, Downie JA, et al. 2006. Positional cloning identifies *Lotus japonicus* NSP2, a putative transcription factor of the GRAS family, required for *NIN* and *ENOD40* gene expression in nodule initiation. *DNA Res.* 13:255–65
100. Murray J, Karas B, Ross L, Brachmann A, Wagg C, et al. 2006. Genetic suppressors of the *Lotus japonicus har1-1* hypernodulation phenotype. *Mol. Plant Microbe. Interact.* 19:1082–91
101. Murray JD, Karas BJ, Sato S, Tabata S, Amyot L, Szczyglowski K. 2007. A cytokinin perception mutant colonized by *Rhizobium* in the absence of nodule organogenesis. *Science* 315:101–4
102. Nakagawa T, Kawaguchi M. 2006. Shoot-applied MeJA suppresses root nodulation in *Lotus japonicus*. *Plant Cell Physiol.* 47:176–80
103. Nishimura R, Hayashi M, Wu GJ, Kouchi H, Imaizumi-Anraku H, et al. 2002. HAR1 mediates systemic regulation of symbiotic organ development. *Nature* 420:426–29
104. Oka-Kira E, Kawaguchi M. 2006. Long-distance signaling to control root nodule number. *Curr. Opin. Plant Biol.* 9:496–502
105. Oldroyd GE. 2007. Plant science. Nodules and hormones. *Science* 315:52–53
106. Oldroyd GE, Downie JA. 2004. Calcium, kinases and nodulation signalling in legumes. *Nat. Rev. Mol. Cell Biol.* 5:566–76
107. Oldroyd GE, Downie JA. 2006. Nuclear calcium changes at the core of symbiosis signalling. *Curr. Opin. Plant Biol.* 9:351–57
108. Oldroyd GE, Engstrom EM, Long SR. 2001. Ethylene inhibits the Nod factor signal transduction pathway of *Medicago truncatula*. *Plant Cell* 13:1835–49
109. Oldroyd GE, Long SR. 2003. Identification and characterization of *nodulation-signaling pathway 2*, a gene of *Medicago truncatula* involved in Nod actor signaling. *Plant Physiol.* 131:1027–32
110. Oldroyd GE, Mitra RM, Wais RJ, Long SR. 2001. Evidence for structurally specific negative feedback in the Nod factor signal transduction pathway. *Plant J.* 28:191–99
111. Ooki Y, Banba M, Yano K, Maruya J, Sato S, et al. 2005. Characterization of the *Lotus japonicus* symbiotic mutant *lot1* that shows a reduced nodule number and distorted trichomes. *Plant Physiol.* 137:1261–71
112. Patil S, Takezawa D, Poovaiah BW. 1995. Chimeric plant calcium/calmodulin-dependent protein kinase gene with a neural visinin-like calcium-binding domain. *Proc. Natl. Acad. Sci. USA* 92:4897–901
113. Peiter E, Sun J, Heckmann AB, Venkateshwaran M, Riley BK, et al. 2007. The *Medicago truncatula* DMI1 protein modulates cytosolic calcium signaling. *Plant Physiol.* 145:192–203
114. Penmetsa RV, Cook DR. 1997. A legume ethylene-insensitive mutant hyperinfected by its rhizobial symbiont. *Science* 275:527–30
115. Penmetsa RV, Frugoli JA, Smith LS, Long SR, Cook DR. 2003. Dual genetic pathways controlling nodule number in *Medicago truncatula*. *Plant Physiol.* 131:998–1008

116. Portin P. 2002 General outlines of the molecular genetics of the Notch signalling pathway in *Drosophila melanogaster*: a review. *Hereditas* 136:89–96
117. Radutoiu S, Madsen LH, Madsen EB, Felle HH, Umehara Y, et al. 2003. Plant recognition of symbiotic bacteria requires two LysM receptor-like kinases. *Nature* 425:585–92
118. Radutoiu S, Madsen LH, Madsen EB, Jurkiewicz A, Fukai E, et al. 2007. LysM domains mediate lipochitin-oligosaccharide recognition and *Nfr* genes extend the symbiotic host range. *EMBO J.* 26:3923–35
119. Riely BK, Ane JM, Penmetsa RV, Cook DR. 2004. Genetic and genomic analysis in model legumes bring Nod-factor signaling to center stage. *Curr. Opin. Plant Biol.* 7:408–13
120. Riely BK, Lougnon G, Ane JM, Cook DR. 2007. The symbiotic ion channel homolog DMI1 is localized in the nuclear membrane of *Medicago truncatula* roots. *Plant J.* 49:208–16
121. Roche P, Debellé F, Maillet F, Lerouge P, Faucher C, et al. 1991. Molecular basis of symbiotic host specificity in *Rhizobium meliloti*: *nodH* and *nodPQ* genes encode the sulfation of lipo-oligosaccharide signals. *Cell* 67:1131–43
122. Saito K, Yoshikawa M, Yano K, Miwa H, Uchida H, et al. 2007. NUCLEOPORIN85 is required for calcium spiking, fungal and bacterial symbioses, and seed production in *Lotus japonicus*. *Plant Cell* 19:610–24
123. Sakakibara H. 2005. Cytokinin biosynthesis and regulation. *Vitam. Horm.* 72:271–87
124. Sanchez-Contreras M, Bauer WD, Gao M, Robinson JB, Downie JA. 2007. Quorum-sensing regulation in rhizobia and its role in symbiotic interactions with legumes. *Philos. Trans. R. Soc. London Ser. B* 362:1149–63
125. Sandal N, Petersen TR, Murray J, Umehara Y, Karas B, et al. 2006. Genetics of symbiosis in *Lotus japonicus*: recombinant inbred lines, comparative genetic maps, and map position of 35 symbiotic loci. *Mol. Plant Microbe. Interact.* 19:80–91
126. Schauser L, Handberg K, Sandal N, Stiller J, Thykjaer T, et al. 1998. Symbiotic mutants deficient in nodule establishment identified after T-DNA transformation of *Lotus japonicus*. *Mol. Gen. Genet.* 259:414–23
127. Schauser L, Roussis A, Stiller J, Stougaard J. 1999. A plant regulator controlling development of symbiotic root nodules. *Nature* 402:191–95
128. Scheres B, van de Wiel C, Zalensky A, Horvath B, Spaink H, et al. 1990. The *ENOD12* gene product is involved in the infection process during the pea-*Rhizobium* interaction. *Cell* 60:281–94
129. Schnabel E, Journet EP, de Carvalho-Niebel F, Duc G, Frugoli J. 2005. The *Medicago truncatula SUNN* gene encodes a CLV1-like leucine-rich repeat receptor kinase that regulates nodule number and root length. *Plant Mol. Biol.* 58:809–22
130. Searle IR, Men AE, Laniya TS, Buzas DM, Iturbe-Ormaetxe I, et al. 2003. Long-distance signaling in nodulation directed by a CLAVATA1-like receptor kinase. *Science* 299:109–12
131. Shaw SL, Long SR. 2003. Nod factor elicits two separable calcium responses in *Medicago truncatula* root hair cells. *Plant Physiol.* 131:976–84
132. Smit G, Swart S, Lugtenberg BJJ, Kijne JW. 1992. Molecular mechanisms of attachment of *Rhizobium* bacteria to plant roots. *Mol. Microbiol.* 6:2897–903
133. Smit P, Limpens E, Geurts R, Fedorova E, Dolgikh E, et al. 2007. Medicago LYK3, an entry receptor in rhizobial nod factor signaling. *Plant Physiol.* 145:183–91
134. Smit P, Raedts J, Portyanko V, Debellé F, Gough C, et al. 2005. NSP1 of the GRAS protein family is essential for rhizobial Nod factor-induced transcription. *Science* 308:1789–91
135. Spaink HP, Kondorosi A, Hooykaas PJJ, eds. 1998. *The Rhizobiaceae*. Dordrecht: Kluwer Acad.

136. Spaink HP, Sheeley DM, van Brussel AAN, Glushka J, York WS, et al. 1991. A novel highly unsaturated fatty acid moiety of lipo-oligosaccharide signals determines host specificity of *Rhizobium*. *Nature* 354:125–30
137. Stacey G, McAlvin CB, Kim SY, Olivares J, Soto MJ. 2006. Effects of endogenous salicylic acid on nodulation in the model legumes *Lotus japonicus* and *Medicago truncatula*. *Plant Physiol.* 141:1473–81
138. Starker CG, Parra-Colmenares AL, Smith L, Mitra RM, Long SR. 2006. Nitrogen fixation mutants of *Medicago truncatula* fail to support plant and bacterial symbiotic gene expression. *Plant Physiol.* 140:671–80
139. Stracke S, Kistner C, Yoshida S, Mulder L, Sato S, et al. 2002. A plant receptor-like kinase required for both bacterial and fungal symbiosis. *Nature* 417:959–62
140. Subramanian S, Stacey G, Yu O. 2006. Endogenous isoflavones are essential for the establishment of symbiosis between soybean and *Bradyrhizobium japonicum*. *Plant J.* 48:261–73
141. Sun J, Cardoza V, Mitchell DM, Bright L, Oldroyd G, Harris JM. 2006. Crosstalk between jasmonic acid, ethylene and Nod factor signaling allows integration of diverse inputs for regulation of nodulation. *Plant J.* 46:961–70
142. Sun J, Miwa H, Downie JA, Oldroyd GE. 2007. Mastoparan activates calcium spiking analogous to Nod factor-induced responses in *Medicago truncatula* root hair cells. *Plant Physiol.* 144:695–702
143. Suzuki A, Akune M, Kogiso M, Imagama Y, Osuki K, et al. 2004. Control of nodule number by the phytohormone abscisic acid in the roots of two leguminous species. *Plant Cell Physiol.* 45:914–22
144. Takezawa D, Ramachandiran S, Paranjape V, Poovaiah BW. 1996. Dual regulation of a chimeric plant serine/threonine kinase by calcium and calcium/calmodulin. *J. Biol. Chem.* 271:8126–32
145. Tansengco ML, Hayashi M, Kawaguchi M, Imaizumi-Anraku H, Murooka Y. 2003. *crinkle*, a novel symbiotic mutant that affects the infection thread growth and alters the root hair, trichome, and seed development in *Lotus japonicus*. *Plant Physiol.* 131:1054–63
146. Tirichine L, Imaizumi-Anraku H, Yoshida S, Murakami Y, Madsen LH, et al. 2006. Deregulation of a Ca^{2+}/calmodulin-dependent kinase leads to spontaneous nodule development. *Nature* 441:1153–56
147. Tirichine L, James EK, Sandal N, Stougaard J. 2006. Spontaneous root-nodule formation in the model legume *Lotus japonicus*: a novel class of mutants nodulates in the absence of rhizobia. *Mol. Plant-Microbe Interact.* 19:373–82
148. Tirichine L, Sandal N, Madsen LH, Radutoiu S, Albrektsen AS, et al. 2007. A gain-of-function mutation in a cytokinin receptor triggers spontaneous root nodule organogenesis. *Science* 315:104–7
149. Urzainqui A, Walker GC. 1992. Exogenous suppression of the symbiotic deficiencies of *Rhizobium meliloti exo* mutants. *J. Bacteriol.* 174:3403–6
150. van Batenburg FHD, Jonker R, Kijne JW. 1986. *Rhizobium* induces marked root hair curling by redirection of tip growth: a computer simulation. *Physiol. Plant.* 66:476–80
151. van Brussel AAN, Bakhuizen R, Van Spronsen PC, Spaink HP, Tak T, et al. 1992. Induction of pre-infection thread structures in the leguminous host plant by mitogenic lipo-oligosaccharides of *Rhizobium*. *Science* 257:70–72
152. van Noorden GE, Ross JJ, Reid JB, Rolfe BG, Mathesius U. 2006. Defective long-distance auxin transport regulation in the *Medicago truncatula* super numeric nodules mutant. *Plant Physiol.* 140:1494–506
153. van Rhijn P, Goldberg RB, Hirsch AM. 1998. Lotus corniculatus nodulation specificity is changed by the presence of a soybean lectin gene. *Plant Cell* 10:1233–49

154. Veereshlingam H, Haynes JG, Penmetsa RV, Cook DR, Sherrier DJ, Dickstein R. 2004. *nip*, a symbiotic *Medicago truncatula* mutant that forms root nodules with aberrant infection threads and plant defense-like response. *Plant Physiol.* 136:3692–702
155. Wais RJ, Galera C, Oldroyd G, Catoira R, Penmetsa RV, et al. 2000. Genetic analysis of calcium spiking responses in nodulation mutants of *Medicago truncatula*. *Proc. Natl. Acad. Sci. USA* 97:13407–12
156. Walker SA, Downie JA. 2000. Entry of *Rhizobium leguminosarum* bv. *viciae* into root hairs requires minimal nod factor specificity, but subsequent infection thread growth requires nodO and nodE. *Mol. Plant Microbe. Interact.* 13:754–62
157. Walker SA, Viprey V, Downie JA. 2000. Dissection of nodulation signaling using pea mutants defective for calcium spiking induced by Nod factors and chitin oligomers. *Proc. Natl. Acad. Sci. USA* 97:13413–18
158. Wasson AP, Pellerone FI, Mathesius U. 2006. Silencing the flavonoid pathway in *Medicago truncatula* inhibits root nodule formation and prevents auxin transport regulation by rhizobia. *Plant Cell* 18:1617–29
159. Wopereis J, Pajuelo E, Dazzo FB, Jiang Q, Gresshoff PM, et al. 2000. Short root mutant of *Lotus japonicus* with a dramatically altered symbiotic phenotype. *Plant J.* 23:97–114
160. Yano K, Tansengco ML, Hio T, Higashi K, Murooka Y, et al. 2006. New nodulation mutants responsible for infection thread development in *Lotus japonicus*. *Mol. Plant-Microbe. Interact.* 19:801–10
161. Yoshida S, Parniske M. 2005. Regulation of plant symbiosis receptor kinase through serine and threonine phosphorylation. *J. Biol. Chem.* 280:9203–9

Structural and Signaling Networks for the Polar Cell Growth Machinery in Pollen Tubes

Alice Y. Cheung[1,2,3] and Hen-ming Wu[1,2]

[1]Department of Biochemistry and Molecular Biology, [2]Molecular Cell Biology Program, and [3]Plant Biology Program, University of Massachusetts, Amherst, Massachusetts 01003; email: acheung@biochem.umass.edu, hmwu@biochem.umass.edu

Annu. Rev. Plant Biol. 2008. 59:547–72

The *Annual Review of Plant Biology* is online at plant.annualreviews.org

This article's doi:
10.1146/annurev.arplant.59.032607.092921

1543-5008/08/0602-0547$20.00

Key Words

actin, ion dynamics, oscillatory growth, membrane trafficking, Rab and Rho GTPases, receptor kinases

Abstract

Pollen tubes elongate within the pistil to transport sperms to the female gametophytes for fertilization. Pollen tubes grow at their tips through a rapid and polarized cell growth process. This tip growth process is supported by an elaborate and dynamic actin cytoskeleton and a highly active membrane trafficking system that together provide the driving force and secretory activities needed for growth. A polarized cytoplasm with an abundance of vesicles and tip-focused Ca^{2+} and H^+ concentration gradients are important for the polar cell growth process. Apical membrane–located Rho GTPases regulate Ca^{2+} concentration and actin dynamics in the cytoplasm and are crucial for maintaining pollen tube polarity. Pollen tube growth is marked by periods of rapid and slow growth phases. Activities that regulate and support this tip growth process also show oscillatory fluctuations. How these activities correlate with the rapid, polar, and oscillatory pollen tube growth process is discussed.

Contents

INTRODUCTION

Plants rely on a dramatic polar cell growth process, pollen tube elongation within the pistil, to achieve fertilization. The tip growth pollen tubes elongate rapidly, deriving nutrients and directional cues from the female tissues to target the female gametophyte. Obviously highly collaborative, pollen tube growth has long been studied to understand how the pollen and pistil interact to facilitate or inhibit fertilization (74, 88, 93, 125). Pollen grains from many species can germinate and their tubes can grow to considerable lengths in vitro, providing unparalleled opportunities to observe and manipulate this fascinating polar cell growth process. Although our discussions here rely considerably on studies based on pollen tubes grown in vitro, we also include studies that examined their in vivo efficacy.

Tip growth is utilized by only a few cell types, including pollen tubes and root hairs in plants, hyphae in fungi, and neurites in animals. The rapidity of pollen tube growth and its sensitivity to growth- and polarity-regulating cues suggest its underlying cellular and signaling activities would be considerably more amplified and easily perturbed than those operating in diffusely growing cells. However, growth and regulatory mechanisms that underlie pollen tube growth should share a general blueprint with cells that rely on more subtle, but fundamentally similar, cellular activities for their expansion. Moreover, pollen tube growth mechanisms also likely overlap with those that underlie other polarity-dependent cellular processes, such as cell division and polarized transport of cellular components (70, 105, 141). Therefore, pollen tubes provide a dramatic cell growth system whose understanding will impact our overall knowledge on cell expansion, proliferation, and differentiation.

One classical (130) and several recent reviews (14, 21, 22, 37, 56, 83, 92, 122) on pollen tube or plant polar cell growth in general provide an excellent background to the discussions here. Recent advances in cellular, molecular, and genetic resources, such as imaging tools, pollen transcriptomic and proteomic information (5, 25, 60, 61, 110), mutants and, more importantly, the combined use of these resources to probe the pollen tube growth system, have added significant depth and new insights to our understanding of this polar cell growth process. Here we focus on integrating recent findings, primarily from tobacco, lily, and *Arabidopsis*, that together reveal a host of regulatory factors that interact in hierarchical signaling pathways and feedback loops to relay extracellular cues and intracellular metabolic and signaling fluctuations to drive a spatially and temporally regulated cell growth process.

THE POLAR CELL GROWTH PROCESS

Upon landing on the stigmatic surface of the pistil, pollen grains hydrate and germinate, and each extrudes a polarized outgrowth to form a pollen tube. Pollen tubes elongate rapidly within specific pistil tissues, targeting ovules that are often located at distances thousands of times that of the diameter of the grain away from the stigma. Growth is restricted to the tube apex; as the tip advances, periodic callose deposition occurs distal to the migrating cell front, compartmentalizing the pollen protoplast to the most proximal region of the elongating tube (**Figure 1*a***). Beyond these common parameters, pollen tubes from different species show a broad range of growth efficiency. For instance, lily pollen tubes grow at an astounding average speed of 200–300 nm/sec in vitro, exceeding that of neurite outgrowth in culture (56). Growth rates ranging from ~25–30 to ~80–100 nm/sec have been reported for in vitro–grown tobacco pollen tubes (17, 66, 81). In vivo, tobacco pollen tubes may reach 4.5 cm within the pistil in approximately 30 h to reach the ovules (19). The *Arabidopsis* pistil is approximately 2.5 mm long; pollen tubes reach the most distal ovules approximately 10–15 h after pollination (124). In vitro, *Arabidopsis* pollen tubes may attain lengths as long as 800 μm within the first 6 hours of growth (7). Pollen tubes also show pronounced oscillatory growth patterns, marking rapid and slow growth phases (40, 59, 67). We discuss the current understanding of how the pollen tube cell surface, intracellular components, cytoplasmic conditions, and signaling cascades contribute to this polar cell growth process. For both structural and functional reasons, most of the efforts aimed at dissecting the cellular and regulatory aspects of pollen tube growth have focused on the most proximal region, within 50 μm from the tip, which is subdivided and referred to in our discussion as the apex, apical flank, subapical region, and shank of the tube (**Figure 2*a***).

THE POLLEN TUBE CELL SURFACE

The pollen tube surface permits rapid cell expansion at the tip and provides support for the structural, biochemical, and signal-response demands needed for the growth process. The pollen tube tip wall is thin and pectinaceous (10). Esterified pectin is secreted at the pollen tube tip and presumed to provide a strong but malleable surface that permits rapid cell expansion. As the tip extends, this pectin is deesterified by pectin methylesterase (PME) and trails to the more distal region. The exposed carboxyl groups of pectin cross-link into the pollen tube wall, which is composed of an outer cellulosic and an inner callose layer. Increasing or reducing PME activity results in reduced pollen tube growth rates, altered tube morphology and tube rupture in vitro, and mildly compromised male transmission in vivo (9, 11, 68, 106, 135). Pollen tube growth is compromised even when total PME activity is nondetectably or moderately (~20%) reduced and when just one out of the twelve *Arabidopsis* PME genes is mutated. These observations support the notion that the chemical difference between pectin in the tip and the subapical walls is tightly regulated, and possibly relies on multiple PMEs each having overlapping and unique roles in sculpting the pollen tube wall. Moreover, PME inhibitors are also localized to the pollen tube tip and interact with PME to modulate growth rates (118). Cellulose synthase mutants show an almost 90% reduction in male transmission efficiency and their pollen tubes are less competitive than wild-type pollen in reaching the distal end of the ovary (49). Regular deposition of callose plugs is often considered a characteristic of normally elongating pollen tubes and seems to be tightly coupled to localized [H^+] conditions (A.C. Certal, A. Cheung, J. Feijo, unpublished observations). However, an *Arabidopsis* callose synthase mutant producing pollen tubes lacking detectable callose walls and plugs is nevertheless fertile, showing only a slight disadvantage when in competition with wild-type (101). Whether a floral architecture–dependent reliance on callose walls and plugs exists remains to be determined. The importance of the plasmalemma to pollen tube growth is discussed in detail below, but male deficiency observed in *Arabidopsis* mutants compromised in their ability to insert lipid-modified proteins into membranes (84) underscores the general importance of a properly decorated cell membrane.

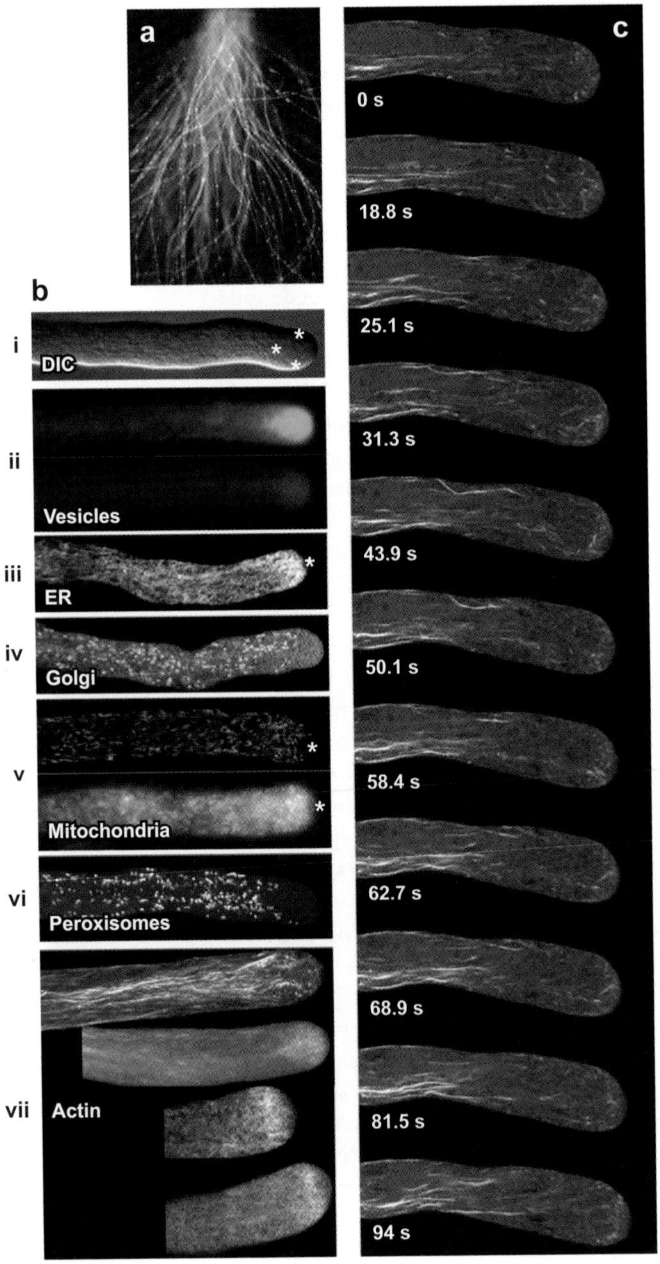

INTRACELLULAR ORGANIZATION

The polarized pollen tube morphology is accompanied by a polarized intracellular organization pattern that is highly structured yet extremely dynamic (see references in 21 and 56) (**Figures 1** and **2**, **Supplemental Movies 1–6**; Follow the **Supplemental Material** link from the Annual Reviews home page at **http://www.annualreviews.org**). Most noticeable is the segregation of an abundance of transport vesicles to an inverted cone-shaped domain at the apical region referred to as the "clear zone" from which most granular organelles are excluded. This cytoplasmic zonation is essential for the polar cell growth process. Also apparent are an extensive endoplasmic reticulum (ER) network and large numbers of secretory and biosynthetic organelles. Networks of actin microfilaments and microtubules (41, 48) are both prominent in pollen tubes. The actin cytoskeleton is essential for angiosperm pollen tube growth but the role of microtubules remains unclear. In the considerably slower growing gymnosperm pollen tubes (~20 μm/h), both cytoskeleton systems are needed for growth (1).

The Endomembrane System, Intracellular Trafficking, and Its Regulation

A bidirectional, "reverse fountain" cytoplasmic streaming pattern is one of the hallmark features of growing angiosperm pollen tubes (**Supplemental Movies 1** and **3**). The bulk flow of cytoplasm with its granular organelles and subresolution vesicles moves toward the proximal region of the tube along the cell cortex, reaching the subapical region and flanking the inverted cone of vesicles, then reverses direction and moves back to the distal region within the core cytoplasm. Flows of cytoplasm can be seen gushing from the clear zone to join the backward stream of organelles. Depending on the plant species, the clear zone typically occupies the apical 5–20 μm of the pollen tube and the inverted cone region is almost exclusively occupied by densely packed transport vesicles (28, 85). Similar to other structural and functional elements that have been examined in the pollen tube, the clear zone is not a rigidly defined domain but is instead dynamic; the inverted cone of vesicles periodically expands from and compresses against the apical membrane (26, 108) (**Supplemental Movie 2**). The region where the cytoplasmic streams reverse direction is also dynamic; it oscillates back and forth from the apex. These oscillatory patterns are likely to be part of the cellular design that underlies pollen tube oscillatory growth (see below). Whereas individual organelle classes reach different distances from the tube apex (**Figure 1*b***) and traffic into the inverted cone region occasionally and at different frequencies (89), wholesale invasions of these organelles into the apical cytoplasm are signs of compromised growth, often exhibited as slowed and, more severely, depolarized, or "ballooned" growth. The differential organelle distribution seems a rational design to achieve functional zonation whereby the transport vesicles deliver membrane and copious amounts

Cytoplasmic streaming: movement of the cytoplasm driven by intracellular motility systems

Figure 1

The intracellular organization and dynamics of pollen tubes. **Supplemental Movies 1–6** accompany this figure. (*a*) Tobacco pollen tubes grown in a semi–in vivo growth system (see Semi–In Vivo Pollen Tube Growth System). Aniline blue staining highlights the periodic callose plugs that maintain the pollen tube protoplast in the most proximal region. (*b*) Polarized cytoplasmic organization in tobacco pollen tubes elongating in vitro. From top to bottom: (*i*) Differential inference contrast (DIC) image of an unstained pollen tube. Asterisks mark the boundary of the clear zone. See **Supplemental Movie 1** for cytoplasmic streaming pattern. (*ii*) GFP-Rab11 labeled (*upper*) and FM4–64 labeled (*lower*) vesicles were coimaged in the same tube. See **Supplemental Movie 2** for periodic expansion and compression of the GFP-Rab11 labeled inverted cone; see **Supplemental Movie 3** for trafficking of small vesicular congregates into and out of the clear zone. (*iii*) The endoplasmic reticulum (ER) was labeled by expressing GFP-HDEL. (*iv*) Golgi bodies were labeled by expressing GFP-Rab2. (*v*) Mitochondria were labeled by expressing a mitochondrial transit peptide fused to GFP. A medial confocal optical section (*upper*) reveals a small apical invert cone region devoid of mitochondria. An epifluorescence image (*lower*) shows the subapical congregation of these organelles. (*vi*) Peroxisomes were labeled by expressing a peroxisome-targeted GFP. (*vii*) Pollen tubes expressing GFP-NtADF1 reveal a range of actin cytoskeleton structures. Top panel: the extensive labeling approximates most closely the actin structures observed in fixed immunostained pollen tubes (91). Second panel: apparent funneling of subapical actin into the rearward cytoplasmic streams (see **Supplemental Movie 4** for "reverse fountain"-streaming actin cables in the subapical region), reminiscent of the funnel-shaped structure revealed by phalloidin staining (45, 137). Bottom two panels: confocal medial sections of a turning pollen tube 3 min apart in a time series (see **Supplemental Movie 5**). GFP-NtADF1 localizes to a dynamic subapical actin mesh. (*a*) and (*b*) are adapted from Reference 21 with permission. (*c*) Actin dynamics at the apical region. The elongating pollen tube was labeled by GFP-NtADF1 expression and grows at rates ~30 nm/s, comparable to unlabeled control cells. Apical actin is seen cycling between a mesh-like organization (e.g., at 18.8 s, 31.3 s, 81.5 s, 94 s), 3–5 μm from the apex, and more disorganized collections of short cables. **Supplemental Movie 6** covers 6 min of growth for this tube, and slow and fast growing phases are evident. Not shown are the male germ unit (MGU, the tube nucleus and two sperm cells) and vacuoles. The MGU usually trails the apical cytoplasm; its integrity and transport are dependent on the microtubules (3). A large vacuole occupies the most distal part of the cell and an extensive network of streaming tubular vacuolar membranes distributes throughout the cytoplasm, reaching around the base of the clear zone (57, 89).

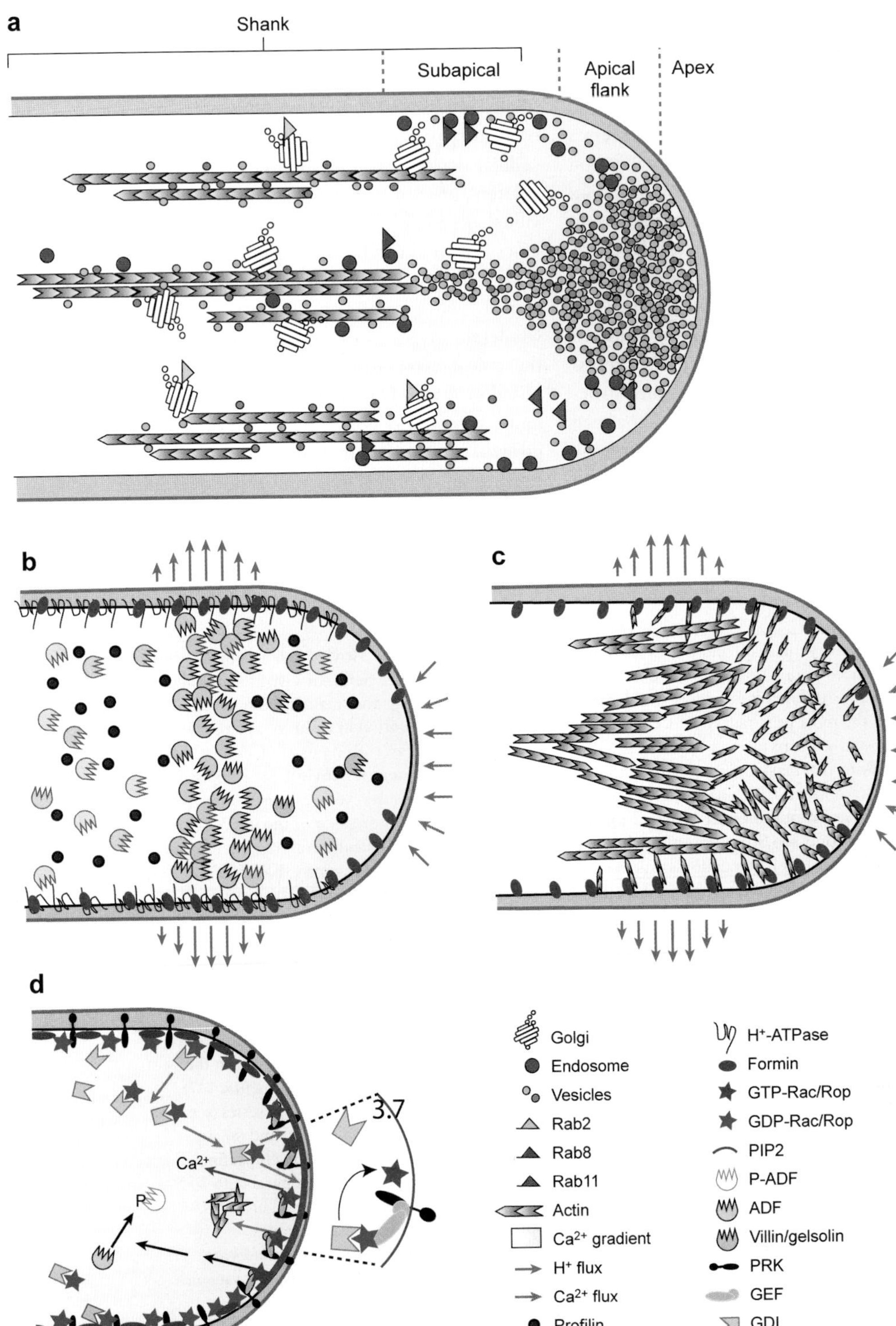
a
Shank
Subapical
Apical flank
Apex
b
c
d
Ca2+
P
3.7
Golgi
Endosome
Vesicles
Rab2
Rab8
Rab11
Actin
Ca2+ gradient
H+ flux
Ca2+ flux
Profilin
H+-ATPase
Formin
GTP-Rac/Rop
GDP-Rac/Rop
PIP2
P-ADF
ADF
Villin/gelsolin
PRK
GEF
GDI
GAP

of cell wall materials to the tip while the subtending cytoplasm cycles organelles to ensure a continuous supply of freshly loaded vesicles.

Polar growth, the accumulation of vesicles in the inverted cone region, and cytoplasmic streaming are all inhibited by actin cycling inhibitors (26, 56, 108), providing compelling evidence for the actin cytoskeleton as the major underlying motility system that supports growth and intracellular trafficking. How vesicles and different organelle classes are differentially trafficked beyond the base of the clear zone remains unclear. Conceivably, a structural element that is also dynamic could permit differential passage of vesicles and different organelle classes; actin structures in the subapical region have been suggested to provide such a role (81).

Exocytosis and Endocytosis

Cell growth and maintenance rely on continuous exocytic and endocytic activities to deliver and recycle membrane and uptake extracellular matrix components. As much as 80% of the secreted membrane is estimated to be recycled during pollen tube growth (109). Pollen tubes also internalize molecules secreted from the female tissues and sometimes sequester them into storage or degradative organelles (47, 76). A precise understanding of exocytic and endocytic events remains undescribed. Transformed pollen tubes expressing GFP-labeled membrane or cell wall proteins or secreted GFP show reverse fountain cytoplasmic streams and an inverted cone region marked by green fluorescence (18, 26). These observations support the conventional view that the apical and apical flank membrane

Actin cycling: continuous polymerization and depolymerization at the two ends of actin filaments giving rise to differential rates of polymerization and depolymerization at the two ends; inhibitors include latrunculin B and cytochalasin D

Figure 2

Schematic representations of key structural, regulatory, and signaling elements in pollen tubes. The yellow shading represents the tip-focused [Ca^{2+}] gradient. Concentrations reaching 10 μM at the tip to a basal level of 150–200 nM around the base of the clear zone have been reported (59). Components are not shown to scale in terms of size or abundance. Many aspects of the figures are deduced from existing literature. (*a*) The shank actin cytoskeleton and apical inverted cone of vesicles. Streaming Golgi bodies, endosomes, newly synthesized (*light blue*) and recycled (*light purple*) vesicles, and Rab GTPases are shown. Long actin cables are shown with their rapidly polymerizing ends pointing in the direction of streaming. Microtubules (41, 48) are not shown. (*b*) Ca^{2+} and H^+ fluxes and a model for how they may affect actin binding proteins (ABPs) such as actin depolymerizing factor (ADF), gelsolin/villin, and profilin. Lighter shading of ABPs indicates weaker activity. (*c*) Actin organization in the apical and subapical region. Although not to scale, the width of actin cables is intended to reflect relative actin bundle thickness. Nascent actin filaments are stimulated by formins along the cell periphery. A working model is that short nascent cables are remodeled by surrounding ABPs, including severing by ADF and gelsolin, providing new filament ends for polymerization and assembly into higher order structures. The exact configuration of actin in the apical dome remains to be revealed; it is displayed relatively randomly to reflect high levels of actin sculpting and restructuring activities implicated by cytoplasmic conditions and actin motility patterns in the apical and subapical regions. These activities include disassembling arriving shank actin cables and reassembly of actin into the reverse stream, actin assembly along the apical/subapical cell periphery, and incorporation of nascent cables from the cell periphery into the subapical cytoplasm where many short cables can be seen joining the higher order assemblies in the subapical region, subsequently feeding into the rearward stream in funnel-shaped sprints. (*d*) Pollen-specific receptor kinase (PRK)-Rac/Rop signaling apparatus. PRK, guanine nucleotide exchange factor (GEF), the Rac/Rop molecular switch, and the three targets Ca^{2+}, apical actin assembly, and ADF inactivation are shown. The collaborators in maintaining tip-localized Rac/Rop activity, GTPase activating protein (GAP), guanine nucleotide dissociation inhibitor (GDI), and phosphatidylinositol 4,5-bisphosphate (PIP2) at the apical membrane, are also shown. The red, pink, and black arrows that emanate from the Rac/Rop signaling apparatus indicate pathways mediated by ROP-interactive Cdc42/Rac-interactive binding (CRIB) motif-containing protein 3 and 4 (RIC3 and RIC4) and yet to be identified effectors. The PRK-Rac/Rop signaling apparatus and the cycling of GDP- and GTP-Racs/Rops are magnified.

domain defined by the inverted cone is the prominent site for secretion. However, in similar experiments, a PME (NtPME1-GFP) is deposited at the apical wall where PME activity is believed to be most critically needed without accumulating at the inverted cone region, suggesting an exocytic pathway not targeted at the apex (9). Furthermore, H^+-ATPases have been localized distal to the tip, most prominently occupying the subapical membrane region, and their localization pattern is functionally correlated to the polar cell growth process (87; A. Certal, A. Cheung, J. Feijo, unpublished results). Determining where exocytosis and recycling of PME and H^+-ATPases occur and how these proteins are translocated after delivery to the membrane should reveal specific regulatory designs that contribute to functional specialization in the different membrane domains of elongating pollen tubes.

Lipophilic FM dyes have been used to follow endocytic events in pollen tubes grown in vitro (13, 108). Uptake of the dyes is rapid and occurs most prevalently behind the tube apex. Internalized membrane traffics from the subapical region toward the tip along the forward cytoplasmic stream. Within minutes, apical FM accumulation overlaps entirely with the inverted cone region and flows of FM-labeled vesicles and some small organelles can be seen tracking the reverse fountain cytoplasmic streams. Together with transmission electron microscopy data that revealed prevalent coated pits and vesicles along the subapical membrane (28, 85), these observations are consistent with prominent endocytic activity at the subapical membrane, followed by incorporation of endocytic organelles into the reverse fountain cytoplasmic streams, with vesicles derived from recycled membrane cycling into and out of and accumulating in the inverted cone region along with vesicles freshly derived from the biosynthetic route (**Figures 1*b*, 2*a***). Dissecting exocytic and endocytic events (139) and determining if differential hotspots exist for specific proteins will be challenging, especially considering the dynamics of these events in rapidly growing pollen tubes.

Regulators for Vesicle Trafficking

A properly regulated membrane trafficking system is evidently an important aspect of pollen tube growth. However, mutations in what may be considered key regulatory elements for vesicular transport often have no or very subtle effects on pollen tubes, whereas similar, or even the same, mutations more profoundly affect root hairs, a slower-growing polar growth cell type (55, 127). Possibly, pollen tube growth, a process that is intricately regulated yet essential for the survival of a plant species, is genetically hardwired with functional overlaps and genetic redundancy (5, 61, 110). Pollen tubes may also be functionally adapted to function adequately to ensure fertilization even under suboptimal conditions.

Rab GTPases

Rab GTPases are members of the Ras-related superfamily of small GTPases. Rab GTPases regulate vesicle budding and targeting specificity and mediate vesicle fusion, thus they are crucial for membrane trafficking (121, 136). Although the details will most likely vary, plant Rabs examined thus far show considerable conservation with their counterparts from mammalian and yeast cells. As is the case for other Ras-related proteins, Rabs shuttle between the inactive GDP-bound and the activated GTP-bound forms. The distribution of these two activity states is tightly monitored and regulated: Guanine nucleotide exchange factors (GEFs) activate Rabs; guanine nucleotide dissociation inhibitors (GDIs) and GTPase-activating proteins (GAPs) keep them inactivated.

Most of the insights into the functional role of Rabs came from studies of transformed pollen expressing dominant negative

(DN) and constitutively active (CA) forms of these GTPases. DN Rabs preferentially bind GDP and are believed to compete with their wild-type counterparts for endogenous Rab-interacting factors, thus conferring DN effects on Rab-mediated processes. CA Rabs are maintained predominantly in the GTP-bound activated state, conferring runaway activity. In transformed tobacco pollen tubes, Rab2 regulates vesicle trafficking between the ER and Golgi and Rab11 targets vesicles to the inverted cone and may also mediate their recycling (18, 26) (**Figure 2*a***). Downregulating Rab activity by overexpressing DN mutant proteins noticeably increases retention of GFP-labeled cargo proteins within the secretory system but does not prohibit their delivery to the cell surface. Both pollen tube growth and male fertility are noticeably but moderately reduced. Apparently, reduced trafficking along the apex-targeted route, perhaps supplemented by activity from alternate routes regulated by other Rabs, is adequate to sustain growth, albeit at reduced rates. Conversely, the expression of CA Rab11 strongly inhibits pollen germination and significantly inhibits tube growth and male fertility. The compensatory activity needed to counteract an overstimulated secretory process, for instance accelerated membrane retrieval and retrograde trafficking, may be lacking. Alternatively, the level and location of signaling molecules delivered to the cell membrane may be deregulated, and the consequential impact on cellular signaling cascades is not easily reversed. Compromised Rab11-regulated targeting of vesicles to the inverted cone region also results in pronounced pollen tube meandering, underscoring the importance of focused secretion for restricted growth at the tip. Beyond assigning Rab functional localization within the endomembrane trafficking pathway, it is important to examine how different Rab classes or different isoforms within the same class of Rabs participate in regulating spatially defined exocytosis. Moreover, an *Arabidopsis* Rab11 homolog (RabA4b), important for root hair growth, interacts with a phosphoinositide kinase, which interacts with a Ca^{2+} binding protein, thus potentially linking local lipid and $[Ca^{2+}]$ conditions to vesicular processes (114). It is reasonable to expect a similar capacity for pollen Rab GTPases, but this remains to be explored.

Exocysts

Exocysts are octameric protein complexes important for tethering approaching vesicles to specific exocytic sites (98). Exocyst mutants in yeast are defective in secretion and budding, which is also a polarized cell growth process; exocysts also differentially regulate mammalian exocytic pathways. Homologs of all eight exocyst subunits are present in plants (31). Severe mutant alleles in *Arabidopsis* SEC8, a single gene for an exocyst subunit, confer male sterility (23). Upon pollination, mutant pollen grains fail to extrude a tube, suggesting defects in the initial establishment of growth polarity. Less severe *sec8* alleles induce modest pollen tube growth defects, observed only when in competition with wild-type pollen. In a semi–in vivo pollen tube growth assay (See Semi–In Vivo Pollen Tube Growth System), mutant pollen tubes show a mild reduction in growth rates relative to wild-type. Mutations in two other plant exocyst subunits, the maize SEC3 (142) and an *Arabidopsis* Exo70 (132), one out of 39 related genes, also result in defective root hairs. The importance of Exo70 for pollen tube growth remains to be determined. In yeast, exocysts are known to interact with Rabs and another class of Ras-related GTPase, Rhos, to regulate localized exocytosis (102). A Rho GTPase-interacting protein from *Arabidopsis* interacts with SEC3 (86). Given the importance of Rabs and Rhos (see below) in pollen tube growth, exocysts likely play crucial roles in this polar cell growth process, possibly integrating Rho signaling and Rab-regulated vesicular events.

SEMI-IN VIVO POLLEN TUBE GROWTH SYSTEM

In this assay (19), pollen tubes initially grow within the pollinated pistil, i.e., in the in vivo environment. After they have penetrated and elongated for some distance into the pistil, the pistil is excised and cultured on in vitro pollen tube growth media. Pollen tubes elongating in the pistil will emerge from the cut end of the pistil and continue the polar growth process in vitro (**Figure 1*a***). This system is most suited for pollen tube tropic response assays (19, 58, 104). Operationally, the uniformity of pollen tube growth direction as these tip growth cells emerge from the pistil onto the medium allows easier observation and scoring of tropic responses. Biologically, the passage through the pistil may, on the one hand, have exhausted nutrient resources stored in the grain and, on the other hand, primed the elongating pollen tubes with female factors. These biological consequences may together confer higher pollen tube sensitivity for directional cues presented in the medium. This assay is also gaining popularity in *Arabidopsis* pollen tube growth comparison assays (23, 146).

THE ACTIN CYTOSKELETON AND ITS REGULATION

Organization and Function

Numerous studies of pollen tubes from different plant species reveal an elaborate and dynamic actin cytoskeleton in these polar growth cells (**Figures 1**, **2**; **Supplemental Movies 4–6**). Long actin cables extend along the length of the tube shank and reach the base of the inverted cone region where a dynamic network of shorter actin cables congregate. The subapical structure has been referred to as a ring (81), collar (43, 46), mesh (17, 45), funnel-like structure (137), or a fringe (91), reflecting its dynamic, and perhaps also fragile, nature. Actin filaments within the apical dome and along the tip membrane were historically more difficult to observe, probably because they are substantially finer and their existence more variable and dependent on growth conditions than the progressively more assembled structures in the subapical and shank cytoplasm. An actin marker (See Actin Markers), GFP-mTalin, reveals a prevalent collection of short actin bundles in the apical region of tobacco pollen tubes (43, 66), similar to, but considerably more subtle than, those observed with phalloidin staining of lily pollen tubes (41). The dynamic nature of actin in the apical and subapical region is also revealed by GFP-NtADF1–expressing pollen tubes (17) (**Figure 1*b*,*c***; **Supplemental Movies 4–6**). Moreover, nascent actin cables can be seen emanating from the apical and flanking membrane when actin nucleation is stimulated (20). Furthermore, vesicles in the inverted cone are rapidly dissipated and reassembled upon application and withdrawal, respectively, of actin dynamics inhibitors, supporting a functional role for apical actin in transporting vesicles to and from the tube apex (26, 108).

GFP-mTalin: GFP-labeled actin binding domain from mouse Talin

GFP-NtADF1: GFP-labeled actin depolymerizing factor 1 from tobacco

Actin nucleation: stimulates formation of actin dimers and trimers to provide nuclei for rapid actin polymerization; the rate-determining step in actin polymerization

As there are apparent differences in actin organization, there is also a separation of labor between the different actin structures. That the long actin cables in the shank show a reverse-fountain motility pattern and cytoplasmic streaming and growth both cease upon treatment with actin dynamics inhibitors provide strong evidence for the actomyosin system as the underlying cellular machinery for intracellular motility, secretion, and growth (56). Several studies showed that tip growth ceases and the subapical actin structures are disrupted by low dosages of actin dynamics inhibitors, whereas cytoplasmic streaming and actin organization in the shank are not affected, suggesting that the actin structures at the subapical and apical region are more closely correlated with growth (46, 137). Moreover, the levels of apical actin seem to increase before growth rates peak, leading to the suggestion that actin assembly drives growth (66).

Microtubules are important for the cohesive transport of the male germ unit and they may support slow and short range trafficking of vesicles and organelles (3, 119). Interestingly, deploymerization of microtubules results in considerably straighter pollen tubes than normal and microtubule integrity seems to be dependent on the actin cytoskeleton (48). Perhaps by interacting with the actin cytoskeleton, microtubules somehow enable pollen tubes to better negotiate their growth paths.

Actin Binding Proteins

The functional significance of several key actin binding proteins (ABPs) to plant development and pollen tube growth was reviewed recently (65, 116, 129). ABPs regulate actin polymerization and dynamics but are regulated by multiple conditions that are known to impact pollen tube growth, such as Ca^{2+}, pH, and phosphoinositides (42, 90, 95). We discuss briefly how these ABPs affect pollen tube growth to highlight how intricately this polar cell growth process may be regulated.

Profilin binds monomeric actin, modulates actin nucleation, and enhances actin polymerization. Injecting profilin into an already rather abundant endogenous pool of profilin severely disrupts actin organization and inhibits tube growth (137). Profilins are distributed throughout the pollen tube, but the actin sequestering activity of some profilins is sensitive to Ca^{2+} (82), which displays a concentration gradient at the tube tip that fluctuates with growth (see below) and thus can profoundly affect profilin activity spatially and temporally.

Actin depolymerizaing factor (ADF) binds to actin filaments cooperatively and severs and stimulates the depolymerization of actin filaments. Pollen tubes monitor their ADF level and activity stringently. Mild overexpression of ADF severely disrupts actin organization and inhibits growth (17). The actin binding activity of ADF is inhibited by phosphorylation at a conserved serine residue in the N-terminal region; the phosphorylation is under the control of a Rho GTPase signaling cascade (see below). Overexpression of Rho GTPases increases the level of phosphorylated ADF, disrupts actin organization, and induces depolarized growth (see below). The in vitro actin binding activity of pollen ADF is enhanced by slightly alkaline conditions. H^+ is differentially distributed in the pollen tube cytoplasm, giving rise to an acidic tip and an alkaline subapical region (see below) where ADF and AIP, an actin interacting protein that enhances the actin depolymerizing activity of ADF (72), are predominantly located (17, 90). Thus, local augmentation of ADF activity in the subapical region is possible (**Figure 2*b***). Given the dynamics observed for actin structures in this region, ADF is well positioned to play a pivotal role in regulating subapical actin organization and dynamics. Moreover, the apical membrane domain is enriched in phosphatidylinositol 4,5-bisphosphate (PIP2) (29, 54) and ADF activity in vitro is inhibited by PIP2 binding. An acidic tip cytoplasm and a PIP2-enriched apical membrane should preclude high ADF activity around the apical cortex and this could be important for nascent actin assembly along the apical and apical flank membrane.

ACTIN MARKERS

Fixed and stained pollen tubes provide the best snapshot of the entire actin collection in an elongating pollen tube (91), but achieving optimum fixation and efficient actin staining efficiency to preclude artifacts is technically challenging. GFP-mTalin and GFP-NtADF1 are the predominant actin markers used in live cell studies in pollen tubes. These live cell markers capture the dynamics of actin structures, but each probe has differential affinity for and different effects on various actin configurations. GFP-mTalin stabilizes actin and inhibits pollen tube growth (20, 66, 73, 81, 144); it can reveal subtle actin structures (43, 66). GFP-NtADF1 binds actin filaments efficiently. To its advantage as an actin marker, the GFP fusion results in substantial reduction in its actin depolymerizing activity compared with NtADF1 alone (17), allowing GFP-NtADF1 to be used at a range of expression levels. At moderate expression levels, GFP-NtADF1 decorates the subapical actin mesh most prominently. At higher but not yet growth inhibiting levels, GFP-NtADF1 labeling reveals the shank actin cables (17) (**Figure 1*b*,*c***). Wilsen and colleagues (144) performed a comparative study with these markers and a Fimbrin-derived actin marker. A usable GFP-actin fusion protein in plants has not been reported.

As a family, villins/gelsolins are actin severing proteins, although some also show bundling, capping, and actin-nucleating activity. With no identifiable gelsolin homologs in plant genomes, it appears that alternative splicing of villin transcripts could have given rise to several gelsolin-like proteins (35, 62, 78, 147). Overexpression of lily ABP29 appears to almost obliterate the actin cytoskeleton (147), and a reduction in the activity of ABP41 (35) by antibody injection in lily pollen tubes results in growth inhibition. The in vitro actin-modifying activities associated with these proteins show different sensitivity to regulatory elements such as Ca^{2+} (64). The combination of coexisting villin/gelsolin isoforms that may be differentially sensitive to Ca^{2+} and the fluctuating apical Ca^{2+} conditions potentially provides a powerful means whereby even subtle changes in the cytoplasmic environment could be sensitively utilized to modify the actin cytoskeleton.

Capping proteins (CP) bind and modulate polymerization on the rapidly growing end of actin filaments. The capping activity of AtCP1, a heterodimeric CP from *Arabidopsis*, is inhibited by phosphatidic acid (PA), resulting in increased actin polymerization. When poppy pollen is treated with PA, the level of actin filaments increases significantly (63). PA is derived from phospholipase D (PLD) hydrolysis of phosphatidylcholine (94, 138). Altering PLD activity or PA levels results in disruptions in the pollen tube actin cytoskeleton and growth (95, 111). Thus, CPs may provide a link to lipid-mediated regulation of this polar cell growth process.

The two families of actin nucleating proteins, formins and the actin-related protein 2 and 3 (Arp2/3) complex, are both expressed in pollen. Arp2/3 is a seven-subunit protein complex that stimulates actin assembly from pre-existng actin filaments to produce branched actin networks. Its action in pollen tubes has not yet been reported, although Arp2/3 is known to be regulated by Rho GTPases, key regulators for polar growth (see below). Conversely, formins stimulate actin assembly de novo to produce linear actin cables from the cell membrane and their activity is enhanced by interacting with profilin. Overexpression of AFH1 (*Arabidopsis* formin homology 1) in transformed tobacco pollen tubes stimulates actin assembly along the cell membrane, allowing nascent actin structures to be observed readily as short actin bundles emanating from the cell periphery (20). Growth is moderately stimulated by slight increases in AFH1 levels, whereas overexpression of AFH1 induces supernumerary actin cables and pollen tube depolarization. The *Arabidopsis* genome contains 21 formin genes (24). Analysis of the pollen-expressed members of this protein family suggests their activities may overlap partially around the apical and subapical membrane domain (A. Cheung and H.-M. Wu, unpublished observations). How these formins collaborate to maintain and modulate actin polymerization during pollen tube growth and reorientation remains to be examined.

IONIC AND METABOLIC REGULATION OF POLLEN TUBE GROWTH

The recent status of our understanding of ion dynamics and their relationship to the pollen polar cell growth process was discussed extensively (40, 59, 96, 117). Here, we only review this briefly to provide a background for our discussion on recent findings that aimed toward understanding how ion distribution, in particular Ca^{2+} and H^+, in the pollen tube is maintained and how the effect of ionic fluctuations may be mediated to regulate the polar cell growth process. We also discuss how metabolic regulation may be integrated into this tip growth process.

Ionic Regulation

Elongating pollen tubes exhibit a steep tip-focused $[Ca^{2+}]$ gradient that is dissipated when growth ceases. The $[Ca^{2+}]$ gradient is maintained largely by Ca^{2+} influx at the pollen tube tip membrane. How the cell wall, whose assembly consumes a large amount of Ca^{2+}, may buffer incoming Ca^{2+} is not known. Considering the extensive endomembrane system in pollen tubes and that the pollen transcriptome has hundreds of transporter genes (8), internal stores likely also contribute to cytoplasmic Ca^{2+} homeostasis. In fact, *Arabidopsis* mutants defective in a cell membrane–associated Ca^{2+}-ATPase (124) or an endomembrane-associated Ca^{2+}-ATPase (H. Sze, personal communication) are male deficient and show reduced seed sets. Mutant pollen tubes also show reduced growth rates in vitro.

Although a large collection of Ca^{2+}-binding signaling proteins is expressed in pollen (5, 61, 110), how the cytoplasmic Ca^{2+} conditions may be sensed and mediated to regulate the polar tube growth is unknown. Among the potential Ca^{2+} sensors, two calcium-dependent protein kinases (CDPKs) from *Petunia* differentially affect pollen tube growth (53). Pertubation of the cell membrane–localized PiCDPK1 results in severely depolarized pollen tubes, increased intracellular Ca^{2+}, and abolition of the tip-focused $[Ca^{2+}]$ gradient, whereas perturbation of the organelle-located PiCDPK2 has only a moderate influence on growth (148). It was noted in this study that PiCDPK1 might interact with GDI; if so, this interaction may provide a link between cytoplasmic Ca^{2+} conditions and an important regulatory apparatus for the polar cell growth process (see below).

Pollen tubes maintain a slightly acidic tip that is subtended by a cytoplasm of increasing pH, culminating in a slightly alkaline region around the base of the clear zone (39, 90). The acidic tip is closely associated with growth, whereas the alkaline region appears to be constitutive but may play an important role in regulating actin remodeling in the subapical region where the cytoplasmic streams reverse direction. The polarized cytoplasmic H^+ distribution is maintained by H^+ influx at the apex and efflux along the subapical membrane. This pattern of H^+ flow into and out of the pollen tube is believed to be maintained by subapical membrane–localized H^+-ATPases that are excluded from the tip (87; A. Certal, A. Cheung, J. Feijo, unpublished observations).

K^+ influx occurs at the pollen tube tip. Analyses of channel mutants in *Arabidopsis* support an important physiological role for K^+ uptake in pollen tubes and in male efficiency (4, 33, 34, 97). The flow of Cl^- in and out of the pollen tube at its tip and distal membrane domains, respectively, is believed to regulate hydrodynamic conditions in the cytoplasm and thus may be vital for the tube growth process (149; but also see 117).

Metabolic Regulation

Early studies of pollen tube growth placed considerable emphasis on how this process is metabolically supported by the paternal reserve from the pollen cell and maternal resources derived from the female tissues. In *Petunia* a novel fermentation pathway operates to adjust to growth within the anoxic condition in the pistil. Mutants defective in this bypass pathway are male deficient. In vitro, pollen tube growth is substantially more severely inhibited relative to wild-type when subjected to anoxic conditions (44). Furthermore, studies in the self-incompatibility response in poppy showed that soluble pyrophosphatases (sPPases) are important to pollen tube growth; their reduction or inhibition is associated with reduced or arrested growth (27). However, sPPases are rare in plant cytosol although increased pyrophosphastase activity enhances resource mobilization in transformed potato tubers (128). Together, these observations support the view that pollen has indeed evolved metabolic strategies that are particularly suited to generate biosynthetic resources for tube growth.

Although plastids and mitochondria do not contribute genetically to offspring in most angiosperms, they are nonetheless abundant throughout the cytoplasm of elongating pollen tubes. Mitochondria can stream deep into the apical dome and congregate there to densities noticeably higher than in the more distal region of the tube (89) (**Figure 2*b***). $NADP^+$ and ATP generated from these mitochondria are proposed to be important for growth propensity (15). Moreover, extracellular ATP (eATP) status apparently also impacts pollen polarity establishment because pollen germination, tube growth, and male transmission are inhibited in *Arabidopsis* plants defective in pollen-expressed apyrases, membrane anchored extracellular proteins with tri- and diphosphatase activities that target primarily eATP (120, 131, 146). Pollen tubes release ATP as they grow; one possible route for how eATP may regulate this tip growth is via NADPH-dependent superoxide production in the extracellular matrix (126). This leads to the potential role of reactive oxygen species (ROS), which are detected prevalently at the subapical mitochondria congregate in lily pollen tubes (15) and along the tobacco pollen tube cell periphery (112). Given the growing evidence of ROS involvement in Rho GTPase–regulated polar cell growth (52, 100) and that multiple cytoplasmic factors (e.g., $[Ca^{2+}]$) can impact ROS status, metabolic or signaling outputs that affect ROS production and distribution most likely participate in regulating the polar tube growth process. Moreover, although pollen tubes normally do not accumulate detectable levels of nitric oxide (NO), exogenously applied NO severely repels these cells in a cGMP-dependent manner, causing them to change growth direction as much as 180° (113). How factors that contribute to oxidoreductive conditions in the pollen tube interact to impact growth needs further analyses.

CELL MEMBRANE–ASSOCIATED SIGNALING APPARATUS

Over the past decade attention has focused on a family of pollen-specific receptor kinases (PRKs) and a family of Ras-related Rho-type GTPases, referred to as Racs/Rops (12). Recent studies provide evidence that they comprise a major signaling apparatus for the polar tube growth process (52, 100).

Rac/Rop GTPases

Like the Rab GTPases, Racs/Rops are switched on and off by GTP and GDP binding. Racs/Rops regulate multiple linear as well as intersecting signaling pathways in plants (see References 52 and 100 and references therein). Overexpression of CA Racs/Rops in pollen tubes results in severe depolarization. DN Racs/Rops reduce growth rate and induce mild tip swelling. Upregulation of Rac/Rop GTPases is accompanied by increased apical actin polymerization and intracellular $[Ca^{2+}]$, dissipating the $[Ca^{2+}]$ gradient. The actin cytoskeleton becomes overpolymerized and highly disorganized. The depolarizing effect can be overcome by overexpressing ADF, which apparently is inactivated by a Rac/Rop regulated kinase (16) (**Figure 2*d***). Moreover, Racs/Rops physically associate with a phosphatidylinositol monophosphate (PIP) kinase, whose product, PIP2, colocalizes with Racs/Rops at the pollen tube tip membrane (80). Therefore, the impact Racs/Rops have on pollen tube growth must result from cascading effects that involve interactions between multiple cellular and biochemical pathways, ultimately impacting the actin cytoskeleton and membrane trafficking. The effect of loss of Rac/Rop functions on male fertility has been more difficult to discern. Nevertheless, mutations in one of these small GTPases in maize results in reduced male competitiveness (2).

A PRK-Rac/Rop Signaling Apparatus

Racs/Rops partition between the cytoplasm and plasmalemma. Their activity is restricted to the apical membrane in elongating pollen tubes; when delocalized across a broader apical domain, growth depolarizes. How does a pollen tube ensure the spatial and temporal distribution of Rac/Rop activity to the apical membrane domain, especially considering that the tip membrane and its constituents are rapidly displaced to the flank as the tip advances?

After a long search, the key upstream activators, GEFs, for Racs/Rops (RopGEFs) were identified (6). When expressed as GFP-labeled proteins, several of them localize to the pollen tube tip membrane and induce Rac/Rop-dependent depolarized growth, establishing a functional linkage among these proteins (51). The more far-reaching implication is that RopGEFs provide the connection between the Rac/Rop molecular switch and signal perception at the pollen tube cell surface. Earlier studies on tomato (*Lycopersicon esculentum*) PRKs (LePRKs) identified a kinase-associated phosphoprotein (LeKPP, for *L. esculentum* kinase partner protein), which turned out to be a member of the GEF protein family (71). When overexpressed, LeKPP induces pollen tube depolarization and disrupts cytoplasmic streaming and actin organization in a manner reminiscent of Rac/Rop- and RopGEF-induced phenotypes. Previous studies on LePRKs suggest they may be important regulators for pollen germination and tube growth (69). In pollen grains and germinating tubes, LePRK2 is phosphorylated, whereas LePRK1 is not. LePRKs associate in a high molecular weight complex, which may also include Rac/Rop GTPases (143). The extracellular matrix domain of LePRKs interacts with distinct pollen and stigma factors prior to and after germination, suggesting possible alterations of their activity state (133, 134). A low-molecular-weight stylar factor added to in vitro grown pollen tubes dephosphorylates LePRK2 and dissociates the protein complex. These interactions potentially regulate LePRK signaling activity to downstream pathways, regulating growth within the pistil. Although upstream regulators for RopGEFs remain to be definitively established, observations thus far are quite compelling and support a signaling pathway whereby LePRKs and their functionally analogous relatives recruit cytosolic GEFs to the cell membrane, possibly phosphorylate them to alter their nucleotide exchange activity, and induce changes in Rac/Rop signaling capacity (**Figure 2*d***). However, these PRKs are localized constitutively along the pollen tube plasmalemma (18, 99), so how is Rac/Rop signaling prevented from spilling from the tip to the subapical region?

The negative regulators GAP and GDI apparently play important roles in ensuring spatial restriction of activated Racs/Rops to the apical membrane (77, 79) (**Figure 2*d***). YFP-GAP localizes to the plasmalemma starting just distal to the apical membrane domain. As the tip advances, activated Racs/Rops are displaced to the apical flank membrane. GAPs positioned there accelerate their inactivation and restrict Rac/Rop activity from spreading beyond the apex, preventing depolarized growth. In another series of experiments, two Rac/Rop mutants, NtRac5 (DN) and NtRac5 (R69A), both unable to bind to GDI, fail to locate to the apical membrane but instead occupy a broader membrane span along the apical flank and shank. Curiously, although NtRac5(R69A) retains its GTPase activity and ability to interact with its regulators and effectors, it nevertheless fails to induce growth depolarization, unlike its wild-type and CA counterparts. These observations together led to the suggestion that cytoplasmic GDI actively extracts the inactivated Racs/Rops from the subapical membrane to the cytoplasm. The GDI-Rac/Rop interaction is needed not only to recycle the GDP-bound Racs/Rops back to the apical region but is also important in some ways for their activation. Once Racs/Rops are inserted into the apical membrane, GDP/GTP exchange takes place to activate them. As the tip advances the activated Racs/Rops are displaced to the subapical flank and the GTP-bound Racs/Rops are inactivated by GAPs (**Figure 2*d***) (79). Many of the details, such as mechanisms that target the RhoGDI-Rac/Rop complexes to the apex and GAP to the subapical flanks, and the full impact of GDI on the cycling of Rac/Rops between its two activity states, remain to be defined.

RICs: ROP-interactive CRIB motif-containing proteins, where CRIB stands for Cdc42/Rac-interactive binding

How are signal inputs to the Rac/Rop molecular switch propagated to downstream pathways to maintain tip-focused cell expansion? The Rac/Rop-regulated lipid environment at the apical membrane and the apical [Ca^{2+}] gradients are obvious candidates to mediate multiple downstream pathways. As mentioned earlier, Racs/Rops interact with PIP-kinase, whose product PIP2 colocalizes with Racs/Rops at the pollen tube tip membrane (80). Phospholipase C, which hydrolyzes PIP2 to inositol 1,4,5-triphosphate (IP3) and diacylglycerol (DAG), localizes to the apical flank and distal membrane (29, 54). These second messengers would be produced at the subapical flank where enzymes and substrates meet, although DAG is detected specifically at the apical membrane and is believed to be delivered there via membrane recycling (54). PIP2 regulates ADF; IP3 may regulate internal Ca^{2+} stores; DAG may serve as a precursor for PA. ADF, Ca^{2+}, and PA are all known regulators for pollen tube growth, potentially acting through their ability to regulate ABPs and vesicular events to impact the actin cytoskeleton and membrane trafficking. The cascading effect from Rac/Rop signaling is therefore both immense and plastic.

RICs are a small family of Rac/Rop immediate targets and were identified from *Arabidopsis* (145). When overexpressed in tobacco pollen tubes, several of these cytosolic proteins, some showing membrane association, induce defects ranging from growth reduction to depolarization. The normally tip-membrane association of GFP-RIC4 is significantly enhanced and delocalizes to the shank when *Arabidopsis* Rop1 is co-overexpressed, consistent with recruitment of these effectors by activated Racs/Rops. Conversely, GFP-RIC3 shows a predominantly cytosolic localization. When GFP-RIC3 is co-overexpressed with Rop1, its localization is enhanced along the cortical cytoplasm and pollen tube depolarization is significantly augmented. The differential interactions of RIC3 and RIC4 with Rop1 affect two downstream pathways, leading to a model whereby RIC4 promotes apical actin polymerization and RIC3 increases intracellular [Ca^{2+}], which would enhance Ca^{2+}-dependent F-actin disassembly in the apex, counteracting the action of the RIC4-mediated pathway (50) (**Figure 2*d***).

LEADERS AND FOLLOWERS IN OSCILLATORY POLLEN TUBE GROWTH

Diverse biological systems display a rhythmic regularity that is for sure underpinned by oscillatory cellular events that can be correlated with output behavior. Pollen tubes grown in vitro show notable oscillatory growth patterns, with periods of 20–90 s and robust amplitudes of a 3- to 4-fold difference between peak and trough growth rates (40, 59, 96, 107, 117). Shorter and longer suboscillations have also been recorded (96). The levels of short actin cables in the apical region, secretion, apical [Ca^{2+}] and [H^+], metabolic activities, and ion fluxes around the membrane all oscillate with growth periods but show variant phase relationships with growth. Time resolution of such rapid events inevitably presents considerable challenges and probably is one of the reasons why events that were previously recorded as occuring after growth have been corrected to lead growth (66), and vice versa (59). Much of the information, controversy, and unresolved issues have been discussed extensively (59, 96, 117). What underlies the polar cell growth process are apparently multiple hierarchical, intersecting signaling pathways as well as feedback loops. For our attempt to extrapolate a probable hierarchical relationship between these events, a brief recapitulation of the major findings will suffice.

Peak metabolic activity, as reflected by the biochemical status at the subapical region where mitochondria congregate (15), and peak secretion, as reflected by oscillation at the FM dye–labeled inverted cone region (108), both precede growth peaks in lily pollen tubes. These strategies seem intuitive because growth requires energy and is dependent on new wall and membrane deposits. Interestingly, secretory oscillations continue even when growth has ceased, suggesting the existence of an inherent oscillator independent of growth (107). In terms of signaling activity, Hwang and coworkers (66) showed that in tobacco pollen tubes Rop1 activation and apical actin assembly, as revealed by tip localization of GFP-RIC4 and GFP-mTalin intensity, respectively, are ahead of peak growth, although the authors noted that these GFP-mTalin–expressing pollen tubes grow slower and show longer oscillation periods compared with control tubes. The Rac/Rop-activated apical actin assembly was proposed to be sufficient to drive growth surges. Subapical alkalinity in lily pollen tubes also peaks before growth (90). Presumably, ADF activity would be enhanced by the more alkaline condition, thus accelerating actin dynamics and driving growth. Increases in Ca^{2+} influx and intracellular [Ca^{2+}] both lag behind peak growth rates in lily pollen tubes (59). Growth was thus proposed to provide modulation for intracellular Ca^{2+} conditions, perhaps by activating putative Ca^{2+} channels (30, 115, 140) during apical membrane expansion.

Although debate will continue on the precision of data collection and the interpretation of the data (59, 96, 117), key questions remain: How can phasing of these growth and regulatory events be used to identify the master regulator that sets the clock and establishes the functional hierarchy among the various factors that underlie the polar cell growth process? Published studies that examined Rac/Rop signaling activities and those related to ion dynamics, secretion, and metabolism have been carried out in pollen tube growth systems that show vastly different rates and oscillatory properties (59, 66, 96, 107), and with experimental probes that could significantly affect growth rates and oscillatory periods (66). Although cross-correlation analysis may alleviate some of these complications (59), it would be more instructive if phase correlations of these multiple factors are made in the same pollen tube growth system and whenever possible, with probes that are least perturbing for the normal pollen tube growth process. Moreover, actin assembly and Ca^{2+} distribution appear to feed back on Rop1 activity because disrupting actin dynamics or partially dissipating the intracellular [Ca^{2+}] gradient suppresses RIC4 accumulation at the tip (66). A pollen tube poised to surge in growth seems to be already modulating the Rac/Rop signaling pathway to prepare for growth deceleration. Thus, examining how each of the oscillatory events impacts the others will increase our understanding of how these interactions together orchestrate this fascinating polar cell growth process.

PERSPECTIVE

With many of the players that support and regulate the pollen tube polar cell growth process in place and the availability of genetic and cell biological resources, connecting the dots for the major interacting components is likely to be imminently possible. Live-cell manipulations of pollen tubes grown in vitro provide powerful means to examine multiple regulatory elements combinatorially. These studies will allow the dissection of intricate signaling cross talk and feedback mechanisms. It is important now to learn whether the activities that orchestrate the optimum in vitro growth process are actually deployed and/or modified in the in vivo pollen tube growth processing within the pistil. The secrets of how stylar and ovule factors contribute to pollen tube growth, guidance, and repulsion are unfolding (19, 32, 58, 75, 103, 104). We are poised to examine how female factors contribute to regulatory and cellular events that underlie the polar cell growth process. Although fine imaging of the cellular machinery during pollen tube growth in the pistil is not yet possible, efforts are ongoing to explore such methodology (34, 36, 38, 67). The original quest to understand how pollen interacts with the pistil to achieve fertilization will also be the next frontier when we explore the pollen tube growth process as it occurs within the female tissues.

SUMMARY POINTS

1. A highly structured but dynamic intracellular organization of organelles and vesicles and an elaborate and dynamic actin cytoskeleton underlie the pollen polar cell growth process.
2. Polarized ionic conditions—a tip-focused Ca^{2+} gradient, an acidic tip, and an alkaline subapical cytoplasm—are crucial for growth polarity.
3. A Rho GTPase molecular switch mediates cell surface signals to establish and maintain polarity.
4. Pollen tube growth and the underlying cellular and regulatory processes all oscillate with the same period but with variant phase relationships with each other. Studying the phasing of these events may provide information toward identifying the master regulator of the polar cell growth process.
5. A future challenge is to understand how pistil factors impact the polar cell growth process as pollen tubes strive to achieve fertilization.

DISCLOSURE STATEMENT

The authors are not aware of any biases that might be perceived as affecting the objectivity of this review.

ACKNOWLEDGMENTS

We thank colleagues on and off the UMass campus, including Jose Feijó, Ilse Foissner, Dave Gross, Benedikt Kost, Stan Roux, Otto Schmidt, Heven Sze, and Shaul Yalovsky for providing comments and suggestions for parts of or the whole manuscript. We also thank Peter Hepler for continual discussions on pollen tubes. Recent work in our lab was supported by grants from the United States Department of Agriculture (CSREES 2004-35304-14873, 2005-35304-16030) and the National Science Foundation (IOB0544222, MCB0618339).

LITERATURE CITED

1. Anderhag P, Hepler P, Lazzaro M. 2000. Microtubules and microfilaments are both responsible for pollen tube elongation in the conifer *Picea abies* (Norway spruce). *Protoplasma* 214:141–57
2. Arthur KM, Vejlupkova Z, Meeley RB, Fowler JE. 2003. Maize ROP2 GTPase provides a competitive advantage to the male gametophyte. *Genetics* 165:2137–51
3. Astrom H, Sorri O, Raudaskoski M. 1995. Role of microtubules in the movement of the vegetative nucleus and generative cell in tobacco pollen tubes. *Sex. Plant Reprod.* 8:61–69
4. Becker D, Geiger D, Dunkel M, Roller A, Bertl A, et al. 2004. AtTPK4, an *Arabidopsis* tandem-pore K^+ channel, poised to control the pollen tube membrane voltage in a pH- and Ca^{2+}-dependent manner. *Proc. Natl. Acad. Sci. USA* 101:15621–26
5. Becker JD, Feijó JA. 2007. How many genes are needed to make a pollen tube? Lessons from transcriptomics. *Ann. Bot.* 100:1117–23
6. **Berken A, Thomas C, Wittinghofer A. 2005. A new family of RhoGEFs activates the Rop molecular switch in plants. *Nature* 436:1176–80**

6. Describes the isolation of the GEF of Racs/Rops, which is unlike GEFs from many other organisms; supports the theory that the Rac/Rop molecule switch system has evolved specific regulatory characteristics.

7. Boavida LC, McCormick S. 2007. Temperature as a determinant factor for increased and reproducible in vitro pollen germination in *Arabidopsis*. *Plant J.* 52:570–82
8. Bock KW, Honys D, Ward JM, Padmanaban S, Nawrocki EP, et al. 2006. Integrating membrane transport with male gametophyte development and function through transcriptomics. *Plant Physiol.* 140:1151–68
9. Bosch M, Cheung AY, Hepler PK. 2005. Pectin methylesterase, a regulator of pollen tube growth. *Plant Physiol.* 138:1334–46
10. Bosch M, Hepler PK. 2005. Pectin methylesterases and pectin dynamics in pollen tubes. *Plant Cell* 17:3219–26
11. Bosch M, Hepler PK. 2006. Silencing of the tobacco pollen pectin methylesterase NtPPME1 results in retarded in vivo pollen tube growth. *Planta* 223:736–45
12. Brembu T, Winge P, Bones AM, Yang Z. 2006. A RHOse by any other name: a comparative analysis of animal and plant Rho GTPases. *Cell Res.* 16:435–45
13. Camacho L, Malho R. 2003. Endo/exocytosis in the pollen tube apex is differentially regulated by Ca^{2+} and GTPases. *J. Exp. Bot.* 54:83–92
14. Campanoni P, Blatt MR. 2007. Membrane trafficking and polar growth in root hairs and pollen tubes. *J. Exp. Bot.* 58:65–74
15. Cardenas L, McKenna ST, Kunkel JG, Hepler PK. 2006. NAD(P)H oscillates in pollen tubes and is correlated with tip growth. *Plant Physiol.* 142:1460–68
16. Chen CY, Cheung AY, Wu HM. 2003. Actin-depolymerizing factor mediates Rac/Rop GTPase-regulated pollen tube growth. *Plant Cell* 15:237–49

16. One of three papers cited here that describe downstream target systems for Rac/Rop signaling.

17. Chen CY, Wong EI, Vidali L, Estavillo A, Hepler PK, et al. 2002. The regulation of actin organization by actin-depolyerizing factor in elongating pollen tubes. *Plant Cell* 14:2175–90
18. Cheung AY, Chen CY, Glaven RH, de Graaf B, Vidali L, et al. 2002. Rab2 GTPase regulates vesicle trafficking between the endoplasmic reticulum and the Golgi bodies and is important to pollen tube growth. *Plant Cell* 14:945–62
19. Cheung AY, Wang H, Wu HM. 1995. A floral transmitting tissue-specific glycoprotein attracts pollen tubes and stimulates their growth. *Cell* 82:383–93
20. Cheung AY, Wu HM. 2004. Overexpression of an *Arabidopsis* formin stimulates supernumerary actin cable formation from pollen tube cell membrane. *Plant Cell* 16:257–69
21. Cheung AY, Wu HM. 2007. Structural and functional compartmentalization in pollen tubes. *J. Exp. Bot.* 58:75–82
22. Cole RA, Fowler JE. 2006. Polarized growth: maintaining focus on the tip. *Curr. Opin. Plant Biol.* 9:579–88
23. Cole RA, Synek L, Zárský V, Fowler JE. 2005. SEC8, a subunit of the putative *Arabidopsis* exocyst complex, facilitates pollen germination and competitive pollen tube growth. *Plant Physiol.* 138:2005–18
24. Cvrcková F, Novotný M, Picková D, Zárský V. 2004. Formin homology 2 domains occur in multiple contexts in angiosperms. *BMC Genmonics* 5:44–52
25. Dai S, Li L, Chen T, Chong K, Xue Y, Wang T. 2006. Proteomic analyses of *Oryza sativa* mature pollen reveal novel proteins associated with pollen germination and tube growth. *Proteomics* 6:2504–29
26. de Graaf BH, Cheung AY, Andreyeva T, Levasseur K, Kieliszewski M, Wu HM. 2005. Rab 11 GTPase-regulated membrane trafficking is crucial for tip-focused pollen tube growth in tobacco. *Plant Cell* 17:2564–79
27. de Graaf BH, Rudd JJ, Wheeler MJ, Perry RM, Bell EM, et al. 2006. Self-incompatibility in *Papaver* targets soluble inorganic pyrophosphatases in pollen. *Nature* 444:490–93

28. Derksen J, Rutten TLM, van Amstel T, de Win A, Doris F, Steer M. 1995. Regulation of pollen tube growth. *Acta Bot. Neerl.* 44:93–119
29. Dowd PE, Coursol S, Skirpan AL, Kao T, Gilroy S. 2006. *Petunia* phospholipase C1 is involved in pollen tube growth. *Plant Cell* 18:1483–53
30. Dutta R, Robinson KR. 2004. Identification and characterization of stretch-activated ion channels in pollen protoplasts. *Plant Physiol.* 135:1398–406
31. Elias M, Drdova E, Ziak D, Bavlnka B, Hala M, et al. 2003. The exocyst complex in plants. *Cell Biol. Int.* 27:199–201
32. Escobar-Restrepo JM, Huck N, Kessler S, Gagliardini V, Gheyselinck J. 2007. The FERONIA receptor-like kinase mediates male-female interactions during pollen tube reception. *Science* 317:656–60
33. Fan LM, Wang YF, Wang H, Wu WH. 2001. In vitro *Arabidopsis* pollen germination and characterization of the inward potassium currents in *Arabidposis* pollen grain protoplasts. *J. Exp. Bot.* 52:1604–14
34. Fan LM, Wang YF, Wu WH. 2003. Outward K^+ channels in *Brassica chinensis* pollen protoplasts are regulated by external and internal pH. *Protoplasma* 220:143–52
35. Fan X, Hou J, Chen X, Chaudhry F, Staiger CJ, Ren H. 2004. Identification and characterization of a Ca^{2+}-dependent actin filament-severing protein from lily pollen. *Plant Physiol.* 136:3979–89
36. Faure JE, Rotman N, Fortune P, Dumas C. 2002. Fertilization in *Arabidopsis thaliana* wild type: developmental stages and time course. *Plant J.* 30:481–88
37. Feijó JA, Costa SS, Prado AM, Becker JD, Certal AC. 2004. Signalling by tips. *Curr. Opin. Plant Biol.* 7:89–98
38. Feijó JA, Moreno N. 2004. Imaging plant cells by two-photon excitation. *Protoplasma* 223:1–32
39. Feijó JA, Sainhas J, Hackett GR, Kunkel JG, Hepler PK. 1999. Growing pollen tubes possess a constitutive alkaline band in the clear zone and a growth-dependent acidic tip. *J. Cell Biol.* 144:483–96
40. Feijó JA, Sainhas J, Holdaway-Clarke T, Cordeiro MS, Kunkel JG, Hepler PK. 2001. Cellular oscillations and the regulation of growth: the pollen tube paradigm. *BioEssays* 23:86–94
41. Fossiner I, Grolig F, Obermeyer G. 2002. Reversible protein phosphorylation regulates the dynamic organization of the pollen tube cytoskeleton: effects of calyculin A and okadaic acid. *Protoplasma* 220:1–15
42. Franklin-Tong VE, Drobak BK, Allan AC, Watkins PAC, Trewavas AJ. 1996. Growth of pollen tubes of *Papaver rhoeas* is regulated by a slow-moving calcium wave propagated by inositol 1,4,5-trisphosphate. *Plant Cell* 8:1305–21
43. Fu Y, Wu G, Yang Z. 2001. Rop GTPase-dependent dynamics of tip-localized F-actin controls tip growth in pollen tubes. *J. Cell Biol.* 152:1019–32
44. Gass N, Glagotskaia T, Mellema S, Stuurman J, Barone M, et al. 2005. Pyruvate decarboxylase provides growing pollen tubes with a competitive advantage in Petunia. *Plant Cell* 17:2355–68
45. Geitmann A, Snowman BN, Emons AMC, Franklin-Tong VE. 2000. Alterations in the actin cytoskeleton of pollen tubes are induced by the self-incompatibility reaction in *Papaver rhoeas*. *Plant Cell* 12:1239–51
46. Gibbon BC, Kovar DR, Staiger CJ. 1999. Latrunculin B has different effects on pollen germination and tube growth. *Plant Cell* 11:2349–63
47. Goldraij A, Kondo K, Lee CB, Hancock CN, Sivaguru M, et al. 2006. Compartmentalization of S-RNase and Ht-B degradation in self-incompatible *Nicotiana*. *Nature* 439:805–10

48. Gossot O, Geitmann A. 2007. Pollen tube growth: coping with mechanical obstacles involves the cytoskeleton. *Planta* 226:405–16

49. Goubet F, Misrahi A, Park SK, Zhang Z, Twell D, Dupree P. 2003. AtCSLA7, a cellulose synthase-like putative glycosyltransferase, is important for pollen tube growth and embryogenesis in *Arabidopsis*. *Plant Physiol.* 131:547–57

50. Gu Y, Fu Y, Dowd P, Li S, Vernoud V, et al. 2005. A Rho-family GTPase controls actin dynamics and tip growth via two counteracting downstream pathways in pollen tubes. *J. Cell Biol.* 169:127–38

51. Gu Y, Li S, Lord EM, Yang Z. 2006. Members of a novel class of *Arabidopsis* Rho guanine nucleotide exchange factors control Rho GTPase-dependent polar growth. *Plant Cell* 18:366–81

52. Gu Y, Wang Z, Yang Z. 2004. Rop/RAC GTPase: an old new master regulator for plant signaling. *Curr. Opin. Curr. Biol.* 7:527–36

53. Harper JF, Breton G, Harmon A. 2004. Decoding Ca^{2+} signals through plant protein kinases. *Annu. Rev. Plant Biol.* 55:263–88

54. Helling D, Possart A, Cottier S, Klahre U, Kost B. 2006. Pollen tube tip growth depends on plasma membrane polarization mediated by tobacco PLC3 activity and endocytic membrane recycling. *Plant Cell* 18:3519–34

55. Hemsley PA, Kemp AC, Grierson CS. 2005. The TIP GROWTH DEFECTIVE1 S-acyl transferase regulates plant cell growth in *Arabidopsis*. *Plant Cell* 17:2554–63

56. Hepler PK, Vidali L, Cheung AY. 2001. Polarized cell growth in higher plants. *Annu. Rev. Cell Dev. Biol.* 17:159–87

57. Hicks GR, Rojo E, Hong S, Carter DG, Raikhel NV. 2004. Germinating pollen has tubular vacuoles, displays highly dynamic vacuole biogenesis, and requires VACUOLESS1 for proper function. *Plant Physiol.* 134:1227–39

58. Higashiyama T, Yabe S, Sasaki N, Nishimura Y, Miyagishima S, et al. 2001. Pollen tube attraction by the synergid cell. *Science* 293:1480–83

59. Holdaway-Clarke T, Hepler PK. 2003. Control of pollen tube growth: role of ion gradients and fluxes. *New Phytol.* 159:539–63

60. Holmes-Davis R, Tanaka CK, Vensel WH, Hurkman WJ, McCormick S. 2005. Proteome mapping of mature pollen of *Arabidopsis thaliana*. *Proteomics* 5:4864–84

61. Honys D, Twell D. 2004. Transcriptome analysis of haploid male gametophyte development in *Arabidopsis*. *Genome Biol.* 5:R85

62. Huang S, Blanchoin L, Chaudhry F, Franklin-Tong VE, Staiger CJ. 2004. A gelsolin-like protein from *Papaver rhoeas* pollen (PrABP80) stimulates calcium-regulated severing and depolymerization of actin filaments. *J. Biol. Chem.* 279:23364–75

63. Huang S, Gao L, Blanchoin L, Staiger CJ. 2006. Heterodimeric capping protein from *Arabidopis* is regulated by phosphatidic acid. *Mol. Biol. Cell* 17:1946–58

64. Huang S, Robinson RC, Gao LY, Matsumoto T, Brunet A, et al. 2005. *Arabidopsis* VILLIN1 generates actin filaments cables that are resistant to depolymerization. *Plant Cell* 17:486–501

65. Hussey PJ, Ketelaar T, Deeks MJ. 2006. Control of the actin cytoskeleton in plant cell growth. *Annu. Rev. Plant Biol.* 57:109–25

66. Hwang JU, Gu Y, Lee YJ, Yang Z. 2005. Oscillatory ROP GTPase activation leads the oscillatory polarized growth of pollen tubes. *Mol. Biol. Cell* 16:5385–99

67. Iwano M, Shiba H, Miwa T, Che FS, Takayama S, et al. 2004. Ca^{2+} dynamics in a pollen grain and papilla cell during pollination of *Arabidopsis*. *Plant Physiol.* 136:3562–71

50. One of three papers cited here that describe downstream target systems for Rac/Rop signaling.

56. Provides an overview of the status of polar cell growth up to 2000.

59. One of two extensive reviews cited here on oscillatory pollen tube growth; provides an encyclopedic discussion on the area.

68. Jiang L, Yang SL, Xie LF, Puah CS, Zhang XQ, et al. 2005. *VANGUARD1* encodes a pectin methylesterase that enhances pollen tube growth in the *Arabidopsis* style and transmitting tract. *Plant Cell* 17:584–96
69. Johnson MA, Preuss D. 2003. On your marks, get set, GROW! LePRK2-LAT52 interactions regulate pollen tube growth. *Trends Plant Sci.* 8:97–99
70. Jurgen G. 2005. Plant cytokinesis: fission by fusion. *Trends Cell Biol.* 15:277–83
71. **Kaothien P, Ok SH, Shuai B, Wengier D, Cotter R, et al. 2005. Kinase partner protein interacts with the LePRK1 and LePRK2 receptor kinases and plays a role in polarized pollen tube growth. *Plant J.* 42:492–503**

71. Identifies what turned out to be a ROPGEF homolog, potentially linking the Rac/Rop molecular switch to the reception of extracellular signals.

72. Ketelaar T, Allwood EG, Anthony R, Voigt B, Menzel D, Hussey PJ. 2004. The actin-interacting protein AIP1 is essential for actin organization and plant development. *Curr. Biol.* 14:145–49
73. Ketelaar T, Anthony RG, Hussey PJ. 2004. Green fluorescent protein-mTalin causes defects in actin organization and cell expansion in *Arabidopsis* and inhibits actin depolymerizing factor's actin depolymerizing activity in vitro. *Plant Physiol.* 136:3390–98
74. Kim S, Dong J, Lord EM. 2004. Pollen tube guidance: the role of adhesion and chemtropic molecules. *Curr. Top. Dev. Biol.* 61:61–79
75. Kim S, Mollet JC, Dong J, Zhang K, Park SY, Lord EM. 2003. Chemocyanin, a small basic protein from the lily stigma, induces pollen tube chemotropism. *Proc. Natl. Acad. Sci. USA* 100:16125–30
76. Kim S, Zhang K, Dong J, Lord EM. 2006. Exogenous free ubiquitin enhances lily pollen tube adhesion to an in vitro stylar matrix and may facilitate endocytosis of SCA. *Plant Physiol.* 142:1397–411
77. Klahre U, Baker C, Schmitt AC, Kost B. 2006. NtRhoGDI12 regulates Rac/Rop signaling and polar cell growth in tobacco pollen tubes. *Plant J.* 46:1018–31
78. Klahre U, Friederich E, Kost B, Louvard D, Chua NH. 2000. Villin-like actin-binding proteins are expressed ubiquitously in *Arabidopsis*. *Plant Physiol.* 122:35–47
79. Klahre U, Kost B. 2006. Tobacco RhoGTPase ACTIVATING PROTEIN1 spatially restricts signaling of RAC/Rop to the apex of pollen tubes. *Plant Cell* 18:3033–46
80. **Kost B, Lemichez E, Spielhofer P, Hong Y, Tolias K, et al. 1999. Rac homologues and compartmentalized phosphatidylinsitol 4,5-bisphosphate act in a common pathway to regulate polar pollen tube growth. *J. Cell Biol.* 145:317–30**

80. One of three papers cited here that describe downstream target systems for Rac/Rop signaling.

81. Kost B, Spielhofer P, Chua NH. 1998. A GFP-mouse talin fusion protein labels plant actin filaments in vivo and visualizes the actin cytoskeleton in growing pollen tubes. *Plant J.* 16:393–401
82. Kovar DR, Drobak BK, Staiger CJ. 2000. Maize profilin isoforms are functionally distinct. *Plant Cell* 12:583–98
83. Krichevsky A, Kozlovsky SV, Tian GW, Chen MH, Zaltsman A, Citovsky V. 2006. How pollen tubes grow. *Dev. Biol.* 303:405–20
84. Lalanne E, Honys D, Johnson A, Borner GHH, Lilley KS, et al. 2004. SETH1 and SETH2, two components of the glycosylphosphatidylinositol anchor biosynthetic pathway, are required for pollen germination and tube growth in *Arabidopsis*. *Plant Cell* 16:229–40
85. Lancelle SA, Hepler PK. 1992. Ultrastructure of freeze-substituted pollen tubes of *Lilium longiflorum*. *Protoplasma* 167:215–30
86. Lavy M, Bloch D, Hazak O, Gutman I, Poraty L, et al. 2007. A novel RAC/ROP effector links cell polarity, root meristem maintenance, and vesicle trafficking. *Curr. Biol.* 17:947–52

87. Lefebvre B, Arango M, Oufattole M, Crouzet J, Purnelle B, Boutry M. 2005. Identification of a *Nicotiana plumbaginifolia* plasma membrane H^+-ATPase gene expressed in the pollen tube. *Plant Mol. Biol.* 58:775–87

88. Lord EM, Russell SD. 2002. The mechanisms of pollination and fertilization in plants. *Annu. Rev. Cell Dev. Biol.* 18:81–105

89. Lovy-Wheeler A, Cardenas L, Kunkel JG, Hepler PK. 2007. Differential organelle movement on the actin cytoskeleton in lily pollen tubes. *Cell Moti. Cytoskelet.* 64:217–32

90. Lovy-Wheeler A, Kunkel JG, Allwood EG, Hussey PJ, Hepler PK. 2006. Oscillatory increases in alkalinity anticipate growth and may regulate actin dynamics in pollen tubes of lily. *Plant Cell* 18:2182–93

91. Lovy-Wheeler A, Wilsen KL, Baskin TI, Hepler PK. 2005. Enhanced fixation reveals the apical cortical fringe of actin filaments as a consistent feature of the pollen tube. *Planta* 221:95–104

92. Malho R, ed. 2006. *The Pollen Tube—A Cellular and Molecular Perspective*. Berlin: Springer-Verlag

93. McClure BA, Franklin-Tong V. 2006. Gametophytic self-incompatibility: understanding the cellular mechanisms involved in "self" pollen tube inhibition. *Planta* 224:233–45

94. Meijer HJ, Munnik T. 2003. Phospholipid-based signaling in plants. *Annu. Rev. Plant Biol.* 54:265–306

95. Monteiro D, Coelho PC, Rodrigues C, Camacho L, Quader H, Malhó R. 2005. Modulation of endocytosis in pollen tube growth by phosphoinositides and phospholipids. *Protoplama* 226:31–38

96. Moreno N, Colaço R, Feijó J. 2007. The pollen tube oscillator: integrating biophysics and biochemistry into cellular growth and morphogenesis. In *Rhythms in Plants: Phenomenology, Mechanisms, and Adaptive Significance*, ed. S Manuso, S Shalaba, pp. 39–62. Berlin/Heidelberg: Springer-Verlag

97. Mouline K, Véry AA, Gaymard F, Boucherez J, Pilot G, et al. 2002. Pollen tube development and competitive ability are impaired by disruption of a Shaker K^+ channel in *Arabidopsis*. *Dev. Biol.* 16:339–50

98. Munson M, Novick P. 2006. The exocysts defrocked, a framework of rods revealed. *Nat. Struct. Mol. Biol.* 13:577–81

99. Muschietti J, Eyal Y, McCormick S. 1998. Pollen tube localization implies a role in pollen-pistil interactions for the tomato receptor-like protein kinases LePRK1 and LePRK2. *Plant Cell* 10:319–30

100. Nibau C, Wu HM, Cheung AY. 2006. RAC/ROP GTPases: hubs for signal integration and diversification in plants. *Trends Plant Sci.* 11:309–15

101. Nishikawa S, Zinkl GM, Swanson RJ, Maruyama D, Preuss D. 2005. Callose (β-1,3 glucan) is essential for *Arabidopsis* pollen cell patterning, but not tube growth. *BMC Plant Biol.* 5:22

102. Novick P, Medkova M, Dong G, Hutagulung A, Reinisch K, Grosshans B. 2006. Interactions between Rabs, tethers, SNAREs and their regulators in exocysts. *Biochem. Soc. Trans.* 34:683–86

103. Palanivelu R, Brass L, Edlund AF, Preuss D. 2003. Pollen tube growth and guidance is regulated by *POP2*, an *Arabidopsis* gene that controls GABA levels. *Cell* 114:47–59

104. Palanivelu R, Preuss D. 2006. Distinct short-range ovule signals attract or repel *Arabidopsis thaliana* pollen tubes in vitro. *BMC Plant Biol.* 6:7

105. Paponov IA, Teale WD, Trebar M, Blilou I, Palme K. 2005. The PIN auxin efflux facilitators: evolutionary and functional perspectives. *Trends Plant Sci.* 10:170–77

88. Provides a good review of pollination and fertilization, areas not covered in depth here.

96. Provides a critical analysis of various studies on oscillatory pollen tube growth, and the challenges faced.

106. Parre E, Geitmann A. 2005. Pectin and the role of the physical propterties of the cell wall in pollen tube growth of *Solanum chacoense*. *Planta* 220:582–92
107. Parton RM, Fischer-Parton S, Trewavas AJ, Watahiki MK. 2003. Pollen tubes exhibit regular periodic membrane trafficking events in the absence of apical extension. *J. Cell Sci.*
108. Parton RM, Fischer-Parton S, Watahiki MK, Trewavas AJ. 2001. Dynamics of the apical vesicle accumulation and the rate of growth are related in individual pollen tubes. *J. Cell Sci.* I114:2685–95
109. Picton JM, Steer MW. 1983. Membrane recycling and the control of secretory activity in pollen tubes. *J. Cell Sci.* 63:303–10
110. Pina C, Pinto F, Feijó JA, Becker JD. 2005. Gene family analysis of the *Arabidopsis* pollen transcriptome reveals biological implications for cell growth, division control and gene expression regulation. *Plant Physiol.* 138:744–56
111. Potocký M, Eliás M, Profotová B, Novotná Z, Valentová O, Zárský V. 2003. Phosphatidic acid produced by phospholipase D is required for tobacco pollen tube growth. *Planta* 217:122–30
112. Potocký M, Jones MA, Bezvoda R, Smirnoff N, Zárský V. 2007. Reactive oxygen species produced by NADPH oxidase are involved in pollen tube growth. *New Phytol.* 174:742–51
113. Prado AM, Porterfield DM, Feijó JA. 2004. Nitric oxide is involved in growth regulation and reorientation of pollen tubes. *Development* 131:2707–14
114. Preuss ML, Schmitz AJ, Thole JM, Bonner HKS, Otegui MS, Nielsen E. 2006. A role for the RabA4b effector protein PI4Kb1 in polarized expansion of root hair cells in *Arabidopsis thaliana*. *J. Cell. Biol.* 172:991–98
115. Qu HY, Shang ZL, Zhang SL, Liu LM, Wu JY. 2007. Identification of hyperpolarization-activated calcium channels in apical pollen tubes of *Pyrus pyrifolia*. *New Phytol.* 174:524–36
116. Ren H, Xiang Y. 2007. The function of actin-binding proteins in pollen tube growth. *Protoplasma* 230:171–82

116. Provides a detailed discussion on the properties of various ABPs and how they are known to or could impact pollen tube growth.

117. Robinson KR, Messerli MA. 2002. Pulsating ion fluxes and growth at the pollen tube tip. *Science STKE* 2002(162):pe51–53
118. Rockel N, Wolf S, Kost B, Rausch T, Greiner S. 2007. Elaborate spatial patterning of cell wall PME and PMEI at the pollen tube tip involves PMEI endocytosis and reflects the distribution of esterified and deesterified pectins. *Plant J.* In press
119. Romagnoli S, Cai G, Cresti M. 2003. In vitro assays demonstrate that pollen tube organelles use kinesin-related motor proteins to move along microtubules. *Plant Cell* 15:251–69
120. Roux SJ, Steinebrunner I. 2007. Extracellular ATP: an unexpected role as a signaler in plants. *Trends Plant Sci.* In press
121. Rutherford S, Moore I. 2002. The *Arabidopsis* Rab GTPase family: another enigma variation. *Curr. Opin. Plant Biol.* 5:518–28
122. Samaj J, Müller J, Beck M, Böhm N, Menzel D. 2006. Vesicular trafficking, cytoskeleton and signaling in root hairs and pollen tubes. *Trends Plant Sci.* 11:594–60
123. Schiefelbein J, Galway M, Masucci J, Ford S. 1993. Pollen tube and root-hair tip growth is disrupted in a mutant of *Arabidopsis thaliana*. *Plant Physiol.* 103:979–85
124. Schiøtt M, Romanowsky SM, Baekgaard L, Jakobsen MK, Palmgren MG, Harper JF. 2004. A plant plasma membrane Ca^{2+} pump is required for normal pollen tube growth and fertilization. *Proc. Natl. Acad. Sci. USA* 101:9502–7
125. Sherman-Broyles S, Boggs N, Farkas A, Liu P, Vrebalov J, et al. 2007. *S* locus genes and the evolution of self-fertility in *Arabidopsis thaliana*. *Plant Cell* 19:94–106

126. Song CJ, Steinebrunner I, Wang X, Stout SC, Roux SJ. 2006. Extracellular ATP induces the accumulation of superoxide via NADPH oxidases in *Arabidopsis*. *Plant Physiol.* 140:1222–22
127. Song XF, Yang CY, Liu J, Yang WC. 2006. RPA, a class II ARFGAP protein activates ARF1 and U5 and plays a role in the root hair development in *Arabidopsis thaliana*. *Plant Physiol.* 141:966–76
128. Sonnewald U. 1992. Expression of *E. coli* inorganic phyrophosphatase in transgenic plants alters photoassimilate partitioning. *Plant J.* 2:571–81
129. Staiger CJ. 2000. Signaling to the actin cytoskeleton in plants. *Annu. Rev. Plant Physiol. Plant Mol. Biol.* 51:257–88
130. Steer MW, Steer JM. 1989. Pollen tube tip growth. *New Phytol.* 111:323–35
131. Steinebrunner I, Wu J, Su Y, Corbett A, Roux SJ. 2003. Disruption of apyrases inhibits pollen germination in *Arabidopsis*. *Plant Physiol.* 131:1638–47
132. Synek L, Schlager N, Eliás M, Quentin M, Hauser MT, Zárský V. 2006. AtEXO70A1, a member of a family of putative exocyst subunits specifically expanded in land plants, is important for polar growth and plant development. *Plant J.* 48:54–72
133. Tang W, Ezcurra I, Muschietti J, McCormick S. 2002. A cysteine-rich extracellular protein, LAT52, interacts with the extracellular domain of the pollen receptor kinase LePRK2. *Plant Cell* 14:2277–87
134. Tang W, Kelly D, Ezcurra I, Cotter R, McCormick S. 2004. LeSTIG1, an extracellular binding partner for the pollen receptor kinases LePRK1 and LePRK2, promotes pollen tube growth in vitro. *Plant J.* 39:343–53
135. Tian GW, Chen MH, Zaltsman A, Citovsky V. 2006. A pollen-specific pectin methylesterase involved in pollen tube growth. *Development* 294:83–91
136. Vernoud V, Horton AC, Yang Z, Nielsen E. 2003. Analysis of the small GTPase gene superfamily of *Arabidopsis*. *Plant Physiol.* 131:1191–208
137. Vidali L, McKenna ST, Hepler PK. 2001. Actin polymerization is essential for pollen tube growth. *Mol. Biol. Cell* 12:2534–45
138. Wang X. 2005. Regulatory functions of phospholipase D and phosphatidic acid in plant growth, development, and stress responses. *Plant Physiol.* 139:566–73
139. Wang X, Teng Y, Wang Q, Li X, Sheng X, et al. 2006. Imaging dynamic secretory vesicles in living pollen tubes of Picea meyeri using evanescent wave microscopy. *Plant Physiol.* 141:1591–603
140. Wang YF, Fan LM, Zhang WZ, Zhang W, Wu WH. 2004. Ca^{2+}-permeable channels in the plasma membrane of *Arabidopsis* pollen are regulated by actin microfilaments. *Plant Physiol.* 136:3892–904
141. Weijers D, Jurgens G. 2005. Auxin and embryo axis formation: the ends in sight? *Curr. Opin. Plant Biol.* 8:32–37
142. Wen TJ, Hochholdinger F, Sauer M, Bruce W, Schnable PS. 2005. The *roothairless1* gene of maize encodes a homolog of sec3, which is involved in polar exocytosis. *Plant Physiol.* 138:1637–43
143. Wengier D, Valsecchi I, Cabanas ML, Tang WH, McCormick S, Muschietti J. 2003. The receptor kinases LePRK1 and LePRK2 associate in pollen when expressed in yeast, but dissociate in the presence of style extract. *Proc. Natl. Acad. Sci. USA* 100:6860–65
144. Wilsen KL, Lovy-Wheeler A, Voigt B, Menzel D, Kunkel J, Hepler PK. 2006. Imaging the actin cytoskeleton in growing pollen tubes. *Sex Plant Reprod.* 19:51–62
145. Wu G, Gu Y, Li S, Yang ZB. 2001. A genome-wide analysis of *Arabidopsis* Rop-interactive CRIB motif-containing proteins that act as Rop GTPase targets. *Plant Cell* 13:2841–56

146. Wu J, Steinebrunner I, Sun Y, Butterfield T, Torres J, et al. 2007. Apyrase (nucleoside triphosphate-diphosphohydrolases) play a key role in growth control in *Arabidopsis*. *Plant Physiol.* 144:961–75
147. Xiang Y, Huang X, Wang T, Zhang Y, Liu Q, et al. 2007. ACTIN BINING PROTEIN29 from *Lilium* pollen plays an important role in dynamic actin remodeling. *Plant Cell* 19:1930–46
148. Yoon GM, Dowd PE, Gilroy S, McCubbin AG. 2006. Calcium-dependent protein kinase isoforms in *Petunia* have distinct functions in pollen tube growth, including regulating polarity. *Plant Cell* 18:867–78
149. Zonia L, Cordeiro S, Tupý J, Feijó JA. 2002. Oscillatory chloride efflux at the pollen tube apex has a role in growth and cell volume regulation and is targeted by inositol 3,4,5,6-tetrakisphosphate. *Plant Cell* 14:2233–49

Regulation and Identity of Florigen: FLOWERING LOCUS T Moves Center Stage

Franziska Turck, Fabio Fornara, and George Coupland

Max Planck Institute for Plant Breeding, D 50829 Cologne, Germany; email: coupland@mpiz-koeln.mpg.de

Annu. Rev. Plant Biol. 2008. 59:573–94

The *Annual Review of Plant Biology* is online at plant.annualreviews.org

This article's doi: 10.1146/annurev.arplant.59.032607.092755

1543-5008/08/0602-0573$20.00

Key Words

photoperiod, systemic signaling, floral transition, light-dependent protein stability, CONSTANS

Abstract

The transition from vegetative to reproductive growth is controlled by day length in many plant species. Day length is perceived in leaves and induces a systemic signal, called florigen, that moves through the phloem to the shoot apex. At the shoot apical meristem (SAM), florigen causes changes in gene expression that reprogram the SAM to form flowers instead of leaves. Analysis of flowering of *Arabidopsis thaliana* placed the *CONSTANS/FLOWERING LOCUS T* (*CO/FT*) module at the core of a pathway that promotes flowering in response to changes in day length. We describe progress in defining the molecular mechanisms that activate this module in response to changing day length and the increasing evidence that FT protein is a major component of florigen. Finally, we discuss conservation of FT function in other species and how variation in its regulation could generate different flowering behaviors.

Contents

INTRODUCTION

The life cycles of many plants are synchronized to the changing seasons. This response is particularly important at high latitudes, where extreme changes in environmental conditions occur at different times of the year. Perception of changes in day length is one of the major ways in which plants detect the changing seasons. Garner & Allard (24, 25), who were the first to describe this process in detail, referred to it as photoperiodism. These observations captured the imagination of plant researchers and attempts to explain the underlying mechanisms led to the discovery of fundamental plant processes such as the existence of phytochrome as a photoreceptor, systemic signaling from the leaf to the shoot apex during the initiation of flower development, and the role of circadian rhythms as the timekeeping mechanism. Many influential reviews dealing with these issues have appeared in various *Annual Reviews* series during the past 50 years, and each generation of researchers has approached the same biological problem with the tools available to them (8, 22, 46, 48, 83, 93, 102). This review describes the recent progress made mainly in *Arabidopsis* using the tools of molecular genetics, and it summarizes our current answers to the questions posed by the observations of Garner & Allard (24, 25).

INDUCTION OF FLOWERING BY PHOTOPERIOD IN *ARABIDOPSIS* AND THE EXTERNAL COINCIDENCE MODEL

Genetic approaches applied in *Arabidopsis thaliana* provided insight into the molecular mechanisms controlling photoperiodic responses. Recent reviews have described in detail the results of these approaches (4, 6, 32, 34, 38, 67, 79). *Arabidopsis* is a facultative long-day plant that flowers earlier under long days (LDs) of 16 h of light than under short days (SDs) of 8 or 10 h of light. The photoperiodic pathway mutants *co* (*constans*), *gi* (*gigantea*), *cry2* (*cryptochrome*), *flowering locus d* (*fd*), *flowering locus t* (*ft*), *fe*, and *fwa* flowered later than wild-type plants under LDs but at the same time as wild-type plants under SDs. The sequences of all these genes have now been published, with the exception of *FE* (1, 23, 27, 40, 44, 70, 84, 95), and they were proposed to comprise a single regulatory pathway, called the photoperiodic or long-day pathway, that promotes flowering specifically in response to LDs.

The GI-CO-FT proteins act in this order at the core of the photoperiodic pathway, and their regulation results in *FT* transcription under LDs but not SDs (**Figures 1** and **2**). *CO* mRNA is present under both LDs and SDs and is regulated by the circadian clock, so that it rises in abundance between 10 h and 12 h after dawn. GI increases *CO* mRNA abundance (62, 78, 85). Under SDs *CO* mRNA accumulates only during the night, whereas under LDs substantial expression is detected toward the end of the day. Furthermore, CO-mediated activation of *FT* transcription occurs at the end of the day under LDs but not under SDs (85). These comparisons

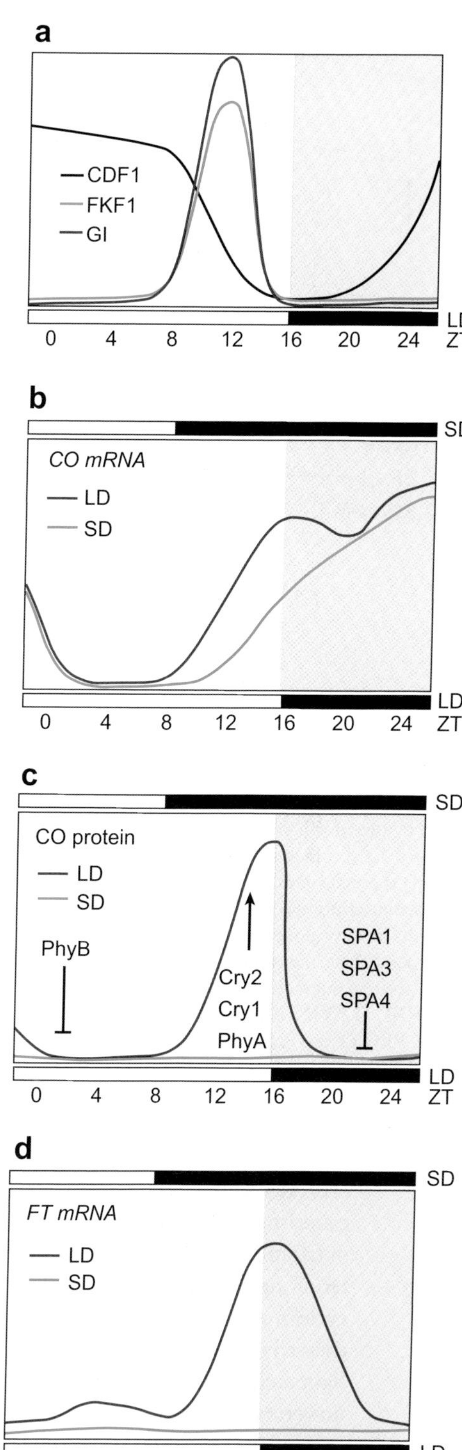

Figure 1

Circadian expression of key components in the photoperiod pathway. (*a*) GI and CDF1 are circadian clock-controlled positive and negative transcriptional regulators of *CO*, respectively. CDF1 directly binds to AAAG-elements within the *CO* promoter. FKF1 is required for CDF1 degradation toward the middle of the day, thus permitting *CO* mRNA levels to rise. (*b*) *CO* mRNA expression differs between LDs and SDs such that a biphasic curve is observed only in LDs. (*c*) Accumulation of CO protein is strongly dependent on the coincidence of light and mRNA expression. CO protein is degraded by a proteasome-dependent mechanism, but it is stabilized toward the end of LDs through the concerted action of CRY2, CRY1, and PhyA. During the night, CO degradation is dependent on the presence of SPA1, SPA3, and SPA4. In the early morning, PhyB negatively regulates CO stability, which counteracts an early peak in CO that could be caused by high *CO* mRNA levels at the end of the night. (*d*) *FT* mRNA production is a direct result of CO protein accumulation toward the end of LDs. White area: duration of light during LDs and SDs. Yellow area: light in LDs but dark in SDs. Blue area: dark in LDs and SDs. Time in hours from dawn is represented below each diagram. ZT, zeitgeber time; SD, short day; LD, long day; SPA1, SUPRESSOR OF PHYA-105-1; GI, GIGANTEA; CDF1, CYCLING DOF FACTOR 1; CO, CONSTANS; FKF1, FLAVIN-BINDING FACTOR 1, KELCH REPEAT, F-BOX PROTEIN; CRY, CRYPTOCHROME; Phy, PHYTOCHROME; *FT*, *FLOWERING LOCUS T*.

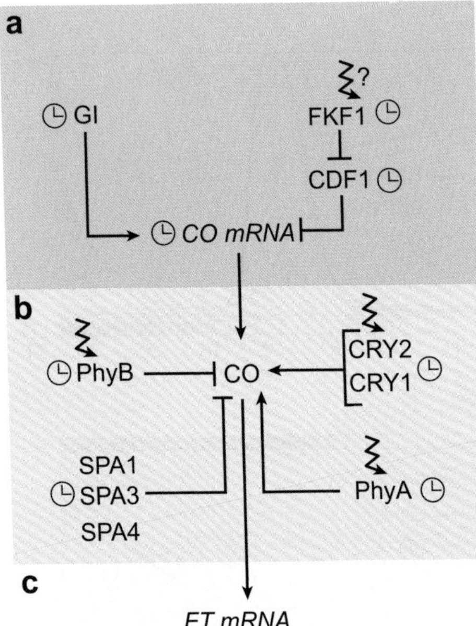

Figure 2

Network that regulates *CONSTANS* (*CO*) mRNA expression and CO protein stability. The circadian clock is a master regulator of photoperiod pathway components and associated genes. Several photoreceptor classes regulate the pathway. Clock symbols indicate that transcription of these genes is regulated by the circadian clock. Zigzag arrows indicate proteins that directly perceive light, which is more thoroughly characterized for phytochromes and cryptochromes than for FKF1. (*a*) Transcriptional regulation. (*b*) Posttranscriptional regulation. (*c*) CO protein accumulation results in activation of *FLOWERING LOCUS T* (*FT*) transcription. Perpendicular lines represent inhibitory interactions. Arrows represent positive interactions. GI, GIGANTEA; CDF1, Cycling DOF Factor 1; FKF1, FLAVIN-BINDING FACTOR 1, KELCH REPEAT, F-BOX PROTEIN; PhyB, PHYTOCHROME B; CRY1, CRYPTOCHROME 1, SPA1, SUPRESSOR OF PHYA-105-1.

suggested that posttranscriptional activation of CO may occur only when *CO* mRNA is expressed in the light. Support for this model came from manipulating the circadian rhythm of *CO* mRNA expression using the *toc1-1* mutation or by altering the length of the daily cycle from 24 h. Both of these approaches showed that if *CO* mRNA accumulates in the light under SDs, then *FT* expression and early flowering occur (75, 99).

Under LDs the peak of *CO* mRNA abundance is broader and extends into the light (**Figure 1**). This response requires the FLAVIN-BINDING, KELCH REPEAT, F-BOX PROTEIN 1 (FKF1) protein. In *fkf1* mutants the abundance of *CO* mRNA in the light at the end of an LD is reduced (36) (**Figure 1**). *FKF1* encodes the F-box protein subunit of an SCF ubiquitin ligase, suggesting that FKF1 directs the degradation of substrate proteins by catalyzing their ubiquitination. FKF1 interacts with GI in vivo and light is required to stabilize their interaction (78). Thus the FKF1-GI complex might target for degradation a negative regulator of *CO* transcription and thereby increase *CO* mRNA levels at the end of the day. Consistent with this idea, *FKF1* and *GI* transcription is also regulated by the circadian clock and their mRNA abundance peaks around the time *CO* transcription rises (**Figure 1**). The transcription factor CYCLING DOF FACTOR 1 (CDF1) likely plays a part in this negative regulation of *CO*. CDF1 physically interacts with FKF1 and GI (35, 78), and overexpression of CDF1 from the *CaMV 35S* promoter causes late flowering and represses *CO* transcription. HA-CDF1 expressed from the *CDF1* promoter accumulates only early in the day in wild-type plants but persists for longer in *fkf1* mutants, consistent with a role for FKF1 in the degradation of CDF1 protein. Chromatin immunoprecipitation data suggest that FKF1, GI, and CDF1 proteins bind the CO promoter and that degradation of CDF1 possibly takes place on the DNA at the *CO* locus (78). However, plants in which *CDF1* mRNA levels were severely reduced by *CDF1* double-standed RNAi exhibited a weak early-flowering phenotype and no increase in *CO* mRNA levels (35). Thus the requirement for CDF1 in regulating *CO* transcription in wild-type plants is relatively weak, perhaps because it is genetically redundant with other repressors of *CO* transcription.

The observation that expression of *CO* mRNA during the night under SDs does not promote flowering suggested that exposure to light activates CO function at the posttranscriptional level. Analysis of CO:GFP fusion protein expression demonstrated that this activation occurs at the level of accumulation of the CO protein (92). In *35S::CO:GFP* plants, GFP is detected in the nucleus when plants are exposed to light, but disappears within a few hours of shifting plants to darkness. Endogenous CO protein is below the level of detection on Western blots, but when expressed from the *CaMV 35S* promoter, CO protein is easily detected. The protein accumulates to highest levels at the end of an LD and falls rapidly in abundance in the dark, whereas in these plants *CO* mRNA is present at constant levels. Furthermore, the abundance of the protein is increased by application of a proteasome inhibitor, supporting the idea that CO protein is degraded via ubiquitination. These data suggest that turnover of CO protein is increased during the night and at the beginning of the day, but reduced at the end of the day, and therefore that post-transcriptional regulation provides an independent layer of regulation that limits CO activity to the end of the day (**Figure 1**).

The effect of light quality on CO protein levels was then tested in photoreceptor mutants carrying the *35S::CO* transgene (92). These experiments indicated that PhyB is required for the degradation of the protein early in the day.

In contrast, cryptochromes, in particular CRYPTOCHROME 2 (CRY2), as well as PHYTOCHROME A (PhyA), contribute to the stabilization of the protein at the end of the day, although single mutations in these photoreceptors have a small effect on protein abundance, suggesting that the photoreceptors might be functionally redundant (92) (**Figure 1**). The photoreceptors PhyA, CRY2, and CRYPTOCHROME 1 (CRY1) promote CO stability, whereas the photoreceptor PHYTOCHROME B (PhyB) destablizes CO. These data are in agreement with the flowering times of photoreceptor mutants, because the *cry2* and *phyA* photoreceptor mutants are late flowering, whereas *phyB* mutants are early flowering (63, 99). Finally, degradation of the CO protein likely involves the SUPPRESSOR OF PHYA-105-1 protein (SPA1). SPA1 was previously shown to act in concert with the E3 ubiquitin ligase CONSTITUTIVE PHOTOMORPHOGENESIS 1 (COP1) to regulate photomorphogenesis. Mutations in *SPA1* cause early flowering under SDs, and this phenotype is enhanced by combining mutations in related *SPA* genes, so that the *spa1 spa3 spa4* triple mutant flowers at the same time under LDs and SDs (49). SPA proteins physically interact with CO both in vitro and in vivo, and mutations in *CO* suppress the early flowering of *spa1* mutants. Also the abundance of the CO protein is markedly increased in a *spa1 spa3 spa4* triple mutant. These results suggest that the SPA proteins are important in mediating the degradation of the CO protein. Factors involved in CO degradation include SPA1 (SUPRESSOR OF PHYA-105-1), SPA3, and SPA4.

The analysis of the temporal regulation of *CO* mRNA and protein suggests that the photoperiodic flowering response in *Arabidopsis* is controlled by an external coincidence model similar to that originally proposed by Bünning (14) and Pittendrigh & Minis (68). According to this model, the photoperiodic response is triggered when the product of an enzymic reaction reaches a threshold level. The abundance of the substrate of this reaction exhibits a circadian rhythm, and the enzyme that converts the substrate to the product is active in the light but reverts to an inactive state in the dark. Therefore, the photoperiodic response would only occur when exposure to light, which activates the enzyme, coincides with the peak in the circadian rhythm of the substrate. This model has striking similarities to the regulation of CO, in which the circadian rhythm in the substrate is represented by the rhythm in *CO* mRNA abundance, and inactivity of the enzyme in the dark is represented by the degradation of CO protein in darkness. Although at first sight the *CO* system appears even simpler than the original model because it includes only one component, the reality is likely much more complex. For example, external coincidence between circadian regulation and exposure to light probably also acts on other components within the pathway (**Figure 2**). FKF1 binds flavin mononucleotide, the chromophore of the photoreceptor phototropin, and according to spectroscopic data FKF1 forms photointermediates similar to those formed by phototropin (36). This observation suggests that FKF1 activity is influenced by light. Furthermore, *GI* transcription is regulated by the circadian clock and activated by light and the GI protein requires light for the interaction with FKF1. Therefore, exposure to light can influence the activity of *GI* at the transcriptional and posttranscriptional level (62, 78). Thus, although our understanding of *CO* regulation is most advanced, similar interactions between light and circadian regulation likely control the activity of multiple components in the photoperiodic pathway (**Figure 2**).

Eukaryotic CCAAT-box binding complex: CBF-B/CBF-C/ CBF-A or NF-YA/ NF-YB/NF-YC in animals; HAP2/ HAP3/HAP5 and HAP4 in yeast

ACTIVATION OF *FT* TRANSCRIPTION BY CO

In general, understanding the biochemical function of CO has not advanced as rapidly as understanding its regulation and general contribution to photoperiodic responses. Genetic analysis placed *FT* downstream of *CO* and experiments performed with a chemically inducible CO:GR fusion protein suggested that it plays a direct role in *FT* transcriptional activation (40, 44, 47, 77, 85).

CO contains two distinct, well-defined protein domains called the B-box (Zinc finger domain) and the CCT (CONSTANS, CO-LIKE, TIMING OF CAB 1) domain (26, 70, 74). Zinc-binding B-boxes are found in many animal transcription factors (89); one or two B-boxes are usually associated with a RING and a coiled-coil domain to form the so-called tripartite motif (11), which has been implicated in protein-protein interactions rather than DNA binding. The amino-terminal B-box of CO is the founding member of a plant-specific B-box subvariant, which occurs either as a single or duplicated domain, often but not always in combination with a CCT domain. CO and 16 related COL (CO-LIKE) proteins in *Arabidopsis* carry the combination of B-box and CCT domains (26, 74), whereas additional proteins contain the CCT domain but no B-boxes.

Difficulty in demonstrating direct DNA binding led to the suggestion that CO is recruited to DNA by an unidentified protein partner (85). As CO B-box:Gal4 DNA binding domain fusion proteins transactivate gene expression in yeast, the role of CO may be to add transactivation function to a protein complex (7). A recent alternative hypothesis is that CO requires protein partners to enhance the affinity of an otherwise weak DNA binding activity of the CCT domain. This hypothesis is based on the finding that the CCT domain of CO and several *Arabidopsis* or tomato COLs interact with subunits of the eukaryotic CCAAT-box binding complex (7, 94) and that the CCT domain shows structure and sequence homology to the sequence-specific DNA binding domain of HAP2 (94).

Metazoan CBF/NFY and yeast HAP complexes are formed by three and four distinct subunits, respectively (57). The preassembled HAP3 and HAP5 dimer recruits the structurally unrelated HAP2 subunit to the complex. None of the subunits alone can stably bind DNA, but the preassembled trimeric complex stably associates with canonical CCAAT box *cis* elements. Amino acid residues required for HAP2 interaction with HAP3/5 and CCAAT-element recognition are most conserved in the CCT domain. Furthermore, mutations that impair the activity of CCT domain–containing proteins affect these conserved amino acids (94).

Genetic evidence that HAP proteins regulate *FT* transcription has been difficult to obtain because in *Arabidopsis* approximately 10 genes encode each of the different subunits (20, 28). Nevertheless, perturbation of subunit stoichiometry by overexpression of HAP2 or HAP3 subunits strongly delays flowering of *Arabidopsis*, and this effect can be counterbalanced by increasing CO concentration (94).

Is *FT* the only gene activated by CO? Studies using *35S::CO:GR* transgenic plants, in which CO activity can be induced with dexamethasone, initially identified that *FT* and several other genes, including *SOC1* (*SUPPRESSOR OF OVEREXPRESSION OF CONSTANS*), are directly activated by CO. However, expression of CO from the *CaMV 35S* promoter in this experiment, at a higher level than in wild-type plants and in a broader set of cell types, may have led to the activation of genes that are not regulated by CO in wild-type plants. Microarray analysis comparing genes expressed in leaves of wild-type, *co*, and *ft* plants shifted from SDs to LDs identified *FT* as the only gene whose expression was higher under LDs than under SDs in wild-type plants but not in *co* mutants (95). Also, an mRNA null allele of *FT* (*ft-10*) apparently suppressed the early-flowering phenotype caused by overexpression of *CO* from the *CaMV 35S* promoter (100). These experiments suggest that *FT* is the only gene activated by CO and the only gene that promotes flowering downstream of CO. However, the *FT*-like gene, *TWIN SISTER OF FT* (*TSF*), also appears to be activated by CO and promotes flowering (97). So far these observations have not been completely reconciled, but they suggest that CO probably activates at least the expression of *FT* and *TSF* in leaves (**Figure 3**).

CLASSICAL STUDIES DEMONSTRATED THE INVOLVEMENT OF SYSTEMIC SIGNALING IN PHOTOPERIODIC FLOWERING

Photoperiod perception takes place predominantly in expanded leaves. These leaves evolved to absorb light during photosynthesis and do so more effectively than the SAM, the site of organ formation, which is often shaded by newly formed leaves. Studies performed from the 1930s onward led to the proposal that one or more mobile signals synthesized in the leaves are transported through the phloem to the SAM and that perception of this mobile signal(s) causes the meristem to change from vegetative development to reproductive development (102). The nature of the signal was further characterized in different plant species over many years. Once induced, the synthesis and effectiveness of the leaf signal can be astonishingly persistent. In *Perilla* spp., successive grafting of an induced leaf to a noninduced shoot could be successfully repeated with the same leaf up to seven times over a period of three months (43). Furthermore, floral induction across interspecies grafts has been reported and long-day and short-day plants are capable of inducing plants of the other response type to flower, suggesting that the floral stimulus appears to be the same or at least functionally equivalent in both types. These experiments supported the hypothesis that a flowering hormone, termed florigen (15), or the floral stimulus, exists in plants and moves from its site of production in the source leaves through the phloem toward the SAM and potentially other sink tissues. None of the classical phytohormones appear to correspond to the definition of a universal floral stimulus, although particularly in *Lolium* spp. a strong argument has been made for gibberellins (GAs) acting as a systemic floral signal (42).

Florigen: compound produced in the leaf that moves through the phloem to the shoot apex to induce flowering

ANALYSIS OF THE SPATIAL REGULATION OF THE PHOTOPERIODIC PATHWAY LINKS FT PROTEIN AND FLORIGEN

The connection between the florigen hypothesis and the *CO/FT* module became apparent when the tissues in which *CO* and *FT* act to regulate flowering were identified. In young plants, *CO* and *FT* are expressed in phloem companion cells, particularly in those of the distal minor veins of source leaves (3, 86). For *FT* this seems to be the only site of expression; however, because of the difficulty in detecting the endogenous transcript by in situ hybridization, these data rely only on promoter reporter gene studies and therefore

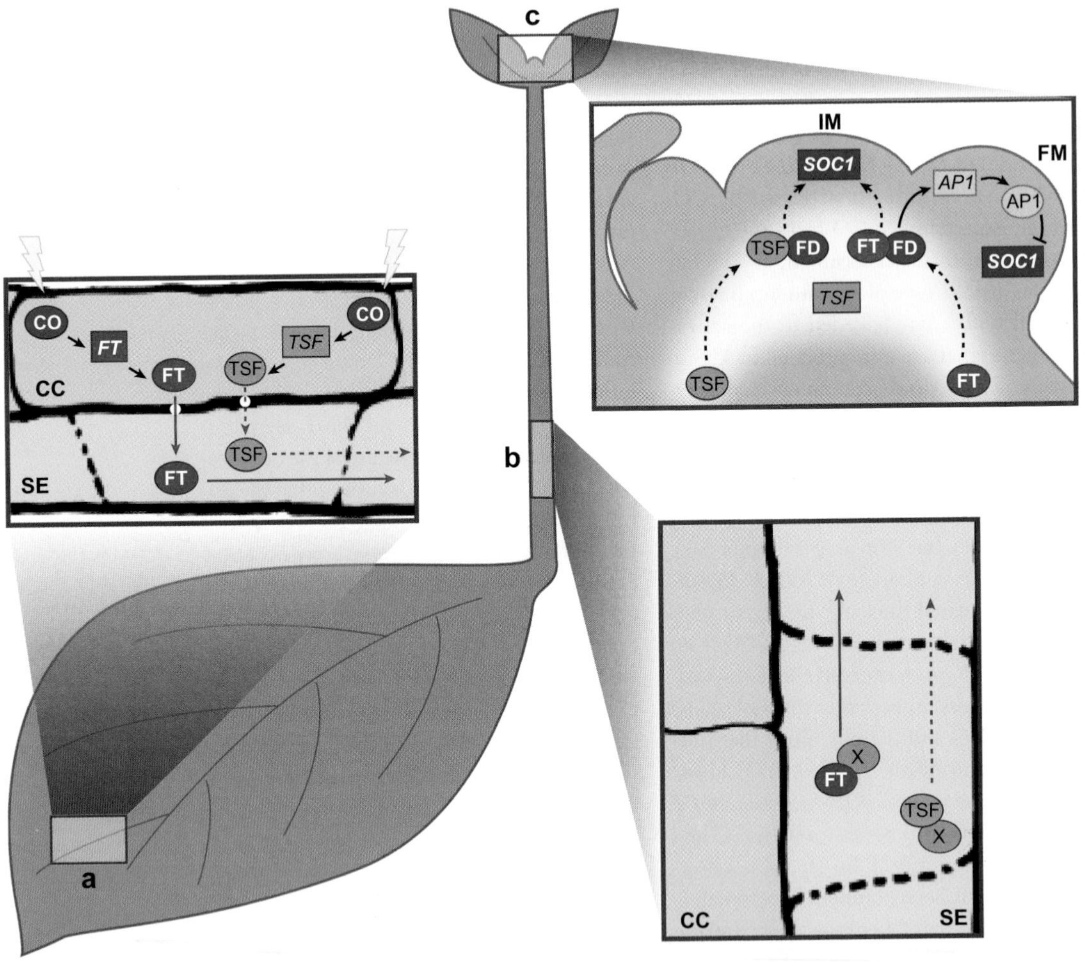

Figure 3

FLOWERING LOCUS T (FT) as a systemic signal. (*a*) Coincidence of *CONSTANS* (*CO*) mRNA accumulation and light at the end of long days (LDs) stabilizes the CO protein. CO then allows transcription of *FT* and *TWIN SISTER OF FT* (*TSF*) in the phloem companion cells within the distal part of the leaf. FT protein is uploaded into the sieve elements either by diffusion through plasmodesmata or by an unidentified active transport mechanism (*white circle*). The similarity between FT and TSF proteins suggests they behave similarly, but no evidence for movement of the TSF protein has been presented. (*b*) Long-distance transport of FT toward sink tissues occurs in the phloem translocation stream. FT may associate with other as yet unknown factors (X) during this step. (*c*) FT unloading from the phloem and transport within the apex probably involves cell-to-cell transport through plasmodesmata. The yellow area indicates a possible gradient of FT and TSF protein distribution in the shoot apical meristem (SAM). Whether diffusion or directed active transport is involved is unclear. Induction of *SUPPRESSOR OF OVEREXPRESSION OF CONSTANS* (*SOC1*) is the first detectable event in the inflorescence meristem (IM) and depends on the presence of FT and the bZIP transcription factor FLOWERING LOCUS D (FD), but whether these directly activate SOC1 transcription is unknown. FT and FD interact physically and the complex is directly involved in *APETALA 1* (*AP1*) transcriptional activation, which occurs during the formation of the first floral bud. AP1 directly represses *SOC1* in the floral meristem (FM). TSF protein might follow the same systemic path toward the SAM as does FT. In addition, promoter *TSF::GUS* fusions indicate that the *TSF* transcript could be directly produced in cells at the periphery of the SAM. CC, companion cells; SE, sieve elements; boxes, mRNA; circles, protein; solid black arrows, experimentally confirmed interconnection; dotted arrows, inferred interconnection.

require further validation (86). In contrast to *FT*, *CO* mRNA is found in the apical regions above the protophloem and expression is less restricted to the phloem tissue in younger leaves (3, 82). However, CO protein stability is tightly regulated (see above) and studies with *CO::CO:GFP* fusions indicated that the spatial pattern of CO protein is restricted to the phloem (3).

Misexpression of *CO* from heterologous promoters and grafting experiments placed *CO* upstream of a leaf-borne transmissible signal. Thus, expression of *CO* driven by the promoter of *SUC2* in the companion cells throughout the phloem system or by the *GAS1* promoter, which is more restricted to the companion cells of the minor veins, generates a graft-transmissible signal that is sufficient to cause a *co* mutant scion to flower (3, 5). In contrast, expression of *CO* in the SAM does not promote flowering (3). Conversely, *FT* causes early flowering when expressed in the phloem or the SAM, and expression of *FT* in either of these tissues promotes the floral transition even in the absence of functional *CO* (3). This observation confirms that *CO* acts upstream in the signaling cascade of *FT* and of the transmissible signal. Indeed, these experiments indicate that the signal must reside downstream of *FT* transcription (3, 86).

Although *FT* is expressed only in the vascular tissue (86), the known biochemical function of FT is in the meristem (1, 95), as is described in detail below. This discrepancy between the spatial pattern of *FT* mRNA expression and the location at which the protein acts provided evidence that a product of *FT* might represent the mobile signal. Two general models emerged to explain the relationship between *FT* and florigen. A direct model proposed that *FT* encodes florigen, so that either *FT* mRNA or protein (or both) move from source leaves to the meristematic tissue. Alternatively, an indirect or relay model proposed that FT activates a transmissible signal in the leaf, and that this moves to the meristem, where it activates expression of *FT* or an *FT*-like gene. The involvement of an *FT*-like gene would be more plausible because *FT* expression has not been detected at the meristem.

The first experiments performed to test movement of an FT product focused on the *FT* mRNA. Experiments describing movement of *FT* mRNA from the leaf to the meristem using a fusion of a promoter from a heat shock–inducible gene (from soybean *Gmhsp 17.6L*) to *FT* were subsequently retracted (9). Furthermore, *FT* mRNA movement was excluded on the basis of grafting experiments performed in tomato, where mutations in the *FT* ortholog *SINGLE FLOWER TRUSS* (*SFT*) cause late flowering (64). Tomato plants overexpressing *SFT* are early flowering. Grafting a *35S::SFT* donor to an *sft* recipient shoot corrected the mutant phenotype of the recipient shoot. Similarly, *35S::SFT* donors could rescue the late-flowering phenotype of Maryland Mammoth tobacco plants (51, 52). These experiments indicated that the systemic signal must cross the graft junction between these shoots, but careful PCR analysis using RNA of the recipient shoot did not detect *SFT* mRNA that had crossed the graft junction. A similar result was obtained with grafted *Arabidopsis* plants, in which no movement of *FT* mRNA could be detected across graft junctions (18). *FT* mRNA requirement in the apex was also excluded by expressing artificial miRNAs targeted against *FT* in the SAM and the phloem. Expression of artificial miRNAs in the SAM did not alter flowering time, whereas when expressed in the phloem they phenocopied the *ft* mutant (59). Taken together these experiments argue against long-distance movement of *FT* mRNA and against a requirement for the mRNA in the SAM.

In contrast, several results support movement of the FT protein. Expression of FT:GFP fusion proteins from the phloem-specific *SUC2* promoter allowed detection of a GFP signal in the phloem and the SAM region (18), suggesting that the fusion protein can move from the phloem to the meristem. Similar results were obtained in rice using the rice ortholog of *FT*, *Hd3a* (87). In *Arabidopsis*, the fusion protein but not its mRNA moved toward sink tissue across graft junctions (18). Protein movement was further detected using FT:MYC fusion protein also expressed under the control of the phloem-specific *SUC2* promoter (39). Finally, in grafted *Cucurbita moschata*, protein mass spectrometry was used to show that an FT-like protein moved through the phloem system across graft junctions and that this correlated with flowering (53). Taken together these experiments seem to convincingly demonstrate that FT protein can move long distances through the phloem system and that this is associated with floral induction (**Figure 3**).

However, diffusion of small proteins expressed in companion cells into the sieve element and subsequent transport toward sink tissues may be a general phenomenon, such that movement of a small (20 kDa) protein such as FT may be the expected result (37, 56, 66). Therefore, demonstrating movement of the FT protein is not sufficient to prove that it acts as a transmissible signal, but rather evidence that movement of FT protein is necessary for flowering to occur is required. Such evidence was provided by several experiments. When expressed in the phloem, FT protein fused to a fluorescent protein is impaired in its ability to complement *ft* mutations. Although FT:GFP complements an *ft* mutation when expressed in the SAM or in the major veins from the *SUC2* promoter, its expression in the minor veins of the leaves from the *GAS1* promoter does not complement the mutation (18). This is in contrast to *GAS1::FT*, which does complement *ft*. Furthermore, *GAS1::FT:GFP* plants exhibit altered gene expression patterns in the leaves similar to those caused by *35S::FT* (88). Therefore FT:GFP is active in the leaves of *GAS1::FT:GFP* plants. These experiments suggested that FT movement from the minor veins is required to promote flowering, and that this movement is impaired in *GAS1::FT:GFP* plants (18).

Similarly, FT protein fused to three consecutive YFP proteins did not induce earlier flowering of wild-type plants if expressed from the *SUC2* promoter, but did if expressed ubiquitously from the *CaMV 35S* promoter. This experiment suggests that FT:3xYFP is biochemically active but cannot move from the phloem when expressed from the *SUC2* promoter. Because this fusion protein also contained a viral peptidase recognition site, free FT protein could be cleaved from the fusion protein in the presence of the viral peptidase. Expression of the viral peptidase from the *SUC2* promoter released free FT protein, which induced earlier flowering of wild-type plants (59). This result suggests that movement of free FT but not FT:3xYFP induces early flowering of these plants.

Finally, FT protein was engineered for efficient targeting to the nucleus and a MYC epitope-tag was added (MYC:NLS:FT) (39). Expression of this fusion protein from the *SUC2* promoter in an *ft-10* mutant did not affect the flowering time of the mutant, whereas when expressed from the *CaMV 35S* promoter it caused extreme early flowering. *SUC2::MYC:FT ft-10* plants were early flowering and MYC:FT protein could be detected beyond the vascular tissue in the meristem region, whereas the late flowering of *SUC2::MYC:NLS:FT ft-10* plants correlated with reduced movement of the protein beyond the phloem (39). Taken together, all these experiments based on different approaches provide evidence that movement of FT protein is required for the induction of flowering and that there is no need to postulate an intermediate signal acting between FT activity in the leaf and flowering at the SAM.

Although the experiments described above demonstrate that FT protein movement is required for flowering, they do not unequivocally show that FT protein and florigen are equivalent. For example, a second signal, perhaps induced by expression of *FT* in the leaf, might move along with FT protein. If this second signal were required to optimize movement of FT or to increase the efficiency of the system, then its requirement might be bypassed by direct expression of *FT* in the meristem. Therefore, the possibility that FT protein acts together with a second mobile component cannot be formally excluded, and active florigen could still be a mixture of substances of which FT protein is only a part.

THE ROLE OF FT IN THE SHOOT APICAL MERISTEM

The developmental program that initiates flower development occurs at the apical meristem after synthesis of FT in the leaves and its transport through the phloem system, but what is the function of FT at the SAM? A breakthrough in this area came from the demonstration that FT interacts in the yeast two-hybrid system with the bZIP transcription factor FLOWERING LOCUS D (FD) (1, 95). Furthermore, mutations in *FD* cause late flowering (47), and *fd* mutations suppress the early flowering of *35S::FT* plants (1, 95). *FD* mRNA is strongly expressed at the SAM, suggesting that this is the major site of FD action, although it is also present at the root meristem and at lower levels throughout the plant (1, 95) (**Figure 4**).

The FT/FD heterodimer is involved in the activation of the floral meristem identity genes *APETALA 1* (*AP1*) and *FRUITFUL (FUL)* at the shoot apex. Occurrence of *AP1* at the apex is strongly delayed in *fd* mutants (95) and abolished in either *fd lfy* or *ft lfy* double mutant plants, indicating that the FT/FD complex acts redundantly with LFY to activate *AP1* (1, 95). Whereas *lfy* mutant plants form abnormal flowers, introduction of either *fd* or *ft* as a second mutation causes the resulting plants to form leaves instead of flowers (1, 76, 95). Furthermore, *FD* overexpression under the control of the *CaMV 35S* promoter causes ectopic expression of *AP1* and *FUL* in leaves of LD-grown but not SD-grown plants,

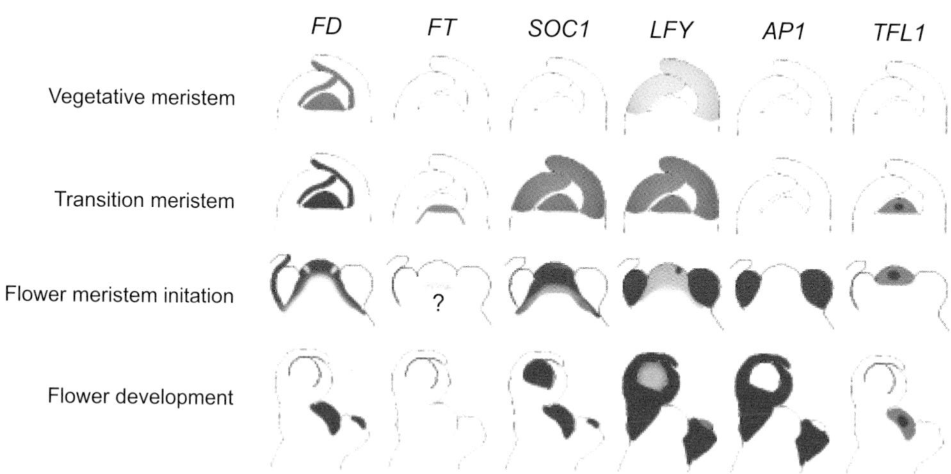

Figure 4

Dynamics of gene expression in the shoot apical meristem upon floral transition. From top to bottom: progression of the apical meristem from a fully vegetative state (vegetative meristem) to a reproductive state (flower development). Two intermediate stages are shown: the transition meristem stage, where morphological changes are not yet visible but induction is taking place, and the flower meristem initiation stage, where the first flower primordia are arising on the flanks of the inflorescence meristem. The mRNA (*red*) and protein (*blue*) patterns of key regulators of floral transition are shown. The varying intensity of the color accounts for the expression level of the gene. The question mark referring to *FLOWERING LOCUS T* (*FT*) in later stages indicates that the pattern is inferred. Abbreviations: *FD, FLOWERING LOCUS D*; *SOC 1, SUPPRESSOR OF OVEREXPRESSION OF CONSTANS 1*; *LFY, LEAFY*; *AP1, APETALA 1*; *TFL1, TERMINAL FLOWER 1*.

suggesting that FT is required in leaf tissue for this expression to occur (1, 95). Similarly, *CaMV 35S* promoter–driven overexpression of *FT* causes ectopic expression of *AP1*, *FUL*, and *SEP3* in leaves, which is strongly reduced if the transgene is expressed in an *fd* mutant background (88). These observations are consistent with the idea that the FT/FD heterodimer regulates *AP1*, *FUL*, and *SEP3* expression in the meristem, and that overexpression of *FT* or *FD* in the leaves causes ectopic expression of the downstream genes.

FT/FD probably activates *AP1* by directly binding to its promoter, presumably via the DNA binding domain of FD. A C-box, a *cis* element bound by bZIP factors, is present in a functionally important region of the *AP1* promoter in close proximity to LFY binding sites (95). The role of FT in the heterodimer is currently unclear, but it might provide a coactivator function to the FT/FD complex, and this is supported by a chromatin immunoprecipitation experiment that detected FT associated with the *AP1* promoter (95). Alternatively, FT might be necessary for posttranslational modification of FD, thereby activating it or targeting it to the nucleus. A putative calcium-dependent protein kinase target site in FD appears to be required for the interaction with FT in yeast two-hybrid assays, supporting the idea that posttranslational modification regulates the interaction (1).

Robust *AP1* expression is detectable at the SAM four days after a shift from SD to LD in Landsberg *erecta*, at a time when the first stage 1 floral bud is visible (**Figure 4**). By this stage production of the FT signal in the leaves is not required any longer, and the meristem is fully committed to flower independently of *FT* expression in the leaves (18). Therefore, the first molecular event controlled by FT at the SAM upon floral induction is unlikely to be the activation of *AP1*. In contrast, induction of *SOC1* expression in the SAM is detected much earlier than *AP1* expression, approximately 16 h after a shift from SD to LD and prior to macroscopic changes at the meristem (12, 80) (**Figure 4**). Induction of *SOC1* is strongly delayed in either *ft* or *fd* mutant plants, so that FT and FD are required for the earliest marker of floral induction in the meristem that is currently available (80), consistent with gene activation by FT/FD as the earliest step in the floral transition that occurs at the meristem.

SOC1 acts as a floral integrator and is activated by FT-dependent and FT-independent pathways (50, 65, 77, 100). Mutations in *SOC1* cause late flowering under LDs or SDs (12). So far, there has not been a report on the identification of direct SOC1 target genes, so the order of events after *SOC1* activation is unclear. However, the inverse correlation of *SOC1* and *AP1* expression (**Figure 4**) may be indicative of a complex feedback loop relationship between different FT/FD target genes (54).

FT-RELATED GENES IN *ARABIDOPSIS*

A small family of six *FT*-like genes exists in *Arabidopsis*, and these genes might have related functions in floral induction. The proteins encoded by these genes contain a phosphatidylethanolamine binding domain (PEPB) (16). The physiological function of PEPB proteins is widely studied in animals in which they are proposed to act in signaling cascades via protein-protein interactions (16). In *Arabidopsis* the PEPB family comprises, in addition to FT and TSF, BFT (BROTHER OF FT), ATC (ARABIDOPSIS THALIANA RELATIVE OF CENTRORADIALIS), MFT (MOTHER OF FT AND TFL1), and TFL1 (TERMINAL FLOWER 1) (13, 61, 97, 101).

Of these proteins TSF is the most similar to FT, such that the proteins are 81.3% identical. *FT* and *TSF* show similar, but not overlapping, expression patterns in the phloem and significant homology is detected in the proximal parts of their promoters. However, in contrast to *FT*, *TSF* is also expressed at low levels in the basal part of the apical meristem. Expression analyses confirmed that, similar to

FT, *TSF* responds rapidly to varying levels of CO and is repressed by FLC and EARLY BOLTING IN SHORT DAYS (EBS) (97). In contrast to *FT*, *TSF* expression is not increased in *tfl2/lhp1* mutants, although chromatin immunoprecipitation on chip data suggest TFL2/LHP1 is associated with the *TSF* locus (90). At least in young plants, *TSF* is expressed at a low level, possibly because of the presence of large retrotransposon and repetitive sequence insertions at the 3′ end of the gene. The *tsf* mutation has only a minor effect on flowering time under LDs in the presence of an active *FT* gene, but *ft tsf* double mutants show an additive phenotype, indicating genetic redundancy between the genes (97). The spatial requirement for *FT* and *TSF* mRNA was analyzed using an artificial microRNA directed against both genes (59). Transgenic plants expressing the *amiR-FT/TSF* in the phloem phenocopied the *ft tsf* double mutant, but flowering time was not affected when *amiR-FT/TSF* was expressed in the *FD* domain. This experiment indicates that *TSF* mRNA, like *FT* mRNA, is active in the companion cells of the phloem and is not required in the meristem. Taken together these data indicate that *TSF* could regulate flowering by a mechanism similar to that proposed for *FT*, but so far it has not been reported whether TSF protein can move to the SAM along with FT (**Figure 3**).

TFL1 has an antagonistic effect on *FT* in the regulation of flowering. Loss-of-function *tfl1* mutant plants flower early independently of day length and form a terminal flower, similar to *FT*-overexpressing plants (13, 40, 44). Conversely, *35S::TFL1* plants flower late in LDs and have a prolonged inflorescence phase in which cauline leaves rather than flowers are produced, a phenotype related to that of *ft* mutants (71). Paradoxically, the *TFL1* transcript is upregulated in the inflorescence meristem through activation of *CO* (82). A current hypothesis is that TFL1 acts as a competitor of FT in the apex to prevent FT from converting the SAM into a floral meristem (2). Consistent with this hypothesis, whereas *TFL1* mRNA is restricted to the center of the SAM, the TFL1 protein moves beyond its mRNA expression domain and spreads into the entire meristem (17) (**Figure 4**). Although a mechanism of reciprocal competitive binding of FT and TFL1 to FD has been proposed as the mechanism underlying this function, at present it is not clear whether the TFL1 and FD proteins can physically interact, because two reports have shown contradictory yeast two-hybrid results (1, 95). A reciprocal single amino acid exchange of FT and TFL1 is sufficient to reverse the function of these proteins (29). The homologs most similar to *TFL1* are *BFT* and *ATC*, but their roles in plant development are unclear. No mutant alleles of *BFT* have been described so far, and *atc* mutants do not show any obvious alteration in flowering time or flower development (61).

TERMINAL FLOWER 2/LIKE-HETERO-CHROMATIN PROTEIN 1 (TFL2/LHP1): a repressor of genes that are regulated by the Polycomb pathway in Arabidopsis

The third class of FT-like protein is represented by MFT (101). MFT is equally related to FT and TFL1 and, at the critical position proposed to distinguish FT and TFL1, MFT has an amino acid different from both. *MFT* does not belong to the *FT/TSF* category; nevertheless, overexpression of *MFT* can also cause slightly early flowering in LDs (101), although mutations in *MFT* do not have a perceptible effect on flowering. Nevertheless, to fully understand how these genes contribute to the systemic signaling and meristem functions currently ascribed to FT, it will be important to describe the patterns of expression of each gene, to systematically combine null alleles of the different family members, and to determine how these combinations alter flowering time.

FLOWERING OF *ARABIDOPSIS* UNDER SHORT DAYS

Arabidopsis is a facultative long-day plant and therefore eventually flowers under SDs. Under LDs *ft* mutants are late flowering, but reports on the effects of *FT/TSF* under SDs differ. For example, whereas Michaels and colleagues (60) found no effect of *ft* or *tsf* mutations under SDs, Yamaguchi and coworkers

(97) found an effect of *tsf* and a strong enhancement in the *ft tsf* double mutant (60, 97). Nevertheless, even in the absence of both FT and TSF, flowering does occur under SDs, indicating that absence of the systemic signal represented by FT/TSF can eventually be overcome under SDs.

An attractive possibility is that an alternative pathway promotes flowering in the absence of *FT/TSF* and under SDs. Genetic data suggest a major role for GA in controlling flowering of *Arabidopsis* under SDs (96). The *ga1-3* mutation, which strongly impairs GA biosynthesis, prevents flowering under SDs and strongly enhances the *co2* mutation under LDs, so that the *co2 ga1-3* double mutant never flowers under these conditions (72). GA may therefore compensate for the reduced effect of the FT system on SD-grown plants and *co* mutants, and GA does accumulate at the meristem of *Arabidopsis* during the transition to flowering under SDs (21). In *Lolium* GA was proposed to represent a systemic signal that induces flowering at the apex, and GA could represent a second signal in *Arabidopsis* that acts in parallel to the FT system and is not as strongly regulated by photoperiod (42).

CONSERVATION OF THE CO/FT MODULE AND ITS REGULATION IN OTHER SPECIES

Homologs of the *CO* and *FT* genes have been isolated from many monocotyledonous and dicotyledonous species (26, 33, 41, 45, 55, 58, 69, 73, 81, 91, 98). In particular, the function of FT as a promoter of flowering appears to be remarkably conserved in all species tested in detail. Overexpression of *FT* homologs causes extreme early flowering in the dicotyledonous plants poplar (10, 33), tomato, tobacco (51), and *Pharbitis nil* (31) as well as in the monocotyledonous plant rice (45). If *FT* directly encodes the floral stimulus, as discussed above, then this would be consistent with the physiological data suggesting that at least in some cases different plant species produce the same systemic signal. Furthermore, *FT* mRNA abundance is increased in response to exposure to photoperiods that induce flowering in barley and rice as well as *Arabidopsis* (30, 85, 91, 99). However, in the day-neutral plant tomato, expression of the *FT* ortholog *SFT* is not regulated by photoperiod, although overexpression of *SFT* promotes early flowering and *sft* mutations delay flowering (52). These observations indicate that regulation of *FT* expression by photoperiod through the activity of CO homologous proteins is likely to be highly conserved in plants as distantly related as *Arabidopsis* and rice, but that this connection can be severed in photoperiod-insensitive plants such as tomato.

Activation of *CO* under LDs can be explained by an external coincidence model, as described above. However, in the short-day plant rice, the regulation of the *FT* ortholog is reversed so that its transcription is activated under SDs and repressed under LDs (45). Elegant genetic experiments based on natural genetic variation for photoperiod response in rice, isolation of induced mutations, and construction of transgenic plants demonstrated that the core photoperiod pathway is conserved and promotes flowering under SDs. In rice the *HEADING DATE 1* (*Hd1*) locus encodes the *CO* ortholog (98) and *Hd3a* encodes an *FT* homolog (45). *Hd3a* plays a role similar to that of *FT* in *Arabidopsis*, so that *Hd3a* mRNA levels are higher under SDs than under LDs, *Hd3a* loss-of-function alleles delay flowering under SDs, and overexpression of *Hd3a* causes early flowering (45). However, the role of *Hd1* in rice is more complex than the role of *CO* in *Arabidopsis*, because *Hd1* both promotes flowering and *Hd3a* expression under inductive SDs and delays flowering and represses *Hd3a* expression under noninductive LDs, whereas in *Arabidopsis* *CO* only promotes flowering under inductive LDs (98) (**Figure 5**). How does *Hd1* have opposite effects on *Hd3a* expression under LDs and SDs? The repression of *Hd3a* expression under LDs could be explained by an external coincidence model similar to that proposed

for *Arabidopsis*. According to this model, under LDs *Hd1* expression coincides with exposure of plants to light, leading to the modification of Hd1 protein and to the repression of *Hd3a* expression. In contrast under SDs, *Hd1* mRNA accumulates only during the night, and in a dark-synthesized form, the Hd1 protein would activate *Hd3a* transcription and thereby induce flowering. Although these results provide a convincing model for how flowering of rice responds to short photoperiods, the response of other short-day plants might be controlled by different mechanisms. Recent evidence suggests that flowering of *Pharbitis nil*, a classical short-day model species for physiological experiments, is controlled by a circadian rhythm set by dusk that induces *Pharbitis nil FT* (*PnFT*) expression only if the night is sufficiently long (31) (**Figure 5**). The role of PnCO in activation of *PnFT* remains unclear. These experiments suggest that *Pharbitis* measures day length by a different mechanism than that of rice.

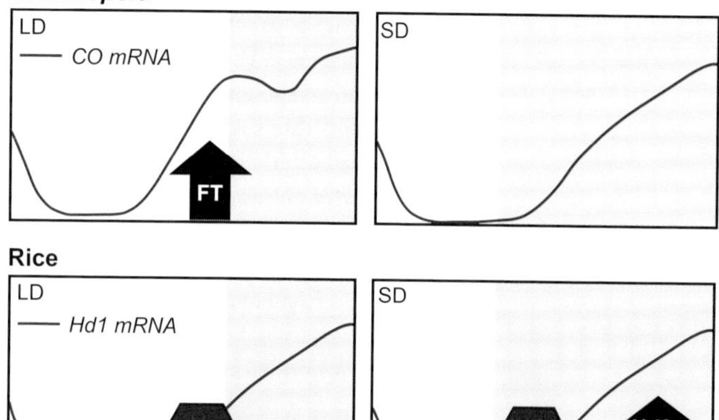

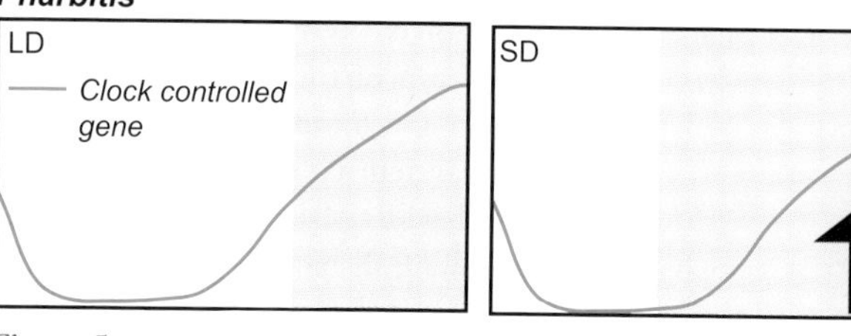

Figure 5

Regulation of *FT* mRNA expression by day length in different species. In Arabidopsis the expression of *CO* at the end of a LD and the light-induced stabilization of the CO protein cause activation of *FT* transcription. Under SD the CO protein does not accumulate, *FT* transcription is not activated, and flowering is delayed. In rice the photoperiodic response is reversed so that the CO ortholog HEADING DATE 1 (Hd1) activates *HEADING DATE 3a* (*Hd3a*) transcription under SD but represses it under LD. The effect of Hd1 on *Hd3a* activation is proposed to be due to light-induced modification of Hd1. According to this model, when rice plants are exposed to light the Hd1 protein is synthesized in a form that represses *Hd3a* transcription, whereas in a dark-synthesized form the same protein acts as a promoter of *Hd3a* expression. In *Pharbitis PnFT* transcription is induced under SD, when the rhythm in the activity of a clock-controlled gene (CCG) reaches its peak of expression during the long night. In contrast, during LDs *PnFT* does not accumulate because expression of the CCG is suppressed by light at dawn and never reaches a critical threshold sufficient for *PnFT* induction. White areas denote light, blue areas denote darkness. The blue arrows represent transcriptional activation of the gene named in the arrow. The red hexagons represent transcriptional repression of *Hd3a*. *FT*, *FLOWERING LOCUS T*; *CO*, *CONSTANS*; SD, short day; LD, long day.

Analysis of the *CO/FT* system in poplar provided evidence for the importance of these genes in adaptation to growth at different latitudes. In poplar, the *FT* ortholog *PnFT1* has important functions in bud dormancy as well as flowering (10, 33). In poplar, growth terminates in autumn and bud dormancy is initiated. This is a photoperiodic response induced by exposure to SDs during autumn, and in wild-type plants *PnFT1* expression is reduced on exposure to SDs. Transgenic poplar plants overexpressing *PnFT1* do not terminate growth on exposure to SDs, whereas those with reduced *PnFT1* expression are more sensitive to SDs. Böhlenius and colleagues (21) then tested whether the day length recognized as an SD in the regulation of *PnFT1* expression differed between poplar accessions, and whether this was related to the timing of *PnCO* expression. They studied four accessions collected from locations extending from Germany at 51°N to northern Sweden at 63°N. In day lengths of 17, 19, and 21 h they observed that *PnCO* is expressed at an earlier phase in the southern accessions. Under 19-h day lengths, *PnCO* mRNA expression coincides with exposure of plants to light for the two most-southern accessions but not for the two northern accessions and *PnFT* is expressed under these conditions for the southern accessions but not the northern accessions. Northern accessions recognize longer day lengths as SDs and therefore induce bud dormancy earlier in the autumn in anticipation of the earlier onset of winter conditions, and this response appears to be adapted to the latitude in which poplar accessions grow through modification of the timing of *PnCO* expression and the consequent expression of *PnFT*.

PERSPECTIVES

Tremendous progress has been made in recent years in understanding the basis of florigen and the control of its expression by photoperiod (see above). However, major questions remain to be solved both in understanding the mechanistic basis of the system in the *Arabidopsis* model and in determining how variation in the system confers the diversity in flowering behaviors observed in nature. Understanding long-distance signaling by FT crucially requires determining whether FT protein is sufficient for this process and acts alone or whether it requires other molecules that are transported along with FT. Similarly, little is known of the mechanisms by which the protein is transported through the phloem and loaded into the meristem. We do not know in which cells FT first acts to promote the earliest steps in floral induction nor the nature of the first signaling steps that are initiated by the arrival of FT protein.

Although the core photoperiod pathway appears to be widely conserved, the broader context in which the photoperiodic response functions is likely to differ significantly in other angiosperm systems. For example, the intersection between photoperiod response and pathways controlling other environmental responses appears not to be conserved. In *Arabidopsis* the vernalization and photoperiod responses appear to be independent and converge on the regulation of transcription of *FT* and other floral integrators. However, transcription of the wheat *VERNALIZATION 2* gene, which encodes a repressor of flowering that plays a central role in the vernalization response, is reduced either by exposure to vernalization or by exposure to noninductive SDs (19). Such observations suggest that in other species environmental responses that influence flowering time are likely to intersect with the photoperiod pathway and regulate *FT* transcription in ways that could not be predicted from the analysis of *Arabidopsis*.

Finally, time of flowering of widely used summer annual accessions of *Arabidopsis* such as Landsberg *erecta* and Columbia seems to be determined largely by whether *FT* is expressed. Within 1 day of inducing *FT* expression in the leaves the mRNAs of genes associated with flowering are detected at the meristem, and within three days Landsberg *erecta* plants are stably committed to flower. Such observations indicate that regulatory steps in the meristem do not play a large part in determining the flowering time of these accessions, but rather that the meristem response is determined by the timing of *FT* expression in the leaves. However, this cannot be the case in all plants. For example, in perennials different meristems on the same plant respond differently to floral induction, so that some remain vegetative, whereas others are induced to form flowers. Such polycarpic behavior suggests either the existence of mechanisms in the meristem to regulate responsiveness or that leaf-derived signals such as FT are transported differently to particular meristems. The nature of such processes will be elucidated by future experiments and will add to the surprises this beautiful system has given us during the past 70 years.

DISCLOSURE STATEMENT

The authors are not aware of any biases that might be perceived as affecting the objectivity of this review.

ACKNOWLEDGMENTS

The laboratory of G.C. is supported by the Max Planck Society through a core grant and work on systemic signaling is partly funded by the Deutsche Forschungsgemeinschaft through SFB 572.

LITERATURE CITED

1. Abe M, Kobayashi Y, Yamamoto S, Daimon Y, Yamaguchi A, et al. 2005. FD, a bZIP protein mediating signals from the floral pathway integrator FT at the shoot apex. *Science* 309:1052–56
2. Ahn JH, Miller D, Winter VJ, Banfield MJ, Lee JH, et al. 2006. A divergent external loop confers antagonistic activity on floral regulators FT and TFL1. *EMBO J.* 25:605–14
3. An H, Roussot C, Suarez-Lopez P, Corbesier L, Vincent C, et al. 2004. CONSTANS acts in the phloem to regulate a systemic signal that induces photoperiodic flowering of *Arabidopsis*. *Development* 131:3615–26
4. Ausin I, Alonso-Blanco C, Martinez-Zapater JM. 2005. Environmental regulation of flowering. *Int. J. Dev. Biol.* 49:689–705
5. Ayre BG, Turgeon R. 2004. Graft transmission of a floral stimulant derived from CONSTANS. *Plant Physiol.* 135:2271–78
6. Baurle I, Dean C. 2006. The timing of developmental transitions in plants. *Cell* 125:655–64
7. Ben-Naim O, Eshed R, Parnis A, Teper-Bamnolker P, Shalit A, et al. 2006. The CCAAT binding factor can mediate interactions between CONSTANS-like proteins and DNA. *Plant J.* 46:462–76
8. Bernier G. 1988. The control of floral evocation and morphogenesis. *Annu. Rev. Plant Physiol. Plant Mol. Biol.* 39:175–219
9. Bohlenius H, Eriksson S, Parcy F, Nilsson O. 2007. Retraction. *Science* 316:367
10. Bohlenius H, Huang T, Charbonnel-Campaa L, Brunner AM, Jansson S, et al. 2006. CO/FT regulatory module controls timing of flowering and seasonal growth cessation in trees. *Science* 312:1040–43
11. Borden KL, Campbelldwyer EJ, Carlile GW, Djavani M, Salvato MS. 1998. Two RING finger proteins, the oncoprotein PML and the arenavirus Z protein, colocalize with the nuclear fraction of the ribosomal P proteins. *J. Virol.* 72:3819–26
12. Borner R, Kampmann G, Chandler J, Gleissner R, Wisman E, et al. 2000. A MADS domain gene involved in the transition to flowering in *Arabidopsis*. *Plant J.* 24:591–99
13. Bradley D, Ratcliffe O, Vincent C, Carpenter R, Coen E. 1997. Inflorescence commitment and architecture in *Arabidopsis*. *Science* 275:80–83
14. Bünning E. 1936. Die endogene Tagesrhythmik als Grundlage der photoperiodischen Reaktion. *Ber. Dtsch. Bot. Ges.* 54:590–607
15. Chailakhyan M. 1937. *Gormonal'naya Teoriya Razvitiya Rastenii*. Moscow: Akad. Nauk SSSR
16. Chardon F, Damerval C. 2005. Phylogenomic analysis of the PEBP gene family in cereals. *J. Mol. Evol.* 61:579–90
17. Conti L, Bradley D. 2007. TERMINAL FLOWER1 is a mobile signal controlling *Arabidopsis* architecture. *Plant Cell* 19:767–78
18. Corbesier L, Vincent C, Jang S, Fornara F, Fan Q, et al. 2007. FT protein movement contributes to long-distance signaling in floral induction of *Arabidopsis*. *Science* 316:1030–33

19. Dubcovsky J, Loukoianov A, Fu D, Valarik M, Sanchez A, Yan L. 2006. Effect of photoperiod on the regulation of wheat vernalization genes VRN1 and. *Plant Mol. Biol.* 60:469–80
20. Edwards D, Murray JA, Smith AG. 1998. Multiple genes encoding the conserved CCAAT-box transcription factor complex are expressed in *Arabidopsis*. *Plant Physiol.* 117:1015–22
21. Eriksson S, Böhlenius H, Moritz T, Nilsson O. 2006. GA4 is the active gibberellin in the regulation of LEAFY transcription and *Arabidopsis* floral initiation. *Plant Cell* 18:2172–81
22. Evans LT. 1971. Flower induction and the florigen concept. *Annu. Rev. Plant Physiol.* 22:365–94
23. Fowler S, Lee K, Onouchi H, Samach A, Richardson K, et al. 1999. GIGANTEA: a circadian clock-controlled gene that regulates photoperiodic flowering in *Arabidopsis* and encodes a protein with several possible membrane-spanning domains. *EMBO J.* 18:4679–88
24. Garner WW, Allard HA. 1920. Effect of the relative length of day and night and other factors of the environment on growth and reproduction in plants. *J. Agric. Res.* 18:553–606
25. Garner WW, Allard HA. 1923. Further studies on photoperiodism, the response of plants to relative length of day and night. *J. Agric. Res.* 23:871–920
26. Griffiths S, Dunford RP, Coupland G, Laurie DA. 2003. The evolution of CONSTANS-like gene families in barley, rice, and *Arabidopsis*. *Plant Physiol.* 131:1855–67
27. Guo H, Duong H, Ma N, Lin C. 1999. The *Arabidopsis* blue light receptor cryptochrome 2 is a nuclear protein regulated by a blue light-dependent post-transcriptional mechanism. *Plant J.* 19:279–87
28. Gusmaroli G, Tonelli C, Mantovani R. 2002. Regulation of novel members of the *Arabidopsis thaliana* CCAAT-binding nuclear factor Y subunits. *Gene* 283:41–48
29. Hanzawa Y, Money T, Bradley D. 2005. A single amino acid converts a repressor to an activator of flowering. *Proc. Natl. Acad. Sci. USA* 102:7748–53
30. Hayama R, Coupland G. 2003. Shedding light on the circadian clock and the photoperiodic control of flowering. *Curr. Opin. Plant Biol.* 6:13–19
31. Hayama R, Agashe B, Luley E, King R, Coupland G. 2007. A circadian rhythm set by dusk determines the expression of *FT* homologs and the short-day photoperiodic flowering response in Pharbitis. *Plant Cell* 19:2988–3000
32. Hayama R, Coupland G. 2004. The molecular basis of diversity in the photoperiodic flowering responses of *Arabidopsis* and rice. *Plant Physiol.* 135:677–84
33. Hsu CY, Liu Y, Luthe DS, Yuceer C. 2006. Poplar FT2 shortens the juvenile phase and promotes seasonal flowering. *Plant Cell* 18:1846–61
34. Imaizumi T, Kay SA. 2006. Photoperiodic control of flowering: not only by coincidence. *Trends Plant Sci.* 11:550–58
35. Imaizumi T, Schultz TF, Harmon FG, Ho LA, Kay SA. 2005. FKF1 F-box protein mediates cyclic degradation of a repressor of CONSTANS in *Arabidopsis*. *Science* 309:293–97
36. Imaizumi T, Tran HG, Swartz TE, Briggs WR, Kay SA. 2003. FKF1 is essential for photoperiodic-specific light signalling in *Arabidopsis*. *Nature* 426:302–6
37. Imlau A, Truernit E, Sauer N. 1999. Cell-to-cell and long-distance trafficking of the green fluorescent protein in the phloem and symplastic unloading of the protein into sink tissues. *Plant Cell* 11:309–22
38. Jaeger KE, Graf A, Wigge PA. 2006. The control of flowering in time and space. *J. Exp. Bot.* 57:3415–18
39. Jaeger KE, Wigge PA. 2007. FT protein acts as a long-range signal in *Arabidopsis*. *Curr. Biol.* 17:1050–54

40. Kardailsky I, Shukla VK, Ahn JH, Dagenais N, Christensen SK, et al. 1999. Activation tagging of the floral inducer FT. *Science* 286:1962–65
41. Kim SJ, Moon J, Lee I, Maeng J, Kim SR. 2003. Molecular cloning and expression analysis of a CONSTANS homologue, PnCOL1, from *Pharbitis nil*. *J. Exp. Bot.* 54:1879–87
42. King RW, Evans LT. 2003. Gibberellins and flowering of grasses and cereals: prizing open the lid of the "florigen" black box. *Annu. Rev. Plant Biol.* 54:307–28
43. King RW, Zeevaart JA. 1973. Floral stimulus movement in *Perilla* and flower inhibition caused by noninduced leaves. *Plant Physiol.* 51:727–38
44. Kobayashi Y, Kaya H, Goto K, Iwabuchi M, Araki T. 1999. A pair of related genes with antagonistic roles in mediating flowering signals. *Science* 286:1960–62
45. Kojima S, Takahashi Y, Kobayashi Y, Monna L, Sasaki T, et al. 2002. Hd3a, a rice ortholog of the *Arabidopsis* FT gene, promotes transition to flowering downstream of Hd1 under short-day conditions. *Plant Cell Physiol.* 43:1096–105
46. Koornneef M, Alonso-Blanco C, Peeters AJM, Soppe W. 1998. Genetic control of flowering time in *Arabidopsis*. *Annu. Rev. Plant Physiol. Plant Mol. Biol.* 49:345–70
47. Koornneef M, Hanhart CJ, van der Veen JH. 1991. A genetic and physiological analysis of late flowering mutants in *Arabidopsis thaliana*. *Mol. Gen. Genet.* 229:57–66
48. Lang A. 1952. Physiology of flowering. *Annu. Rev. Plant Physiol.* 3:265–306
49. Laubinger S, Marchal V, Le Gourrierec J, Wenkel S, Adrian J, et al. 2006. *Arabidopsis* SPA proteins regulate photoperiodic flowering and interact with the floral inducer CONSTANS to regulate its stability. *Development* 133:3213–22
50. Lee H, Suh SS, Park E, Cho E, Ahn JH, et al. 2000. The AGAMOUS-LIKE 20 MADS domain protein integrates floral inductive pathways in *Arabidopsis*. *Genes Dev.* 14:2366–76
51. Lifschitz E, Eshed Y. 2006. Universal florigenic signals triggered by FT homologues regulate growth and flowering cycles in perennial day-neutral tomato. *J. Exp. Bot.* 57:3405–14
52. Lifschitz E, Eviatar T, Rozman A, Shalit A, Goldshmidt A, et al. 2006. The tomato FT ortholog triggers systemic signals that regulate growth and flowering and substitute for diverse environmental stimuli. *Proc. Natl. Acad. Sci. USA* 103:6398–403
53. Lin MK, Belanger H, Lee YJ, Varkonyi-Gasic E, Taoka K, et al. 2007. FLOWERING LOCUS T protein may act as the long-distance florigenic signal in the cucurbits. *Plant Cell* 19:1488–506
54. Liu C, Zhou J, Bracha-Drori K, Yalovsky S, Ito T, Yu H. 2007. Specification of *Arabidopsis* floral meristem identity by repression of flowering time genes. *Development* 134:1901–10
55. Liu J, Yu J, McIntosh L, Kende H, Zeevaart JA. 2001. Isolation of a CONSTANS ortholog from *Pharbitis nil* and its role in flowering. *Plant Physiol.* 125:1821–30
56. Lough TJ, Lucas WJ. 2006. Integrative plant biology: role of phloem long-distance macromolecular trafficking. *Annu. Rev. Plant Biol.* 57:203–32
57. Maity SN, de Crombrugghe B. 1998. Role of the CCAAT-binding protein CBF/NF-Y in transcription. *Trends Biochem. Sci.* 23:174–78
58. Martin J, Storgaard M, Andersen CH, Nielsen KK. 2004. Photoperiodic regulation of flowering in perennial ryegrass involving a CONSTANS-like homolog. *Plant Mol. Biol.* 56:159–69
59. Mathieu J, Warthmann N, Kuttner F, Schmid M. 2007. Export of FT protein from phloem companion cells is sufficient for floral induction in *Arabidopsis*. *Curr. Biol.* 17:1055–60
60. Michaels SD, Himelblau E, Kim SY, Schomburg FM, Amasino RM. 2005. Integration of flowering signals in winter-annual *Arabidopsis*. *Plant Physiol.* 137:149–56

61. Mimida N, Goto K, Kobayashi Y, Araki T, Ahn JH, et al. 2001. Functional divergence of the TFL1-like gene family in *Arabidopsis* revealed by characterization of a novel homologue. *Genes Cells* 6:327–36
62. Mizoguchi T, Wright L, Fujiwara S, Cremer F, Lee K, et al. 2005. Distinct roles of GIGANTEA in promoting flowering and regulating circadian rhythms in *Arabidopsis*. *Plant Cell* 17:2255–70
63. Mockler T, Yang H, Yu X, Parikh D, Cheng YC, et al. 2003. Regulation of photoperiodic flowering by *Arabidopsis* photoreceptors. *Proc. Natl. Acad. Sci. USA* 100:2140–45
64. Molinero-Rosales N, Latorre A, Jamilena M, Lozano R. 2004. SINGLE FLOWER TRUSS regulates the transition and maintenance of flowering in tomato. *Planta* 218:427–34
65. Onouchi H, Igeno MI, Perilleux C, Graves K, Coupland G. 2000. Mutagenesis of plants overexpressing CONSTANS demonstrates novel interactions among *Arabidopsis* flowering-time genes. *Plant Cell* 12:885–900
66. Oparka KJ, Cruz SS. 2000. The great escape: phloem transport and unloading of macromolecules. *Annu. Rev. Plant Physiol. Plant Mol. Biol.* 51:323–47
67. Parcy F. 2005. Flowering: a time for integration. *Int. J. Dev. Biol.* 49:585–93
68. Pittendrigh CS, Minis DH. 1964. The entrainment of circadian oscillations by light and their role as photoperiodic clocks. *Am. Nat.* 98:261–322
69. Pnueli L, Carmel-Goren L, Hareven D, Gutfinger T, Alvarez J, et al. 1998. The SELF-PRUNING gene of tomato regulates vegetative to reproductive switching of sympodial meristems and is the ortholog of CEN and TFL1. *Development* 125:1979–89
70. Putterill J, Robson F, Lee K, Simon R, Coupland G. 1995. The CONSTANS gene of *Arabidopsis* promotes flowering and encodes a protein showing similarities to zinc finger transcription factors. *Cell* 80:847–57
71. Ratcliffe OJ, Amaya I, Vincent CA, Rothstein S, Carpenter R, et al. 1998. A common mechanism controls the life cycle and architecture of plants. *Development* 125:1609–15
72. Reeves PH, Coupland G. 2001. Analysis of flowering time control in *Arabidopsis* by comparison of double and triple mutants. *Plant Physiol.* 126:1085–91
73. Robert LS, Robson F, Sharpe A, Lydiate D, Coupland G. 1998. Conserved structure and function of the *Arabidopsis* flowering time gene CONSTANS in *Brassica napus*. *Plant Mol. Biol.* 37:763–72
74. Robson F, Costa MM, Hepworth SR, Vizir I, Pineiro M, et al. 2001. Functional importance of conserved domains in the flowering-time gene CONSTANS demonstrated by analysis of mutant alleles and transgenic plants. *Plant J.* 28:619–31
75. Roden LC, Song HR, Jackson S, Morris K, Carre IA. 2002. Floral responses to photoperiod are correlated with the timing of rhythmic expression relative to dawn and dusk in *Arabidopsis*. *Proc. Natl. Acad. Sci. USA* 99:13313–18
76. Ruiz-García L, Madueño F, Wilkinson M, Haughn G, Salinas J, Martínez-Zapater JM. 1997. Different roles of flowering-time genes in the activation of floral initiation genes in *Arabidopsis*. *Plant Cell* 9:1921–34
77. Samach A, Onouchi H, Gold SE, Ditta GS, Schwarz-Sommer Z, et al. 2000. Distinct roles of CONSTANS target genes in reproductive development of *Arabidopsis*. *Science* 288:1613–16
78. Sawa M, Nusinow DA, Kay SA, Imaizumi T. 2007. FKF1 and GIGANTEA complex formation is required for day-length measurement in *Arabidopsis*. *Science* 318:261–65
79. Searle I, Coupland G. 2004. Induction of flowering by seasonal changes in photoperiod. *EMBO J.* 23:1217–22

80. Searle I, He Y, Turck F, Vincent C, Fornara F, et al. 2006. The transcription factor FLC confers a flowering response to vernalization by repressing meristem competence and systemic signaling in *Arabidopsis*. *Genes Dev.* 20:898–912
81. Shin BS, Lee JH, Lee JH, Jeong HJ, Yun CH, Kim JK. 2004. Circadian regulation of rice (*Oryza sativa* L.) CONSTANS-like gene transcripts. *Mol. Cells* 17:10–16
82. Simon R, Igeno MI, Coupland G. 1996. Activation of floral meristem identity genes in *Arabidopsis*. *Nature* 384:59–62
83. Simpson GG, Gendall AR, Dean C. 1999. When to switch to flowering. *Annu. Rev. Cell Dev. Biol.* 15:519–50
84. Soppe WJ, Jacobsen SE, Alonso-Blanco C, Jackson JP, Kakutani T, et al. 2000. The late flowering phenotype of fwa mutants is caused by gain-of-function epigenetic alleles of a homeodomain gene. *Mol. Cell* 6:791–802
85. Suarez-Lopez P, Wheatley K, Robson F, Onouchi H, Valverde F, Coupland G. 2001. CONSTANS mediates between the circadian clock and the control of flowering in *Arabidopsis*. *Nature* 410:1116–20
86. Takada S, Goto K. 2003. Terminal flower2, an *Arabidopsis* homolog of heterochromatin protein1, counteracts the activation of flowering locus T by constans in the vascular tissues of leaves to regulate flowering time. *Plant Cell* 15:2856–65
87. Tamaki S, Matsuo S, Wong HL, Yokoi S, Shimamoto K. 2007. Hd3a protein is a mobile flowering signal in rice. *Science* 316:1033–36
88. Teper-Bamnolker P, Samach A. 2005. The flowering integrator FT regulates SEPALLATA3 and FRUITFULL accumulation in *Arabidopsis* leaves. *Plant Cell* 17:2661–75
89. Torok M, Etkin LD. 2001. Two B or not two B? Overview of the rapidly expanding B-box family of proteins. *Differentiation* 67:63–71
90. Turck F, Roudier F, Farrona S, Martin-Magniette ML, Guillaume E, et al. 2007. *Arabidopsis* TFL2/LHP1 specifically associates with genes marked by trimethylation of histone H3 lysine 27. *PLoS Genet.* 3:e86
91. Turner A, Beales J, Faure S, Dunford RP, Laurie DA. 2005. The pseudoresponse regulator Ppd-H1 provides adaptation to photoperiod in barley. *Science* 310:1031–34
92. Valverde F, Mouradov A, Soppe W, Ravenscroft D, Samach A, Coupland G. 2004. Photoreceptor regulation of CONSTANS protein in photoperiodic flowering. *Science* 303:1003–6
93. Weigel D. 1995. The genetics of flower development: from floral induction to ovule morphogenesis. *Annu. Rev. Genet.* 29:19–39
94. Wenkel S, Turck F, Singer K, Gissot L, Le Gourrierec J, et al. 2006. CONSTANS and the CCAAT box binding complex share a functionally important domain and interact to regulate flowering of *Arabidopsis*. *Plant Cell* 18:2971–84
95. Wigge PA, Kim MC, Jaeger KE, Busch W, Schmid M, et al. 2005. Integration of spatial and temporal information during floral induction in *Arabidopsis*. *Science* 309:1056–59
96. Wilson RN, Heckman JW, Somerville CR. 1992. Gibberellin is required for flowering in *Arabidopsis thaliana* under short days. *Plant Physiol.* 100:403–8
97. Yamaguchi A, Kobayashi Y, Goto K, Abe M, Araki T. 2005. TWIN SISTER OF FT (TSF) acts as a floral pathway integrator redundantly with FT. *Plant Cell Physiol.* 46:1175–89
98. Yano M, Katayose Y, Ashikari M, Yamanouchi U, Monna L, et al. 2000. Hd1, a major photoperiod sensitivity quantitative trait locus in rice, is closely related to the *Arabidopsis* flowering time gene CONSTANS. *Plant Cell* 12:2473–84

99. Yanovsky MJ, Kay SA. 2002. Molecular basis of seasonal time measurement in *Arabidopsis*. *Nature* 419:308–12
100. Yoo SK, Chung KS, Kim J, Lee JH, Hong SM, et al. 2005. CONSTANS activates SUPPRESSOR OF OVEREXPRESSION OF CONSTANS 1 through FLOWERING LOCUS T to promote flowering in *Arabidopsis*. *Plant Physiol.* 139:770–78
101. Yoo SY, Kardailsky I, Lee JS, Weigel D, Ahn JH. 2004. Acceleration of flowering by overexpression of MFT (MOTHER OF FT AND TFL1). *Mol. Cells* 17:95–101
102. Zeevaart JAD. 1976. Physiology of flower formation. *Annu. Rev. Plant Physiol.* 27:321–48

Plant Aquaporins: Membrane Channels with Multiple Integrated Functions

Christophe Maurel, Lionel Verdoucq, Doan-Trung Luu, and Véronique Santoni

Biochimie et Physiologie Moléculaire des Plantes, SupAgro/INRA/CNRS/UM2 UMR 5004, F-34060 Montpellier Cedex 1, France; email: maurel@supagro.inra.fr, verdoucq@supagro.inra.fr, luu@supagro.inra.fr, santoniv@supagro.inra.fr

Annu. Rev. Plant Biol. 2008. 59:595–624

The *Annual Review of Plant Biology* is online at plant.annualreviews.org

This article's doi:
10.1146/annurev.arplant.59.032607.092734

1543-5008/08/0602-0595$20.00

Key Words

environmental stress, gating, major intrinsic protein, nutrient, transport selectivity, water relations

Abstract

Aquaporins are channel proteins present in the plasma and intracellular membranes of plant cells, where they facilitate the transport of water and/or small neutral solutes (urea, boric acid, silicic acid) or gases (ammonia, carbon dioxide). Recent progress was made in understanding the molecular bases of aquaporin transport selectivity and gating. The present review examines how a wide range of selectivity profiles and regulation properties allows aquaporins to be integrated in numerous functions, throughout plant development, and during adaptations to variable living conditions. Although they play a central role in water relations of roots, leaves, seeds, and flowers, aquaporins have also been linked to plant mineral nutrition and carbon and nitrogen fixation.

Contents

INTRODUCTION

Aquaporins are small integral membrane proteins that belong to the ancient family of major intrinsic proteins (MIPs), with members in animals, microbes, and plants. Fifteen years after their discovery in plants, it now appears that studies on aquaporins have provided unique perspectives into multiple integrated aspects of plant biology. Aquaporins first raised considerable interest because of their water channel activity. This finding was unexpected in plants and, although it may not have induced a real paradigm shift in understanding of membrane water transport (124, 140), it led researchers to revisit many aspects of plant water relations and to link these aspects to novel physiological contexts. More recently, MIPs were proved to be more than water channels (141), and other transport substrates of great physiological significance have been identified.

MIP: major intrinsic protein

PIP: plasma membrane intrinsic protein

TIP: tonoplast intrinsic protein

NIP: nodulin-26–like intrinsic protein

SIP: small basic intrinsic protein

Although the term aquaporin was initially restricted to water-transporting MIPs, we now use this term in a broader sense, referring to all plant MIPs as aquaporins. The molecular and cellular properties of aquaporins were recently reviewed in detail (18, 91). The aim of the present review is to examine how a wide range of selectivity profiles and regulation properties allows aquaporins to be integrated in numerous functions throughout plant development and during adaptations to variable environmental conditions.

MOLECULAR AND CELLULAR PROPERTIES

The Plant Aquaporin Family

Subfamilies. Plant aquaporins show a high multiplicity of isoforms, with 35 and 33 homologs in *Arabidopsis* and rice, respectively (62, 113, 120). On the basis of sequence homology, aquaporins in most plant species can be divided into four subgroups. The plasma membrane intrinsic proteins (PIP) (with two phylogenic subgroups, PIP1 and PIP2, and 13 isoforms in *Arabidopsis*) and the tonoplast intrinsic proteins (TIP) (10 homologs in *Arabidopsis*) are the most abundant aquaporins in the plasma membrane and vacuolar membrane (tonoplast), respectively (62, 113). The third subfamily comprises the nodulin-26–like intrinsic membrane proteins (NIPs), which were named after soybean (*Glycine max*) nodulin-26 (*Gm*NOD26), an abundant aquaporin expressed in the peribacteroid membrane of N_2-fixing symbiotic root nodules. NIPs are also present in nonlegume plant species (9 homologs in *Arabidopsis*) (149). A fourth class comprises small basic intrinsic proteins (SIPs) (3 homologs in *Arabidopsis*) (56, 62, 113). Although these four classes are conserved among all plant species, the aquaporin gene family shows signs of rapid and recent evolution and orthologs cannot necessarily be distinguished between species (120). In addition, some plant species have acquired additional, novel types of aquaporins.

For instance, a homolog of the bacterial glycerol facilitator GlpF has been acquired by the moss *Physcomitrella patens* by horizontal gene transfer (45), and the genome of this organism and some higher plants (such as poplar) encodes a fifth class of aquaporins, which are closely related to but yet clearly distinct from PIPs (139; U. Johanson, personal communication).

Subcellular localization. Plant aquaporins localize in all subcellular compartments forming or derived from the secretory pathway. This broad localization pattern reflects the high degree of compartmentation of the plant cell and the need for the cell to control water and solute transport not only across the plasma membrane but also across intracellular membranes. Similar to PIPs, some NIPs localize in the plasma membrane (82, 134). By contrast, the three *Arabidopsis* SIP homologs reside mainly in the endoplasmic reticulum (56).

However, aquaporins cannot simply be assigned to homogeneous subcellular compartments. For instance, immunocytochemical studies using isoform-specific anti-TIP antibodies revealed that distinct types of vacuole that can coexist in the same cell are equipped with specific combinations of TIP isoforms; TIP1 and TIP2 isoforms are preferentially associated with the large lytic vacuoles and vacuoles accumulating vegetative storage proteins, respectively (59). More recently, *Arabidopsis thaliana At*TIP1;1 was shown to accumulate in spherical structures named bulbs, tentatively identified as intravacuolar invaginations made of a double tonoplast membrane (118). Preferential expression of PIPs in plasmalemmasomes (convoluted plasma membrane invaginations that dip into the vacuole) has also been observed in *Arabidopsis* leaves (116). Finally, preferential expression of a PIP and a NIP homolog on the distal side of root exo- and endodermal cells has been described in maize and rice, respectively (46, 82). Such cell polarization is consistent with the uptake and centripetal transport of water and solute in roots (see below). A future challenge is to understand how aquaporins can be specifically targeted to membrane subdomains in the plant cell and how targeting contributes to their functional specialization.

Plasmalemmasome: convoluted plasma membrane invagination

Mechanisms of Transport

Pore structure and transport mechanisms. X-ray crystallography determination of atomic structures of microbial, animal, and plant homologs points to highly conserved structural features in the aquaporin family (38, 137). Aquaporins are 23–31 kDa proteins comprising six membrane-spanning domains tilted along the plane of the membrane and linked by five loops (*A* to *E*) located on the intra- (*B*, *D*) or extracytoplasmic (*A*, *C*, *E*) side of the membrane. The N- and C-terminal extremities are both exposed to the cytosol (**Figure 1**). A central aqueous pore is delineated by the transmembrane domains and loops *B* and *E*, which both carry a conserved Asn-Pro-Ala (NPA) motif and dip from either side of the membrane into the center of the molecule. Projection structures determined by cryo-electron microscopy indicate that, similar to their animal and microbial counterparts, PIPs and TIPs occur as tetramers in their native membranes (24, 34). X-ray structures have confirmed this type of assembly (38, 137) and in combination with molecular dynamics simulations have provided critical insights into the fundamental principles of aquaporin transport selectivity (38, 133) (**Figure 1**). In brief, the substrate specificity of aquaporins can be explained by several mechanisms, including size exclusion at two main pore constrictions [aromatic/Arg (Ar/R) and NPA] and stereospecific recognition of the substrate mediated by spatially defined H-bonding and hydrophobic interactions within the pore. The remarkable impermeability of aquaporins to protons is explained by electrostatic repulsion, dipole orientation, and transient isolation of the water molecule as it passes within a single

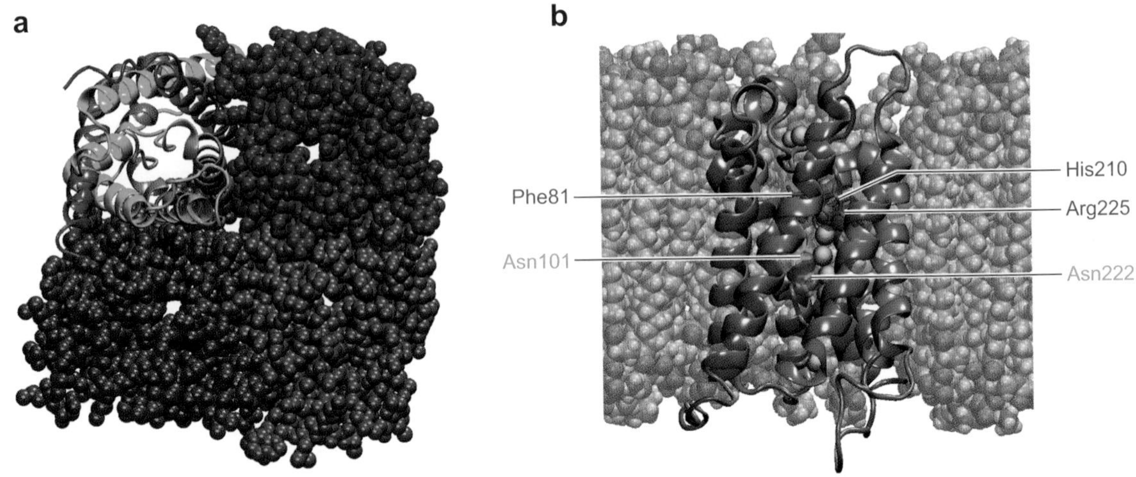

Figure 1

Representative atomic structure of a plant aquaporin (*a*) and general molecular mechanisms of transport selectivity (*b*). (*a*) Structure of the open conformation of *Spinacia oleracea* plasma membrane intrinsic protein 2;1 (*So*PIP2;1) [Protein Data Bank (PDB) ID 2B5F] (137) showing a typical tetrameric arrangement. Each monomer is composed of six tilted transmembrane helices; the N-terminal (*red*) and C-terminal (*green*) helices of the top left monomer are shown. The pores of individual monomers are emphasized by the space-filling representation of the three other monomers. (*b*) The two highly conserved Asn-Pro-Ala (NPA) motifs (represented by Asn101 and Asn222, *green*) are in close proximity to form one of the main pore constrictions. Another constriction called Ar/R (*red*) is formed on the extracytoplasmic side of the membrane by a spatial arrangement of aromatic (Ar) residues, such as Phe81 and His210, facing an Arg (R) residue, here Arg225. Proton transport is blocked by electrostatic repulsion in the Ar/R constriction and the dipole orientation of the water molecule by the two Asn residues of the NPA motifs. This results in a transient isolation of the water molecule within the single file of water molecules that fills the pore (*orange spheres*).

file of water molecules through the center of the pore (11, 38, 133) (**Figure 1**).

The molecular basis of plant aquaporin selectivity has been investigated more specifically by homology modeling of pore structures at the Ar/R constriction (8, 150). Analysis of all 35 *Arabidopsis* homologs yielded up to nine pore types (150) and additional types exist in maize and rice (8). Whereas all PIPs exhibit a narrow pore structure typical of orthodox, water-selective aquaporins, larger substrate specificity was predicted for other plant homologs. According to this analysis, *At*NIP6;1 belongs to one of two NIP subgroups and as such exhibits a low and high permeability to water and urea, respectively (151). An Ala119Trp substitution, made to mimic the pore configuration of members of the other NIP subgroup, also confers novel permeability properties, i.e., higher permeability to water and failure to transport urea. This result and other examples in animal aquaporins (11) show that point mutations can drastically alter transport specificity and that these proteins may be engineered to accommodate novel substrates of interest.

Transport assays and aquaporin substrates. Functional expression in *Xenopus* oocytes or yeast was essential to show that plant MIP homologs of all four subclasses can function as water channels (56, 66, 94, 115). Enhanced water permeability of proteoliposomes containing a purified aquaporin provides the ultimate proof of water channel activity. Such functional reconstitution has been performed with *Gm*NOD26 purified from native peribacteroid membranes (27) or after production of *Spinacia oleracea So*PIP2;1 in *Pichia pastoris* (67). Although strict comparative measurements have not been performed in plants, plant aquaporins may, similar to their animal homologs, exhibit marked differences (up to 30-fold) in intrinsic water transport activity (154).

Expression studies in *Xenopus* oocytes also show that, similar to animal and bacterial aquaglyceroporins, some plant aquaporin isoforms can transport small neutral solutes such as glycerol (12), urea (42), formamide, acetamide (115), methylammonium (53), boric acid (134), silicic acid (82), or lactic acid (20). Ammonia (NH_3) and CO_2 transport is detected using substrate-induced extra- and intracellular acidification, respectively, whereas ammonium (NH_4^+) transport by *Triticum aestivum Ta*TIP2;1 results in inward currents (53, 144). Finally, expression in yeast cells deficient in endogenous systems responsible for urea or hydrogen peroxide uptake has proved efficient to screen, on the basis of a survival assay, aquaporin isoforms that possibly transport these molecules; these properties are subsequently confirmed by true transport assays (13, 77).

Several approaches have established that aquaporins contribute significantly to the permeability of plant membranes to water and small neutral solutes. In most studies, mercury derivatives, which act through oxidation and binding to Cys residues, were used as common aquaporin blockers. Plant aquaporins do not have Cys residues at conserved positions and various residues may be involved in plant aquaporin inhibition (23). We also note that mercury-resistant PIPs have been described in *Arabidopsis* and tobacco (12, 25). In some studies, the permeability profiles of the vacuolar, peribacteroid, and plasma membranes were characterized by stopped-flow spectrophotometry on purified membrane vesicles, and mercury induced a marked (50%–90%) inhibition of water transport in the first two types of membranes (42, 95, 104, 105, 115). In addition, a good parallel was established between the high permeability of the tobacco tonoplast and soybean peribacteroid membrane to urea and formamide, respectively, and the capacity of *Nicotiana tabacum Nt*TIPa and *Gm*NOD26 to transport these solutes (42, 115). In other studies, the respective water permeabilities of the plasma membrane and the tonoplast and their sensitivity to mercury were inferred from independent osmotic swelling assays on protoplasts and isolated vacuoles and calculations using a three-compartment model (92, 99, 102). **Figure 2** summarizes the contribution of plant aquaporins to water and solute transport in multiple subcellular compartments.

Molecular Mechanisms of Regulation

Cotranslational and posttranslational modifications. Because of their high abundance in plant membranes, and despite their high hydrophobicity, some aquaporins have proved to be particularly amenable to biochemical analysis, in comparison with other membrane proteins (34, 48, 63). Proteomics, and mass spectrometry techniques in particular, have recently been added to more classical techniques to produce a thorough description of aquaporin co- and posttranslational modifications (26, 121, 122). For instance, N-terminal maturation of PIP1s and PIP2s occurs through N-α-acetylation or cleavage of the initiating residue, respectively (121). In vivo and in vitro labeling studies, experiments with antiphosphopeptide antibodies, and mass spectrometry analyses have provided direct evidence for phosphorylation of Ser residues in the N-terminal and C-terminal tails of *Phaseolus vulgaris Pv*TIP3;1, *Gm*NOD26, and *So*PIP2;1 (26, 43, 63, 64, 96). PIPs show a conserved phosphorylation site in loop *B* and multiple (up to three) and interdependent phosphorylations occur in adjacent sites of their C-terminal tail (63, 64; S. Prak, S. Hem, J. Boudet, N. Sommerer, G. Viennois, M. Rossignol, C. Maurel & V. Santoni, unpublished results). Purification of calcium-dependent protein kinases acting on aquaporins has been undertaken by several laboratories (48, 129). Although most plant aquaporins do not exhibit glycosylation, this type of modification has been observed in *Gm*NOD26 and in an ice plant TIP (96, 146). In the latter case, glycosylation was required for subcellular redistribution (described below). Aquaporins were also

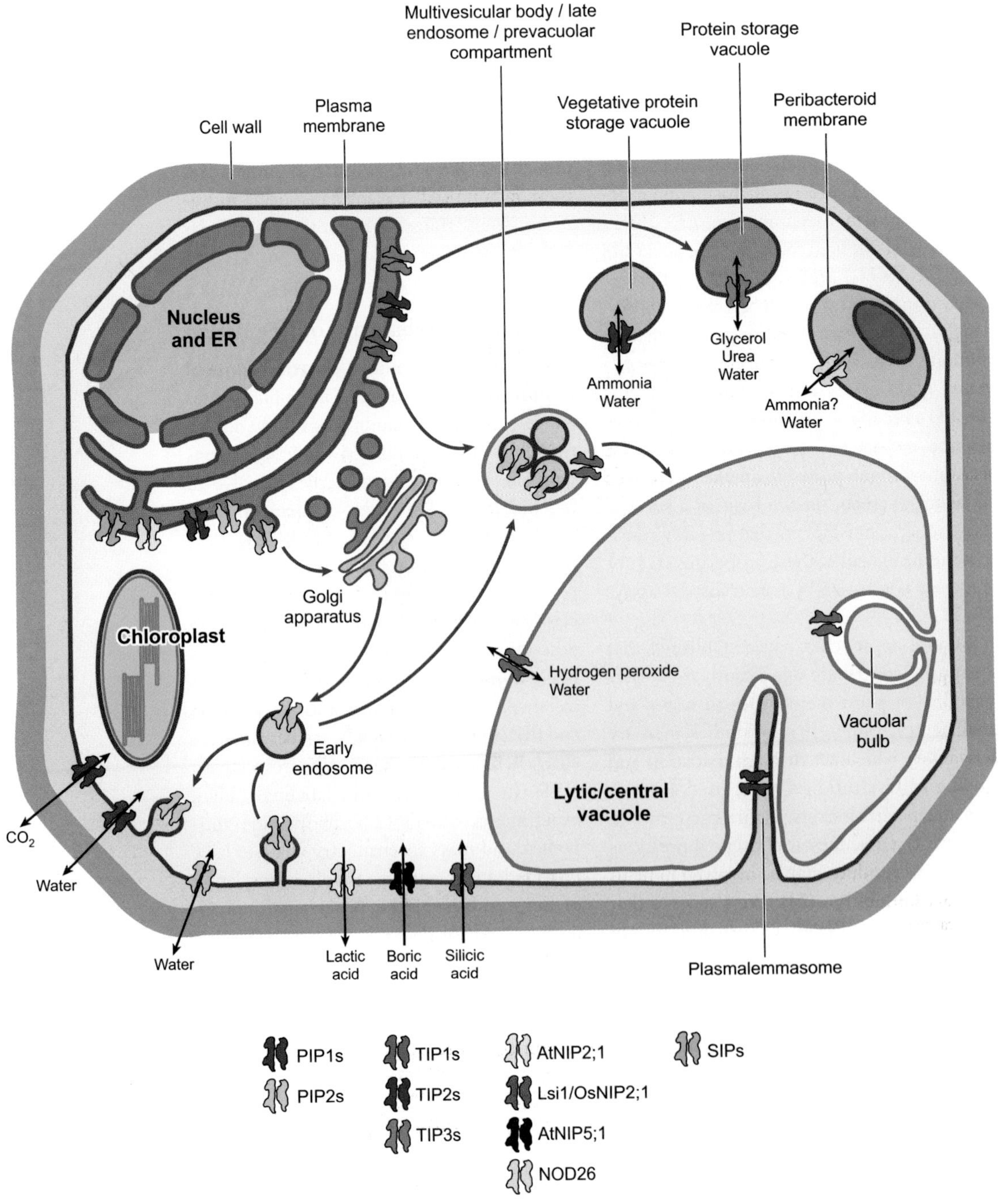

the first plant membrane proteins found to be methylated (121). For instance, *At*PIP2;1 can carry one or two methyl groups on its Lys3 and Glu6 residues, respectively. These data show that, in addition to a high isoform multiplicity, plant aquaporins occur in a large variety of modified forms, which suggests intricate co- and posttranslational regulation mechanisms.

Gating. The gating of aquaporins, i.e., the opening and closing of the pore, can be regulated by multiple factors. A role for phosphorylation in gating *Pv*TIP3;1, *Gm*NOD26, and *So*PIP2;1 was first deduced from functional expression in oocytes of these aquaporins, either wild-type or with point mutations at their phosphorylation sites (43, 63, 93), and by using pharmacological alterations of endogenous protein phosphatases and kinases. A role for phosphorylation in *Gm*NOD26 gating has been unambiguously established by stopped-flow measurements in purified peribacteroid membranes, showing that alkaline phosphatase-mediated dephosphorylation leads to reduced water permeability (43). Water transport measurements in plasma membrane vesicles purified from *Arabidopsis* suspension cells or *Beta vulgaris* roots also suggest that PIPs can be gated from the cytosolic side by protons and divalent cations (4, 41). A half-inhibition of water transport is observed at ~pH 7.5 and for free Ca^{2+} concentrations in the 100 μM range (4, 41). Beet plasma membranes exhibit an additional affinity component in the 10 nM range (4).

Gating: opening and closing of a membrane channel pore

The molecular bases of aquaporin gating have been elucidated from structure-function analyses in *Xenopus* oocytes and more recently from the atomic structures of *So*PIP2;1 in its open and closed conformations (137, 138). These studies established that protons are sensed by a His residue that is perfectly conserved in loop *D* of all PIPs (138). The molecular mechanisms that lead to a conformational change of loop *D* and occlusion of the pore upon protonation of the His residue or binding of divalent cations are detailed in **Figure 3**. The atomic structure of *So*PIP2;1 also indicates how phosphorylation of loop *B* would unlock loop *D* to allow the open conformation. By contrast, phosphorylation of the C-terminal tail would act in trans to prevent loop *D* of an adjacent monomer from adopting a closed-pore conformation (137).

A role for solutes in gating aquaporins has been proposed, based mainly on pressure probe measurements in *Chara* cells (155). Inhibition of cell water permeability is linked to the presence of the solute on either side of the membrane and is strongly dependent on solute molecular size. A tension/cohesion model

←

Figure 2

The multiple cellular functions of plant aquaporins. The figure illustrates the variety of transport functions achieved by aquaporins in various subcellular compartments. The different aquaporin subclasses or isoforms are identified below the illustration in distinct colors. Isoforms of the plasma membrane intrinsic protein 1 (PIP1) and PIP2 subfamilies are thought to follow the secretory pathway, which carries cargo from the endoplasmic reticulum (ER) toward the plasma membrane through the Golgi apparatus. PIPs also undergo repeated cycles of endocytosis and recycling through endosomal compartments before being eventually targeted to the lytic vacuole through the multivesicular body. In *Arabidopsis* leaves, PIP1s label plasmalemmasomes (116). Tonoplast intrinsic protein 1s (TIP1s) are found in the lytic vacuole membrane. *At*TIP1;1 localizes in spherical structures named bulbs in epidermal cells of young cotyledons or salt-treated roots (15, 118). TIP2s and TIP3s are preferentially associated with vacuoles that accumulate vegetative storage proteins and seed protein storage vacuoles, respectively. Nodulin-26–like intrinsic membrane proteins (NIPs) show a broad range of subcellular localization patterns. *At*NIP2;1 is localized in the endoplasmic reticulum and the plasma membrane (20, 97), the *Oryza sativa* silicon influx transporter low silicon rice 1 (Lsi1, also named*Os*NIP2;1) and the *Arabidopsis thaliana* boric acid channel *At*NIP5;1 are localized in the plasma membrane, whereas *Glycine max* nodulin-26 (*Gm*NOD26) is exclusively expressed in the peribacteroid membrane.

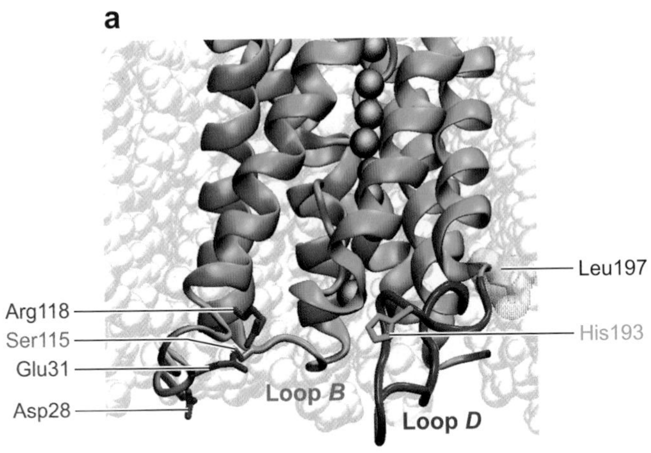

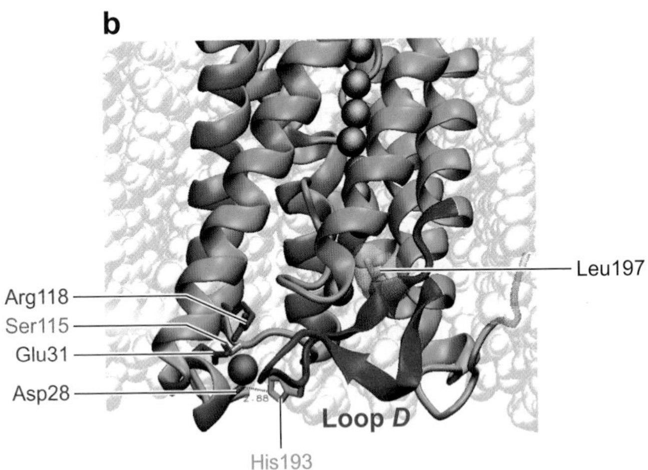

Figure 3

Molecular mechanisms of plasma membrane intrinsic protein (PIP) gating. The *Spinacia oleracea So*PIP2;1 structure was solved in an open (*a*) [Protein Data Bank (PDB) ID 2B5F] and in a closed (*b*) (PDB ID 1Z98) conformation (137). The His193 residue (*green*) is perfectly conserved in loop *D* of all PIPs. In the open conformation (*a*), His193 is not protonated and loop *D* is distal from the other cytoplasmic loop *B*. By contrast, the protonation of His193 (*b*) allows interaction with an acidic residue of the N terminus, Asp28 (*purple*). This in turn drives a conformational change of loop *D* and occlusion of the pore by displacement of the hydrophobic side chain of Leu197 (*yellow*) into the cytosolic pore mouth. Binding of divalent cations [Cd^{2+} in the atomic structure, (*purple sphere*)] would also involve Asp28 and an adjacent acidic residue (Glu31). Loop *D* would then be stabilized in the closed pore conformation through a network of H-bond and hydrostatic interactions, involving Arg118. In this model, phosphorylation of loop *B*, at Ser115 (*pink*), would disrupt this network of interactions and unlock loop *D* to allow the open conformation.

was proposed in which exclusion of the solute from the narrow vestibule of the pore would result in osmotic forces and tensions, which in turn would collapse the pore (155). Hydroxyl radicals also induce a marked (≥90%) and reversible inhibition of water transport in *Chara* cells, which was interpreted in terms of direct oxidative gating of aquaporins (50). By contrast, the inhibition of aquaporins by reactive oxygen species (ROS) in the *Arabidopsis* root seems to involve cell signaling mechanisms (Y. Boursiac, J. Boudet, O. Postaire, D.-T. Luu, C. Tournaire-Roux & C. Maurel, unpublished results).

Tetramer assembly and cellular trafficking of PIPs. Recent studies have pointed to aquaporin trafficking as a critical point for regulating aquaporin expression and function. The inability of some PIP1 isoforms to be functionally expressed in *Xenopus* oocytes has been reported by several laboratories. Fetter and coworkers (31) explained this inability by a failure of these aquaporins to traffic to the oocyte plasma membrane, and showed that coexpression of maize PIP1s in *Xenopus* oocytes with reduced amounts of PIP2 isoforms could alleviate this defect. Affinity copurification and coimmunopurification studies provided the first biochemical evidence that PIP1s and PIP2s physically interact, both in oocytes and plants (31, 158). The results of fluorescence resonance energy transfer (FRET) imaging in living maize protoplasts coexpressing PIP1s and PIP2s further support a model in which aquaporins of the two classes directly interact, very likely by heterotetramerization, to facilitate PIP1 trafficking (158). A possible role for PIP1 phosphorylation was recently added to this model (135). Phosphorylation on loop *B* of a *Mimosa* PIP1 is not necessary for aquaporin interaction but enhances the overall water transport activity of PIP1-PIP2 complexes in oocytes (135). Whereas interaction-dependent trafficking of PIP1s and PIP2s offers a broad range of combinatorial regulations, a future challenge is to determine to what extent this process can dominate the expression of PIP1 or PIP2 homotetramers. Antisense inhibition experiments in *Arabidopsis* of PIP1s and PIP2s, alone or in combination, have suggested that the two classes of aquaporins contribute to the same functional water transport units (90).

Similar to other membrane proteins, PIP2 aquaporins are subjected to constitutive cycling. Their endocytosis is clathrin-dependent (28) and reduced by auxin (108). Export of PIP2 aquaporins from the endoplasmic reticulum is also critically controlled and the role of a di-acidic motif contained in the N-terminal tail of PIP2s was recently uncovered in maize and *Arabidopsis* (F. Chaumont, personal communication; M. Sorieul, D.-T. Luu, V. Santoni & C. Maurel, unpublished results). The cellular mechanisms that determine aquaporin trafficking and their subcellular relocalization in response to stimuli will surely fuel intense investigations in the coming years.

AQUAPORIN FUNCTIONS THROUGHOUT PLANT GROWTH AND DEVELOPMENT

Water Transport

Principles of plant water transport. A wide range of cell water permeabilities can be observed between distinct cell types and throughout plant development. For instance, cell pressure probe measurements indicate that, in growing epicotyls of pea, cortical cells have a ~30-fold higher hydraulic conductivity than epidermal cells (130). Also, swelling assays on isolated protoplasts from rape roots indicate that their osmotic water permeability coefficient increases from 10 to 500 $\mu m\ sec^{-1}$ within less than two days (114). Although the contribution of the lipid membranes should be taken into account, one challenge will be to determine how the aquaporin equipment of each individual cell can determine such strikingly different water transport properties. In these respects, attempts have been made to regulate the cell-specific expression of aquaporin isoforms in radish taproots and maize primary roots and the water permeability of protoplasts derived from the various cell types of these materials (46, 132).

Hydraulic conductivity: water permeability (i.e., intrinsic capacity to transport water) of a membrane, cell, or tissue

In the whole plant, long-distance transport of fluids occurs mostly through vascular tissues, which do not present significant membrane barriers. Yet, living tissues can be the site of intense flows of water during transpiration or expansion growth. For this, water can flow along various paths: (*i*) the apoplastic path, i.e., within the cell wall continuum, (*ii*) the symplastic route through cytoplasmic continuities and plasmodesmata, and (*iii*) the transcellular path across cell membranes (mainly plasma membranes), which in many tissues is mostly mediated by aquaporins. Although it is not very specific and is inactive on certain aquaporins (see above), mercury represents one of the very few tools available to evaluate the contribution of aquaporins to water transport in plant tissues. The general toxicity of this compound in vivo must be carefully evaluated (reviewed in 61), and researchers checked that mercury does not perturb xylem solute transport and respiration in aspen roots. By contrast, mercury depolarizes wheat root cells in parallel to inhibition of water transport (61). A reversibility of mercury effects by reducing agents is also required to show that the blocking effects are due to oxidation mechanisms and not to irreversible damage of the cells. Despite all these restrictions, the effects of mercury on water transport have been characterized in a large variety of physiological contexts. Overall, these studies provide a consistent picture of the role of aquaporins, in particular during root water transport (61). Yet, new specific aquaporin blockers are critically needed. Gold and silver ions have been described as potent aquaporin blockers in vitro but the use of these compounds in vivo seems to be problematic and their mode of action is as yet unknown (106).

Transpiration. Because it induces an intense renewal of water throughout the plant,

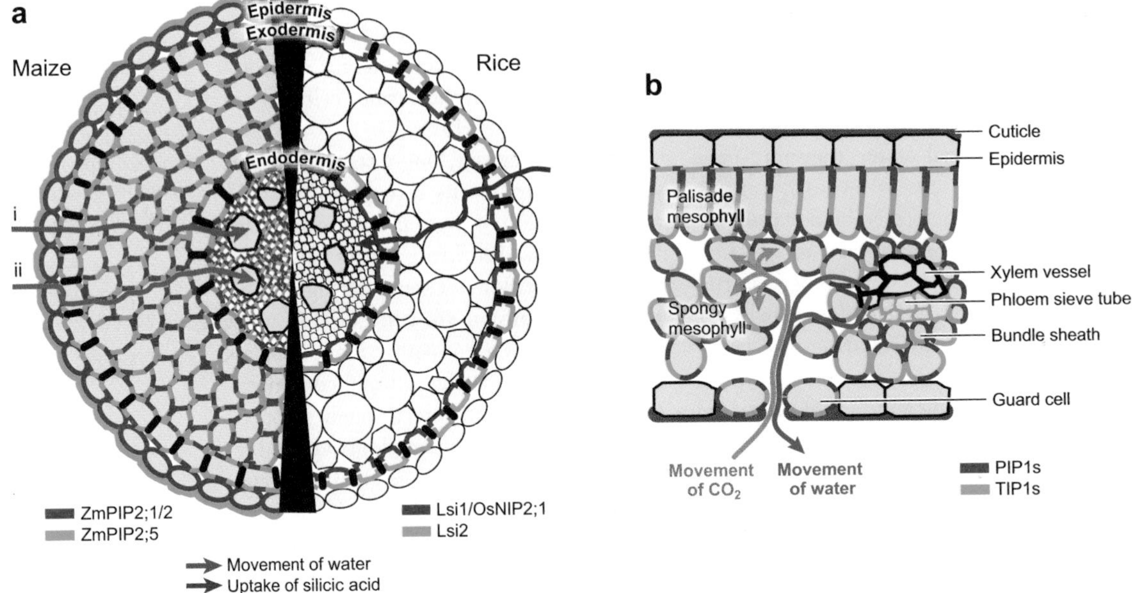

Figure 4

Aquaporin-mediated transport of water and solutes in roots (*a*) and leaves (*b*). Schematic cross sections with representations of the tissue-specific expression patterns of aquaporins and paths of transport are shown. Aquaporin expression and water transport in maize roots is summarized according to Reference 46, whereas uptake of silicic acid in rice roots by *Oryza sativa* Lsi1 (*Os*NIP2;1) in combination with the efflux transporter Low silicon rice 2 (Lsi2) is drawn according to References 82 and 83. Expression of plasma membrane intrinsic protein 1s (PIP1s) and tonoplast intrinsic protein 1s (TIP1s) in *Brassica napus* leaves was summarized according to Reference 35. The movement of water can follow the cell-to-cell (symplastic and transcellular) (*i*) or apoplastic (*ii*) path.

transpiration represents an obvious context in which to investigate aquaporin function in roots and leaves. A thorough description of cell-specific expression of aquaporins in roots was recently performed in maize using in situ and quantitative RT-PCR and immunolocalization (46). Strong expression of *Zm*PIP2;1 and *Zm*PIP2;5 is observed in both the exodermis and endodermis of the mature zone, suggesting that because of the presence of Casparian strips a bypass of the apoplastic path may be necessary in these cell layers (46) (**Figure 4*a***). Also, a strong expression in the stele and vascular tissues is consistently observed in roots of several plant species (46, 124, 132). Several lines of functional evidence also show that aquaporins significantly contribute to water uptake by roots. Firstly, mercury inhibits the root hydraulic conductivity (Lp_r) by 30%–90% in more than ten plant species (61). In addition, antisense inhibition of aquaporins of the PIP1 and/or PIP2 subclasses reduced Lp_r by approximately 50% in tobacco or *Arabidopsis* (90, 128). Finally, two allelic *Arabidopsis pip2;2* knockout mutants show, with respect to wild-type plants, a reduction of 25%–30% in hydraulic conductivity of root cortex cells (60). In addition, the osmotic hydraulic conductivity of entire roots, as derived from free exudation measurements, is decreased by 14% in the mutants, pointing to PIP2;2 as an aquaporin specialized in osmotic fluid transport in the *Arabidopsis* root (60). Further analysis of mutants corresponding to aquaporin genes with distinct cell-specific expression patterns may help

Lp_r: root hydraulic conductivity

dissect the contribution of the various cell layers to distinct modes (i.e., osmotic or hydrostatic) of water transport within the root.

The preferential expression of some aquaporin isoforms in vascular tissues and cell types such as tracheary elements, xylem parenchyma cells, and phloem-associated cells suggests a general role of aquaporins in sap transport throughout the plant body (reviewed in 92). In the leaf, the water supply at the evaporating sites is sustained by a flow of liquid water from the vascular system through the extravascular compartment, including the vascular bundles and the mesophyll (**Figure 4*b***). A role for aquaporins in mediating water transfer from the veins to the stomatal chamber has been proposed on the basis of two lines of evidence. Firstly, mercury can inhibit leaf hydraulic conductance (K_{leaf}) in sunflower and in six temperate deciduous trees (1, 103). Secondly, light-dependent changes in K_{leaf} in walnut occur within one hour, are associated with changes in expression of PIP2 aquaporin transcripts, and both are inhibited by 100 μM cycloheximide, indicating a role for protein synthesis in K_{leaf} regulation (22). In a recent study, mesophyll protoplasts were isolated from *Arabidopsis* genotypes differing in stomatal aperture or from plants grown at varying relative air humidity (98). Surprisingly, researchers observed an inverse relationship between the rate of transpiration in the plant and the water permeability of the isolated protoplasts. These variations occur without any alteration in the leaf PIP content, suggesting that aquaporin function is controlled at the posttranslational level. The physiological significance of this control and its occurrence in other plant species are as yet unknown. Expression of aquaporins has also been reported in stomatal guard cells (36, 123). Despite the critical role played by these cells in maintaining the whole plant water status, the function of aquaporins in stomatal movements is as yet unclear and deserves more attention for future research.

Tissue expansion. Although some aquaporin isoforms seem to be specific to dividing cells (9), a strong link between PIP and TIP aquaporin expression and cell expansion has been observed in numerous plant materials. For instance, expression of the *AtTIP1;1* promoter is associated with cell enlargement in *Arabidopsis* roots, hypocotyls, leaves, and flower stems (81), and transcript accumulation is enhanced by the growth-promoting hormone gibberellic acid (GA3) (109), suggesting that *At*TIP1;1 may contribute to the differentiation of a large central vacuole in fully elongated cells (81).

Because most plant cells have short half-times of water exchange (130), water influx into a single plant cell can hardly be limiting during expansion growth. Membrane water transport in growing tissues should rather be envisioned in the context of a transcellular delivery of water from vascular tissues toward peripheral expanding tissues (148). The presence, in certain physiological conditions, of significant water potential gradients within growing tissues supports the idea that this type of water transport can be limiting. Accordingly, mercury blocks tissue growth in maize roots, but exclusively in the older cells, distal to the apex (55). These cells are characterized, with respect to younger cells, by a high, mercury-sensitive cell hydraulic conductivity and reduced symplastic connections with the phloem, suggesting that aquaporin-mediated transcellular water transport is necessary for delivery of water from the phloem into the cells. In castor bean hypocotyls, the transcript abundance of a specific PIP2 isoform and a high hydraulic conductivity of cortical cells both show the same light- and spatial-dependence as that of tissue expansion (30). Finally, diurnal epinastic movements (unfolding) of tobacco leaves can be accounted for by a differential growth of the upper and lower surfaces of the petiole. A limiting role for tobacco aquaporin 1 (*Nt*AQP1) in this process was proposed on the basis of observations that expression of *Nt*AQP1 in the petiole shows a diurnal rhythm that coincides

K_{leaf}: leaf hydraulic conductance

g_m: mesophyll conductance to CO_2

with leaf unfolding and that antisense inhibition of *Nt*AQP1 impairs leaf movement (127). These studies draw a convincing, but qualitative, picture of aquaporin function in expansion growth. Future studies will have to quantitatively integrate growth rates, cell and tissue water relation parameters, and aquaporin expression in time and space (148). Fruit development and ripening, which involve cell enlargement and cotransport of sugar and water, will also represent important processes in which to investigate aquaporin function (19, 110).

Tissue desiccation and imbibition. Plant reproduction requires the intense desiccation of certain organs, which then acquire specific dissemination and resistance properties. TIP isoforms specific to pollen grains have been reported in *Arabidopsis* but their function during pollen desiccation and/or pollen tube growth is as yet unclear (111). By contrast, antisense inhibition of PIP2 aquaporins in tobacco delays anther dehydration and dehiscence, suggesting that these aquaporins are involved in water flow out of the anther via the vascular bundle and/or evaporation (14). Seed germination represents another remarkable context, during early tissue imbibition and subsequent embryo growth, in which aquaporins may mediate a fine temporal and spatial control of water transport; evidence for aquaporin function in seeds is emerging. In *Brassica napus*, the germination rate of seeds that have gone through various priming treatments is strongly correlated with the transcript abundance of a PIP2 aquaporin (39). In pea and *Arabidopsis*, mercurials reduce the speed of seed imbibition and seed germination, respectively (145, 147). Finally, expression in tobacco and rice of sense and antisense *PIP1* transgenes shows that the speed and extent of germination of seeds in normal and/or water stress conditions is positively correlated with aquaporin expression (76, 156). Liu and coworkers (76) suggested a role for PIP1s in stimulating seed germination by nitric oxide (NO) in rice.

Nitrogen, Carbon, and Micronutrient Acquisition

Nitrogen fixation. A first link between aquaporins and nitrogen (N) assimilation came from the observation that expression of some aquaporin genes is dependent on N compounds; some genes, such as *ZmPIP1;5b*, are strongly induced by nitrate (40), whereas others, such as *AtTIP2;1*, are induced under long-term N starvation or short term NH_4^+ supply (79). This type of regulation was first interpreted as a reflection of well-known connections between water relations and N metabolism. However, evidence was recently presented that aquaporins of the PIP, NIP, and TIP subfamilies can transport N compounds. Transport of urea by TIPs (42, 70, 140) may contribute to urea equilibration within the cell and storage into and remobilization from the vacuole (70). Wheat and *Arabidopsis* TIP2 homologs also show a remarkable permeability to NH_3 and may therefore contribute to significant loading of this compound and acid-trapping of the protonated form (NH_4^+) in the vacuole (53, 57, 79). However, studies of transgenic *Arabidopsis* that overexpresses *At*TIP2;1 failed to establish any significant role for this aquaporin in NH_4^+ accumulation (79).

CO_2 transport and carbon metabolism. CO_2 transport by aquaporins in planta was first evaluated by treating *Vicia faba* and *Phaseolus vulgaris* leaves with mercury (136). In these two experiments, mercury altered the dependency of photosynthesis on intercellular but not on chloroplastic CO_2. This effect was interpreted to mean that CO_2 diffusion into the chloroplast [i.e., mesophyll conductance to CO_2 (g_m)] is blocked and therefore involves proteins, possibly aquaporins. Transgenic plants with altered aquaporin expression provide systems in which to explore this issue further (47, 144). In tobacco plants with antisense inhibition or an antibiotic-inducible overexpression of *Nt*AQP1, g_m positively correlates with the *Nt*AQP1 expression level

(33, 144). In view of the CO_2 transport activity of *Nt*AQP1 in oocytes, this result was interpreted as evidence that this PIP1 homolog serves as a CO_2 pore in tobacco leaves (33, 144). Interestingly, in various genetic and physiological contexts g_m is positively correlated with maximal stomatal conductance and CO_2 assimilation capacity (see 33 and references therein). Up to now, it was unclear whether changes in g_m can be accounted for by changes in leaf anatomy or by changes in cell permeability to CO_2 (47). Following evidence that PIP contributes to both g_m and leaf hydraulic conductance, the hypothesis that aquaporins coregulate CO_2 and H_2O transport in the mesophyll emerged (**Figure 4*b***).

A role for aquaporins in carbohydrate storage and compartmentation has also been suggested. In a first study, tomato fruits with antisense inhibition of a PIP homolog showed increases in organic acid content and decreases in sugar content; these defects are associated with a marked alteration of the ripening process (19). In another study, metabolomic analysis of *Arabidopsis* plants lacking *At*TIP1;1 expression revealed complex alterations in the accumulation of various sugars, organic acids, and starch (84). Although this provocative hypothesis remains to be confirmed, reduced expression of *At*TIP1;1 was proposed to alter vesicle trafficking and therefore carbohydrate compartmentation.

Nutrient uptake. Two recent studies unraveled novel functions of aquaporins in plant nutrient uptake. Transcriptome analysis of *Arabidopsis* roots revealed striking upregulation of *At*NIP5;1 in response to boron (B) deficiency (134). Interestingly, *At*NIP5;1 transports boric acid in *Xenopus* oocytes and significantly contributes to root B uptake, as shown in two independent *nip5;1* insertion lines. The physiological significance of *At*NIP5;1 was further underscored by mutant plants that, under B limitation, display a striking growth retardation of shoot and roots and an inhibition of flower and silique formation (134). We note that a role for membrane channels in B transport was first proposed in an early study on squash roots (29). However, the role of aquaporins had remained uncertain owing to the low B transport activity of the PIPs and NIPs investigated in that study.

Silicon is a major mineral component of certain plants, such as Gramineae, and more generally, helps plants withstand abiotic stresses and pathogen attacks. Molecular characterization of *low silicon rice1* (*lsi1*), a mutant of rice defective in silicon uptake into roots, led to the unexpected finding that Lsi1 encodes a NIP homolog (82). Lsi1 transports silicon after heterologous expression in oocytes. Lsi1 is expressed on the distal side of exodermal and endodermal root cells and may contribute, in combination with the efflux transporter Lsi2 (83), to a vectorial transport of silicic acid from the soil solution into the xylem, a limiting step for translocation of silicon to the aerial parts (**Figure 4*a***). A similar function can be expected in other important crops such as maize, which also accumulates significant amounts of silicon and has close Lsi1 homologs (82).

AQUAPORINS IN A VARIABLE ENVIRONMENT

Changes in Irradiance

Light is a key environmental parameter that, besides its long-term effects on plant growth and development, diurnally affects the plant metabolic regime and therefore affects water relations. A primary effect of light is to control stomatal aperture, and therefore transpiration. In guard cells of sunflower leaves, the transcript abundance of a TIP homolog (SunTIP7) is under diurnal regulation and is maximal at the end of the day, during stomatal closure, suggesting that this aquaporin contributes to water efflux from the guard cell (123). Light also enhances K_{leaf} in many plant species (22, 103, 142). For instance in sunflower, the $\sim 50\%$ increase in K_{leaf} induced by light is fully sensitive to mercury inhibition, suggesting that the variations in K_{leaf} are due to changes in aquaporin activity (103). This was confirmed in walnut twigs, where K_{leaf} shows a very tight kinetic correlation with the abundance of two major *PIP2* transcripts during a transition from dark to high light (22). Enhanced activity of leaf aquaporins during the day, and therefore increased K_{leaf}, may favor water transport into the inner leaf tissues when transpiration is maximal. This process would avoid excessive drops in leaf water potential, reduce xylem tensions, and therefore prevent possible xylem embolization.

Light interception is optimized by diurnal movements of leaves, a process in which aquaporins also participate. In the Mimosaceae, the movement of leaves and leaflets is determined by coordinate swelling and shrinking of cells on opposing sides of a motor organ, the pulvinus. In *Samanea saman*, the osmotic water permeability of protoplasts isolated from the pulvinus shows diurnal regulation and is maximal in the mornings and evenings, concomitant with leaf movement (100). Accumulation of a PIP2 homolog in these cells is under circadian control and in phase with these rhythmic changes in water transport. In *Mimosa pudica*, motor cells harbor both a tannin and a central aqueous vacuole. Immunocytochemistry experiments indicate that the latter type of vacuoles shows an approximate tenfold higher density of TIP1 aquaporins as compared with the former type, in agreement with the major contribution of the central vacuole to water exchanges during cell volume regulation (32).

Diurnal variations of root Lp_r, with a two- to threefold increase during the day, have been observed in many plant species and may contribute, together with light-dependent regulation of K_{leaf}, to reducing xylem tension under conditions of high transpiration demand (16, 49, 78). In *Lotus japonicus* and maize, for instance, root water transport is maximally enhanced around midday and is matched or slightly preceded by an increase in the abundance of *PIP1* and *PIP2* transcripts (49, 78). In maize, *Zm*PIP1;5 transcripts are detected in all root cell types during the day but restricted to the epidermis during the night (40). However, the abundance of PIP proteins in maize roots shows a more complex diurnal variation profile than that of transcripts, suggesting a role for posttranslational regulation (78). The mechanisms that allow light perception and long-distance control of aquaporins in the plant root deserve more precise investigation.

Water, Salt, and Nutrient Stresses

Regulation of turgor and intracellular water movements. Because it is central for plant water relations, the regulation of water transport during water deficit has been the object of extensive research. Understanding the role of aquaporins in this context now requires integration of numerous observations made at the molecular, cell, and tissue levels. Fundamental regulation properties that explain the remarkable ability of plant cells to withstand water deprivation have emerged from basic knowledge of plant cell water relations and from more recent research on aquaporins. Water deficit induces primarily an efflux of water, which can result in a marked drop in cell turgor and ultimately, but more rarely, in cell plasmolysis or cytorrhysis. In this context, the cytosol, which contributes to a minor fraction of the plant cell volume, may be very sensitive to differential flow of water across the plasma membrane and the tonoplast. Abrupt changes in cytosolic volume can theoretically be avoided if mobilization of water from or into the vacuole is nonlimiting (92, 140). Studies with membranes purified from wheat and tobacco have confirmed that, in these preparations at least, the tonoplast shows much higher water permeability and aquaporin activity than the plasma membrane (95, 104).

Osmotic stress also requires an adjustment of plasma membrane surface area; recent results link this process to the regulation of membrane water permeability. In *Vicia faba* guard cells, a pretreatment with inhibitors of membrane trafficking (wortmannin, cytochalasin D) slows down cell shrinkage in response to hypertonicity, suggesting that a reduction of cell hydraulic conductivity and possibly aquaporin downregulation is induced (126). When protoplasts isolated from maize suspension cells are hypotonically challenged, a subset of these protoplasts exhibits a retarded swelling, which was interpreted to mean that their initial water permeability is extremely low and is dynamically adjusted during the course of cell swelling and mobilization of membrane material at the cell surface (101). In agreement with these functional data, dynamic changes in aquaporin subcellular localization were observed in osmotically challenged cells. These processes may also reflect transfer of aquaporins to subcellular compartments devoted to protein degradation. For instance, mannitol-induced osmotic stress in ice plant suspension cells induces the relocalization of *Mc*TIP1;2 from the tonoplast to a putative endosomal compartment (146). This process is dependent on aquaporin glycosylation and a cAMP-dependent pathway. In salt-treated *Arabidopsis* roots, *At*TIP1;1, but not the *At*TIP2;1 homolog, is relocalized in vacuolar bulbs (15). In addition, redistribution of PIPs from the plasma membrane to internal compartments contributes to the downregulation of root water uptake (15).

The regulation of water transport in *Chara* cells in response to changing osmotic or hydrostatic pressures has been interpreted as the result of a direct gating of aquaporins by these factors (152, 155). In higher plant cells, aquaporins are more likely under the control of osmo- and pressure-sensing molecules and downstream signaling cascades. For instance, the downregulation of water permeability in melon protoplasts by salt can be counteracted by okadaic acid, a protein phosphatase inhibitor (89). More specifically, phosphorylation of *So*PIP2;1 in spinach leaf fragments decreases in response to a hyperosmotic treatment (64). A general model of cell osmoregulation involving stretch-activated Ca^{2+} channel and Ca^{2+}-dependent phosphorylation of *So*PIP2;1 was proposed to explain that aquaporin phosphorylation, and therefore cell hydraulic conductivity, would be maximal at high water potential to favor water entry in fully turgid cells (63). Finally, several authors proposed that aquaporins themselves may function as osmosensors, but the molecular and cellular mechanisms involved remain elusive (51, 86).

Whole plant level. At the whole plant level, a major effect of drought is to reduce transpiration through stomatal closure. Yet, in extreme drought conditions, high tension in the xylem can lead to vessel occlusion by embolization. A specific role for aquaporins in embolism refilling and recovery of stem axial conductance after drought was proposed in grapevine on the basis of mercury inhibition experiments (80). In roots of most plant species investigated, drought or salt stresses also result in a marked decrease in Lp_r (61). In *Arabidopsis* for instance, exposure to 100 mM NaCl reduces Lp_r by 70% with a half-time of approximately 45 min. The fact that residual Lp_r of salt-stressed *Arabidopsis* or paprika roots becomes resistant to mercury was interpreted to mean that aquaporin activity is downregulated in these conditions (17, 88). During the day, this early response may provide a hydraulic signal to the leaf to trigger stomatal closure, whereas during the night, it may avoid a backflow of water to the drying soil.

Numerous early studies reported on water stress–dependent expression of aquaporin genes and a large variety of individual regulation profiles were described (92). A more comprehensive understanding of the processes involved has emerged from recent studies in maize, rice, radish, and *Arabidopsis*, in which expression of the whole aquaporin family was considered (3, 15, 44, 58, 73, 85, 131, 159). In salt-stressed roots of *Arabidopsis* and maize, a coordinated downregulation of most aquaporin transcripts occurs, which over the first 24 h of stress can contribute to Lp_r downregulation (3, 15, 85). A recovery toward initial transcript abundance occurs over longer term stresses (85, 159). Transcriptional control of aquaporins in drought-stressed leaves appears to be more complex and, although a tendency to overall aquaporin gene downregulation is also observed, specific upregulation of certain *PIP* transcripts occurs in rice and *Arabidopsis* leaves (3, 44). Interestingly, the two transcripts that are upregulated in *Arabidopsis* are specifically expressed in aerial parts (3). Although their tissue expression pattern is as yet unknown, these isoforms may facilitate water flow toward critical cell types. Studies in *Hordeum vulgare* (barley) leaves suggest that increased abundance of *HvPIP1;6* transcripts in response to salt may reflect a role for this aquaporin in promoting residual growth of the leaf under stress (37).

In agreement with its central role in plant responses to water stress, abscisic acid (ABA) seems to mediate, at least in part, drought- and salt stress-induced aquaporin regulation. For instance, treatment of maize roots with ABA results over 1–2 h in a transient increase in hydraulic conductivity of the whole organ and of cortical cells, by factors of 3–4 and 7–27, respectively (54). Consistent with these effects, ABA also rapidly enhances the expression of some PIP isoforms (159). In rice roots, a strong induction of several PIPs is observed in response to water deficit, specifically in an upland cultivar that shows an enhanced production of ABA (73). This response may optimize uptake of residual soil water at the onset of soil drying.

Genetic approaches have also been useful to investigate the function of aquaporins during drought. Transgenic tobacco plants with antisense inhibition of PIP1 and transgenic *Arabidopsis* plants with antisense inhibition of PIP1 expression and PIP2 expression showed lower leaf water potentials than wild-type plants under drought stress conditions (90, 128). Most strikingly, the recovery following rewatering of leaf wilting in tobacco and leaf water potential and plant hydraulic conductance in *Arabidopsis* is significantly delayed in the antisense plants (90, 128). Therefore, PIP aquaporins contribute to adaptation of the plants to drought by mechanisms that remain to be determined, and even more significantly, contribute to rehydration of the whole plant body after drought. Another genetic strategy is to enhance aquaporin expression in transgenic plants. Although spectacular phenotypes are observed in most studies, aquaporin overexpression has either beneficial (44, 72, 156) or adverse (2, 68) effects on drought tolerance, depending on the aquaporin gene or the plant species investigated. Therefore, the relevance of this approach for biotechnological improvement of plant tolerance to water stress remains uncertain. One reason may be that many studies relied on overexpression of an aquaporin in a heterologous plant species (2, 44, 68, 156). Inadequate regulation of the foreign aquaporin may disturb the endogenous stress response. In these respects, more relevant insights were provided by a study showing that *Oryza sativa* *Os*PIP1;3 is specifically induced by water stress in an upland, drought-avoidant cultivar of rice (72). Furthermore, the performance of a lowland cultivar under drought can be significantly enhanced by expression of this aquaporin under a stress-responsive promoter (72). In future studies it will be important to evaluate the capacity to recover from water stress after rewatering in transgenic plants that ectopically express an aquaporin.

Responses to nutrient stress. Strong interactions exist between the nutrient and water status of plants; integration of these two aspects seems to be critical for a deeper understanding of plant stress responses. For instance, deprivation of N, phosphorus (P), or sulfur (S) in plants results after a few days in a significant inhibition of water transport in whole roots or individual root cells; initial root water transport properties can be restored in the 24 h following nutrient resupply (16, 21, 125). A downregulation of water channels under N and P deprivation is invoked on the basis of the insensitivity of residual Lp_r to mercury (16). The adverse effects of nutrient starvation on plant water relations have also been studied in sorghum under drought stress. As compared with replete conditions, P starvation enhances the inhibition of Lp_r by a polyethylene glycol treatment and slows down its recovery after water resupply (125).

The molecular and cellular mechanisms involved in these regulations remain unclear. Stimulation of maize Lp_r by NO_3^- is blocked in the presence of tungstate, an inhibitor of nitrate reductase, suggesting that products of the N assimilation pathway are required for activation of aquaporin functions (10). A general transcriptional control of aquaporins by nutrient stress is also observed in the *Arabidopsis* root and, for instance, calcium deprivation results in an overall transcriptional downregulation of aquaporins (85). The effects of potassium (K) starvation are more moderate but a downregulation of *Arabidopsis* PIPs is also induced in the long term. By contrast, K deprivation in rice induces a twofold stimulation of Lp_r after 4–6 h and enhances expression of some PIP isoforms, in parallel to expression of K channels (75). Coregulation of aquaporins and K transport systems has also been observed in roots treated with CsCl, which in addition to blocking K transport, reduces Lp_r and aquaporin expression (75). These data suggest tight interactions between water and K transport during cell turgor regulation.

Cold Stress

Chilling of plant roots (i.e., exposure to 4°C–8°C) reduces root pressure, sap flow, and Lp_r in a few hours (5, 71, 157). These effects in turn induce water deficit symptoms in shoots, such as decreased leaf water potential and stomatal closure (157). In maize, both a chilling-tolerant and a chilling-sensitive variety show an initial, >80% decline in Lp_r but the tolerant variety shows a unique capacity to spontaneously overcompensate Lp_r upon prolonged (>3 d) chilling (5). The speed and reversibility of inhibition of Lp_r by chilling in cucumber and rice and a concomitant six- to ninefold reduction in cortex cell hydraulic conductivity in cucumber roots suggest that inhibition of aquaporin activity is involved (71, 157).

Comprehensive gene expression analyses in roots and shoots of rice, maize, and *Arabidopsis* show that chilling induces a marked (two- to fourfold) decrease in abundance for most *PIP* transcripts (5, 58, 120, 157). Normal gene expression is restored in the 24 h following the return to permissive temperature. However, in maize and rice roots under cold stress or recovery, the abundance of aquaporin transcripts and proteins is not always correlated, suggesting the occurrence of posttranscriptional regulation (5, 157). In addition, the abundance of PIP1s and of phosphorylated PIP2 forms (as monitored by immunodetection) increases during prolonged chilling in roots of both a chilling-tolerant and a chilling-sensitive variety of maize; intriguingly, this response is not correlated to their differential Lp_r regulation (5). Because the sensitivities to chilling and H_2O_2 are correlated in the tolerant and sensitive varieties, it was proposed that ROS-induced damage probably dominates the aquaporin response and determines the poor performance of the sensitive variety during stress (5). A more direct relationship between aquaporins and ROS was determined in cucumber (71). In this species, H_2O_2 accumulates in response to chilling and treatment of roots by exogenous H_2O_2 inhibits Lp_r to the same extent as chilling.

Flowers can also perceive temperature. In tulip, diurnal movements of petals are controlled in part by changes in temperature (7). Petal opening and an associated water retention can be induced at 20°C and are linked to phosphorylation in a microsomal membrane fraction of a 31-kDa protein, tentatively identified as a PIP isoform. Petal closure is induced at 5°C and is associated with decreased phosphorylation of the putative aquaporin. The effects of a calcium chelator [1,2-bis(o-aminophenoxy)ethane-N,N,N′,N′-tetraacetic acid, or BAPTA] and a calcium channel blocker on petal movement and the associated phosphorylation of the aquaporin suggest a role for calcium signaling in this process (7).

AM: arbuscular mycorrhiza

Finally, freeze-thaw cycles occurring during winter can, similar to severe drought stress, embolize xylem vessels of woody plants (119). Embolism repair may be achieved by hydrolysis of starch in adjacent parenchyma cells, exudation of the resulting sugars in the vessel, and concomitant water influx to chase out the air bubble. In walnut twigs, the transcripts and proteins corresponding to two PIP2 homologs show seasonal variations and preferentially accumulate in the xylem parenchyma during winter, suggesting a role for these aquaporins in embolism repair (119).

Anoxia

Flooding or compaction of soils results in acute oxygen deprivation (anoxia) of plant roots, which is a major stress for cultivated plants. Most plant species investigated show a rapid inhibition of Lp_r in response to anoxia. Tournaire-Roux and coworkers (138) delineated the organ and cell bases of this process in *Arabidopsis* roots. They showed that anoxic stress results in acidosis of root cells and that the Lp_r of excised roots diminishes in parallel to cytosolic pH. These observations can be linked to the molecular mechanism of PIP aquaporin gating by cytosolic protons, which is conserved in PIPs of all plants and therefore can explain how an anoxic stress results in a massive inhibition of root water uptake. This regulation may avoid excessive dilution of xylem sap after flooding or, on a longer term, favor ethylene accumulation, which in turn induces aerenchyma differentiation (52). Ethylene, which enhances Lp_r in hypoxic aspen roots, may also compensate for the initial inhibition of water transport in response to oxygen deprivation (65). Consistent with the physiological inhibition of Lp_r, a general downregulation of *PIP* and *TIP* genes in response to hypoxia occurs in *Arabidopsis* (74). By contrast, expression of *AtNIP2;1* is markedly induced upon flooding stress and hypoxia (20, 74). *At*NIP2;1 transports lactic acid and may therefore provide a path for release of this fermentation product from root cells, to contribute to cytosolic pH regulation and metabolic adaptation to long-term hypoxia (20).

Biotic Interactions

Rhizobia-legume symbiosis. Interactions of plants with soil microorganisms, which have long been known as central for plant mineral nutrition and metabolism, more recently appear to play an important role in plant water relations and tolerance to environmental stresses (6, 43, 143). Notably, *Gm*NOD26, the first plant aquaporin to be identified, is specifically expressed in symbiotic nitrogen-fixing nodules formed after infection of soybean by *Rhizobiaceae* bacteria (149). Similar nodulins have been identified in other legumes. *Gm*NOD26 is a major component of the peribacteroid membrane, a membrane of plant origin that surrounds the bacteroid and mediates exchanges with the root cell. Antibodies raised against either the native or phosphorylated form of *Gm*NOD26 reveal that maximal expression of the protein and its subsequent phosphorylation coincide with bacteroid maturation (43). Because of its solute transporting activity, *Gm*NOD26 has been tentatively linked to a channel-mediated import of NH_3 from the bacteroid, but unequivocal evidence for such function is still lacking (105, 149). The water transport activity of *Gm*NOD26 may also help the plant cell to couple osmoregulation of the plant cytosol and peribacteroid space. Accordingly, drought and salt stress result in a threefold increase in *Gm*NOD26 phosphorylation, suggesting that enhanced water permeability is required for nodule osmoregulation and adaptation to water stress. (43).

Mycorrhiza. Arbuscular mycorrhizas (AM) represent the most common form of symbiosis between land plants and soil fungi. Similar to the *Rhizobia*-legume symbiosis, this interaction results in deep anatomical changes of root cells, involving in this case the differentiation of convoluted, periarbuscular membrane structures that are the site of extensive exchanges of mineral nutrient (phosphate), carbohydrates (photosynthates), and water with the fungus. This membrane specialization results in marked changes in *PIP* and *TIP* gene expression, with a specific profile depending on the plant host or the symbiotic fungus (reviewed in 143). In poplar, mycorrhized plants show, with respect to non-mycorrhized plants, a 55% increase in Lp_r; besides changes in root anatomy (internal surface), this increase can be accounted for by enhanced expression of most of the PIPs expressed in roots (87). By contrast, the Lp_r of mycorrhized *Phaseolus vulgaris* plants is reduced approximately threefold and this reduction is associated with a decreased abundance of PIP2s and their phosphorylated forms (6). Plant aquaporins expressed during AM symbiosis may also contribute to NH_3 import from the fungus (143).

AM symbiosis also exerts beneficial effects on tolerance of plants to water stress, whether induced by drought, salinity, or chilling (6, 143). These effects may be mediated through alteration of both root water uptake and transpiration to promote water economy. A specific role for aquaporins was deduced in a study on transgenic tobacco, showing that antisense inhibition of *Nt*AQP1 reduces the positive effects of mycorrhiza on root and leaf growth under drought (112). Two recent studies in lettuce, soybean, and tomato drew an interesting parallel between the effects of AM and drought stress, which synergistically regulate *PIP* genes in roots and leaves (reviewed in 143).

Nematode and other infections. Specific aquaporins also seem to be involved in plant-pathogen interactions as an adaptive response to infection-induced changes in plant cell morphology. For instance, infection of roots by nematodes leads to the differentiation of giant cells that serve as feeding sites for the parasite. Regulatory sequences that are specifically responsive to nematode infection were identified in the promoter sequence of a tobacco *TIP* gene (107). Enhanced expression of this aquaporin might be necessary to achieve extensive delivery of water and solutes to the parasite, together with proper osmotic regulation of the giant cells. In tomato, incompatible interaction with the parasite *Cuscuta reflexa* induces the expression of a PIP1 homolog, probably in relation to the auxin-dependent elongation of hypodermal cells induced after pathogen attachment (153).

CONCLUSIONS

Aquaporins have provided a unique molecular entry into plant water relations and their study has significantly improved our understanding of integrated mechanisms of water transport, in roots in particular. Yet, in view of the complex expression and regulation profiles of aquaporins, their role in regulating water transport in many other physiological and developmental contexts, including seed germination, stomatal regulation, and leaf water transport, deserves further investigation (**Figure 5**). In most studies, aquaporin function is experimentally monitored through water flow intensities and kinetics. However, in the whole plant the overall flow of water across plant tissues is determined by stomatal regulation and/or solute transport. Therefore, it will be important to consider how, in this context, aquaporins may critically determine local water potential gradients rather than water flow intensities. These new considerations may lead to a better understanding of the role of aquaporins during cell elongation and water stress.

Studies on aquaporins have also led us far beyond membrane water transport. The transport of solutes of great physiological significance, such as CO_2, H_2O_2, B, or silicic acid, is now well established and has linked aquaporins to many functions, including carbon metabolism, oxidative stress responses, and plant mineral nutrition (**Figure 5**). Yet,

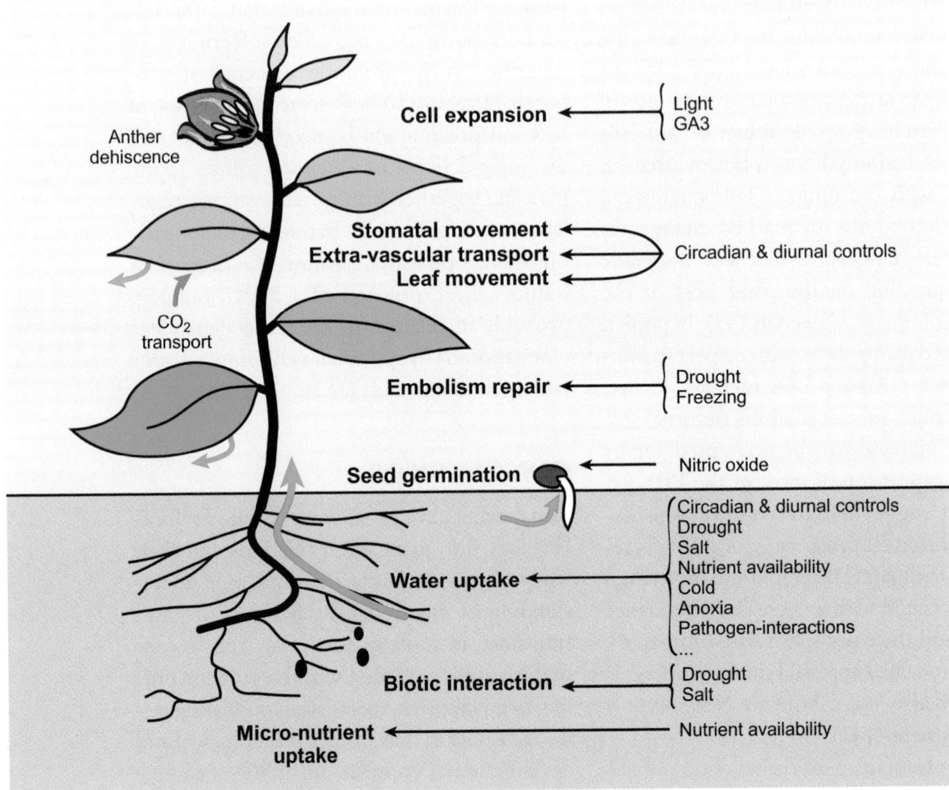

Figure 5

Integrated functions of plant aquaporins. The endogenous and environmental factors acting on each of the indicated aquaporin functions are shown. GA3, gibberellin.

novel putative substrates of plant aquaporins such as arsenate, NO, and NO_3^- await further investigation. We also note that several plant aquaporins, in the NIP and SIP subgroups in particular, have unknown functions and that new aquaporin subclasses are being discovered (139).

Finally, aquaporin functions need to be further integrated in the whole plant physiology. This will first require a better understanding of how the various transport activities of aquaporins are coupled with those of other transport proteins (75, 83, 134). The chains of events that lead to control of aquaporin functions by local or long-distance signals, during development or in response to biotic or abiotic signals, will also have to be elucidated. Finally, and although the field of aquaporin research has already enlarged considerably, we may not be at the end of our surprises because novel primary functions as diverse as cell proliferation (117) or virus replication (69) might be anticipated for plant aquaporins.

SUMMARY POINTS

1. Aquaporins are membrane channels that have a conserved structure and facilitate the transport of water and/or small neutral solutes (urea, boric acid, silicic acid) or gases (ammonia, carbon dioxide).

2. Aquaporins exhibit a high isoform multiplicity that reflects distinct transport specificities and subcellular localizations.
3. Aquaporin transport activity can be regulated by multiple mechanisms, including regulation of transcript or protein abundance, subcellular trafficking, or gating by phosphorylation or cytosolic protons.
4. Aquaporins play a central role in plant water relations. They mediate the regulation of root water transport in response to a variety of environmental stimuli. They facilitate water transport through inner leaf tissues during transpiration and in expanding tissues.
5. Multiple integrated roles of aquaporins in carbon and nitrogen assimilation and micronutrient uptake are being uncovered.

FUTURE ISSUES

1. The transport specificity of aquaporins lacking function and, in particular, of novel classes of aquaporins recently discovered in certain plant species should be investigated.
2. The mechanisms governing aquaporin subcellular trafficking should be investigated, and in particular it will be important to evaluate in planta how the functional expression of aquaporins of the plasma membrane intrinsic proteins 1 and 2 (PIP1 and PIP2) subclasses is determined by mutual physical interactions.
3. Investigation of the function and regulation of aquaporins in poorly explored physiological contexts, such as stomatal regulation or seed germination, will be required.
4. The mechanisms that determine regulation of aquaporins by light in inner leaf tissues should be dissected, and the role of aquaporins in coregulating CO_2 and H_2O transport in these tissues should be deciphered.
5. The relevance of altered aquaporin expression for biotechnological improvement of plant tolerance to water stress must be explored. The role of aquaporins during water stress recovery and in conditions similar to those experienced by crops in the field will have to be specified.

DISCLOSURE STATEMENT

The authors are not aware of any biases that might be perceived as affecting the objectivity of this review.

ACKNOWLEDGMENTS

Work in our laboratory is supported by grants from INRA (AgroBI AIP300) and Génoplante (ANR-05-GPLA-034-06). We thank members of our group for fruitful discussions and apologize to all colleagues whose valuable work could not be cited owing to space limitations.

LITERATURE CITED

1. Aasamaa K, Sober A. 2005. Seasonal courses of maximum hydraulic conductance in shoots of six temperate deciduous tree species. *Funct. Plant Biol.* 32:1077–87
2. Aharon R, Shahak Y, Wininger S, Bendov R, Kapulnik Y, Galili G. 2003. Overexpression of a plasma membrane aquaporin in transgenic tobacco improves plant vigor under favorable growth conditions but not under drought or salt stress. *Plant Cell* 15:439–47
3. Alexandersson E, Fraysse L, Sjövall-Larsen S, Gustavsson S, Fellert M, et al. 2005. Whole gene family expression and drought stress regulation of aquaporins. *Plant Mol. Biol.* 59:469–84
4. Alleva K, Niemietz CM, Sutka M, Maurel C, Parisi M, et al. 2006. Plasma membrane of *Beta vulgaris* storage root shows high water channel activity regulated by cytoplasmic pH and a dual range of calcium concentrations. *J. Exp. Bot.* 57:609–21
5. Aroca R, Amodeo G, Fernández-Illescas S, Herman EM, Chaumont F, Chrispeels MJ. 2005. The role of aquaporins and membrane damage in chilling and hydrogen peroxide induced changes in the hydraulic conductance of maize roots. *Plant Physiol.* 137:341–53
6. Aroca R, Porcel R, Ruiz-Lozano JM. 2007. How does arbuscular mycorrhizal symbiosis regulate root hydraulic properties and plasma membrane aquaporins in *Phaseolus vulgaris* under drought, cold or salinity stresses? *New Phytol.* 173:808–16
7. Azad AK, Sawa Y, Ishikawa T, Shibata H. 2004. Phosphorylation of plasma membrane aquaporin regulates temperature-dependent opening of tulip petals. *Plant Cell Physiol.* 45:608–17
8. Bansal A, Sankararamakrishnan R. 2007. Homology modeling of major intrinsic proteins in rice, maize and *Arabidopsis*: comparative analysis of transmembrane helix association and aromatic/arginine selectivity filters. *BMC Struct. Biol.* 7:27
9. Barrieu F, Thomas D, Marty-Mazars D, Charbonnier M, Marty F. 1998. Tonoplast intrinsic proteins from cauliflower (*Brassica oleracea* L. var. *botrytis*): immunological analysis, cDNA cloning and evidence for expression in meristematic tissues. *Planta* 204:335–44
10. Barthes L, Deléens E, Bousser A, Hoarau J, Prioul J-L. 1996. Xylem exudation is related to nitrate assimilation pathway in detopped maize seedlings: use of nitrate reductase and glutamine synthetase inhibitors as tools. *J. Exp. Bot.* 47:485–95
11. Beitz E, Wu B, Holm LM, Schultz JE, Zeuthen T. 2006. Point mutations in the aromatic/arginine region in aquaporin 1 allow passage of urea, glycerol, ammonia, and protons. *Proc. Natl. Acad. Sci. USA* 103:269–74
12. Biela A, Grote K, Otto B, Hoth S, Hedrich R, Kaldenhoff R. 1999. The *Nicotiana tabacum* plasma membrane aquaporin NtAQP1 is mercury-insensitive and permeable for glycerol. *Plant J.* 18:565–70
13. Bienert GP, Møller AL, Kristiansen KA, Schulz A, Møller IM, et al. 2007. Specific aquaporins facilitate the diffusion of hydrogen peroxide across membranes. *J. Biol. Chem.* 282:1183–92
14. Bots M, Vergeldt F, Wolters-Arts M, Weterings K, van As H, Mariani C. 2005. Aquaporins of the PIP2 class are required for efficient anther dehiscence in tobacco. *Plant Physiol.* 137:1049–56
15. Boursiac Y, Chen S, Luu D-T, Sorieul M, van den Dries N, Maurel C. 2005. Early effects of salinity on water transport in *Arabidopsis* roots. Molecular and cellular features of aquaporin expression. *Plant Physiol.* 139:790–805
16. Carvajal M, Cooke DT, Clarkson DT. 1996. Responses of wheat plants to nutrient deprivation may involve the regulation of water-channel function. *Planta* 199:372–81

17. Carvajal M, Martinez V, Alcaraz CF. 1999. Physiological function of water channels as affected by salinity in roots of paprika pepper. *Physiol. Plant.* 105:95–101
18. Chaumont F, Moshelion M, Daniels MJ. 2005. Regulation of plant aquaporin activity. *Biol. Cell* 97:749–64
19. Chen GP, Wilson ID, Kim SH, Grierson D. 2001. Inhibiting expression of a tomato ripening-associated membrane protein increases organic acids and reduces sugar levels of fruit. *Planta* 212:799–807
20. Choi WG, Roberts DM. 2007. *Arabidopsis* NIP2;1, a major intrinsic protein transporter of lactic acid induced by anoxic stress. *J. Biol. Chem.* 282:24209–18
21. Clarkson DT, Carvajal M, Henzler T, Waterhouse RN, Smyth AJ, et al. 2000. Root hydraulic conductance: diurnal aquaporin expression and the effects of nutrient stress. *J. Exp. Bot.* 51:61–70
22. Cochard H, Venisse JS, Barigah TS, Brunel N, Herbette S, et al. 2007. New insights into the understanding of variable hydraulic conductances in leaves. Evidence for a possible implication of plasma membrane aquaporins. *Plant Physiol.* 143:122–33
23. Daniels MJ, Chaumont F, Mirkov TE, Chrispeels MJ. 1996. Characterization of a new vacuolar membrane aquaporin sensitive to mercury at a unique site. *Plant Cell* 8:587–99
24. Daniels MJ, Chrispeels MJ, Yeager M. 1999. Projection structure of a plant vacuole membrane aquaporin by electron cryo-crystallography. *J. Mol. Biol.* 294:1337–49
25. Daniels MJ, Mirkov TE, Chrispeels MJ. 1994. The plasma membrane of *Arabidopsis thaliana* contains a mercury-insensitive aquaporin that is a homolog of the tonoplast water channel protein TIP. *Plant Physiol.* 106:1325–33
26. Daniels MJ, Yeager M. 2005. Phosphorylation of aquaporin PvTIP3;1 defined by mass spectrometry and molecular modeling. *Biochemistry* 44:14443–54
27. Dean RM, Rivers RL, Zeidel ML, Roberts DM. 1999. Purification and functional reconstitution of soybean Nodulin 26. An aquaporin with water and glycerol transport properties. *Biochemistry* 38:347–53
28. Dhonukshe P, Aniento F, Hwang I, Robinson DG, Mravec J, et al. 2007. Clathrin-mediated constitutive endocytosis of PIN auxin efflux carriers in *Arabidopsis*. *Curr. Biol.* 17:520–27
29. Dordas C, Chrispeels MJ, Brown PH. 2000. Permeability and channel-mediated transport of boric acid across membrane vesicles isolated from squash roots. *Plant Physiol.* 124:1349–61
30. Eisenbarth DA, Weig AR. 2005. Dynamics of aquaporins and water relations during hypocotyl elongation in *Ricinus communis* L. seedlings. *J. Exp. Bot.* 56:1831–42
31. Fetter K, Van Wilder V, Moshelion M, Chaumont F. 2004. Interactions between plasma membrane aquaporins modulate their water channel activity. *Plant Cell* 16:215–28
32. Fleurat-Lessard P, Frangne N, Maeshima M, Ratajczak R, Bonnemain JL, Martinoia E. 1997. Increased expression of vacuolar aquaporin and H^+-ATPase related to motor cell function in *Mimosa pudica* L. *Plant Physiol.* 114:827–34
33. Flexas J, Ribas-Carbó M, Hanson DT, Bota J, Otto B, et al. 2006. Tobacco aquaporin NtAQP1 is involved in mesophyll conductance to CO_2 in vivo. *Plant J.* 48:427–39
34. Fotiadis D, Jenö P, Mini T, Wirtz S, Müller SA, et al. 2001. Structural characterization of two aquaporins isolated from native spinach leaf plasma membranes. *J. Biol. Chem.* 276:1707–14
35. Frangne N, Maeshima M, Schaffner AR, Mandel T, Martinoia E, Bonnemain JL. 2001. Expression and distribution of a vacuolar aquaporin in young and mature leaf tissues of *Brassica napus* in relation to water fluxes. *Planta* 212:270–78

36. Fraysse L, Wells B, McCann MC, Kjellbom P. 2005. Specific plasma membrane aquaporins of the PIP1 subfamily are expressed in sieve elements and guard cells. *Biol. Cell.* 97:519–34
37. Fricke W, Akhiyarova G, Wei W, Alexandersson E, Miller A, et al. 2006. The short-term growth response to salt of the developing barley leaf. *J. Exp. Bot.* 57:1079–95
38. Fujiyoshi Y, Mitsuoka K, de Groot BL, Philippsen A, Grubmüller H, et al. 2002. Structure and function of water channels. *Curr. Opin. Struct. Biol.* 12:509–15
39. Gao YP, Young L, Bonham-Smith P, Gusta LV. 1999. Characterization and expression of plasma and tonoplast membrane aquaporins in primed seed of *Brassica napus* during germination under stress conditions. *Plant Mol. Biol.* 40:635–44
40. Gaspar M, Bousser A, Sissoëff I, Roche O, Hoarau J, Mahe A. 2003. Cloning and characterization of *ZmPIP1–5b*, an aquaporin transporting water and urea. *Plant Sci.* 165:21–31
41. Gerbeau P, Amodeo G, Henzler T, Santoni V, Ripoche P, Maurel C. 2002. The water permeability of *Arabidopsis* plasma membrane is regulated by divalent cations and pH. *Plant J.* 30:71–81
42. Gerbeau P, Güclü J, Ripoche P, Maurel C. 1999. Aquaporin Nt-TIPa can account for the high permeability of tobacco cell vacuolar membrane to small neutral solutes. *Plant J.* 18:577–87
43. Guenther JF, Chanmanivone N, Galetovic MP, Wallace IS, Cobb JA, Roberts DM. 2003. Phosphorylation of soybean nodulin 26 on serine 262 enhances water permeability and is regulated developmentally and by osmotic signals. *Plant Cell* 15:981–91
44. Guo L, Wang ZY, Lin H, Cui WE, Chen J, et al. 2006. Expression and functional analysis of the rice plasma-membrane intrinsic protein gene family. *Cell Res.* 16:277–86
45. Gustavsson S, Lebrun A, Norden K, Chaumont F, Johanson U. 2005. A novel plant major intrinsic protein in *Physcomitrella patens* most similar to bacterial glycerol channels. *Plant Physiol.* 139:287–95
46. Hachez C, Moshelion M, Zelazny E, Cavez D, Chaumont F. 2006. Localization and quantification of plasma membrane aquaporin expression in maize primary root: a clue to understanding their role as cellular plumbers. *Plant Mol. Biol.* 62:305–23
47. Hanba YT, Shibasaka M, Hayashi Y, Hayakawa T, Kasamo K, et al. 2004. Overexpression of the barley aquaporin HvPIP2;1 increases internal CO_2 conductance and CO_2 assimilation in the leaves of transgenic rice plants. *Plant Cell Physiol.* 45:521–29
48. Harvengt P, Vlerick A, Fuks B, Wattiez R, Ruysschaert JM, Homble F. 2000. Lentil seed aquaporins form a hetero-oligomer which is phosphorylated by a Mg^{2+}-dependent and Ca^{2+}-regulated kinase. *Biochem. J.* 352:183–90
49. Henzler T, Waterhouse RN, Smyth AJ, Carvajal M, Cooke DT, et al. 1999. Diurnal variations in hydraulic conductivity and root pressure can be correlated with the expression of putative aquaporins in the roots of *Lotus japonicus*. *Planta* 210:50–60
50. Henzler T, Ye Q, Steudle E. 2004. Oxidative gating of water channels (aquaporins) in *Chara* by hydroxyl radicals. *Plant Cell Environ.* 27:1184–95
51. Hill AE, Shachar-Hill B, Shachar-Hill Y. 2004. What are aquaporins for? *J. Membr. Biol.* 197:1–32
52. Holbrook NM, Zwieniecki MA. 2003. Plant biology: water gate. *Nature* 425:361
53. Holm LM, Jahn TP, Møller AL, Schjoerring JK, Ferri D, et al. 2005. NH_3 and NH_4^+ permeability in aquaporin-expressing *Xenopus* oocytes. *Pflügers Arch.* 450:415–28
54. Hose E, Steudle E, Hartung W. 2000. Abscisic acid and hydraulic conductivity of maize roots: a study using cell- and root-pressure probes. *Planta* 211:874–82

55. Hukin D, Doering-Saad C, Thomas CR, Pritchard J. 2002. Sensitivity of cell hydraulic conductivity to mercury is coincident with symplasmic isolation and expression of plasmalemma aquaporin genes in growing maize roots. *Planta* 215:1047–56
56. Ishikawa F, Suga S, Uemura T, Sato MH, Maeshima M. 2005. Novel type aquaporin SIPs are mainly localized to the ER membrane and show cell-specific expression in *Arabidopsis thaliana*. *FEBS Lett.* 579:5814–20
57. Jahn TP, Møller AL, Zeuthen T, Holm LM, Klaerke DA, et al. 2004. Aquaporin homologues in plants and mammals transport ammonia. *FEBS Lett.* 574:31–36
58. Jang JY, Kim DG, Kim YO, Kim JS, Kang H. 2004. An expression analysis of a gene family encoding plasma membrane aquaporins in response to abiotic stresses in *Arabidopsis thaliana*. *Plant Mol. Biol.* 54:713–25
59. Jauh GY, Fischer AM, Grimes HD, Ryan CA Jr, Rogers JC. 1998. δ-Tonoplast intrinsic protein defines unique plant vacuole functions. *Proc. Natl. Acad. Sci. USA* 95:12995–99
60. Javot H, Lauvergeat V, Santoni V, Martin-Laurent F, Güclü J, et al. 2003. Role of a single aquaporin isoform in root water uptake. *Plant Cell* 15:509–22
61. Javot H, Maurel C. 2002. The role of aquaporins in root water uptake. *Ann. Bot.* 90:301–13
62. Johanson U, Karlsson M, Johansson I, Gustavsson S, Sjövall S, et al. 2001. The complete set of genes encoding major intrinsic proteins in *Arabidopsis* provides a framework for a new nomenclature for major intrinsic proteins in plants. *Plant Physiol.* 126:1358–69
63. Johansson I, Karlsson M, Shukla VK, Chrispeels MJ, Larsson C, Kjellbom P. 1998. Water transport activity of the plasma membrane aquaporin PM28A is regulated by phosphorylation. *Plant Cell* 10:451–60
64. Johansson I, Larsson C, Ek B, Kjellbom P. 1996. The major integral proteins of spinach leaf plasma membranes are putative aquaporins and are phosphorylated in response to Ca^{2+} and apoplastic water potential. *Plant Cell* 8:1181–91
65. Kamaluddin M, Zwiazek JJ. 2002. Ethylene enhances water transport in hypoxic aspen. *Plant Physiol.* 128:962–69
66. Kammerloher W, Fischer U, Piechottka GP, Schäffner AR. 1994. Water channels in the plant plasma membrane cloned by immunoselection from a mammalian expression system. *Plant J.* 6:187–99
67. Karlsson M, Fotiadis D, Sjövall S, Johansson I, Hedfalk K, et al. 2003. Reconstitution of water channel function of an aquaporin overexpressed and purified from *Pichia pastoris*. *FEBS Lett.* 537:68–72
68. Katsuhara M, Koshio K, Shibasaka M, Hayashi Y, Hayakawa T, Kasamo K. 2003. Overexpression of a barley aquaporin increased the shoot/root ratio and raised salt sensitivity in transgenic rice plants. *Plant Cell Physiol.* 44:1378–83
69. Kim MJ, Kim HR, Paek KH. 2006. *Arabidopsis* tonoplast proteins TIP1 and TIP2 interact with the cucumber mosaic virus 1a replication protein. *J. Gen. Virol.* 87:3425–31
70. Kojima S, Bohner A, von Wirén N. 2006. Molecular mechanisms of urea transport in plants. *J. Membr. Biol.* 212:83–91
71. Lee SH, Singh AP, Chung GC. 2004. Rapid accumulation of hydrogen peroxide in cucumber roots due to exposure to low temperature appears to mediate decreases in water transport. *J. Exp. Bot.* 55:1733–41
72. Lian HL, Yu X, Lane D, Sun WN, Tang ZC, Su W. 2006. Upland rice and lowland rice exhibited different PIP expression under water deficit and ABA treatment. *Cell Res.* 16:651–60
73. Lian HL, Yu X, Ye Q, Ding XS, Kitagawa Y, et al. 2004. The role of aquaporin RWC3 in drought avoidance in rice. *Plant Cell Physiol.* 45:481–89

74. Liu F, Vantoai T, Moy LP, Bock G, Linford LD, Quackenbush J. 2005. Global transcription profiling reveals comprehensive insights into hypoxic response in *Arabidopsis*. *Plant Physiol.* 137:1115–29
75. Liu HY, Sun WN, Su WA, Tang ZC. 2006. Co-regulation of water channels and potassium channels in rice. *Physiol. Plant.* 128:58–69
76. Liu HY, Yu X, Cui DY, Sun MH, Sun WN, et al. 2007. The role of water channel proteins and nitric oxide signaling in rice seed germination. *Cell Res.* 17:638–49
77. Liu LH, Ludewig U, Gassert B, Frommer WB, von Wirén N. 2003. Urea transport by nitrogen-regulated tonoplast intrinsic proteins in *Arabidopsis*. *Plant Physiol.* 133:1220–28
78. Lopez F, Bousser A, Sissoëff I, Gaspar M, Lachaise B, et al. 2003. Diurnal regulation of water transport and aquaporin gene expression in maize roots: contribution of PIP2 proteins. *Plant Cell Physiol.* 44:1384–95
79. Loqué D, Ludewig U, Yuan L, von Wirén N. 2005. Tonoplast intrinsic proteins AtTIP2;1 and AtTIP2;3 facilitate NH_3 transport into the vacuole. *Plant Physiol.* 137:671–80
80. Lovisolo C, Schubert A. 2006. Mercury hinders recovery of shoot hydraulic conductivity during grapevine rehydration: evidence from a whole-plant approach. *New Phytol.* 172:469–78
81. Ludevid D, Höfte H, Himelblau E, Chrispeels MJ. 1992. The expression pattern of the tonoplast intrinsic protein γ-TIP in *Arabidopsis thaliana* is correlated with cell enlargement. *Plant Physiol.* 100:1633–39
82. Ma JF, Tamai K, Yamaji N, Mitani N, Konishi S, et al. 2006. A silicon transporter in rice. *Nature* 440:688–91
83. Ma JF, Yamaji N, Mitani N, Tamai K, Konishi S, et al. 2007. An efflux transporter of silicon in rice. *Nature* 448:209–12
84. Ma S, Quist TM, Ulanov A, Joly R, Bohnert HJ. 2004. Loss of TIP1;1 aquaporin in *Arabidopsis* leads to cell and plant death. *Plant J.* 40:845–59
85. Maathuis FJ, Filatov V, Herzyk P, Krijger GC, Axelsen KB, et al. 2003. Transcriptome analysis of root transporters reveals participation of multiple gene families in the response to cation stress. *Plant J.* 35:675–92
86. MacRobbie EA. 2006. Osmotic effects on vacuolar ion release in guard cells. *Proc. Natl. Acad. Sci. USA* 103:1135–40
87. Marjanovic Z, Uehlein N, Kaldenhoff R, Zwiazek JJ, Weiss M, et al. 2005. Aquaporins in poplar: what a difference a symbiont makes! *Planta* 222:258–68
88. Martínez-Ballesta MC, Aparicio F, Pallás V, Martínez V, Carvajal M. 2003. Influence of saline stress on root hydraulic conductance and PIP expression in *Arabidopsis*. *J. Plant Physiol.* 160:689–97
89. Martínez-Ballesta MC, Martínez V, Carvajal M. 2000. Regulation of water channel activity in whole roots and in protoplasts from roots of melon plants grown under saline conditions. *Aust. J. Plant Physiol.* 27:685–91
90. Martre P, Morillon R, Barrieu F, North GB, Nobel PS, Chrispeels MJ. 2002. Plasma membrane aquaporins play a significant role during recovery from water deficit. *Plant Physiol.* 130:2101–10
91. Maurel C. 2007. Plant aquaporins: novel functions and regulation properties. *FEBS Lett.* 581:2227–36
92. Maurel C, Javot H, Lauvergeat V, Gerbeau P, Tournaire C, et al. 2002. Molecular physiology of aquaporins in plants. *Int. Rev. Cytol.* 215:105–48
93. Maurel C, Kado RT, Guern J, Chrispeels MJ. 1995. Phosphorylation regulates the water channel activity of the seed-specific aquaporin α-TIP. *EMBO J.* 14:3028–35

94. Maurel C, Reizer J, Schroeder JI, Chrispeels MJ. 1993. The vacuolar membrane protein γ-TIP creates water specific channels in *Xenopus* oocytes. *EMBO J.* 12:2241–47
95. Maurel C, Tacnet F, Güclü J, Guern J, Ripoche P. 1997. Purified vesicles of tobacco cell vacuolar and plasma membranes exhibit dramatically different water permeability and water channel activity. *Proc. Natl. Acad. Sci. USA* 94:7103–8
96. Miao GH, Hong Z, Verma DP. 1992. Topology and phosphorylation of soybean nodulin-26, an intrinsic protein of the peribacteroid membrane. *J. Cell Biol.* 118:481–90
97. Mizutani M, Watanabe S, Nakagawa T, Maeshima M. 2006. Aquaporin NIP2;1 is mainly localized to the ER membrane and shows root-specific accumulation in *Arabidopsis thaliana*. *Plant Cell Physiol.* 47:1420–26
98. Morillon R, Chrispeels MJ. 2001. The role of ABA and the transpiration stream in the regulation of the osmotic water permeability of leaf cells. *Proc. Natl. Acad. Sci. USA* 98:14138–43
99. Morillon R, Lassalles JP. 1999. Osmotic water permeability of isolated vacuoles. *Planta* 210:80–84
100. Moshelion M, Becker D, Biela A, Uehlein N, Hedrich R, et al. 2002. Plasma membrane aquaporins in the motor cells of *Samanea saman*: diurnal and circadian regulation. *Plant Cell* 14:727–39
101. Moshelion M, Moran N, Chaumont F. 2004. Dynamic changes in the osmotic water permeability of protoplast plasma membrane. *Plant Physiol.* 135:2301–17
102. Murai-Hatano M, Kuwagata T. 2007. Osmotic water permeability of plasma and vacuolar membranes in protoplasts I: high osmotic water permeability in radish (*Raphanus sativus*) root cells as measured by a new method. *J. Plant Res.* 120:175–89
103. Nardini A, Salleo S, Andri S. 2005. Circadian regulation of leaf hydraulic conductance in sunflower (*Helianthus annuus* L. cv Margot). *Plant Cell Environ.* 28:750–59
104. Niemietz CM, Tyerman SD. 1997. Characterization of water channels in wheat root membrane vesicles. *Plant Physiol.* 115:561–67
105. Niemietz CM, Tyerman SD. 2000. Channel-mediated permeation of ammonia gas through the peribacteroid membrane of soybean nodules. *FEBS Lett.* 465:110–14
106. Niemietz CM, Tyerman SD. 2002. New potent inhibitors of aquaporins: silver and gold compounds inhibit aquaporins of plant and human origin. *FEBS Lett.* 531:443–47
107. Opperman CH, Taylor CG, Conkling MA. 1994. Root-knot nematode-directed expression of a plant root-specific gene. *Science* 263:221–23
108. Paciorek T, Zazímalová E, Ruthardt N, Petrásek J, Stierhof YD, et al. 2005. Auxin inhibits endocytosis and promotes its own efflux from cells. *Nature* 435:1251–56
109. Phillips AL, Huttly AK. 1994. Cloning of two gibberellin-regulated cDNAs from *Arabidopsis thaliana* by subtractive hybridization: expression of the tonoplast water channel, γ-TIP, is increased by GA_3. *Plant Mol. Biol.* 24:603–15
110. Picaud S, Becq F, Dédaldéchamp F, Ageorges A, Delrot S. 2003. Cloning and expression of two plasma membrane aquaporins expressed during the ripening of grape berry. *Funct. Plant Biol.* 30:621–30
111. Pina C, Pinto F, Feijó JA, Becker JD. 2005. Gene family analysis of the *Arabidopsis* pollen transcriptome reveals biological implications for cell growth, division control, and gene expression regulation. *Plant Physiol.* 138:744–56
112. Porcel R, Gómez M, Kaldenhoff R, Ruiz-Lozano JM. 2005. Impairment of *NtAQP1* gene expression in tobacco plants does not affect root colonisation pattern by arbuscular mycorrhizal fungi but decreases their symbiotic efficiency under drought. *Mycorrhiza* 15:417–23

113. Quigley F, Rosenberg JM, Shachar-Hill Y, Bohnert HJ. 2001. From genome to function: the *Arabidopsis* aquaporins. *Genome Biol.* 3:1–17
114. Ramahaleo T, Morillon R, Alexandre J, Lassalles J-P. 1999. Osmotic water permeability of isolated protoplasts. Modifications during development. *Plant Physiol.* 119:885–96
115. Rivers RL, Dean RM, Chandy G, Hall JE, Roberts DM, Zeidel ML. 1997. Functional analysis of Nodulin 26, an aquaporin in soybean root symbiosomes. *J. Biol. Chem.* 272:16256–61
116. Robinson DG, Sieber H, Kammerloher W, Schäffner AR. 1996. PIP1 aquaporins are concentrated in plasmalemmasomes of *Arabidopsis thaliana* mesophyll. *Plant Physiol.* 111:645–49
117. Saadoun S, Papadopoulos MC, Hara-Chikuma M, Verkman AS. 2005. Impairment of angiogenesis and cell migration by targeted aquaporin-1 gene disruption. *Nature* 434: 786–92
118. Saito C, Ueda T, Abe H, Wada Y, Kuroiwa T, et al. 2002. A complex and mobile structure forms a distinct subregion within the continuous vacuolar membrane in young cotyledons of *Arabidopsis*. *Plant J.* 29:245–55
119. Sakr S, Alves G, Morillon R, Maurel K, Decourteix M, et al. 2003. Plasma membrane aquaporins are involved in winter embolism recovery in walnut tree. *Plant Physiol.* 133:630–41
120. Sakurai J, Ishikawa F, Yamaguchi T, Uemura M, Maeshima M. 2005. Identification of 33 rice aquaporin genes and analysis of their expression and function. *Plant Cell Physiol.* 46:1568–77
121. Santoni V, Verdoucq L, Sommerer N, Vinh J, Pflieger D, Maurel C. 2006. Methylation of aquaporins in plant plasma membrane. *Biochem. J.* 400:189–97
122. Santoni V, Vinh J, Pflieger D, Sommerer N, Maurel C. 2003. A proteomic study reveals novel insights into the diversity of aquaporin forms expressed in the plasma membrane of plant roots. *Biochem. J.* 372:289–96
123. Sarda X, Tousch D, Ferrare K, Legrand E, Dupuis JM, et al. 1997. Two TIP-like genes encoding aquaporins are expressed in sunflower guard cells. *Plant J.* 12:1103–11
124. Schäffner AR. 1998. Aquaporin function, structure, and expression: are there more surprises to surface in water relations? *Planta* 204:131–39
125. Shangguan Z-P, Lei T-W, Shao M-A, Xue Q-W. 2005. Effects of phosphorus nutrient on the hydraulic conductivity of sorghum (*Sorghum vulgare* Pers.) seedling roots under water deficiency. *J. Integr. Plant Biol.* 47:421–27
126. Shope JC, Mott KA. 2006. Membrane trafficking and osmotically induced volume changes in guard cells. *J. Exp. Bot.* 57:4123–31
127. Siefritz F, Otto B, Bienert GP, van der Krol A, Kaldenhoff R. 2004. The plasma membrane aquaporin NtAQP1 is a key component of the leaf unfolding mechanism in tobacco. *Plant J.* 37:147–55
128. Siefritz F, Tyree MT, Lovisolo C, Schubert A, Kaldenhoff R. 2002. PIP1 plasma membrane aquaporins in tobacco: from cellular effects to function in plants. *Plant Cell* 14:869–76
129. Sjövall-Larsen S, Alexandersson E, Johansson I, Karlsson M, Johanson U, Kjellbom P. 2006. Purification and characterization of two protein kinases acting on the aquaporin SoPIP2;1. *Biochim. Biophys. Acta* 1758:1157–64
130. Steudle E. 1989. Water flow in plants and its coupling to other processes: an overview. *Methods Enzymol.* 174:183–225
131. Suga S, Komatsu S, Maeshima M. 2002. Aquaporin isoforms responsive to salt and water stresses and phytohormones in radish seedlings. *Plant Cell Physiol.* 43:1229–37

132. Suga S, Murai M, Kuwagata T, Maeshima M. 2003. Differences in aquaporin levels among cell types of radish and measurement of osmotic water permeability of individual protoplasts. *Plant Cell Physiol.* 44:277–86
133. Tajkhorshid E, Nollert P, Jensen MØ, Miercke LJ, O'Connell J, et al. 2002. Control of the selectivity of the aquaporin water channel family by global orientational tuning. *Science* 296:525–30
134. Takano J, Wada M, Ludewig U, Schaaf G, von Wirén N, Fujiwara T. 2006. The *Arabidopsis* major intrinsic protein NIP5;1 is essential for efficient boron uptake and plant development under boron limitation. *Plant Cell* 18:1498–509
135. Temmei Y, Uchida S, Hoshino D, Kanzawa N, Kuwahara M, et al. 2005. Water channel activities of *Mimosa pudica* plasma membrane intrinsic proteins are regulated by direct interaction and phosphorylation. *FEBS Lett.* 579:4417–22
136. Terashima I, Ono K. 2002. Effects of $HgCl_2$ on CO_2 dependence of leaf photosynthesis: Evidence indicating involvement of aquaporins in CO_2 diffusion across the plasma membrane. *Plant Cell Physiol.* 43:70–78
137. Törnroth-Horsefield S, Wang Y, Hedfalk K, Johanson U, Karlsson M, et al. 2006. Structural mechanism of plant aquaporin gating. *Nature* 439:688–94
138. Tournaire-Roux C, Sutka M, Javot H, Gout E, Gerbeau P, et al. 2003. Cytosolic pH regulates root water transport during anoxic stress through gating of aquaporins. *Nature* 425:393–97
139. Tuskan GA, Difazio S, Jansson S, Bohlmann J, Grigoriev I, et al. 2006. The genome of black cottonwood, *Populus trichocarpa* (Torr. & Gray). *Science* 313:1596–604
140. Tyerman SD, Bohnert HJ, Maurel C, Steudle E, Smith JA. 1999. Plant aquaporins: their molecular biology, biophysics and significance for plant water relations. *J. Exp. Bot.* 50:1055–71
141. Tyerman SD, Niemietz CM. 2002. Plant aquaporins: multifunctional water and solute channels with expanding roles. *Plant Cell Environ.* 25:173–94
142. Tyree MT, Nardini A, Salleo S, Sack L, El Omari B. 2005. The dependence of leaf hydraulic conductance on irradiance during HPFM measurements: any role for stomatal response? *J. Exp. Bot.* 56:737–44
143. Uehlein N, Fileschi K, Eckert M, Bienert G, Bertl A, Kaldenhoff R. 2007. Arbuscular mycorrhizal symbiosis and plant aquaporin expression. *Phytochemistry* 68:122–29
144. Uehlein N, Lovisolo C, Siefritz F, Kaldenhoff R. 2003. The tobacco aquaporin NtAQP1 is a membrane CO_2 pore with physiological functions. *Nature* 425:734–37
145. Vander Willigen C, Postaire O, Tournaire-Roux C, Boursiac Y, Maurel C. 2006. Expression and inhibition of aquaporins in germinating *Arabidopsis* seeds. *Plant Cell Physiol.* 47:1241–50
146. Vera-Estrella R, Barkla BJ, Bohnert HJ, Pantoja O. 2004. Novel regulation of aquaporins during osmotic stress. *Plant Physiol.* 135:2318–29
147. Veselova TV, Veselovskii VA, Usmanov PD, Usmanova OV, Kozar VI. 2003. Hypoxia and imbibition injuries to aging seeds. *Russ. J. Plant. Physiol.* 50:835–42
148. Volkov V, Hachez C, Moshelion M, Draye X, Chaumont F, Fricke W. 2007. Water permeability differs between growing and nongrowing barley leaf tissues. *J. Exp. Bot.* 58:377–90
149. Wallace IS, Choi WG, Roberts DM. 2006. The structure, function and regulation of the nodulin 26-like intrinsic protein family of plant aquaglyceroporins. *Biochim. Biophys. Acta* 1758:1165–75

150. Wallace IS, Roberts DM. 2004. Homology modeling of representative subfamilies of *Arabidopsis* major intrinsic proteins. Classification based on the aromatic/arginine selectivity filter. *Plant Physiol.* 135:1059–68

151. Wallace IS, Roberts DM. 2005. Distinct transport selectivity of two structural subclasses of the nodulin-like intrinsic protein family of plant aquaglyceroporin channels. *Biochemistry* 44:16826–34

152. Wan X, Steudle E, Hartung W. 2004. Gating of water channels (aquaporins) in cortical cells of young corn roots by mechanical stimuli (pressure pulses): effects of ABA and of $HgCl_2$. *J. Exp. Bot.* 55:411–22

153. Werner M, Uehlein N, Proksch P, Kaldenhoff R. 2001. Characterization of two tomato aquaporins and expression during the incompatible interaction of tomato with the plant parasite *Cuscuta reflexa*. *Planta* 213:550–55

154. Yang BX, Verkman AS. 1997. Water and glycerol permeabilities of aquaporins 1–5 and MIP determined quantitatively by expression of epitope-tagged constructs in *Xenopus* oocytes. *J. Biol. Chem.* 272:16140–46

155. Ye Q, Wiera B, Steudle E. 2004. A cohesion/tension mechanism explains the gating of water channels (aquaporins) in *Chara* internodes by high concentration. *J. Exp. Bot.* 55:449–61

156. Yu QJ, Hu YL, Li JF, Wu Q, Lin ZP. 2005. Sense and antisense expression of plasma membrane aquaporin *BnPIP1* from *Brassica napus* in tobacco and its effects on plant drought tolerance. *Plant Sci.* 169:647–56

157. Yu X, Peng YH, Zhang MH, Shao YJ, Su WA, Tang ZC. 2006. Water relations and expression analysis of plasma membrane intrinsic proteins in sensitive and tolerant rice during chiling and recovery. *Cell Res.* 16:599–608

158. Zelazny E, Borst JW, Muylaert M, Batoko H, Hemminga MA, Chaumont F. 2007. FRET imaging in living maize cells reveals that plasma membrane aquaporins interact to regulate their subcellular localization. *Proc. Natl. Acad. Sci. USA* 104:12359–64

159. Zhu C, Schraut D, Hartung W, Schäffner AR. 2005. Differential responses of maize *MIP* genes to salt stress and ABA. *J. Exp. Bot.* 56:2971–81

Metabolic Flux Analysis in Plants: From Intelligent Design to Rational Engineering

Igor G.L. Libourel and Yair Shachar-Hill

Department of Plant Biology, Michigan State University, East Lansing, Michigan 48824; email: libourel@msu.edu, yairhill@msu.edu

Annu. Rev. Plant Biol. 2008. 59:625–50

The *Annual Review of Plant Biology* is online at plant.annualreviews.org

This article's doi:
10.1146/annurev.arplant.58.032806.103822

1543-5008/08/0602-0625$20.00

Key Words

rational metabolic engineering, metabolic networks, *Arabidopsis*, flux balance analysis, predictive modeling, systems biology

Abstract

Metabolic flux analysis (MFA) is a rapidly developing field concerned with the quantification and understanding of metabolism at the systems level. The application of MFA has produced detailed maps of flow through metabolic networks of a range of plant systems. These maps represent detailed metabolic phenotypes, contribute significantly to our understanding of metabolism in plants, and have led to the discovery of new metabolic routes. The presentation of thorough statistical evaluation with current flux maps has set a new standard for the quality of quantitative flux studies. In microbial systems, powerful methods have been developed for the reconstruction of metabolic networks from genomic and transcriptomic data, pathway analysis, and predictive modeling. This review brings together the recent developments in quantitative MFA and predictive modeling. The application of predictive tools to high quality flux maps in particular promises to be important in the rational metabolic engineering of plants.

Contents

INTRODUCTION

Stoichiometry: the stoichiometry of a reaction is the molar balance between metabolites consumed and produced

Metabolism is a complex network of interdependent chemical reactions catalyzed by highly regulated enzymes. Metabolic flux analysis (MFA) aims to characterize fluxes through the network and to give insight into their regulation (107). The resulting flux maps form a detailed metabolic phenotype that is more closely related to biological function than phenotypes defined by metabolic profiles or other biological parts lists. Flux mapping goes beyond providing a rich phenotypic description, and has yielded a great deal of novel insight into the metabolic operation of plant cells (67, 81, 87). MFA has contributed to our fundamental understanding of metabolism by helping to determine which of the known alternative routes carry fluxes through the metabolic network (13, 64), and by uncovering novel routes and cycles (3, 98). Flux maps obtained under different growth conditions or from mutants also aid in the generation of hypotheses about metabolic regulation (2, 28, 43, 91).

Defining the structure and stoichiometry of the network is the first step in MFA; for microbial systems, this first step can be performed in an objective, almost routine way from the annotated genome together with transcript, protein, and metabolite datasets. The structure of the network can be used to define the range of possible flux maps that a network can support, and to determine which of these best meet particular cellular objectives (evolutionary selection pressures), such as maximizing growth (77, 78, 83, 115). The comparison of fluxes estimated from experimentally based MFA and those calculated to best meet evolutionary incentives can be a valuable tool to evaluate the validity of the postulated incentives. Experimentally based approaches to quantify fluxes through cells and tissues are based on either steady-state or kinetic isotopic labeling experiments and their interpretation by computer-aided modeling. Two recent reviews (81, 87) provide detailed tutorial-style explanations of kinetic and steady-state MFA approaches, whereas we focus on the principles involved, and on illustrating the sort of information these approaches have yielded when applied to plants. Because of the diversity of approaches used for MFA of plant systems, we include a discussion of the statistical confidence of the flux values reported in plant MFA studies.

In the microbial world, MFA is the basis of rational metabolic engineering (73). Plant metabolic engineering, which has thus far been largely based on intelligent tinkering, is severely hampered by a lack of understanding of metabolic network structure, function, and regulation (19). Indeed, with the exception of some notable successes (for example, Reference 124), the great majority of plant metabolic engineering efforts are unsuccessful. Thus, the quest for better methods for predicting the effects of genetic or environmental alterations is important. Predictive metabolic modeling techniques that derive from MFA can be highly effective in microbial systems (23, 46, 101, 104, 115), which suggests that predictive modeling is poised to make significant contributions to rational metabolic engineering in plants. The current interest in plant-based biofuels, whose production is expected to require the development of plants with altered biomass composition (122), adds impetus for improved predictive modeling. An increasingly urgent need to foresee the effects of climatic changes on plants will also stimulate efforts in predictive metabolic flux modeling.

Metabolic flux analysis also has a central part to play in plant systems biology (51), a field in which the development and application of high-throughput analytical technologies still exceed our ability to use the resulting data to understand plant function. The use of metabolic network analysis in plant systems biology is currently hampered by the lack of a common platform for the dissemination of models. Such a platform is widely used in microbial and mammalian flux modeling studies and we believe that its adoption by plant researchers would accelerate the integration of metabolic modeling into plant systems biology.

This review focuses on subjects that have so far received little attention in the plant literature and whose importance has been outlined above: (*a*) network reconstruction, (*b*) quantitative aspects of flux mapping, and (*c*) predictive modeling. These are exciting times in plant metabolic flux analysis, as illustrated by the recent appearance of an entire issue of *Phytochemistry* devoted to theoretical analyses, experimental findings, and methodological developments. Our hope is to stimulate the interest of plant biologists in what we believe is an important area of research, and to commend to current and future plant MFA practitioners some of the techniques developed in the microbial field.

NETWORK DEFINITION

The first requirement for the analysis of metabolic fluxes is to define a network; values obtained through the use of a model that is based on an erroneous network are likely to be wrong, even if the model explains the measured data well. Network reconstruction has traditionally been done using the physiological, biochemical, and molecular genetic literature. The present availability of annotated genomes and rich databases of transcription and protein composition information makes it possible to assemble such networks in a more efficient and unbiased manner, and allows networks to be created for systems that have not been studied intensively by traditional means (8, 17, 18, 54, 55).

The most complex network reconstructed to date is *Homo sapiens* Recon 1 (21). This genome-scale model is based on the primary literature (>1500 papers, referred to as the bibliome) and its creation was guided by the Kyoto encyclopedia of genes and genomes (KEGG) database (44). Recon 1 is a network reconstructed from the bottom up, where relationships between gene expression and protein function are deterministic (82). Recon 1 includes eight subcellular compartments and consists of 1496 open reading frames (ORFs), 2004 proteins, 2766 metabolites, and 3311 metabolic reactions. This bottom-up approach of starting with the molecular components allows the application of gap analysis to identify metabolites or enzymes that are unconnected or incompletely connected to the network. In the human metabolic network, this approach was used iteratively to identify missing components. The 356 metabolites that still remain disconnected in the published version serve to highlight areas where more detailed work is required.

In the world of microbial network analysis, genome-scale network construction began with *Escherichia coli* and is now well advanced (18, 78, 82). Genome-scale network construction is applied in an almost routine way to an increasing number of organisms (8, 54). Gap analysis was used to assign putative function to 55 ORFs (86) for *E. coli* K-12 MG1655, and was followed up with the development of algorithms to predict missing reactions to reconcile the model with experimental data. This work led to the assignment of function to 8 more ORFs, 5 of which were verified experimentally (85). Genome-based network reconstruction is thus not only a starting point for metabolic flux analysis but also a powerful tool for functional genomics.

In *Arabidopsis thaliana*, gene annotation and deterministic gene-to-protein-to-metabolic reaction descriptions are not yet available to the same extent as in bacterial or mammalian models (108). Annotation of plant genes is often putative and based on sequence similarity. The need for a system-wide approach to network construction in plants has been recognized (34) and the most comprehensive plant (*Arabidopsis*) network to date (33) integrates the regulatory and metabolic networks and contains 7635 nodes (6176 genes and 1459 metabolites) in total and 230,900 interactions between these nodes (**Figure 1**).

Correlation-based information from omics approaches can also be used to generate candidates for network components (44). Metabolic genes involved in the same pathway are often expressed at the same time and in the same tissue (95). Using this observation, clustering analysis techniques have been applied in the plant fields (7, 123) to find unknown genes involved in secondary metabolism. Coexpression analysis holds promise for metabolic gene discovery, which is especially important in plant systems where metabolic networks are not yet fully resolved.

METABOLIC FLUX ANALYSIS AND THE STOICHIOMETRY OF THE NETWORK

MFA is the investigation of the flow of metabolites through a metabolic network. Biological model systems that have a nearly constant metabolism, in which fluxes and the levels of metabolites (except stored or excreted ones) are constant, are said to be in metabolic (pseudo) steady state. Examples of such systems include cell cultures during exponential growth and many mature differentiated tissues. Certain growing plant tissues, such as developing embryos during seed filling (99), also have nearly constant patterns of metabolic flux for extended periods. Computationally, steady-state models are easiest to manage, and steady-state systems have been used productively in plant studies over the last dozen years to yield extensive and detailed flux maps of central metabolism. For recent summaries and discussion of the findings of such plant studies see References 81 and 87.

The stoichiometry of the network is defined in a stoichiometric matrix $S_{(m*n)}$, which is constructed from mass balance equations around the internal metabolites. Usually a metabolic network contains more reactions (n) than metabolites (m) and is thus said to be underdetermined. Because no metabolites build up during steady state, multiplication of the stoichiometric matrix (S) with the flux vector (v) returns a null vector:

$$S.v = 0$$

This all-important relationship constrains the value that the internal fluxes (those within the metabolic network) may assume. The number of underdeterminacy (n-m) defines the number of free variables (fluxes) in the metabolic network model that can be varied independently without violating the steady-state assumption. However, the free variables do constrain each other, reducing the allowed

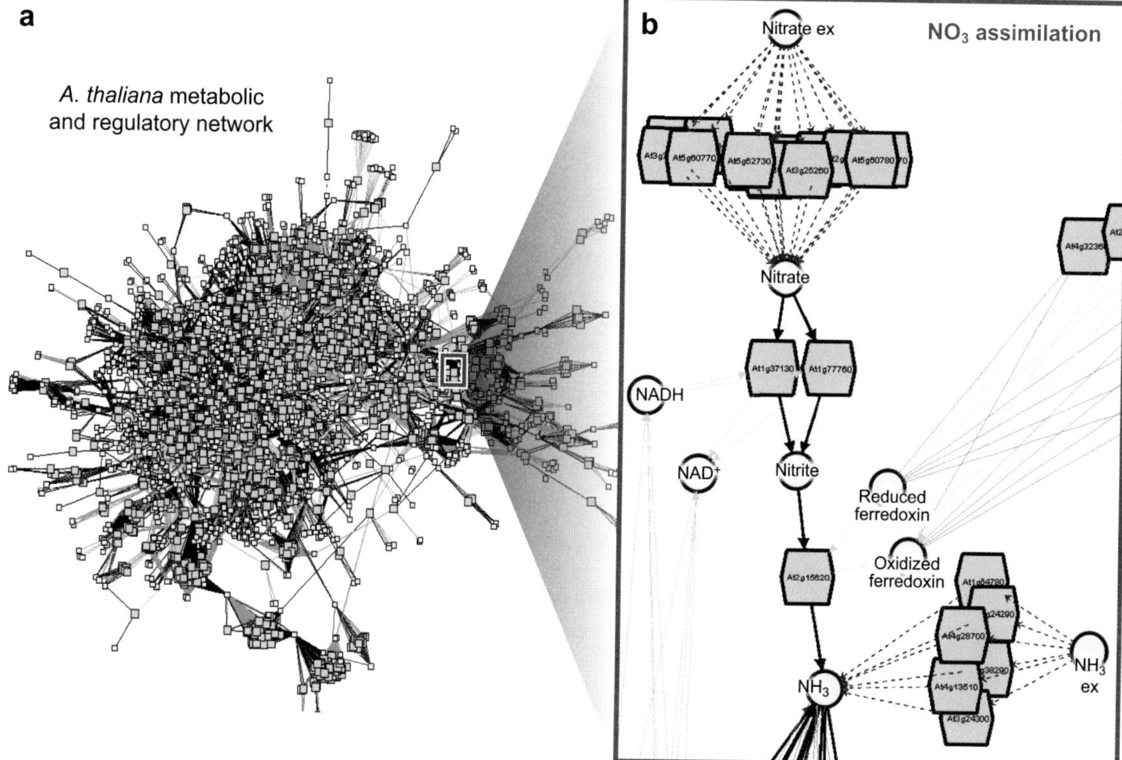

Figure 1

Reconstruction of a qualitative network model of a generic plant cell (taken from Reference 33 with permission). (*a*) A birds-eye view of the integrated network model. Metabolic data were compiled from the KEGG and Aracyc databases. In addition to interaction information pooled from three different databases, interactions were predicted or experimentally determined. A detailed description of this network is posted on the VirtualPlant website (**http://www.virtualplant.org**). (*b*) A close-up view of the genes and metabolites involved in the NO_3^- reduction and assimilation pathway. Yellow circles represent metabolites. Grey hexagons represent genes coding for transporters or enzymes. From top to bottom: extracellular NO_3^- is connected by blue dotted arrows to several genes that code for known or putative transporters. The transporters are in turn connected to intracellular NO_3^-. Intracellular NO_3^- is converted to NO_2^- by the action of nitrate reductase, for which there are two genes in *Arabidopsis*. NO_2^- is then reduced to NH_3 by the single gene enzyme nitrite reductase. Black arrows and thin grey arrows denote association through enzymatic reactions.

relative values that fluxes may assume to a hyper cone in the m-n dimensional flux space (**Figure 2**). Stoichiometric analysis can be used to reveal network properties such as complexity using singular value decomposition of S (21) and flux-coupling analysis (12, 14). Flux-coupling analysis is a method that identifies metabolic reactions that exclusively belong to a single metabolic pathway, which can be instrumental in the identification of targets in a given pathway available for manipulation.

Examining the stoichiometries of a pathway directly can also be informative. For example, stoichiometric balancing of protons and the cofactor NADH was used to resolve a longstanding error in the field of plant responses to hypoxia/anoxia. The balancing of protons and cofactors demonstrated that during anoxia, nitrate reduction in roots

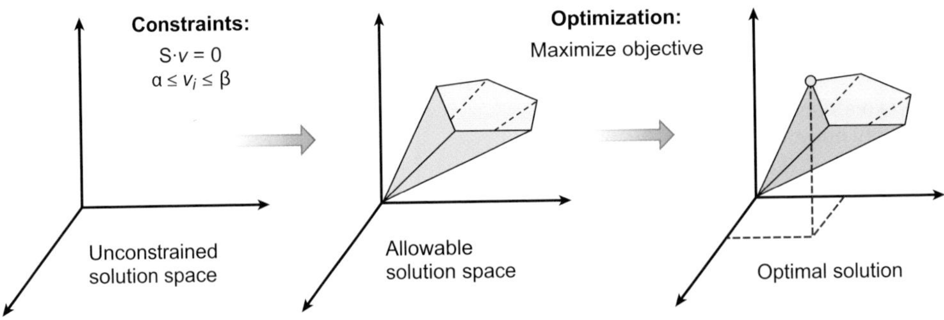

Figure 2

Computation of flux values using flux balance analysis (FBA) (taken from Reference 86 with permission). In the three-dimensional unconstrained flux space of a hypothetical network, fluxes can assume any value. After considering the stoichiometry and enzymatic limitations of the network's reactions, the feasible solution space is reduced to a cone. Using an objective function, such as maximizing biomass accumulation, FBA can identify a coordinate (set of flux values) on an edge of the feasible flux cone.

contributes to acidification instead of reducing it, despite the consumption of a proton in the conversion of nitrate to nitrite (110). Follow-up research (57) showed that the reduced cytoplasmic acidification observed in the presence of nitrate (88) could be mimicked by nitrite alone, which suggests a possible signaling role for nitrite or a downstream metabolite of nitrite, and provided support for the initial assertion based on stoichiometric balancing (57).

Elementary Mode Analysis and Extreme Pathway Analysis

Insight into the functional capabilities of a metabolic network can also be obtained from its stoichiometry by deriving operating modes of a metabolic network. Two of these methods, elementary mode analysis (EMA) and extreme pathway analysis (EPA) (**Figure 2**), are based on analysis of the flux space (96). The EMA description of a flux map is exhaustive and unique (72); each mode is a minimal pathway that can operate independently. The weighted sum of these minimal pathways describes the entire flux cone (97) (**Figure 2**). The number of modes of complex networks is often very large (30), but fortunately many elementary modes can be combined into families that share the overall mass balance. EMA has been applied to plant flux maps and has provided insight into futile cycling in sugarcane (89) and the role of photosynthesis and a unique role of Rubisco in the carbon conversion efficiency in developing *Brassica napus* embryos (98).

EPA is closely related to EMA and plays an important role in flux balance analysis (FBA), which is discussed below. EPA and EMA methods were recently reviewed and compared in depth (72). The primary distinctions between EMA and EPA are as follows: in EPA (*a*) the flux cone of feasible flux values is capped by restricting the pathways not to exceed the V_{max} deduced from external flux measurements, (*b*) futile substrate cycles are omitted, and (*c*) no linear combinations of modes are included. This results in a closed hypervolume rather than a cone, of which only the edges are feasible solutions. As a consequence, the number of extreme pathways is much smaller than the number of elementary modes for a typical metabolic network (72).

Flux Balance Analysis

FBA is a constraint-based method that solves the underdetermined mass balancing problem by finding the set of flux values that is optimal for a particular goal, referred to as an objective function (114). The use of an objective function allows for solutions of internal fluxes, which are represented as points on the edge of an n-dimensional flux cone (83, 86) (**Figure 2**). Biomass accumulation is a popular choice as an objective function for microbial models because for fast-growing laboratory or industrial strains it is reasonable to argue that biomass accumulation is indeed the prevalent selective pressure.

Many bacterial networks, as well as those of yeast (22) and mammalian cell cultures (21), have been analyzed with FBA, amongst which the photosynthetic prokaryote *Synechocystis* sp. PCC 6803 (102) is of special interest to plant biologists as a model system. Under photoautotrophic conditions all carbon is converted to biomass, which led to the selection of light-use efficiency as the objective function. In applying FBA to heterotrophic growth conditions a two-step approach was chosen. Firstly, the efficiency of biomass accumulation from substrate was used as the objective function, followed by efficiency of light use for biomass accumulation. The mixotrophic mode of operation is of particular interest for developing plant embryos, where the balance between photosynthesis and carbon substrate uptake influences the carbon conversion efficiency during seed filling (32). FBA has yet to be applied to a plant model but promises to be a useful tool for developing embryos, in which optimal biomass accumulation and light use-efficiency are also reasonable assumptions. Academic software packages such as FluxAnalyzer (48) and MetaFluxNet (52) and proprietary software (SimPheny) have been developed to facilitate FBA. For a more comprehensive list of software tools see References 54 and 87.

The development of FBA as a technique continues because solutions to the FBA objective function are typically not unique, and mixed-integer linear programming techniques have been used to identify equivalent flux maps (53, 84, 86). Within the FBA framework, solutions having identical flux values are said to be silent phenotypes (79, 84). Efforts have been ongoing to increase the number of constraints used in genome-scale FBA models to reduce the number of equivalent solutions, with attention directed to thermodynamic constraints on extreme pathways (energy balance analysis; see Reference 11) and measured transcript levels in the cells under study (11, 16, 35). Such information is also available for plant systems and we expect them to be productively applied there as well.

Steady-State Isotope Labeling Experiments

In experimentally based MFA, isotopically labeled substrates are supplied to a biological system and the resulting labeling patterns are analyzed to obtain internal flux information. Internal metabolic fluxes—including their reversibilities—can be estimated on the basis of modeling analysis of the labeling data. In an isotope labeling experiment (ILE), isotopically labeled substrates are supplied to cells in metabolic steady state until the pattern of labeling has stopped changing noticeably (isotopic steady state). The isotopes used are usually nonradioactive ones (^{2}H, ^{15}N, and most commonly, ^{13}C) and isotopic enrichment in metabolic intermediates and products is detected by nuclear magnetic resonance (NMR) spectroscopy and/or mass spectrometry (MS). Isotopic labeling information is used in conjunction with measurements of fluxes into (uptake) and out of (excretion, growth, and storage) the network. The details of such labeling experiments and the analysis of the labeling results in plant systems are explained for the nonspecialist in a recent review (81).

For simple (sub)networks, algebraic expressions can often be derived that directly relate the flux values to measurable positional isotopic labeling. In such fully determined cases the flux values in the system can be obtained by inserting the labeling measurements into the derived expressions (93). This approach has been used to obtain information on the fluxes of glycolysis/gluconeogenesis and the oxidative pentose phosphate pathway in heterotrophic plant cells, and specifically to shed light on the role of fructose 2,6-bisphosphate in regulating fluxes in this part of metabolism (28). Solutions for larger metabolic networks are hard to obtain manually; Dieuaide-Noubhani and coworkers (20, 91) used algebraic solving software to derive relationships between positional labeling levels and the values of metabolic fluxes. These studies yielded flux maps for growing maize root tips and tomato cell suspensions and provided evidence for a dramatic rate of ATP dissipation via the turnover of sucrose.

This analytical approach is attractive because it is mathematically tangible, but it has at least two significant disadvantages. The first is that solutions have to be obtained afresh for every alteration in the network architecture that one wishes to explore. The second is that this approach does not easily allow the use of all the available experimental information. This is because the number of measurements from a labeling experiment is usually much larger than the number of fluxes to be measured, which makes the flux estimation an overdetermined problem, whereas the analytical solution approach uses only the amount of labeling information required to solve the relationships directly.

To take advantage of all available data and to provide flexibility in exploring alternative network models, theory and software have been developed to convert the problem of obtaining fluxes from measurements into one of optimizing the fit between predicted and observed labeling patterns. The principle of this approach is to construct a model based on the network structure that includes the stoichiometries of the metabolic reactions and tracks the transformation of positional isotopic labeling in reactions. The model is used to compute the expected labeling patterns from the network architecture, the values of the fluxes, and the labeling of the substrate(s) provided. The computed labeling patterns are compared with the measured ones and the flux values are iteratively changed to minimize the difference between the computed and observed labeling (117). The details of obtaining flux estimates based on the cumomer concept are well explained in a series of papers by Weichert and coworkers (66, 117, 118, 121). Alternative methods, such as the bondomer (111) and elementary metabolite units (5) concepts that aim to reduce the computational cost, have since been developed.

A significant number of studies in plant systems using ILE and variations upon it have appeared in the plant literature in the last several years (for reviews see References 81 and 87). Developing plant embryo cultures in particular has been the subject of many of these studies because they are amenable to in vitro growth under (pseudo) steady-state conditions. The striking findings to date include the following: the discovery of a new metabolic route in developing *B. napus* embryos (98), the observation that mitochondrial metabolism in these embryos operates differently than the canonical modes found in other biological systems (100), and the finding of a new substrate cycle involving the phosphorylation and dephosphorylation of glucose in maize roots (3).

QUANTITATIVE FLUX ANALYSIS USING ISOTOPE LABELING EXPERIMENTS

The number of the internal fluxes to be determined is the total number of internal fluxes minus the number of internal metabolite balances. In addition, ILEs also resolve the reversibility of fluxes, implying that reverse fluxes must be estimated as well. If more measurements are available than the number of fluxes to be estimated, the flux estimation problem is said to be overdetermined and can, in principle, be solved. However, if the label measurements report on only part of the network, it is possible that the flux estimation may still not be fully resolved, in which case the problem is said to be structurally undeterminable (41, 112, 113). In practice, many more measurements are required than the number of fluxes to be determined if one is to be able to estimate all the network fluxes.

Once flux estimates have been made, each flux value must be associated with a confidence interval to make quantitative interpretation possible. Because the estimation of internal flux values is an indirect method, the parameters of interest are not measured directly, but are inferred from measurements of input and output rates (external fluxes) and labeling data. As a result, confidence estimation for internal flux measurements is less straightforward. Fortunately, the theory of obtaining confidence intervals for inverse problems is well established and is based on the measurement sensitivity matrix (See Quantitative Flux Measurements). The sensitivity matrix contains the predicted responses of all measurements to a small change in the value of any of the fluxes. Together with the confidence range of each of the measurements, this information determines the flux covariance matrix, which contains linear approximations of all flux variances (See Quantitative Flux Measurements). Because the relationship between fluxes and label measurements is highly nonlinear, linear flux confidence estimates can easily be in error by a factor of two or more (4). To improve the quality of the confidence estimates, Wiechert and coworkers (121) transformed forward and reverse fluxes to net and exchange fluxes, and used a compactification mapping of the exchange fluxes (See Quantitative Flux Measurements). For a detailed description of flux confidence estimation see References 4 and 121.

Alternatively, flux variance estimates can be obtained using Monte Carlo sampling. For this approach, each measured label and external flux value must be replaced with a chance distribution of values generated from the mean and variance of each (label) measurement. By performing thousands of optimization runs using appropriately sampled measurement values, a distribution of flux values, and therefore variance estimates, will be found for each flux. Given enough trials, this method is very precise (4). In practice this method is complicated by the inability of optimization algorithms to reliably find the global best fit for each run. In fact, one can never be certain that a global minimum (minimal difference between actual and simulated measurements) has been found, and many optimization trials using the mean measurement values are usually performed to increase the likelihood of finding the global best fit.

The probability that the determined flux map differs from nature is usually determined using the χ^2-test. This test evaluates the goodness of fit of the model by considering the difference between the number of label measurements and the number of estimated fluxes, the precision of the label measurements, and the difference between the simulated and observed label measurements.

Interpretation of Flux Estimates in the Plant Literature

Owing to the specialist nature of internal flux estimation, flux values and their associated confidence intervals presented in the plant literature are not always straightforward to interpret. A flux estimate value with a standard deviation on the order of the largest flux values in the flux map is obviously poorly determined. However, evaluation of the validity of the reported confidence interval is more difficult. In the plant literature, reported flux standard deviations are determined in many different ways and often do not represent true confidence estimates. Several plant studies do not report variance estimates and therefore values in these studies cannot be interpreted quantitatively. In other studies, standard deviations associated with fluxes are a description of the size of the feasible solution space of underdetermined labeling systems (90). Even in one of the more advanced studies published to date (105), the reported standard deviations associated with the fluxes in developing soy beans do not represent confidence intervals. In this study a few hundred optimizations were run from different initial flux values, and the standard deviation of the distribution of optimized flux estimates was reported. Because no chance distributions of

a Relationship between label measurements and flux values:

Label measurements (y) are a function of the forward ($V^{\rightarrow}$) and reverse ($V^{\leftarrow}$) fluxes (117). Assuming that ε_y is normally distributed, the matrix Σ_y describes the variance σ^2 associated with y.

$$y = \Gamma\left(\frac{V^{\rightarrow}}{V^{\leftarrow}}\right) + \varepsilon_y$$

$$V_{net} = V^{\rightarrow} - V^{\leftarrow}, \quad V_{ex} = \min(V^{\rightarrow}, V^{\leftarrow})$$

It should be noted that good estimates of measurement σs must be based on $n > 30$. Therefore, it is good practice to enter σs associated with the measurement technique used to prevent bias in the fitting procedure. Flux maps should still be based on multiple labeling experiments to ensure reproducibility and better mean labeling values.

$$\Sigma_y = \begin{bmatrix} \sigma^2 & \cdot \\ \cdot & \sigma^2 \end{bmatrix}$$

b The inverse problem:

An optimizer is used to minimize the residuum, which is the sum of the weighted residuals (differences between simulated and observed values) where Θ are the flux estimates, $F_w(\Theta)$ and $F_y(\Theta)$ are simulated flux and label measurements, and w and y are flux and label measurements. At the minimum residuum value, flux values are said to be best estimates ($\hat{\Theta}$).

$$\min_{\Theta} \left\| F_w(\Theta) - w \right\|^2_{\Sigma_w} + \left\| F_y(\Theta) - y \right\|^2_{\Sigma_y}$$

c χ^2-test

To test whether the flux model cannot explain the measurements and must be rejected, the residuum must fail (be larger than) the χ^2-test. The χ^2-test value is calculated on the basis of the degrees of freedom (number of independent measurements minus parameters) and a defined confidence level α.

d The weighted sensitivity matrix of the label measurements:

This matrix expresses the change in measurements in response to a change in flux. Variances of the label measurements are used to weight the sensitivities.

$$Sens^{w,y}_{\Theta} = \Sigma_y^{-1/2} \cdot \left(\frac{\partial F_y}{\partial \Theta}\right)$$

e The flux covariance matrix:

The diagonal entries of the covariance matrix form a linear approximation of the flux estimates. Estimation of the confidence intervals is improved by nonlinear compactification mapping of the exchange fluxes (121). An even more precise estimate of flux variances can be calculated using an algorithm presented in Reference 4.

$$Cov_{\Theta} = \left[\left(\frac{\partial F_y}{\partial \Theta}\right)^T \cdot \Sigma_y^{-1} \cdot \left(\frac{\partial F_y}{\partial \Theta}\right)\right]^{-1}$$

$$V_{ex}^{[0,1]} = \frac{V_{ex}}{1 + V_{ex}}$$

f Individual flux confidence intervals:

Here $\hat{\Theta}_i$ is the ith flux estimate and $Cov(\hat{\Theta})_{ij}$ is the ith diagonal entry of the flux covariance matrix (flux variance of $\hat{\Theta}_i$).

$$[\hat{\Theta}_i - \Delta, \hat{\Theta}_i + \Delta] \quad \text{where } \Delta = \sqrt{\chi^2_1(1-\alpha) \cdot Cov(\hat{\Theta})_{ij}}$$

g The system variance:

The system-wide variance can be described by the D- or A-criterion, which are scaled to the average geometric or arithmetic mean, respectively. Criterion values have been used for optimal design studies (9, 56, 66).

$$D_{crit} = \sqrt[2n]{\det(Cov_{\Theta})}, \quad A_{crit} = \sqrt{\frac{tr(Cov_{\Theta})}{n}}$$

QUANTITATIVE FLUX MEASUREMENTS

Variance estimates of internal flux measurements are indispensable for a quantitative interpretation of internal flux estimates. An overview of the steps required for a quantitative assessment of an isotope labeling experiment (ILE) is presented as follows: (*a*) definition of the relationship between fluxes and measurements, (*b*) finding best estimates for internal fluxes using an optimization routine, (*c*) statistical evaluation of whether the model must be rejected, (*d*) calculation of the flux covariance matrix on the basis of the weighted sensitivity matrix (using nonlinear mapping of exchange fluxes), (*e*) calculation of confidence intervals from flux covariances, and (*f*) description of system-wide statistics that can be used for optimal design studies.

This section is intended to give a feeling for the theory involved. Comprehensive coverage of the theory involved can be found in parameter estimation textbooks (74).

measurements were used (as in Monte Carlo analysis), the ranges reported for the flux values reflect an evaluation of the performance of the optimization routine. In addition, taking the mean values of normal distribution fits to the flux distributions that were found this way has led to the presentation of a flux map that is not mass balanced. Although standard deviations obtained by this approach are likely qualitatively indicative of the determinability of the fluxes, they cannot be interpreted as flux confidence intervals.

Plant studies that used the 13C flux software suite (119) reported a nonlinearly mapped linear approximation of flux confidence estimates (121) as discussed above (See Quantitative Flux Measurements). Finally, flux value ranges should always be interpreted with caution, even if the method of calculation is appropriate. Systematic errors in label measurements and simplifications of the true metabolic network also contribute to error and are not easily estimated. A pragmatic approach to errors is therefore necessary, but this should not conceal the large variation in quality and meaning of flux standard deviations presented in the plant literature.

Design of Optimal Substrates and Labeling Measurements

Once a flux map has been determined, the quality of the flux estimates can be greatly improved by designing an optimal experimental strategy (66). The quality of the flux estimates of a metabolic flux map depends on the following: (*a*) network structure, (*b*) flux values, (*c*) design of the labeling substrate, and (*d*) label measurements performed. The first two parameters are dictated by nature, but the choice of the substrate label and the measurements made are to some extent controlled by the experimenter. Recently, two studies considered optimal designs for models of interest to the plant community. One study used the metabolic flux map of developing *Brassica napus* embryos (56). This study explores the value of optimal substrate label designs obtained with statistical criteria based on properties of the flux covariance matrix of simulated label designs. A partial optimal design aimed at best resolving the oxidative branch and the flux carried by Rubisco presented in this study confirmed the previous theoretically derived importance of 2-^{13}C-glucose (93). In a separate optimal design study, based on the assessment of simulated experimental data, Shastri & Morgan (103) determined optimal conditions and measurements for a transient labeling study of photoautotrophic bacteria. These studies show that effort spent in optimizing the choice of labeled substrate(s) is well repaid by improved resolution of the resulting flux maps. This is especially the case for the medium- or high-throughput studies that we expect for plant systems in the next several years, similar to those recently carried out for microbial systems (94).

KINETIC MODELS

As discussed above, the use of steady state metabolic flux analysis requires a system to be in metabolic and isotopic steady state. However, with some notable exceptions, plants and their tissues are usually not in metabolic steady state long enough to reach an isotopic steady state during labeling. Fortunately, two types of approach allow metabolic flux analysis to be carried out effectively in these situations: kinetic (or dynamic) and instationary metabolic flux analysis methods. Indeed, such "explicit kinetic models still allow for the most detailed and quantitative evaluation of the dynamics and function of metabolic systems" (109). Of these dynamic methods the approach that is in principle most generally applicable, kinetic modeling, is also the best established, because it has been applied to microbes since the 1960s and to plant systems shortly thereafter (45); see References 67 and 81 for reviews.

In studies of this type, a sequence of samples is taken while the labeling patterns, metabolite levels, and/or metabolic fluxes are changing. Time course data on metabolite

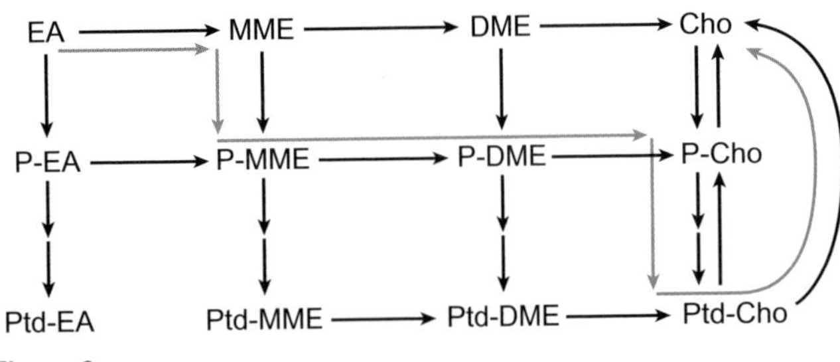

Figure 3

The network of reactions that could participate in choline (Cho, trimethylethanolamine) synthesis in flowering plants (adapted from Reference 64 with permission). Methylation reactions proceed from left to right whereas reactions involving the making or breaking of phosphoester bonds (phosphorylation, phosphotransesterase, and phosphodiester hydrolysis) proceed from top to bottom (or in the case of hydrolysis, from bottom to top). The predominant route of synthesis as found by McNeil and coworkers (64) is shown in orange. Abbreviations: EA, ethanolamine; MME, monomethylethanolamine; DME, dimethylethanolamine; P-base, phospho-bases; Ptd-base, phosphatidyl-bases.

levels and their labeling are then analyzed using rate equations written to represent the metabolic and transport steps of the network under investigation.

An example of this approach is a study to determine the route by which choline is synthesized in leaves (64). The metabolic network under consideration is shown in **Figure 3**, which shows the existence of multiple routes by which the precursor, ethanolamine, could be converted to choline. In one set of experiments researchers supplied ^{33}P-radiolabeled phosphoethanolamine or phosphomonomethylethanolamine to follow the phosphorylated species; in another set of experiments they provided ^{14}C-labeled formate to track methylation. In these experiments they obtained time courses of labeling and of the levels of the intermediates and products of the network. The model that was used to analyze the data is illustrated in **Figure 4**. By fitting the model parameters to the experimental data these authors showed that the first methylation step occurs solely at the phospho-base level, the second and third methylations occur largely at the phospho-base level (the remainder occur

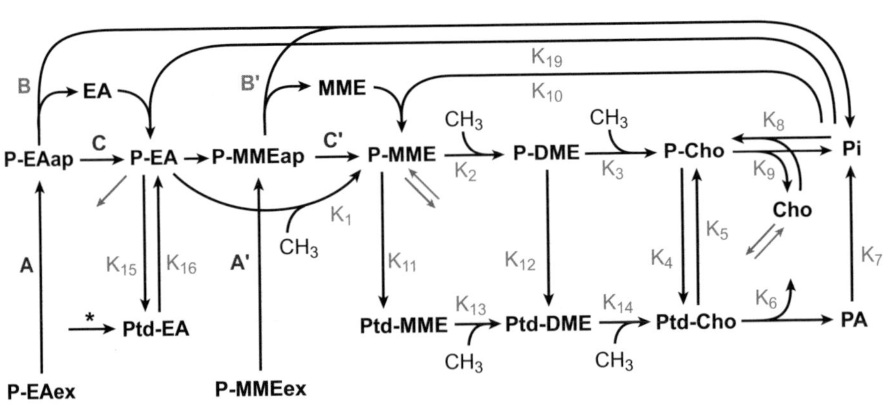

Figure 4

Illustration of the model of the kinetics of flux through the network shown in **Figure 3** that was used to analyze the results of labeling experiments (adapted from Reference 64 with permission). The notation K1–K16, A, A′, B, B′, C, and C′ next to the flux arrows refer to fluxes whose sizes were used as parameters in modeling the data. All fluxes were assumed to remain constant (metabolic steady state) except for rates A, A′, B, B′, C, and C′, which describe the uptake and apoplastic hydrolysis of supplied phosphomonomethylethanolamine (P-MME) and phosphoethanolamine (P-EA). These rates were set to be proportional to the substrate pool sizes. Thus, exogenously supplied ^{33}P-MME (33P-MMEex) or ^{33}P-EA (33P-EAex) was taken up into the apoplast at a rate proportional to the exogenous pool size ($A = [33P\text{-}EAex] \times K_A$; $A' = [33P\text{-}MMEex] \times K_{A'}$ where K_A and $K_{A'}$ are first order rate constants that were used as parameters and whose values were assigned to optimize the fit to the time course data). Diagonal arrows (*grey*) designate transport to and from separate storage pools. Abbreviations: EA, ethanolamine; DME, dimethylethanolamine; Cho, choline; PA, phosphatidic acid; P-base, phospho-bases; Ptd-base, phosphatidyl-bases.

at the phosphatidyl-base level), and that free choline originates predominantly from phosphatidylcholine rather than from phosphocholine. This study contributed significantly to our understanding of choline metabolism in plants, and was instrumental in metabolic engineering of increased stress tolerance by introducing betaine synthesis from choline.

Other studies by Rhodes and his collaborators over several decades used more or less similar kinetic modeling approaches and contributed substantially to pathway delineation and understanding the regulation of primary nitrogen metabolism (63), different aspects of one-carbon metabolism (65, 70), and more recently, the synthesis of floral scent compounds through the complex network of benzenoid metabolism (13, 71). Other significant recent studies utilizing similar kinetic flux analysis methods include work by Matsuda and coworkers (60, 61) on pathway delineation and regulation of fluxes of phenylpropanoid synthesis after wounding or exposure to an elicitor. These and other kinetic flux analysis studies, of which a substantial proportion are aimed at understanding the regulation of photosynthesis, have been reviewed elsewhere (81, 87). Additional studies analyzing tryptophan biosynthesis in cultured rice cells (62) and describing the kinetics of label distribution through central metabolism in heterotrophically growing *Arabidopsis* cells (10) have appeared since then.

Here we consider the study of choline synthesis in tobacco (64) in greater detail because it serves to illustrate several general features of this class of kinetic model. First, kinetic modeling is a powerful tool for determining the route that material takes through branched and interconnected parts of metabolism. This can be challenging to study by other means, because the complexity of time course data makes it impossible to discern the active route through the network by eye. Second, kinetic rather than steady state modeling is the toolset of choice when the substrate contains only one suitable atomic position for labeling. This is the case for important plant nutrients such as sulfate, nitrate, ammonia, carbon dioxide, or as in the study under consideration here: phosphate or methyl groups. For such substrates the labeling pattern reached in metabolic intermediates and products at isotopic steady state contains no information on fluxes because they all become equally labeled.

A third important issue in kinetic modeling encountered in the work of McNeil and coworkers (64) is the choice of the form of rate terms used in the model. Rate equations describing flow through a network are coupled linear differential equations whose parameters may be of various levels of complexity. In a related study by McNeil and coworkers (65) of choline conversion to betaine, rate equations were written with Michaelis-Menten terms, where each rate depends on substrate concentration and two parameters (K_m and V_{max}) that were fitted during modeling. In that study the smaller size of the network under consideration permitted, and the predictive aim of the study required, the use of more realistic rate terms with an attendant increase in the number of parameters.

A fourth issue illustrated by the study of McNeil and coworkers (64) is encountered in every flux analysis study of eukaryotic systems, whether dynamic or steady-state in character: compartmentation. To account for the fact that the cells were exposed to the externally supplied label gradually because diffusion into the leaf tissue proceeds at a finite rate, the analysis required that an apoplastic compartment be included. Cell suspensions present no such challenges (e.g., References 10 and 62), nor do studies in isotopic steady state in which the tissue under study can be treated as approximately uniform (such as those on root segments or embryos in culture) (2, 20, 105). However, compartmentation should not be neglected when there may be significant metabolic conversion of the substrate either in the apoplast or in tissue through which label passes before reaching the tissue under study (26). Nor can intracellular compartmentation be ignored when multiple pools of the same metabolite contribute significantly to the redistribution of label, measured pool sizes, or specific enrichments. McNeil and coworkers (65) showed that three pools (vacuolar, cytosolic, and chloroplastic) are involved in determining flux to betaine and should be included in the model. The large artifacts that could arise in steady-state experiments from a failure to account for the potential effects of different metabolic pools of sucrose were recently explored (49). Obtaining information on labeling in different pools of the same metabolic intermediates, such as hexose and triose phosphates and acetyl-CoA, in different subcellular compartments can therefore be of central importance. Advances in making such measurements by analyzing compartmentally specific products as reporters were recently reported by Allen and coworkers (1). An exception to the requirement for a model to include multiple pools of the same metabolite is the case in which pools in different compartments are in rapid exchange relative to the rates of the relevant metabolic conversions (100).

Another important issue for both kinetic and steady-state analyses that arose in the work of McNeil and coworkers (64) concerns the simplification of a model compared with the actual metabolic network. In this study, the model represents the conversion of phospho-bases to phosphatidyl-bases as a single kinetic step, omitting the cytidyldiphospho-bases that are intermediates in this conversion (the omission is represented by double arrows in **Figure 3**). Reactions are collapsed in this way in kinetic, steady-state, and other flux models in which there are no measurements to allow meaningful modeling of the process. In kinetic flux analysis this occurs frequently when measurements on levels and/or labeling in extracted intermediates are unavailable owing to their low concentrations, lability, and/or uncertain or mixed compartmental origins. In steady-state labeling studies and other stoichiometric analyses, the network model is simplified relative to the actual metabolic network so that fluxes between metabolic branch points are represented as single quantities without regard to the number of enzymatic steps that actually take place between these points.

Instationary State Models

The successes of steady-state experimental MFA have motivated a number of leading microbial flux analysis groups to develop theoretical frameworks and experimental methods to study systems that are either in metabolic but not isotopic steady state (26, 68, 69, 120), or in neither metabolic nor isotopic steady state (6). Although they treat the same non-steady-state conditions as the classical kinetic modeling approaches described in the preceding section do, the new instationary approaches, whose formalisms derive from steady-state flux analysis, use positional labeling information to greatly increase the information content of experimental data. To apply the approach of Noh and coworkers (68, 69), the concentrations of most of the intracellular metabolic intermediates, in addition to their labeling patterns, must be measured. In prokaryotic systems this can be achieved using modern mass spectrometric tools and we anticipate that flux analysis of photosynthetic prokaryotes will soon be forthcoming. Indeed, a recent study (103) describes a detailed experimental design for studying cyanobacterial photosynthetic metabolism using this approach. According to this design, cells are labeled with $^{13}CO_2$ and the labeling and pool sizes for metabolic intermediates are analyzed by gas chromatography–mass spectrometry (GCMS) for a time course leading to isotopic steady state. Analysis of the design shows that useful information on the kinetics and ultimately on the regulation of photoautotrophic metabolism could be obtained by this instationary approach. Provided that sufficient subcellular compartmental information can be obtained on the levels and labeling of plant metabolic intermediates, this instationary approach would allow kinetic flux mapping in higher plant systems. The success of this approach would allow for flux analysis of metabolic states that are not sustained for long enough to be analyzed with established isotopic steady-state techniques.

In contrast, the instationary approach recently presented by Antoniewicz and coworkers (6) requires neither pool size measurements, information on labeling in intermediates, nor metabolic steady state. This approach uses experimental steady-state MFA with the analysis modified to include dilution factors that account for changing labeling in precursor and product pools. The underlying assumption is that the metabolic intermediates reach isotopic pseudo steady state rapidly compared with changes in the metabolic flux values through the network. This assumption makes the approach suitable for slow rather than abrupt changes in conditions or development and it may prove useful for studying some plant tissues. However, because the turnover rates of plant metabolites are often on the order of hours rather than the seconds or minutes that characterize bacterial metabolite turnover, the pseudo–steady-state assumption may not be valid for many plant systems.

INTEGRATION AND CROSS-VALIDATION OF FLUX MODELS

The existence of different experimental and theoretical approaches to predicting or estimating fluxes through metabolic networks invites comparison between their results. In the microbial fields, ^{13}C-based flux measurements from steady-state flux analysis have been compared with FBA predictions (104) and isotope label–derived flux measurements have also aided to constrain FBA models (116). A schematic of how MFA technologies and concepts relate to each other is presented in **Figure 5**.

Flux models of central metabolism can be validated with simple physiological measurements, as was done with gas exchange rates in a recent study of central metabolism in developing sunflower embryos (2). In that case, the O_2 consumption rate was compared with the total NADH production rate predicted by the flux map, and measured CO_2 emission was compared with the total CO_2 production estimated from the flux map. Alternatively, key enzyme activities may be checked to verify whether a certain pathway branch has the capacity to carry the estimated flux (43).

Other methods exist that could be used to directly measure fluxes to validate the results of metabolic flux analysis. For example, exchange spectroscopy (EXSY) is an NMR technique that can provide direct measurements of forward and reverse fluxes in vivo. In principle, EXSY measures the chemical exchange rates between metabolites directly, without the requirement of a metabolic network. However, the insensitivity of this powerful technology has so far limited its application to biological systems (reviewed in Reference 80). The only in vivo ^{31}P-EXSY study reported to date in plants resolved reactions of glycolysis, hexose transformations, and ATP metabolism in maize root tips (92).

Metabolic flux analysis is a core component of systems biology (47) and its integration with other systems analyses requires that its models be accessible beyond flux analysis research groups. Cross-platform compatibility facilitates the integration of information obtained by different methods, and allows the systems biologist to begin integrating metabolic models into broader cellular, physiological, and ultimately, ecological contexts. The need for the adoption of a platform such as systems biology markup language (SBML) is even more pressing for flux analysis because of the incompatibility among, and great variety of, software used. The systems biology community has developed the extensible markup language (XML) standard SBML to communicate all systems biology data, and SBML definitions for kinetic models (37) were among the first to appear. Flux models in the microbial community have been published in SBML for some time now (125) and current metabolic flux analysis software generally accepts and exports SBML files

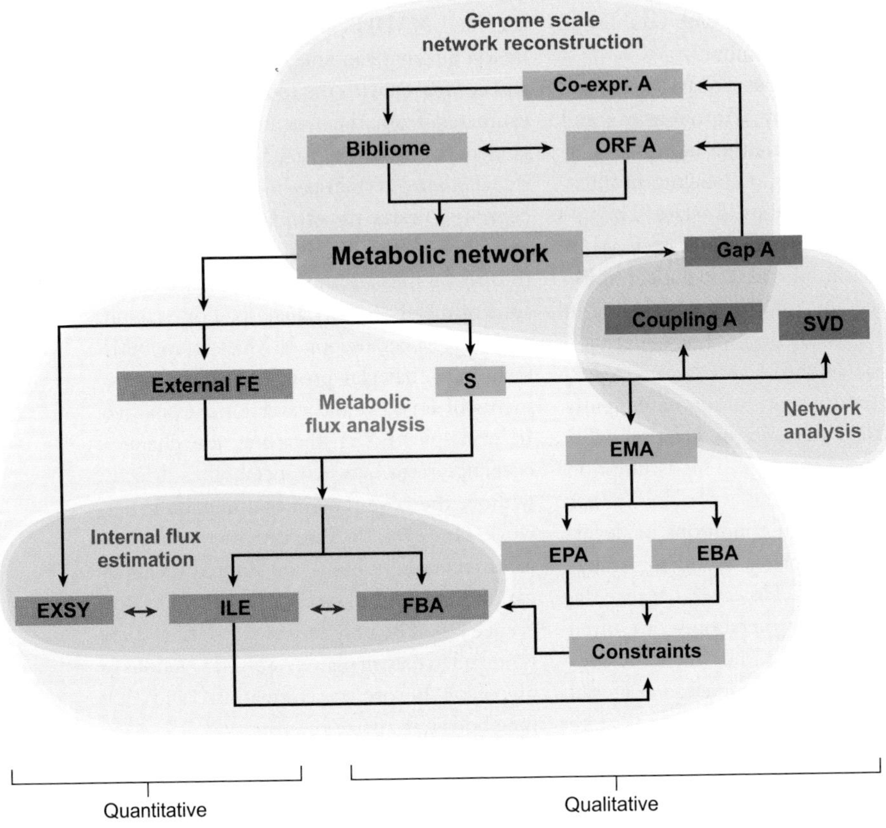

Figure 5

Schematic overview of metabolic network analysis. The different aspects of metabolic analysis are grouped into four functionally interconnected clusters: i) reconstruction of the network (*gray*), ii) analysis of the network structure (*red*), iii) metabolic flux analysis (*blue*), and iv) internal flux estimation (*green*). Genome-scale network reconstruction is an iterative process used to reconstruct the metabolic network from the literature (bibliome). Network analysis is used to evaluate the integrity of the metabolic network by gap analysis (Gap A). Network gaps prompt a targeted search for missing genes through open reading frame analysis (ORF A) and coexpression analysis (Co-expr. A). Additional network properties, such as coupling of pathways (Coupling A) and the more abstract determination of network complexity by singular value decomposition (SVD), can be determined via the use of the network stoichiometry (S). Only external flux estimation (External FE, direct measurements of input and output fluxes), internal flux estimation through in vivo nuclear magnetic resonance exchange spectroscopy (EXSY), and isotope label experiments (ILE) are quantitative (i.e., include confidence estimates). Flux balance analysis (FBA) forms a qualitative constraint-based alternative approach to determine internal flux values. Constraints can be based entirely on qualitative metabolic flux analysis of the network, such as extreme pathway analysis (EPA) and energy balance analysis (EBA). EPA and EBA are both related to elementary mode analysis (EMA), which is based on S, together with information about the reversibility of fluxes. EXSY, ILE, and FBA are largely independent methods used to estimate internal fluxes and can therefore serve to mutually validate findings (*red arrows*).

(54, 76). Unfortunately, with rare exceptions (58), plant flux models have not been made available in SBML, which hampers cross-comparison and validation of flux models.

PREDICTIVE MODELING

The next level of development for any set of methods, and a prime objective of plant systems biology, is to make useful predictions about the effects of genetic or environmental interventions. The ability to make quantitative predictions of flux maps in response to a perturbation is also an excellent test of our understanding of the regulation of metabolism. Furthermore, the ability to predict the effects of a pathway manipulation provides a powerful tool for rational design of flux maps. Predictive modeling of the functioning of metabolic networks is already possible in plants using kinetic models, and several other approaches have been applied to microbial systems and successfully make qualitative and quantitative predictions of the effects of metabolic perturbations on flux maps.

Predictions Using Mechanistic Models

The most sophisticated kinetic models form complete mechanistic descriptions of metabolic networks and therefore contain all the information needed to predict the effects of environmental or genetic change. Such a model is thus the ultimate description of a metabolic network. However, to produce a useful model all the kinetic parameters of each enzyme must be included in the model. In practice this makes kinetic models of even moderate size underdetermined. Predictive kinetic models have been constructed and successfully tested for the limited and well-studied metabolism of mammalian red blood cells but the complexity of metabolic networks in most cells makes comprehensive predictive kinetic models unmanageable. One mechanistically realistic kinetic model in a plant system is that of glycine betaine production from choline (65). As part of a multistudy metabolic engineering effort by Hanson and coworkers to increase stress tolerance by introducing the synthesis of osmoprotectants, mechanistic kinetic modeling revealed that several factors in the structure and kinetic parameters of the network would need to be engineered before large amounts of betaine could be produced in a naturally nonproducing species. This model provides an excellent illustration of the potential uses of mechanistic models in plants and is available online in a user-friendly, interactive form that allows one to explore the predicted effects of putative interventions (**http://www.hort.purdue.edu/cfpesp/models/mo00014.htm**). A recent mechanistic model of C3 photosynthetic carbon metabolism uses kinetic parameters from the extensive literature on photosynthetic enzymes to successfully model CO_2-fixation rates under different conditions (126). Importantly, this model indicates that rising atmospheric CO_2 levels make the relative enzyme levels in C3 plant leaves suboptimal for carbon fixation.

Flux Balance Analysis (FBA)

Flux balance analysis is innately predictive because the computed fluxes are calculated on the basis of the network structure and one or more assumptions about the functional goal(s) of its operation. Indeed, predicted optimal metabolic operation modes for different culturing conditions have been confirmed experimentally (23). FBA also predicts the fluxes through a perturbed metabolic network, assuming that the network is still operating to maximize fluxes toward the initial objective (46). Knockout mutations can be simulated using the original network by including an additional constraint in which the gene knockout corresponds to a zero flux through the coded enzyme (24). This approach has been used to predict the lethality and other effects of knockouts. For microbes, FBA-based predictions of metabolic flux adaptations in response to perturbation are close to experimentally determined ones (36, 42, 75, 101, 115).

The cause of the predictive success of FBA in microbes is suggested to be twofold: (*a*) Redundancy in the network design and regulatory mechanisms adjust metabolism so that the original objective function is still closely approached, and (*b*) microbial cultures undergo adaptive evolution after a perturbation and evolve to optimize the original objective function (biomass accumulation) (24, 25, 29, 39). For plants, the first mechanism likely also applies. Adaptive evolution is not applicable to most plant systems on an experimental time scale, except for models such as unicellular algae or cell cultures. However, the applicability of the first mechanism should provide sufficient impetus to the plant community to apply FBA to a plant model and evaluate the predictive potency of FBA for plant models. We note, however, that the choice of system will be important, because the objective functions of many plant tissues are not obvious and are likely not as straightforward as maximal growth rate.

Minimization of Metabolic Adjustment (MOMA)

A promising method for the prediction of metabolic flux adaptation in response to a perturbation is based on the principle of minimization of metabolic adjustment (MOMA) (101). In this approach, only the original flux values are used to determine the nearest feasible flux map after imposing the perturbation. The nearest feasible flux map is defined as the closest Euclidian location on the feasible flux cone to the location of the original flux map, which is found using quadratic programming and thought to be unique (101). Because often a genetically perturbed organism is not functioning optimally, MOMA is an important alternative predictive tool in the microbial world (46, 59, 106) (**Figure 6**).

MOMA has the great advantage that only flux values are required, which makes this technique directly applicable as soon as a flux map of a model has been established. When put to the test, MOMA often outperforms other methods such as FBA and ROOM (see below) in matching experimental results obtained with knockout mutants (101, 104). We believe that MOMA has significant promise for use in those plant systems where flux maps have now been established (87).

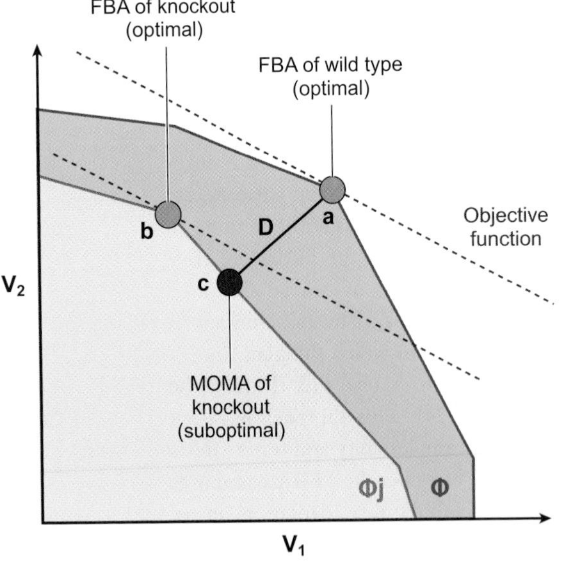

Figure 6

Predictive modeling of a knockout mutant using the minimization of metabolic adjustment (MOMA), taken from Reference 101 with permission. The green and yellow areas define the feasible flux space for the values of two fluxes V1 and V2 in a metabolic network. The outer red line is defined by the flux balance analysis (FBA) objective function, which forms a tangent to the feasible space and solves for V1 and V2 at point a. For a knockout mutant, for which the feasible space is reduced to the yellow area, the original FBA objective function now solves V1 and V2 at point b. In contrast with the outcome predicted by FBA, MOMA (which minimizes the metabolic adjustment) predicts that V1 and V2 for the mutant will be defined by point c. Thus, c is the nearest feasible point to a, and D is perpendicular to the nearest edge of the allowed flux space. Φj, feasible space of knockout (*yellow*); Φ, feasible space of wild type (*green*).

Regulatory On/Off Minimization (ROOM)

Another recently developed flux-based method to predict the metabolic state of an organism after a perturbation is regulatory on/off minimization (ROOM) (104). Related to but distinct from MOMA, ROOM is a constraint-based method that aims to minimize the number of changes required to adjust the flux map following a perturbation using mixed integer linear programming. The development of this method was inspired by the observation that organisms undergo a depression in growth shortly after a (genetic) perturbation that coincides with a large change in gene expression. After an adaptation period, gene expression often returns to a state close to the state prior to perturbation (31, 40). By analogy to the minimal change in gene regulation, ROOM minimizes the number of significant flux changes compared with the unperturbed state

(104). ROOM-based predictions of knockout mutant phenotypes closely resemble FBA prediction and match flux patterns after the adaptation phase better than MOMA, but during the adaptation phase MOMA predictions most closely match experimental results (104). A drawback of ROOM-based prediction, as is the case for FBA predictions, is that the solutions are often not unique.

The applicability of ROOM to plant models will depend on the nature of the changes that occur during the adaptation phase. If all changes are regulation based, similar results can be expected for plant systems as those that were found for yeast (104). However, if point mutations (adaptive evolution) underlie the predictive success, perturbations in plant systems cannot be expected to be predicted by ROOM successfully.

Flux-Based Plant Metabolic Rational Design is Within Reach

The approach suitable for rational design of a metabolic pathway depends on the context. Mechanistic kinetic modeling is appropriate for subnetworks in which the understanding of the pathway is detailed. Plant one-carbon and amino acid metabolism, as well as phenylpropanoid and other better-studied areas of secondary metabolism, are good examples. We note that multiple studies in each area are likely needed before the relevant network structure and enzymatic kinetic parameters are sufficiently well understood for more than occasional success.

ROOM and MOMA require only a flux map of the system of interest to make predictions of the effects of perturbations. Both methods can therefore be applied directly to plant models in which flux maps have been generated. Successful prediction of the metabolic adaptation following a perturbation will depend on the quality and the level of detail of the map (current flux maps of central carbon metabolism in plants contain 50–150 reactions). Their potential use in predictive modeling should provide a strong incentive for the production of detailed, validated flux maps of high statistical quality.

Other theoretical approaches to understanding the regulation of metabolism that are not covered in this article also have a part to play in guiding successful rational design. In particular, the lessons of metabolic control analysis should be considered (for explanation and review see References 27 and 87). Especially important is that control over flux is exerted throughout a pathway, so single gene overexpression rarely results in great increases in flux. Consequently, gene overexpression is less likely to be a successful approach to pathway manipulation than gene knockdowns. Mechanistic kinetic models yield flux control coefficients for all the elements in a network, but these coefficients can be obtained independently of such modeling efforts by piecemeal experiments that measure fluxes in perturbed systems.

CONCLUDING REMARKS

Metabolic flux analysis in plants provides a rich description of plant cellular function. Studies to date have yielded insights into the nature and regulation of integrated metabolic processes and have led to the discovery of novel routes and cycles that operate in plant cells and tissues. Metabolic network reconstruction, analysis, and predictive modeling methods developed in microbial systems have seen rapid progress in recent years and there are grounds for considerable optimism about their fruitful application to plants.

With the creation of metabolic flux maps in plants now becoming routine, extra attention should be paid to the quality of flux estimates. The wider use of appropriate and transparent confidence metrics in plant studies will greatly facilitate the interpretation and portability of flux maps. Transparency of flux data will aid in integration into plant systems biology, which provides another incentive for quality and consistency as well as for the adoption of a common format for the exchange of flux models.

The plant community can utilize the tools for network generation and predictive flux analysis that have been developed by microbial engineers. Predictive modeling is a potent tool for hypothesis testing with regards to the regulation of metabolism, and allows for the systematic in silico evaluation of perturbations, which promises to improve success in the genetic alteration of plant metabolism.

DISCLOSURE STATEMENT

The authors are not aware of any biases that might be perceived as affecting the objectivity of this review.

ACKNOWLEDGMENTS

Y.S-H is supported by grants from the National Science Foundation, the U.S. Department of Agriculture, and the Michigan State University Foundation

LITERATURE CITED

1. Allen DK, Shachar-Hill Y, Ohlrogge JB. 2007. Compartment-specific labeling information in ^{13}C metabolic flux analysis of plants. *Phytochemistry* 68:2197–210
2. Alonso AP, Raymond P, Rolin D, Dieuaide-Noubhani M. 2007. Substrate cycles in the central metabolism of maize root tips under hypoxia. *Phytochemistry* 68:2222–31
3. Alonso AP, Vigeolas H, Raymond P, Rolin D, Dieuaide-Noubhani M. 2005. A new substrate cycle in plants. Evidence for a high glucose-phosphate-to-glucose turnover from in vivo steady-state and pulse-labeling experiments with [^{13}C] glucose and [^{14}C] glucose. *Plant Physiol.* 138:2220–32
4. Antoniewicz MR, Kelleher JK, Stephanopoulos G. 2006. Determination of confidence intervals of metabolic fluxes estimated from stable isotope measurements. *Metab. Eng.* 8:324–37
5. Antoniewicz MR, Kelleher JK, Stephanopoulos G. 2007. Elementary metabolite units (EMU): A novel framework for modeling isotopic distributions. *Metab. Eng.* 9:68–86
6. Antoniewicz MR, Kraynie DF, Laffend LA, Gonzalez-Lergier J, Kelleher JK, Stephanopoulos G. 2007. Metabolic flux analysis in a nonstationary system: Fed-batch fermentation of a high yielding strain of *E. coli* producing 1,3-propanediol. *Metab. Eng.* 9:277–92
7. Aoki K, Ogata Y, Shibata D. 2007. Approaches for extracting practical information from gene coexpression networks in plant biology. *Plant Cell Physiol.* 48:381–90
8. Arakawa K, Yamada Y, Shinoda K, Nakayama Y, Tomita M. 2006. GEM System: automatic prototyping of cell-wide metabolic pathway models from genomes. *BMC Bioinformatics* 7:168
9. Arauzo-Bravo MJ, Shimizu K. 2003. An improved method for statistical analysis of metabolic flux analysis using isotopomer mapping matrices with analytical expressions. *J. Biotechnol.* 105:117–33
10. Baxter CJ, Redestig H, Schauer N, Repsilber D, Patil KR, et al. 2007. The metabolic response of heterotrophic *Arabidopsis* cells to oxidative stress. *Plant Physiol.* 143:312–25
11. Beard DA, Liang SC, Qian H. 2002. Energy balance for analysis of complex metabolic networks. *Biophys. J.* 83:79–86

12. Becker SA, Price ND, Palsson BØ. 2006. Metabolite coupling in genome-scale metabolic networks. *BMC Bioinformatics* 7:111
13. Boatright J, Negre F, Chen X, Kish CM, Wood B, et al. 2004. Understanding in vivo benzenoid metabolism in petunia petal tissue. *Plant Physiol.* 135:1993–2011
14. Burgard AP, Nikolaev EV, Schilling CH, Maranas CD. 2004. Flux coupling analysis of genome-scale metabolic network reconstructions. *Genome Res.* 14:301–12
15. Cai R, Arntfield SD. 2001. A rapid high-performance liquid chromatographic method for the determination of sinapine and sinapic acid in canola seed and meal. *J. Am. Oil Chem. Soc.* 78:903–10
16. Croes D, Couche F, Wodak SJ, van Helden J. 2006. Inferring meaningful pathways in weighted metabolic networks. *J. Mol. Biol.* 356:222–36
17. DeJongh M, Formsma K, Boillot P, Gould J, Rycenga M, Best A. 2007. Toward the automated generation of genome-scale metabolic networks in the SEED. *BMC Bioinformatics* 8:139
18. De Keersmaecker SCJ, Thijs IMV, Vanderleyden J, Marchal K. 2006. Integration of omics data: how well does it work for bacteria? *Mol. Microbiol.* 62:1239–50
19. DellaPenna D. 2001. Plant metabolic engineering. *Plant Physiol.* 125:160–63
20. Dieuaide-Noubhani M, Raffard G, Canioni P, Pradet A, Raymond P. 1995. Quantification of compartmented metabolic fluxes in maize root tips using isotope distribution from ^{13}C- or ^{14}C-labeled glucose. *J. Biol. Chem.* 270:13147–59
21. Duarte NC, Becker SA, Jamshidi N, Thiele I, Mo ML, et al. 2007. Global reconstruction of the human metabolic network based on genomic and bibliomic data. *Proc. Natl. Acad. Sci. USA* 104:1777–82
22. Duarte NC, Herrgard MJ, Palsson BO. 2004. Reconstruction and validation of *Saccharomyces cerevisiae* iND750, a fully compartmentalized genome-scale metabolic model. *Genome Res.* 14:1298–309
23. Edwards JS, Ibarra RU, Palsson BO. 2001. In silico predictions of *Escherichia coli* metabolic capabilities are consistent with experimental data. *Nat. Biotechnol.* 19:125–30
24. Edwards JS, Palsson BO. 2000. Metabolic flux balance analysis and the in silico analysis of *Escherichia coli* K-12 gene deletions. *BMC Bioinformatics* 1:1
25. Edwards JS, Palsson BO. 2000. The *Escherichia coli* MG1655 in silico metabolic genotype: Its definition, characteristics, and capabilities. *Proc. Natl. Acad. Sci. USA* 97:5528–33
26. Ettenhuber C, Spielbauer G, Margl L, Hannah LC, Gierl A, et al. 2005. Changes in flux pattern of the central carbohydrate metabolism during kernel development in maize. *Phytochemistry* 66:2632–42
27. Fell DA, Thomas S. 1999. Increasing the flux in a metabolic pathway: a metabolic control analysis perspective. In *Regulation of Primary Metabolic Pathways in Plants*, ed. NJ Kruger, SA Hill, RG Ratcliffe, pp. 257–73. Dordrecht: Kluwer Acad.
28. Fernie AR, Roscher A, Ratcliffe RG, Kruger NJ. 2001. Fructose 2,6-bisphosphate activates pyrophosphate:fructose-6-phosphate 1-phosphotransferase and increases triose phosphate to hexose phosphate cycling in heterotrophic cells. *Planta* 212:250–63
29. Fong SS, Marciniak JY, Palsson BO. 2003. Description and interpretation of adaptive evolution of *Escherichia coli* K-12 MG1655 by using a genome-scale in silico metabolic model. *J. Bacteriol.* 185:6400–8
30. Gagneur J, Klamt S. 2004. Computation of elementary modes: a unifying framework and the new binary approach. *BMC Bioinformatics* 5:175
31. Gasch AP, Spellman PT, Kao CM, Carmel-Harel O, Eisen MB, et al. 2000. Genomic expression programs in the response of yeast cells to environmental changes. *Mol. Biol. Cell* 11:4241–57

32. Goffman FD, Alonso AP, Schwender J, Shachar-Hill Y, Ohlrogge JB. 2005. Light enables a very high efficiency of carbon storage in developing embryos of rapeseed. *Plant Physiol.* 138:2269–79
33. Gutierrez RA, Lejay LV, Dean A, Chiaromonte F, Shasha DE, Coruzzi GM. 2007. Qualitative network models and genome-wide expression data define carbon/nitrogen-responsive molecular machines in *Arabidopsis*. *Genome Biol.* 8:R7; doi:10.1186/gb-2007-8-1-r7
34. Gutierrez RA, Shasha DE, Coruzzi GM. 2005. Systems biology for the virtual plant. *Plant Physiol.* 138:550–4
35. Henry CS, Broadbelt LJ, Hatzimanikatis V. 2007. Thermodynamics-based metabolic flux analysis. *Biophys. J.* 92:1792–805
36. Hua Q, Yang C, Baba T, Mori H, Shimizu K. 2003. Responses of the central metabolism in *Escherichia coli* to phosphoglucose isomerase and glucose-6-phosphate dehydrogenase knockouts. *J. Bacteriol.* 185:7053–67
37. Hucka M, Finney A, Sauro HM, Bolouri H, Doyle JC, et al. 2003. The systems biology markup language (SBML): a medium for representation and exchange of biochemical network models. *Bioinformatics* 19:524–31
38. Huege J, Sulpice R, Gibon Y, Lisec J, Koehl K, Kopka J. 2007. GC-EI-TOF-MS analysis of in vivo carbon-partitioning into soluble metabolite pools of higher plants by monitoring isotope dilution after $^{13}CO_2$ labelling. *Phytochemistry* 68:2258–72
39. Ibarra RU, Edwards JS, Palsson BO. 2002. *Escherichia coli* K-12 undergoes adaptive evolution to achieve in silico predicted optimal growth. *Nature* 420:186–89
40. Ideker T, Thorsson V, Ranish JA, Christmas R, Buhler J, et al. 2001. Integrated genomic and proteomic analyses of a systematically perturbed metabolic network. *Science* 292:929–34
41. Isermann N, Wiechert W. 2003. Metabolic isotopomer labeling systems. Part II: structural flux identifiability analysis. *Math. Biosci.* 183:175–214
42. Jiao Z, Baba T, Mori H, Shimizu K. 2003. Analysis of metabolic and physiological responses to *gnd* knockout in *Escherichia coli* by using C-13 tracer experiment and enzyme activity measurement. *FEMS Microbiol. Lett.* 220:295–301
43. Junker BH, Lonien J, Heady LE, Rogers A, Schwender J. 2007. Parallel determination of enzyme activities and in vivo fluxes in *Brassica napus* embryos grown on organic or inorganic nitrogen source. *Phytochemistry* 68:2232–42
44. Kanehisa M, Goto S, Hattori M, Aoki-Kinoshita KF, Itoh M, et al. 2006. From genomics to chemical genomics: new developments in KEGG. *Nucleic Acids Res.* 34:D354–57
45. Katz J, Rognstad R. 1967. Labeling of pentose phosphate from glucose-^{14}C and estimation of rates of transaldolase transketolase contribution of pentose cycle and ribose phosphate synthesis. *Biochemistry* 6:2227–47
46. Kauffman KJ, Prakash P, Edwards JS. 2003. Advances in flux balance analysis. *Curr. Opin. Biotechnol.* 14:491–96
47. Kitano H. 2002. Computational systems biology. *Nature* 420:206–10
48. Klamt S, Stelling J, Ginkel M, Gilles ED. 2003. FluxAnalyzer: exploring structure, pathways, and flux distributions in metabolic networks on interactive flux maps. *Bioinformatics* 19:261–69
49. Kruger NJ, Le Lay P, Ratcliffe RG. 2007. Vacuolar compartmentation complicates the steady-state analysis of glucose metabolism and forces reappraisal of sucrose cycling in plants. *Phytochemistry* 68:2189–96
50. Kugel H, Mayer A, Kirst GO, Leibfritz D. 1990. The energy requirements of pH homeostasis define the limits of pH regulation—a model. *Biochim. Biophys. Acta* 1054:33–40

51. Lange BM. 2006. Integrative analysis of metabolic networks: from peaks to flux models? *Curr. Opin. Plant Biol.* 9:220–26
52. Lee DY, Yun H, Park S, Lee SY. 2003. MetaFluxNet: the management of metabolic reaction information and quantitative metabolic flux analysis. *Bioinformatics* 19:2144–46
53. Lee S, Phalakornkule C, Domach MM, Grossmann IE. 2000. Recursive MILP model for finding all the alternate optima in LP models for metabolic networks. *Comput. Chem. Eng.* 24:711–16
54. Lee SY, Lee DY, Kim TY. 2005. Systems biotechnology for strain improvement. *Trends Biotechnol.* 23:349–58
55. Li S, Wu LJ, Zhang ZQ. 2006. Constructing biological networks through combined literature mining and microarray analysis: a LMMA approach. *Bioinformatics* 22:2143–50
56. Libourel IGL, Gehan JP, Shachar-Hill Y. 2007. Design of substrate label for steady state flux measurements in plant systems using the metabolic network of *Brassica napus* embryos. *Phytochemistry* 68:2211–21
57. Libourel IGL, van Bodegom PM, Fricker MD, Ratcliffe RG. 2006. Nitrite reduces cytoplasmic acidosis under anoxia. *Plant Phys.* 142:1710–17
58. Locke JCW, Southern MM, Kozma-Bognar L, Hibberd V, Brown PE, et al. 2005. Extension of a genetic network model by iterative experimentation and mathematical analysis. *Mol. Syst. Biol.* 1:13
59. Luo R-Y, Liao S, Tao G-Y, Li Y-Y, Zeng SQ, et al. 2006. Dynamic analysis of optimality in myocardial energy metabolism under normal and ischemic conditions. *Mol. Syst. Biol.* 2:2006.0031; doi:10.1038/msb4100071
60. Matsuda F, Morino K, Ano R, Kuzawa M, Wakasa K, Miyagawa H. 2005. Metabolic flux analysis of the phenylpropanoid pathway in elicitor-treated potato tuber tissue. *Plant Cell Physiol.* 46:454–66
61. Matsuda F, Morino K, Miyashita M, Miyagawa H. 2003. Metabolic flux analysis of the phenylpropanoid pathway in wound-healing potato tuber tissue using stable isotope-labeled tracer and LC-MS spectroscopy. *Plant Cell Physiol.* 44:510–17
62. Matsuda F, Wakasa K, Miyagawa H. 2007. Metabolic flux analysis in plants using dynamic labeling technique: Application to tryptophan biosynthesis in cultured rice cells. *Phytochemistry* 68:2290–301
63. Mayer RR, Cherry JH, Rhodes D. 1990. Effects of heat shock on amino acid metabolism of cowpea cells. *Plant Physiol.* 94:796–810
64. McNeil SD, Nuccio ML, Rhodes D, Shachar-Hill Y, Hanson AD. 2000. Radiotracer and computer modeling evidence that phospho-base methylation is the main route of choline synthesis in tobacco. *Plant Physiol.* 123:371–80
65. McNeil SD, Rhodes D, Russell BL, Nuccio ML, Shachar-Hill Y, Hanson AD. 2000. Metabolic modeling identifies key constraints on an engineered glycine betaine synthesis pathway in tobacco. *Plant Physiol.* 124:153–62
66. Mollney M, Wiechert W, Kownatzki D, de Graaf AA. 1999. Bidirectional reaction steps in metabolic networks: IV. Optimal design of isotopomer labeling experiments. *Biotechnol. Bioeng.* 66:86–103
67. Morgan JA, Rhodes D. 2002. Mathematical modeling of plant metabolic pathways. *Metab. Eng.* 4:80–88
68. Nöh K, Grönke K, Luo B, Takors R, Oldiges M, Wiechert W. 2007. Metabolic flux analysis at ultra short time scale: Isotopically nonstationary ^{13}C labeling experiments. *J. Biotechnol.* 129:249–67
69. Nöh K, Wiechert W. 2006. Experimental design principles for isotopically instationary ^{13}C labeling experiments. *Biotechnol. Bioeng.* 94:234–51

70. Nuccio ML, McNeil SD, Ziemak MJ, Hanson AD, Jain RK, Selvaraj G. 2000. Choline import into chloroplasts limits glycine betaine synthesis in tobacco: analysis of plants engineered with a chloroplastic or a cytosolic pathway. *Metab. Eng.* 2:300–11
71. Orlova I, Marshall-Colon A, Schnepp J, Wood B, Varbanova M, et al. 2006. Reduction of benzenoid synthesis in petunia flowers reveals multiple pathways to benzoic acid and enhancement in auxin transport. *Plant Cell* 18:3458–75
72. Papin JA, Stelling J, Price ND, Klamt S, Schuster S, Palsson BO. 2004. Comparison of network-based pathway analysis methods. *Trends Biotechnol.* 22:400–5
73. Patil KR, Akesson M, Nielsen J. 2004. Use of genome-scale microbial models for metabolic engineering. *Curr. Opin. Biotechnol.* 15:64–69
74. Pázman A. 1986. *Foundations of Optimum Experimental Design.* Dordrecht: Reidel
75. Peng L, Arauzo-Bravo MJ, Shimizu K. 2004. Metabolic flux analysis for a *ppc* mutant *Escherichia coli* based on ^{13}C-labelling experiments together with enzyme activity assays and intracellular metabolite measurements. *FEMS Microbiol. Lett.* 235:17–23
76. Pettinen A, Aho T, Smolander OP, Manninen T, Saarinen A, et al. 2005. Simulation tools for biochemical networks: evaluation of performance and usability. *Bioinformatics* 21:357–63
77. Price ND, Papin JA, Schilling CH, Palsson BO. 2003. Genome-scale microbial in silico models: the constraints-based approach. *Trends Biotechnol.* 21:162–69
78. Price ND, Reed JL, Palsson BO. 2004. Genome-scale models of microbial cells: Evaluating the consequences of constraints. *Nat. Rev. Microbiol.* 2:886–97
79. Raamsdonk LM, Teusink B, Broadhurst D, Zhang NS, Hayes A, et al. 2001. A functional genomics strategy that uses metabolome data to reveal the phenotype of silent mutations. *Nat. Biotechnol.* 19:45–50
80. Ratcliffe RG, Shachar-Hill Y. 2001. Probing plant metabolism with NMR. *Annu. Rev. Plant Physiol. Plant Mol. Biol.* 52:499–526
81. Ratcliffe RG, Shachar-Hill Y. 2006. Measuring multiple fluxes through plant metabolic networks. *Plant J.* 45:490–511
82. Reed JL, Famili I, Thiele I, Palsson BO. 2006. Towards multidimensional genome annotation. *Nat. Rev. Genet.* 7:130–41
83. Reed JL, Palsson BO. 2003. Thirteen years of building constraint-based in silico models of *Escherichia coli*. *J. Bacteriol.* 185:2692–99
84. Reed JL, Palsson BO. 2004. Genome-scale in silico models of *E. coli* have multiple equivalent phenotypic states: Assessment of correlated reaction subsets that comprise network states. *Genome Res.* 14:1797–805
85. Reed JL, Patel TR, Chen KH, Joyce AR, Applebee MK, et al. 2006. Systems approach to refining genome annotation. *Proc. Natl. Acad. Sci. USA* 103:17480–84
86. Reed JL, Vo TD, Schilling CH, Palsson BO. 2003. An expanded genome-scale model of *Escherichia coli* K-12 (iJR904 GSM/GPR). *Genome Biol.* 4:R54
87. Rios-Estepa R, Lange BM. 2007. Experimental and mathematical approaches to modeling plant metabolic networks. *Phytochemistry* 68:2351–74
88. Roberts JKM, Lane AN, Clark RA, Nieman RH. 1985. Relationships between the rate of synthesis of ATP and the concentrations of reactants and products of ATP hydrolysis in maize root tips, determined by ^{31}P nuclear magnetic resonance. *Arch. Biochem. Biophys.* 240:712–22
89. Rohwer JM, Botha FC. 2001. Analysis of sucrose accumulation in the sugar cane culm on the basis of in vitro kinetic data. *Biochem. J.* 358:437–45

90. Römisch-Margl W, Schramek N, Radykewicz T, Ettenhuber C, Eylert E, et al. 2007. $^{13}CO_2$ as a universal metabolic tracer in isotopologue perturbation experiments. *Phytochemistry* 68:2273–89
91. Rontein D, Dieuaide-Noubhani M, Dufourc EJ, Raymond P, Rolin D. 2002. The metabolic architecture of plant cells. Stability of central metabolism and flexibility of anabolic pathways during the growth cycle of tomato cells. *J. Biol. Chem.* 277:43948–60
92. Roscher A, Emsley L, Raymond P, Roby C. 1998. Unidirectional steady state rates of central metabolism enzymes measured simultaneously in a living plant tissue. *J. Biol. Chem.* 273:25053–61
93. Roscher A, Kruger NJ, Ratcliffe RG. 2000. Strategies for metabolic flux analysis in plants using isotope labelling. *J. Biotechnol.* 77:81–102
94. Sauer U. 2004. High-throughput phenomics: experimental methods for mapping fluxomes. *Curr. Opin. Biotechnol.* 15:58–63
95. Schilling CH, Palsson BO. 2000. Assessment of the metabolic capabilities of *Haemophilus influenzae* Rd through a genome-scale pathway analysis. *J. Theor. Biol.* 203:249–83
96. Schilling CH, Schuster S, Palsson BO, Heinrich R. 1999. Metabolic pathway analysis: Basic concepts and scientific applications in the postgenomic era. *Biotechnol. Prog.* 15:296–303
97. Schuster S, Dandekar T, Fell DA. 1999. Detection of elementary flux modes in biochemical networks: a promising tool for pathway analysis and metabolic engineering. *Trends Biotechnol.* 17:53–60
98. Schwender J, Goffman FD, Ohlrogge JB, Shachar-Hill Y. 2004. Rubisco without the Calvin cycle improves the carbon efficiency of developing green seeds. *Nature* 432:779–82
99. Schwender J, Ohlrogge JB. 2002. Probing in vivo metabolism by stable isotope labeling of storage lipids and proteins in developing *Brassica napus* embryos. *Plant Physiol.* 130:347–61
100. Schwender J, Shachar-Hill Y, Ohlrogge JB. 2006. Mitochondrial metabolism in developing embryos of *Brassica napus*. *J. Biol. Chem.* 281:34040–47
101. Segre D, Vitkup D, Church GM. 2002. Analysis of optimality in natural and perturbed metabolic networks. *Proc. Natl. Acad. Sci. USA* 99:15112–17
102. Shastri AA, Morgan JA. 2005. Flux balance analysis of photoautotrophic metabolism. *Biotechnol. Prog.* 21:1617–26
103. Shastri AA, Morgan JA. 2007. A transient isotopic labeling methodology for ^{13}C metabolic flux analysis of photoautotrophic microorganisms. *Phytochemistry* 68:2302–12
104. Shlomi T, Berkman O, Ruppin E. 2005. Regulatory on/off minimization of metabolic flux changes after genetic perturbations. *Proc. Natl. Acad. Sci. USA* 102:7695–700
105. Sriram G, Fulton DB, Iyer VV, Peterson JM, Zhou RL, et al. 2004. Quantification of compartmented metabolic fluxes in developing soybean embryos by employing biosynthetically directed fractional ^{13}C labeling, [^{13}C, ^{1}H] two-dimensional nuclear magnetic resonance, and comprehensive isotopomer balancing. *Plant Physiol.* 136:3043–57
106. Stephanopoulos G, Alper H, Moxley J. 2004. Exploiting biological complexity for strain improvement through systems biology. *Nat. Biotechnol.* 22:1261–67
107. Stephanopoulos G, Aristidou AA, Nielsen J. 1998. *Metabolic Engineering Principles and Methodologies*. San Diego: Academic
108. Sterck L, Rombauts S, Vandepoele K, Rouze P, Van de Peer Y. 2007. How many genes are there in plants (... and why are they there)? *Curr. Opin. Plant Biol.* 10:199–203
109. Steuer R. 2007. Computational approaches to the topology, stability and dynamics of metabolic networks. *Phytochemistry* 68:2302–12

110. Stoimenova M, Libourel IGL, Ratcliffe RG, Kaiser WM. 2003. The role of nitrate reduction in the anoxic metabolism of roots—II. Anoxic metabolism of tobacco roots with or without nitrate reductase activity. *Plant Soil* 253:155–67

111. van Winden WA, Heijnen JJ, Verheijen PJT. 2002. Cumulative bondomers: A new concept in flux analysis from 2D [C-13,H-1] COSY NMR data. *Biotechnol. Bioeng.* 80:731–45

112. van Winden WA, Heijnen JJ, Verheijen PJT, Grievink J. 2001. A priori analysis of metabolic flux identifiability from ^{13}C-labeling data. *Biotechnol. Bioeng.* 74:505–16

113. Van der Heijden RTJM, Romein B, Heijnen JJ, Hellinga C, Luyben KCAM. 1994. Linear constraint relations in biochemical reaction systems. 1. Classification of the calculability and the balanceability of conversion rates. *Biotechnol. Bioeng.* 43:3–10

114. Varma A, Palsson BO. 1994. Metabolic flux balancing—Basic concepts, scientific and practical use. *Bio-Technology* 12:994–98

115. Varma A, Palsson BO. 1994. Stoichiometric flux balance models quantitatively predict growth and metabolic by-product secretion in wild-type *Escherichia coli* W3110. *Appl. Environ. Microbiol.* 60:3724–31

116. Wiback SJ, Mahadevan R, Palsson BO. 2004. Using metabolic flux data to further constrain the metabolic solution space and predict internal flux patterns: The *Escherichia coli* spectrum. *Biotechnol. Bioeng.* 86:317–31

117. Wiechert W, de Graaf AA. 1997. Bidirectional reaction steps in metabolic networks. I. Modeling and simulation of carbon isotope labeling experiments. *Biotechnol. Bioeng.* 55:101–17

118. Wiechert W, Mollney M, Isermann N, Wurzel W, de Graaf AA. 1999. Bidirectional reaction steps in metabolic networks: III. Explicit solution and analysis of isotopomer labeling systems. *Biotechnol. Bioeng.* 66:69–85

119. Wiechert W, Mollney M, Petersen S, de Graaf AA. 2001. A universal framework for ^{13}C metabolic flux analysis. *Metab. Eng.* 3:265–83

120. Wiechert W, Nöh K. 2005. From stationary to instationary metabolic flux analysis. *Adv. Biochem. Eng. Biotechnol.* 92:145–72

121. Wiechert W, Siefke C, de Graaf AA, Marx A. 1997. Bidirectional reaction steps in metabolic networks. II. Flux estimation and statistical analysis. *Biotechnol. Bioeng.* 55:118–35

122. Wilke D, Gleba Y. 2006. Starting at the front end processes for new renewables as feedstocks of the future. In *Feedstocks for the Future: Renewables for the Production of Chemicals and Materials*, ACS Symp. Ser., ed. JJ Bozell, MK Patel, pp. 27–39. Washington, DC: Am. Chem. Soc.

123. Wille A, Zimmermann P, Vranová E, Fürholz A, Laule O, et al. 2004. Sparse graphical Gaussian modeling of the isoprenoid gene network in *Arabidopsis thaliana*. *Genome Biol.* 5:R92

124. Ye XD, Al-Babili S, Kloti A, Zhang J, Lucca P, et al. 2000. Engineering the provitamin A (β-carotene) biosynthetic pathway into (carotenoid-free) rice endosperm. *Science* 287:303–5

125. Yun H, Lee DY, Jeong J, Lee S, Lee SY. 2005. MFAML: a standard data structure for representing and exchanging metabolic flux models. *Bioinformatics* 21:3329–30

126. Zhu XG, de Sturler E, Long SP. 2007. Optimizing the distribution of resources between enzymes of carbon metabolism can dramatically increase photosynthetic rate: a numerical simulation using an evolutionary algorithm. *Plant Physiol.* 145:513–26

Mechanisms of Salinity Tolerance

Rana Munns[1] and Mark Tester[2]

[1]CSIRO Plant Industry, Canberra, ACT, Australia; email: rana.munns@csiro.au

[2]Australian Center for Plant Functional Genomics and University of Adelaide, SA, Australia; email: mark.tester@acpfg.com.au

Annu. Rev. Plant Biol. 2008. 59:651–81

The *Annual Review of Plant Biology* is online at plant.annualreviews.org

This article's doi:
10.1146/annurev.arplant.59.032607.092911

1543-5008/08/0602-0651$20.00

Key Words

salt tolerance, salinity stress, sodium toxicity, chloride, stress tolerance

Abstract

The physiological and molecular mechanisms of tolerance to osmotic and ionic components of salinity stress are reviewed at the cellular, organ, and whole-plant level. Plant growth responds to salinity in two phases: a rapid, osmotic phase that inhibits growth of young leaves, and a slower, ionic phase that accelerates senescence of mature leaves. Plant adaptations to salinity are of three distinct types: osmotic stress tolerance, Na^+ or Cl^- exclusion, and the tolerance of tissue to accumulated Na^+ or Cl^-. Our understanding of the role of the *HKT* gene family in Na^+ exclusion from leaves is increasing, as is the understanding of the molecular bases for many other transport processes at the cellular level. However, we have a limited molecular understanding of the overall control of Na^+ accumulation and of osmotic stress tolerance at the whole-plant level. Molecular genetics and functional genomics provide a new opportunity to synthesize molecular and physiological knowledge to improve the salinity tolerance of plants relevant to food production and environmental sustainability.

Contents

INTRODUCTION

Soil salinity stresses plants in two ways. High concentrations of salts in the soil make it harder for roots to extract water, and high concentrations of salts within the plant can be toxic. Salts on the outside of roots have an immediate effect on cell growth and associated metabolism; toxic concentrations of salts take time to accumulate inside plants before they affect plant function. We discuss the physiology and molecular biology of mechanisms that allow plants to adapt to these stresses.

Stress: an adverse circumstance that disturbs, or is likely to disturb, the normal physiological functioning of an individual

More than 800 million hectares of land throughout the world are salt affected (31). This amount accounts for more than 6% of the world's total land area. Most of this salt-affected land has arisen from natural causes, from the accumulation of salts over long periods of time in arid and semiarid zones (107). Weathering of parental rocks releases soluble salts of various types, mainly chlorides of sodium, calcium, and magnesium, and to a lesser extent, sulfates and carbonates (124). Sodium chloride is the most soluble and abundant salt released. The other cause of accumulation is the deposition of oceanic salts carried in wind and rain. Rainwater contains 6–50 mg/kg of sodium chloride; the concentration decreases with distance from the coast. Rain containing 10 mg/kg of sodium chloride would deposit 10 kg/ha of salt for each 100 mm of rainfall per year.

Apart from natural salinity, a significant proportion of recently cultivated agricultural land has become saline owing to land clearing or irrigation, both of which cause water tables to rise and concentrate the salts in the root zone. Of the 1500 million ha of land farmed by dryland agriculture, 32 million ha (2%) are affected by secondary salinity to varying degrees. Of the current 230 million ha of irrigated land, 45 million ha (20%) are salt affected (31). Irrigated land accounts for only 15% of total cultivated land, but because irrigated land has at least twice the productivity of rainfed land, it produces one third of the world's food.

Salinity is a soil condition characterized by a high concentration of soluble salts. Soils are classified as saline when the ECe is 4 dS/m or more (131), which is equivalent to approximately 40 mM NaCl and generates an osmotic pressure of approximately 0.2 MPa. This definition of salinity derives from the ECe that significantly reduces the yield of most crops.

Because NaCl is the most soluble and widespread salt, it is not surprising that all plants have evolved mechanisms to regulate its accumulation and to select against it in favor of other nutrients commonly present in low concentrations, such as K^+ and NO_3^-. In most plants, Na^+ and Cl^- are effectively excluded by roots while water is taken up from the soil (89). Halophytes, the natural flora of highly saline soils, are able to maintain this exclusion at higher salinities than glycophytes. For example, sea barleygrass, *Hordeum marinum*, excludes both Na^+ and Cl^- until at least 450 mM NaCl (44). It is also not surprising that because salinity is a common feature of arid and semiarid lands, plants have evolved mechanisms to tolerate the low soil water potential caused by salinity, as well as by drought, and so tolerance to osmotic stress is a feature of most glycophytes and halophytes.

Former reviews in this series on plant responses to salinity were published either 20 or more years ago (35, 53, 104) or much more recently (58, 145). The 20-year gap and the recent revival in activity is indicative of the breakthroughs now emerging owing to the application of molecular genetics to increase our understanding of the physiological and molecular mechanisms of salinity tolerance in plants. This recent flurry of activity may also reflect the current excitement in plant science for making practical contributions to food production in the face of increasing salinization of agricultural regions and global climate change (75).

ECe: the electrical conductivity of the saturated paste extract; equivalent to the concentration of salts in saturated soil or in a hydroponic solution

Aim of This Review

The focus of this review is mechanisms of salinity tolerance at the molecular, cellular, and whole plant levels. The aim is to provide a fundamental biological understanding and knowledge to underpin future applications. The great opportunity for salinity tolerance research now is the ability to marry together new molecular techniques with the body of literature on whole plant physiology. This new opportunity in salinity tolerance research provides exciting prospects for ameliorating the impact of salinity stress on plants, and improving the performance of species important to human health and agricultural and environmental sustainability.

Ultimately, plant function is explained by the operation of genes in cells and tissues to regulate plant growth in coordination with environmental constraints. As such, gene and cell function must always be considered in the context of the whole plant. This is especially so in the case of salinity tolerance, where cell-specific processes are of particular importance. A salt-tolerant cell does not necessarily make a salt-tolerant plant.

THE BASES FOR PLANT VARIATION IN TOLERANCE

Plants Vary in Tolerance

Plants differ greatly in their tolerance of salinity, as reflected in their different growth responses. Of the cereals, rice (*Oryza sativa*) is the most sensitive and barley (*Hordeum vulgare*) is the most tolerant (**Figure 1**). Bread wheat (*Triticum aestivum*) is moderately

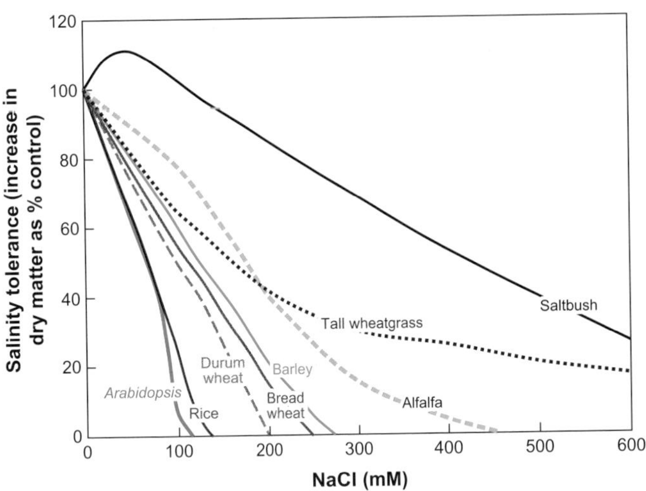

Figure 1

Diversity in the salt tolerance of various species, shown as increases in shoot dry matter after growth in solution or sand culture containing NaCl for at least 3 weeks, relative to plant growth in the absence of NaCl. Data are for rice (*Oryza sativa*) (6), durum wheat (*Triticum turgidum* ssp *durum*) (19), bread wheat (*Triticum aestivum*) (19), barley (*Hordeum vulgare*) (19), tall wheatgrass (*Thinopyrum ponticum*, syn. *Agropyron elongatum*) (19), *Arabidopsis* (*Arabidopsis thaliana*) (21), alfalfa (*Medicago sativa*) (70), and saltbush (*Atriplex amnicola*) (7).

tolerant and durum wheat (*Triticum turgidum* ssp. *durum*) is less so. Tall wheatgrass (*Thinopyrum ponticum*, syn. *Agropyron elongatum*) is a halophytic relative of wheat and is one of the most tolerant of the monocotyledonous species (**Figure 1**); its growth proceeds at concentrations of salt as high as in seawater.

Osmotic stress: affects growth immediately and is caused by the salt outside the roots

The variation in salinity tolerance in dicotyledonous species is even greater than in monocotyledonous species. Some legumes are very sensitive, even more sensitive than rice (74); alfalfa or lucerne (*Medicago sativa*) is very tolerant, and halophytes such as saltbush (*Atriplex* spp.) continue to grow well at salinities greater than that of seawater (**Figure 1**). Many dicotyledonous halophytes require a quite high concentration of NaCl (100–200 mM) for optimum growth (35). *Arabidopsis*, when compared with other species under similar conditions of light and humidity (that is, at high transpiration rates), is a salt-sensitive species (**Figure 1**). This sensitive plant may provide limited insights into mechanisms of salinity tolerance unless it is compared with a tolerant relative such as *Thellungiella halophila*. The differences between these two species are highlighted by their responses to 100 mM NaCl under conditions of high transpiration. Continued exposure to 100 mM does not allow *Arabidopsis* to complete its life cycle (116), but has little effect on the growth rate of *Thellungiella* (69).

Table 1 The effects of salinity stress on plants

Effect of stress	Osmotic stress	Stress due to high leaf Na^+ (ionic stress)
Speed of onset	Rapid	Slow
Primary site of visible effect	Decreased new shoot growth	Increased senescence of older leaves

Plant Responses Can Occur in Two Distinct Phases Through Time

To understand the physiological mechanisms responsible for the salinity tolerance of these species, it is necessary to know whether their growth is being limited by the osmotic effect of the salt in the soil, or the toxic effect of the salt within the plant. In the simplest analysis of the response of a plant to salinity stress, the reduction in shoot growth occurs in two phases: a rapid response to the increase in external osmotic pressure, and a slower response due to the accumulation of Na^+ in leaves (**Table 1**).

In the first, osmotic phase, which starts immediately after the salt concentration around the roots increases to a threshold level, the rate of shoot growth falls significantly. The threshold level is approximately 40 mM NaCl for most plants (see definition of salinity above), or less for sensitive plants like rice and *Arabidopsis*. This is largely (but not entirely) due to the osmotic effect of the salt outside the roots. **Figure 2*a*** shows the effect on the rate of shoot growth, that is, the rate of increase in shoot dry matter or in leaf area over time. The rate at which growing leaves expand is reduced, new leaves emerge more slowly, and lateral buds develop more slowly or remain quiescent, so fewer branches or lateral shoots form.

In cereals, the major effect of salinity on total leaf area is a reduction in the number of tillers; in dicotyledonous species, the major effect is the dramatic curtailing of the size of individual leaves or the numbers of branches. Curiously, shoot growth is more sensitive than root growth, a phenomenon that also occurs in drying soils and for which there is as yet no mechanistic explanation (see the following section). The teleological explanation is that a reduction in leaf area development relative to root growth would decrease the water use by the plant, thus allowing it to conserve soil moisture and prevent an escalation in the salt concentration in the soil.

The second, ion-specific, phase of plant response to salinity starts when salt accumulates to toxic concentrations in the old leaves (which are no longer expanding and so no longer diluting the salt arriving in them as younger growing leaves do), and they die. If the rate at which they die is greater than the rate at which new leaves are produced, the photosynthetic capacity of the plant will no longer be able to supply the carbohydrate requirement of the young leaves, which further reduces their growth rate (**Figure 2*a***).

The osmotic stress not only has an immediate effect on growth, but also has a greater effect on growth rates than the ionic stress. Ionic stress impacts on growth much later, and with less effect than the osmotic stress, especially at low to moderate salinity levels (**Figure 2*a***). Only at high salinity levels, or in sensitive species that lack the ability to control Na^+ transport, does the ionic effect dominate the osmotic effect. The effect of increased tolerance to the osmotic stress, with no change in ionic stress tolerance, is shown by the dotted line in **Figure 2*a***. A significant genetic variation within species may exist in the osmotic response, but this has not yet been documented. An increase in ionic tolerance takes longer to appear (**Figure 2*b***). Within many species, documented genetic variation exists in the rate of accumulation of Na^+ and Cl^- in leaves, as well as in the degree to which these ions can be tolerated. An increase in tolerance to both stresses would enable a plant to grow at a reasonably rapid rate throughout its life

Ionic stress: develops over time and is due to a combination of ion accumulation in the shoot and an inability to tolerate the ions that have accumulated

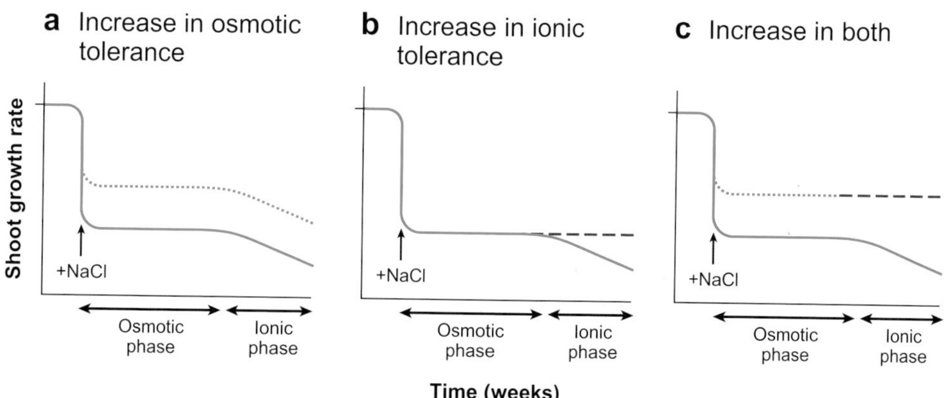

Figure 2

The growth response to salinity stress occurs in two phases: a rapid response to the increase in external osmotic pressure (the osmotic phase), and a slower response due to the accumulation of Na^+ in leaves (the ionic phase). The solid green line represents the change in the growth rate after the addition of NaCl. (*a*) The broken green line represents the hypothetical response of a plant with an increased tolerance to the osmotic component of salinity stress. (*b*) The broken red line represents the response of a plant with an increased tolerance to the ionic component of salinity stress (based on Reference 93). (*c*) The green-and-red line represents the response of a plant with increased tolerance to both the osmotic and ionic components of salinity stress.

cycle. This combined tolerance is shown in **Figure 2c**.

For most species, Na^+ appears to reach a toxic concentration before Cl^- does, and so most studies have concentrated on Na^+ exclusion and the control of Na^+ transport within the plant. However for some species, such as soybean, citrus, and grapevine, Cl^- is considered to be the more toxic ion (74, 119). The evidence for this is the association between genetic differences in the rate of Cl^- accumulation in leaves and the plant's salinity tolerance. This difference may arise because Na^+ is withheld so effectively in the woody roots and stems that little reaches the leaves, and K^+ becomes the major cation. Thus Cl^-, which continues to pass to the lamina, becomes the more significant toxic component of the saline solution.

Three Distinct Types of Plant Response or Tolerance

The mechanisms of salinity tolerance fall into three categories (**Table 2**):

1. Tolerance to osmotic stress. The osmotic stress immediately reduces cell expansion in root tips and young leaves, and causes stomatal closure. A reduced response to the osmotic stress would result in greater leaf growth and stomatal conductance, but the resulting increased leaf area would benefit only plants that have sufficient soil water. Greater leaf area expansion would be productive when a supply of water is ensured such as in irrigated food production systems, but could be undesirable in water-limited systems, and cause the

Table 2 Mechanisms of salinity tolerance, organized by plant processes and their relevance to the three components of salinity tolerance

		Osmotic stress	Ionic stress	
Process involved	**Candidate genes[a]**	**Osmotic tolerance**	**Na^+ exclusion**	**Tissue tolerance**
Sensing and signaling in roots	*SOS3, SnRKs*	Modification of long-distance signaling	Control of net ion transport to shoot	Control of vacuolar loading
Shoot growth	?	Decreased inhibition of cell expansion and lateral bud development	Not applicable[b]	Delay in premature senescence of old (carbon source) leaves
Photosynthesis	*ERA1, PP2C, AAPK, PKS3*	Decreased stomatal closure	Avoidance of ion toxicity in chloroplasts	Delay in ion toxicity in chloroplasts
Accumulation of Na^+ in shoots	*HKT, SOS1*	Increased osmotic adjustment	Reduced long distance transport of Na^+	Reduced energy spent on Na^+ exclusion
Accumulation of Na^+ in vacuoles	*NHX, AVP*	Increased osmotic adjustment	Increased sequestration of Na^+ into root vacuoles	Increased sequestration of Na^+ into leaf vacuoles
Accumulation of organic solutes	*P5CS, OTS, MT1D, M6PR, S6PDH, IMT1*	Increased osmotic adjustment	Alteration of transport processes to reduce Na^+ accumulation	Accumulation of high concentrations of compatible solutes in cytoplasm

[a]This list is not comprehensive, please see reviews such as Bartels & Sunkar (8), Munns (89), and Zhu (145), as well as the Clickable Guard Cell available at **http://www-biology.ucsd.edu/labs/schroeder/clickablegc.html**

[b]Ions do not accumulate to toxic levels in growing tissues.

soil water to be used up before the grain is fully matured.[1]

2. Na^+ exclusion from leaf blades. Na^+ exclusion by roots ensures that Na does not accumulate to toxic concentrations within leaves. A failure in Na^+ exclusion manifests its toxic effect after days or weeks, depending on the species, and causes premature death of older leaves.
3. Tissue tolerance, i.e., tolerance of tissue to accumulated Na^+, or in some species, to Cl^-. Tolerance requires compartmentalization of Na^+ and Cl^- at the cellular and intracellular level to avoid toxic concentrations within the cytoplasm, especially in mesophyll cells in the leaf. Toxicity occurs with time, after leaf Na^+ increases to high concentrations in the older leaves.

Table 2 summarizes some of the mechanisms relevant to the three components of salinity tolerance, classified by various plant processes.

Relative Importance of the Three Tolerance Mechanisms

The relative importance of these various processes clearly varies with the species (i.e., the strategy a particular plant species has evolved for responding to the salinity stress), but probably also varies with the length of exposure to the salinity, the concentration of the salt, and possibly the local environmental conditions, notably soil water supply and air humidity, and thus transpiration rate and leaf water potential.

For example, in some conditions a high shoot Na^+ may be beneficial by helping the plant maintain turgor. This may become particularly important in drying soils, where access by the plant to other beneficial nutrients (such as N, P, and K) becomes increasingly difficult. A balance probably needs to be struck between the use of Na^+ and Cl^- by the plant to maintain turgor and the need to avoid chemical toxicity. Where that balance lies will depend on the species and conditions. This dilemma has been likened to that of Ulysses who had to steer a course through treacherous waters between the twin perils of Scylla and Charybdis (53).

Methods to Distinguish the Three Tolerance Mechanisms

The two-phase effects of salinity on plants are not obvious if the salinity is high, or if the species is particularly sensitive to Na^+. The roots of some species, such as rice, are leaky and Na^+ may be taken up apoplastically (48). Then, the first phase, or osmotic effect, might last only a few hours or days at the most before the Na^+ levels build up to toxic levels within the leaves (142). However, for most plants in most conditions, the two phases are clearly separated in time (93), which facilitates the experimental separation of the three tolerance mechanisms.

Distinguishing the osmotic effect from the ion-specific effect requires observations over time of the rate of new leaf production and the rate of increase in injury of old leaves. The effect of the osmotic stress is seen as a rapid inhibition of the rate of expansion of young leaves and reduced stomatal conductance of mature leaves. Daily measurements of the length of a growing leaf, or spot measurements of stomatal conductance with a porometer, are good indicators of growth rate.

Ion-specific toxicity is seen as an increase in the rate of senescence of older leaves, due to either high leaf Na^+ concentrations or to low tolerance of the accumulated Na^+. Leaf Na^+ concentration is best measured in a defined leaf of a defined age if the plant was exposed to Na^+ at around the time of the

[1]The focus of this review is on tolerance in agricultural systems, where growth and productivity of annual crops is more important than survival per se. Thus, tolerance to osmotic stress is considered in this review to be the ability to maintain growth. However, in an ecological context, especially for perennial species, survival is often more important than growth, so the emphasis on growth maintenance as an adaptive (beneficial) response is less pronounced.

emergence of that leaf (91, 141). Leaf senescence can be measured nondestructively with a chlorophyll meter or image analysis. Combining rates of senescence in older leaves with measures of leaf Na^+ concentration provides an estimate of tolerance to Na^+ that has accumulated (tissue tolerance). The use of nondestructive assays, exploiting image analysis, thermography, and hyperspectral reflectance techniques, greatly facilitates the separation of these different types of Na^+ tolerance.

Increased osmotic tolerance and increased tissue tolerance will both lead to an increased ability to maintain growth for a given accumulation of Na^+ in the leaf tissue. However, they can be distinguished because of their differential effects on younger versus older tissue. Increased osmotic tolerance will be mainly evident by an increased ability to continue production of new leaves, whereas tissue tolerance will be primarily evident by the increased survival of older leaves (**Table 1**).

Interestingly, the *sos* (*salt overly sensitive*) mutants of *Arabidopsis* were identified from a screen based on the maintenance of root growth in nontranspiring conditions, where the delivery of Na^+ to the shoot in the transpiration stream would be low. The *sos* mutant screen might detect mutants that are related to the osmotic component of salinity stress because in the nontranspiring conditions used for the initial screen, the primary effect of salinity would be osmotic. In nontranspiring conditions, salinity tolerance in *Arabidopsis* is unrelated to the extent of shoot Na^+ accumulation; however, in transpiring conditions salinity tolerance is related to the extent of shoot Na^+ accumulation (86).

In the following three sections, each of the three tolerance mechanisms is discussed in more detail.

OSMOTIC STRESS TOLERANCE

Growth

The decreased rate of leaf growth after an increase in soil salinity is primarily due to the osmotic effect of the salt around the roots. A sudden increase in soil salinity causes leaf cells to lose water, but this loss of cell volume and turgor is transient. Within hours, cells regain their original volume and turgor owing to osmotic adjustment, but despite this, cell elongation rates are reduced (21, 42, 97, 142). Over days, reductions in cell elongation and also cell division lead to slower leaf appearance and smaller final size. Cell dimensions change, with more reduction in area than depth, so leaves are smaller and thicker.

For a moderate salinity stress, an inhibition of lateral shoot development becomes apparent over weeks, and over months there are effects on reproductive development, such as early flowering or a reduced number of florets. During this time, a number of older leaves may die. However, production of younger leaves continues. All these changes in plant growth are responses to the osmotic effect of the salt, and are similar to drought responses.

The reduction in leaf development is due to the salt outside the roots. That this reduction is largely due to the osmotic effect of the salt is supported by experiments using mixed salts such as concentrated Hoagland's solution (125), other single salts such as KCl (142), and nonionic solutes such as mannitol or polyethylene glycol (PEG) (121, 142). These different osmotica all have a similar qualitative effect as NaCl on leaf expansion.

However, the salt outside the roots may affect plant growth not only through its effect on osmotic pressure. Sümer and coworkers (121) found evidence for Na^+ but not Cl^- toxicity during the first phase of salt stress in maize in innovative experiments with different salts and PEG, via the use of additional PEG to adjust the equimolar solutions to equivalent osmotic pressures. Further, Cramer (20) found evidence for the effect of supplemental Ca^{2+} in the rooting solution affecting rapid responses of leaf elongation rate from working with two maize cultivars of different salinity tolerance. A possible Na^+-specific effect associated with the growth response is discussed below in the section on signaling.

The mechanism that downregulates leaf growth and shoot development under stress is not precisely known. The reduction in leaf growth must be regulated by long distance signals in the form of hormones or their precursors, because the reduced leaf growth rate is independent of carbohydrate supply (90) and water status (42, 90). The reduction occurs in the absence of nutrient deficiency (61) and ion toxicity, as evidenced by very low concentrations of Na^+ and Cl^- in expanding cells or tissues that do not correlate with growth rates (38, 61, 62, 94). Changes in wall properties must occur (22), but their exact nature remains unknown. The long distance and local signals regulating these wall properties and expansion rates are still obscure.

Abscisic acid (ABA) plays a central role in root-to-shoot and cellular signaling in drought stress and in the regulation of growth and stomatal conductance (26, 145). However, measurements of ABA in growing zones of barley and maize leaves in saline soil do not support a simple ABA control theory. ABA concentrations in the growing zone of salt-treated barley increase transiently but return to the original low value after 24 h, whereas leaf growth rate is still reduced (39). ABA-deficient mutants in maize and tomato generally have the same leaf growth rates as wild-type in drying soil and saline soil (80, 132), indicating that there is another limiting factor. Gibberellins (GAs) are a good candidate. ABA can inhibit leaf elongation in barley by lowering the content of active GA, as indicated by exogenous treatments with ABA and GA and measurements of endogenous GAs in the elongating zone (P.M. Chandler, M. Maheswari & R. Munns, unpublished data). Accumulating evidence shows that members of a class of negative regulators of growth, the DELLA proteins, mediate the growth-promoting effects of gibberellins in a number of species, and integrate signals from a range of hormones and abiotic stress conditions, including salinity (2). DELLA proteins may be the central coordinators that adapt plant growth to different environments (2).

Root growth is usually less affected than leaf growth, and root elongation rate recovers remarkably well after exposure to NaCl or other osmotica (88). Recovery from a moderate stress of up to 0.4 MPa of mannitol, KCl, or NaCl (i.e., an osmotic shock that does not cause plasmolysis) is complete within an hour (37). Even so, recovery from NaCl concentrations as high as 150 mM can occur within a day (88). In contrast to leaves, these recoveries take place despite turgor not being fully restored (37). This indicates different changes in cell wall properties compared with leaves, but the mechanism is unknown. With time, reduced initiation of new seminal or lateral roots probably occurs, but little is known about this.

Photosynthesis and Stomatal Conductance

The most dramatic and readily measurable whole plant response to salinity is a decrease in stomatal aperture. Stomatal responses are undoubtedly induced by the osmotic effect of the salt outside the roots. Salinity affects stomatal conductance immediately, firstly and transiently owing to perturbed water relations and shortly afterward owing to the local synthesis of ABA (39). A short-lived increase in ABA is detected in the photosynthetic tissues within 10 minutes of the addition of 100 mM NaCl to barley (39, 40); the rapidity of the increase suggesting in situ synthesis of ABA rather than transport from the roots. However, a new reduced rate of transpiration stabilizes within hours (40) while ABA tissue levels return to control concentrations (39, 40). This stomatal response is probably regulated by root signals in common with plants in a drying soil (26), as evidenced by stomatal closure in salt-treated plants whose water status is kept high by applying a balance pressure (126).

Rates of photosynthesis per unit leaf area in salt-treated plants are often unchanged, even though stomatal conductance is reduced (68).

This paradox is explained by the changes in cell anatomy described above that give rise to smaller, thicker leaves and result in a higher chloroplast density per unit leaf area. When photosynthesis is expressed on a unit chlorophyll basis, rather than a leaf area basis, a reduction due to salinity can usually be measured. In any case, the reduction in leaf area due to salinity means that photosynthesis per plant is always reduced.

Cause-effect relationships between photosynthesis and growth rate can be difficult to untangle. It is always difficult to know whether a reduced rate of photosynthesis is the cause of a growth reduction, or the result. With the onset of salinity stress, a reduced rate of photosynthesis is certainly not the sole cause of a growth reduction because of the rapidity of the change in leaf expansion rates described earlier (22, 39, 97), and also because of the increase in stored carbohydrate, which indicates unused assimilate (90). However, with time, feedback inhibition from sink to source may fine tune the rate of photosynthesis to match the reduced demand arising from growth inhibition (98). Reduced leaf expansion resulting in a buildup of unused photosynthate in growing tissues may generate feedback signals to downregulate photosynthesis.

At high salinity, salts can build up in leaves to excessive levels. Exactly how the salts exert their toxicity remains unknown. Salts may build up in the apoplast and dehydrate the cell, they may build up in the cytoplasm and inhibit enzymes involved in carbohydrate metabolism, or they may build up in the chloroplast and exert a direct toxic effect on photosynthetic processes.

Oxidative Stress

The reduced rate of photosynthesis increases the formation of reactive oxygen species (ROS), and increases the activity of enzymes that detoxify these species (4, 36, 78). When plants acclimate to a changed environment, they undergo adjustments in leaf morphology, chloroplast pigment composition, and in the activity of biochemical processes that prevent oxidative damage to photosystems. The two processes that avoid photoinhibition owing to excess light are heat dissipation by the xanthophyll pigments and electron transfer to oxygen acceptors other than water. The latter response necessitates the upregulation of key enzymes for regulating ROS levels such as superoxide dismutase, ascorbate peroxidase, catalase, and the various peroxidases (4, 78). The coordinated activity of the multiple forms of these enzymes in the different cell compartments achieves a balance between the rate of formation and removal of ROS, and maintains hydrogen peroxide (H_2O_2) at the levels required for cell signaling.

All these ROS detoxifying mechanisms are present naturally in surfeit (4, 36, 78), and are "woven into the regulatory regimes of the chloroplast" (78), to protect the photosystems from photoinhibition that might otherwise occur from the rapidly increasing light loads experienced by leaves under naturally variable situations. If a plant has sufficient capacity to adjust to the instant, large changes in light intensity as the sun emerges from behind a cloud, it has more than enough capacity to adjust to the slower changes in the rate of photosynthesis induced by a saline soil. The only situation in which antioxidants appear to be insufficient is when an oxidative burst is induced. However, this does not occur under abiotic stress, but is confined to pathogen attack, when a massive rise in ROS triggers programmed cell death (4).

Therefore, genetic differences in salinity tolerance are not necessarily due to differences in the ability to detoxify ROS. Many studies have found differences in levels of expression or activity of antioxidant enzymes; these differences are sometimes associated with the more tolerant genotype, and sometimes with the more sensitive genotype. We suggest that differences in antioxidant activity between genotypes may be due to genotypic differences in degrees of stomatal closure or in other responses that alter the rate of CO_2 fixation, differences that bring into play the processes that avoid photoinhibition and for which the plant has abundant capacity. For such basic and important defense mechanisms, the biochemical pathways are complex, interactive, and have built-in redundancy. More than 150 genes make up the complex ROS network in *Arabidopsis* (84). Knowledge of the many possible functions of these genes, and the coordination, degree of redundancy, and cross talk between different branches of the ROS network, is still incomplete (84). Doubt has been expressed that the manipulation of a single gene related to oxidative stress tolerance can enhance the tolerance to any abiotic stress (78). Recently *Arabidopsis* mutants lacking either or both a cytosolic and chloroplastic ascorbate peroxidase (H_2O_2 removal enzymes) were found to be actually more tolerant of salinity stress (83), illustrating the plasticity of ROS regulatory pathways, and the redundancy of pathways for ROS regulation and protection.

Cellular Signaling

Long-distance signaling of salinity stress to the shoot from the roots, mediated at least in part by ABA, is discussed above in the context of the rapid inhibition of growth upon addition of NaCl. Although this initial response appears similar at the whole plant level with addition of NaCl or isosmotic concentrations of PEG or mannitol (see Growth, above), comparison of cytosolic Ca^{2+} responses in solutions with physiologically realistic ionic composition revealed that responses of roots to addition of NaCl and sorbitol differ (129). Thus, cells in the roots initially must sense both the ionic and osmotic components of the addition of Na^+ and then respond rapidly to changes in its external concentration. The responses root cells need to make are necessary not only to maintain their own correct function in the face of the new elevated external Na^+, but also for them to signal to the shoot that shoot function must also be altered. In this section, we focus on signaling within root cells, which is likely to be independent of ABA.

Plants respond directly and specifically to the addition of Na^+ within seconds (73, 129), yet the mechanism by which plants sense the addition of Na^+ and the change in osmotic pressure remains obscure. The extracellular Na^+ is either sensed at the plasma membrane, or if it is sensed intracellularly, then it must first cross the plasma membrane. Thus, a plasma membrane protein must either be the sensor or be immediately upstream of the sensor. This gap in our knowledge is surprising given the importance of this first step in the response by a plant to changes in its environment. A similar notable absence of knowledge exists about the molecular basis for turgor sensing.

The first recorded response to an increase in Na^+ around roots is an increase in cytosolic free Ca^{2+} ($[Ca^{2+}]_{cyt}$); the extracellular addition of Na^+ is apparently able to activate the flux of Ca^{2+} into the cytosol across the plasma membrane and also, interestingly, the tonoplast (71–73, 87, 129). The changes in $[Ca^{2+}]_{cyt}$ are complex, and are modulated by differences in extracellular composition, including Na^+ concentration, providing opportunities for information to be encoded by the $[Ca^{2+}]_{cyt}$ changes (129). An additional level of complexity in NaCl-induced $[Ca^{2+}]_{cyt}$ increases has been demonstrated by root cell type–specific expression of aequorin in *Arabidopsis* (71). In response to 220 mM NaCl, the increase in $[Ca^{2+}]_{cyt}$ is lower in the pericycle than in the other cell types (71).

The best-characterized signaling pathway specific to salinity stress likely involves these increases in $[Ca^{2+}]_{cyt}$ (145). In this pathway, the Na^+-induced increase in $[Ca^{2+}]_{cyt}$ may be sensed by a calcineurin B-like protein (CBL4), originally identified as SOS3. Although the affinity for Ca^{2+} binding of this protein is unknown, physiologically realistic increases in cytosolic Ca^{2+} likely facilitate the dimerization of CBL4/SOS3 and the subsequent interaction with a CBL-interacting protein kinase (CIPK24, originally identified as SOS2) (55). The CBL4/CIPK24 (SOS3/SOS2) complex is targeted to the plasma membrane via a myristoyl fatty acid chain covalently bound to CBL4/SOS3 (65), enabling the phosphorylation and thus the activation of the membrane-bound Na^+/H^+ antiporter, SOS1 (102, 103, 115).

However, the role of SOS1 in plant salinity tolerance remains uncertain, because reconciliation of its pattern of expression with its function remains incomplete. Measurement of the effects of SOS1 knockout on long-distance transport of Na^+ is confounded because most experiments are performed in non-transpiring conditions (86).

Although which aspect of salinity tolerance is contributed to by this pathway remains uncertain, this pathway is likely important for some aspects of salinity tolerance, because *sos* mutants of *Arabidopsis thaliana* are less tolerant to salinity stress than wild-type plants (146).

Many other components of signaling pathways have also been implicated in plant responses to salinity, inferred by a range of approaches such as transcriptomics and reverse genetics. These are reviewed extensively elsewhere (e.g., 18, 137, 145). However, invoking the adaptive relevance of a particular response to Na^+ in a plant that is poorly adapted to salinity (*Arabidopsis*) is risky. These approaches could be strengthened by comparing responses in salt-tolerant and salt-sensitive lines—if the response is greater in the tolerant line, this suggests a role in the tolerance, but if the response is smaller, this may indicate the response is not related to the tolerance per se, but is a downstream response to the stress.

Genetic approaches, such as the screening of mutant populations of *Arabidopsis* for altered salinity tolerance (115, 145) and the identification of the genetic alteration causing observed differences in tolerance (12, 64), are essential for identifying significant genes for tolerance. More work is necessary to disentangle the complexities of the myriad signal transduction networks in plants. It is essential that these experiments are performed in physiologically relevant conditions. Future work may also be able to allow the identification of the different processes that are relevant to particular aspects of salinity tolerance (as summarized in this review).

Signaling pathways identified in salt-tolerant species (e.g., *Thellungiella halophila*) (50, 133, 135) are more likely to deliver results relevant to adaptive, rather than dysfunctional, responses to salinity, than those in the salt-sensitive *Arabidopsis*—unless, of course, screens of *Arabidopsis* are designed to identify salt-tolerant, rather than salt-sensitive, mutants. This is reflected in two components of ionic stress tolerance—ion exclusion and tissue tolerance.

Overall, cells respond to the perceived difference in extracellular Na^+ with changes in diverse aspects of function—from biochemistry and gene transcription to physiology, growth, and development. Transcription factors and small RNAs are central in controlling the core aspects of the longer-term plant transcriptional responses, as reviewed in this series and elsewhere; readers are referred to these detailed overviews (123, 139).

ACCUMULATION OF SODIUM IONS IN SHOOTS

The main site of Na^+ toxicity for most plants is the leaf blade, where Na^+ accumulates after being deposited in the transpiration stream, rather than in the roots (88). A plant transpires 50 times more water than it retains in leaves (92), so excluding Na^+ from the leaf blades is important, even more so for perennial than for annual species, because the leaves of perennials live and transpire for longer. Most Na^+ that is delivered to the shoot remains in the shoot, because for most plants, the movement of Na^+ from the shoot to the roots in the phloem can likely recirculate only a small proportion of the Na^+ that is delivered to the shoot. As such, the processes determining Na^+ accumulation in the shoot are primarily the processes controlling the net delivery of Na^+ into the root xylem.

The net delivery of Na^+ to the xylem can be divided into four distinct components (127):

1. Influx into cells in the outer half of the root;
2. Efflux back out from these cells to the soil solution;
3. Efflux from cells in the inner half of the root to the xylem; and
4. Influx back into these cells from the xylem before the transpiration stream delivers the Na^+ to the leaf blade.

Thermodynamics of Na^+ Transport

The thermodynamics of each of these processes for Na^+ are illustrated in **Figure 3*a***, and the likely molecular mechanisms are shown in **Figure 3*b***. The thermodynamic analysis assumes cytosolic Na^+ concentrations of 30 mM and an electrical potential of −120 mM, but even if values differ by a factor of two, the principles remain unchanged. For example, at the xylem parenchyma, the efflux of Na^+ from the cells would be active even if the xylem Na^+ concentrations were nearly ten times lower than cytosolic Na^+ concentrations (owing to the xylem parenchyma cytoplasm potential being 60 mV negative of the potential in the xylem apoplast). With a xylem Na^+ free concentration of 10 mM and a potential difference between the xylem parenchyma cell cytoplasm and xylem apoplast of −60 mV, active influx of Na^+ into the xylem parenchyma cells would

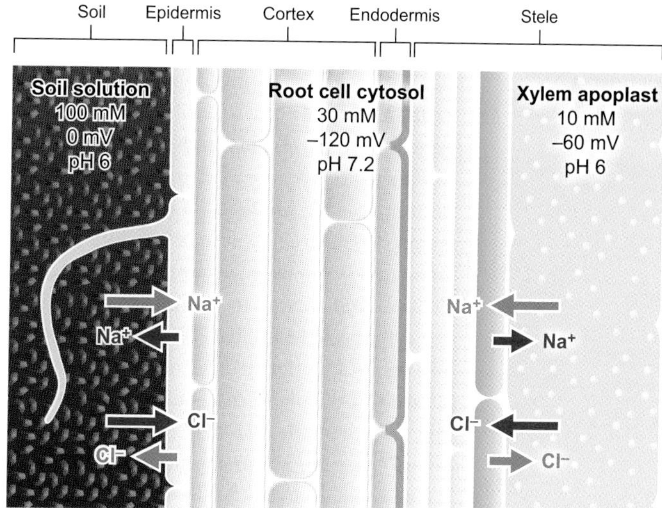

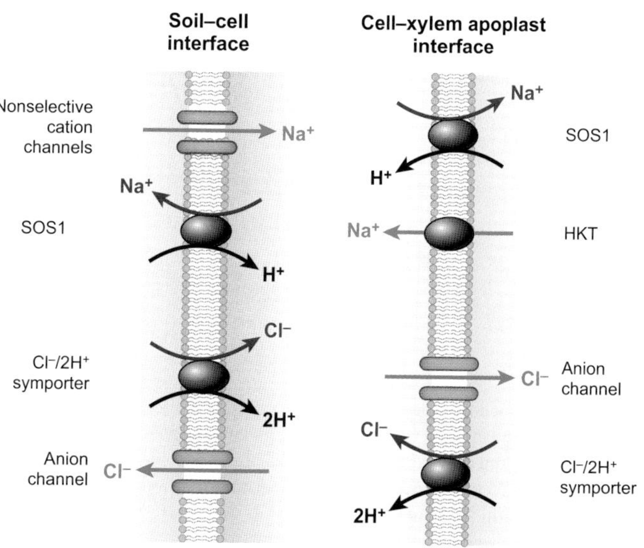

Figure 3

The thermodynamics and mechanisms of Na^+ and Cl^- transport at the soil-root and stelar cell–xylem vessel interfaces in roots. Indicative cytosolic pH, ion concentrations, and voltages are derived from the literature (127, 134). (*a*) Longitudinal section of wheat root (provided by Dr. Michelle Watt). The cells between the endodermis and the xylem vessel are not labeled, but include pericycle cells and xylem parenchyma (*darker blue*) as well as phloem parenchyma. The stele of dicotyledonous plants is more complex because it includes cambial vascular elements. The thermodynamics of ion movements are indicated by the arrow colors: Active transport is shown as a red arrow, passive transport is shown as a blue arrow. (*b*) The proposed mechanisms of passive and active Na^+ and Cl^- transport at the two interfaces, mediated by ion channels and carriers (uniporters and H^+-coupled antiporters and symporters). Abbreviations: SOS1, salt overly sensitive mutant 1; HKT, high-affinity K^+ transporter.

Net Na^+ influx: the result of unidirectional influx and unidirectional efflux; Na^+ influx is passive, as opposed to efflux, which requires energy

Unidirectional Na^+ influx into roots: very rapid, requires high rates of efflux to control net Na^+ accumulation

only be necessary with cytoplasmic free Na^+ concentrations greater than approximately 100 mM (which, with an activity coefficient of 0.7, is a total concentration of around 140 mM). Another way to look at this is if the cytoplasmic free Na^+ were 30 mM and the membrane potential difference were −60 mV, active influx would only be necessary with xylem apoplastic concentrations below 3 mM.

Consideration of the thermodynamics of a Na^+/H^+ antiporter is simpler, because the electroneutral exchange this antiporter catalyzes is unaffected by membrane potential. Thus, the direction of Na^+ movement is determined simply by the differences in free concentrations of Na^+ and H^+. A Na^+/H^+ antiporter could only work in the opposite direction to that indicated (i.e., it could only pump Na^+ into cells) if, for a pH difference of one unit (xylem more acidic), the xylem concentration increased to 10 times that found in the cytoplasm (i.e., to over 300 mM for a cytoplasmic Na^+ concentration of 30 mM). Alternatively, if the pH became more alkaline than pH 7.7, then the Na^+/H^+ antiporter could pump Na^+ into xylem parenchyma cells from a free concentration of 10 mM. These conditions would rarely, if ever, occur, and thus, the Na^+/H^+ antiporter will mostly act to pump Na^+ out of cells.

The various processes of Na^+ transport are each briefly considered here, but the reader is referred to the more extensive analysis of these processes in Tester & Davenport (127).

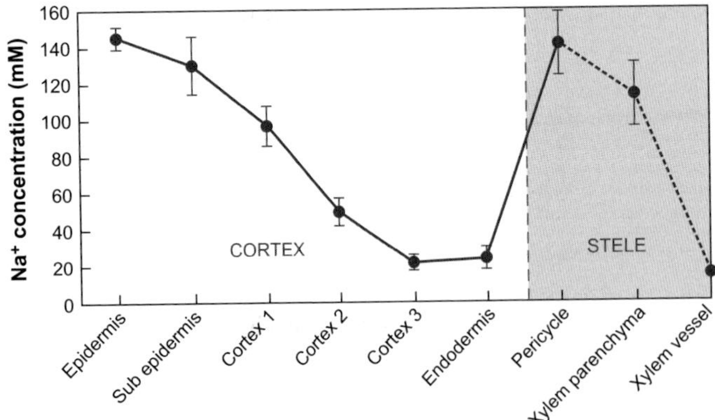

Figure 4

Differences in vacuolar concentrations of Na^+ across roots of transpiring wheat plants growing in 150 mM NaCl. Concentrations were measured by quantitative and calibrated X-ray microanalysis of snap-frozen sections using a cryo-SEM (scanning electron microscope) method on root tissues 10 cm from the tip (A. Läuchli, R.A. James, R. Munns, C.X. Huang & M. McCully, unpublished data).

Net Na^+ Influx Into the Outer Half of Roots

Na^+ enters roots passively, via voltage-independent (or weakly voltage-dependent) nonselective cation channels (3, 127) and possibly via other Na^+ transporters such as some members of the high-affinity K^+ transporter (HKT) family (57, 76). High affinity Na^+ influx is also mediated by some members of the HKT transporter family in low salt roots (60), but this is repressed by moderate concentrations of Na^+ and so is unlikely to be relevant to salinity tolerance. The identities of the genes encoding nonselective cation channels remain uncertain, although there are several candidates, including cyclic nucleotide–gated channels and ionotropic glutamate receptor–like channels (27).

The main site of Na^+ entry in roots is uncertain, although it seems intuitively likely that as water moves across the root cortex toward the stele, ions are removed from this stream into cells, where they are then sequestered in the vacuoles of these cells. This is supported by X-ray microanalysis of roots from rapidly transpiring wheat plants (A. Läuchli, R.A. James, R. Munns, C.X. Huang, & M. McCully, unpublished data), which shows that vacuolar Na^+ and Cl^- concentrations decrease across the cortex; vacuolar Na^+ and Cl^- concentrations are highest in the epidermis and subepidermis and lowest in the endodermis (**Figure 4**).

Most of the Na^+ that enters root cells in the outer part of the root is likely pumped back out again via plasma membrane Na^+/H^+ antiporters (127), a process that likely consumes significant energy, given the large fluxes that have been measured. The identities of the genes encoding these Na^+ efflux proteins are uncertain—in *Arabidopsis*, only two members of the *SOS1* gene family exist, *SOS1* and a currently uncharacterized gene at locus *At1g14660* (95). Plasma membrane Na^+/H^+ antiporter activity has been demonstrated for the *Arabidopsis* protein SOS1 (101); although, as discussed above, the levels of expression in the outer half of the mature root are currently uncertain.

Given that active Na^+ efflux is required in all cells throughout the plant, it is likely that other genes encoding Na^+/H^+ antiporters also exist. Many efflux proteins may be encoded in *Arabidopsis* by the gene at locus *At1g14660* (95), but members of other gene families, particularly the large family of *CHX* genes, may also be important (95). The possibility of other mechanisms for Na^+ efflux, such as primary pumping by Na^+-translocating ATPases, also needs to be kept in mind (14, 82).

Na^+ remaining in the root can be sequestered in vacuoles or transported to the shoot. Compartmentation in vacuoles is achieved by tonoplast Na^+/H^+ antiporters such as those belonging to the Na^+/H^+ exchanger (NHX) family in *Arabidopsis* (95). There is passive leakage of Na^+ back to the cytosol from vacuoles (possibly via tonoplast nonselective cation channels), requiring constant resequestration of Na^+ into vacuoles. Constitutive overexpression of *NHX1* or the gene encoding the *Arabidopsis thaliana* vacuolar H^+-translocating pyrophosphatase (AVP1), which contributes to the electrochemical potential difference for H^+, which energizes the pumping of Na^+ into the vacuole, increases both Na^+ accumulation and Na^+ tolerance in *Arabidopsis*, suggesting that more efficient sequestration may improve tissue tolerance, perhaps by reducing cytosolic Na^+ concentrations (5, 45).

Na^+ Loading Into and Retrieval From the Xylem

Na^+ moves in the symplast across the endodermis, is released from stelar cells into the stelar apoplast, and then moves to the xylem in the transpiration stream. The plasma membrane Na^+/H^+ antiporter, SOS1, is expressed in stelar cells and could be involved in the efflux of Na^+ from stelar cells into the xylem. However, this statement needs to be reconciled with the observation that the knockout of this gene causes elevated, not reduced, shoot Na^+ levels. The effect of the knockout on Na^+ efflux in the outer half of the root may possibly be greater than the effect of the knockout on loading in the inner half of the root.

In another attempt to reconcile the observations, SOS1 has also been implicated in retrieval of Na^+ from the xylem (115). However, given the likely difference in pH between the stelar cytosol and apoplast (**Figure 3**), this electroneutral exchange would only be possible with a large (at least an approximately 50-fold) difference in Na^+ activity (the apoplast with higher activity), which is extremely unlikely (see section above, Thermodynamics of Na^+ Transport).

Increasing evidence exists for the role of some members of the *HKT* gene family in retrieval of Na^+ from the xylem. In the *Arabidopsis* root, *AtHKT1;1* is involved in the retrieval of Na^+ from the xylem before it reaches the shoot (25, 122). Good evidence is accumulating for a similar function for members of the closely related *HKT1;5* gene family in rice (106) and wheat (12, 24, 66). The candidate gene for the classic K^+/Na^+ discrimination (*Kna1*) locus on the long arm of chromosome 4D, described more than 20 years ago by Gorham and colleagues (51) and mapped by Dubcovsky and coworkers (28) and Luo and coworkers (79), is likely an *HKT1;5* gene (12). *Kna1* was associated with a higher leaf K^+/Na^+ ratio (mainly determined by the variation in Na^+ concentration), and was attributed with providing bread wheat with its superior salinity tolerance over tetraploid wheats (51).

Furthermore, good evidence exists that a closely related gene, *TmHKT1;4-A2*, is the candidate gene for the Na^+ exclusion (*Nax1*)

AtHKT1;1, A CASE STUDY OF CONFUSION

The HKT family of proteins comprises a structurally diverse group that separates naturally into two distinct subfamilies (99). This diversity led to early reports of apparently contradictory properties, because the same name used for the first two genes studied, *HKT1*, from wheat and *Arabidopsis*, suggested similar function. Members of the HKT family function as Na^+/K^+ symporters and as Na^+-selective transporters of both high and low affinity. Subfamily 1 contains low affinity Na^+ uniporters.

Different patterns of expression within the plant also affect the role of these transporters in net cation uptake to the shoot; expression of a protein that catalyzes influx in the outer half of the root (epidermis and cortex) increases influx into the plant, but an influxer in the stele reduces net influx into the plant (**Figure 3**).

Although the first *HKT* gene identified was from subfamily 2 (114), this group is less well characterized than subfamily 1. The wheat TaHKT2;1 protein functions as a Na^+/K^+ symporter when expressed in *Xenopus* oocytes (109), and downregulation of expression in planta reduces root Na^+ accumulation and improves growth in saline conditions (76). In rice, OsHKT2;1 catalyzes high affinity Na^+ influx in low salt roots, conditions where Na^+ influx is beneficial (60). At higher external Na^+ concentrations, OsHKT2;1 is rapidly downregulated, to reduce potentially toxic Na^+ influx.

The most studied member of the *HKT1* subfamily is in *Arabidopsis*, which contains a single *HKT* homolog, *AtHKT1;1*. AtHKT1;1 functions as a Na^+-selective uniporter when expressed in *Xenopus* oocytes and yeast, but it also complements an *E. coli* K^+ uptake deficient mutant and increases its K^+ accumulation, suggesting some role in K^+ transport (130).

Athkt1;1 mutants are salt-sensitive compared with wild-type and hyperaccumulate Na^+ in the shoot but show reduced accumulation of Na^+ in the root (10, 81, 110). Several hypotheses have been advanced concerning the function of AtHKT1;1 in *Arabidopsis*.

Because *hkt1;1* mutations ameliorated the *sos* phenotypes and reduced whole seedling Na^+ in the *sos3* background, Rus and coworkers (111) proposed that AtHKT1;1 is an influx pathway for Na^+ uptake into the root. However, Berthomieu and colleagues (10) and Essah and coworkers (30) showed that *hkt1;1* mutants do not have lower root Na^+ influx and Berthomieu and coworkers proposed instead that AtHKT1;1

(*Continued*)

locus in durum wheat (64), which is associated with Na^+ exclusion and a high leaf K^+/Na^+ ratio. The protein encoded by this gene retrieves Na^+ from the xylem, and has activity in the leaf sheaths as well as in the root (66).

In *Arabidopsis*, the importance of retrieval of Na^+ from the xylem as a primary controller of shoot Na^+ concentration and plant salinity tolerance is suggested by forward genetic studies that have revealed *AtHKT1;1* as a primary determinant of these parameters (10, 49, 111). It is noteworthy that, to date, no other genes have been revealed from forward genetic screens for altered shoot Na^+ concentration. A suppressor screen of *Athkt1;1* plants may usefully reveal other steps in the Na^+ transport process.

It should be noted that the *HKT* gene family is quite diverse, which has confused issues in the past (see *AtHKT1;1*, A Case Study of Confusion), and this sequence diversity likely reflects a diversity of function. As such, increased clarity has been provided by dividing the *HKT* gene family into two distinct subfamilies (99). These subfamilies largely, although not exclusively, reflect differences in a likely selectivity-determining amino acid residue in the first so-called 'pore loop' region of the protein, and differences in the cation selectivity. Subfamily 1 members contain an important serine residue, and are largely Na^+-selective; subfamily 2 members have the serine replaced by a glycine, and can catalyze the transport of K^+ and probably also can catalyze high affinity Na^+ influx (60).

TISSUE TOLERANCE OF SODIUM IONS

At the cellular level, high amounts of Na^+ and Cl^- arriving in leaves can be tolerated by anatomical adaptations and intracellular partitioning. Dicotyledonous halophytes exemplify two types of anatomical adaptations: salt-induced increase in cell size due to increases in vacuole volume (succulence), and the excretion of Na^+ and Cl^- by salt glands (modified trichomes) or bladders (modified epidermal cells) (34). Succulence is extremely rare in monocotyledonous species, and salt glands occur in only approximately 15% of monocotyledonous halophytes (T.J. Flowers, personal communication), but in all species, intercellular transport processes can promote partitioning across the leaf.

The effect of salinity on intercellular partitioning of ions has been particularly studied in barley, a cereal known for its ability to tolerate high leaf tissue concentrations of Na^+ and Cl^- (19, 67), by measurement of vacuolar concentrations by scanning electron microscope X-ray microanalysis, either in situ (67) or in sap taken from single cells using a microcapillary (41). In salt-treated barley, there is a greater accumulation of Cl^- in epidermal compared with mesophyll cells (41, 63, 67, 77). The converse is true for K^+, that is, there is a greater accumulation of K^+ in mesophyll compared with epidermal cells (23, 41, 67), but there is no evidence of partitioning of Na^+ between different cell types (67).

Intracellular Compartmentation of Na^+

Na^+ must be partitioned within cells so that concentrations in the cytoplasm are kept low, possibly as low as 10–30 mM. No direct measurements of cytosolic concentrations in leaves have been reported, but in roots, direct measurements of cytosolic Na^+ in salt-treated plants via the use of ion-sensitive microelectrodes indicate cytosolic Na^+ concentrations range from 10 to 30 mM (13). In animal cells, cytosolic concentrations are also of this order (9). However, the concentration at which Na^+ becomes toxic is not well defined. In vitro studies showed Na^+ starts to inhibit most enzymes at concentrations approaching 100 mM (54), although some enzymes are sensitive to lower concentrations (33). The concentration at which Cl^- becomes toxic is even less well defined, but is probably similar to that for Na^+ (33). Even K^+ starts to inhibit enzymes at concentrations above 100 mM (33, 54).

(Continued)

functions in Na^+ recirculation from shoots to roots, by loading Na^+ from the shoot into phloem and then unloading it into the roots for efflux.

However, Sunarpi and colleagues (122) demonstrated that AtHKT1;1 localizes to the plasma membrane of xylem parenchyma cells in the shoot. They found both reduced phloem Na^+ and elevated xylem Na^+ in the shoot of *hkt1;1* mutants and proposed that AtHKT1;1 functions primarily to retrieve Na^+ from the xylem, at least in the shoot, and that retrieval of Na^+ into the symplast has a secondary effect on phloem Na^+ levels.

Most recently, Davenport and coworkers (25) used radioactive tracers to dissect the individual transport processes contributing to Na^+ and K^+ accumulation in intact, transpiring plants to provide the most direct evidence to date that AtHKT1;1 is involved in Na^+ retrieval from the xylem.

Results from closely related members of the HKT1 subfamily in rice and wheat are also consistent with a function of AtHKT1;1 in retrieval of Na^+ from the xylem. Thus, even though AtHKT1;1 catalyzes Na^+ influx into cells, its effect at the level of the whole plant is to reduce net Na^+ influx into the shoot.

Hypotheses regarding the role of AtHKT1;1 in Na^+ transport have relied mainly on measurements of tissue ion contents, which are the net result of a number of different transport processes, or on disruptive measurements of phloem and xylem contents. These measurements can often be interpreted in many ways.

In addition, many of the experiments have been conducted in plants grown on agar plates (where transpiration is extremely limited). Transpiring conditions have a major influence on Na^+ transport and tolerance (86). This is especially important when studying a gene whose function appears to be to remove Na^+ from the transpiration stream.

In *Arabidopsis*, although AtHKT1;1 function is now well defined in roots, its function in the shoot remains obscure, and the hypotheses of Berthomieu and colleagues (10) require careful consideration. In rice, functions for the nine *HKT*-like genes identified thus far remain largely unknown. Although *OsHKT1;5* appears to have a similar role to that of the *Arabidopsis* gene, the functions of other members of the gene family may well be quite distinct, as indicated by Horie and coworkers (60). Much more work is required to properly elucidate the functions of this important gene family.

Na^+ **activity:** the total amount of freely diffusing Na^+ available for transport per unit volume of solution

Ideally, Na^+ and Cl^- should be largely sequestered in the vacuole of the cell. That this sequestering occurs is indicated by the high concentrations of Na^+ found in leaves that are still functioning normally. Concentrations well over 200 mM on a tissue basis are common, yet these same concentrations will completely repress enzyme activity in vitro and are beyond all known direct measurements of cytosolic Na^+ in both eukaryotic and prokaryotic cells, other than the extremely halophilic prokaryotes (127). Importantly, enzymes in halophytes are not more tolerant of salt in vitro than the corresponding enzymes in nonhalophytes, suggesting compartmentation of Na^+ is an essential mechanism in all plants, rather than a result of the evolution of tolerance of enzymatic functions in plants from saline environments.

Thus, differences in the expression levels of *AtNHX1* or *AtAVP1* may affect the potential to sequester Na^+ in vacuoles of the leaves. Increased salinity tolerance of a range of plant species overexpressing *NHX* genes (5, 11, 15, 59, 138, 143, 144) or *AtAVP1* (45) indicates the feasibility of such a mechanism and suggests that this process is important for Na^+ tolerance not only in *Arabidopsis* but also across plant species.

Increased efficiency of intracellular compartmentation may explain differences in salinity tolerance between closely related species. This hypothesis is supported by findings of a much greater salt stress–induced Na^+/H^+ antiporter activity in the salt-tolerant species *Plantago maritima* than in the salt-sensitive species *Plantago media* (118).

Increased vacuolar Na^+ concentrations would require a coordinated increase in the osmotic pressure of the other subcellular compartments, including the cytosol, to maintain their volume. This can be achieved by an increase in the concentration of K^+ to sub-toxic levels, as well as the concentration of compatible solutes.

Increased Accumulation of Compatible Solutes

If Na^+ and Cl^- are sequestered in the vacuole of a cell, organic solutes that are compatible with metabolic activity even at high concentrations (hence 'compatible solutes') must accumulate in the cytosol and organelles to balance the osmotic pressure of the ions in the vacuole (35, 136). The compounds that accumulate most commonly are sucrose, proline, and glycine betaine, although other molecules can accumulate to high concentrations in certain species (35, 58, 89).

In many halophytes, proline or glycine betaine occur at sufficiently high concentrations in leaves (over 40 mM on a tissue water basis) to contribute to the osmotic pressure (over 0.1 MPa) in the cell as a whole (35). In glycophytes, the concentrations of compatible solutes that accumulate are not so high, on the order of 10 mM, but if partitioned exclusively to the cytoplasm, they could generate a significant osmotic pressure and function as an osmolyte. At low concentrations, these solutes presumably have another role, perhaps in stabilizing the tertiary structure of proteins, and function as osmoprotectants (108). An osmolyte role has been suggested for glycine betaine accumulation in maize; comparison of near-isogenic maize lines with contrasting glycine betaine accumulation showed that lines that were homozygous for the *Bet1* (glycine betaine accumulation) gene had a 10%–20% higher biomass under saline conditions (113).

Accumulation of these compatible solutes, such as proline and mannitol, also occurs under drought stress and sometimes under other stresses that reduce growth, such as low temperature. Many studies of genes controlling the synthesis or metabolism of these solutes have indicated their essential role in tolerance to abiotic stresses (16, 56, 108). For example, the lower expression of a gene encoding proline dehydrogenase (*PDH*) may contribute to the higher salt tolerance of *Thellungiella halophila* compared with its salt-sensitive relative *Arabidopsis thaliana* (69). Enhancement of mannitol accumulation in *Arabidopsis* by overexpression of a mannose-6-phosphate reductase from celery caused substantial and sustained increases in growth rate and photosynthesis in saline treatment but not drought, suggesting that mannitol protects the chloroplasts against salt (116). The transgene had no effect on growth in control conditions (116). This is noteworthy, because most reports of transgenic alterations in levels of enzymes that catalyze rate-limiting steps describe plants whose growth is significantly reduced. This may be because uncontrolled accumulation of the solutes perturbs other metabolic pathways, diverting substrates from essential processes such as protein synthesis and cell wall synthesis.

Compatible solute synthesis comes with an energy cost and hence involves a potential growth penalty. In leaf cells, approximately seven moles of ATP are needed to accumulate one mole of NaCl as an osmoticum, whereas the amount of ATP required to synthesize one mole of an organic compatible solute is an order of magnitude higher (105). The ATP requirement for the synthesis or accumulation of solutes has been estimated as 3.5 for Na^+, 34 for mannitol, 41 for proline, 50 for glycine betaine, and approximately 52 for sucrose (105). These values assume a production of 0.5 mole of ATP per photon and nitrate as the source of N. The synthesis of these compounds occurs at the expense of plant growth, but may allow the plant to survive and recover from the presence of high external concentrations of salt.

Tolerance of leaf tissue to high Na^+ concentrations is clearly an adaptive mechanism, as exemplified by most halophytes (34) and glycophytes such as barley, which can tolerate at least 400 mM Na^+ in leaf blades (67). The high Na^+ and the accompanying Cl^- allows barley to osmotically adapt and to maintain turgor in the face of high soil salinities. This is the "cheapest" form of osmotic adaptation. The mechanism of Na^+ exclusion enables the plant to avoid or postpone the problem of ion toxicity, but unless the exclusion of Na^+ is compensated for by the uptake of K^+, it creates a greater demand for organic solutes for osmotic adjustment. The synthesis of organic solutes jeopardizes the energy balance of the plant. Thus, the plant must steer a course through ion toxicity on the one hand, and turgor loss on the other, in analogy to the Scylla versus Charybdis dilemma faced by Ulysses.

OBSERVATIONS IN WHICH SALINITY TOLERANCE IS CLEARLY INDEPENDENT OF TISSUE SODIUM ION CONCENTRATIONS

A negative correlation between salinity tolerance and Na^+ accumulation in leaves is often seen when comparing different genotypes within a species (88, 127), but this is not the case when comparing different species, such as wheat and barley. **Figure 5** illustrates the relationship between salinity tolerance and leaf Na^+ concentration found within a species, in

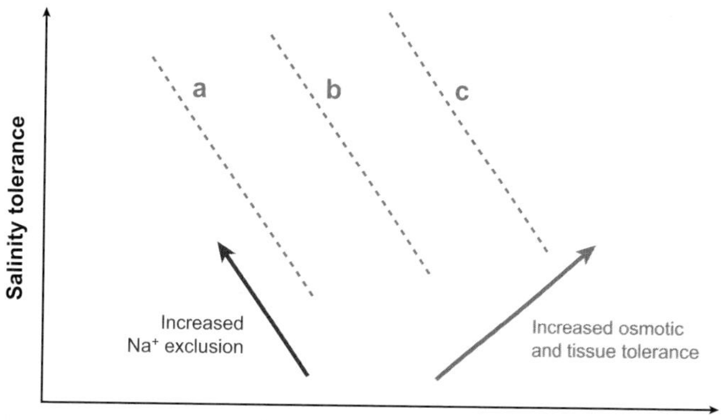

Figure 5

Hypothetical relationships between salinity tolerance and leaf Na^+ concentration for three different species, denoted by a, b, and c for rice, durum wheat, and barley. Within most species, there is a negative correlation between salinity tolerance and shoot Na^+ concentration, as in rice (141) and durum wheat (91) and, with less conviction, in barley (19). A larger intercept on the x-axis indicates an increased tolerance to the osmotic pressure of the soil solution or to high internal concentrations of Na^+ or Cl^-.

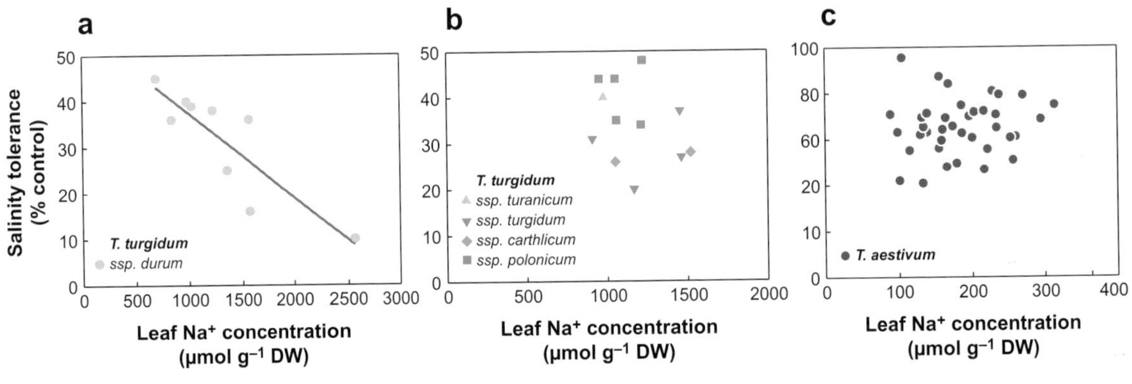

Figure 6

Relationships measured between salinity tolerance (biomass in salt as a % of biomass in control conditions) and leaf Na^+ concentration in different wheat species. (*a*) Negative relationship for durum wheat (91). (*b*) Lack of relationship for other tetraploid wheats (91). (*c*) Lack of relationship for bread wheat (46).

this case rice (141), durum wheat (91), and the *Hordeum* genus, including barley (44); the figure also shows that this relationship shifts for different species. This shift can reflect differences in tissue tolerance of Na^+ between different species, differences in tolerance of Cl^-, or differences in tolerance of the osmotic pressure of the soil solution.

Although Na^+ exclusion is often a primary determinant of variability in salinity tolerance within a species (**Figure 6*a***), many exceptions to this generalization exist, such as within certain subspecies of tetraploid wheat, *Triticum turgidum* (**Figure 6*b***), in which differences in salt tolerance do not correlate with differences in Na^+ exclusion. One study observed a lack of correlation within bread wheat (*Triticum aestivum*) (**Figure 6*c***), possibly because at the moderate salinity of 100 mM NaCl, the leaf Na^+ concentration was below the toxic level. The genetic variation in Na^+ exclusion may contribute to greater salinity tolerance only in highly saline soil that causes higher leaf Na^+ accumulation. We conclude that Na^+ exclusion remains an important factor, and increasing Na^+ exclusion by conventional or transgenic methods could increase salinity tolerance, but these results indicate other mechanisms may be important in many species, especially at high salinity.

Mechanisms of Salinity Tolerance Other than Na^+ Exclusion

In addition to tissue tolerance mechanisms discussed above, other mechanisms of salinity tolerance unrelated to Na^+ exclusion could also be important in these plants.

Osmotic tolerance. The relative importance of variation in osmotic tolerance remains unknown for most species, which likely reflects the relative difficulty of quantifying this parameter. A close association likely exists between osmotic tolerance and tissue tolerance of Na^+, because genotypes that tolerate high internal Na^+ concentrations in leaves by compartmentalizing it in the vacuole should also be more tolerant of the osmotic stress owing to their elevated osmotic adjustment. However, this speculation remains to be tested.

K^+ accumulation in cytoplasm. The concentration of K^+ in the cytoplasm relative to that of Na^+ may be a contributing factor to salinity tolerance. In *Arabidopsis*, an additional supply of K^+ alleviated the phenotype of the *sos* mutants (145), which may be due to an increase in cytoplasmic K^+ concentrations. In barley, Shabala and colleagues (17) found a negative correlation between Na^+-activated net K^+ efflux in 3d-old seedlings and salinity tolerance of mature barley plants. This phenomenon may be related to root K^+ status, although a strong relationship between leaf K^+ concentrations and salinity tolerance has not been found.

Cl^- tolerance. The question is often asked: "Why focus only on Na^+, why not also consider Cl^-?" This question relates particularly to species that accumulate high concentrations of Cl^- and not Na^+ in leaves, such as soybean, woody perennials such as avocado, and those species that are routinely grown on Cl^--excluding rootstocks such as grapevines and citrus. For these species, Cl^- toxicity is more important than Na^+ toxicity. However, this statement does not imply that Cl^- is more metabolically toxic than Na^+, rather these species are better at excluding Na^+ from the leaf blades than Cl^-. For example, Na^+ does not increase in the leaf blade of grapevines until after several years of exposure to saline soil, then the exclusion within the root, stem, and petiole breaks down, and Na^+ starts to accumulate in the leaf blade, whereas leaf blade Cl^- concentrations increase progressively (100). Thus, Na^+ may be a more toxic solute, but because the plant is managing the Na^+ transport better than Cl^- transport, Cl^- becomes the potentially more toxic component.

Many studies have been undertaken to determine whether Na^+ is more or less toxic than Cl^-. The use of different salts has produced only equivocal results, because of the difficulty in changing the external concentration of one ion versus another without changing the osmotic pressure of the external solution or the rate of uptake of other ions. The most convincing approaches to test the toxicity of Na^+ versus Cl^- are genetic approaches. Between different species of wheat, genetic variation in salinity tolerance correlates with leaf Na^+ accumulation but not Cl^- accumulation (51, 52). However, genetic variation in salinity tolerance correlates with leaf Cl^- accumulation in citrus (119). Cl^- influx is likely active. See The Thermodynamics and Mechanisms Controlling Cl^- Transport.

Cl^- loading into the xylem is most likely a passive mechanism mediated by anion channels such as those characterized by Gilliham & Tester (47). These channels are downregulated by ABA, which may serve to limit Cl^- transfer to the shoot in saline conditions. Radioactive tracer studies have shown that net Cl^- loading into the root xylem is lower in grapevine genotypes that have lower shoot Cl^- accumulation (J. Tregeagle, M. Tester & R. Walker, unpublished results). The control of Cl^- transport to shoots may be due to reduced loading of Cl^- via anion channels, but may also be due to increased active retrieval

THE THERMODYNAMICS AND MECHANISMS CONTROLLING CL^- TRANSPORT

Mechanisms of Cl^- transport are shown in **Figure 3**. In most situations, Cl^- influx requires energy and is probably catalyzed by a $Cl^-/2H^+$ symporter (32, 112), although Skerrett & Tyerman (117) have shown that passive uptake could occur in saline conditions if the membrane potential is depolarized and cytosolic Cl^- is low (less than 20 mM). The cytosolic Cl^- concentration is likely in the range of 10 to 20 mM, but may be higher in saline conditions. Felle (32) showed that the cytoplasmic concentration doubled (from 15 to 33 mM) within minutes of increasing the external Cl^- concentration from 0 to 20 mM. Given the uncertainties surrounding the thermodynamics, useful speculation on the role of net influx processes in salinity tolerance is difficult. Nevertheless, if Cl^- influx is active, and thus efflux is passive, the opening of a Cl^--permeable channel in nonsaline conditions would favor the passive efflux of Cl^-. Thus, activation of a Cl^--permeable channel in saline conditions could be useful for reducing the net influx of Cl^-. Yamashita and coworkers (140) observed an increase in Cl^- permeability of protoplasts isolated from barley roots after plants were pretreated with 200 mM NaCl, supporting such a role for Cl^- channels. Comparisons of Cl^- transport in lines with different levels of Cl^- accumulation in the shoot would reveal the significance of different transport processes in whole plant accumulation.

of Cl^- from the xylem stream. Sites of tissue Cl^- accumulation indicate that Cl^- can be retrieved from the xylem in petioles, woody stems, and roots.

Results from biochemical approaches (study of the effects of different salts on protein synthesis or enzyme activity) have been equivocal, as have attempts to estimate Cl^- concentrations in the cytoplasm or organelles such as chloroplast and mitochondria. Yet tissue concentrations as high as 400 mM are tolerated by most species, and even the sensitive species like citrus can tolerate tissue concentrations of 250 mM, so Cl^- must be compartmentalized in the vacuole. The thermodynamics and mechanisms of Cl^- transport at the tonoplast are largely unknown, and differences in properties between tolerant and sensitive lines are regrettably obscure.

APPROACHES FOR FUTURE STUDIES

The Importance of Cell Type–Specific Processes

Gene expression studies using constitutive promoters provide limited biological information compared with the use of inducible promoters (120) or cell type–specific promoters (127, 128). The choice of promoters can significantly affect the results from a transgenic manipulation. The constitutive expression of genes encoding compatible solutes often inhibits plant growth, as shown by stunted growth and sterility of lines with higher concentrations of mannitol (1). Expression that is inducible upon plant stress should have little effect on growth in control conditions, but can increase tolerance to the applied stress, as shown for trehalose accumulation in rice (43). In a similar vein, constitutive expression of *AtHKT1;1* causes increased shoot accumulation of Na^+ and reduced salinity tolerance, whereas expression specifically in the stele of mature roots has the opposite effect (85).

Relevant Growth Conditions and Salinity Treatments

There are several easily adopted methods of growing plants that could greatly facilitate the interpretation of results, comparisons between experiments in different laboratories, and the relevance of experiments to field situations.

The time of exposure to salinity and the severity of the salt treatment determine the physiological and molecular changes that are observed. Metabolomics and transcriptomics studies produce different answers depending on the tissue examined and whether the plant is growing or dying. Whether the plant is transpiring or not is also important, as shown for the HKT gene family (See *AtHKT1;1*, A Case Study of Confusion). A high-salt treatment for a sensitive plant like *Arabidopsis* will induce changes predominantly associated with senescence; however, a low-salt treatment may not result in discernable changes in gene expression and metabolite levels. Finding the right balance can be difficult. For application to the agricultural context, experiments should focus on growth and reproductive yield, rather than survival. Tolerance of extreme stress is of ecological relevance to perennial species, but is generally not relevant to annual species.

Osmotic effects could be distinguished from ionic effects by analyzing growing tissues for the osmotic effect, and analyzing older transpiring leaf blades for the ionic effect (**Table 1**). Short times of exposure may be useful for signaling studies; however, it is important to recognize that transient cell shrinkage and recovery of volume occur after a salt shock, and to relate measurements to the new steady state reached.

Addition of Na^+ or any electrolyte reduces Ca^{2+} activity in solutions. If Ca^{2+} activity is not maintained by addition of Ca^{2+} with the Na^+, uncertainty remains about whether the effects of Na^+ addition are due to the increase in Na^+ or the decrease in available Ca^{2+}. Thus, salt treatments need to include supplemental Ca^{2+} to maintain stable Na^{+}/Ca^{2+} ratios, or constant Ca^{2+} activity (as calculated using programs such as Geochem (96) or MINTEQ (**http://www.lwr.kth.se/English/OurSoftware/vminteq/**). Consideration should also be given to the addition of silicon to solutions (29, 48) as sodium silicate (or 'liquid glass', mainly Na_2SiO_3), taking care to adjust the pH after its addition.

Without a good understanding of the physiology involved and the phenotype to measure, complemented by the discovery of key genes in model systems, the recent fast progress on control of shoot Na^+ in rice and wheat would not have been possible. Elucidating more basic physiology and the molecular genetics of other aspects of salinity responses (notably osmotic tolerance) will facilitate the generation of further applications in major crops.

SUMMARY POINTS

1. Plant responses to salinity occur in two phases: a rapid, osmotic phase that inhibits growth of young leaves, and a slower, ionic phase that accelerates senescence of mature leaves.
2. Plant adaptations to salinity are of three distinct types: osmotic stress tolerance; Na^+ exclusion; and tissue tolerance, i.e., tolerance of tissue to accumulated Na^+, and possibly Cl^-.
3. Our understanding of Na^+ exclusion from leaves and the role of the HKT gene family is increasing, although the molecular bases for many other transport processes remain obscure.
4. The salt overly sensitive (SOS) signal transduction pathway is clearly important in salinity tolerance, although the mechanism of action at the whole plant level remains to be established.
5. Osmotic tolerance and tissue tolerance both increase the ability to maintain growth for a given accumulation of Na^+ in the leaf tissue. Increased osmotic tolerance is evident mainly by the increased ability to continue production of new leaves, whereas tissue tolerance is evident primarily by the increased survival of older leaves.
6. Na^+ sequestration and compatible solute synthesis are important processes for tissue tolerance. Mechanisms of osmotic tolerance remain unknown.
7. To benefit more from the new genomics approaches, molecular studies with plants grown in physiologically realistic conditions are needed.

FUTURE ISSUES

1. Significant breakthroughs have been made on the mechanisms and control of Na^+ accumulation by the high-affinity K^+ transporter (*HKT*) gene family and the importance of the intraplant management of Na^+. Nevertheless, large gaps remain in our knowledge of Na^+ transport, notably the control of phloem transport, the identity of the genes encoding nonselective cation channels responsible for the initial entry of Na^+ into plants, and the role of other solutes in salinity tolerance, including K^+ and Cl^-.

2. Molecular processes that control Na^+ compartmentalization in vacuoles have received much attention, but other essential processes in tissue tolerance of Na^+ and Cl^- and osmotic adjustment remain relatively unknown.
3. Signaling pathways at the intracellular level have been well described, but long-distance signaling requires more attention. How do the leaves know the roots are in saline soil, when so little salt is delivered in the xylem to the leaves? Yet, the leaf growth rate and stomatal conductance are reduced in proportion to the concentration of salt in the soil solution, and not in proportion to the salt concentration in the xylem or the leaves.
4. Forward genetic approaches will provide significant breakthroughs in the coming years, and the use of genomics to address fundamental questions regarding, for example, the basis for the high tissue tolerance of barley, will provide us with new dimensions of understanding of salinity tolerance. Complementing genomics with phenomics to design screens for the other aspects of salinity tolerance, notably the osmotic component, will also open exciting new avenues of research.

DISCLOSURE STATEMENT

The authors are not aware of any biases that might be perceived as affecting the objectivity of this review.

ACKNOWLEDGMENTS

We thank many colleagues for helpful discussions and encouragement to write this review, and Carl Davies from CSIRO Plant Industry for illustrations. M.T. thanks the Australian Research Council for a Federation Fellowship.

LITERATURE CITED

1. Abebe T, Guenzi AC, Martin B, Cushman JC. 2003. Tolerance of mannitol-accumulating transgenic wheat to water stress and salinity. *Plant Physiol.* 131:1748–55
2. Achard P, Cheng H, De Grauwe L, Decat J, Schoutteten H, et al. 2006. Integration of plant responses to environmentally activated phytohormonal signals. *Science* 311:91–94
3. Amtmann A, Sanders D. 1999. Mechanisms of Na^+ uptake by plant cells. *Adv. Bot. Res.* 29:75–112
4. Apel K, Hirt H. 2004. Reactive oxygen species: metabolism, oxidative stress and signal transduction. *Annu. Rev. Plant Biol.* 55:373–99
5. Apse MP, Aharon GS, Snedden WA, Blumwald E. 1999. Salt tolerance conferred by overexpression of a vacuolar Na^+/H^+ antiport in *Arabidopsis*. *Science* 285:1256–58
6. Aslam M, Qureshi RH, Ahmed N. 1993. A rapid screening technique for salt tolerance in rice (*Oryza sativa* L.). *Plant Soil.* 150:99–107
7. Aslam Z, Jeschke WD, Barrett-Lennard EG, Greenway H, Setter TL, Watkin E. 1986. Effects of external NaCl on the growth of *Atriplex amnicola* and the ion relations and carbohydrate status of the leaves. *Plant Cell Environ.* 9:571–80
8. Bartels D, Sunkar R. 2005. Drought and salt tolerance in plants. *CRC Crit. Rev. Plant Sci.* 24:23–58

9. Bers DM, Barry WH, Despa S. 2003. Intracellular Na^+ regulation in cardiac myocytes. *Cardiovasc. Res.* 57:897–912
10. Berthomieu P, Conéjéro G, Nublat A, Brackenbury WJ, Lambert C, et al. 2003. Functional analysis of *AtHKT1* in *Arabidopsis* shows that Na^+ recirculation by the phloem is crucial for salt tolerance. *EMBO J.* 22:2004–14
11. Brini F, Hanin M, Mezghani I, Berkowitz GA, Masmoudi K. 2007. Overexpression of wheat Na^+/H^+ antiporter TNHX1 and H^+-pyrophosphatase TVP1 improve salt- and drought-stress tolerance in *Arabidopsis thaliana* plants. *J. Exp. Bot.* 58:301–8
12. Byrt CS, Platten JD, Spielmeyer W, James RA, Lagudah ES, et al. 2007. HKT1;5-like cation transporters linked to Na^+ exclusion loci in wheat, *Nax2* and *Kna1*. *Plant Physiol.* 143:1918–28
13. Carden DE, Walker DJ, Flowers TJ, Miller AJ. 2003. Single-cell measurements of the contributions of cytosolic Na^+ and K^+ to salt tolerance. *Plant Physiol.* 131:676–83
14. Cheeseman JM. 1982. Pump-leak sodium fluxes in low salt corn roots. *J. Membr. Biol.* 70:157–64
15. Chen H, An R, Tang J-H, Cui X-H, Hao F-S, et al. 2007. Over-expression of a vacuolar Na^+/H^+ antiporter gene improves salt tolerance in an upland rice. *Mol. Breed.* 19:215–25
16. Chen THH, Murata N. 2002. Enhancement of tolerance of abiotic stress by metabolic engineering of betaines and other compatible solutes. *Curr. Opin. Plant Biol.* 5:250–57
17. Chen Z, Newman I, Zhou M, Mendham N, Zhang G, Shabala S. 2005. Screening plants for salt tolerance by measuring K^+ flux: a case study for barley. *Plant Cell Environ.* 28:1230–46
18. Cheong MS, Yun DJ. 2007. Salt-stress signaling. *J. Plant Biol.* 50:148–55
19. Colmer TD, Munns R, Flowers TJ. 2005. Improving salt tolerance of wheat and barley: future prospects. *Aust. J. Exp. Agric.* 45:1425–43
20. Cramer GR. 1992. Kinetics of maize leaf elongation. II. Responses of a Na-excluding cultivar and a Na-including cultivar to varying Na/Ca salinities. *J. Exp. Bot.* 43:857–64
21. Cramer GR. 2002. Response of abscisic acid mutants of *Arabidopsis* to salinity. *Funct. Plant Biol.* 29:561–67
22. Cramer GR, Bowman DC. 1991. Kinetics of maize leaf elongation. I. Increased yield threshold limits short-term, steady-state elongation rates after exposure to salinity. *J. Exp. Bot.* 42:1417–26
23. Cuin TA, Miller AJ, Laurie SA, Leigh RA. 2003. Potassium activities in cell compartments of salt-grown barley leaves. *J. Exp. Bot.* 54:657–61
24. Davenport RJ, James RA, Zakrisson-Plogander A, Tester M, Munns RJ. 2005. Control of sodium transport in durum wheat. *Plant Physiol.* 137:807–18
25. Davenport RJ, Muñoz-Mayor A, Jha D, Essah PA, Rus A, Tester M. 2007. The Na^+ transporter AtHKT1 controls xylem retrieval of Na^+ in *Arabidopsis*. *Plant Cell Environ.* 30: 497–507
26. Davies WJ, Kudoyarova G, Hartung W. 2005. Long-distance ABA signaling and its relation to other signaling pathways in the detection of soil drying and the mediation of the plant's response to drought. *J. Plant Growth Regul.* 24:285–95
27. Demidchik V, Davenport RJ, Tester M. 2002. Nonselective cation channels. *Annu. Rev. Plant Biol.* 53:67–107
28. Dubcovsky J, Santa Maria G, Epstein E, Luo MC, Dvoák J. 1996. Mapping of the K^+/Na^+ discrimination locus *Kna1* in wheat. *Theor. Appl. Genet.* 92:448–54
29. Epstein E. 1994. The anomaly of silicon in plant biology. *Proc. Natl. Acad. Sci. USA* 91:11–17

30. Essah PA, Davenport RJ, Tester M. 2003. Sodium influx and accumulation in *Arabidopsis thaliana*. *Plant Physiol.* 133:307–18
31. FAO. 2008. *FAO Land and Plant Nutrition Management Service*. **http://www.fao.org/ag/agl/agll/spush**
32. Felle H. 1994. The H^+/Cl^- symporter in root-hair cells of *Sinapis alba*. An electrophysiological study using ion-selective microelectrodes. *Plant Physiol.* 106:1131–36
33. Flowers TJ, Dalmond D. 1992. Protein synthesis in halophytes: the influence of potassium, sodium and magnesium in vitro. *Plant Soil.* 146:153–61
34. Flowers TJ, Hajibagheri MA, Clipson NJW. 1986. Halophytes. *Q. Rev. Biol.* 61:313–37
35. Flowers TJ, Troke PF, Yeo AR. 1977. The mechanism of salt tolerance in halophytes. *Annu. Rev. Plant Physiol.* 28:89–121
36. Foyer CH, Noctor G. 2005. Oxidant and antioxidant signalling in plants: a re-evaluation of the concept of oxidative stress in a physiological context. *Plant Cell Environ.* 28:1056–71
37. Frensch J, Hsiao TC. 1994. Transient responses of cell turgor and growth of maize roots as affected by changes in water potential. *Plant Physiol.* 104:247–54
38. Fricke W. 2004. Rapid and tissue-specific accumulation of solutes in the growth zone of barley leaves in response to salinity. *Planta* 219:515–25
39. Fricke W, Akhiyarova G, Veselov D, Kudoyarova G. 2004. Rapid and tissue-specific changes in ABA and in growth rate response to salinity in barley leaves. *J. Exp. Bot.* 55:1115–23
40. Fricke W, Akhiyarova G, Wei W, Alexandersson E, Miller A, et al. 2006. The short-term growth response to salt of the developing barley leaf. *J. Exp. Bot.* 57:1079–95
41. Fricke W, Leigh RA, Tomos AD. 1996. The intercellular distribution of vacuolar solutes in the epidermis and mesophyll of barley leaves changes in response to NaCl. *J. Exp. Bot.* 47:1413–26
42. Fricke W, Peters WS. 2002. The biophysics of leaf growth in salt-stressed barley. A study at the cell level. *Plant Physiol.* 129:374–88
43. Garg AK, Kim JK, Owens TG, Ranwala AP, Choi YD, et al. 2002. Trehalose accumulation in rice plants confers high tolerance levels to different abiotic stresses. *Proc. Natl. Acad. Sci. USA* 99:15898–903
44. Garthwaite AJ, von Bothmer R, Colmer TD. 2005. Salt tolerance in wild *Hordeum* species is associated with restricted entry of Na^+ and Cl^- into the shoots. *J. Exp. Bot.* 56:2365–78
45. Gaxiola RA, Li JS, Undurraga S, Dang LM, Allen GJ, et al. 2001. Drought- and salt-tolerant plants result from overexpression of the AVP1 H^+-pump. *Proc. Natl. Acad. Sci. USA* 98:11444–49
46. Genc Y, McDonald GK, Tester M. 2007. Re-assessment of tissue Na^+ concentration as a criterion for salinity tolerance in bread wheat. *Plant Cell Environ.* 30:1486–1498.
47. Gilliham M, Tester M. 2005. The regulation of anion loading to the maize root xylem. *Plant Physiol.* 137:819–28
48. Gong HJ, Randall DP, Flowers TJ. 2006. Silicon deposition in the root reduces sodium uptake in rice *(Oryza sativa* L.) seedlings by reducing bypass flow. *Plant Cell Environ.* 29:1970–79
49. Gong JM, Waner DA, Horie T, Li SL, Horie R, et al. 2004. Microarray-based rapid cloning of an ion accumulation deletion mutant in *Arabidopsis thaliana*. *Proc. Natl. Acad. Sci. USA* 101:15404–9
50. Gong QQ, Li PH, Ma SS, Rupassara SI, Bohnert HJ. 2005. Salinity stress adaptation competence in the extremophile *Thellungiella halophila* in comparison with its relative *Arabidopsis thaliana*. *Plant J.* 44:826–39

51. Gorham J, Hardy C, Wyn Jones RG, Joppa LR, Law CN. 1987. Chromosomal location of a K/Na discrimination character in the D genome of wheat. *Theor. Appl. Genet.* 74:584–88
52. Gorham J, Wyn Jones RG, Bristol A. 1990. Partial characterization of the trait for enhanced K^+-Na^+ discrimination in the D genome of wheat. *Planta* 180:590–97
53. Greenway H, Munns R. 1980. Mechanisms of salt tolerance in nonhalophytes. *Annu. Rev. Plant Physiol.* 31:149–90
54. Greenway H, Osmond CB. 1972. Salt responses of enzymes from species differing in salt tolerance. *Plant Physiol.* 49:256–59
55. Halfter U, Ishitani M, Zhu JK. 2000. The *Arabidopsis* SOS2 protein kinase physically interacts with and is activated by the calcium-binding protein SOS3. *Proc. Natl. Acad. Sci. USA* 97:3735–40
56. Hare PD, Cress WA, Van Staden J. 1998. Dissecting the roles of osmolyte accumulation during stress. *Plant Cell Environ.* 21:535–53
57. Haro R, Bañuelos MA, Senn MAE, Barrero-Gil J, Rodríguez-Navarro A. 2005. HKT1 mediates sodium uniport in roots. Pitfalls in the expression of HKT1 in yeast. *Plant Physiol.* 139:1495–506
58. Hasegawa PM, Bressan RA, Zhu J-K, Bohnert HJ. 2000. Plant cellular and molecular responses to high salinity. *Annu. Rev. Plant Physiol. Plant Mol. Biol.* 51:463–99
59. He CX, Yan JQ, Shen GX, Fu LH, Holaday AS, et al. 2005. Expression of an *Arabidopsis* vacuolar sodium/proton antiporter gene in cotton improves photosynthetic performance under salt conditions and increases fiber yield in the field. *Plant Cell Physiol.* 46:1848–54
60. Horie T, Costa A, Kim TH, Han MJ, Horie R, et al. 2007. Rice OsHKT2;1 transporter mediates large Na^+ influx component into K^+-starved roots for growth. *EMBO J.* 26:300–14
61. Hu Y, Burucs Z, von Tucher S, Schmidhalter U. 2007. Short-term effects of drought and salinity on mineral nutrient distribution along growing leaves of maize seedlings. *Environ. Exp. Bot.* 60:268–75
62. Hu Y, Fricke W, Schmidhalter U. 2005. Salinity and the growth of nonhalophytic grass leaves: the role of mineral nutrient distribution. *Funct. Plant Biol.* 32:973–85
63. Huang CX, van Steveninck RFM. 1989. Maintenance of low Cl^- concentrations in mesophyll cells of leaf blades of barley seedlings exposed to salt stress. *Plant Physiol.* 90:1440–43
64. Huang S, Spielmeyer W, Lagudah ES, James RA, Platten JD, et al. 2006. A sodium transporter (HKT7) is a candidate for *Nax1*, a gene for salt tolerance in durum wheat. *Plant Physiol.* 142:1718–27
65. Ishitani M, Liu JP, Halfter U, Kim CS, Shi WM, Zhu J-K. 2000. SOS3 function in plant salt tolerance requires N-myristoylation and calcium binding. *Plant Cell* 12:1667–77
66. James RA, Davenport RJ, Munns R. 2006. Physiological characterisation of two genes for Na^+ exclusion in durum wheat: *Nax1* and *Nax2*. *Plant Physiol.* 142:1537–47
67. James RA, Munns R, von Caemmerer S, Trejo C, Miller C, Condon AG. 2006. Photosynthetic capacity is related to the cellular and subcellular partitioning of Na^+, K^+ and Cl– in salt-affected barley and durum wheat. *Plant Cell Environ.* 29:2185–97
68. James RA, Rivelli AR, Munns R, von Caemmerer S. 2002. Factors affecting CO_2 assimilation, leaf injury and growth in salt-stressed durum wheat. *Funct. Plant Biol.* 29:1393–403
69. Kant S, Kant P, Raveh E, Barak S. 2006. Evidence that differential gene expression between the halophyte *Thellungiella halophila*, and *Arabidopsis thaliana* is responsible for higher levels of the compatible osmolyte proline and tight control of Na^+ uptake in *T. halophila*. *Plant Cell Environ.* 29:1220–34

70. Kapulnik Y, Tueber LR, Phillips DA. 1989. Lucerne (*Medicago sativa* L.) selected for vigor in a nonsaline environment maintained growth under salt stress. *Aust. J. Agric. Res.* 40:1253–59
71. Kiegle E, Moore C, Haseloff J, Tester M, Knight M. 2000. Cell-type specific calcium responses to drought, NaCl, and cold in *Arabidopsis* root: a role for endodermis and pericycle in stress signal transduction. *Plant J.* 23:267–78
72. Knight H. 2000. Calcium signaling during abiotic stress in plants. *Int. Rev. Cytol.* 192:269–324
73. Knight H, Trewavas AJ, Knight MR. 1997. Calcium signalling in *Arabidopsis thaliana* responding to drought and salinity. *Plant J.* 12:1067–78
74. Läuchli A. 1984. Salt exclusion: an adaptation of legumes for crops and pastures under saline conditions. In *Salinity Tolerance in Plants: Strategies for Crop Improvement*, ed. RC Staples, pp. 171–87. New York: Wiley
75. Läuchli A. 2002. Introduction to *Salinity: Environment—Plants—Molecules*, ed. A Läuchli, U Lüttge, pp. ix–x. Dordrecht, Netherlands: Kluwer
76. Laurie S, Feeney KA, Maathuis FJM, Heard PJ, Brown SJ, Leigh RA. 2002. A role for HKT1 in sodium uptake by wheat roots. *Plant J.* 32:139–49
77. Leigh RA, Storey R. 1993. Intercellular compartmentation of ions in barley leaves in relation to potassium nutrition and salinity. *J. Exp. Bot.* 44:755–62
78. Logan BA. 2005. Reactive oxygen species and photosynthesis. In *Antioxidants and Reactive Oxygen Species in Plants*, ed. N Smirnoff, pp. 250–67. Oxford: Blackwell
79. Luo MC, Dubcovsky J, Goyal S, Dvorak J. 1996. Engineering of interstitial foreign chromosome segments containing the K^+/Na^+ selectivity gene *Kna1* by sequential homoeologous recombination in durum wheat. *Theor. Appl. Genet.* 93:1180–84
80. Mäkelä P, Munns R, Colmer TD, Peltonen-Sainio P. 2003. Growth of tomato and its ABA-deficient mutant (*sitiens*) under saline conditions. *Physiol. Plant.* 117:58–63
81. Mäser P, Eckelman B, Vaidyanathan R, Horie T, Fairbairn DJ, et al. 2002. Altered shoot/root Na^+ distribution and bifurcating salt sensitivity in *Arabidopsis* by genetic disruption of the Na^+ transporter AtHKT1. *FEBS Lett.* 531:157–61
82. Mennen H, Jacoby B, Marschner H. 1990. Is sodium proton antiport ubiquitous in plant cells? *J. Plant Physiol.* 137:180–83
83. Miller G, Suzuki N, Rizhsky L, Hegie A, Koussevitzky S, Mittler R. 2007. Double mutants deficient in cytosolic and thylakoid acsorbate peroxidase reveal a complex mode of interaction between reactive oxygen species, plant development, and a response to abiotic stress. *Plant. Physiol.* 144:1777–85
84. Mittler R, Vanderauwera S, Gollery M, Van Breusegem F. 2004. Reactive oxygen gene network of plants. *Trends Plant Sci.* 9:490–98
85. Møller IS, Gilliham M, Jha D, Roy S, Coates J, et al. 2008. Salinity tolerance (and Na^+ exclusion) engineered by cell type-specific overexpression of a sodium transporter in the *Arabidopsis* root. *Science.* In review
86. Møller IS, Tester M. 2007. Salinity tolerance of Arabidopsis: a good model for cereals? *Trends Plant Sci.* 12:534–40
87. Moore CA, Bowden HC, Scrase-Field S, Knight MR, White PJ. 2002. The deposition of suberin lamellae determines the magnitude of cytosolic Ca^{2+} elevations in root endodermal cells subjected to cooling. *Plant J.* 30:457–65
88. Munns R. 2002. Comparative physiology of salt and water stress. *Plant Cell Environ.* 25:239–50
89. Munns R. 2005. Genes and salt tolerance: bringing them together. *New Phytol.* 167:645–63

90. Munns R, Guo J, Passioura JB, Cramer GR. 2000. Leaf water status controls day-time but not daily rates of leaf expansion in salt-treated barley. *Aust. J. Plant Physiol.* 27:949–57
91. Munns R, James RA. 2003. Screening methods for salinity tolerance: a case study with tetraploid wheat. *Plant Soil.* 253:201–18
92. Munns R, James RA, Läuchli A. 2006. Approaches to increasing the salt tolerance of wheat and other cereals. *J. Exp. Bot.* 57:1025–43
93. Munns R, Schachtman DP, Condon AG. 1995. The significance of a two-phase growth response to salinity in wheat and barley. *Aust. J. Plant Physiol.* 22:561–69
94. Neves-Piestun BG, Bernstein N. 2005. Salinity-induced changes in the nutritional status of expanding cells may impact leaf growth inhibition in maize. *Funct. Plant Biol.* 32:141–52
95. Pardo JM, Cubero B, Leidi EO, Quintero FJ. 2006. Alkali cation exchangers: roles in cellular homeostasis and stress tolerance. *J. Exp. Bot.* 57:1181–99
96. Parker DR, Norvell WA, Chaney RL. 1995. GEOCHEM-PC: A chemical speciation program for IBM and compatible computers. In *Chemical Equilibrium and Reaction Models*, SSSA Spec. Publ., ed. RH Loeppert, AP Schwab, S Goldberg, 42:253–59. Madison, WI: Soil Sci. Soc. Am./Am. Soc. Agronomy
97. Passioura JB, Munns R. 2000. Rapid environmental changes that affect leaf water status induce transient surges or pauses in leaf expansion rate. *Aust. J. Plant Physiol.* 27:941–48
98. Paul MJ, Foyer CH. 2001. Sink regulation of photosynthesis. *J. Exp. Bot.* 52:1383–400
99. Platten JD, Cotsaftis O, Berthomieu P, Bohnert H, Bressan R, et al. 2006. Nomenclature for *HKT* genes, key determinants of plant salinity tolerance. *Trends Plant Sci.* 11:372–74
100. Prior LD, Grieve AM, Bevington KB, Slavich PG. 2007. Long-term effects of saline irrigation water on 'Valencia' orange trees: relationships between growth and yield, and salt levels in soil and leaves. *Aust. J. Agric. Res.* 58:349–58
101. Qiu QS, Barkla BJ, Vera-Estrella R, Zhu J-K, Schumaker KS. 2003. Na^+/H^+ exchange activity in the plasma membrane of *Arabidopsis*. *Plant Physiol.* 132:1041–52
102. Qiu QS, Guo Y, Dietrich MA, Schumaker KS, Zhu J-K. 2002. Regulation of SOS1, a plasma membrane Na^+/H^+ exchanger in *Arabidopsis thaliana*, by SOS2 and SOS3. *Proc. Natl. Acad. Sci. USA* 99:8436–41
103. Quintero FJ, Ohta M, Shi HZ, Zhu J-K, Pardo JM. 2002. Reconstitution in yeast of the *Arabidopsis* SOS signaling pathway for Na^+ homeostasis. *Proc. Natl. Acad. Sci. USA* 99:9061–66
104. Rains DW. 1972. Salt transport by plants in relation to salinity. *Annu. Rev. Plant Physiol.* 23:367–88
105. Raven JA. 1985. Regulation of pH and generation of osmolarity in vascular plants: A cost-benefit analysis in relation to efficiency of use of energy, nitrogen and water. *New Phytol.* 101:25–77
106. Ren ZH, Gao JP, Li LG, Cai XL, Huang W, et al. 2005. A rice quantitative trait locus for salt tolerance encodes a sodium transporter. *Nat. Genet.* 37:1141–46
107. Rengasamy P. 2002. Transient salinity and subsoil constraints to dryland farming in Australian sodic soils: an overview. *Aust. J. Exp. Agric.* 42:351–61
108. Rhodes D, Nadolska-Orczyk A, Rich PJ. 2002. Salinity, osmolytes and compatible solutes. In *Salinity: Environment—Plants—Molecules*, ed. A Läuchli, U Lüttge, pp. 181–204. Dordrecht, Netherlands: Kluwer
109. Rubio F, Gassmann W, Schroeder JI. 1995. Sodium-driven potassium uptake by the plant potassium transporter HKT1 and mutations conferring salt tolerance. *Science* 270:1660–63
110. Rus A, Lee BH, Munoz-Mayor A, Sharkhuu A, Miura K, et al. 2004. AtHKT1 facilitates Na^+ homeostasis and K^+ nutrition in planta. *Plant Physiol.* 136:2500–11

111. Rus A, Yokoi S, Sharkhuu A, Reddy M, Lee BH, et al. 2001. AtHKT1 is a salt tolerance determinant that controls Na^+ entry into plant roots. *Proc. Natl. Acad. Sci. USA* 98:1415–15
112. Sanders D. 1980. The mechanism of Cl^- transport at the plasma-membrane of chara-corallina. 1. Cotransport with H^+. *J. Membr. Biol.* 53:129–41
113. Saneoka H, Nagasaka C, Hahn DT, Yang WJ, Premechandra GS, et al. 1995. Salt tolerance of glycinebetaine-deficient and -containing maize lines. *Plant Physiol.* 107:631–38
114. Schachtman DP, Schroeder JI. 1994. Structure and transport mechanism of a high-affinity potassium uptake transporter from higher-plants. *Nature* 370:655–58
115. Shi HZ, Quintero FJ, Pardo JM, Zhu J-K. 2002. The putative plasma membrane Na^+/H^+ antiporter SOS1 controls long-distance Na^+ transport in plants. *Plant Cell* 14:465–77
116. Sickler CM, Edwards GE, Kiirats O, Gao Z, Loescher W. 2007. Response of mannitol-producing *Arabidopsis thaliana* to abiotic stress. *Funct. Plant Biol.* 34:382–91
117. Skerrett M, Tyerman SD. 1994. A channel that allows inwardly directed fluxes of anions in protoplasts derived from wheat roots. *Planta* 192:295–305
118. Staal M, Maathuis FJM, Elzenga JTM, Overbeek JHM, Prins HBA. 1991. Na^+/H^+ antiport activity in tonoplast vesicles from roots of the salt-tolerant *Plantago maritima* and the salt-sensitive *Plantago media*. *Physiol. Plant.* 82:179–84
119. Storey R, Walker RR. 1999. Citrus and salinity. *Sci. Hortic.* 78:39–81
120. Su J, Hirji R, Zhang L, He CK, Selvaraj G, Wu R. 2006. Evaluation of the stress-inducible production of choline oxidase in transgenic rice as a strategy for producing the stress-protectant glycine betaine. *J. Exp. Bot.* 57:1129–35
121. Sümer A, Zörb C, Yan F, Schubert S. 2004. Evidence of sodium toxicity for the vegetative growth of Maize (*Zea mays* L.) during the first phase of salt stress. *J. Appl. Bot.* 78:135–39
122. Sunarpi HT, Motoda J, Kubo M, Yang H, Yoda K, et al. 2005. Enhanced salt tolerance mediated by AtHKT1 transporter-induced Na^+ unloading from xylem vessels to xylem parenchyma cells. *Plant J.* 44:928–38
123. Sunkar R, Zhu J-K. 2007. Micro RNAs and short-interfering RNAs in plants. *J. Integr. Plant Biol.* 49:817–26
124. Szabolcs I. 1989. *Salt-Affected Soils*. Boca Raton, FL: CRC Press
125. Termaat A, Munns R. 1986. Use of concentrated macronutrient solutions to separate osmotic from NaCl-specific effects on plant growth. *Aust. J. Plant Physiol.* 13:509–22
126. Termaat A, Passioura JB, Munns R. 1985. Shoot turgor does not limit shoot growth of NaCl-affected wheat and barley. *Plant Physiol.* 77:869–72
127. Tester M, Davenport RJ. 2003. Na^+ transport and Na^+ tolerance in higher plants. *Ann. Bot.* 91:503–27
128. Tester M, Leigh RA. 2001. Partitioning of transport processes in roots. *J. Exp. Bot.* 52:445–57
129. Tracy FE, Gilliham M, Dodd AN, Webb AAR, Tester M. 2008. Cytosolic free Ca^{2+} in *Arabidopsis thaliana* are heterogeneous and modified by external ionic composition. *Plant Cell Environl.* In press
130. Uozumi N, Kim EJ, Rubio F, Yamaguchi T, Muto S, et al. 2000. The *Arabidopsis* HKT1 gene homolog mediates inward Na^+ currents in *Xenopus laevis* oocytes and Na^+ uptake in *Saccharomyces cerevisiae*. *Plant Physiol.* 122:1249–59
131. USDA-ARS. 2008. Research Databases. Bibliography on Salt Tolerance. *George E. Brown, Jr. Salinity Lab. US Dep. Agric., Agric. Res. Serv. Riverside, CA.* **http://www.ars.usda.gov/Services/docs.htm?docid=8908**

132. Voisin A, Reidy B, Parent B, Rolland G, Redondo E, et al. 2006. Are ABA, ethylene or their interaction involved in the response of leaf growth to soil water deficit? An analysis using naturally occurring variation or genetic transformation of ABA production in maize. *Plant Cell Environ.* 29:1829–40
133. Volkov V, Amtmann A. 2006. *Thellungiella halophila*, a salt-tolerant relative of *Arabidopsis thaliana*, has specific root ion-channel features supporting K^+/Na^+ homeostasis under salinity stress. *Plant J.* 48:342–53
134. White PJ, Broadley MR. 2001. Chloride in soils and its uptake and movement within the plant: A review. *Ann. Bot.* 88:967–88
135. Wong CE, Li Y, Labbe A, Guevara D, Nuin P, et al. 2006. Transcriptional profiling implicates novel interactions between abiotic stress and hormonal responses in *Thellungiella*, a close relative of *Arabidopsis*. *Plant Physiol.* 140:1437–50
136. Wyn Jones RG, Storey R, Leigh RA, Ahmad N, Pollard A. 1977. A hypothesis on cytoplasmic osmoregulation. In *Regulation of Cell Membrane Activities in Plants*, ed. E Marré, O Cifferi, pp. 121–36. Amsterdam, Netherlands: Elsevier
137. Xiong LM, Schumaker KS, Zhu J-K. 2002. Cell signaling during cold, drought, and salt stress. *Plant Cell* 14:S165–83
138. Xue ZY, Zhi DY, Xue GP, Zhang H, Zhao YX, Xia GM. 2004. Enhanced salt tolerance of transgenic wheat (*Triticum aestivum* L.) expressing a vacuolar Na^+/H^+ antiporter gene with improved grain yields in saline soils in the field and a reduced level of leaf Na^+. *Plant Sci.* 167:849–59
139. Yamaguchi-Shinozaki K, Shinozaki K. 2006. Transcriptional regulatory networks in cellular responses and tolerance to dehydration and cold stresses. *Annu. Rev. Plant Biol.* 57:781–803
140. Yamashita K, Kasai M, Yamamoto Y, Matsumoto H. 1994. Stimulation of plasma-membrane H^+-transport activity in barley roots by salt stress—possible role of increase in chloride permeability. *Soil Sci. Plant Nutr.* 40:555–63
141. Yeo AR, Flowers TJ. 1986. Salinity resistance in rice (*Oryza sativa* L.) and a pyramiding approach to breeding varieties for saline soils. *Aust. J. Plant Physiol.* 13:161–73
142. Yeo AR, Lee KS, Izard P, Boursier PJ, Flowers TJ. 1991. Short- and long-term effects of salinity on leaf growth in rice (*Oryza sativa* L.). *J. Exp. Bot.* 42:881–89
143. Zhang HX, Blumwald E. 2001. Transgenic salt-tolerant tomato plants accumulate salt in foliage but not in fruit. *Nat. Biotech.* 19:765–68
144. Zhang HX, Hodson JN, Williams JP, Blumwald E. 2001. Engineering salt-tolerant *Brassica* plants: Characterization of yield and seed oil quality in transgenic plants with increased vacuolar sodium accumulation. *Proc. Natl. Acad. Sci. USA* 98:12832–36
145. Zhu J-K. 2002. Salt and drought signal transduction in plants. *Annu. Rev. Plant Biol.* 53:247–73
146. Zhu J-K, Liu JP, Xiong LM. 1998. Genetic analysis of salt tolerance in *Arabidopsis*: Evidence for a critical role of potassium nutrition. *Plant Cell* 10:1181–91

Sealing Plant Surfaces: Cuticular Wax Formation by Epidermal Cells

Lacey Samuels,[1] Ljerka Kunst,[1] and Reinhard Jetter[1,2]

[1]Department of Botany, University of British Columbia, Vancouver, BC V6T1Z4, Canada; [2]Department of Chemistry, University of British Columbia, Vancouver, BC V6T1Z4, Canada; email: lsamuels@interchange.ubc.ca; kunst@interchange.ubc.ca; jetter@interchange.ubc.ca

Annu. Rev. Plant Biol. 2008. 59:683–707

The *Annual Review of Plant Biology* is online at plant.annualreviews.org

This article's doi:
10.1146/annurev.arplant.59.103006.093219

1543-5008/08/0602-0683$20.00

Key Words

fatty acid elongation, alkanes, primary alcohols, ABC transporters, regulation of wax biosynthesis, *Arabidopsis*

Abstract

The vital importance of plant surface wax in protecting tissue from environmental stresses is reflected in the huge commitment of epidermal cells to cuticle formation. During cuticle deposition, a massive flux of lipids occurs from the sites of lipid synthesis in the plastid and the endoplasmic reticulum to the plant surface. Recent genetic studies in *Arabidopsis* have improved our understanding of fatty acid elongation and of the subsequent modification of the elongated products into primary alcohols, wax esters, secondary alcohols, and ketones, shedding light on the enzymes involved in these pathways. In contrast, the biosynthesis of alkanes is still poorly understood, as are the mechanisms of wax transport from the site of biosynthesis to the cuticle. Currently, nothing is known about wax trafficking from the endoplasmic reticulum to the plasma membrane, or about translocation through the cell wall to the cuticle. However, a first breakthrough toward an understanding of wax export recently came with the discovery of ATP binding cassette (ABC) transporters that are involved in releasing wax from the plasma membrane into the apoplast. An overview of our present knowledge of wax biosynthesis and transport and the regulation of these processes during cuticle assembly is presented, including the evidence for coordination of cutin polyester and wax production.

Contents

INTRODUCTION

The plant cuticle is a hydrophobic layer coating the epidermis of the primary plant body. Structurally, the cuticle forms a continuous seal over the outer walls of the epidermal pavement, guard, and trichome cells. Cuticle ultrastructure varies widely among plant species, organ types, and their developmental states, ranging from a procuticle on emerging organs to a mature cuticle that is complete only some time after tissue expansion has ceased (reviewed in References 51 and 52). Despite this variability, all cuticles consist of the same two types of highly lipophilic materials. One of them, cutin, is a polymer consisting mainly of ω- and mid-chain hydroxy and epoxy C_{16} and C_{18} fatty acids, as well as glycerol (44, 95, 124). Owing to covalent linkages between its monomers, cutin resists mechanical damage and forms the structural backbone of the cuticle. In contrast, the second component, cuticular wax, is monomeric and can be extracted by organic solvents. Wax components typically constitute 20%–60% of the cuticle mass (44). Cuticular wax is a complex mixture of straight-chain C_{20} to C_{60} aliphatics and may include secondary metabolites such as triterpenoids, phenylpropanoids, and flavonoids (55). Physical separation and careful constituent analysis have demonstrated that the intracuticular wax, interspersed within the cutin polymer, has a distinct chemical composition from the epicuticular wax lying on the outer surface of the cutin polymer (56). Clearly, this segregation of wax components and the diversity of the wax chemical compositions greatly affect the physical properties of plant surfaces, but the exact implications of this compositional variation for the biological functions of the cuticle are only poorly understood.

Cutin: a fatty acid–based polyester that forms the structural skeleton of the cuticle

Wax: a mixture of highly lipophilic aliphatics surrounding and covering the cutin and sealing the plant surface

Cuticular wax serves the essential function of limiting nonstomatal water loss, and is therefore one of the key adaptations in the evolution of land plants (107). Epicuticular wax, because it is exposed at the outermost surface of plant organs, also plays important roles in the interactions of the plant with its environment. The wax surface influences plant-insect interactions, helps to prevent germination of pathogenic microbes, and causes shedding of water droplets and dust particles as well as spores (110). Together with cutin, wax also plays a pivotal role in cell-cell interactions, e.g., mediating pollen-stigma contact and preventing postgenital organ fusions (128).

The functional importance of the cuticle to the whole plant is evidenced by the significant commitment of epidermal cells to cuticle production. For example, over half of the fatty acids made by epidermal cells of the rapidly expanding *Arabidopsis* stem are estimated to be channeled into the cuticular lipids (cutin and wax), more than intracellular membrane and storage lipids combined (127). The huge investment of epidermal cells to cuticle production is reflected in the epidermis transcriptome during stem expansion (127). Epidermal cells exhibit increased expression of genes encoding proteins involved in lipid metabolism, as well as membrane-associated and extracellular proteins. The expression of wax biosynthetic genes is also upregulated in epidermal cells, including the *CER* genes that were identified in forward genetic screens for the *Arabidopsis* wax-deficient *eceriferum* mutants (75).

This review focuses on the formation of cuticular wax in *Arabidopsis thaliana*, because most of the recent advances in identification and functional characterization of genes involved in wax biosynthesis and transport have been made in this plant species. Evidence from *Arabidopsis* is complemented with important, mostly biochemical information obtained from other species. For more comprehensive reviews of the biochemical literature and the genetic evidence from other species, readers are referred to previous reviews (14, 67, 68, 139). Because a parallel review summarizes our current knowledge of cutin formation (103), this cuticle component is addressed here only where its formation intersects with wax pathways.

WAX BIOSYNTHESIS

Wax components are synthesized in epidermal cells by joining C_2 building blocks of acetyl-coenzyme A (acetyl-CoA) together into straight-chain aliphatics with 24 to 34 carbon atoms. Wax biosynthesis comprises three distinct stages: First, C_{16} and C_{18} fatty acids are synthesized de novo by the plastid. These ubiquitous fatty acids serve as central intermediates for all lipid classes, and this first stage of wax formation is thus shared with other lipid biosynthetic processes. In contrast, the second stage of the biosynthetic pathway, involving the elongation of C_{16} and C_{18} fatty acids in the endoplasmic reticulum (ER) into very-long-chain fatty acids (VLCFAs) with C_{20}–C_{34} chains, is largely dedicated to generating cuticular waxes (and to a degree to sphingolipid production). In the final stages of wax production in the ER, VLCFAs are modified into the major wax products, including alcohols, esters, aldehydes, alkanes, and ketones (**Figure 1**).

Synthesis of Very-Long-Chain Fatty Acid Wax Precursors

Cuticular lipid formation begins with synthesis of C_{16} and C_{18} fatty acids in leucoplasts, the small nonphotosynthetic plastids found in the epidermis. In this process, long carbon chains are assembled, starting with the condensation of an acetyl-CoA with a C_2 moiety from malonyl-acyl carrier protein (ACP), which originates from acetyl-CoA. After the condensation step, a sequence of reactions including reduction of β-ketoacyl-ACP, dehydration of β-hydroxyacyl-ACP, and reduction of *trans*-Δ^2-enoyl-ACP yields an acyl-ACP product two carbons longer than the original acetyl molecule. Similar elongation cycles, now starting with the condensation of malonyl-ACP with an acyl-ACP and completed by reductive removal of the β-keto group, are repeated six to seven times (43, 97). This process is catalyzed by fatty acid synthases (FASs), complexes of four soluble, dissociable enzymes. Two or three different types of FAS complexes are required for the formation of a C_{16} or C_{18} fatty acid, respectively. FAS complexes differ in their condensing enzymes, which have strict acyl chain length specificities: ketoacyl ACP synthase III (KASIII) (C_2 to C_4) (28), KASI (C_4 to C_{16}), and KASII (C_{16} to C_{18}) (118). In contrast, the two reductases and the dehydratase have no particular acyl chain length specificity and are shared by all three plastidial FAS complexes (126).

Further extension of C_{16} and C_{18} fatty acids to VLCFA chains requires their liberation from ACP by an acyl-ACP thioesterase, activation to CoA thioesters by a long-chain acyl-CoA synthetase (LACS), and transfer to the ER. These processes are important for partitioning of C_{16} and C_{18} acyl chains between pathways leading to cuticlar lipid formation and those leading to membrane

eceriferum (*cer*): *Arabidopsis* and barley mutants with altered cuticular wax amounts and/or composition (literally, "not carrying wax")

CoA: coenzyme A

VLCFAs: very-long-chain fatty acids (C_{20}–C_{34})

ACP: acyl carrier protein

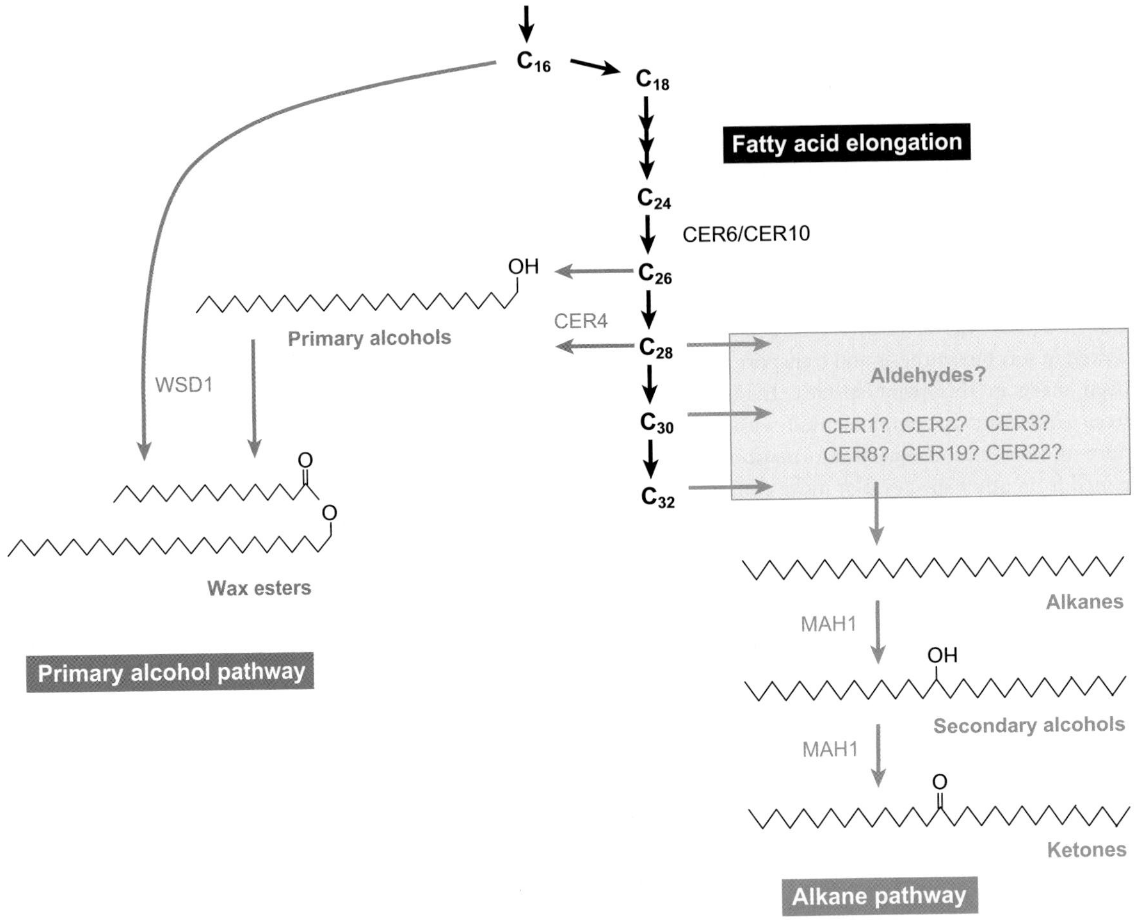

Figure 1

Simplified pathways for wax biosynthesis in *Arabidopsis* stems. CER, ECERIFERUM; WSD, wax synthase/diacylglycerol acyltransferase; MAH, mid-chain alkane hydroxylase.

glycerolipid synthesis within and outside of the plastid of epidermal cells.

Details of fatty acid partitioning into different biosynthetic pathways at this control point are still vague, but substrate flux seems to be determined by activities and specificities of the enzymes involved, including the KASII enzyme (101), acyl-ACP acyltransferases, thioesterases, and the $C_{18:0}$ acid desaturase in the plastid, as well as extraplastidial acyltransferases and fatty acid elongase enzymes in the ER. For example, for C_{16} acyl-ACP, the possible fates are further elongation to C_{18} acyl-ACP by KASII, transfer onto a glycerol backbone in the plastid to form a prokaryotic-type membrane lipid, or cleavage by a fatty acyl–ACP thioesterase B (FATB) with subsequent export of the free fatty acid out of the plastid (43, 136). In *Arabidopsis*, the *fatb* loss-of-function mutant shows a 50% reduction in total wax load in stems and a 20% reduction in leaves (**Table 1**) (20). Based on this mutant wax phenotype it can be speculated that, in an elongating epidermal cell actively synthesizing cuticle, a major portion of C_{16} (and an unknown proportion of C_{18}) acyl-ACPs are channeled through thioesterase cleavage toward wax biosynthesis.

FATA and FATB: class A and class B fatty acyl-ACP thioesterases

Table 1 Summary of genes reported to encode proteins involved in wax biosynthesis and secretion in *Arabidopsis*

	Gene	MIPS Accession number	Cuticle phenotype	Reference
Biosynthesis				
Fatty acyl-ACP thioesterase, B class	*FATB*	At1g08510	Stem wax load 50% of WT. Leaf wax load 80% of WT	(20)
β-keto acyl-CoA synthases (KCS)	*CER6*	At1g68530	Stem wax load 10% of WT. Reduced levels of all wax components; accumulation of C_{24}/C_{26} acyl groups	(35, 92)
Enoyl-CoA reductase (ECR)	*CER10*	At3g55360	Stem wax load 40% of WT. Reduced levels of all wax components	(150)
Fatty acyl-CoA reductase (FAR)	*CER4*	At4g33790	Stem wax load similar to WT. Reduced primary alcohols and wax esters in stem wax. When expressed in yeast, makes C24 and C26 primary alcohols	(113)
Wax synthase/ DGAT (WSD)	*WSD1*	At5g37300	Stem wax load similar to WT. Reduced wax esters in stem wax	F. Li, X. Wu, L. Samuels, R. Jetter & L. Kunst, unpublished.
Midchain alkane hydroxylase (CYP96A15)	*MAH1*	At1g57750	Stem wax load 60–85% of WT. Reduced levels of secondary alcohols and ketones in stem wax	(38)
Secretion				
ABC transporter	*CER5*	At1g51500	Stem wax load 45% of WT. Reduced levels of alkanes in stem wax	(102)
ABC transporter	*WBC11*	At1g17840	Stem wax load 44–60% of WT. Reduced levels of alkanes in stem wax	(17, 87, 98, 133)
Regulation				
Exosome subunit (RRP45)	*CER7*	At3g60500	Stem wax load 30% of WT. Reduced levels of all stem wax components	(49)
Unknown function				
	CER1	At1g02205	Stem wax load 13% of WT. Reduced levels of all stem wax components; C_{30} aldehyde accumulation	(1, 42, 90)
	CER2	At4g24510	Stem wax load 25% of WT. Reduced levels of alkanes, secondary alcohols and ketones; accumulation of C_{26}/C_{28} acyl groups, primary alcohols and wax esters	(54, 79, 96, 142, 143)
	CER3/WAX2/ YRE/FLP1	At5g57800	Stem wax load 20% of WT. Reduced levels of aldehydes, alkanes, secondary alcohols and ketones; higher levels of C_{30} primary alcohols	(5, 25, 54, 77, 112)

The process of fatty acid export from the plastid is not well understood. Fatty acids released from ACP by a thioesterase in the plastid must undergo conversion to acyl-CoAs by LACSs in the outer envelope membrane (4, 57, 116). Based on the kinetics of labeled fatty acid export from the plastid, the fatty acyl movement from the thioesterase to LACS was

PLAMs: plastid-ER associated membranes

FAEs: fatty acid elongases

KCS: β-ketoacyl-CoA synthase

proposed to occur by some type of facilitated diffusion (74), but the mechanism of transfer between the two enzymes has not been established. There are nine *LACS* genes annotated in the *Arabidopsis* genome (119), and one of them, *LACS2*, has been implicated in cuticle biosynthesis (115). A recent analysis of the *lacs2* phenotype demonstrated that the cuticular defect is in the cutin, rather than the wax, of rosette leaves (12). Indeed, the wax levels on the surface of *lacs2* mutants are increased rather than decreased, a common phenomenon in plants with disrupted cutin (12, 78, 115, 121). Thus, the LACS isozyme(s) that would be primarily responsible for CoA esterification of fatty acids en route to wax biosynthesis has yet to be identified.

Once the fatty acids are esterified to CoA, they are translocated to the ER, where additional acyl chain elongation and modification of VLCFAs to diverse aliphatic wax components occur. Recent work has experimentally verified the intimate connection between the plastid and the ER of *Arabidopsis* leaf protoplasts. Physical manipulation of green fluorescent protein (GFP)-labeled ER strands, using laser scalpels and optical tweezers, demonstrated that ER membranes are firmly attached to isolated plastids (3). Sensitivity to proteases and the strength of the attachment is consistent with protein-protein interactions maintaining these plastid-ER associated membranes (PLAMs), which may be major routes for lipid transfer between the two organelles.

The extension of fatty acids from long (C_{16}, C_{18}) to very long chains ($\geq C_{20}$) is carried out by fatty acid elongases (FAEs), multienzyme complexes residing on the ER membrane (76, 145, 150). Analogous to plastidial fatty acid synthesis, VLCFA formation involves four consecutive enzymatic reactions, and results in a two-carbon extension of the acyl chain in each elongation cycle. However, unlike the FAS, which uses malonyl-ACP as a C_2 donor, FAE utilizes C_2 units from malonyl-CoA. Extraplastidial malonyl-CoA is generated by the multifunctional acetyl-CoA carboxylase (ACCase). In *Arabidopsis*, two genes, *ACC1* and *ACC2*, encode the multifunctional ACCases. Even though both genes appear to be ubiquitously expressed, studies of mutants disrupted in the *ACC* genes unequivocally established that ACC1 is involved in supplying malonyl-CoA for VLCFA elongation (8, 9).

Multiple elongation cycles are needed to generate C_{24} to C_{34} acyl chains for the production of aliphatic wax components (**Figure 1**). These elongation cycles are carried out by several distinct elongases with unique substrate chain length specificities (137, 138). The specificity of each elongation reaction lies in the condensing enzyme (β-ketoacyl-CoA synthase, KCS) of the elongase complex (18, 81, 93, 99, 132). Because single condensing enzymes can catalyze a few consecutive elongation steps, and various FAEs may have overlapping ranges of substrate chain lengths, it is not clear how many condensing enzymes participate in the elongation of a C_{18} to C_{34} fatty acid. Consistent with the requirement for multiple FAEs to handle fatty acyl precursors of various chain lengths, a large family of 21 *KCS*-like sequences has been identified in *Arabidopsis* (18, 34, 82). A second gene family of putative condensing enzymes, related to the *Saccharomyces cerevisiae* condensing enzymes *ELONGASE 1* (*ELO1*), *ELO2*, and *ELO3*, has also been annotated (34).

The only wax-specific KCS characterized to date is CER6, involved in elongation of fatty acyl-CoAs longer than C_{22} (35, 50, 92) (**Table 1**). In addition to *CER6*, seven other *KCS* genes were found to be upregulated in *Arabidopsis* stem epidermal cells in a microarray experiment (127), including *FIDDLEHEAD* and *KCS1*, although the functions of these *KCS* genes remain enigmatic (131, 146). Because a major reduction of CER6 activity in *cer6* mutants or in transgenic sense-suppressed plants nearly abolishes stem wax accumulation (35, 92), there is clearly no significant functional overlap of CER6 with other condensing enzymes in *Arabidopsis* stems. Thus, KCSs may have cell-type-specific functions and may not be expressed in the epidermal pavement cells, but instead may be expressed only in trichomes or guard cells, as shown for the condensing enzyme named HIC (for high carbon dioxide) (37).

The identification of the additional enzymes of the plant FAE has recently become possible due to progress in research on yeast sphingolipid biosynthesis, beginning with the isolation of the β-keto acyl reductase (KCR) (10, 41) and the enoyl-CoA reductase (ECR) (62) genes from *Saccharomyces cerevisiae*.

The wax phenotype of the maize *glossy8* mutant led to the proposal that GLOSSY8 functions as a KCR, catalyzing the reduction of β-keto acyl-CoA during VLCFA synthesis for wax production (144). The sequence homology between maize GLOSSY8 and the yeast KCR, whose biochemical function was demonstrated (10), further supported this proposal. More recently, a closely related gene designated *GL8b* was identified in maize, which shows overlapping expression patterns and function with the original *GL8a* (33). Loss of both GL8a and GL8b activities is embryo lethal, a phenotype attributed to the essential role of VLCFAs in sphingolipid assembly. A BLAST search using the yeast KCR sequence resulted in the identification of two putative homologs in the *Arabidopsis* genome, both of which show high levels of expression in the stem epidermis (127). One of these sequences, At1g67730, rescues the growth phenotype of the yeast *ybr159w* mutant defective in KCR (41). Taken together, this information makes it very likely that the two *Arabidopsis* genes encode KCRs. However, additional molecular and biochemical characterization is needed to establish their biochemical and biological role in cuticular wax formation.

Similarly, the isolation of the *TSC13* gene encoding the yeast ECR (62) allowed the identification of a single-copy *ECR* gene from *Arabidopsis*, responsible for the reduction of enoyl-CoA during FAE. Functional complementation of the yeast *tsc13-1elo2*Δ mutant with the *Arabidopsis* sequence demonstrated that it is indeed a true ECR, and that this protein can physically interact with the yeast Elo2p and Elo3p condensing enzymes (36). The *Arabidopsis ECR* gene is identical to the *CER10* gene (150) (**Table 1**), which is defective in the *cer10* mutant originally identified by Koornneef and colleagues (75). *CER10* is ubiquitously expressed in *Arabidopsis*; analysis of the *cer10* mutants demonstrated that *CER10/ECR* is required for the synthesis of all the VLCFA-containing lipids, including cuticular waxes, seed triacylglycerols (TAGs), and sphingolipids (150). Surprisingly, the ECR-deficient *cer10* mutants still accumulate 40% of wild-type cuticular wax as well as VLCFAs in sphingolipids and seed TAGs, suggesting that another ECR exists in *Arabidopsis*. Alternatively, unknown enzymes functionally similar to the ECR may complement the *cer10* deficiency to maintain critical levels of VLCFA synthesis (150).

KCR: β-keto acyl reductase

ECR: enoyl CoA reductase

The last of the enzymes in the FAE complex, the β-hydroxyacyl-CoA dehydratase, was for many years elusive in both yeast and plants (129). Recent studies using proteoliposome reconstitution of the *Saccharomyces cerevisiae* FAE have demonstrated that PHS1p, an ER-localized transmembrane protein, has dehydratase activity (30). This work is expected to prompt rapid progress in the identification of the dehydratase enzyme in plants.

Synthesis of Primary Alcohols and Wax Esters

One branch of the wax biosynthetic reactions, generally called the acyl reduction pathway, is responsible for the formation of constituents with predominantly even numbers of carbons (**Figure 1**). In diverse plant species and organs, the most important of these compounds are primary alcohols, synthesized with a chain length preference of C_{26} or C_{28} and in some systems C_{30} or C_{32} (7). The alcohols are frequently found in free form and esterified to various acyl groups, including aromatic and short (C_2), long (C_{16}, C_{18}), or very-long-chain aliphatic acids (55). Biosynthesis has long been investigated, and both *Brassica oleracea* and *Arabidopsis* have proven to be suitable model systems for these investigations, because in both species the cuticles of all above-ground organs accumulate high concentrations of primary alcohols and their esters (6, 42, 54).

FAR: fatty acyl-CoA reductase

Closely matching chain length distributions between alcohols and acids in the waxes of diverse plant species suggest that these compounds are biosynthetically related (14). Consequently, Chibnall & Piper (27) proposed that alcohols are generated by reduction of VLCFA precursors and there is now direct evidence that supports this hypothesis. The reduction of fatty acids to the corresponding alcohols must occur via intermediate aldehydes, and much research has focused on whether both reactions are catalyzed by two independent enzymes, or whether one fatty acyl-CoA reductase (FAR) can catalyze both steps (68).

Biochemical support for the two-step process leading to alcohol formation comes from experiments in *B. oleracea*, where an aldehyde intermediate could be isolated (66). The chemical phenotype of the *gl5* mutant of *Zea mays* was initially thought to provide further support for the two-step reduction hypothesis (15), but was later found to be caused by mutations in two genes, *GL5* and *GL20* (139). Because neither gene has been cloned, it is not clear whether one or both of them code for relevant reductases, and a case cannot be made for or against the two-step hypothesis for wax alcohol biosynthesis in *Z. mays*.

There is also substantial evidence for the direct reduction of acyl CoAs to primary alcohols. Initially, the green alga *Euglena gracilis* was found to generate alcohols from acyl CoA precursors without releasing aldehyde intermediates (65). Subsequent biochemical studies showed that single FARs were also responsible for direct reduction to wax alcohols in jojoba embryos (*Simmondsia chinensis*) (104) and pea leaves (*Pisum sativum*) (135). Functional expression of genes specifying alcohol-forming FARs from jojoba (91), silkmoth (*Bombyx mori*) (94), mouse (*Mus musculus*), and human (*Homo sapiens*) cells (26) in heterologous systems confirmed that the reduction of VLCFAs to alcohols in these species is also carried out by single alcohol-forming FARs.

Based on the biochemical results from experiments performed in various species, it seemed likely that a similar FAR enzyme was also involved in primary alcohol biosynthesis in *Arabidopsis*. Eight FAR-like genes were identified in the *Arabidopsis* genome, one of which is *CER4* (113) (**Table 1**). *cer4* mutants exhibit major decreases in primary alcohols and wax esters, suggesting that *CER4* encodes an alcohol-forming FAR (42, 54). Molecular characterization of *CER4* alleles, genomic complementation, and heterologous expression in yeast confirmed that CER4 is indeed the major FAR responsible for primary alcohol formation in *Arabidopsis* stems (113). The enzyme is capable of carrying out both reduction steps from acyl precursors to primary alcohols, thus showing that the direct reduction process is operating in this species.

The alcohols generated by CER4 likely serve as precursors for ester biosynthesis (**Figure 1**). This hypothesis implies that a pool of primary alcohols is generated in the epidermal cells, which are available either for direct export to the cuticle or for ester formation. Detailed analyses of esterified and free alcohols of various mutants of *Arabidopsis* show a clear correlation of alcohol chain lengths in both types of compounds. This study demonstrated that the alcohols formed by CER4 are indeed incorporated into the wax esters, and that the levels of alcohols limit ester production (79).

Ester biosynthesis in higher plants, mammals, and bacteria is catalyzed by wax synthase (WS) enzymes, which fall into three groups based on sequence information. The first class is exemplified by jojoba WS, which is capable of using a wide array of saturated and unsaturated acyl CoAs, ranging between C_{14} and C_{24}; unsaturated C_{18} alcohol is the prefered second substrate (80). In *Arabidopsis* twelve homologs of the jojoba type wax synthase exist, but none have yet been characterized. In contrast, the second class, which includes the mammalian WS enzymes, has no known homologs in plants. They have the highest activity with acyl-CoAs between C_{12} and C_{16} in length and efficiently use alcohols shorter than C_{20} (26). Finally, in *Acinetobacter calcoaceticus*, a third class of WS has been identified as a bifunctional WS/DGAT enzyme with a preference for C_{14} and C_{16} acyl-CoA together with C_{14} to C_{18} alcohols (125). Nearly one hundred WS/DGAT homologs from over twenty different microorganisms have been identified so far (140), as well as ten sequences in the *Arabidopsis* genome.

Very recently, one of the WS/DGATs from *Arabidopsis* was characterized and shown to be responsible for the formation of cuticular wax esters in stems of this species (F. Li, X. Wu, L. Samuels, R. Jetter & L. Kunst, unpublished observations) (**Table 1**). This enzyme utilizes mostly C_{16} acyl-CoA precursors, indicating that these very early intermediates of wax biosynthesis must come together with the alcohols formed as much later products of the pathway by acyl elongation and reduction.

Synthesis of Alkanes, Secondary Alcohols, and Ketones

A second branch of the wax biosynthetic pathway is responsible for the formation of compounds with predominantly odd numbers of carbons. Among these, the alkanes are the most prominent because they are ubiquitous in the wax mixtures from various plants and organs, where they frequently accumulate to high concentrations. Secondary alcohols and ketones with similar chain length distributions often accompany alkanes, pointing to a direct biosynthetic relationship between all three classes of compounds (55). Biochemical experiments in the 1960s and 70s addressed the biosynthesis of these compounds and led to a model describing the pathway as a series of reactions leading first from VLCFA precursors to alkanes and then from alkanes to ketones (**Figure 1**). Subsequent experiments confirmed that this pathway indeed occurs in two sets of reactions, with the alkanes as central intermediates or as end products (if the second set is not carried out). Although the second part of the pathway is relatively well characterized, the first part remains poorly understood.

WS/DGAT: dual function wax synthase and diacylglycerol acyl transferase

Compelling evidence exists that the VLCFA precursors described above are utilized for alkane biosynthesis. This conclusion was first drawn from feeding experiments in diverse plant species that showed incorporation of elongation products into various classes of wax compounds, including alkanes, secondary alcohols, and ketones (63, 64, 69, 72). These biochemical results were confirmed by molecular genetic studies in *Arabidopsis*, where two mutants known to be defective in VLCFA elongation, *cer6* and *cer10*, showed drastic reductions of the longer acyl chains together with depleted levels of all the odd-numbered wax constituents (alkanes, secondary alcohols, and ketones) (54, 105). Based on combined biochemical and molecular genetic evidence, it is now well-established that elongation precedes decarbonylation and that, therefore, both the primary alcohol and the alkane pathways compete for acyl-CoA precursors of various chain lengths. However, a comparison between the wax phenotypes of *Arabidopsis* wild-type and *cer6* stems shows that the primary alcohol pathway can utilize C_{26} precursors quite well, whereas the alkane pathway cannot (92).

Although the conversion of VLCFA precursors into alkanes as the first odd-numbered products could formally proceed in one step, both experimental data and theoretical considerations make it very unlikely that a direct decarboxylation reaction occurs. Instead, it is generally accepted that the net decarboxylation of the acyl substrates is brought about by a sequence of transformations. Accordingly, a number of different *Arabidopsis* mutants showing a stem wax phenotype with reduced alkane levels have been described, at least some of them likely due to defects in genes coding for enzymes of the first stage of this pathway (42, 54, 105, 106). Unfortunately, several of these genes have not been cloned (*CER8*, *CER19*, *CER22*), and the biochemical function of the corresponding proteins cannot be deduced on the basis of changes in wax composition alone. Three other genes have been isolated (*CER1*, *CER2*, *CER3/WAX2/YRE/FLP*) (**Table 1**), but all attempts to characterize their products have failed so far (1, 5, 25, 77, 96, 112, 142, 143). Nevertheless, both deduced protein sequence similarity of selected domains to known enzymes, and double mutant phenotypes, make it very plausible that these genes encode pathway enzymes.

The central reaction of the alkane-forming pathway (the step that makes the transition from even- to odd-numbered carbon chains) is thought to involve the loss of one carbon atom from the acyl precursors, rather than C_1 addition. Early indications for C_1 loss came from wax analyses of diverse species, in which the compound classes with odd-numbered carbon chains have homolog patterns shifted one carbon down from the accompanying even-numbered classes, including fatty acids (27). A similar correlation was found in *Arabidopsis* mutants affected in stem wax biosynthesis, in which a reduction in alkane-derived C_{29} compounds is sometimes accompanied by an accumulation of C_{30} compounds (42, 54, 105). The C_1 loss was further confirmed by biochemical experiments showing that, in vitro, labeled carboxyl carbons are lost in the reaction, whereas in-chain labels are retained. For example, C_{30} and C_{32} acids are converted into C_{29} alkane and C_{31} alkane by *B. oleracea* leaf discs (69) and *P. sativum* epidermal peels (61), respectively, whereas *Allium porrum* leaf microsomes form C_{23} alkane from C_{24} acid (23).

Although the overall C_1 loss is thus well established, the reaction details are not understood. Various hypotheses have been proposed, mostly differing in the central reactions in which the C_1 unit is cleaved off (14, 19, 27), but only one of the hypotheses has been tested to a certain degree. In this model, the central C-C cleavage step is decarbonylation (i.e., the loss of a CO molecule) by an aldehyde intermediate, and therefore alkane formation is frequently described as the decarbonylation pathway (19). Several biochemical experiments have been carried out with the explicit goal of confirming decarbonylation, and evidence supporting this hypothesis has been acquired (22, 24, 31, 32, 114, 135, 141). However, final biochemical proof for decarbonylation is currently missing, because the two enzymes predicted to be involved in the process (an aldehyde-forming acyl-CoA reductase and an aldehyde decarbonylase) have only been partially purified and some of their most important characteristics remain to be determined.

A multistep pathway hypothesis also seems to be supported by a number of *Arabidopsis* mutants that show correlations between alkane and aldehyde levels. Most notably, stem waxes of *cer1* and *cer22* have decreased levels of wax alkanes, partially compensated by increased levels of aldehydes (42, 54, 106). *CER1* and *CER22* were therefore postulated to encode enzymes catalyzing aldehyde decarbonylation. However, the observed correlation between aldehyde and alkane levels could also be explained by aldehydes being a side product of the pathway, with disrupted alkane formation leading to a backup into this side branch. Consequently, on the basis of the phenotype alone it cannot be decided whether CER1 or CER22 is indeed a decarbonylase involved in alkane formation. Even the cloning of the *CER1* gene did not reveal the function of the protein that it encodes (1). In summary, experimental evidence has not fully validated the decarbonylation hypothesis, and alkane formation remains by far the least understood part of wax biosynthesis.

In *Arabidopsis* leaves, alkanes are the final product of this pathway, whereas in the stem wax of this species, as well as in leaf wax of *B. oleracea*, the alkanes are accompanied by corresponding secondary alcohols and ketones (6, 54). In these instances additional reactions are carried out, in which the alkanes are modified by midchain hydroxylation to secondary alcohols and a second oxidation into ketones. Direct evidence for the oxidation reactions was provided by the incorporation of labeled alkanes and secondary alcohols into ketones, and by inhibitor studies pointing to mixed function oxidases (70, 71, 73).

A reverse genetic approach led to the recent discovery of a cytochrome P450-dependent enzyme (CYP96A15) involved in secondary alcohol and ketone formation in *Arabidopsis* stems (38). The protein is a mid-chain alkane hydroxylase (MAH1) that can catalyze both reaction steps by first hydroxylating alkanes on the central -CH_2- group, and then likely rebinding the resulting secondary alcohol for the second oxidation reaction (**Table 1**). Based on all the available biochemical and molecular genetic information, these two steps of the wax biosynthetic pathway are now well characterized, and confirm the original hypothesis that the pathway proceeds via alkanes as the central intermediates that may or may not be further oxidized depending on plant species and organ type.

TRANSPORT OF CUTICULAR WAX

Intracellular Sites of Wax Synthesis

Enzymes that catalyze the initial steps of wax synthesis, the formation of VLCFA wax precursors, are associated with the ER in all plant species investigated to date. For example, fatty acid elongation activities found in the microsomal fraction of leek (*Allium porrum*) colocalize with ER markers (13, 84). Furthermore, subcellular fractionation in *Zea mays* reveals that the β-ketoacyl reductase resides in the ER (145). Similarly, *Arabidopsis* CER6 condensing enzyme and enoyl-CoA reductase GFP fusion proteins localize to the ER (76, 150).

The ER was recently reported to also be the subcellular compartment in which VLCFAs are further metabolized via the primary alcohol and the alkane pathways. The site of primary alcohol formation was determined by localization of the *Arabidopsis* CER4 FAR, the enzyme that catalyzes the conversion of acyl-CoA to primary alcohols, after expression in yeast (113). Similarly, the mid-chain alkane hydroxylase MAH1, which catalyzes the oxidation of alkanes to secondary alcohols and ketones in *Arabidopsis* stems, was localized to the ER of stem epidermal pavement cells (38). MAH1 is the last enzyme on this wax biosynthetic pathway, and thus its intracellular location implies that both the intermediate metabolites and the final products of the pathway are located in the ER, and must be delivered from this compartment to the plasma membrane for export toward the cuticle.

MAH1: mid-chain alkane hydroxylase, a cytochrome P450-dependent enzyme that forms secondary alcohols and ketones

Delivery of Wax Constituents to the Plasma Membrane

Because conventional sample preparation techniques for electron microscopy extract lipophilic compounds (109), it is difficult to visualize cell structures that may be involved in intracellular wax transport. For this reason, the mechanisms for transport of wax molecules within epidermal cells are currently unknown. On the basis of circumstantial evidence and by analogy with other intracellular lipid transport processes, two hypothetical routes for wax molecules from the ER to the PM have been suggested (76, 117): 1) Golgi-mediated vesicular traffic through the secretory pathway, or 2) direct molecular transfer at ER-PM contact sites (**Figure 2**).

Consistent with the first hypothesis, epidermal cells of sorghum (*Sorghum bicolor*) and rice (*Oryza sativa*) contain dark-staining vesicles (46, 53). However, further cytochemical investigations in deep-water rice showed that these osmiophilic particles tested negative for cutin and candidate proteins for cuticle formation (e.g., lipid transfer proteins) although they did contain other unidentified proteins (47). Thus, the role of these vesicles in the transport of cuticle precursors from the ER to the PM remains unresolved.

In agreement with the second hypothesis that wax components may be transferred from the ER to the PM by a nonvesicular route, membrane contact sites have been

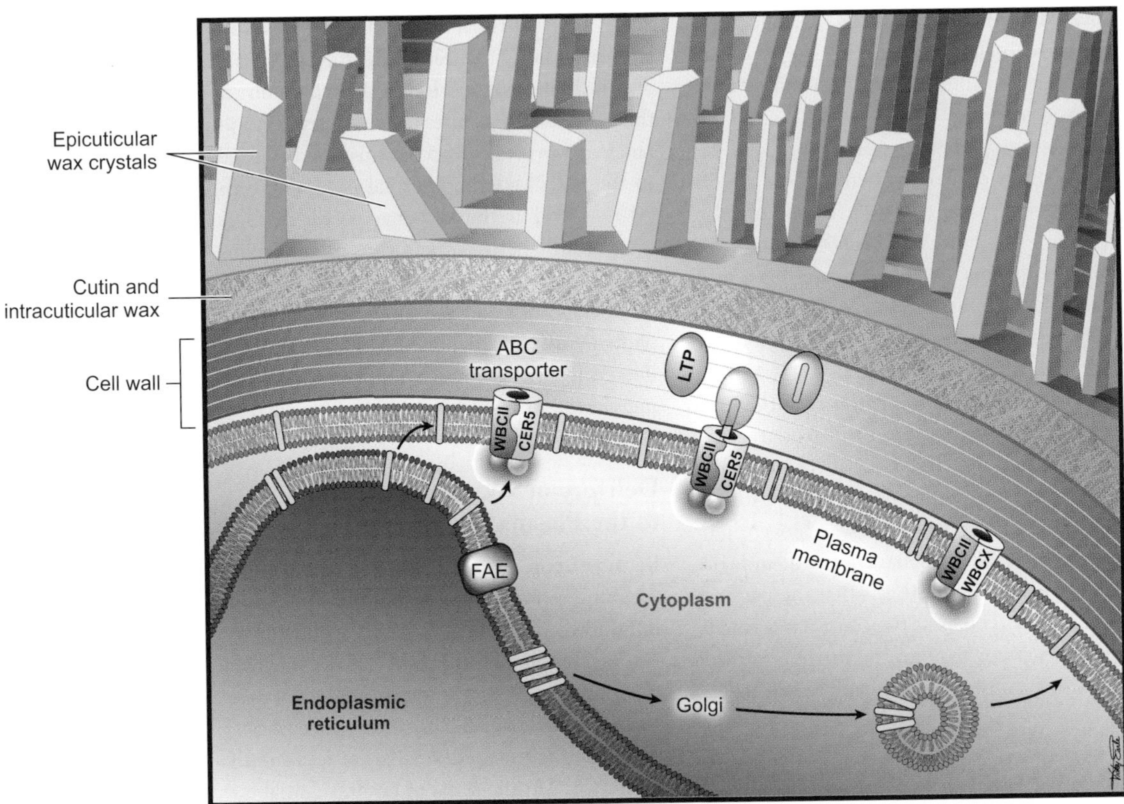

Figure 2

A current model of wax export from an epidermal cell to the cuticle. ABC transporter, ATP binding cassette transporter; CER5, ECERIFERUM 5; FAE, fatty acid elongase; LTP, lipid transfer protein; WBC, WHITE-BROWN COMPLEX.

described in plant cells where cortical ER is in close proximity (within 10 nm) to the PM (122, 123). Similar contact sites in *S. cerevisiae* have been designated as PM-associated membranes (PAMs) (48, 100). PAMs have been defined morphologically by transmission electron microscopy and biochemically by fractionation, which demonstrates the enrichment of some lipid biosynthetic proteins in these domains (100). Cargo selection proteins, such as intracellular lipid transfer proteins, are postulated to be enriched at these sites to facilitate nonvesicular lipid traffic (85). In plants, the monomolecular exchange of lipids at such sites is a suggested mechanism for membrane recycling (123) and/or wax trafficking (76).

Intermediates and products of wax biosynthesis are expected to partition into membrane bilayers within the epidermal cells due to their high hydrophobicity (29, 148). However, nothing is known about the local concentrations and the physical behavior of waxes in the complex lipid mixtures found in biological membranes. High wax concentrations in the epidermal ER could locally disturb the membrane structure (39, 45, 134) and have detrimental effects on housekeeping ER membrane domains. To maintain membrane homeostasis, specialized domains of ER might be dedicated to wax production in the epidermis, similar to oil domains dedicated to storage triglyceride biosynthesis in seeds (120).

Export of Wax from the Plasma Membrane

After wax molecules have been delivered to the PM, they must be released from the lipid bilayer into the apoplastic environment. First progress was recently made toward a more detailed understanding of wax export when two transporters, CER5 and WBC11, required for this process were discovered in *Arabidopsis* stems (17, 102). These ATP binding cassette (ABC) transporters from the ABCG/WHITE-BROWN COMPLEX (WBC) subfamily were shown to be involved in cuticle formation, because both *cer5* and *wbc11* mutants have reduced surface wax loads combined with intracellular wax accumulation (17, 87, 98, 102, 133). Both transporters were localized to the PM of stem epidermal cells using functional transporter–fluorescent protein fusions and confocal microscopy (17, 98, 102, 133).

Although the phenotypes of *cer5* and *wbc11* mutants show that the two ABC transporters are required for wax export from the PM, there is no direct evidence that these proteins actually move wax molecules as substrates. However, given the sequence similarity between CER5 and WBC11 with known lipid transporters of the ABCG subfamily in humans, it seems probable that CER5 and WBC11 are handling wax molecules. Additional questions remain, such as how is substrate presented to the transporter? Can the wax molecules be extracted directly from the ER? The presence of intracellular inclusions in the *cer5* or *wbc11* mutants, rather than PM defects, is consistent with substrate pooling in intracellular membranes such as the ER.

If the CER5 and WBC11 transporters function independently to export wax, then knocking both out should produce a more severe surface wax phenotype than the loss of each protein alone. When *cer5wbc11* double mutants were generated and analyzed, their stems were found to have wax loads and compositions similar to the single mutants, suggesting that the two transporters act in the same pathway or complex (17). ABC transporters of the WBC subfamily are half-transporter proteins requiring dimerization to function (16, 108). An attractive hypothesis is that CER5 and WBC11 form a heterodimer which transports wax across the plasma membrane of the epidermal cells (**Figure 2**). *cer5wbc11* double mutants still accumulate some stem wax; thus, further research is needed to characterize additional protein(s) that are involved in the export of wax from the PM of *Arabidopsis* epidermal cells.

wbc11 mutant lines, but not the *cer5* mutants, also exhibit organ fusions and decreased cutin levels (17, 87, 98), suggesting that WBC11 additionally functions in cutin export. This function might be accomplished by WBC11 homodimers, or by heterodimers formed by WBC11 and members of the WBC subfamily other than CER5. The latter model, in which CER5/WBC11 complexes transport wax components and WBC11/WBCX complexes transport cutin (**Figure 2**), does have a precedent in the eye pigment transporter system of *Drosophila melanogaster*. There, WHITE and BROWN proteins, members of the WBC subfamily, form a heterodimer to transport the red drosopterin pigment precursors, whereas the WHITE/SCARLET heterodimer transports the brown ommochrome pigment precursors (88). Future investigations will show whether another ABC transporter is indeed involved in cutin export in *Arabidopsis*, and how it interacts with WBC11.

ABC transporters: ATP binding cassette transporters

WBC: WHITE-BROWN COMPLEX subfamily of ABC transporters, equivalent to the ABCG subfamily

LTPs: lipid transfer proteins

Transport of Wax Through the Cell Wall to the Cuticle

Once wax components have been exported from the epidermal cell, they must cross the hydrophilic cell wall to reach the cuticle. Even though lipid transfer proteins (LTPs) have long been attractive candidates for wax transport across the cell wall (58), because they are abundantly expressed in the epidermis, are secreted into the apoplast (130), are small enough to traverse the pores of the cell wall, and contain a hydrophobic pocket that binds long-chain fatty acids in vitro (147), no experimental evidence exists for this hypothesis. This lack of information is partially due to difficulties in verifying roles for LTPs in planta, and partially due to the large number of candidate genes. Of the 72 LTP genes annotated in the *Arabidopsis* genome, only *DIR1* has been characterized, and mutant plants with defects in this type 3 LTP (as defined by Reference 11) are defective in long distance signaling for systemic acquired resistance upon pathogen attack (89). From the remaining 71 LTPs, candidates involved in wax transport can be selected on the basis of their epidermis-specific expression. Recently published microarray data indicate that a number of type 1 and type 5 LTPs are highly expressed in the epidermis (127). Reverse genetic approaches may soon reveal whether these proteins indeed function as cuticular lipid carriers within the epidermal cell wall.

REGULATION OF WAX BIOSYNTHESIS

Cuticular wax formation is known to be tightly regulated in response to both developmental and environmental cues. For example, wax loads on rapidly elongating *Arabidopsis* stems remain remarkably constant, indicating that wax production is closely matched to surface area expansion (127). Furthermore, expression analyses carried out for two *Arabidopsis* genes encoding wax biosynthetic enzymes, *CER2* and *CER6* (50, 143), confirmed that these genes are transcriptionally regulated during development. *CER6* transcription is also induced by light and osmotic stress, environmental factors known to stimulate wax accumulation (50). Somewhat unexpectedly, *CER2* expression is not light, heat, cold, or wound inducible, and is unaffected by osmotic stress (143). Despite solid evidence that wax production is under transcriptional control, transcription factors regulating this process have not yet been identified.

Currently, the only transcription factors known to affect wax biosynthesis are the WAX INDUCER (WIN)/SHINE family in *Arabidopsis* and WAX PRODUCTION 1 (WXP1) in *Medicago truncatula*. Overexpression of these APETALA2 (AP2)/ethylene-responsive element binding protein (EREBP)-type transcription factors dramatically enhances wax accumulation in transgenic plants and results in a strikingly glossy leaf phenotype (2, 21, 149). A detailed examination of *35S:WIN1/SHINE 1* (*SHN1*) transgenic plants demonstrated that WIN1/SHN1 overexpression results in the induction of several wax-related genes, including *CER1*, *CER2*, and *KCS1*, and consequently results in a dramatic increase in leaf alkane levels (2, 21). Extreme leaf glossiness and increased wax deposition on leaves and stems are also detected in transgenic plants overexpressing the *WIN1/SHN1* paralogs *SHN2* and *SHN3* (2). In addition, RNA-blot and microarray analyses showed that other genes predicted to encode lipid biosynthetic enzymes and proteins involved in cellular trafficking, including one unidentified ABC transporter, are upregulated in the *35S:WIN1/SHN1* overexpressors (21).

Surprisingly, an investigation into the mode of action of the WIN1/SHN1 transcription factor revealed that it rapidly activates genes encoding cutin biosynthetic enzymes and that this activation, at least for *LACS2*, is a result of direct binding of WIN1/SHN1 to the target gene promoter. This study also confirmed that WIN1/SHN1 is capable of activating wax biosynthetic genes, but that their induction lags behind genes involved in cutin formation (59). This delayed induction of wax-related genes suggests that the control of wax formation by WIN1/SHN1 may be indirect and may require additional transcription factors acting downstream of WIN1/SHN1. Alternatively, wax biosynthetic genes may be regulated in a similar way as the genes encoding enzymes of the cutin biosynthetic pathway, but are induced more slowly than the cutin genes.

Finally, WIN1/SHN1 may impact wax production indirectly by affecting the composition or amount of cutin produced, thus altering the physical properties of the cuticle. This in turn may, possibly through facilitated transport of signaling molecules, activate wax biosynthesis (59). *Arabidopsis* mutants with altered cutin, including *bodyguard* (78) and *lacs2* (12, 115), as well as transgenic plants expressing a fungal cutinase (121), all accumulate more cuticular wax than wild-type plants.

While the search for the elusive components involved in transcriptional activation of wax biosynthesis continues, an intriguing new regulatory pathway controlling cuticular wax accumulation was recently discovered in *Arabidopsis* (49). The key component of this pathway is the CER7 ribonuclease, a core subunit of the exosome, the evolutionarily conserved complex of 3′-5′ exoribonucleases involved in RNA processing and degradation (**Table 1**). In addition to performing general exosomal functions, as described for other eukaryotes, the CER7 ribonuclease has a unique role in epidermis-specific control of wax biosynthesis. The proposed target of this ribonuclease in epidermal cells is a mRNA encoding a repressor of transcription of the key wax biosynthetic gene *CER3*. In wild-type cells, at the onset of wax biosynthesis, the CER7 ribonuclease degrades the mRNA specifying the repressor, thereby allowing CER3 expression and wax production via the alkane-forming pathway to proceed (49). Further work in this area is needed to identify the mRNA target of the CER7 ribonuclease and define the individual steps involved in this process.

Finally, it is interesting to consider how cuticle biosynthetic pathways are regulated in the epidermis during organ development so that wax deposition is synchronized with cutin formation. The constant amounts and compositions of both wax and cutin along all areas of the elongating inflorescence stem of *Arabidopsis* (127) indicate that synthesis and transport of these two components of the cuticle are closely coordinated. Further proof of cross talk between both pathways is that reduced cutin amounts in *Arabidopsis* mutants and transgenics cause increased wax accumulation. Although this result may be explained by the fact that the two pathways share common fatty acid precursors, it may also point to regulatory interactions between the pathways, to common biosynthetic steps, or to (partially) shared mechanisms for transport of cuticle components. A first example for common steps between wax biosynthesis and a cutin-like pathway was provided by the characterization of glycerol 3-phosphate acyltransferase 5 (GPAT5), an acyltransferase involved in the synthesis of aliphatic suberin and waxes in *Arabidopsis* roots (86). Ectopic expression of *GPAT5* results in accumulation of free VLCFAs and corresponding monoacylglycerols in *Arabidopsis* stem cuticular wax at the expense of standard stem wax components (86), implying that GPAT5 is present in the same subcellular compartment and competes with wax biosynthetic enzymes for the same pool of very-long-chain acyl-CoA substrates.

Exosome: multiprotein complex with RNase activity implicated in control of mRNA levels in eukaryotes

SUMMARY POINTS

1. Primary plant surfaces are covered with a cuticle consisting of cutin and wax, and developing epidermal cells make a strong commitment to cuticle biosynthesis during cell expansion.

2. A central stage in wax biosynthesis is elongation of C_{16} and C_{18} acids to very-long-chain fatty acids ($C_{>20}$), mediated by elongase complexes. There has been exciting progress in characterization of three out of the four components of the complex, namely the β-keto acyl-CoA synthase condensing enzyme (KCS), the β-keto acyl-CoA reductase (KCR), and the enoyl-CoA reductase (ECR).

3. On one branch of the wax biosynthetic pathway, even-numbered primary alcohols are formed by reduction of very-long-chain fatty acyl-CoAs. The fatty acyl-CoA reductase (FAR) responsible for this reaction in *Arabidopsis* has been recently identified, showing that both reduction steps from very-long-chain fatty acids to aldehydes and on to the primary alcohols can be catalyzed by one enzyme.
4. On a second branch of the wax biosynthetic pathway, alkanes are formed and further converted into secondary alcohols and ketones by two consecutive oxidation steps. A reverse genetic approach recently led to the discovery of a cytochrome P450–dependent mid-chain alkane hydroxylase (MAH1) that catalyzes these final steps of the pathway.
5. All the wax biosynthetic enzymes investigated to date are localized to the endoplasmic reticulum. Because some of these enzymes catalyze early steps, and some catalyze final steps in the pathway, the entire process of wax biosynthesis likely occurs in this single intracellular compartment.
6. Export of cuticular lipids from the plasma membrane of epidermal cells has been demonstrated to be carried out by CER5 and WBC11 proteins in *Arabidopsis*, members of the ABCG/WHITE-BROWN COMPLEX (WBC) subfamily of ATP binding cassette (ABC) transporters.
7. Wax accumulation in *Arabidopsis* is, at least in part, controlled by the mRNA stability of a proposed repressor of transcription of the key wax biosynthetic gene *ECERIFERUM 3* (*CER3*). At the onset of wax biosynthesis, the mRNA specifying the repressor is recognized and degraded by the CER7 ribonuclease, a core subunit of the exosome, which results in *CER3* expression and wax production via the alkane-forming pathway.

FUTURE ISSUES

1. Wax biosynthesis requires unique lipid biochemical machinery and unique regulation mechanisms in epidermal cells. What are the proportions and how is the flux of C_{16} and C_{18} saturates leaving the plastid controlled?
2. How many KCS homologs are involved in the various elongation rounds during fatty acid elongation? How do chain length preferences of KCSs overlap? Even more importantly, the fourth enzyme of the plant elongase complex, the β-hydroxyacyl-CoA dehydratase, must be identified.
3. Whether one or two FARs are operating in the alcohol pathway of various plant species remains unclear. Intriguing *Arabidopsis* mutant phenotypes and biochemical data from other systems suggest multiple mechanisms could be at work. Is there more than one reductase involved in wax alcohol formation in *Arabidopsis*?
4. An examination of earlier biochemical data on the early steps in the alkane pathway leaves many unanswered questions. This remains the least understood part of wax biosynthesis, despite an array of *Arabidopsis* mutants impaired in this pathway. These mutants provide excellent tools to test the various possible mechanisms for alkane biosynthesis, including decarbonylation.

5. Many aspects of wax export remain enigmatic. How are the highly hydrophobic aliphatic wax components accommodated in cellular membranes? Is wax transport from the endoplasmic reticulum to the plasma membrane vesicular or nonvesicular? How are cuticular lipids transferred across the cell wall?
6. Identification of the mRNA target of the CER7 ribonuclease is essential for defining the mechanism of CER7-based regulation of wax biosynthesis.

DISCLOSURE STATEMENT

The authors are not aware of any biases that might be perceived as affecting the objectivity of this review.

ACKNOWLEDGMENTS

The authors acknowledge the artwork of Vicki Earle, UBC Media Group, for **Figure 2**. Funding for the 'Roadmap to the Plant Cuticle' was provided by a Natural Sciences and Engineering Research Council of Canada Special Research Opportunity program grant to the authors. The authors thank Miao Wen and David Bird for helpful comments on the manuscript.

LITERATURE CITED

1. Aarts MGM, Keijzer CJ, Stiekema WJ, Pereira A. 1995. Molecular characterization of the *CER1* gene of *Arabidopsis* involved in epicuticular wax biosynthesis and pollen fertility. *Plant Cell* 7:2115–27
2. Aharoni A, Dixit S, Jetter R, Thoenes E, van Arkel G, Pereira A. 2004. The SHINE clade of AP2 domain transcription factors activates wax biosynthesis, alters cuticle properties, and confers drought tolerance when overexpressed in *Arabidopsis*. *Plant Cell* 16:2463–80
3. Andersson MX, Goksör M, Sandelius AS. 2007. Optical manipulation reveals strong attracting forces at membrane contact sites between endoplasmic reticulum and chloroplasts. *J. Biol. Chem.* 282:1170–74
4. Andrews J, Keegstra K. 1983. Acyl-CoA synthetase is located in the outer membrane and acyl-CoA thioesterase in the inner membrane of pea chloroplast envelopes. *Plant Physiol.* 72:735–40
5. Ariizumi T, Hatakeyama K, Hinata K, Sato S, Kato T, et al. 2003. A novel male-sterile mutant of *Arabidopsis thaliana*, *faceless pollen-1*, produces pollen with a smooth surface and an acetolysis-sensitive exine. *Plant Mol. Biol.* 53:107–16
6. Baker E. 1974. The influence of environment on leaf wax development in *Brassica oleracea* var. *gemmifera*. *New Phytol.* 73:955–66
7. Baker E. 1982. Chemistry and morphology of plant epicuticular waxes. In *The Plant Cuticle*, ed. D Cutler, KL Alvin, CE Price, pp. 139–65. London: Academic
8. Baud S, Bellec Y, Miquel M, Bellini C, Caboche M, et al. 2004. *gurke* and *pasticcino3* mutants affected in embryo development are impaired in acetyl-CoA carboxylase. *EMBO Rep.* 5:515–20
9. Baud S, Guyon V, Kronenberger J, Wuillème S, Miquel M, et al. 2003. Multifunctional acetyl-CoA carboxylase 1 is essential for very long chain fatty acid elongation and embryo development in *Arabidopsis*. *Plant J.* 33:75–86

10. Beaudoin F, Gable K, Sayanova O, Dunn T, Napier JA. 2002. A *Saccharomyces cerevisiae* gene required for heterologous fatty acid elongase activity encodes a microsomal β-keto-reductase. *J. Biol. Chem.* 277:11481–88
11. Beisson F, Koo AJK, Ruuska S, Schwender J, Pollard M, et al. 2003. *Arabidopsis* genes involved in acyl lipid metabolism. A 2003 census of the candidates, a study of the distribution of expressed sequence tags in organs, and a web-based database. *Plant Physiol.* 132:681–97
12. Bessire MCC, Jacquat A-C, Humphry M, Borel S, Petétot JMC, et al. 2007. A permeable cuticle in *Arabidopsis* leads to a strong resistance to *Botrytis cinerea*. *EMBO J.* 26:2158–68
13. Bessoule J-J, Lessire R, Cassagne C. 1989. Partial purification of the acyl-CoA elongase of *Allium porrum* leaves. *Arch. Biochem. Biophys.* 268:475–84
14. Bianchi G. 1995. Plant waxes. See Ref. 40, pp. 176–222
15. Bianchi G, Avato P, Salamini F. 1978. Glossy mutants of maize. VIII. Accumulation of fatty aldehydes in surface waxes of *gl5* maize seedling. *Biochem. Genet.* 16:1015–21
16. Bird D. 2007. The role of ABC transporters in cuticular lipid transport. *Plant Sci.* In press
17. Bird D, Beisson F, Brigham A, Shin J, Greer S, et al. 2007. Characterization of *Arabidopsis* ABCG11/WBC11, an ATP binding cassette (ABC) transporter that is required for cuticular lipid secretion. *Plant J.* 52:485–498
18. Blacklock BJ, Jaworski JG. 2006. Substrate specificity of *Arabidopsis* 3-ketoacyl-CoA synthases. *Biochem. Biophys. Res. Commun.* 346:583–90
19. Bognar AL, Paliyath G, Rogers L, Kolattukudy PE. 1984. Biosynthesis of alkanes by particulate and solubilized enzyme preparations from pea leaves (*Pisum sativum*). *Arch. Biochem. Biophys.* 235:8–17
20. Bonaventure G, Salas JJ, Pollard MR, Ohlrogge JB. 2003. Disruption of the *FATB* gene in *Arabidopsis* demonstrates an essential role of saturated fatty acids in plant growth. *Plant Cell* 15:1020–33
21. Broun P, Poindexter P, Osborne E, Jiang C-Z, Riechmann JL. 2004. WIN1, a transcriptional activator of epidermal wax accumulation in *Arabidopsis*. *Proc. Natl. Acad. Sci. USA* 101:4706–11
22. Buckner J, Kolattukudy PE. 1973. Specific inhibition of alkane synthesis with accumulation of very long chain compounds by dithioerythritol, dithiothreitol, and mercaptoethanol in *Pisum sativum*. *Arch. Biochem. Biophys.* 156:34–45
23. Cassagne C, Lessire R. 1974. Studies on alkane biosynthesis in epidermis of *Allium porrum* L. leaves. *Arch. Biochem. Biophys.* 165:274–80
24. Cheesbrough T, Kolattukudy PE. 1984. Alkane biosynthesis by decarbonylation of aldehydes catalyzed by a particulate preparation from *Pisum sativum*. *Proc. Natl. Acad. Sci. USA* 81:6613–17
25. Chen X, Goodwin SM, Boroff VL, Liu X, Jenks MA. 2003. Cloning and characterization of the *WAX2* gene of *Arabidopsis* involved in cuticle membrane and wax production. *Plant Cell* 15:1170–85
26. Cheng JB, Russell DW. 2004. Mammalian wax biosynthesis: I. Identification of two fatty acyl-Coenzyme A reductases with different substrate specificities and tissue distributions. I. *J. Biol. Chem.* 279:37789–97
27. Chibnall A, Piper SH. 1934. The metabolism of plant and insect waxes. *Biochem. J.* 28:2209–19
28. Clough R, Matthis AL, Barnum SR, Jaworski JG. 1992. Purification and characterization of 3-ketoacyl-acyl carrier protein synthase from spinach: a condensing enzyme utilizing acetyl-CoA to initiate fatty acid synthesis. *J. Biol. Chem.* 267:20992–98

29. Coll EP, Kandt C, Bird DA, Samuels AL, Tieleman DP. 2007. The distribution and conformation of very long-chain plant wax components in a lipid bilayer. *J. Phys. Chem. B* 111:8702–4
30. Denic V, Weissman JS. 2007. A molecular caliper mechanism for determining very long-chain fatty acid length. *Cell* 130:663–88
31. Dennis M, Kolattukudy PE. 1991. Alkane biosynthesis by decarbonylation of aldehyde catalyzed by a microsomal preparation from *Botryococcus braunii*. *Arch. Biochem. Biophys.* 287:268–75
32. Dennis M, Kolattukudy PE. 1992. A cobalt-porphyrin enzyme converts a fatty aldehyde to a hydrocarbon and CO. *Proc. Natl. Acad. Sci. USA* 89:5306–10
33. Dietrich CR, Perera MADN, Yandeau-Nelson MD, Meeley RB, Nikolau BJ, Schnable PS. 2005. Characterization of two *GL8* paralogs reveals that the 3-ketoacyl reductase component of fatty acid elongase is essential for maize (*Zea mays* L.) development. *Plant J.* 42:844–61
34. Dunn TM, Lynch DV, Michaelson LV, Napier JA. 2004. A postgenomic approach to understanding sphingolipid metabolism in *Arabidopsis thaliana*. *Ann. Bot.* 93:483–97
35. Fiebig A, Mayfield JA, Miley NL, Chau S, Fischer RL, Preuss D. 2000. Alterations in *CER6*, a gene identical to *CUT1*, differentially affect long-chain lipid content on the surface of pollen and stems. *Plant Cell* 12:2001–8
36. Gable K, Garton S, Napier JA, Dunn TM. 2004. Functional characterization of the *Arabidopsis thaliana* orthologue of *Tsc13p*, the enoyl reductase of the yeast microsomal fatty acid elongating system. *J. Exp. Bot.* 55:543–45
37. Gray JE, Holroyd GH, van der Lee FM, Bahrami AR, Sijmons PC, et al. 2000. The HIC signalling pathway links CO_2 perception to stomatal development. *Nature* 408:713–16
38. Greer S, Wen M, Bird D, Wu X, Samuels L, Kunst L, Jetter R. 2007. The cytochrome P450 enzyme *CYP96A15* is the mid-chain alkane hydroxylase responsible for formation of secondary alcohols and ketones in stem cuticular wax of *Arabidopsis thaliana*. *Plant Physiol.* 145:653–67
39. Hamilton JA. 1998. Fatty acid transport: Difficult or easy? *J. Lipid Res.* 39:467–81
40. Hamilton RJ, ed. 1995. *Waxes: Chemistry, Molecular Biology and Functions*. Dundee: Oily Press
41. Han G, Gable K, Kohlwein SD, Beaudoin F, Napier JA, Dunn TM. 2002. The *Saccharomyces cerevisiae YBR159w* gene encodes the 3-ketoreductase of the microsomal fatty acid elongase. *J. Biol. Chem.* 277:35440–49
42. Hannoufa A, McNevin J, Lemieux B. 1993. Epicuticular waxes of *eceriferum* mutants of *Arabidopsis thaliana*. *Phytochemistry* 33:851–55
43. Harwood JL. 2005. Fatty acid biosynthesis. In *Plant Lipids: Biology, Utilisation and Manipulation*, ed. D Murphy, pp. 27–66. Oxford: Blackwell
44. Heredia A. 2003. Biophysical and biochemical characteristics of cutin, a plant barrier biopolymer. *Biochim. Biophys. Acta* 1620:1–7
45. Ho JK, Moser H, Kishimoto Y, Hamilton JA. 1995. Interactions of a very long chain fatty acid with model membranes and serum albumin: Implications for the pathogenesis of adrenoleukodystrophy. *J. Clin. Invest.* 96:1455–63
46. Hoffmann-Benning S, Kende H. 1994. Cuticle biosynthesis in rapidly growing internodes of deepwater rice. *Plant Physiol.* 104:719–23
47. Hoffmann-Benning S, Klomparens KL, Kende H. 1994. Characterization of growth-related osmiophilic particles in corn coleoptiles and deepwater rice internodes. *Ann. Bot.* 74:563–72

48. Holthius J, Levine TP. 2005. Lipid traffic: Floppy drives and a superhighway. *Nat. Rev. Mol. Cell Biol.* 6:209–20
49. Hooker TS, Lam P, Zheng H, Kunst L. 2007. A core subunit of the RNA-processing/degrading exosome specifically influences cuticular wax biosynthesis in *Arabidopsis. Plant Cell* 19:904–13
50. Hooker TS, Millar AA, Kunst L. 2002. Significance of the expression of the CER6 condensing enzyme for cuticular wax production in *Arabidopsis. Plant Physiol.* 129:1568–80
51. Jeffree CE. 1996. Structure and ontogeny of plant cuticles. See Ref. 60, pp. 33–83
52. Jeffree CE. 2006. The fine structure of the plant cuticle. See Ref. 111, pp. 11–125
53. Jenks MA, Rich PJ, Ashworth EN. 1994. Involvement of cork cells in the secretion of epicuticular wax filaments on Sorghum bicolor (L) Moench. *Int. J. Plant Sci.* 155:506–18
54. Jenks MA, Tuttle HA, Eigenbrode SD, Feldman KA. 1995. Leaf epicuticular waxes of the *eceriferum* mutants in *Arabidopsis. Plant Physiol.* 108:369–77
55. Jetter R, Kunst L, Samuels L. 2006. Composition of plant cuticular waxes. See Ref. 111, pp. 145–81
56. Jetter R, Schäffer S. 2001. Chemical composition of the *Prunus laurocerasus* leaf surface. Dynamic changes of the epicuticular wax film during leaf development. *Plant Physiol.* 126:1725–37
57. Joyard J, Stumpf PK. 1981. Synthesis of long-chain acyl-CoA in chloroplast envelope membranes. *Plant Physiol.* 67:250–56
58. Kader J-C. 1996. Lipid-transfer proteins in plants. *Annu. Rev. Plant Physiol. Plant Mol. Biol.* 47:627–54
59. Kannangara R, Branigan C, Liu Y, Penfield T, Rao V, et al. 2007. The transcription factor WIN1/SHN1 regulates cutin biosynthesis in *Arabidopsis thaliana. Plant Cell* 19:1278–94
60. Kerstiens G, ed. 1996. *Plant Cuticles: An Integrated Functional Approach.* Oxford. UK: Bios Sci.
61. Khan A, Kolattukudy PE. 1994. Decarboxylation of long chain fatty acids to alkanes by cell free preparations of pea leaves (*Pisum sativum*). *Biochem. Biophys. Res. Commun.* 61:1379–86
62. Kohlwein SD, Eder S, Oh C-S, Martin CE, Gable K, et al. 2001. Tsc13p is required for fatty acid elongation and localizes to a novel structure at the nuclear-vacuolar interface in *Saccharomyces cerevisiae. Mol. Cell. Biol.* 21:109–25
63. Kolattukudy PE. 1965. Biosynthesis of wax in *Brassica oleracea. Biochemistry* 4:1844–55
64. Kolattukudy PE. 1968. Tests whether a head to head condensation mechanism occurs in the biosynthesis of n-hentriacontane, the paraffin of spinach and pea leaves. *Plant Physiol.* 43:1466–70
65. Kolattukudy PE. 1970. Reduction of fatty acids to alcohols by cell-free preparation of *Euglena gracilis. Biochemistry* 9:1095–102
66. Kolattukudy PE. 1971. Enzymatic synthesis of fatty alcohols in *Brassica oleracea. Arch. Biochem. Biophys.* 142:701–9
67. Kolattukudy PE. 1980. Cutin, suberin and waxes. In *The Biochemistry of Plants*, ed. PK Stumpf, pp. 571–645. London: Academic
68. Kolattukudy PE. 1996. Biosynthetic pathways of cutin and waxes, and their sensitivity to environmental stresses. See Ref. 60, pp. 83–108
69. Kolattukudy PE, Buckner JS, Brown L. 1972. Direct evidence for a decarboxylation mechanism in the biosynthesis of alkanes in *B. oleracea. Biochem. Biophys. Res. Commun.* 47:1306–13

70. Kolattukudy PE, Buckner JS, Liu T-Y. 1973. Biosynthesis of secondary alcohols and ketones from alkanes. *Arch. Biochem. Biophys.* 156:613–20
71. Kolattukudy PE, Croteau R, Brown L. 1974. Structure and biosynthesis of cuticular lipids. Hydroxylation of palmitic acid and decarboxylation of C28, C30 and C32 acids in *Vicia faba* flowers. *Plant Physiol.* 54:670–77
72. Kolattukudy PE, Jaeger R, Robinson R. 1971. Biogenesis of nonacosan-15-one in *Brassica oleracea*. *Phytochemistry* 10:3047–51
73. Kolattukudy PE, Liu T-Y. 1970. Direct evidence for biosynthetic relationships among hydrocarbons, secondary alcohols and ketones in *Brassica oleracea*. *Biochem. Biophys. Res. Commun.* 41:1369–74
74. Koo AJK, Ohlrogge JB, Pollard M. 2004. On the export of fatty acids from the chloroplast. *J. Biol. Chem.* 279:16101–10
75. Koornneef M, Hanhart CJ, Thiel F. 1989. A genetic and phenotypic description of *Eceriferum* (*cer*) mutants in *Arabidopsis thaliana*. *J. Hered.* 80:118–22
76. Kunst L, Samuels AL. 2003. Biosynthesis and secretion of plant cuticular wax. *Progr. Lipid Res.* 42:51
77. Kurata T, Kawabata-Awai C, Sakuradani E, Shimizu S, Okada K, Wada T. 2003. The *YORE-YORE* gene regulates multiple aspects of epidermal cell differentiation in *Arabidopsis*. *Plant J.* 36:55–66
78. Kurdyukov S, Faust A, Nawrath C, Bär S, Voisin D, et al. 2006. The epidermis-specific extracellular *BODYGUARD* controls cuticle development and morphogenesis in Arabidopsis. *Plant Cell* 18:321–39
79. Lai C, Kunst L, Jetter R. 2007. Composition of alkyl esters in the cuticular wax on inflorescence stems of *Arabidopsis thaliana cer* mutants. *Plant J.* 50:189–96
80. Lardizabal KD, Metz JG, Sakamoto T, Hutton WC, Pollard MR, Lassner MW. 2000. Purification of a jojoba embryo wax synthase, cloning of its cDNA, and production of high levels of wax in seeds of transgenic *Arabidopsis*. *Plant Physiol.* 122:645–56
81. Lassner MW, Lardizabal K, Metz JG. 1996. A jojoba β-ketoacyl-CoA synthase cDNA complements the canola fatty acid elongation mutation in transgenic plants. *Plant Cell* 8:281–92
82. Lechelt-Kunze C, Meissner RC, Drewes M, Tietjen K. 2003. Flufenacet herbicide treatment phenocopies the *fiddlehead* mutant in *Arabidopsis thaliana*. *Pest Manag. Sci.* 59:847–56
83. Lemieux B, McNevin J, Hannoufa A, Espelie K, Feldmann K. 1992. GC-MS analysis of the wax of *eceriferum* (*cer*) mutants of *Arabidopsis thaliana* and isolation of *CER* genes from T-DNA tagged *Arabidopsis* mutant lines. *Plant Physiol.* 99:14
84. Lessire R, Juguelin H, Moreau P, Cassagne C. 1985. Elongation of acyl-CoAs by microsomes from etiolated leek seedlings. *Phytochemistry* 24:1187–92
85. Levine T. 2004. Short-range intracellular trafficking of small molecules across endoplasmic reticulum junctions. *Trends Cell Biol.* 14:483–90
86. Li Y, Beisson F, Ohlrogge J, Pollard M. 2007. Monoacylglycerols are components of root waxes and can be produced in the aerial cuticle by ectopic expression of a suberin-associated acyltransferase. *Plant Physiol.* 144:1267–77
87. Luo B, Xue XY, Hu WL, Wang LJ, Chen XY. 2007. An ABC transporter gene of *Arabidopsis thaliana*, *AtWBC11*, is involved in cuticle development and prevention of organ fusion. *Plant Cell Physiol.* doi:10.1093/pcp/pcm152
88. Mackenzie S, Howells A, Cox G, Ewart G. 2000. Sub-cellular localisation of the White/Scarlet ABC transporter to pigment granule membranes within the compound eye of *Drosophila melanogaster*. *Genetica* 108:239

89. Maldonado A, Doerner P, Dixon RA, Lamb CJ, Cameron RK. 2002. A putative lipid transfer protein involved in systemic resistance signalling in *Arabidopsis*. *Nature* 419:399–403
90. McNevin JP, Woodward W, Hannoufa A, Feldmann KA, Lemieux B. 1993. Isolation and characterization of *eceriferum* (*cer*) mutants induced by T-DNA insertions in *Arabidopsis thaliana*. *Genome* 36:610–18
91. Metz JG, Pollard MR, Anderson L, Hayes TR, Lassner MW. 2000. Purification of a jojoba embryo fatty acyl-Coenzyme A reductase and expression of its cDNA in high erucic acid rapeseed. *Plant Physiol.* 122:635–44
92. Millar AA, Clemens S, Zachgo S, Giblin EM, Taylor DC, Kunst L. 1999. *CUT1*, an *Arabidopsis* gene required for cuticular wax biosynthesis and pollen fertility, encodes a very-long-chain fatty acid condensing enzyme. *Plant Cell* 11:825–38
93. Millar AA, Kunst L. 1997. Very-long-chain fatty acid biosynthesis is controlled through the expression and specificity of the condensing enzyme. *Plant J.* 12:121–31
94. Moto Ki, Yoshiga T, Yamamoto M, Takahashi S, Okano K, et al. 2003. Pheromone gland-specific fatty-acyl reductase of the silkmoth, *Bombyx mori*. *Proc. Natl. Acad. Sci. USA* 100:9156–61
95. Nawrath C. 2006. Unraveling the complex network of cuticular structure and function. *Curr. Opin. Plant Biol.* 9:281–87
96. Negruk V, Yang P, Subramanian M, McNevin JP, Lemieux B. 1996. Molecular cloning and characterization of the *CER2* gene of *Arabidopsis thaliana*. *Plant J.* 9:137–45
97. Ohlrogge J, Browse J. 1995. Lipid biosynthesis. *Plant Cell* 7:957–70
98. Panikashvili D, Savaldi-Goldstein S, Mandel T, Yifhar T, Franke RB, et al. 2007. The Arabidopsis *DESPERADO/AtWBC11* transporter is required for cutin and wax secretion. *Plant Physiol.* doi: 10.1104/pp.107.105676
99. Paul S, Gable K, Beaudoin F, Cahoon E, Jaworski J, et al. 2006. Members of the *Arabidopsis* FAE1-like 3-ketoacyl-CoA synthase gene family substitute for the Elop proteins of *Saccharomyces cerevisiae*. *J. Biol. Chem.* 281:9018–29
100. Pichler H, Gaigg B, Hrastnik C, Achleitner G, Kohlwein SD, et al. 2001. A subfraction of the yeast endoplasmic reticulum associates with the plasma membrane and has a high capacity to synthesize lipids. *Eur. J. Biochem.* 268:2351–61
101. Pidkowich MS, Nguyen HT, Heilmann I, Ischebeck T, Shanklin J. 2007. Modulating seed β-ketoacyl-acyl carrier protein synthase II level converts the composition of a temperate seed oil to that of a palm-like tropical oil. *Proc. Natl. Acad. Sci. USA* 104:4742–47
102. Pighin JA, Zheng H, Balakshin LJ, Goodman IP, Western TL, et al. 2004. Plant cuticular lipid export requires an ABC transporter. *Science* 306:702–4
103. Pollard M, Beisson F, Li Y, Ohlrogge J. 2007. Polyesters in plants. *Trends Plant Sci.* In press
104. Pollard M, McKeon T, Gupta LM, Stumpf PK. 1979. Studies on biosynthesis of waxes by developing jojoba seed. II. The demonstration of wax biosynthesis by cell-free homogenates. *Lipids* 14:651–62
105. Rashotte AM, Jenks MA, Feldmann KA. 2001. Cuticular waxes of *eceriferum* mutants of *Arabidopsis thaliana*. *Phytochemistry* 57:115–23
106. Rashotte AM, Jenks MA, Ross A, Feldmann KA. 2004. Novel *eceriferum* mutants in *Arabidopsis thaliana*. *Planta* 219:5–13
107. Raven JA, Edwards D. 2004. Physiological evolution of lower embryophytes: adaptations to the terrestrial environment. In *The Evolution of Plant Physiology: From Whole Plants to Ecosystems*, ed. A Hemsley, I Poole, pp. 17–41. Amsterdam: Elsevier

108. Rea PA. 2007. Plant ATP-binding cassette transporters. *Annu. Rev. Plant Biol.* 58:347–75
109. Reed DW. 1982. Wax alteration and extraction during electron microscopy preparation of leaf cuticles. In *The Plant Cuticle*, ed. D Cutler, KL Alvin, CE Price, pp. 181–96. London: Academic
110. Riederer M. 2006. Introduction: Biology of the plant cuticle. See Ref. 111, pp. 1–8
111. Riederer M, Müller C, eds. 2006. *Biology of the Plant Cuticle*. Oxford, UK: Blackwell
112. Rowland O, Lee R, Franke R, Schreiber L, Kunst L. 2007. The *CER3* wax biosynthetic gene from *Arabidopsis thaliana* is allelic to *WAX2/YRE/FLP1*. *FEBS Lett.* 581:3538–44
113. Rowland O, Zheng H, Hepworth SR, Lam P, Jetter R, Kunst L. 2006. *CER4* encodes an alcohol-forming fatty acyl-Coenzyme A reductase involved in cuticular wax production in *Arabidopsis*. *Plant Physiol.* 142:866–77
114. Schneider-Belhaddad F, Kolattukudy PE. 2000. Solubilization, partial purification, and characterization of a fatty aldehyde decarbonylase from a higher plant, *Pisum sativum*. *Arch. Biochem. Biophys.* 377:341–49
115. Schnurr J, Shockey J, Browse J. 2004. The acyl-CoA synthetase encoded by *LACS2* is essential for normal cuticle development in *Arabidopsis*. *Plant Cell* 16:629–42
116. Schnurr JA, Shockey JM, de Boer G-J, Browse JA. 2002. Fatty acid export from the chloroplast: Molecular characterization of a major plastidial acyl-Coenzyme A synthetase from *Arabidopsis*. *Plant Physiol.* 129:1700–9
117. Schulz B, Frommer WB. 2004. A plant ABC transporter takes the lotus seat. *Science* 306:622–25
118. Shimakata T, Stumpf P. 1982. Isolation and function of spinach leaf β-ketoacyl-[acyl-carrier-protein] synthases. *Proc. Natl. Acad. Sci. USA* 79:5808–12
119. Shockey JM, Fulda MS, Browse JA. 2002. *Arabidopsis* contains nine long-chain acyl-Coenzyme A synthetase genes that participate in fatty acid and glycerolipid metabolism. *Plant Physiol.* 129:1710–22
120. Shockey JM, Gidda SK, Chapital DC, Kuan J-C, Dhanoa PK, et al. 2006. Tung tree DGAT1 and DGAT2 have nonredundant functions in triacylglycerol biosynthesis and are localized to different subdomains of the endoplasmic reticulum. *Plant Cell* 18:2294–313
121. Sieber P, Schorderet M, Ryser U, Buchala A, Kolattukudy P, et al. 2000. Transgenic *Arabidopsis* plants expressing a fungal cutinase show alterations in the structure and properties of the cuticle and postgenital organ fusions. *Plant Cell* 12:721–38
122. Staehelin LA. 1997. The plant ER: a dynamic organelle composed of a large number of discrete functional domains. *Plant J.* 11:1151–65
123. Staehelin LA, Chapman RL. 1987. Secretion and membrane recycling in plant cells: novel intermediary structures visualized in ultrarapidly frozen sycamore and carrot suspension-culture cells. *Planta* 171:43–57
124. Stark RE, Tian S. 2006. The cutin biopolymer matrix. See Ref. 111, pp. 126–41
125. Stoveken T, Kalscheuer R, Malkus U, Reichelt R, Steinbuchel A. 2005. The wax ester synthase/acyl Coenzyme A:diacylglycerol acyltransferase from *Acinetobacter* sp. strain ADP1: characterization of a novel type of acyltransferase. *J. Bacteriol.* 187:1369–76
126. Stumpf P. 1984. Fatty acid biosynthesis in higher plants. In *Fatty acid Metabolism and Its Regulation*, ed. S Numa, pp. 155–79. Amsterdam: Elsevier Sci.
127. Suh MC, Samuels AL, Jetter R, Kunst L, Pollard M, et al. 2005. Cuticular lipid composition, surface structure, and gene expression in *Arabidopsis* stem epidermis. *Plant Physiol.* 139:1649–65
128. Tanaka H, Machida Y. 2006. The cuticle and cellular interactions. See Ref. 111, pp. 312–33

129. Tehlivets O, Scheuringer K, Kohlwein SD. 2007. Fatty acid synthesis and elongation in yeast. *Biochim. Biophys. Acta* 1771:255–70
130. Thoma S, Kaneko Y, Somerville C. 1993. A nonspecific lipid transfer protein from *Arabidopsis* is a cell wall protein. *Plant J.* 3:427–36
131. Todd J, Post-Beittenmiller D, Jaworski JG. 1999. *KCS1* encodes a fatty acid elongase 3-ketoacyl-CoA synthase affecting wax biosynthesis in *Arabidopsis thaliana*. *Plant J.* 17:119–30
132. Trenkamp S, Martin W, Tietjen K. 2004. Specific and differential inhibition of very-long-chain fatty acid elongases from *Arabidopsis thaliana* by different herbicides. *Proc. Natl. Acad. Sci. USA* 101:11903–8
133. Ukitsu H, Kuromori T, Toyooka K, Goto Y, Matsuoka K, et al. 2007. Cytological and biochemical analysis of *COF1*, an Arabidopsis mutant of an ABC transporter gene. *Plant Cell Phsyiol.* 48:1524–33
134. Urbina P, Alonso A, Contreras FX, Goni FM, Lopez DJ, et al. 2006. Alkanes are not innocuous vehicles for hydrophobic reagents in membrane studies. *Chem. Phys. Lipids* 139:107
135. Vioque J, Kolattukudy PE. 1997. Resolution and purification of an aldehyde-generating and an alcohol-generating fatty acyl-CoA reductase from pea leaves (*Pisum sativum* L.). *Arch. Biochem. Biophys.* 340:64–72
136. Voelker TA. 1996. Plant acyl-ACP thioesterases: chain-length determining enzymes in plant fatty acid biosynthesis. In *Genetic Engineering*, ed. J Setlow, pp. 111–33. New York: Plenum
137. von Wettstein-Knowles P. 1982. Elongase and epicuticular wax biosynthesis. *Physiol. Vég.* 20:797–809
138. von Wettstein-Knowles P. 1993. Waxes, cutin and suberin. In *Lipid Metabolism in Plants*, ed. T Moore, pp. 127–66. Boca Raton, FL: CRC Press
139. von Wettstein-Knowles P. 1995. Biosynthesis and genetics of waxes. See Ref. 40, pp. 91–129
140. Waltermann M, Stoveken T, Steinbuchel A. 2007. Key enzymes for biosynthesis of neutral lipid storage compounds in prokaryotes: Properties, function and occurrence of wax ester synthases/acyl-CoA:diacylglycerol acyltransferases. *Biochimie* 89:230–42
141. Wang X, Kolattukudy PE. 1995. Solubilization and purification of aldehyde-generating fatty acyl-CoA reductase from green alga *Botryococcus braunii*. *FEBS Lett.* 370:15–18
142. Xia Y, Nikolau BJ, Schnable PS. 1996. Cloning and characterization of *CER2*, an *Arabidopsis* gene that affects cuticular wax accumulation. *Plant Cell* 8:1291–304
143. Xia Y, Nikolau BJ, Schnable PS. 1997. Developmental and hormonal regulation of the *Arabidopsis CER2* gene that codes for a nuclear-localized protein required for the normal accumulation of cuticular waxes. *Plant Physiol.* 115:925–37
144. Xu X, Dietrich CR, Delledonne M, Xia Y, Wen TJ, et al. 1997. Sequence analysis of the cloned *glossy8* gene of maize suggests that it may code for a β-ketoacyl reductase required for the biosynthesis of cuticular waxes. *Plant Physiol.* 115:501–10
145. Xu X, Dietrich CR, Lessire R, Nikolau BJ, Schnable PS. 2002. The endoplasmic reticulum-associated maize GL8 protein is a component of the acyl-Coenzyme A elongase involved in the production of cuticular waxes. *Plant Physiol.* 128:924–34
146. Yephremov A, Wisman E, Huijser P, Huijser C, Wellesen K, Saedler H. 1999. Characterization of the *FIDDLEHEAD* gene of *Arabidopsis* reveals a link between adhesion response and cell differentiation in the epidermis. *Plant Cell* 11:2187–202
147. Zachowski A, Guerbette F, Grosbois M, Jolliot-Croquin A, Kader J-C. 1998. Characterisation of acyl binding by a plant lipid-transfer protein. *Eur. J. Biochem.* 257:443–48

148. Zhang F, Kamp F, Hamilton JA. 1996. Dissociation of long and very long chain fatty acids from phospholipid bilayers. *Biochemistry* 35:16055–60
149. Zhang J-Y, Broeckling C, Sumner L, Wang Z-Y. 2007. Heterologous expression of two *Medicago truncatula* putative ERF transcription factor genes, WXP1 and WXP2, in *Arabidopsis* led to increased leaf wax accumulation and improved drought tolerance, but differential response in freezing tolerance. *Plant Mol. Biol.* 64:265–78
150. Zheng H, Rowland O, Kunst L. 2005. Disruptions of the *Arabidopsis* enoyl-CoA reductase gene reveal an essential role for very-long-chain fatty acid synthesis in cell expansion during plant morphogenesis. *Plant Cell* 17:1467–81

Ionomics and the Study of the Plant Ionome

David E. Salt,[1,2] Ivan Baxter,[2] and Brett Lahner[1]

[1]Horticulture and Landscape Architecture, Purdue University, West Lafayette, Indiana 47907

[2]Bindley Bioscience Center, Purdue University, West Lafayette, Indiana 47907; email: dsalt@purdue.edu

Annu. Rev. Plant Biol. 2008. 59:709–33

First published online as a Review in Advance on February 5, 2008

The *Annual Review of Plant Biology* is online at plant.annualreviews.org

This article's doi: 10.1146/annurev.arplant.59.032607.092942

1543-5008/08/0602-0709$20.00

Key Words

elemental analysis, mineral nutrient, trace element, functional genomics, bioinformatics, gene discovery

Abstract

The ionome is defined as the mineral nutrient and trace element composition of an organism and represents the inorganic component of cellular and organismal systems. Ionomics, the study of the ionome, involves the quantitative and simultaneous measurement of the elemental composition of living organisms and changes in this composition in response to physiological stimuli, developmental state, and genetic modifications. Ionomics requires the application of high-throughput elemental analysis technologies and their integration with both bioinformatic and genetic tools. Ionomics has the ability to capture information about the functional state of an organism under different conditions, driven by genetic and developmental differences and by biotic and abiotic factors. The relatively high throughput and low cost of ionomic analysis means that it has the potential to provide a powerful approach to not only the functional analysis of the genes and gene networks that directly control the ionome, but also to the more extended gene networks that control developmental and physiological processes that affect the ionome indirectly. In this review we describe the analytical and bioinformatics aspects of ionomics, as well as its application as a functional genomics tool.

Contents

CONCEPTS OF THE IONOME AND IONOMICS

The ionome was defined as all the mineral nutrient and trace elements found in an organism (47). This definition extended the previously used term metallome (61, 90) to include biologically significant nonmetals (77). The ionome also includes both essential and nonessential elements. The concept of the ionome has been applied to *Saccharomyces cerevisae*; the mineral nutrient and trace element profile of 4385 mutant strains from the *Saccharomyces* Genome Deletion collection were recently quantified (19). This work in *S. cerevisae* represents the first full genome-wide scan for genes involved in the regulation of the ionome in any organism.

The ionome can be thought of as the inorganic subset of the metabolome, a term originally used to describe the global metabolite pools in *Escherichia coli* and *S. cerevisae* (60, 85) and has now been generalized to describe the "quantitative complement of all the low-molecular weight molecules present in cells in a particular physiological or developmental state" (for a review see Reference 29). Further drawing on these parallels with the metabolome and its study of metabolomics or metabonomics (58), the study of the ionome, called ionomics, is defined here as the quantitative and simultaneous measurement of the elemental composition of living organisms and changes in this composition in response to physiological stimuli, developmental state, and genetic modifications.

This definition captures and highlights several critical concepts in the study of the ionome. Firstly, the study of the ionome is predicated on the fact that it should provide a snapshot of the functional status of a complex biological organism; this information is held in both the quantitative and qualitative patterns of mineral nutrients and trace elements in the various tissues and cells of the organism. Such a concept rests heavily on the early work of Pauling & Robinson (for a review see Reference 74), in which they developed the notion that a quantitative metabolite profile can be indicative of a particular physiological or disease state. To capture this information contained in the ionome, the precise and simultaneous quantification of as many of the components of the ionome as possible is necessary. Secondly, the power of ionomics lies in its ability to precisely capture information about the functional state of an organism under different conditions. These conditions may be driven either by genetic differences or developmental differences or by biotic or abiotic factors.

The underlying cause of an alteration in the ionome may be either direct or indirect. For example, alterations in the mineral nutrient levels in the soil or the loss of function of an important ion transporter would be expected to directly affect the ionome. Conversely, alterations in cell wall structure or acidification of the apoplast, for example, might be expected to indirectly affect the ionome. Given the relatively high throughput and low cost of ionomic analysis (hundreds of samples per day at approximately \$10/sample), compared with metabolomic or proteomic analysis (tens of samples per day at approximately \$100/sample), ionomics has the potential to provide a powerful and relatively low cost approach to not only the functional analysis of the genes and gene networks that directly control the ionome, but also to analysis of the more extended gene networks that control developmental and physiological processes that indirectly affect the ionome.

HISTORY OF IONOMICS

The inception of ionomics occurred with the blending of ideas from both metabolomics and plant mineral nutrition. The conviction held by Pauling & Robinson (for a review see Reference 74) in the late sixties and early seventies that the metabolite profiles of an organism contain a rich source of information that is reflective of the physiological status of an organism has been confirmed many times since their pioneering work, and there are now many recent reviews of metabolomics that provide excellent overviews of this topic (for example, see Reference 80). The ability to explore the information content of an organism's metabolite profile only became truly feasible with the advent of reliable small-molecule profiling technologies such as gas-liquid chromatography–mass spectrometry (GC-MS) and proton-nuclear magnetic resonance (^{1}H-NMR). Similarly, our understanding of the basic biology of mineral nutrient homeostasis in plants has very much paralleled our analytical capability to quantify these mineral nutrients. However, only with the development of reliable inductively coupled plasma (ICP) technologies and the ability to simultaneously analyze all the significant elemental components of a plant was it possible to fuse the early ideas of Pauling and Robinson and others on metabolite profiling with our broad understanding of plant mineral nutrition. This fusion gave rise to the concepts of the ionome and ionomics, and occurred at a time when both bioinformatics tools and genetic tools such as sequenced genomes, DNA microarrays, and gene deletion collections were being developed. Given this milieu, we feel that ionomics is coming of age as a tool to both help unravel the functional complexities of genomes and probe the physiologies of plants and animals, and the future for discoveries in ionomics is bright.

Below we describe the analytical and bioinformatics tools required to perform ionomics, and discuss how ionomics can be applied to advance our knowledge and understanding of biological systems.

ANALYTICAL TECHNOLOGY REQUIRED FOR IONOMICS

To achieve the key analytical requirements of ionomics, the "quantitative and simultaneous measurement of the elemental composition of living organisms," requires choosing specialized instrumentation and sample preparation protocols on the basis of various selection criteria. These criteria include sample throughput, dynamic quantification range, sensitivity, elements to be measured, sample size availability, reliability, cost, portability, and the need to measure the ionome in either a bulk sample (e.g., dried and milled whole maize plant) or with either low spatial resolution (1–10 mm, e.g., sample of leaf or root tissue) or high spatial resolution (10–100 μm, e.g., elemental map of a trichome or *Arabidopsis thaliana* seed) in either two or three dimensions. Furthermore, the optimum analytical solution must always be balanced with the financial support available for the project. Because most ionomic analyses are generally comparative (for example, did the ionome change when gene x was deleted), precision is important analytically, not accuracy. To clarify, precision is a measure of how consistently a result is determined by repeated measurements. Precision is critical if you want to establish that an observed alteration in the ionome is due to the perturbation the experimenter applied to the system rather than due to uncontrolled analytical or environmental error. Conversely, accuracy is a measure of how close a measurement is to the true absolute value. High accuracy in ionomics is required only if the experimenter wants to make conclusive statements about the absolute concentration of particular elements in the ionome. An example of such a statement is "the minimal quota for this element is 2×10^5 atoms of zinc per cell" (61). The need for precision, accuracy, or both has numerous implications for the analytical methodology chosen to perform ionomics, some of which are discussed below.

Methods for elemental analysis fall into two groups: techniques that utilize the electronic properties of an atom (emission, absorption, and fluorescence spectroscopy) or techniques that utilize its nuclear properties (radioactivity or atomic number). Below we review some of the most common methods for the simultaneous quantification of multiple elements (see **Table 1** for summary), along with various other analytical considerations such as sample preparation, standardization, and normalization. We also discuss other auxiliary analytical methods for the acquisition of both spatial ionomics and chemical speciation information.

Inductively Coupled Plasma

The goal of ICP is to ionize analyte atoms for their detection by either optical emission spectroscopy (ICP-OES) [also known as atomic emission spectroscopy (ICP-AES)] or mass spectrometry (ICP-MS). The ICP is designed to generate a plasma, a gas in which atoms are present in the ionized state. To generate a plasma a silica torch is used, situated within a water- or argon-cooled coil of a radio frequency generator (RF coil). Flowing gas (plasma gas) [typically argon (Ar)] is introduced into the plasma torch and the radio frequency field ionizes the gas, making it electrically conductive. The plasma is maintained by the inductive heating of the flowing gas. The plasma, at up to 8000 K, is insulated both electrically and thermally from the instrument, and maintained in position by a flow of cooling argon gas (coolant gas). The sample to be analyzed, as an aerosol, is carried into the plasma by a third argon gas stream (carrier gas). Generally, elements to be analyzed by ICP must be in solution (there are exceptions to this, discussed below under Laser Ablation ICP). An aqueous sample is preferred, and particulates should be avoided because they can clog the instrument. A nebulizer in the instrument transforms the aqueous sample into an aerosol. The sample is pumped into the nebulizer via a peristaltic pump where it is converted into an aerosol, which passes into the spray chamber with the carrier argon gas. In the spray chamber the finest sample droplets are swept into the plasma while the large sample droplets settle out and run to waste. Various nebulizer designs allow sample flow rates to range from less than 20 μL per minute to more than 2 mL per minute, and some designs can accommodate some fine particulate matter as well. The optimal flow rate is determined by the transfer efficiency, sample size, and plasma matrix effects. A system with good transfer efficiency will get more analyte ions to the detector per volume of sample introduced, which allows for a smaller sample size and reduces matrix effects within the plasma. Desolvation systems improve transfer efficiency by increasing the analyte/solvent ratio before the sample enters the plasma. Two methods of desolvation are commonly employed: porous membrane and heating/cooling. On introduction into the plasma atoms in the sample are ionized, generally into singly charged positive ions. Once ionized the analyte atoms are detected using either an optical emission spectrometer or a mass spectrometer.

Table 1 Comparison of various elemental analysis techniques with potential application in ionomics

Technique	Name[a]	Sensitivity[b]	Analysis time[c]	Sample Prep	Matrix Effects	Quantification	Cost	Elements detected	Summary	Notes
ICP-MS	Inductively coupled plasma mass spectrometry	PPT to PPB; PPQ (10E-15 mass fraction) with sector instruments	1 to 3 minutes; depends on number of elements measured, sample uptake, and washout	Simple acid digestion or microwave digestion	Extensive, but can be corrected for using equations or reduced with collision cells or a sector instrument	NIST standards available for calibration; somewhat appropriate SRMs available for plants	\$10 to \$60 per sample; lowest prices for efficient in-house work; instrument price \$125 to \$400k	Most elements, but sensitivity varies; can measure individual isotopes	Possible to run hundreds of samples daily with excellent sensitivity	Both ICP-MS and ICP-OES depend on having a consistent supply of high-quality argon
ICP-OES	Inductively coupled optical emission spectrometry	PPB	1 to 2 minutes; depends mainly on uptake and washout times	Simple acid digestion or microwave digestion	Extensive, can be partly corrected for using equations	NIST standards available for calibration; somewhat appropriate SRMs available for plants	Costs similar to ICP-MS, although purchase prices of instruments are lower	Most elements, but sensitivity varies; in practice fewer elements than ICP-MS due to lower sensitivity	Can achieve higher throughput than ICP-MS at the cost of some elements and sensitivity	Gains some sensitivity compared with ICP-MS by running more concentrated samples
XRF	X-ray fluorescence	sub-PPM	30 seconds to several minutes; may depend on number of elements measured	Extensive; samples are either powdered and compressed into a wafer or fused into a glass	Amount of fluorescence is very sample dependent; samples must be "known" for accurate determinations	Standards may need to be prepared by user; not as accurate as ICP methods	\$10 to \$150 per sample or more, depending on number of elements and type of instrument	Difficult to measure elements with atomic numbers lower than sodium	Versatile system for measuring PPM levels of many elements in solid samples	Instrument forms vary widely and impact type of data obtained; high-end instruments may be used to localize elements
NAA	Neutron activation analysis	10E-15 mass fraction for some elements	Hours to days; requires a neutron source such as a reactor or an accelerator	Sample may be in various states; sample is placed in polyethylene vial; simple prep	Present but correctable; relatively unimportant compared to other methods	Used as a primary analytical method to test other instrumental techniques	Expensive; \$300 to \$450 per sample	Nearly 70% of the elements; more than 30 elements possible simultaneously	Costly, slow, very sensitive, accurate; useful for checking other techniques	Getting all desired elements may be impossible or push the analysis into the highest cost per sample

[a]Proton-induced X-ray emission possible as an alternative.
[b]Sensitivity is element dependent for every technique.
[c]Assumes sample prep is not limiting.
Abbreviations: PPT, parts per trillion; PPB, parts per billion; NIST, National Institute of Standards and Technology; SRM, standard reference materials.

Optical Emission Spectroscopy

When ionized analyte atoms in the ICP plasma fall back to ground state they emit photons at a wavelength characteristic of a given element. For quantification of these analytes the light from the plasma, representing a summation of emitted light from all the atoms introduced into the plasma from the sample, can be focused and passed through optical slits into a spectrometer. Within the spectrophotometer an optical filter is used to separate the collected photons by wavelength, and a charge injection device (CID) detector simultaneously measures the intensities of photons at multiple wavelengths. By comparing these energy intensities to reference standards a quantitative measurement of each element in the sample can be obtained.

Inductively Coupled Plasma Mass Spectrometry

The ability of ICP to ionize atoms makes it an effective ionization source for detection by mass spectroscopy. Ions from the ICP pass through sampling and skimmer cones (typically made of nickel) before being focused by a series of ion lenses into the quadrupole mass analyzer. Ions are transmitted through the quadrupole on the basis of their mass to charge ratio and detected by an electron multiplier. Quantification is achieved by comparison with reference standards for each element of interest.

One critical advantage of ICP-MS over ICP-OES is that it allows for a smaller sample size owing to its greater sensitivity. A small sample size has numerous benefits for ionomic analyses. A small sample size usually requires less sample preparation time, which in turn may be faster and easier. Small samples also allow more samples to be loaded into an autosampler, allowing longer analytical runs. The small sample size required for ICP-MS also makes nondestructive sampling of small plants possible, a prerequisite in a classical genetic screen where interesting mutants need to be saved and not destroyed by sampling. In the deficit column, smaller samples require cleaner conditions, are harder to weigh accurately, and may be more difficult to handle. One additional advantage of ICP-MS over ICP-OES is that individual isotopes may be measured, which introduces the possibility of isotopic spiking for pulse-chase–type experiments and isotope dilution procedures for improved analytical accuracy and precision.

One of the main drawbacks of ICP-MS is that the formation of polyatomic ionic species in the plasma can interfere with the measurement of particular elements; e.g., $^{40}Ar^{16}O^+$ interferes with the determination of ^{56}Fe. These polyatomic species are generated from ions derived from the plasma gas or sample components. The cold/cool plasma approach, which uses a reduced plasma temperature to reduce the formation of argon-based interferences, is effective at minimizing some of these interferences, but is difficult to optimize, and it is time consuming to move back and forth between hot and cold plasma. However, use of the collision/reaction cell alleviates the problems associated with the cold/cool plasma approach by removing polyatomic species from the plasma before they enter the mass analyzer. In this configuration, ions from the ICP enter the mass analyzer interface as normal, where they are now extracted into the collision/reaction cell positioned before the quadrupole. One or two collision/reaction gases such as hydrogen and methane are fed into the cell, where, under the influence of a radio frequency field, the introduced gas(es) collide and react with ions from the sample. Through a number of ion-molecular collisions and reactions polyatomic interfering ions like $^{40}Ar^{16}O^+$ are eliminated. The collision/reaction gases used are chosen on the basis of the interfering polyatomic species to be removed. For example, such technology allows for the use of ICP-MS to measure Se at its most abundant isotope, 80 (49.6%), which is normally covered by Ar_2, by a reaction of the $^{40}Ar^{40}Ar^+$ dimer with hydrogen gas. An even more biologically important element, Fe, can be measured at its most abundant isotope, 56 (91.7%), by reacting the interfering $^{40}Ar^{16}O^+$ ion with methane. A complementary approach to the collision/reaction cell is to use a desolvating sample introduction system.

An alternative approach to the removal or reduction of interfering polyatomic ions is to utilize a single collector magnetic sector high-resolution ICP-MS (HR-ICP-MS). Because of the increased resolution of the mass analyzer of these instruments it is possible to simply resolve the interfering polyatomic ions from the analyte ions of interest. HR-ICP-MS provides the gold standard for the resolution of interfering polyatomics. However, HR-ICP-MS instruments are currently more expensive than quadrupole ICP-MS instruments (though the differential of approximately $150,000 is rapidly shrinking), and scan speeds for detection of multiple elements are lower (though not dramatically).

In summary, ICP-OES or ICP-MS can both be used effectively for ionomics. ICP-OES has the advantage of lower cost and simplicity, whereas ICP-MS has an edge in sensitivity and the ability to detect different isotopes of the same element. Although ICP-OES is less sensitive than ICP-MS, some of this sensitivity is won back by the robustness of ICP-OES in more concentrated sample matrices. Whereas ICP-MS struggles with sample matrices with greater than about 0.1% solids, ICP-OES can handle up to about 3% dissolved solids. Both ICP-OES and ICP-MS have been used successfully for large-scale ionomics projects; Eide and colleagues (19) used ICP-OES to measure approximately 10,000 samples over two years in yeast, and other researchers used ICP-MS to measure approximately 80,000 samples between 2001–2007 in *A. thaliana* (10, 47, 76).

By coupling laser ablation for sample introduction to ICP-MS (LA-ICP-MS), information about the ionome can be acquired without sample preparation and with two-dimensional spatial resolution. Generally, a UV laser light is focused on the sample; spot sizes can be varied from 5–300 μm. At the point of focus the UV laser ablates material from the sample, and this ablated material is introduced into the plasma of the ICP-MS via an argon carrier gas that flows over the sample being ablated. LA-ICP-MS analysis can be carried out on a single spot on the sample, rastered over several spots (e.g., **Figure 1**), or scanned continuously across the sample to develop a two-dimensional elemental map of the sample. By using the laser to sample a single spot over time an elemental depth profile of the sample can also be developed. LA-ICP-MS is well suited for the ionomic analysis of specific tissues or small regions of samples, such as root tips, vascular tissue, etc. This technique would also be useful for the tissue localization of ionomics changes that had previously been identified in bulk samples of leaves, for example. Furthermore, LA-ICP-MS should be applicable to high-throughput ionomic screening of arrayed samples. LA-ICP-MS has been used extensively for the analysis of geological samples, human artifacts, and bone, teeth, and hair. However, LA-ICP-MS has currently had only limited application for plant samples; for example, Punshon and colleagues (70) analyzed U and Ni on the surface of leaves. The limited availability of cooled sample chambers required for the analysis of hydrated samples and difficulties in quantification of elements using LA-ICP-MS may explain this limited application. However, we feel that this technique holds great potential for ionomic analysis.

X-Ray Fluorescence

X-ray fluorescence (XRF) is the emission of secondary or fluorescent X-rays from an atom that has been excited by the absorption of high energy X-rays or gamma rays. The emitted fluorescence X-rays have energies characteristic of the atom from which they were emitted, and therefore can be used to detect and quantify specific elements in a complex mixture. For the primary excitation of the sample, radiation of sufficient energies is required to allow for the removal of tightly held electrons

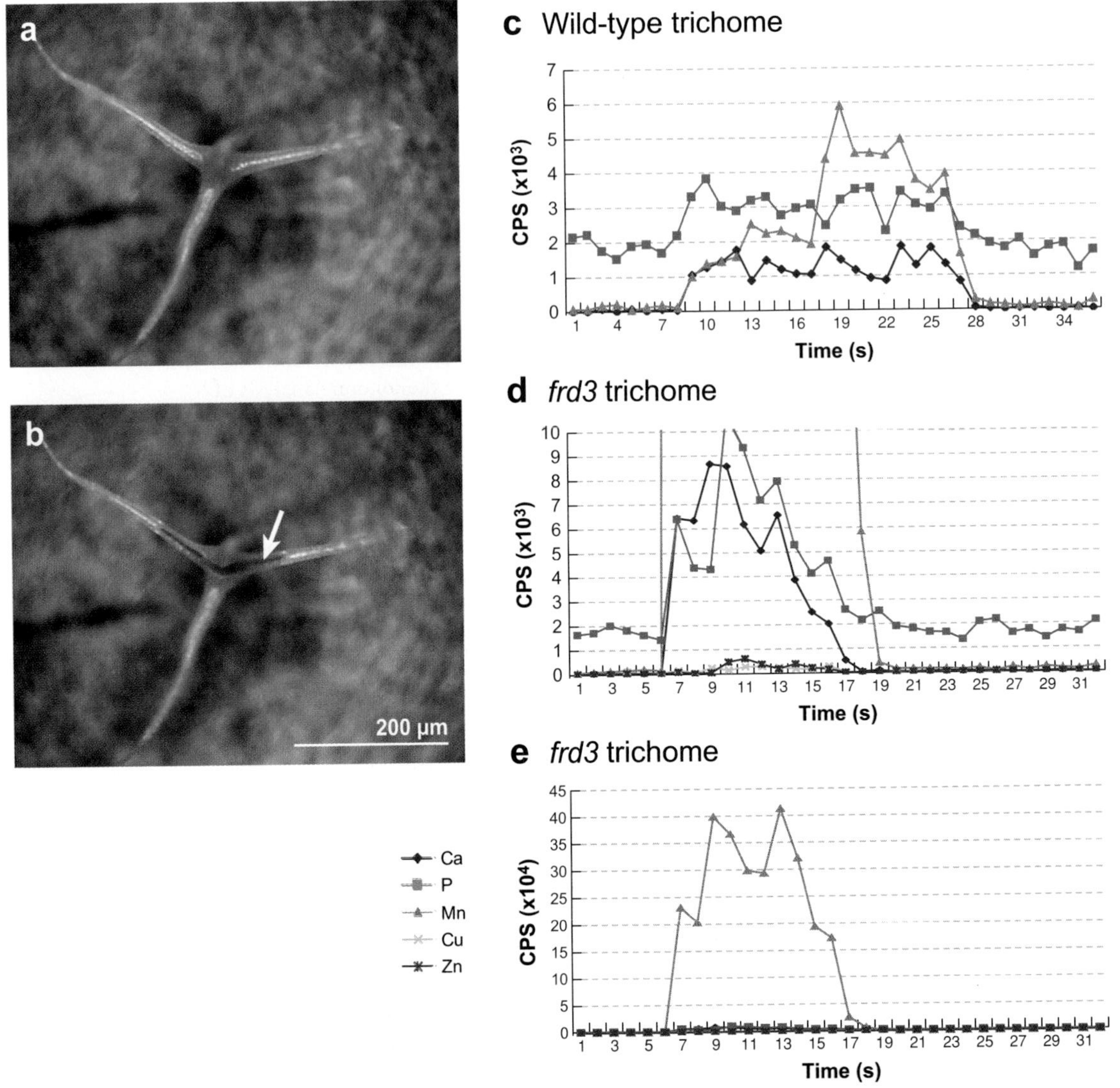

Figure 1

Laser ablation ICP-MS. *Arabidopsis thaliana* trichome analyzed by in situ laser ablation inductively coupled plasma mass spectrometry (ICP-MS). (*a*) Trichome before ablation. (*b*) Trichome after ablation (*arrow*). (*c*) ICP-MS data for trichome on a wild-type leaf showing levels of Ca, P, and Mn. (*d,e*) ICP-MS data for trichome of a mutant (*frd3*) leaf, with different y-axis scales, showing elevated accumulation of Ca, P, Mn, Cu, and Zn. Image and data courtesy of Brett Lahner, Luke Gumaelius, and David E Salt. CPS, counts per second.

in the inner shells of atoms. High-energy electrons from outer shells replace these lost electrons, and in the process release fluorescence X-rays, which can be detected for elemental quantification. This high-energy primary excitation radiation can be supplied from a conventional high-voltage X-ray tube to produce a range of X-ray energies, allowing excitation and quantification of a broad range of atoms. However, gamma-ray sources can also be used to produce an overlapping range of energies, which allows for multielement detection. Such sealed gamma-ray sources are inherently radioactive, and therefore do not require large power supplies and can be used in small portable XRF instruments, which are useful for rapid ionomic analyses in the greenhouse or the field. For example, plant tissue and soil could be analyzed directly in the field, and decisions about collection of fresh tissue for genotyping of a segregating mapping population can be made. Such experiments could be very valuable for the identification of quantitative trait loci (QTL) involved in ionomic adaptation to particular soil conditions. Given that XRF is generally a nondestructive procedure, ionomic analysis by XRF can be performed on living plant specimens without compromising their viability. However, because uniform samples produce more precise analytical data, samples are generally prepared as flat discs thick enough to allow the sample to absorb all the energy of the primary excitation beam.

Synchrotron radiation is a third source of excitation energy for XRF. Here X-rays are focused into a very intense beam with a small cross-sectional area, allowing analysis of both the distribution and concentration of multiple elements with trace-level detection limits and micrometer to submicrometer spatial resolution. Such microXRF techniques can be applied for elemental analysis of a single region of a sample, or be used for sample scanning in two dimensions, without any sample preparation. Furthermore, XRF microtomography and confocal XRF imaging can be used to map the elemental content of a sample in three dimensions. However, given the intensity of the excitation energies used with these synchrotron-based X-ray beams, these procedures can damage the sample, and will quite possibly be detrimental to the viability of living organisms. A related elemental analysis method, based on the same principles as XRF, is particle (or proton) induced X-ray emission (PIXE). In this method a beam of protons is generally used to excite atoms in the sample, which are then detected by their emission of fluorescent X-rays as in XRF.

In the early 1990s, before the ionome or ionomics had been defined, Delhaize and coworkers (18) applied XRF for the successful multielement screening of more than 100,000 mutagenized *A. thaliana* seedlings to identify mutants with altered ionomes. This screen identified three mutants: *pho2*, which accumulates threefold higher P in leaves compared with wild-type; *pho1-2*, which accumulates reduced P in leaves [and was previously identified by Poirier and colleagues (69) in a colorimetric screen for P mutants] (17); and *man1* (now known as *frd3*), which overaccumulates a range of metals in leaves, including manganese, for which it was originally named (16). Owing to the lack of molecular genetics tools for *A. thaliana* when these mutants were first identified, it took several more years before the loci underlying these mutant phenotypes were identified (6, 9, 26, 75). Interestingly, one of the first mutants to be identified in a truly ionomic screen by Delhaize, *frd3* (formally *man1*), was used as the positive control in the second large-scale ionomic screen performed by Salt and coworkers (47), and was in fact rediscovered in this second ICP-MS–based screen.

A second novel application of XRF to ionomics is the recent use of synchrotron-based microXRF as a rapid screening tool for the possible identification of *A. thaliana* seeds with mutant ionomic phenotypes (94). In this proof-of-concept work, *A. thaliana* seeds were arrayed in 5 × 3 blocks, and each block was scanned with a focused X-ray beam to quantify the relative content of Mn, Fe, Ni, Cu, Zn, K, and Ca of each seed in the block. Such a microXRF-based ionomics methodology holds great promise for the rapid screening of many thousands of seeds or other tissue samples. However, a practical application of the method awaits further optimization work.

Synchrotron-based microXRF has also been used successfully both for ionomic analysis of small samples and for two-dimensional imaging of the ionome in several different biological samples, including intact Se-tolerant and Se-sensitive diamondback moths (22), intact zooplankton (20), the growth front of mussel shells (46), and mycorrhizal plant roots (96). Recently, XRF microtomography and confocal imaging were also used for quantitative imaging of the three-dimensional distribution of multiple elements in various plant samples (32, 35, 38, 55) (e.g., XRF microtomography, **Figure 2**). The recent insightful combination of microXRF imaging with nanogold immunolocalization offers the unique opportunity for the simultaneous colocalization of known cellular structures, such as the mitochondria and chloroplast, with particular features revealed by microXRF elemental mapping (50). Such colocalization information could be very important for the biological interpretation of XRF imaging.

Although these XRF imaging techniques do not have the throughput required for ionomics screens, they are proving to be powerful tools for understanding the fundamental biological processes that underlie the ionome. For example, Kim and coworkers (38) recently used XRF microtomography to quantitatively map the three-dimensional distribution of various elements in intact *A. thaliana* seeds (**Figure 2**). Using this technique they were

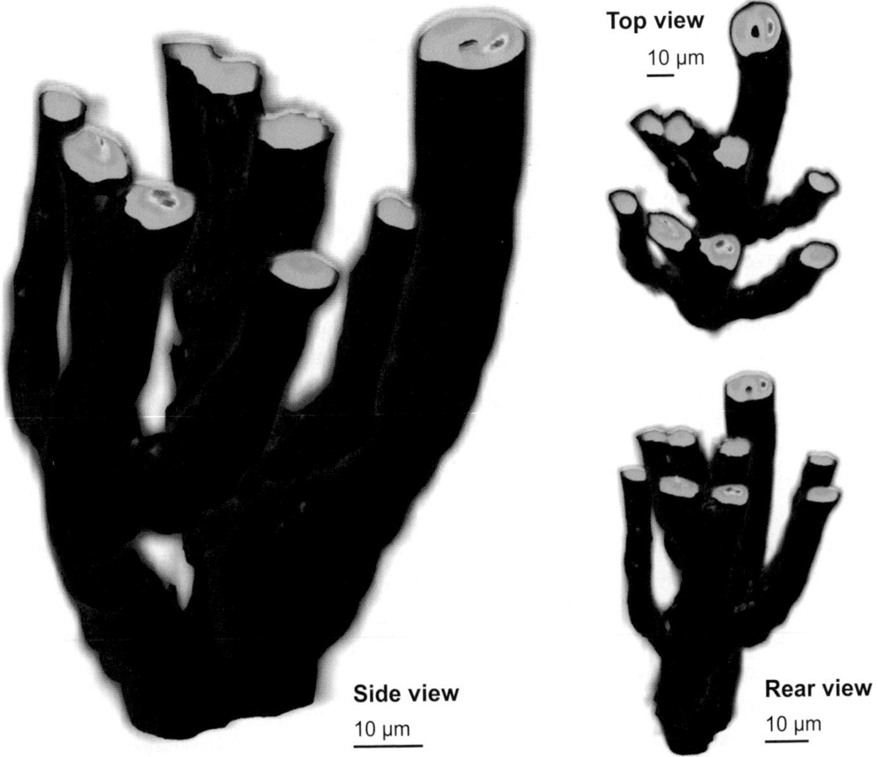

Figure 2

X-ray microtomography. Three-dimensional rendering of Fe K-alpha fluorescence in an *A. thaliana* (Col-0) seed, with in silico transaxial sectioning (z axis, upper 50% removed), showing the Fe localization to a discrete cell layer surrounding the embryonic provasculature. Three views are shown: side (*main panel*), top (*upper inset*), and rear (*lower inset*) views. The branched structures are the Fe surrounding the provasculature of the cotyledons, and the the unbranched structure is the provasculature of the radicle. Warmer colors correspond to higher Fe fluorescence. Image courtesy of Tracy Punshon, Tony Lanzirotti, and Mary Lou Guerinot.

able to determine that the vacuolar Fe uptake transporter VIT1 is directly involved in storage of Fe in the provascular strands of the *A. thaliana* embryo, and without such localized stores of Fe *vit1-1* seedlings fail to thrive.

Neutron Activation Analysis

Neutron activation is the process whereby free neutrons are captured by atomic nuclei. This neutron capture results in the formation of new nuclei that are frequently radioactive. These radioactive nuclei will decay with time, and a proportion of the energy is released as gamma radiation. This emitted gamma radiation can be detected, and gamma rays at a particular energy are indicative of the presence of a specific radionuclide. Processing of the gamma-ray spectra released from a neutron-irradiated sample can therefore yield the concentration of various elements in the sample. This type of technique can allow the nondestructive quantification of multiple major and trace elements in a sample. Because neutrons have no charge they can penetrate and pass through most samples, activating the whole sample. Gamma rays released from the activated sample are also very penetrating and can escape the sample for efficient detection. Therefore, elemental analysis by neutron activation analysis (NAA) in general does not suffer from errors introduced due to the sample matrix. NAA can be performed on a sample directly, without sample preparation. In this configuration the analysis is termed instrument neutron activation analysis (INAA), and it is this approach that is most useful for the large sample numbers required for ionomic analysis. Unfortunately, NAA does require access to a nuclear reactor as a source of neutrons to perform the initial activation step, which could limit the usefulness of NAA for a long-term ionomics project.

Elemental analysis of plant samples by NAA dates back to at least the mid-1960s. Analysis was initially focused on single elements, but by the early 1970s researchers were performing simultaneous analysis of macro, micro and trace elements in plants by NAA (54). The power of elemental profiling using NAA was rapidly applied to environmental toxicology, where the transport of potentially toxic trace elements from the environment, through crop plants and livestock to humans, has been monitored using NAA (15, 23, 33, 83). Multielement analysis of plant samples by NAA was also used to identify and monitor areas of heavy metal pollution across broad geographical areas and multiple years (8, 25). Interestingly, NAA was also used to perform multielement quantification on plant samples collected within and across broad phylogenetic groupings, for the identification of trends in mineral nutrient and trace element accumulation in plants across taxa (62, 87). However, even though the use of NAA for plant samples goes back more than forty years, to our knowledge NAA has not yet been used as a high-throughput elemental analysis tool for ionomic analyses, as defined here. For example, unlike ICP-(OES & MS) and XRF, NAA has not been used as a screening tool for the identification of ionomic mutants. This is surprising given the high throughput and minimal sample preparation required for INAA. We do note that NAA has been applied to perform ionomics in the study of breast cancer (24, 57), colorectal cancer (3, 81), and brain cancer (2); in these studies the ionome was shown to be perturbed in the diseased tissues or organisms.

ANALYTICAL STANDARDIZATION

Because ionomics generally involves the comparison of two nearly identical organisms across an experiment that can last between hours to years, standardization across these timescales can set the lower limit on the discovery and determination of the differences between these two organisms. The sharpest comparison occurs when they are colocated as much as possible both spatially and temporally, starting from the growth stage and continuing through the chemical analysis. In this way the effect of instrument drift (i.e., changes in the instrument's analytical responsiveness with time) is reduced. The effect of drift can be further minimized by the use of internal standards, and by recalibrating as frequently as necessary. For comparing samples in separate runs, or even from different labs, external standards [National Institute of Standards and Technology (NIST) traceable] and standard reference materials (SRMs, available from NIST) become useful. Because the matrix matching of samples is very important, reference material must sometimes be prepared from the same type of material as that under analysis. Note that because differences between these very similar organisms are often due to environmental factors, this careful standardization across time and distance is helpful for elucidating these factors. Environmental factors can also be gauged by the essential inclusion of positive control plants in every group of samples.

The precision of the determination of the amount of material in each analytical sample can be limiting in the ability to discern differences in the ionome if the samples are small or unwieldy. One way to avoid this problem is to normalize samples to their analytical signal and the included matrix-matched reference standards. This method is based on the assumption that all the samples have identical compositions. If, after the calculation is done, a line is found to be ionomically different, then the affected elements are removed from the data set, and the calculation iterated (47). An added advantage of this technique is that it saves the time of determining the sampled amount by the standard method, such as weighing.

An important, often overlooked part of the data analysis is the necessity of presenting the data in a form that is most useful to the end users. Because gigabytes of data may be produced with current technology, and many people with varied backgrounds may need to understand the significance of the results, today's challenge is to reduce the data to easy concepts like percentage change and p-values and make it available through simple and efficient interfaces.

SAMPLE HARVESTING AND PREPARATION

Harvesting is a crucial element in plant ionomics. Getting the equivalent portion of each plant is necessary because plant tissue is far from homogeneous. Even leaves just a week apart in age can show significant differences in their ion profiles. Particularly when using ICP-OES or ICP-MS as the measurement technique, getting the same amount of sample each time can improve the results dramatically. This effect is due to two factors: First, the sample matrix affects the plasma in ways that may not be corrected for by the internal standards. Second, a very small or large sample may be outside the linear dynamic range of some of the calibration curves, or even below the detection limit. Harvesting is also the stage where sample contamination can either be reduced by a good washing technique or introduced from utensils or hands.

Sample preparation for the ICP techniques is typically acid digestion and dilution. Open air or microwave digestion can be used. Both require a fume hood that can handle acid fumes. If laser ablation is used as a sample introduction technique, then sample preparation consists of fixing the sample to a flat surface and possible drying or freezing of the sample. Sample chambers for laser ablation are now available that can accommodate a 96-well plate, which could facilitate the automation of the targeting process for appropriate samples, e.g., seeds. NAA does not require extensive sample preparation. The sample must be sealed in a small vial and can be solid or liquid (or gas). All that matters is the amount of analyte within the vial. XRF has the most difficult preparation; the samples typically must be homogenized and pelletized. However, a large screen has already been undertaken using XRF in which leaf samples were merely pressed onto flat surfaces (18); as noted above, microXRF techniques require only proper mounting.

AUXILIARY IONOMIC METHODOLOGIES

A critical aspect of ionomics is the necessity of follow-up studies to understand the biology that underpins the observed ionomic changes. Such experiments often require different types of analytical approaches than those used to make the initial ionomic observation. A mutant with an altered leaf ionome is a powerful tool for the identification of genes involved in regulating the ionome. However, a better understanding of both the distribution and chemical speciation of the elements altered in the mutant could provide important clues to the function of the gene underlying the mutant phenotype.

We discussed above the use of both LA-ICP-MS and microXRF as methods for the determination of spatial distribution changes in the ionome. However, both these techniques reveal nothing about the chemical environment or oxidation state of the elements of interest. To address these questions of localization and speciation, X-ray spectroscopy and liquid chromatography coupled to ICP-MS and electrospray ionization mass spectrometry (ESI-MS) have been used successfully on plant samples and are discussed further here.

X-Ray Absorbance Spectroscopy

Previously, we discussed the use of XRF as a method for multielement quantification in plant samples. Such an approach involves the excitation of atoms across a broad range of excitation energies, allowing the detection of multiple elements. However, X-ray absorbance spectroscopy (XAS) relies on the excitation of a specific element of interest. The sample is scanned with X-rays of a narrow range of energies, chosen to exclusively excite the element of interest, and the X-ray absorption spectrum is recorded. Features within the recorded X-ray absorption spectrum reveal useful information about the chemical speciation of the element being probed. Such methods require minimal sample preparation, and therefore provide in vivo chemical speciation information. XAS is generally divided into X-ray absorption near edge spectroscopy (XANES) and extended X-ray absorption fine structure analysis (EXAFS). Both approaches provide complementary information. XANES provides information about the oxidation state and overall ligand environment of the element of interest. EXAFS provides detailed information about the bond lengths between the element of interest and the element(s) it is coordinated with, along with qualitative information on the identity of the ligating atoms. These approaches were first applied to plants in the mid-1990s by Salt and colleagues (78) and Krämer and colleagues (44) for the chemical speciation of Cd and Ni in bulk plant tissues, respectively. Since this initial work, XAS has been used by many investigators to probe the speciation of numerous different elements in plants, including As, Cr, Cu, Mn, S, Se, Pb, U, and Zn. Using microfocused X-ray beams, quantification and chemical speciation can also be performed in small localized areas of a sample. For example, Freeman and coworkers (22) used microXANES (μXANES) in an elegant study to probe Se speciation in target tissues of diamondback moth larva. Here, Se was chemically speciated in the thorax, hindgut, and abdominal deposits of the moth, and differences were observed between Se-tolerant and Se-sensitive ecotypes.

The use of microfocused X-ray beams has also been developed further, to allow quantitative chemically specific imaging. Pickering and coworkers (68) initially applied an approach of this type to the quantitative localization and chemical speciation of Se in leaves and roots of the natural Se hyperaccumulator *Astragalus bisulcatus*. In a follow-up study the imaging resolution was increased to 5 μm, allowing, for example, quantification and speciation of Se in the vascular tissue of the plants (67). High-resolution quantitative chemically specific imaging was also used to determine the localization and chemical speciation of As in the As-hyperaccumulating fern *Pteris vittata* (66). This type of imaging revealed in exquisite detail the amount and localization of arsenite, arsenate, and As(III) coordinated with thiol ligands in several tissues in the sporophyte and the gametophyte of *P. vittata*.

As is clear from these examples, the data obtained from XAS can provide important leads in the search to uncover the underlying biology reflected in a change in the bulk properties of the ionome.

Liquid Chromatography–ICP-MS

By coupling chromatographic separation of the chemical species of interest (e.g., arsenate from arsenite) with detection using ICP-MS, specific chemical forms of elements of interest can be quantified. Because coelution with standards is not considered sufficient evidence for molecular identification, several researchers have run liquid chromatography (LC) separation with parallel ICP-MS and ESI-MS (71). However, because extraction is required to prepare the sample for chromatography, great care must be taken when using this technique to avoid the artifactual formation of new chemical species or changes in the quantities of existing species. That said, this approach has been applied successfully to the quantification and speciation of various elements in plant samples, including As and Se (42, 72).

BIOINFORMATICS INVOLVED IN IONOMICS

In any large-scale ionomics project, where many hundreds or thousands of samples are to be analyzed over an extended period of time, it will be critical to implement an information management system to control all aspects of the process. This system will include the management of plant growth, harvesting, sample preparation, elemental analysis, and data processing. These workflow tools will allow, for example, scheduling and tracking of samples within the ionomics pipeline and generation of automated reminders when plants are ready for harvesting or data have been analyzed and stored in the database. Workflow tools can also be developed to control sample submission to the ionomic analysis pipeline from outside laboratories. The Purdue Ionomics Information Management System (PiiMS) is a working example of such a workflow control system (10), in which the ionomics workflow has been broken down into four stages: planting, harvesting, drying, and analysis. Each stage is represented by a portal through which information about the stage is collected, curated, and displayed (**Figure 3**).

Critically, workflow tools also provide for the logical organization of the workflow in the ionomics pipeline into discrete processes, providing a logical framework for the capture of contextual information (metadata such as plant genotype, growth conditions, date planted, etc.) necessary to fully describe the experiment. To implement an efficient system of metadata collection it is critical to develop a standardized nomenclature to describe "objects" within the system. This nomenclature can be a controlled vocabulary in which terms describing each object in the database are predefined (e.g., soil mix 1 = Sunshine Mix LB2, Carl Brehob & Son, Indianapolis, IN or SALK_132258_homo = a homozygous *A. thaliana* line with a T-DNA insert in gene *At2g19110*). This type of controlled vocabulary helps unify and standardize terminology and avoids duplication and contradiction. However, controlled vocabularies generally do not capture relations between the objects and concepts the vocabulary describes, thus limiting their use for data retrieval, data integration, and knowledge extraction. To overcome these limitations of controlled vocabularies, information management systems for ionomics, and other high-throughput omics technologies, should be based on a comprehensive ontology that describes all the entities

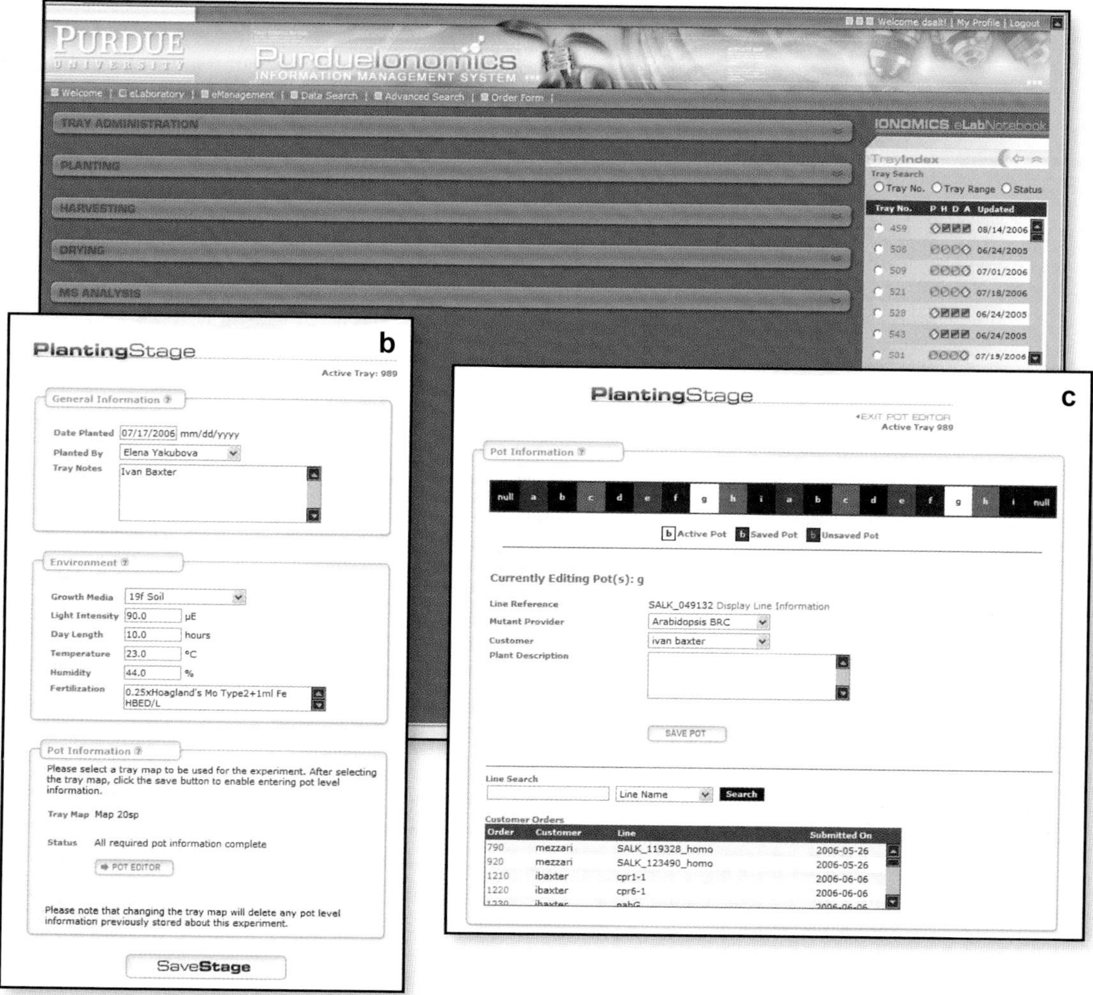

Figure 3

Information Management eLaboratory portal used to control workflow in the Purdue Ionomics Information Management System (*a*), with examples of modules accessed through this portal that are used to collect metadata during the planting stage. These include modules to collect experiment level information (*b*) and information that defines each line and its physical location in the planting tray (*c*). Courtesy of Reference 10.

and their logical relations in both planned and ongoing experiments. Work is progressing in the development of general biological ontologies (4, 53), those for plants (31), and those focused on high-throughput data acquisition technologies (34, 88). However, much still remains to be done to integrate these ontologies into a cohesive whole that can describe all facets of ionomics or other omic technology platforms.

The preprocessing of elemental profile, or ionomic data, is a critical step in the ionomic workflow before data can be analyzed for the extraction of knowledge (see section above on Analytical Standardization). Because such data preprocessing is best done by the analyst that collected the data, tools to accomplish such data preprocessing must be incorporated into the workflow at the stage that the analyst interacts with the information management system. Metadata describing how the preprocessing is performed also should be collected at this stage, so that such preprocessing steps can be recreated at a later date. These types of integrated tools have been implemented in the PiiMS (10).

For an information management system to be useful it must provide tools that allow for the retrieval, display, and download of the ionomics data and associated metadata that it stores. Furthermore, access to integrated and flexible data analysis tools would be a great asset to such an information management system. One example is the ability to select ionomic data from across a series of experiments, format the collected data and merge data from external sources (other databases or user supplied data), and submit it for normalization, statistical tests, clustering, and classification. Ideally, the researcher could build their own custom analysis workflows and upload new analysis algorithms for inclusion in the custom workflow. Such workflows should allow the results of one analysis to become the inputs of another. To the authors' knowledge, integration of such analysis tools into an existing high-throughput data management platform does not yet exist, although several groups are working on developing such systems to facilitate this type of integration using BioMOBY and Taverna (see below).

To further enhance and enrich the ability to extract knowledge from large ionomic datasets it is also critical to be able to incorporate information from other existing databases. National and international efforts have funded the development of a wide array of information and computational resources. Although these provide a rich set of genotypic, phenotypic, and analytical resources, considerable expertise is required to find and use appropriate resources, and integration across datasets is very difficult. Web Services (14, 56) provide a means to knit together disparate resources without requiring the very complex task of integrating the information into the core ionomics database. Currently, the PiiMS (10) is compatible with the Web Services branch of BioMOBY (89), and the development of PiiMS as a client for interaction with the MOBY-S framework for exchange of data and analytical services is currently under development.

Taverna is a recently developed scripting language and set of software tools to facilitate the easy construction of custom analysis workflows and use of distributed computing resources (30). The use of Taverna, integrated with BioMOBY, is one possible solution to the integration of high-throughput ionomic data generation platforms with other external data and computing resources (36). Such a set of tools should provide the ability to develop custom data analysis workflows for hypothesis testing and knowledge generation from large ionomic data sets.

Open access to large publicly funded functional genomics datasets is not only an obligation to the funding agency, but is also critical if the datasets are going to be efficiently mined for valuable biological information. This is as true for ionomic datasets as it is for genome sequence or transcriptomics data, for example. Open access to "raw" data sets would allow multiple investigators to carefully analyze data from many different perspectives, which would help to develop and refine robust biological knowledge. To facilitate this process for ionomics it will be critical to make ionomics data, and its associated metadata, freely available by the deployment of search and retrieval tools, which preferably should be Web Service–enabled to allow integration with systems such as BioMOBY and Taverna, as described above.

To promote rapid knowledge generation about the ionome and the genes and gene networks that underpin it, it will be critical that information obtained through experimental or bioinformatic approaches be retained within this information management system. Such annotation will allow the iteration of ionomic discovery. Currently, systems to allow researcher-driven annotation of genes with biological knowledge are very limited across all current biological models. With the rapid growth in the number of sequenced genes, functional data, and their interrelationship, data systems allowing for such systematized annotation are in great demand.

Finally, because of the complex, interdisciplinary nature of any large-scale ionomics project, the research is almost inevitably going to be collaborative. Collaborative projects such as these, almost by definition, are going to occur across various principle investigators' laboratories, institutions, and field sites. To facilitate such distributed activities it will be important for the information management system designed for the project to be web-enabled and contain tools for the distributed input and output of data, coordination of experiments, and sharing of biological insights.

APPLICATIONS OF IONOMICS

As defined in this review, a central theme of ionomics is the study of changes in the ionome in response to "physiological stimuli, developmental state, and genetic modifications." It is in this context that we discuss the application of ionomics to the discovery of gene function (functional genomics) and the assessment of the physiological status of plants.

Functional Genomics

With genotyping, including sequencing and polymorphism identification, rapidly becoming routine, the identification of phenotypic variation, and its association with genotypic variation, is limiting the leveraging of genomic information for knowledge generation. As a high-throughput phenotyping platform, ionomics offers the possibility of rapidly generating large ionomics data sets on many thousands of individual plants. Utilization of such a phenotyping platform to screen mapping populations with available modern genetic tools provides a very powerful approach for the identification of genes and gene networks that regulate the ionome.

Genetic variation for these screens can either be artificially induced using various mutagens, including ethyl methanesulfonate (EMS), X-rays, fast neutrons (FN) (41), T-DNA (7, 45) and transposable elements such as Dissociation (Ds) (64), or be derived from natural populations. The probability of identifying a plant harboring a mutation in a gene that affects the trait of interest, in this case the ionome, is dependent on both the mutation frequency and size of the gene(s). Mutation frequency varies between mutagens; FN and EMS produce on average 30–60 mutations per diploid genome (41), compared with 1.4 mutations for T-DNA (21). To perform a saturation screen using an EMS- or FN-mutagenized population would therefore require phenotyping of approximately 10,000–20,000 M2 plants, whereas the same screen with T-DNA would require 200,000–400,000 M2 plants. Clearly, even when using an EMS- or FN-mutagenized population the screening system used to identify plants with an altered ionome needs to be relatively high throughput to achieve saturation.

EMS- and FN-mutagenized populations have been successfully used for the identification of various ionomic mutants, including mutants with perturbations in single elements, such as P (17, 69) and Na (59, 76), and mutants with multiple ionomic changes (16, 47). With the efficient identification of ionomics mutants, mapping the causal locus becomes the limiting factor in gene identification. One approach to overcome this potential bottleneck is to use a mutagen, such as T-DNA, that has an easily identifiable sequence tag. This sequence tag can be used for the rapid identification of the mutagenic insertion site using PCR. The main drawback of these technologies is that their relatively low mutation frequencies make screening to saturation impractical with current ionomic throughput. However, the high mutation frequencies of

EMS and FN make them more favorable mutagens for saturation ionomic screens. Unfortunately, identification of the causal locus for a particular mutant phenotype is laborious when using EMS and FN because the mutation is not tagged.

However, the advent of high-throughput genotyping methodologies and the availability of genome-wide knockout collections has started to relieve some of these difficulties. For example, DNA microarray–based technologies are being used to perform bulk segregant analysis (BSA) (51) for the rapid localization of causal loci to within a few cM in mapping populations with no predetermined genetic markers (12, 91). DNA microarray–based genotyping is also being used for the identification of causal deletions underlying phenotypes of interest (12, 27). Deletion detection using DNA microarray–based techniques is limited by the size of the deletion and the number of features on the DNA microarray relative to the genome size. The current version of the Affymetrix *A. thaliana* array contains ~1.6 million features, which provides a probe spacing of ~35 bp across the genome and allows for reliable detection of deletions of >300 bp in length. Furthermore, new massively parallel sequencing, using systems like 454's GS Flex, Illumina's Solexa, and ABI's SOLID, is set to revolutionize the identification of causal mutations by allowing the rapid sequencing of large regions of DNA to identify polymorphisms between mutant and wild-type plants. To illustrate the power of this new sequencing technology, it recently took only two months, using the 454 sequencing technology, to sequence James Watson's entire genome, the "DNA behind the DNA". This contrasts with the 13 years it took to sequence the first human genome, completed in 2003. With several companies and technologies competing, the cost and speed of genotyping should continue to rapidly decrease, removing this step as a roadblock to identifying causal loci.

Once identified, candidate genes can be rapidly tested by screening for the ionomic phenotype of interest in various types of sequence-indexed insertion lines carrying a mutant allele of the gene of interest. Such collections currently exist for various plants, including *A. thaliana* (T-DNA, Ds, and dSpm), rice (T-DNA, tos17, and Ds) and maize (UniformMu). Where sequence-indexed insertion collections do not exist, targeting induced local lesions in genomes (TILLING) (28) is an alternative strategy for the identification of mutant alleles of candidate genes.

Genetic variation among and within natural populations can also be used as a tool for gene discovery, and has been applied extensively in *A. thaliana* (1, 40, 63), maize (79, 84), and rice (5, 39), for example. Further, genetic studies in model organisms can provide a critical bridge between a molecular gene-based approach to analyzing function and an evolutionary investigation of adaptive and natural selection (52, 82).

Via the use of immortalized mapping populations known as recombinant inbred lines (RIL), derived from a variety of natural accessions, researchers have identified QTL for several ionomic traits in various species, including *A. thaliana*, rice, and maize. In *A. thaliana* these traits include phosphate accumulation in seed and shoot (11), shoot Cs accumulation (65), shoot selenate accumulation (97), seed K, Na, Ca, Mg, Fe, Mn, Zn, and P accumulation (86), and sulfate accumulation (49). In rice and maize these traits include P, Si, Na, and K accumulation (43, 48, 73, 92, 93). Once ionomics QTL have been identified, genomic tools available for *A. thaliana* and to some extent rice and maize can be used to locate the genes that underlie these QTL and thus describe the traits at a molecular level (for a review see Reference 13). Such an approach was recently taken to identify the genes responsible for QTL that control Na in rice and *A. thaliana* (73, 76); interestingly, the responsible gene was found to be the Na-transporter HKT1 in both species. Loudet and coworkers (49) recently identified the gene that controls a major QTL for sulfate accumulation in *A. thaliana*; this gene encodes adenosine 5′-phosphosulfate reductase, a central enzyme in sulfate assimilation. Researchers are also well on the way to identifying the gene that controls a major QTL for seed P content in *A. thaliana*, which has currently been narrowed down to only 13 open reading frames (11).

Many species have thousands of natural accessions collected in stock centers that can be used for association mapping (95). Advances in high-throughput genotyping have enabled the genome-wide coverage necessary to use this technique to identify small chromosomal regions containing loci that are associated with a given trait. Although this technique requires the phenotyping of thousands of plants in a single experiment, the causal loci is likely to be within approximately 20 kb in *A. thaliana* (37, 98). The fine resolution of this technique should be extremely useful for gene discovery, and will make it the technique of choice where populations and genotypes are available. Phenotyping platforms like ionomics, which analyze many phenotypes simultaneously on the same sample, are poised to efficiently utilize the resources necessary for association mapping.

The availability of the homozygous full-genome knockout collection for *A. thaliana* from The *Arabidopsis* Information Resource was imminent when this review was written. With this collection in hand loss-of-function alleles can be screened for every gene in the *A. thaliana* genome for ionomic phenotypes. Taking such a reverse genetics approach needs no postscreen gene identification, and would require screening of approximately 52,000 individuals (with two alleles for each gene). At a throughout of 1000 samples per week (the current throughput of the Purdue Ionomics Facility) this screen would take approximately 1–2 years. A similar reverse genetics approach is currently underway, but because homozygous lines are limiting until the full collection is available, as of when this article was written ionomic data were available on only approximately 1500 unique genes (**http://www.purdue.edu/dp/ionomics**; described by Reference 10).

Given the rapid expansion of genetic tools for the established genetic model organisms, including *A. thaliana*, rice, and maize, the future for ionomic gene discovery looks very bright. Extensions of such genetic resources, such as sequenced genomes, mapping populations, and stable transformation systems into other plant species with interesting phenotypic characteristics, will further expand the horizons for ionomics. These new horizons will include new opportunities to understand the regulation of the ionome in other organisms and in relation to their adaptation, ecology, and natural selection.

Assessment of Physiological Status

The ionome of a plant is controlled by a summation of multiple physiological processes, starting in the rhizosphere and ending with evapotranspiration and phloem recycling to and from the shoot. Alterations in any of these processes that are involved in the transport of inorganic ions from the soil solution to the shoot could possibly affect the ionome. Because of this, the shoot ionome is likely very sensitive to the physiological state of the plant, and different ionomic profiles may reflect different physiological states. Such characteristic ionomic profiles, if they exist, could be useful as biomarkers for the particular physiological condition with which they are associated. In plants, ionomic biomarkers may be a simple way to determine if a plant has entered a particular physiological or biochemical state, e.g., cold or drought stress, disease, perturbed cell wall or wax biosynthesis, etc. Ionomic biomarkers may also allow the screening of individual plants for increased susceptibility to particular stresses, or alterations in processes that are not easily measured in high throughput, such as changes in root architecture, cell wall structure, etc. Our recent identification of an ionomic mutant in which low shoot Ca is driven by perturbations in root cell wall structure (I. Baxter, B. Lahner, A. Rus & D.E. Salt, unpublished observations) supports such an approach. To date little work has been done in plants to establish ionomics biomarkers; however, the concept holds promise.

CONCLUSION

With the $1000 genome sequence a rapidly approaching reality, high-throughput phenotyping platforms will be critical for the association of genotype with phenotype for the process of gene discovery. Here we discussed the development and application of ionomics as a high-throughput phenotyping platform, with the capacity to analyze approximately 1000 samples/week with a single analytical instrument. Because the ionome of a plant is the summation of many biological processes, a high-throughput ionomics platform offers a viable system for probing the multiple physiological and biochemical activities that affect the ionome, in tens of thousands of individuals. Ionomics, in combination with other phenotyping platforms such as transcript profiling, proteomics, and metabolomics, therefore offers the potential to close the growing gap between our knowledge of genotype and the phenotypes it controls.

DISCLOSURE STATEMENT

The authors are not aware of any biases that might be perceived as affecting the objectivity of this review.

ACKNOWLEDGMENTS

We would like to gratefully acknowledge helpful discussions with John Danku on ICP-MS, and Mary Lou Guerinot and other members of the National Science Foundation–funded ionomic group. This work was supported by grants from the NSF Plant Genome Research Program (DBI-0077378), NSF *Arabidopsis* 2010 program (IOS-0419695), Indiana 21st Century Research & Technology Fund (912010479), and the National Institutes of Health (5 R33 DK070290-03).

LITERATURE CITED

1. Alonso-Blanco C, El-Assal SE, Coupland G, Koornneef M. 1998. Analysis of natural allelic variation at flowering time loci in the Landsberg erecta and Cape Verde Islands ecotypes of *Arabidopsis thaliana*. *Genetics* 149:749–64
2. Andrási E, Suhajda M, Sáray I, Bezúr L, Ernyei L, Réffy A. 1993. Concentration of elements in human brain: glioblastoma multiforme. *Sci. Total Environ.* 139–140:399–402
3. Arriola H, Longoria L, Quintero A, Guzman D. 1999. INAA of trace elements in colorectal cancer patients. *Biol. Trace Elem. Res.* 71–72:563–68
4. Ashburner M, Ball CA, Blake JA, Botstein D, Butler H, et al. 2000. Gene ontology: tool for the unification of biology. The Gene Ontology Consortium. *Nat. Genet.* 25:25–29
5. Ashikari M, Sakakibara H, Lin S, Yamamoto T, Takashi T, et al. 2005. Cytokinin oxidase regulates rice grain production. *Science* 309:741–45
6. Aung K, Lin SI, Wu CC, Huang YT, Su CL, Chiou TJ. 2006. *pho2*, a phosphate overaccumulator, is caused by a nonsense mutation in a microRNA399 target gene. *Plant Physiol.* 141:1000–11
7. Azpiroz-Leehan R, Feldmann KA. 1997. T-DNA insertion mutagenesis in *Arabidopsis*: going back and forth. *Trends Genet.* 13:152–56

8. Barandovski L, Cekova M, Frontasyeva MV, Pavlov SS, Stafilov T, et al. 2007. Atmospheric deposition of trace element pollutants in Macedonia studied by the moss biomonitoring technique. *Environ. Monit. Assess.* Jul 31 doi: 10.1007/s10661-007-9747-6
9. Bari R, Datt Pant B, Stitt M, Scheible WR. 2006. PHO2, microRNA399, and PHR1 define a phosphate-signaling pathway in plants. *Plant Physiol.* 141:988–99
10. Baxter I, Ouzzani M, Orcun S, Kennedy B, Jandhyala SS, Salt DE. 2007. Purdue Ionomics Information Management System (PiiMS): An integrated functional genomics platform. *Plant Physiol.* 143:600–11
11. Bentsink L, Yuan K, Koorneef M, Vreugdenhil D. 2003. The genetics of phytate and phosphate accumulation in seeds and leaves of *Arabidopsis thaliana*, using natural variation. *Theor. Appl. Genet.* 106:1234–43
12. Borevitz JO, Liang D, Plouffe D, Chang HS, Zhu T, et al. 2003. Large-scale identification of single-feature polymorphisms in complex genomes. *Genome Res.* 13:513–23
13. Borevitz JO, Nordborg M. 2003. The impact of genomics on the study of natural variation in *Arabidopsis*. *Plant Physiol.* 132:718–25
14. Curcin V, Ghanem M, Guo Y. 2005. Web services in the life sciences. *Drug Discov. Today* 10:865–71
15. Dang HS, Jaiswal DD, Wadhwani CN, Somasunderam S, Dacosta H. 1985. Breast feeding: Mo, As, Mn, Zn and Cu concentrations in milk of economically poor Indian tribal and urban women. *Sci. Total Environ.* 44:177–82
16. Delhaize E. 1996. A metal-accumulator mutant of *Arabidopsis thaliana*. *Plant Physiol.* 111:849–55
17. Delhaize E, Randall PJ. 1995. Characterization of a phosphate-accumulator mutant of *Arabidopsis thaliana*. *Plant Physiol.* 107:207–13
18. Delhaize E, Randall PJ, Wallace PA, Pinkerton A. 1993. Screening *Arabidopsis* for mutants in mineral nutrition. *Plant Soil* 155/156:131–34
19. Eide DJ, Clark S, Nair TM, Gehl M, Gribskov M, et al. 2005. Characterization of the yeast ionome: a genome-wide analysis of nutrient mineral and trace element homeostasis in *Saccharomyces cerevisiae*. *Genome Biol.* 6:R77
20. Ezoe M, Sasaki M, Hokura A, Nakai I, Terada Y, et al. 2002. Two-dimensional microbeam imaging of trace elements in a single plankton measured by a synchrotron radiation X-ray fluorescence analysis. *Bunseki Kagaku* 51:883–90
21. Feldmann KA. 1991. T-DNA insertional mutagenesis in *Arabidopsis*—mutational spectrum. *Plant J.* 1:71–82
22. Freeman JL, Quinn CF, Marcus MA, Fakra S, Pilon-Smits EA. 2006. Selenium-tolerant diamondback moth disarms hyperaccumulator plant defense. *Curr. Biol.* 21:2181–92
23. Furr AK, Stoewsand GS, Bache CA, Lisk DJ. 1976. Study of guinea pigs fed Swiss chard grown on municipal sludge-amended soil. Multi-element content of tissues. *Arch. Environ. Health* 31:87–91
24. Garg AN, Singh V, Weginwar RG, Sagdeo VN. 1994. An elemental correlation study in cancerous and normal breast tissue with successive clinical stages by neutron activation analysis. *Biol. Trace Elem. Res.* 46:185–202
25. Grodzińska K, Frontasyeva M, Szarek-Lukaszewska G, Klich M, Kucharska-Fabiś A, et al. 2003. Trace element contamination in industrial regions of Poland studied by moss monitoring. *Environ. Monit. Assess.* 87:255–70
26. Hamburger D, Rezzonico E, MacDonald-Comber Petétot J, Somerville C, Poirier Y. 2002. Identification and characterization of the *Arabidopsis PHO1* gene involved in phosphate loading to the xylem. *Plant Cell* 14:889–902

27. Hazen SP, Borevitz JO, Harmon FG, Pruneda-Paz JL, Schultz TF, et al. 2005. Rapid array mapping of circadian clock and developmental mutations in *Arabidopsis*. *Plant Physiol.* 138:990–97
28. Henikoff S, Till BJ, Comai L. 2004. TILLING. Traditional mutagenesis meets functional genomics. *Plant Physiol.* 135:630–36
29. Hollywood K, Brison DR, Goodacre R. 2006. Metabolomics: current technologies and future trends. *Proteomics* 6:4716–23
30. Hull D, Wolstencroft K, Stevens R, Goble C, Pocock MR, et al. 2006. Taverna: a tool for building and running workflows of services. *Nucleic Acids Res.* 34:W729–32
31. Ilic K, Kellogg EA, Jaiswal P, Zapata F, Stevens PF, et al. 2007. The plant structure ontology, a unified vocabulary of anatomy and morphology of a flowering plant. *Plant Physiol.* 143:587–99
32. Isaure MP, Fraysse A, Devès G, Le Lay P, Fayard B, et al. 2006. Micro-chemical imaging of cesium distribution in *Arabidopsis thaliana* plant and its interaction with potassium and essential trace elements. *Biochimie* 88:1583–90
33. Iskander FY, Bauer TL, Klein DE. 1986. Determination of 28 elements in American cigarette tobacco by neutron-activation analysis. *Analyst* 111:107–9
34. Jones AR, Pizarro A, Spellman P, Miller M; FuGE Working Group. 2006. FuGE: Functional Genomics Experiment Object Model. *OMICS* 10:179–84
35. Kanngießer B, Malzer W, Pagels M, Lühl L, Weseloh G. 2007. Three-dimensional micro-XRF under cryogenic conditions: a pilot experiment for spatially resolved trace analysis in biological specimens. *Anal. Bioanal. Chem.* 389:1171–76
36. Kawas E, Senger M, Wilkinson MD. 2006. BioMoby extensions to the Taverna workflow management and enactment software. *BMC Bioinformatics* 7:523
37. Kim S, Plagnol V, Hu TT, Toomajian C, Clark RM, et al. 2007. Recombination and linkage disequilibrium in *Arabidopsis thaliana*. *Nat. Genet.* 39:1151–55
38. Kim SA, Punshon T, Lanzirotti A, Li L, Alonso JM, et al. 2006. Localization of iron in *Arabidopsis* seed requires the vacuolar membrane transporter VIT1. *Science* 24:1295–98
39. Kojima S, Takahashi Y, Kobayashi Y, Monna L, Sasaki T, et al. 2002. Hd3a, a rice ortholog of the *Arabidopsis* FT gene, promotes transition to flowering downstream of Hd1 under short-day conditions. *Plant Cell Physiol.* 43:1096–105
40. Koornneef M, Alonso-Blanco C, Vreugdenhil D. 2004. Naturally occurring genetic variation in *Arabidopsis thaliana*. *Annu. Rev. Plant Biol.* 55:141–72
41. Koornneef M, Dellaert LW, van der Veen JH. 1982. EMS- and radiation-induced mutation frequencies at individual loci in *Arabidopsis thaliana* (L.) Heynh. *Mutat. Res.* 93:109–23
42. Kotrebai M, Birringer M, Tyson JF, Block E, Uden PC. 2000. Selenium speciation in enriched and natural samples by HPLC-ICP-MS and HPLC-ESI-MS with perfluorinated carboxylic acid ion-pairing agents. *Analyst* 125:71–78
43. Koyama ML, Levesley A, Koebner RM, Flowers TJ, Yeo AR. 2001. Quantitative trait loci for component physiological traits determining salt tolerance in rice. *Plant Physiol.* 125:406–22
44. Krämer U, Cotter-Howells JD, Charnock JM, Baker AJM, Smith JAC. 1996. Free histidine as a metal chelator in plants that accumulate nickel. *Nature* 379:635–38
45. Krysan PJ, Young JC, Sussman MR. 1999. T-DNA as an insertional mutagen in *Arabidopsis*. *Plant Cell* 11:2283–90
46. Kurunczi S, Torok S, Chevallier P. 2001. A micro-XRF study of the element distribution on the growth front of mussel shell (species of *Unio crassus Retzius*). *Mikrochim. Acta* 137:41–48
47. Lahner B, Gong J, Mahmoudian M, Smith EL, Abid KB, et al. 2003. Genomic scale profiling of nutrient and trace elements in *Arabidopsis thaliana*. *Nat. Biotechnol.* 21:1215–21

48. Lin HX, Zhu MZ, Yano M, Gao JP, Liang ZW, et al. 2004. QTLs for Na^+ and K^+ uptake of the shoots and roots controlling rice salt tolerance. *Theor. Appl. Genet.* 108:253–60
49. Loudet O, Saliba-Colombani V, Camilleri C, Calenge F, Gaudon V, et al. 2007. Natural variation for sulfate content in *Arabidopsis thaliana* is highly controlled by APR2. *Nat. Genet.* 39:896–900
50. McRae R, Lai B, Vogt S, Fahrni CJ. 2006. Correlative microXRF and optical immunofluorescence microscopy of adherent cells labeled with ultrasmall gold particles. *J. Struct. Biol.* 155:22–29
51. Michelmore RW, Paran I, Kesseli RV. 1991. Identification of markers linked to disease-resistance genes by bulked segregant analysis: a rapid method to detect markers in specific genomic regions by using segregating populations. *Proc. Natl. Acad. Sci. USA* 88:9828–32
52. Mitchell-Olds T, Schmitt J. 2006. Genetic mechanisms and evolutionary significance of natural variation in *Arabidopsis*. *Nature* 441:947–52
53. Myhre S, Tveit H, Mollestad T, Laegreid A. 2006. Additional gene ontology structure for improved biological reasoning. *Bioinformatics* 22:2020–27
54. Nadkarni RA, Morrison GH. 1973. Multielement instrumental neutron activation analysis of biological materials. *Anal. Chem.* 45:1957–60
55. Nakano K, Tsuji K. 2006. Development of confocal 3D micro XRF spectrometer and its application to rice grain. *Bunseki Kagaku* 55:427–32
56. Neerincx PBT, Leunissen JAM. 2005. Evolution of web services in bioinformatics. *Brief. Bioinform.* 6:178–88
57. Ng KH, Ong SH, Bradley DA, Looi LM. 1997. Discriminant analysis of normal and malignant breast tissue based upon INAA investigation of elemental concentration. *Appl. Radiat. Isot.* 48:105–9
58. Nicholson JK, Lindon JC, Holmes E. 1999. 'Metabonomics': understanding the metabolic responses of living systems to pathophysiological stimuli via multivariate statistical analysis of biological NMR spectroscopic data. *Xenobiotica* 29:1181–89
59. Nublat A, Desplans J, Casse F, Berthomieu P. 2001. *sas1*, an *Arabidopsis* mutant overaccumulating sodium in the shoot, shows deficiency in the control of the root radial transport of sodium. *Plant Cell* 13:125–37
60. Oliver SG, Winson MK, Kell DB, Baganz F. 1998. Systematic functional analysis of the yeast genome. *Trends Biotechnol.* 16:373–78
61. Outten CE, O'Halloran TV. 2001. Femtomolar sensitivity of metalloregulatory proteins controlling zinc homeostasis. *Science* 292:2488–92
62. Ozaki T, Enomoto S, Minai Y, Ambe S, Makide Y. 2000. A survey of trace elements in pteridophytes. *Biol. Trace Elem. Res.* 74:259–73
63. Paran I, Zamir D. 2003. Quantitative traits in plants: beyond the QTL. *Trends Genet.* 19:303–6
64. Parinov S, Sevugan M, Ye D, Yang W-C, Kumaran M, Sundaresan V. 1999. Analysis of flanking sequences from dissociation insertion lines: A database for reverse genetics in *Arabidopsis*. *Plant Cell* 11:2263–70
65. Payne K, Bowen H, Hammond J, Hampton C, Lynn J, et al. 2004. Natural genetic variation in caesium (Cs) accumulation by *Arabidopsis thaliana*. *New Phytol.* 162:535–48
66. Pickering IJ, Gumaelius L, Harris HH, Prince RC, Hirsch G, et al. 2006. Localizing the biochemical transformations of arsenate in a hyperaccumulating fern. *Environ. Sci. Technol.* 40:5010–14
67. Pickering IJ, Hirsch G, Prince RC, Yu EY, Salt DE, George GN. 2003. Imaging of selenium in plants using tapered metal capillary optics. *J. Synchrotron. Radiat.* 10:289–90

68. Pickering IJ, Prince RC, Salt DE, George GN. 2000. Quantitative chemically-specific imaging of selenium transformation in plants. *Proc. Natl. Acad. Sci. USA* 97:10717–22
69. Poirier Y, Thoma S, Somerville C, Schiefelbein J. 1991. Mutant of *Arabidopsis* deficient in xylem loading of phosphate. *Plant Physiol.* 97:1087–93
70. Punshon T, Jackson BP, Bertsch PM, Burger J. 2004. Mass loading of nickel and uranium on plant surfaces: application of laser ablation-ICP-MS. *J. Environ. Monit.* 6:153–59
71. Raab A, Feldmann J, Meharg AA. 2004. The nature of arsenic-phytochelatin complexes in *Holcus lanatus* and *Pteris cretica*. *Plant Physiol.* 134:1113–22
72. Raab A, Schat H, Meharg AA, Feldmann J. 2005. Uptake, translocation and transformation of arsenate and arsenite in sunflower (*Helianthus annuus*): formation of arsenic-phytochelatin complexes during exposure to high arsenic concentrations. *New Phytol.* 168:551–58
73. Ren ZH, Gao JP, Li LG, Cai XL, Huang W, et al. 2005. A rice quantitative trait locus for salt tolerance encodes a sodium transporter. *Nat. Genet.* 37:1141–46
74. Robinson AB, Pauling L. 1974. Techniques of orthomolecular diagnosis. *Clin. Chem.* 20:961–65
75. Rogers EE, Guerinot ML. 2002. FRD3, a member of the multidrug and toxin efflux family, controls iron deficiency responses in *Arabidopsis*. *Plant Cell* 14:1787–99
76. Rus A, Baxter I, Muthukumar B, Gustin J, Lahner B, et al. 2006. Natural variants of *AtHKT1* enhance Na^{+} accumulation in two wild populations of *Arabidopsis*. *PLoS Genet.* 2(12):e210
77. Salt DE. 2004. Update on ionomics. *Plant Physiol.* 136:2451–56
78. Salt DE, Prince RC, Pickering IJ, Raskin I. 1995. Mechanisms of cadmium mobility and accumulation in Indian mustard. *Plant Physiol.* 109:1427–33
79. Salvi S, Sponza G, Morgante M, Tomes D, Niu X, et al. 2007. Conserved noncoding genomic sequences associated with a flowering-time quantitative trait locus in maize. *Proc. Natl. Acad. Sci. USA* 104:11376–81
80. Schauer N, Fernie AR. 2006. Plant metabolomics: towards biological function and mechanism. *Trends Plant Sci.* 11:508–16
81. Shenberg C, Feldstein H, Cornelis R, Mees L, Versieck J, et al. 1995. Br, Rb, Zn, Fe, Se and K in blood of colorectal patients by INAA and PIXE. *J. Trace Elem. Med. Biol.* 9:193–99
82. Shindo C, Bernasconi G, Hardtke CS. 2007. Natural genetic variation in *Arabidopsis*: tools, traits and prospects for evolutionary ecology. *Ann. Bot.* 99:1043–54
83. Tano S, Eguchi H, Koizumi Y, Yamaguchi H. 1979. Comparisons of inorganic elements in barley seeds by neutron activation analysis with respect to varieties and cultivated locations. *Radioisotopes* 28:309–12
84. Thornsberry JM, Goodman MM, Doebley J, Kresovich S, Nielsen D, Buckler ES 4th. 2001. *Dwarf8* polymorphisms associate with variation in flowering time. *Nat. Genet.* 28:286–89
85. Tweeddale H, Notley-McRobb L, Ferenci T. 1998. Effect of slow growth om metabolism of *Escherichia coli*, as revealed by global metabolite pools ("metabolome") analysis. *J. Bacteriol.* 180:5190–16
86. Vreugdenhil D, Aarts MGM, Koornneef M, Nelissen H, Ernst WHO. 2004. Natural variation and QTL analysis for cationic mineral content in seeds of *Arabidopsis thaliana*. *Plant Cell Environ.* 27:828–39
87. Watanabe T, Broadley MR, Jansen S, White PJ, Takada J, et al. 2007. Evolutionary control of leaf element composition in plants. *New Physiol.* 174:516–23
88. Whetzel PL, Brinkman RR, Causton HC, Fan L, Field D, et al. 2006. Development of FuGO: an ontology for functional genomics investigations. *OMICS* 10:199–204

89. Wilkinson M, Schoof H, Ernst R, Haase D. 2005. BioMOBY successfully integrates distributed heterogeneous bioinformatics web services. The PlaNet exemplar case. *Plant Physiol.* 138:5–17
90. Williams RJP. 2001. Chemical selection of elements by cells. *Coord. Chem. Rev.* 216–17:583–95
91. Winzeler EA, Richards DR, Conway AR, Goldstein AL, Kalman S, et al. 1998. Direct allelic variation scanning of the yeast genome. *Science* 281:1194–97
92. Wissuwa M, Wegner J, Ae N, Yano M. 2002. Substitution mapping of Pup1: a major QTL increasing phosphorus uptake of rice from a phosphorus-deficient soil. *Theor. Appl. Genet.* 105:890–97
93. Wu QS, Wan XY, Su N, Cheng ZJ, Wang JK, et al. 2006. Genetic dissection of silicon uptake ability in rice (*Oryza sativa* L.). *Plant Sci.* 171:441–48
94. Young LW, Westcott ND, Attenkofer K, Reaney MJ. 2006. A high-throughput determination of metal concentrations in whole intact *Arabidopsis thaliana* seeds using synchrotron-based X-ray fluorescence spectroscopy. *J. Synchrotron Radiat.* 13:304–13
95. Yu J, Pressoir G, Briggs WH, Vroh Bi I, Yamasaki M, et al. 2006. A unified mixed-model method for association mapping that accounts for multiple levels of relatedness. *Nat. Genet.* 38:203–8
96. Yun W, Pratt ST, Miller RM, Cai Z, Hunter DB, et al. 1998. X-ray imaging and microspectroscopy of plants and fungi. *J. Synchrotron Radiat.* 5:1390–95
97. Zhang L, Byrne PF, Pilon-Smits EA. 2006. Mapping quantitative trait loci associated with selenate tolerance in *Arabidopsis thaliana*. *New Phytol.* 170:33–42
98. Zhao K, Aranzana MJ, Kim S, Lister C, Shindo C, et al. 2007. An *Arabidopsis* example of association mapping in structured samples. *PLoS Genet.* 3:e4

NOTE ADDED IN PROOF

Association mapping of an ionomic trait was recently used for the first time in the identification of a novel mitochondrially localized transporter responsible for regulating molybdenum accumulation in *Arabidopsis*. This was recorded in the following article by Baxter et al.:

Baxter I, Muthukumar B, Park HC, Buchner P, Lahner B, et al. 2008. Variation in molybdenum content across broadly distributed populations of *Arabidopsis thaliana* is controlled by a mitochondrial molybdenum transporter (MOT1). *PLoS Genet.* 4:e1000004. doi:10.1371/journal.pgen.1000004

Alkaloid Biosynthesis: Metabolism and Trafficking

Jörg Ziegler and Peter J. Facchini

Department of Biological Sciences, University of Calgary, Calgary, Alberta T2N 1N4, Canada; email: pfacchin@ucalgary.ca; joerg.ziegler@ucalgary.ca

Annu. Rev. Plant Biol. 2008. 59:735–69

The *Annual Review of Plant Biology* is online at plant.annualreviews.org

This article's doi:
10.1146/annurev.arplant.59.032607.092730

1543-5008/08/0602-0735$20.00

Key Words

benzylisoquinoline alkaloids, cellular compartmentalization, secondary metabolism, monoterpenoid indole alkaloids, tropane alkaloids, metabolic engineering

Abstract

Alkaloids represent a highly diverse group of compounds that are related only by the occurrence of a nitrogen atom in a heterocyclic ring. Plants are estimated to produce approximately 12,000 different alkaloids, which can be organized into groups according to their carbon skeletal structures. Alkaloid biosynthesis in plants involves many catalytic steps, catalyzed by enzymes that belong to a wide range of protein families. The characterization of novel alkaloid biosynthetic enzymes in terms of structural biochemistry, molecular and cell biology, and biotechnological applications has been the focus of research over the past several years. The application of genomics to the alkaloid field has accelerated the discovery of cDNAs encoding previously elusive biosynthetic enzymes. Other technologies, such as large-scale gene expression analyses and metabolic engineering approaches with transgenic plants, have provided new insights into the regulatory architecture of alkaloid metabolism.

Contents

ALKALOID METABOLISM

EST: expressed sequence tag

MIA: monoterpenoid indole alkaloid

Alkaloids are a diverse group of low-molecular-weight, nitrogen-containing compounds derived mostly from amino acids. As secondary metabolites found in approximately 20% of plant species, alkaloids are purported to play a defensive role against herbivores and pathogens. Owing to their potent biological activity, many of the approximately 12,000 known alkaloids have been exploited as pharmaceuticals, stimulants, narcotics, and poisons. Unlike most other types of secondary metabolites, the many classes of alkaloids have unique biosynthetic origins. Despite the diversity of metabolic pathways, several technical breakthroughs have recently contributed to impressive advancements in our understanding of alkaloid biosynthesis. Recent applications of genomics-based technologies, such as expressed sequence tag (EST) databases, DNA microarrays, and proteome analysis, have accelerated the discovery of new components and mechanisms involved in the assembly of alkaloids in plants. Our present ability to investigate secondary metabolism from a combined biochemical, molecular, cellular, and physiological perspective has improved our appreciation for the complex biology of alkaloid pathways. In this review, we discuss recent advances in our understanding of the metabolism and trafficking of alkaloids.

Alkaloid Biosynthetic Pathways

Monoterpenoid indole alkaloids. The monoterpenoid indole alkaloids (MIA) comprise a family of structurally and pharmaceutically diverse alkaloids. Some of the approximately 2,000 known compounds widely used in medicine include vinblastine for the treatment of cancer and ajmaline for antiarrythmic heart disorders. The major sources for these compounds are *Catharanthus roseus* and *Rauvolfia serpentina*. MIAs are condensation products of a nitrogen-containing indole moiety derived from tryptamine and a monoterpenoid component derived from the iridoid glucoside secologanin (**Figure 1**). In the MIA biosynthetic pathway,

Figure 1

Biosynthesis of the monoterpenoid indole alkaloids vinblastine and ajmaline. Enzymes for which corresponding molecular clones have been isolated are shown in bold. Abbreviations: AAE, acetylajmalan esterase; ANAMT, acetylnorajmalan methyltransferase; Cyp72A1, secologanin synthase; Cyp76B6, geraniol 10-hydroxylase; D4H, desacetoxyvindoline 4-hydroxylase; DAT, deacetylvindoline 4-*O*-acetyltransferase; DHVR, dihydrovomilenine reductase; LAMT, loganic acid methyltransferase; MAT, minovincinine acetyltransferase; NAMT, norajmalan methyltransferase; NMT, *N*-methyltransferase; PER, peroxidase; PNAE, polyneuridine aldehyde esterase; RG, raucaffricine *O*-β-glucosidase; SBE, sarpagan bridge enzyme; SGD, strictosidine β-D-glucosidase; STR, strictosidine synthase; T16H, tabersonine 16-hydroxylase; TDC, tryptophan decarboxylase; VH, vinorine hydroxylase; VR, vomilenine reductase; VS, vinorine synthase.

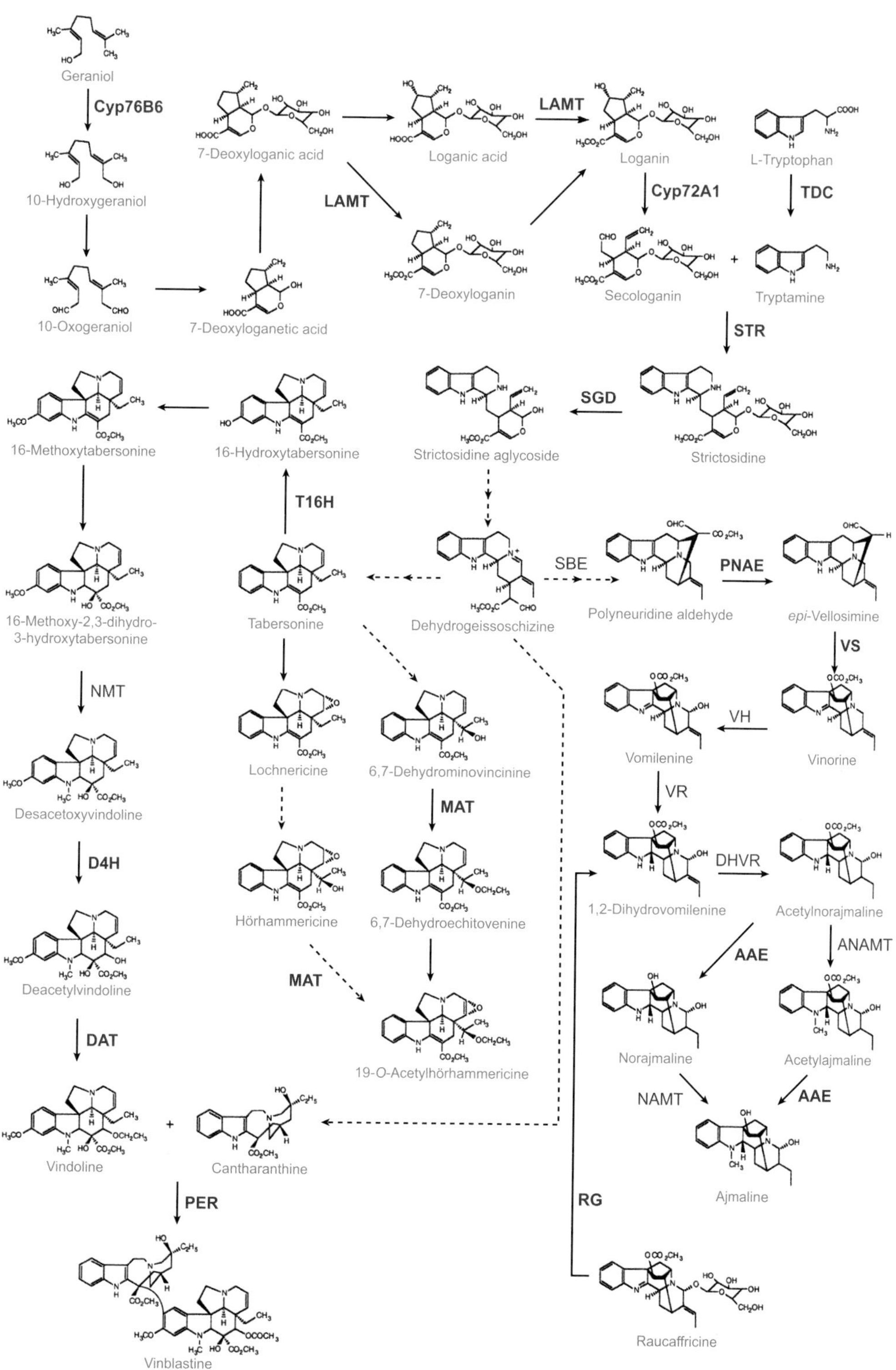
Geraniol
Cyp76B6
10-Hydroxygeraniol
10-Oxogeraniol
7-Deoxyloganetic acid
7-Deoxyloganic acid
Loganic acid
LAMT
Loganin
L-Tryptophan
LAMT
7-Deoxyloganin
Cyp72A1
TDC
Secologanin
Tryptamine
STR
16-Methoxytabersonine
16-Hydroxytabersonine
Strictosidine aglycoside
SGD
Strictosidine
T16H
16-Methoxy-2,3-dihydro-3-hydroxytabersonine
Tabersonine
Dehydrogeissoschizine
SBE
Polyneuridine aldehyde
PNAE
epi-Vellosimine
VS
NMT
Lochnericine
6,7-Dehydrominovincinine
Vomilenine
VH
Vinorine
Desacetoxyvindoline
MAT
VR
D4H
Hörhammericine
6,7-Dehydroechitovenine
1,2-Dihydrovomilenine
DHVR
Acetylnorajmaline
Deacetylvindoline
MAT
AAE
ANAMT
DAT
19-O-Acetylhörhammericine
Norajmaline
Acetylajmaline
NAMT
AAE
Vindoline
Cantharanthine
Ajmaline
PER
RG
Vinblastine
Raucaffricine

tryptophan decarboxylase (TDC) converts tryptophan to tryptamine; the gene encoding this enzyme has been cloned from different MIA-accumulating plants (25, 89, 178). Incorporation experiments with isotopically labeled glucose in *C. roseus* cell cultures showed that the initial steps for the biosynthesis of the monoterpenoid skeleton proceed via the triose phosphate/pyruvate pathway (22). Cognate cDNAs for 1-deoxy-D-xylulose 5-phosphate reductoisomerase and 2C-methyl-D-erythritol 2,4-cyclodiphosphate synthase were isolated from *C. roseus* and the corresponding gene transcripts were upregulated in MIA-producing cell cultures (163). The first committed step in secologanin biosynthesis is catalyzed by the cytochrome P450 monooxygenase geraniol-10-hydroxylase (Cyp76B6), which was purified and cloned from *C. roseus* (20). Several steps in the secologanin pathway have not been characterized, although the availability of *C. roseus* EST databases (108) has led to the recent discovery of loganic acid methyltransferase (LAMT) (V. De Luca, personal communication). The final reaction of this early branch of the pathway involves an oxidative C-C cleavage catalyzed by a second P450 monooxgenase (Cyp72A1), resulting in the conversion of loganin to secologanin (70).

Strictosidine, the common precursor to all MIAs, is formed by a Pictet-Spengler condensation of tryptamine and secologanin (**Figure 1**). Strictosidine synthase (STR) from *R. serpentina* was the first cDNA involved in alkaloid biosynthesis to be cloned and functionally expressed in microorganisms. STR orthologs from *C. roseus* and *Ophiorrhiza pumila* have also been isolated (79, 99, 178). The strictosidine glucose moiety is subsequently removed by a family 1 glucosyl hydrolase enzyme, strictosidine β-D-glucosidase (SGD); a cDNA for SGD was functionally characterized from *C. roseus* and *R. serpentina*. SGD from *R. serpentina* shows exclusive substrate specificity toward strictosidine and closely related analogs (46, 50). The strictosidine-derived aglycone is subsequently converted via several unstable intermediates to dehydrogeissoschizine, which represents a key branchpoint intermediate that leads to several diverse MIA pathways. The branch pathways proceeding through tabersonine and polyneuridine aldehyde have been characterized most thoroughly. Other branch pathways, such as that leading to catharanthine, remain poorly understood.

Hydroxylation of tabersonine at position 16 represents the first reaction leading to vindoline (**Figure 1**). The responsible enzyme, tabersonine 16-hydroxylase (T16H, Cyp71D12), belongs to the P450 monooxygenase family, and the corresponding cDNA was identified from a subset encoding P450-dependent enzymes induced by the treatment of *C. roseus* cultures with light (140). *O*-Methylation at position 16, reduction of the 2,3-double bond, and *N*-methylation result in the conversion of 16-hydroxytabersonine to desacetoxyvindoline. Although cDNAs have not been isolated for the enzymes that participate in these steps, the *N*- and *O*-methylating activities have been characterized in plant extracts (27, 37). The 2-oxoglutarate–dependent dioxygenase desacetoxyvindoline 4-hydroxylase (D4H) produces desacetylvindoline, which is further converted by the acetyl CoA–dependent desacetylvindoline 4-*O*-acetyltransferase (DAT) to vindoline (150, 162). Both enzymes have been cloned and characterized from *C. roseus*. DAT belongs to the BAHD (benzylalcohol *O*-acetyl-, anthocyanin-*O*-hydroxycinnamoyl-, anthranilate-*N*-hydroxycinnamoyl/benzoyl-, and deacetylvindoline 4-*O*-acetyltransferase) family of acyl-CoA dependent acyltransferases; these proteins participate in a variety of plant secondary metabolic pathways. Ultimately, vindoline is coupled to catharanthine by a nonspecific peroxidase to form vinblastine (145). A cDNA with 78% amino acid identity to DAT was obtained from *C. roseus* and encodes minovincinine 19-*O*-acetyltransferase, yielding echitovenine, which is a second pathway originating from the tabersonine branch (80). Whereas minovincinine acetyltransferase (MAT) shows residual activity toward the DAT substrate, deacetoxyvindoline, DAT accepts only its natural substrate.

The polyneuridine aldehyde branch of the MIA pathway is initiated by the formation of a bond, known as the sarpagan bridge, between C5 and C16 of strictosidine-derived intermediate compounds (**Figure 1**). The enzyme characterized from crude extracts of *R. serpentina* shows NADPH and oxygen dependence, and is sensitive to P450 inhibitors, suggesting it is a P450 monooxygenase (139). The resulting polyneuridine aldehyde undergoes desterification to yield *epi*-vellosimine, which is acetylated to form vinorine. Recombinant polyneuridine aldehyde esterase (PNAE) from *R. serpentina* shows esterase activity only to polyneuridine aldehyde and not to structurally related esters, and is a member of the α/β hydrolase superfamily (29). With approximately 30% identity on the amino acid level to DAT and MAT, vinorine synthase (VS) from *R. serpentina* also belongs to the BAHD family of acyltransferases (11). Acetylajmaline is subsequently formed via a series of reactions that includes hydroxylation, two double bond reductions, and an *N*-methylation. The enzymes involved in these steps have been biochemically characterized as the P450-dependent monooxygenase vinorine hydroxylase (VH), which yields vomilenine, and the NADPH-dependent reductases vomilenine reductase and 1,2-dehydrovomilenine reductase (39, 44, 166). Acetylajamaline esterase (AAE) ultimately hydrolyzes the 17-*O*-acetyl group to produce ajmaline. Active recombinant AAE, which could be produced only via a virus expression system in *Nicotiana benthamiana*, shows slight substrate preference for acetylajmaline compared with norajmaline. The latter compound might represent an intermediate in a parallel ajamaline biosynthetic pathway in which *N*-methylation occurs after deesterification (134). Unlike PNAE, AAE belongs to the GDSL lipase family. Raucaffricine, a glucosylated derivative of vomilenine, is found in *R. serpentina* cultures. Although the glucosylating activity has not been reported, researchers found a cDNA encoding the enzyme raucaffricine *O*-β-glucosidase (RG), responsible for deglycosylation of raucaffricine (168). RG shares 60% amino acid identity with SGD and accepts strictosidine as a substrate, whereas SGD is not active against raucaffricine.

Benzylisoquinoline alkaloids. Benzylisoquinoline alkaloids (BIA) represent approximately 2,500 elucidated structures and possess potent pharmacological properties. The most prominent compounds are the narcotic analgesic morphine, the cough suppressant codeine, the muscle relaxant papaverine, and the antimicrobial agents sanguinarine and berberine. Collectively, these alkaloids occur mainly in the Papaveraceae, Ranunculaceae, Berberidaceae, and Menispermaceae; *Papaver somniferum* (opium poppy), *Eschscholzia californcia*, *Thalictrum* species, and *Coptis japonica* are the most extensively investigated species. BIA biosynthesis, which fundamentally involves the condensation of two tyrosine derivatives, begins with the decarboxylation of tyrosine to tyramine or of dihydroxyphenylalanine to dopamine by tyrosine decarboxylase (TYDC). TYDC constitutes a large gene family; approximately 15 members are found in opium poppy (33). Dopamine is the precursor for the isoquinoline moiety, whereas 4-hydroxyphenylacetaldehyde, resulting from the deamination of tyramine, is incorporated as the benzyl component (**Figure 2**). As is the case in MIA biosynthesis, BIA condensation is a Pictet-Spengler–type reaction and is catalyzed by the first committed step of the pathway, norcoclaurine synthase (NCS). The enzyme has been purified from *Thalictrum flavum* and corresponding cDNAs have been isolated and functionally characterized from opium poppy and *T. flavum* (87, 136, 137). NCS is related to the pathogenesis related protein (PR) 10 and Bet v 1 allergen protein families. However, homologous PR10 proteins from opium poppy are not catalytically active. Biochemical characterization of

BIA: benzylisoquinoline alkaloid

Sanguinarine: an antimicrobial benzylisoquinoline alkaloid sometimes used in oral hygiene products

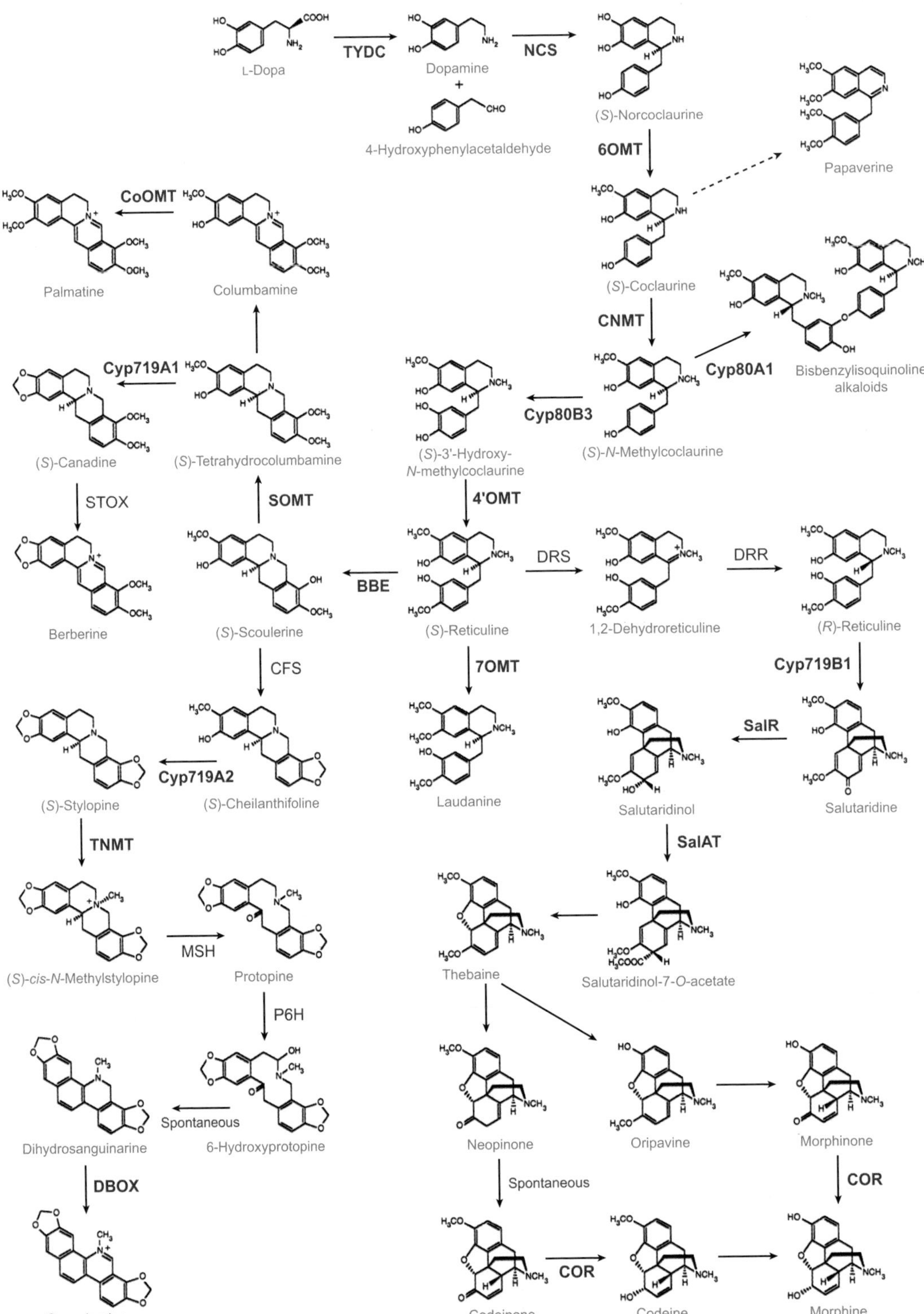
L-Dopa
TYDC
Dopamine
+
4-Hydroxyphenylacetaldehyde
NCS
(S)-Norcoclaurine
6OMT
Papaverine
(S)-Coclaurine
CNMT
Bisbenzylisoquinoline alkaloids
Cyp80A1
(S)-N-Methylcoclaurine
Cyp80B3
(S)-3'-Hydroxy-N-methylcoclaurine
4'OMT
(S)-Reticuline
DRS
1,2-Dehydroreticuline
DRR
(R)-Reticuline
Cyp719B1
Salutaridine
SalR
Salutaridinol
SalAT
Salutaridinol-7-O-acetate
Thebaine
Neopinone
Spontaneous
Codeinone
COR
Codeine
Morphine
Oripavine
Morphinone
COR
7OMT
Laudanine
BBE
(S)-Scoulerine
SOMT
(S)-Tetrahydrocolumbamine
Columbamine
CoOMT
Palmatine
Cyp719A1
(S)-Canadine
STOX
Berberine
CFS
(S)-Cheilanthifoline
Cyp719A2
(S)-Stylopine
TNMT
(S)-cis-N-Methylstylopine
MSH
Protopine
P6H
6-Hydroxyprotopine
Spontaneous
Dihydrosanguinarine
DBOX
Sanguinarine

recombinant *T. flavum* NCS has been accomplished using a continuous enzyme assay based on circular dichroism spectroscopy that follows the generation of the enzyme's chiral product. These studies revealed a reaction mechanism that involves a two-step cyclization with a direct electrophilic aromatic substitution (91). Recently, a second enzyme capable of producing only the (*S*)-norcoclaurine enantiomer was isolated from *C. japonica*; this enzyme displays sequence similarity to 2-oxoglutarate dependent dioxygenases (102). However, this enzyme does not possess a 2-oxoglutarate-binding domain and requires ferrous ions, rather than 2-oxoglutarate or oxygen, for activity. Remarkably, two proteins in two different protein families can catalyze the same reaction in vitro. Nevertheless, the relative participation of each enzyme in BIA biosynthesis in vivo must still be determined.

The conversion of (*S*)-norcoclaurine to (*S*)-reticuline involves *O*-methylation at position 6, *N*-methylation, 3′-hydroxylation, and a second 4′-*O*-methylation (**Figure 2**). Norcoclaurine 6-*O*-methyltransferase (6OMT) and 3′-hydroxy-*N*-methylcoclaurine 4′-*O*-methyltransferase (4′OMT) are both class II *O*-methyltransferases that display strict regiospecificity. Cognate cDNAs have been obtained for each enzyme from opium poppy and *C. japonica* (107, 121, 182). Additional 6OMT homologs from *Thalictrum tuberosum* were functionally characterized and exhibit a broader substrate specificity that includes catechols and phenylpropanoids in addition to various BIA derivatives (42). Coclaurine *N*-methyltransferases (CNMT) have been cloned from opium poppy and *C. japonica* and are more closely related to *S*-adenosyl-*L*-methionine (SAM)-dependent cyclopropane fatty acid synthases than other *N*-methyltransferases (19, 35). The hydroxylation of *N*-methylcoclaurine is catalyzed by a P450 monooxygenase classified in the Cyp subfamily 80B (65, 68, 125, 138).

(*S*)-Reticuline is the central pathway intermediate from which most BIA structural types are derived. Only the dimeric bisbenzylisoquinoline alkaloids are not produced via (*S*)-reticuline. In this pathway, the cytochrome P450 enzyme Cyp80A1 catalyzes the regio- and stereoselective oxidative C-O phenol coupling of the reticuline precursor *N*-methylcoclaurine to produce the bisbenzylisoquinoline alkaloid berbamunine (78). Another exception where reticuline does not represent an intermediate compound might be the biosynthesis of the simple *N*-demethylated BIA papaverine. The recent discovery of a 7-*O*-methyltransferase specific for norreticuline (N7OMT, norreticuline 7-*O*-methyltransferase), but not *N*-methylated analogs, suggests that (*S*)-reticuline precursors might enter the pathway to papaverine (S. Pienkny, J. Ziegler & W. Brandt, manuscript in preparation). A second *O*-methyltransferase that acts on reticuline and catalyzes the formation of laudanine was previously isolated

Figure 2

Biosynthesis of the benzylisoquinoline alkaloids berberine, morphine, and sanguinarine. Enzymes for which corresponding molecular clones have been isolated are shown in bold. Abbreviations: 4′OMT, 3′-hydroxy-*N*-methylcoclaurine 4′-*O*-methyltransferase; 6OMT, norcoclaurine 6-*O*-methyltransferase; 7OMT, reticuline 7-*O*-methyltransferase; BBE, berberine bridge enzyme; CFS, cheilanthifoline synthase; CNMT, coclaurine *N*-methyltransferase; CoOMT, columbamine *O*-methyltransferase; COR, codeinone reductase; Cyp719A1, canadine synthase; Cyp719A2, stylopine synthase; Cyp719B1, salutaridine synthase; Cyp80A1, berbamunine synthase; Cyp80B3, *N*-methylcoclaurine 3′-hydroxylase; DBOX, dihydrobenzophenanthridine oxidase; DRR, 1,2-dehydroreticuline reductase; DRS, 1,2-dehydroreticuline synthase; MSH, *N*-methylstylopine 14-hydroxylase; NCS, norcoclaurine synthase; P6H, protopine 6-hydroxylase; SalAT, salutaridinol 7-*O*-acetyltransferase; SalR, salutaridine:NADPH 7-oxidoreductase; SOMT, scoulerine 9-*O*-methyltransferase; STOX, (*S*)-tetrahydroxyprotoberberine oxidase; TNMT, tetrahydroprotoberberine *cis*-*N*-methyltransferase; TYDC, tyrosine decarboxylase.

from opium poppy (121). (*R,S*)-Reticuline 7-*O*-methyltransferase (7OMT) does not accept *N*-demethylated BIA substrates, but is active toward phenolic compounds.

A major branch pathway that gives rise to many BIA classes begins with the formation of (*S*)-scoulerine by the berberine bridge enzyme (BBE) (**Figure 2**). This enzyme has been cloned from several sources (28, 36, 138) and was recently characterized thoroughly (174, 175). BBE belongs to a novel family of flavoproteins that possess two covalent attachment sites for flavin adenine dinucleotide (FAD); one is histidine and the other is cysteine. The cysteinylation of the cofactor increases the midpoint redox potential to a value higher than that observed for other flavoproteins, thereby facilitating hydride abstraction of (*S*)-reticuline. This step represents the first half reaction toward the conversion to (*S*)-scoulerine. The biosynthesis of benzophenanthridine alkaloids is initiated by the formation of two methylenedioxy bridges resulting in (*S*)-cheilanthifoline and (*S*)-stylopine (**Figure 2**). Both reactions are catalyzed by P450-dependent monooxygenases and two cDNAs coding for stylopine synthase have been cloned from *E. californica* and classified as Cyp719A2 and Cyp719A3 (67). Both recombinant proteins show the same regiospecificity for methylendioxy bridge formation, but Cyp719A2 only converts (*S*)-cheilanthifoline to (*S*)-stylopine. In contrast, Cyp719A3 also accepts compounds without a pre-existing methylenedioxy bridge. (*S*)-Stylopine is subsequently *N*-methylated to (*S*)-*cis*-*N*-methylstylopine by tetrahydroprotoberberine *N*-methyltransferase (TNMT). On the basis of homology to CNMT, a cDNA encoding TNMT has been isolated and functionally characterized from opium poppy (86). The enzyme shows a narrow substrate range in that it converts only tetrahydroprotoberberine alkaloids with dimethoxy or methylenedioxy functional groups at C2/3 and C9/10, respectively. TNMT is also one of only a few plant enzymes able to catalyze the formation of quaternary ammonium compounds. Subsequent hydroxylation by (*S*)-*cis*-*N*-methylstylopine 14-hydroxylase yields protopine, which is further hydroxylated by protopine 6-hydroxylase to dihydrosanguinarine. Both enzymes have been detected in protopine alkaloid-containing cell cultures, and their characterization suggests that they are P450 monooxygenases (132, 156). Dihydrobenzophenanthridine oxidase, which converts dihydrosanguinarine to sanguinarine, has been purified from *Sanguianaria canadensis* (7).

An alternative branch for the metabolism of (*S*)-scoulerine in some species involves the formation of (*S*)-tetrahydrocolumbamine by scoulerine 9-*O*-methyltransferase (SOMT) (**Figure 2**) (155). The cDNA encoding SOMT from *C. japonica* was the first reported clone for an *O*-methyltransferase specifically implicated in BIA metabolism. All *O*-methyltransferases in the BIA pathway exhibit considerable homology. Tetrahydrocolumbamine is converted to columbamine, which is methylated by columbamine *O*-methyltransferase (CoOMT) to yield palmatine (106). Recombinant CoOMT is active only against protoberberine alkaloid substrates, such as scoulerine or tetrahydrocolumbamine, but not against other BIA derivatives. The subsequent formation of a methylenedioxy bridge is catalyzed by canadine synthase, a P450 enzyme that belongs to the Cyp719A family (68). Cyp719A1 displays high substrate specificity for tetrahydrocolumbamine and does not accept columbamine. As such, a parallel path to berberine via this columbamine is unlikely. (*S*)-Canadine, or (*S*)-tetrahydroberberine as it is also called, is oxidized by either (*S*)-canadine oxidase or (*S*)-tetrahydroberberine oxidase (STOX), which catalyze the same reaction but show substantially different biochemical properties.

Whereas all pathways downstream of reticuline begin with the (*S*)-epimer, conversion to the (*R*)-epimer of reticuline is a required entry step into the morphinan alkaloid biosynthetic pathway (**Figure 2**). The epimerization of reticuline is a two-step process that involves the oxidation of (*S*)-reticuline by 1,2-dehydroreticuline synthase and the reduction of 1,2-dehydroreticuline to (*R*)-reticuline. Both steps have been characterized biochemically and the enzymes have been partially purified (23, 63). Intramolecular carbon-carbon phenol coupling between C2 of the benzyl and C4a of the isochinoline moiety leads to the formation of salutaridine. This enzyme belongs to the P450 monooxygenase family (48). The gene encoding salutaridine synthase (SalSyn) was recently cloned from opium poppy on the basis of its higher expression in morphine-containing *Papaver* species and the enzyme was then functionally characterized (A. Gesell, F.C. Huang, J. Ziegler & T.M. Kutchan, manuscript in preparation). The SalSyn protein shows high homology to the methylenedioxybridge-forming P450-dependent enzymes, and was classified as Cyp719B1. The next step in the pathway is catalyzed by salutaridine reductase (SalR); a cognate cDNA was obtained via the same approach used for SalSyn (183). Functional characterization of the recombinant enzyme showed the stereospecific reduction of the keto group to 7(*S*)-salutaridinol, which is also reported for the purified enzyme from opium poppy (49). The enzyme belongs to the family of short chain dehydrogenases/reductases (SDR), but unlike many other enzymes in this family it exhibits a higher molecular weight and is monomeric. The stereospecific reduction of salutaridine is required for the next step, which is catalyzed by salutaridinol 7-*O*-acetyltransferase (SalAT). This enzyme specifically acetylates the 7(*S*)-epimer of salutaridinol to salutaridinol-7-*O*-acetate (82). With considerable sequence homology to the acetylating enzymes from the MIA pathway, SalAT also belongs to the BAHD family of acetyltransferases (52). The introduced acetyl group is eliminated spontaneously, leading to the formation of an oxide bridge between C-4 and C-5 to yield thebaine, the first pentacyclic alkaloid of the pathway (82). The final steps toward the biosynthesis of morphine consist of two demethylations and one reduction. Both the demethylation from thebaine to neopinone, which isomerises to codeinone, and from codeine to morphine are not yet understood and no enzymes capable of catalyzing either reaction have been detected. Codeinone reductase has been purified and cloned from opium poppy, and, in contrast to SalR, belongs to the aldo-keto reductase (AKR) family (83, 160).

SDR: short chain dehydrogenases/reductases

Calystegines: nortropane alkaloids thought to serve as nutritional sources for soil microorganisms

Tropane alkaloids and nicotine. Tropane alkaloids are an important class of plant-derived anticholinergic compounds, such as hyoscyamine and scopolamine, that occur in several *Hyoscyamus*, *Atropa*, and *Datura* species. Calystegines, which function as selective glucosidase inhibitors, are more widely spread than hyoscyamine and scopolamine in the plant kingdom and occur mainly in the Solanaceae and Convolvulaceae (30). Nicotine, the active principle in *Nicotiana* species, acts on nicotinic acetylcholine receptors to cause a variety of physiological effects, including addiction. Tropane alkaloid and nicotine biosynthesis begin with the methylation of putrescine to *N*-methylputrescine by putrescine *N*-methyltransferase (PMT) (**Figure 3**). The isolation of the cDNA encoding PMT from tobacco was one of the first examples of the successful integration of metabolite and gene expression profiles as a strategy to isolate cDNAs implicated in plant secondary metabolite biosynthesis (61). Homologous cDNAs from other plants that produce tropane alkaloids, such as *Hyoscyamus niger*, *Atropa belladonna*, and *Solanum tuberosum*, have also been isolated (147, 153, 157). The second step in the pathway is the oxidative deamination of *N*-methylputrescine to 4-methylaminobutanal by *N*-methylputrescine oxidase (MPO). This enzyme belongs to a class of amine oxidases that require copper as a cofactor. This property was exploited in a homology-based cloning strategy to isolate the MPO cDNA from tobacco (59). The central intermediate *N*-methyl-Δ^1-pyrrolium cation for

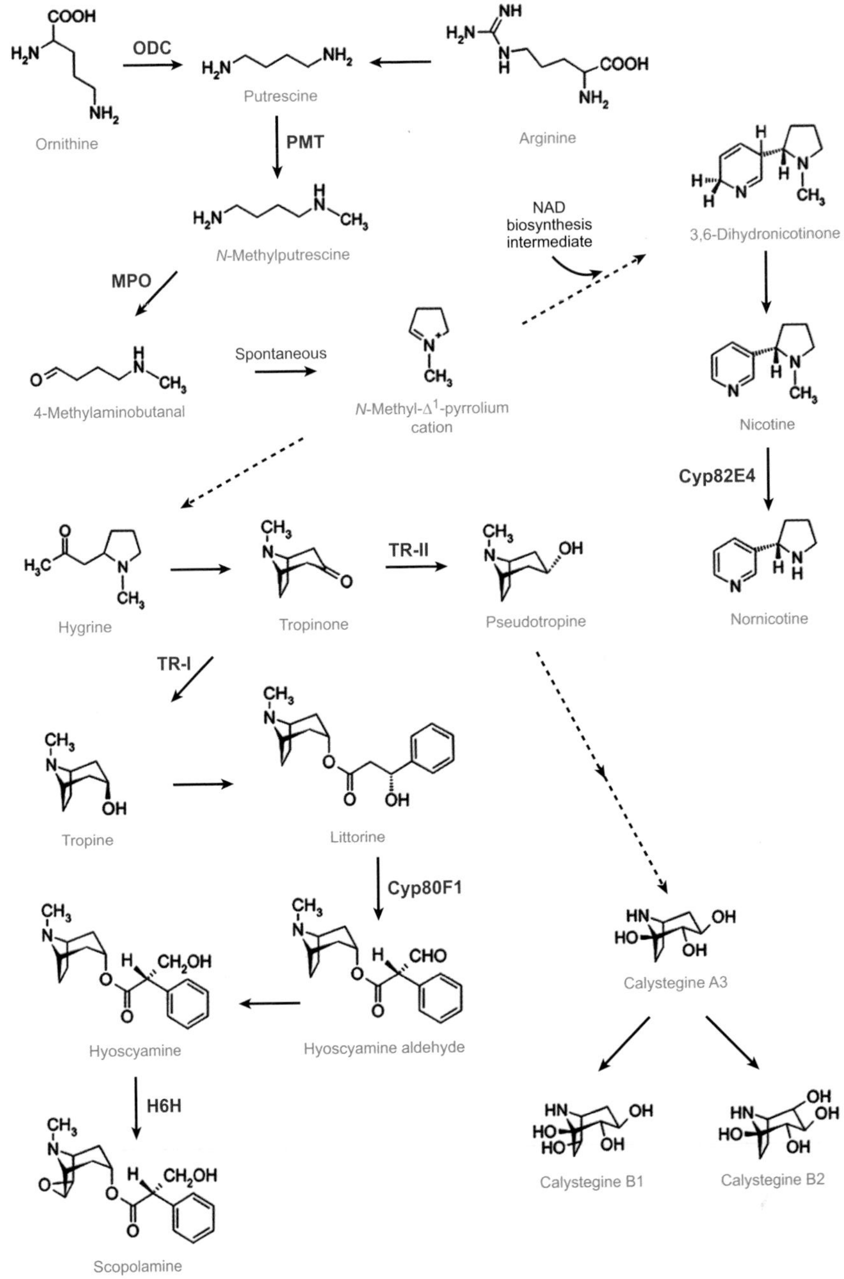

Figure 3

Biosynthesis of the tropane alkaloids hyoscyamine and scopolamine, the calystegines, and nicotine. Molecular clones have been isolated for all enzymes shown. Abbreviations: Cyp80F1, littorine mutase/ monooxygenase; Cyp82E4, nicotine *N*-demethylase; H6H, hyoscyamine 6β-hydroxylase; MPO, methylputrescine oxidase; ODC, ornithine decarboxylase; PMT, putrescine *N*-methyltransferase; TR-I, tropinone reductase I; TR-II, tropinone reductase II.

tropane alkaloid and nicotine biosynthesis results from the spontaneous cyclization of 4-methylaminobutanal. For nicotine, the cation is condensed with nicotinic acid to form 3,6-dihydronicotine, which subsequently undergoes dehydrogenation to nicotine by enzymes that remain poorly characterized. Nicotine can be *N*-demethylated to form nornicotine, which is an undesirable derivative owing to its role as the precursor of the carcinogen *N'*-nitrosonornicotine. On the basis of the differential abundance of transcripts corresponding to several P450-encoding cDNAs in tobacco varieties acccumulating nicotine and nornicotine, a clone for nicotine *N*-demethylase (NND) was identified and classified as Cyp82E4 (144, 176). Recently, Gavilano & Siminszky (45) described an additional cDNA with NND activity (Cyp82E5v2) that shows distinct tissue-specific expression in tobacco.

Although enzymatic activities have not been demonstrated, the condensation of *N*-methyl-Δ^1-pyrrolium cation with acetoacetic acid is purported to yield hygrine, the precursor of tropane alkaloids (**Figure 3**). Hygrine is converted to tropinone, which is subsequently reduced to intermediates that lead to hyoscyamine or calystegines depending on the stereochemistry of the reduction. Tropinone reductase I (TR-I) catalyzes the reduction of tropinone to tropine, which possesses a 3α configuration. In contrast, tropinone reductase II (TR-II) catalyzes the formation of ψ-tropine, which has a 3β configuration. Cognate cDNAs show that both NADPH-dependent enzymes belong to the SDR family and exhibit considerable amino acid sequence similarity (76, 110, 111, 113). Domain-swapping experiments and site-directed mutagenesis led to the identification of the substrate-binding domain responsible for the opposite stereospecificity of each reductase. Tropine then condenses with the phenylalanine-derived (*R*)-phenyllactate to yield littorine, which undergoes rearrangement to form hyoscyamine. Recently, Li and coworkers (84) used functional genomics based on virus-induced gene silencing to isolate a cytochrome P450 involved in littorine rearrangement from *H. niger*. This enzyme was classified as Cyp80F1 and it catalyzes the oxidation of (*R*)-littorine with rearrangement to hyoscyamine aldehyde. Finally, the epoxidation of hyoscyamine yields scopolamine via a two-step reaction: 6β-hydroxylation of the tropane ring followed by intramolecular epoxide formation. The reaction is catalyzed by a 2-oxoglutarate–dependent dioxygenase, hyoscyamine 6β-hydroxylase (H6H), the cDNA for which has been cloned from several tropane alkaloid-containing plants (88, 95, 154).

Purine alkaloids. Purine alkaloids are derived from purine nucleotides. The most prominent members of this class of compounds are theobromine and caffeine. Purine alkaloid biosynthesis begins with the *N*-methylation of xanthosine at position 7 by 7-methylxanthosine synthase (XRS), which is also known as xanthosine 7-*N*-methyltanferase (XMT) (**Figure 4**). Cognate cDNAs for XMT have been isolated from

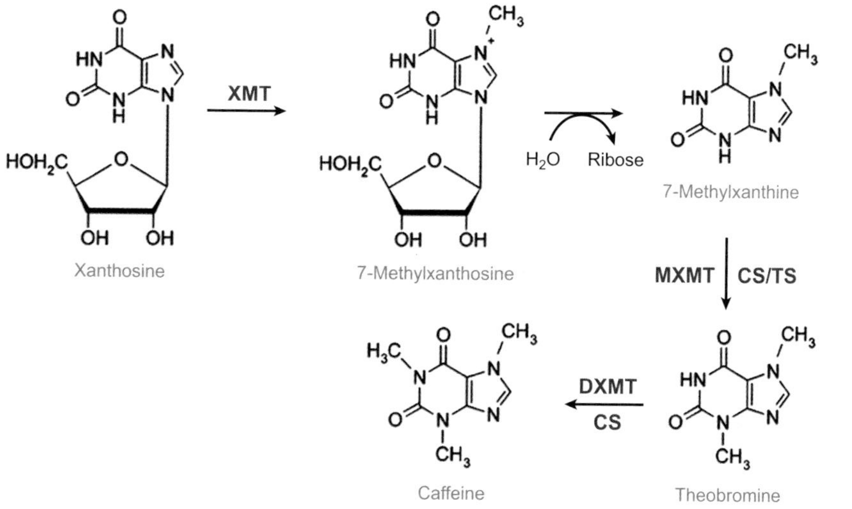

Figure 4

Biosynthesis of the purine alkaloids caffeine and theobromine. Molecular clones have been isolated for all enzymes shown. Abbreviations: CS, caffeine synthase; DXMT, 1,7-dimethylxanthosine methyltransferase; MXMT, 7-methylxanthine methyltransferase; TS, theobromine synthase, XMT, xanthosine 7-*N*-methyltanferase.

Coffea arabica (103, 158). The second step in the purine alkaloid pathway is the hydrolysis of xanthosine to 7-methylxanthine, although the responsible enzyme has not yet been purified or characterized. However, detailed structural investigations of XMT suggest a coupled reaction for 7-*N*-methylation and nucleoside cleavage catalyzed by a single enzyme (97). Several cDNAs with different substrate specificities have been obtained from tea, coffee, or cacao that catalyze the next two *N*-methylations. Caffeine synthase (CS) performs dual methylations, first at position 3 to form theobromine, and then at position 1 to yield caffeine (74, 104). Several cDNAs encoding related enzymes that catalyze only single *N*-methylations have been isolated, including 7-methylxanthine methyltransferase (MXMT1 and MXMT2) and theobromine synthase (TS), which methylate position *N*-3, and 3,7-dimethylxanthine methyltransferase (DXMT), which catalyzes the final methylation at position *N*-1 (117, 158). These *N*-methyltransferases possess more then 80% amino acid similarity and phylogenetic analysis suggests that they are more closely related to carboxyl-methyltransferases than to other *N*-methyltransferases.

Pyrrolizidine alkaloids. Pyrrolizidine alkaloids are produced constitutively in various plants as a defense against hebivores and as a component of the complex chemical ecology between plants and animals (55). These alkaloids are composed of a necine base and one or more necic acids; the latter are responsible for their structural diversity. Necine biosynthesis begins with the condensation of spermidine and putrescine to form homospermidine by homospermidine synthase (HSS) (116) (**Figure 5**). The reaction mechanism is identical to that of deoxyhyposine synthase (DHS), which transfers the aminobutyl moiety to a lysine residue of the eukaryotic

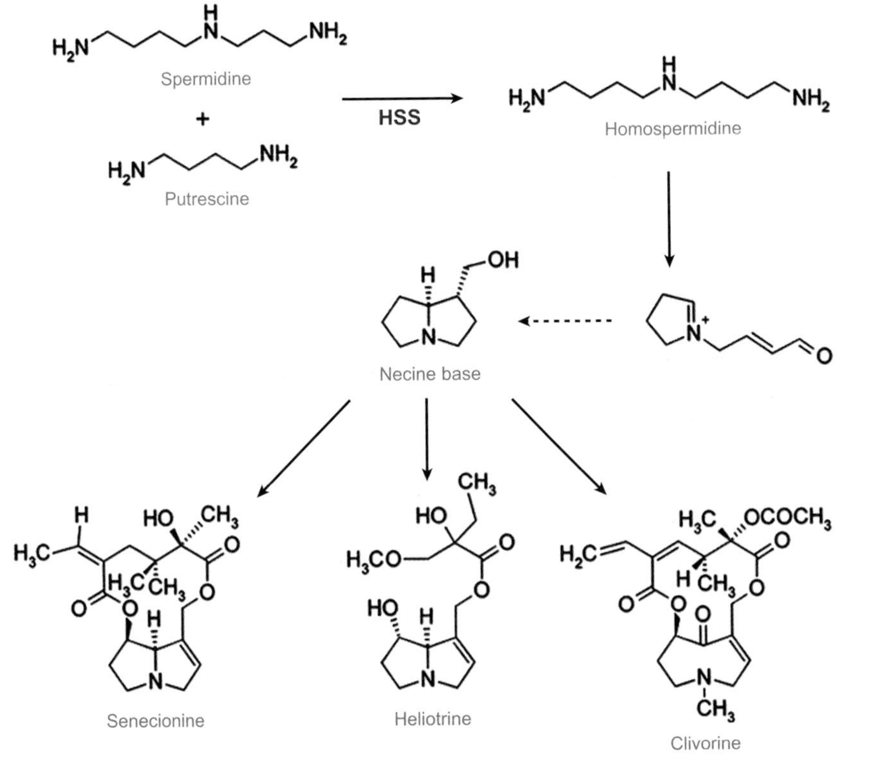

Figure 5

Biosynthesis of pyrrolizidine alkaloids. A molecular clone has been isolated for only one biosynthetic enzyme. Abbreviation: HSS, homospermidine synthase.

initiation factor 5A precursor protein. Additionally, both enzymes share extensive sequence homology, suggesting the recruitment of HSS from DHS, with subsequent optimization to facilitate the role of HSS in secondary metabolism. Phylogenetic analysis of HSS and DHS homologs from angiosperms that represent several unrelated plant lineages suggests at least four independent recruitment events for HSS (128). The remaining components of pyrrolizidine alkaloid metabolism are not well understood.

Structure-Function Relationships in Alkaloid Biosynthetic Enzymes

The biomimetic exploitation of enzymes, especially those that display strict stereospecificity, is an appealing strategy for the commercial production of pharmaceutical alkaloids. Equally intriguing is the synthesis of novel alkaloids via protein engineering aimed at altering the substrate specificity of biosynthetic enzymes. Recent attention has focused on elucidating the reaction and substrate binding mechanisms of key alkaloid biosynthetic enzymes. The structures of several enzymes have been determined and substrate-binding pockets have been characterized.

The first detailed structures of enzymes involved in plant alkaloid metabolism were obtained by X-ray crystallography for TR-I and TR-II, which show strict product specificities and catalyze either tropine or ψ-tropine formation. Site-directed mutagenesis of selected amino acids in the substrate-binding domains resulted in a mutual conversion of the product specificities for TR-I and TR-II (114). A homology-based model of the three-dimensional structure of PMT was generated on the basis of the crystal structure of the putative ancestral enzyme spermidine synthase, which suggested the identity of amino acids responsible for the distinction between these two enzymes (157).

Most X-ray crystallographic data have been obtained for enzymes implicated in MIA metabolism, especially those involved in ajmaline biosynthesis. The structure of STR from *R. serpentina* revealed a novel six-bladed β-propeller protein and site-directed mutagenesis showed the importance of a key glutamate residue in catalysis (93). The structure of the enzyme complexed with the natural substrates tryptamine and secologanine provided insight into the architecture of the substrate binding sites, which could then be engineered to accommodate several different tryptamine and secologanin analogs (18, 90). The three-dimensional structure of SGD revealed the expected $(\beta/\alpha)_8$ barrel fold typical for family 1 glycosidases (9). Site-directed mutagenesis identified amino acid residues required for the catalytic mechanism and the binding site architecture. Ruppert and coworkers (133) reported preliminary X-ray crystallographic data for the homologous enzyme RG. A comparision of the structures of SGD and RG will be interesting because both enzymes occur in the same organism and catalyze the same type of reaction, but differ in substrate specificity. VS was the first BAHD acyltransferase family enzyme for which a three-dimensional structure was obtained (92). The protein consists of two major domains of similar size connected by a large loop. Whereas site-directed mutagenesis and structural analysis confirm the importance of a HXXXD motif for catalysis, a second highly conserved motif in members of the BAHD family is distant from the active site and is considered essential for proper folding rather than catalysis. Molecular modeling and site-directed mutagenesis established the classification of PNAE as a member of the α/β hydrolase superfamily and identified the amino acid residues that participate in the catalytic triad (96).

The structure of SalR (involved in BIA biosynthesis) was analyzed by homology modelling (47). An additional helix near the catalytic site not found in multimeric SDR-type enzymes appears to contribute to substrate specificity. Substrate docking studies and site-directed mutagenesis revealed several amino acids implicated in the binding of the morphinan alkaloid precursor salutaridine. It will be

Homology-based model: an atomic-resolution protein structure based on amino acid sequence

Substrate docking: a mathematical procedure used to identify ligand-binding sites in proteins

Laticifer: a plant cell or vessel that contains latex

interesting to compare the substrate-binding site of SalR with that of COR, which specifically reduces codeinone, an alkaloid with a similar structure, to salutaridine. The potential of homology modelling and substrate docking is well demonstrated in studies involving the *O*-methyltransferases implicated in BIA metabolism (S. Pienkny, J. Ziegler & W. Brandt, manuscript in preparation). Although highly similar to 6OMT, the modelling and substrate docking results for a novel *O*-methyltransferase precluded norcoclaurine as a likely substrate, and rather suggested the *O*-methylation of norreticuline at position 7. Experimental evidence has confirmed this prediction and led to the identification of N7OMT. Furthermore, comparisons of the 6OMT and N7OMT models identified the amino acids responsible for the distinct substrate specificity.

Recently, McCarthy & McCarthy (97) elucidated the structures of the two highly homologous *N*-methyltransferases involved in caffeine biosynthesis, XMT and DXMT. Cocrystallization with the cofactor and either substrate, coupled with structural comparisons, revealed critical elements for substrate selectivity and catalysis.

REGULATION OF ALKALOID BIOSYNTHETIC PATHWAYS

Transcriptome and Metabolome Analyses

Large-scale expression analyses have recently begun to provide a broad picture of the gene expression profiles associated with alkaloid biosynthesis. As a prerequisite for these studies, several EST sequencing projects have been reported and the number of sequences associated with alkaloid-producing plants continues to increase. The first database consisted of 4,500 ESTs from the laticifers of opium poppy (127). Further EST projects involving this plant have yielded a total of 25,000 ESTs from various tissues including seedlings, stems, roots, and elicited cell cultures (182, 183, 184). A recent floral genome project contributed 11,000 ESTs from the BIA-accumulating plant *E. californica* (17), and the release of a *C. japonica* database has also been announced (69, 75). NapGen, a consortium of Canadian investigators, has sequenced more than 400,000 ESTs from a wide variety of plants that produce health-related secondary compounds. In this project, 46,000 ESTs were sequenced from cell cultures of eight BIA-accumulating species including *E. californica*, *T. flavum*, *Nandina domestica*, and *Papaver bracteatum* (D.K. Liscombe, J. Ziegler & P.J. Facchini, manuscript in preparation). More than 56,000 ESTs have been obtained from leaf, leaf epidermis, and roots of the MIA-accumulating plant *C. roseus* (108). Large-scale sequencing projects for tropane alkaloid-containing plants, such as *S. tuberosum*, are also well established. Although research in potato is primarily aimed at the discovery of genes involved in fungal resistance, the 62,000 ESTs from aerial and underground organs are a good source to identify cDNAs implicated in calystegine biosynthesis (131). A sequencing project targeting tropane alkaloid metabolism yielded 2,300 ESTs from roots of *H. niger* (84). In a similar effort to investigate the transcriptional regulation associated with the chemical composition of coffee, Lin and coworkers (85) reported 47,000 ESTs from *Coffea canephora* at different stages of seed development.

Large-scale transcriptome and metabolite profiling has been performed in opium poppy cell cultures treated with a fungal elicitor (184), and in *C. roseus* and tobacco cell cultures treated with methyl jasmonate (51, 129). In all cases, researchers observed a coordinated increase in the expression of genes implicated in alkaloid metabolism. Moreover, profound changes in the level of gene transcripts encoding primary metabolic enzymes also occurred. Interestingly, transcripts involved in SAM recycling increased in all three systems, indicating a high demand for this cofactor in the modification of alkaloid backbone structures. As expected, genes implicated in aromatic amino acid metabolism were also induced in opium poppy and *C. roseus* in response to the increased demand for the precursors of BIA and MIA biosynthesis (129, 184). Surprisingly, the expression of genes associated with nitrogen metabolism was not affected in opium poppy cultures, suggesting that the cells have a constitutive and sufficient capacity for nitrogen assimilation even during periods of increased demand (184). However, substantial changes occurred in the levels of primary metabolites involved in the production of energy molecules potentially required by enzymes and other components required by the induction of alkaloid biosynthesis (184). In *C. roseus*, the construction of correlation networks that integrate transcriptomic and metabolomics data revealed a correlation between the expression of alkaloid biosynthetic genes and corresponding metabolic products (129).

Gene Regulation and Signal Transduction

Progress has continued on the identification of promoter elements and transcription factors involved in the regulation of several MIA biosynthetic genes (165). The recent application of a genomics approach based on DNA macroarrays constructed from ESTs has led to the isolation of the first transcription factor putatively involved in the regulation of BIA metabolism. Transcripts that encode a subset of transcriptional regulators showed coordinate expression with respect to BIA biosynthetic genes in berberine-producing *C. japonica* cell cultures. One of these regulators, a WRKY transcription factor, was shown by RNAi and overexpression analysis to specifically regulate the expression of BIA biosynthetic genes (75). With respect to early signal transduction events, considerable effort has been focused on events associated with the induction of alkaloid metabolism in *E. californica* cell cultures, which accumulate benzophenanthridine alkaloids such as sanguinarine in response to treatment with a fungal elicitor. Two different signal transduction pathways were identified. One cascade is jasmonate-dependent and responds to high elicitor concentrations. The other is jasmonate-independent and is triggered by low elicitor concentrations (38). The jasmonate-independent pathway involves Gα proteins that interact and activate phospholipase A2, which leads to a transient proton efflux from the vacuole and a subsequent activation of other cytoplasmic components (60, 164).

Metabolomics: the systematic study of the chemical fingerprints left behind by specific cellular processes

RNAi: RNA interference

Transgenic Approaches

The application of transgenic technologies to alkaloid-producing plants is primarily intended to increase the synthetic capacity of desired product via the overexpression of certain genes, or to divert pathways to previously under-represented or novel compounds through posttranscriptional gene silencing. However, such experiments also provide insights into the regulatory architecture of alkaloid pathways, especially if the predicted outcome is not observed. Unexpected metabolic consequences resulting from single-enzyme perturbations of alkaloid pathways suggest the existence of key rate-limiting steps, potential multienzyme complexes, or unsuspected compartmentalization.

Metabolic engineering of low-scopolamine *A. belladonna* plants via the introduction of a constitutively expressed H6H transgene led to an increase in scopolamine accumulation (179). Similarly, a shift in the accumulation of hyoscyamine in favor of scopolamine occurred when the H6H transgene was introduced into *A. beatica*, suggesting that the enzyme is a rate-limiting step in scopolamine biosynthesis (180). However, the unpredictability of metabolic engineering in tropane alkaloid biosynthesis was demonstrated by the constitutive coexpression of PMT and H6H. The transgenes caused only modest increases in alkaloid accumulation when expressed alone, but exhibited a synergistic effect on alkaloid levels when expressed together (181).

Latex: the milky cytoplasm of specialized cells called laticifers

In MIA biosynthesis, the first attempts at metabolic engineering focused on the expression of constitutive *TDC* and *STR* transgenes in *C. roseus* cell cultures (31). However, only unsustained increases in alkaloid accumulation were reported, which raises concerns about the actual relationship between the transgenes and the initial phenotype (16). Overexpression of enzymes responsible for production of the indole moiety, such as anthranilate synthase (AS), resulted in higher levels of tryptophan, but not alkaloids (64, 66). Monoterpenoid pathway reactions have long been considered the rate-limiting steps in MIA production. In this context, overexpression of a modified 3-hydroxy-3-methylglutaryl-CoA reductase leads to a predictable increase in alkaloid content (8). The role of secologanin biosynthesis in the control of flux into MIA metabolism is underscored by the ectopic overexpression of transcriptional regulators of the pathway. T-DNA activation tagging in *C. roseus* cell cultures resulted in the isolation of an octadecanoid-derivative responsive *Catharanthus* AP2-domain protein (ORCA3), which activates the expression of genes encoding AS, TDC, STR, D4H, cytochrome P450 reductase, and D-1-deoxyxylulose 5-phosphate synthase, but not those encoding geraniol 10-hydroxylase, SGD, and DAT (161). However, alkaloid accumulation in cells transformed with a constitutively expressed ORCA3 transgene occurred only in the presence of exogenous loganin. The combined overexpression of transcriptional activators, such as ORCA2 and ORCA3, and the silencing of repressors, such as the G-box binding factors 1 and 2 and the zinc finger protein family, might be required to activate the entire pathway (100, 126, 143, 161).

Most of the transgenic work involving BIA metabolism has focused on the modulation of BBE activity. Overexpression of this enzyme in *E. californica* root cultures results in an increased accumulation of downstream alkaloids and decreased levels of certain amino acids (124). Conversely, antisense suppression of *BBE* expression leads to undetectable levels of downstream metabolites and increased cellular pools of amino acids, revealing the impact of perturbations in alkaloid metabolism on primary metabolism (123). Interestingly, antisense suppression of *BBE* does not result in the accumulation of its substrate (*S*)-reticuline or any other upstream alkaloid, suggesting the occurrence of metabolic channels that are abolished in the absence of BBE. In contrast, RNAi lines targeting *BBE* in *E. californica* cell cultures result in high (*S*)-reticuline content (43). Furthermore, laudanine is detected, implying that the pathway is redirected toward the *O*-methylation of reticuline by 7OMT. Transgenic opium poppy plants expressing an antisense-BBE construct show increased flux into the morphinan and tetrahydrobenzylisoquinoline branch pathways (40). Surprisingly, the BBE reaction product (*S*)-scoulerine also accumulates in the latex of these transgenic plants, although the roots show no alterations in metabolite profile. Whether these results are due to an additional role of BBE in BIA metabolism remains unproven. Opium poppy plants transformed with constitutively expressed or antisense-suppressed *Cyp80B3*, which encodes *N*-methylcoclaurine 3′-hydroxylase, also show substantial modulations in alkaloid content (41). However, as expected the alkaloid profile is not altered because Cyp80B3 acts early in the pathway. Overexpression of *COR1*, the penultimate step in morphine biosynthesis, also results in opium poppy plants with increased alkaloid content (81). This increase is attributable to higher levels of morphine, codeine, and—for unexplained reasons—thebaine, which is upstream of COR1 in the pathway. The overexpression of one alkaloid biosynthetic gene might possibly cause the coordinate transcriptional induction of other pathway genes. It would be interesting to subject these transgenic plants to microarray analysis to potentially correlate alterations in transcript abundance with changes in alkaloid profile. In RNAi-silenced *COR1* plants, the expression of other known genes from the pathway is unaffected (4). However, the plants accumulate the far upstream intermediate (*S*)-reticuline rather than codeinone, the substrate of COR. Whether this is based on a feedback mechanism that inhibits the entire morphinan branch pathway or the impairment of a required metabolic channel due to the absence of COR is not known. The presence of multienzyme complexes in morphine biosynthesis is supported by experiments that involve the suppression of *SalAT*. RNAi-silenced *SalAT* plants show an accumulation of salutaridine, which is normally not abundant in opium poppy plants (3). This is surprising because salutaridinol, which does not accumulate, is the substrate for SalAT (**Figure 2**). Salutaridine might be channelled to thebaine through an enzyme complex that includes SalR and SalAT.

Experiments involving the overexpression of two *O*-methyltransferases from the early BIA pathway in *E. californica* cells suggested a rate-limiting role for 6OMT (69). Constitutive overexpression of 6OMT led to increased alkaloid content. In contrast, overexpression of 4′OMT had little effect. The *E. californica* cell culture used in this study appeared to lack a functional 6OMT, which might explain the strong effect of overexpressing a 6OMT transgene. Subsequent biochemical characterization of 4′OMT from *E. californica* revealed low 6OMT activity, suggesting a role for 4′OMT as a surrogate for 6OMT to facilitate BIA biosynthesis.

Transgenic approaches to alter caffeine biosynthesis have recently focused on the generation of *C. arabica* plants with reduced caffeine content for the production of decaffeinated coffee. Suppression of *MXMT*, the second *N*-methyltransferase in the pathway, results in the reduction of theobromine and caffeine by 50% to 70% in *C. arabica* and *C. canephora* (118, 119). However, *MXMT*, *XMT*, and *DXMT* transcripts are all reduced owing to the high homology between the three genes. An alternative biotechnological strategy has targeted the production of caffeine in non-caffeine-producing plants to increase pest resistance. Overexpression of all three *N*-methyltransferases in transgenic *Nicotiana tabacum* leads to a substantial (5 ug g^{-1} fresh weight) accumulation of caffeine in leaves (77, 159). This is sufficient to reduce by 50% pest damage caused by feeding of the tobacco cutworm *Spodoptera litura*.

Idioblast: an individual cell that differs greatly from its neighbors

ALKALOID TRAFFICKING

The cell biology of alkaloid metabolism in plants has recently emerged as an exciting field of research. Although the biosynthetic pathways leading to various alkaloid types are of polyphyletic origin, some intriguing paradigms are apparent, including the involvement of multiple cell types for alkaloid biosynthesis and/or accumulation, the targeting of different pathway enzymes to multiple subcellular compartments, and the possibility that multienzyme complexes are ubiquitous. Such complex organization implicates extensive intra- and intercellular transport of pathway intermediates, products, and biosynthetic enzymes.

Cell Type–Specific Localization of Alkaloid Biosynthetic Enzymes

Alkaloids generally accumulate in specific cell types owing to their cytotoxicity and probable role in plant defense responses. For example, alkaloids are sequestered to isolated idioblasts and laticifers in *C. roseus* (151), root endodermis and stem cortex/pith in *T. flavum* (138), and laticifers in opium poppy (13). The cellular localization of alkaloid pathways is remarkably diverse and complex. Work on the cellular and developmental complexities and organization of alkaloid biosynthesis in *C. roseus* and opium poppy, in particular, have established new paradigms in the cell biology of secondary metabolism.

PMT and H6H, which catalyze the first and last steps, respectively, in the biosynthesis of the tropane alkaloid scopolamine, localize to the pericycle in the roots of *A. belladonna* and *Hyoscyamus muticus* (56, 153, 154) (**Figure 6*a***). PMT also catalyzes the

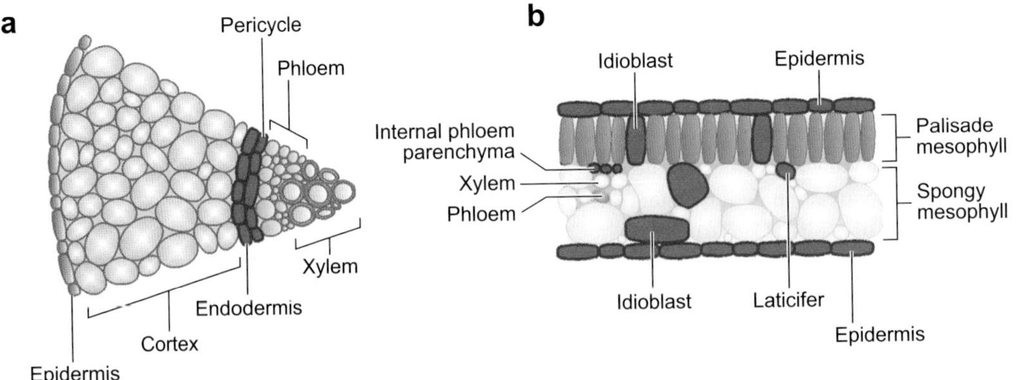

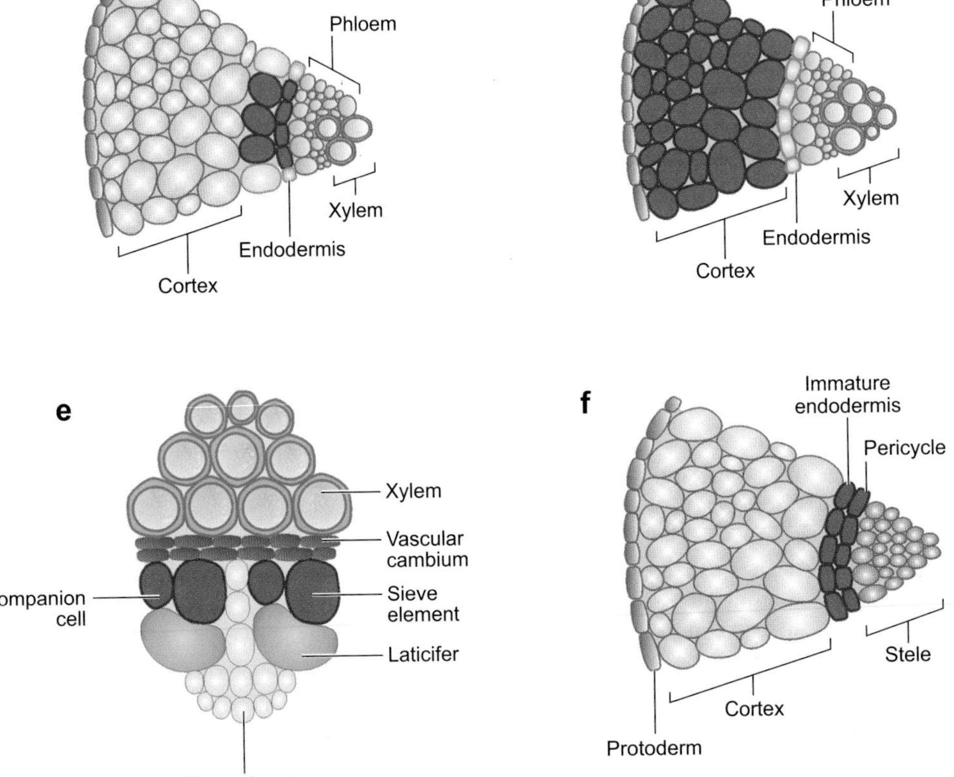

Figure 6

Alkaloid biosynthetic pathways are associated with a diversity of cell types. The tissue-specific localization (*red*) of enzymes and/or gene transcripts are shown for the biosynthesis of tropane alkaloids in (*a*) *Atropa belladonna* and *Hyoscyamus niger* roots, (*b*) terpenoid indole alkaloids in *Catharanthus roseus* leaves, (*c*) pyrrolizidine alkaloids in *Senecio vernalis* roots, (*d*) pyrrolizidine alkaloids in *Eupatorium cannabinum* roots, (*e*) benzylisoquinoline alkaloids in *Papaver somniferum* vascular bundles, and (*f*) benzylisoquinoline alkaloids in *Thalictrum flavum* roots.

first step in nicotine biosynthesis and localizes to the endodermis, outer cortex, and xylem in *Nicotiana sylvestris* (141, 142). In contrast, TR-I, an intermediate enzyme in the production of hyoscyamine and scopolamine, resides in the endodermis and nearby cortical cells (112); thus, tropane alkaloid intermediates must also traffic between cell types (**Figure 7**). The specific pathway intermediates that undergo intercellular translocation are not known. Interestingly, TR-II, which provides pseudotropine for the formation of calystegines, localizes to companion cells of sieve elements in the phloem of potato (73).

Enzymes involved in MIA biosynthesis localize to several different *C. roseus* organs and cell types. TDC and STR are abundant in roots (151), but also occur in photosynthetic organs, whereas T16H (149), D4H (162), and DAT (150) are restricted to young leaves and other shoot organs where vindoline biosynthesis occurs. In situ hybridization and immunocytochemical localization studies have shown that Cyp72A1, TDC, and STR localize to the epidermis of stems, leaves, and flower buds (70, 151) (**Figure 6*b***). In roots, these enzymes occur in cells near the apical meristem. In contrast, D4H and DAT are associated with laticifers and idioblasts of shoots, but are absent from roots. Laticifers and idioblasts are distributed throughout the mesophyll in leaves, often several cell layers away from the epidermis; thus, vindoline biosynthesis involves at least two distinct cell types and requires the intercellular translocation of pathway intermediates. Moreover, gene transcripts that encode enzymes involved in the MEP pathway, along with geraniol 10-hydroxylase, colocalize to the internal phloem parenchyma of young *C. roseus* aerial organs (15, 120). These results suggest the translocation of vindoline biosynthetic intermediates from the internal phloem to the epidermis and from the epidermis to laticifers and idioblasts (**Figure 8**). As is the case in tropane alkaloid metabolism, the specific pathway intermediates that undergo intercellular translocation in MIA biosynthesis in *C. roseus* are not known. Interestingly, the identification of gene transcripts encoding vindoline biosynthetic enzymes in specific cell types isolated by laser-capture microdissection and enriched via carborundum abrasion was interpreted to suggest that the leaf epidermis is independently capable of producing 16-methoxytabersonine (109). Upper leaf epidermis has been implicated in several secondary metabolic pathways (94), complicating the assignment of common precursors to specific cell types. The role of internal phloem

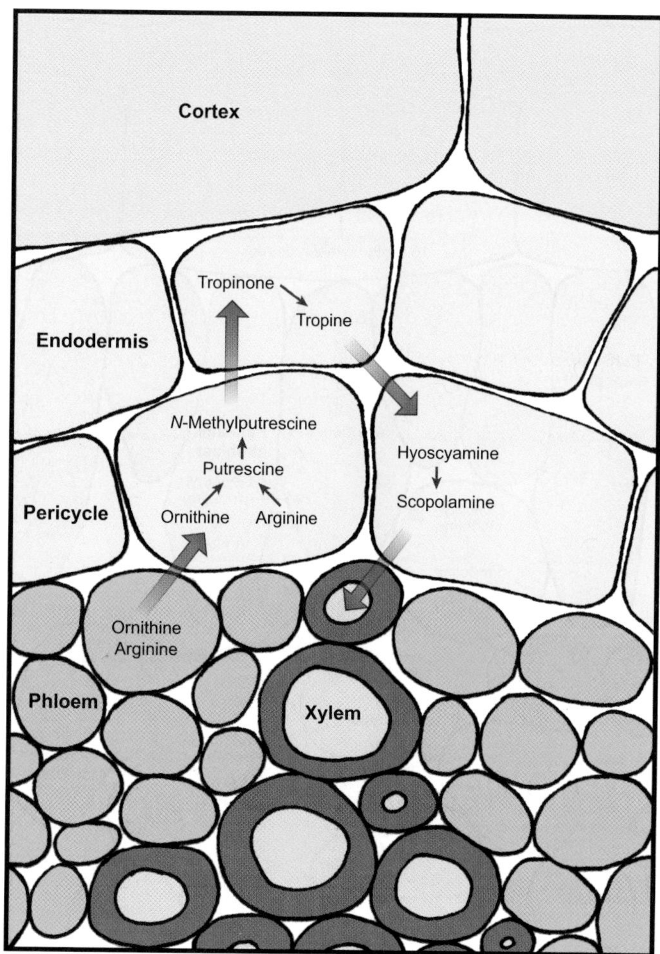

Figure 7

Putative trafficking of pathway intermediates and products in tropane alkaloid metabolism. Red arrows show specific enzyme-catalyzed reactions. Blue arrows represent the purported intercellular translocation of unspecified compounds.

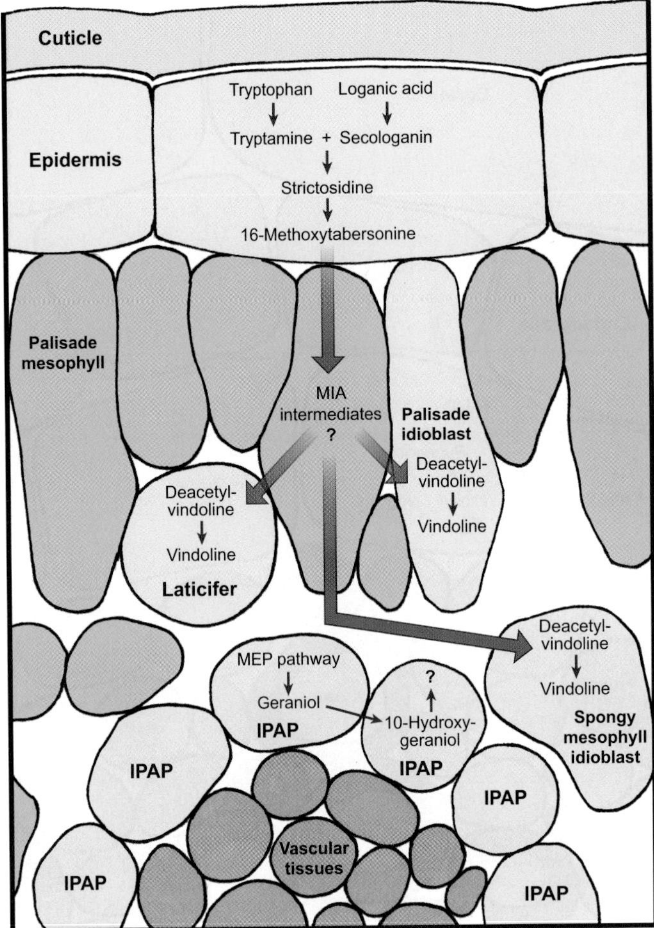

Figure 8

Putative trafficking of pathway intermediates and products in monoterpenoid indole alkaloid metabolism. Red arrows show specific enzyme-catalyzed reactions. Blue arrows represent the purported intercellular translocation of unspecified compounds. IPAP, internal phloem-associated parenchyma.

and epidermis in the supply of terpenoid precursors to alkaloid biosynthesis requires further evaluation.

Pyrrolizidine alkaloids also share a common metabolic pathway in restricted yet diverse taxa (54). In *Senecio* species, pyrrolizidine alkaloids are produced in actively growing roots as senecionine *N*-oxides, which are transported via the phloem to above-ground organs (54). Senecionine *N*-oxides are subsequently modified by one or two species-specific reactions (i.e., hydroxylation, dehydrogenation, epoxidation, or *O*-acetylation) that result in the unique pyrrolizidine alkaloid profile of different plants. Inflorescences are the major sites of pyrrolizidine alkaloid accumulation in *Senecio jacobaea* and *Senecio vernalis*; jacobine occurs in flowers. HSS is the first committed enzyme in pyrrolizidine alkaloid biosynthesis and localizes to the root endodermis and cortex adjacent to the phloem in *S. vernalis* (**Figure 6*c***), which might reflect a functional accommodation for systemic transport of pyrrolizidine alkaloids to the stem (105). However, HSS is found throughout the root cortex in *Eupatorium cannabinum* (**Figure 6*d***), which like *S. vernalis* is a member of the Asteraceae (6). In contrast to the general monophyletic origin of BIA biosynthesis (87), pyrrolizidine alkaloid pathways have evolved in at least four different angiosperm lineages (128). The differential localization of a key enzyme was interpreted to support the polyphyletic origin for pyrrolizidine alkaloid biosynthesis (6). In contrast, the monophyletic origin of BIA biosynthesis (87) and the differential localization of gene transcripts in *T. flavum* and opium poppy suggest the migration of pathway intermediates between cell types.

In opium poppy, BIA accumulation occurs in the articulated laticifers found adjacent or proximal to sieve elements of the phloem (32). The cytoplasm of laticifers—or latex—contains a full complement of cellular organelles and many large vesicles to which alkaloids are sequestered. Although laticifers were long considered to be the site of BIA biosynthesis and accumulation, the cellular localization of BIA biosynthetic enzymes and gene transcripts has shown that alkaloid synthesis involves other cell types (13, 34, 170). Initial in situ hybridization experiments demonstrated the localization of *TYDC* gene transcripts to the phloem, but not to laticifers (34). The morphinan pathway enzymes salutaridine synthase (Cyp719B1) and salutaridine:NADPH 7-oxidoreductase (SalR) are also not detected in isolated latex (48, 49). Seven other biosynthetic enzymes—6OMT,

CNMT, (*S*)-*N*-methylcoclaurine 3′-hydroxylase (Cyp80B3), 4′OMT, BBE, SalAT, and COR—localize to sieve elements in opium poppy and their corresponding gene transcripts localize to associated companion cells (13, 135) (**Figure 6*e***). The localization of BIA metabolism components to phloem cells distinct from laticifers predicts the intercellular transport of alkaloid biosynthetic enzymes and pathway intermediates and/or products. The implication of sieve elements also breaks a long-standing paradigm in plant biology (**Figure 9**). Previously, sieve elements were not known to support complex metabolism, and were assumed to possess only a limited number of proteins required for cell maintenance and solute transport. Recently, the physiological roles for sieve elements have expanded to include the transport of information macromolecules such as RNA (72) and the biosynthesis of jasmonic acid (57), ascorbic acid (53), and defense-related compounds (167). Sieve elements clearly possess a previously unrealized biochemical potential.

T. flavum accumulates BIAs such as the antimicrobial agent berberine. In situ RNA hybridization analysis revealed the cell type–specific expression of BIA biosynthetic genes in roots and rhizomes of *T. flavum* (138). In roots, gene transcripts for all nine enzymes localize to the pericycle—the innermost layer of the cortex—and adjacent cortical cells (**Figure 6*f***). In rhizomes, all biosynthetic gene transcripts are restricted to the protoderm of leaf primordia. The protoderm localization of biosynthetic gene transcripts contrasts with the tissue-specific accumulation of BIAs. In roots, protoberberine alkaloids are restricted to endodermal cells upon the initiation of secondary growth, and are distributed throughout the pith and cortex in rhizomes. Thus, the cell type–specific localization of BIA biosynthesis and accumulation are temporally and spatially separated in *T. flavum* roots and rhizomes, respectively. Despite the close phylogenetic relationships between corresponding biosynthetic enzymes (87), different cell types are involved in the biosynthesis and accumulation of BIAs in opium poppy, *T. flavum*, and perhaps *C. japonica*.

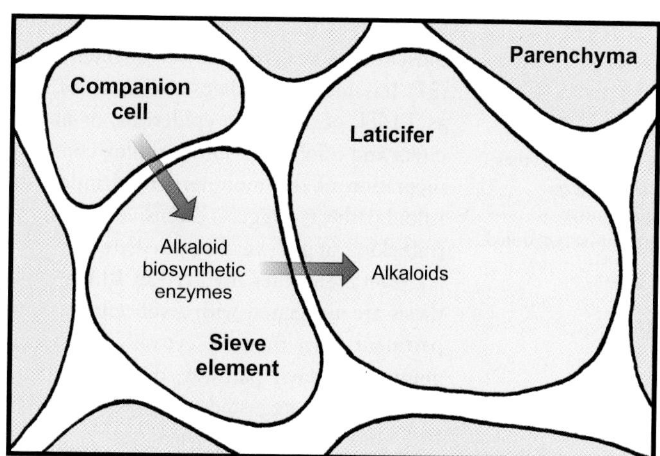

Figure 9

Putative trafficking of benzylisoquinoline alkaloid biosynthetic enzymes and pathway intermediates and/or products.

Subcellular Compartmentalization of Alkaloid Biosynthetic Enzymes

MIA biosynthetic enzymes are associated with at least three different cell types in *C. roseus*—geraniol 10-hydroxylase (G10H) is found in internal phloem parenchyma of aerial organs (15), TDC, secologanin synthase, and STR are localized to the epidermis of aerial organs and the apical meristem of roots (70, 151), and D4H and DAT are restricted to the laticifers and idioblasts of leaves and stems (151); thus, vindoline pathway intermediates must be translocated between cell types. Enzymes involved in monoterpenoid indole alkaloid biosynthesis in *C. roseus* also localize to at least five subcellular compartments—TDC, D4H, and DAT are in the cytosol (24), STR and the peroxidase involved in the coupling of MIA monomers localize to the vacuole (98, 99, 145), SGD is a soluble enzyme purported to associate with the cytoplasmic face of the endoplasmic reticulum (148), the P450-dependent monooxygenases G10H, secologanin synthase (SLS), and T16H are integral endomembrane proteins (20, 149, 177), and

Multienzyme complex: a cluster of distinct enzymes that catalyze consecutive metabolic reactions

the *N*-methyltransferase involved in vindoline biosynthesis localizes to thylakoid membranes (27). It is unclear whether some enzymes, such as T16H, occur in the epidermis, or in laticifers and idioblasts. The complex compartmentation of the monoterpenoid indole alkaloid pathway suggests extensive subcellular trafficking of pathway intermediates.

Several enzymes involved in BIA biosynthesis are associated with a subcellular compartment other than the cytosol. In the sanguinarine branch pathway, density gradient fractionation suggested the localization of BBE and P450 monooxygenases to microsomes with a density slightly higher than that of typical endoplasmic reticulum (ER) (5, 10, 132, 156). Although BBE is not an integral membrane protein, it is initially targeted to the ER and subsequently sorted to a vacuolar compartment (12). NCS is also predicted to possess a signal peptide for targeting to the ER (137), and the final oxidation of alkaloids, such as dihydrosanguinarine, likely occurs in an ER-derived compartment (5). The association of BIA biosynthetic enzymes with endomembranes led to speculation that specialized alkaloid-synthesizing vesicles are present in alkaloid-producing cells (5). Recently, however, Cyp80B3, BBE, and sanguinarine were found to colocalize with the ER in opium poppy cell cultures (2). Moreover, the induction of sanguinarine biosynthesis correlates with extensive dilations of the ER and the accumulation of an electron-dense flocculent material within the ER. Because the pH optimum of BBE is ~8.8 (146), sanguinarine biosynthesis is unlikely to involve the vacuole; thus, alkaloid metabolism could be entirely associated with the ER. Indeed, the vacuole might not even be the site of BIA accumulation in cultured cells, as previously thought. Instead, sanguinarine and related alkaloids could be secreted and bound to cell wall components and reabsorbed, reduced to the less-toxic compound dihydrosanguinarine, and further metabolized (171).

A unique subcellular compartmentalization of enzymes is also present in quinolizidine alkaloid biosynthesis, which occurs in the mesophyll of some legumes. Lysine decarboxylase and the quinolizidine skeleton–forming enzyme have been detected in chloroplasts of *Lupinus polyphyllus* (172). 13α-Hydroxymultifluorine/13α-hydroxylupanine *O*-tigloylase is localized to the mitochondrial matrix rather than to chloroplasts where de novo quinolizidine alkaloid biosynthesis is thought to occur (152). In contrast, epilupinine *O*-*p*-coumaryoltransferase is present in a distinct organelle, but has not been unambiguously localized.

Enzyme Complexes and Metabolic Channels

Many metabolic enzymes are generally assumed to interact physically or be in close proximity with other enzymes that participate in common pathways (173). Theoretically, the existence of multienzyme complexes—also known as metabolic complexes/channels or metabolons—promote the efficiency of cellular metabolism. The direct transfer of a pathway intermediate from one enzyme to another maintains a high local substrate concentration, which avoids the dilution of intermediates released into the cytoplasm. Enzyme complexes also eliminate competition from other enzymes for the same substrate, increase the stability of intermediates, and minimize the deleterious effects of cytotoxic compounds. Recent investigations of the interactions between pathway enzymes have hinted at the importance of metabolic channels in primary and secondary metabolism. The detection of multienzyme complexes has been purported for flavonoid (1, 14, 58) and polyamine (122) metabolism.

The results from the RNAi-mediated silencing of *COR* genes suggested the possible existence of a multienzyme complex in BIA (4). Although seven enzymatic steps occur between (*S*)-reticuline and codeinone—the substrate for COR—only (*S*)-reticuline accumulates at elevated levels. No intermediates between (*S*)-reticuline and morphine are detected. Removal of COR was suggested to disrupt a metabolic channel composed of morphinan branch pathway enzymes, resulting in the accumulation of an alkaloid intermediate produced by enzymes that are not part of the same complex. Interestingly, thebaine and oripavine, intermediates upstream of substrates acted upon by COR, accumulate to high levels in some opium poppy cultivars (101); thus, researchers expected an accumulation of morphinan branch pathway intermediates. An alternative interpretation not considered by Allen and coworkers (4) is the suppression of 1,2-dehydroreticuline reductase as a possible side effect of silencing *COR*. 1,2-Dehydroreticuline reductase is one of two enzymes involved in the epimerization of (*S*)-reticuline to (*R*)-reticuline. The potential homology between the two reductases could lead to cosilencing.

PERSPECTIVE

Major progress in the elucidation of alkaloid biosynthetic pathways and their regulation has been obtained by application of large scale genomic tools. However, there are several techniques, whose applications are still more or less exclusively confined to model organisms, that might further our understanding of plant alkaloid biosynthesis. Proteome analysis in alkaloid-accumulating plants has been undertaken (26, 71, 115), but is still limited by the lack of peptide mass databases for the investigated species, which does not allow protein identification by simple peptide mass fingerprinting. Targeted induced local lesions in genomes (TILLING) as a tool to discover point mutations is also dependent on available sequence information (21). However, the growing sequence database makes the application of this technique feasible in studying mutations in alkaloid-containing plants. The development of sequencing techniques that can generate large datasets within short times will probably be applied to alkaloid producing plants and will provide the basis for many sequence-based approaches that are now limited to plants with sequenced genomes such as *Arabidopsis* and rice. Whether genome sequencing projects in alkaloid-containing plants will be feasible remains to be seen, because the genomes of the investigated plants are very large (4.7 Gbp for *C. roseus* or 7.4 Gbp for opium poppy compared with, for example, 1 Gbp for rice). The predicted function of alkaloid biosynthetic enzymes and other components based on the in vitro characterization of gene products must be confirmed in vivo. However, functional genomics remains problematic for most alkaloid-producing plants owing to general limitations in established genetic transformation technologies. Virus-induced gene silencing is a fast method for the generation of transiently transformed plants and works well in a model organism such as *N. benthamiana* (130), and protocols for opium poppy and *E. californica* have recently been developed (62, 169). Thus, the impact of suppression of candidate genes on alkaloid biosynthesis can be readily examined before stable transformation is applied. Considering the progress in the investigation of alkaloid metabolism achieved in the last 5 years, a look to the future promises further strong developments in the discovery of regulatory networks that lead to alkaloid accumulation in plants.

SUMMARY POINTS

1. The application of genomics technologies has expedited the discovery of new alkaloid biosynthetic genes that encode enzymes and regulatory proteins with novel functions.
2. Large-scale, integrated transcriptomics and metabolomics analyses are providing initial hints about the regulation of alkaloid pathways.

3. Structural analysis of alkaloid biosynthetic enzymes has enabled targeted modifications of substrate-binding sites for the development of biomimetic alkaloid production.
4. Improved transformation protocols have facilitated the establishment of transgenic plants with tailored alkaloid profiles, providing additional insights into the regulation of pathways.
5. Alkaloid biosynthesis and accumulation are associated with a variety of cell types in different plants, including epidermis, endodermis, pericycle, phloem parenchyma, phloem sieve elements and companion cells, specialized mesophyll, and laticifers. A common paradigm is the involvement of multiple cell types and the implied transport of pathway intermediates and/or products.
6. The subcellular compartmentalization of alkaloid biosynthetic enzymes is as complex as the cell type–specific localization of gene transcripts, enzymes, and metabolites. Although the endoplasmic reticulum is a favored site for alkaloid formation, biosynthetic enzymes have been associated with chloroplast thylakoid membranes, mitochondria, vacuoles, and the cytosol.

FUTURE ISSUES

1. Despite impressive advances facilitated by the application of genomics technologies to the discovery of novel genes that encode alkaloid biosynthetic enzymes, a substantial understanding of the regulatory components of alkaloid pathways has been achieved only for terpenoid indole alkaloid metabolism. Genomics approaches should lead to the identification of regulatory genes involved in benzylisoquinoline alkaloid synthesis and other alkaloid pathways.
2. The impact of posttranslational modification of alkaloid biosynthetic enzymes on product accumulation is a black box. Proteomic approaches might explain why the expression levels of some biosynthetic genes do not correlate with alkaloid profiles.
3. Although the involvement of multiple cell types in the biosynthesis and accumulation of many alkaloids has been established, the identity of the pathway intermediates and/or products that undergo intercellular transport is not known. Moreover, the mechanisms of transport—symplastic involving plasmodesmata, or apoplastic involving specific transporters or channels—are poorly understood.
4. The existence of metabolic channels as a common feature of alkaloid biosynthetic pathways has been widely purported, but only scant evidence is available to support their existence. Establishing the interactions among biosynthetic enzymes and other pathway components will facilitate the rational engineering of alkaloid metabolism in plants and microorganisms.

DISCLOSURE STATEMENT

The authors are not aware of any biases that might be perceived as affecting the objectivity of this review.

ACKNOWLEDGMENTS

J.Z. was funded through a Canada Research Chair in Plant Metabolic Processes Biotechnology held by P.J.F. Research support from the Natural Sciences and Engineering Research Council of Canada to P.J.F. is also gratefully acknowledged.

LITERATURE CITED

1. Achnine L, Blancaflor EB, Rasmussen S, Dixon RA. 2004. Colocalization of L-phenylalanine ammonia-lyase and cinnamate 4-hydroxylase for metabolic channeling in phenylpropanoid biosynthesis. *Plant Cell* 16:3098–109
2. Alcantara J, Bird DA, Franceschi VR, Facchini PJ. 2005. Sanguinarine biosynthesis is associated with the endoplasmic reticulum in cultured opium poppy cells after elicitor treatment. *Plant Physiol.* 138:173–83
3. Allen RS, Miller JA, Chitty JA, Fist AJ, Gerlach WL, Larkin PJ. 2007. Metabolic engineering of morphinan alkaloids by overexpression and RNAi suppression of salutaridinol 7-*O*-acetyltransferase in opium poppy. *Plant Biotechnol. J.* doi:10.1111/j.1467-7652.2007.00293.x
4. Allen RS, Millgate AG, Chitty JA, Thisleton J, Miller JA, et al. 2004. RNAi-mediated replacement of morphine with the nonnarcotic alkaloid reticuline in opium poppy. *Nat. Biotechnol.* 22:1559–66
5. Amann M, Wanner G, Zenk MH. 1986. Intracellular compartmentation of two enzymes of berberine biosynthesis in plant cell cultures. *Planta* 167:310–20
6. Anke S, Niemüller D, Moll S, Hänsch R, Ober D. 2004. Polyphyletic origin of pyrrolizidine alkaloids within the Asteraceae. Evidence from differential tissue expression of homospermidine synthase. *Plant Physiol.* 136:4037–47
7. Arakawa H, Clark WG, Psenak M, Coscia CJ. 1992. Purification and characterization of dihydrobenzophenanthridine oxidase from elicited *Sanguinaria canadensis* cell cultures. *Arch. Biochem. Biophys.* 299:1–7
8. Ayora-Talavera T, Chappell J, Lozoya-Gloria E, Loyola-Vargas VM. 2002. Overexpression in *Catharanthus roseus* hairy roots of a truncated hamster 3-hydroxy-3-methylglutaryl-CoA reductase gene. *Appl. Biochem. Biotechnol.* 97:135–45
9. Barleben L, Panjikar S, Ruppert M, Koepke J, Stöckigt J. 2007. Molecular architecture of strictosidine glucosidase: the gateway to the biosynthesis of the monoterpenoid indole alkaloid family. *Plant Cell* 19:2886–97
10. Bauer W, Zenk MH. 1991. Two methylenedioxy bridge forming cytochrome P-450 dependent enzymes are involved in (*S*)-stylopine biosynthesis. *Phytochemistry* 30:2953–62
11. Bayer A, Ma X, Stöckigt J. 2004. Acetyltransfer in natural product biosynthesis–functional cloning and molecular analysis of vinorine synthase. *Bioorg. Med. Chem.* 12:2787–95
12. Bird DA, Facchini PJ. 2001. Berberine bridge enzyme, a key branch-point enzyme in benzylisoquinoline alkaloid biosynthesis, contains a vacuolar-sorting determinant. *Planta* 213:888–97
13. Bird DA, Franceschi VR, Facchini PJ. 2003. A tale of three cell types: alkaloid biosynthesis is localized to sieve elements in opium poppy. *Plant Cell* 15:2626–35
14. Burbulis IE, Winkel-Shirley B. 1999. Interactions among enzymes of the *Arabidopsis* flavonoid biosynthetic pathway. *Proc. Natl. Acad. Sci. USA* 96:12929–34
15. Burlat V, Oudin A, Courtois M, Rideau M, St-Pierre B. 2004. Co-expression of three MEP pathway genes and geraniol 10-hydroxylase in internal phloem parenchyma of *Catharanthus roseus* implicates multicellular translocation of intermediates during the

biosynthesis of monoterpene indole alkaloids and isoprenoid-derived primary metabolites. *Plant J.* 38:131–41

16. Canel C, Lopes-Cardoso MI, Whitmer S, van der Fits L, Pasquali G, et al. 1998. Effects of overexpression of strictosidine synthase and tryptophan decarboxylase on alkaloid production by cell cultures of *Catharanthus* roseus. *Planta* 205:414–19
17. Carlson JE, Leebens-Mack JH, Wall PK, Zahn LM, Mueller LA, et al. 2006. EST database for early flower development in California poppy (*Eschscholzia californica* Cham., Papaveraceae) tags over 6,000 genes from a basal eudicot. *Plant Mol. Biol.* 62:351–69
18. Chen S, Galan MC, Coltharp C, O'Connor SE. 2006. Redesign of a central enzyme in alkaloid biosynthesis. *Chem. Biol.* 13:1137–41
19. Choi KB, Morishige T, Shitan N, Yazaki K, Sato F. 2002. Molecular cloning and characterization of coclaurine *N*-methyltransferase from cultured cells of *Coptis japonica*. *J. Biol. Chem.* 277:830–35
20. Collu G, Unver N, Peltenburg-Looman AM, van der Heijden R, Verpoorte R, Memelink J. 2001. Geraniol 10-hydroxylase, a cytochrome P450 enzyme involved in terpenoid indole alkaloid biosynthesis. *FEBS Lett.* 508:215–20
21. Comai L, Henikoff S. 2006. TILLING: practical single-nucleotide mutation discovery. *Plant J.* 45:684–94
22. Contin A, van der Heijden R, Lefeber AW, Verpoorte R. 1998. The iridoid glucoside secologanin is derived from the novel triose phosphate/pyruvate pathway in a *Catharanthus roseus* cell culture. *FEBS Lett.* 434:413–16
23. De-Eknamkul W, Zenk MH. 1992. Purification and properties of 1,2-dehydroreticuline reductase from *Papaver somniferum* seedlings. *Phytochemistry* 31:813–21
24. De Luca V, Cutler AJ. 1987. Subcellular localization of enzymes involved in indole alkaloid biosynthesis in *Catharanthus roseus*. *Plant Physiol.* 85:1099–102
25. De Luca V, Marineau C, Brisson N. 1989. Molecular cloning and analysis of cDNA encoding a plant tryptophan decarboxylase: comparison with animal dopa decarboxylases. *Proc. Natl. Acad. Sci. USA* 86:2582–86
26. Decker G, Wanner G, Zenk MH, Lottspeich F. 2000. Characterization of proteins in latex of the opium poppy (*Papaver somniferum*) using two-dimensional gel electrophoresis and microsequencing. *Electrophoresis* 21:3500–16
27. Dethier M, De Luca V. 1993. Partial purification of an *N*-methyltransferase involved in vindoline biosynthesis in *Catharanthus roseus*. *Phytochemistry* 32:673–78
28. Dittrich H, Kutchan TM. 1991. Molecular cloning, expression, and induction of berberine bridge enzyme, an enzyme essential to the formation of benzophenanthridine alkaloids in the response of plants to pathogenic attack. *Proc. Natl. Acad. Sci. USA* 88:9969–73
29. Dogru E, Warzecha H, Seibel F, Haebel S, Lottspeich F, Stöckigt J. 2000. The gene encoding polyneuridine aldehyde esterase of monoterpenoid indole alkaloid biosynthesis in plants is an ortholog of the α/β-hydrolase super family. *Eur. J. Biochem.* 267:1397–406
30. Dräger B. 2004. Chemistry and biology of calystegines. *Nat. Prod. Rep.* 21:211–23
31. Facchini PJ. 2001. Alkaloid biosynthesis in plants: biochemistry, cell biology, molecular regulation, and metabolic engineering applications. *Annu. Rev. Plant Physiol. Plant Mol. Biol.* 52:29–66
32. Facchini PJ, Bird DA. 1998. Developmental regulation of benzylisoquinoline alkaloid biosynthesis in opium poppy plants and tissue cultures. *In Vitro Cell. Dev. Biol. Plant* 34:69–79
33. Facchini PJ, De Luca V. 1994. Differential and tissue-specific expression of a gene family for tyrosine/dopa decarboxylase in opium poppy. *J. Biol. Chem.* 269:26684–90

34. Facchini PJ, De Luca V. 1995. Phloem-specific expression of tyrosine/dopa decarboxylase genes and the biosynthesis of isoquinoline alkaloids in opium poppy. *Plant Cell* 7:1811–21
35. Facchini PJ, Park SU. 2003. Developmental and inducible accumulation of gene transcripts involved in alkaloid biosynthesis in opium poppy. *Phytochemistry* 64:177–86
36. Facchini PJ, Penzes C, Johnson AG, Bull D. 1996. Molecular characterization of berberine bridge enzyme genes from opium poppy. *Plant Physiol.* 112:1669–77
37. Fahn W, Laussermair E, Deus-Neumann B, Stöckigt J. 1985. Late enzymes of vindoline biosynthesis *S*-adenosyl-L-methionine:11-*O*-demethyl-17-*O*-deacetylvindoline 11-*O*-methylase and unspecific acetylesterase. *Plant Cell Rep.* 4:337–40
38. Färber K, Schumann B, Miersch O, Roos W. 2003. Selective desensitization of jasmonate- and pH-dependent signaling in the induction of benzophenanthridine biosynthesis in cells of *Eschscholzia californica*. *Phytochemistry* 62:491–500
39. Falkenhagen H, Stöckigt J. 1995. Enzymatic biosynthesis of vomilenine, a key intermediate of the ajmaline pathway, catalyzed by a novel cytochrome P450 dependent enzyme from plant cell cultures of *Rauvolfia serpentina*. *Z. Naturforsch.* 1995:45–53
40. Frick S, Chitty JA, Kramell R, Schmidt J, Allen RS, et al. 2004. Transformation of opium poppy (*Papaver somniferum* L.) with antisense berberine bridge enzyme gene (*anti-bbe*) via somatic embryogenesis results in an altered ratio of alkaloids in latex but not in roots. *Transgenic Res.* 13:607–13
41. Frick S, Kramell R, Kutchan TM. 2007. Metabolic engineering with a morphine biosynthetic P450 in opium poppy surpasses breeding. *Metab. Eng.* 9:169–76
42. Frick S, Kutchan TM. 1999. Molecular cloning and functional expression of *O*-methyltransferases common to isoquinoline alkaloid and phenylpropanoid biosynthesis. *Plant J.* 17:329–39
43. Fujii N, Inui T, Iwasa K, Morishige T, Sato F. 2007. Knockdown of berberine bridge enzyme by RNAi accumulates (*S*)-reticuline and activates a silent pathway in cultured California poppy cells. *Transgenic Res.* 16:363–75
44. Gao S, von Schumann G, Stöckigt J. 2002. A newly-detected reductase from *Rauvolfia* closes a gap in the biosynthesis of the antiarrhythmic alkaloid ajmaline. *Planta Med.* 68:906–11
45. Gavilano LB, Siminszky B. 2007. Isolation and characterization of the cytochrome P450 gene *Cyp82E5v2* that mediates nicotine to nornicotine conversion in the green leaves of tobacco. *Plant Cell. Physiol.* 48:1567–74
46. Geerlings A, Ibanez MM, Memelink J, van Der Heijden R, Verpoorte R. 2000. Molecular cloning and analysis of strictosidine β-D-glucosidase, an enzyme in terpenoid indole alkaloid biosynthesis in *Catharanthus roseus*. *J. Biol. Chem.* 275:3051–56
47. Geissler R, Brandt W, Ziegler J. 2007. Molecular modeling and site-directed mutagenesis reveal the benzylisoquinoline binding site of the short-chain dehydrogenase/reductase salutaridine reductase. *Plant Physiol.* 143:1493–503
48. Gerardy R, Zenk MH. 1993. Formation of salutaridine from (*R*)-reticuline by a membrane-bound cytochrome P-450 enzyme from *Papaver somniferum*. *Phytochemistry* 32:79–86
49. Gerardy R, Zenk MH. 1993. Purification and characterization of salutaridine:NADPH 7-oxidoreductase from *Papaver somniferum*. *Phytochemistry* 34:125–32
50. Gerasimenko I, Sheludko Y, Ma X, Stöckigt J. 2002. Heterologous expression of a *Rauvolfia* cDNA encoding strictosidine glucosidase, a biosynthetic key to over 2000 monoterpenoid indole alkaloids. *Eur. J. Biochem.* 269:2204–13

51. Goossens A, Häkkinen ST, Laakso I, Seppänen-Laakso T, Biondi S, et al. 2003. A functional genomics approach toward the understanding of secondary metabolism in plant cells. *Proc. Natl. Acad. Sci. USA* 100:8595–600
52. Grothe T, Lenz R, Kutchan TM. 2001. Molecular characterization of the salutaridinol 7-*O*-acetyltransferase involved in morphine biosynthesis in opium poppy *Papaver somniferum*. *J. Biol. Chem.* 276:30717–23
53. Hancock RD, McRae D, Haupt S, Viola R. 2003. Synthesis of L-ascorbic acid in the phloem. *BMC Plant Biol.* 3:7
54. Hartmann T, Dierich B. 1998. Chemical diversity and variation of pyrrolizidine alkaloids of the senecionine type: biological need or coincidence? *Planta* 206:443–51
55. Hartmann T. 2004. Plant-derived secondary metabolites as defensive chemicals in herbivorous insects: a case study in chemical ecology. *Planta* 219:1–4
56. Hashimoto T, Hayashi A, Amano Y, Kohno J, Iwanari H, et al. 1991. Hyoscyamine 6β-hydroxylase, an enzyme involved in tropane alkaloid biosynthesis, is localized at the pericycle of the root. *J. Biol. Chem.* 266:4648–53
57. Hause B, Hause G, Kutter C, Miersch O, Wasternack C. 2003. Enzymes of jasmonate biosynthesis occur in tomato sieve elements. *Plant Cell Physiol.* 44:643–48
58. He XZ, Dixon RA. 2000. Genetic manipulation of isoflavone 7-*O*-methyltransferase enhances biosynthesis of 4′-*O*-methylated isoflavonoid phytoalexins and disease resistance in alfalfa. *Plant Cell* 12:1689–702
59. Heim WG, Sykes KA, Hildreth SB, Sun J, Lu RH, Jelesko JG. 2007. Cloning and characterization of a *Nicotiana tabacum* methylputrescine oxidase transcript. *Phytochemistry* 68:454–63
60. Heinze M, Steighardt J, Gesell A, Schwartze W, Roos W. 2007. Regulatory interaction of the Gα protein with phospholipase A_2 in the plasma membrane of *Eschscholzia californica*. *Plant J.* doi:10.1111/j.1365–313X.2007.03300.x
61. Hibi N, Higashiguchi S, Hashimoto T, Yamada Y. 1994. Gene expression in tobacco low-nicotine mutants. *Plant Cell* 6:723–35
62. Hileman LC, Drea S, Martino G, Litt A, Irish VF. 2005. Virus-induced gene silencing is an effective tool for assaying gene function in the basal eudicot species *Papaver somniferum* (opium poppy). *Plant J.* 44:334–41
63. Hirata K, Poeaknapo C, Schmidt J, Zenk MH. 2004. 1,2-Dehydroreticuline synthase, the branch point enzyme opening the morphinan biosynthetic pathway. *Phytochemistry* 65:1039–46
64. Hong SB, Peebles CA, Shanks JV, San KY, Gibson SI. 2006. Expression of the *Arabidopsis* feedback-insensitive anthranilate synthase holoenzyme and tryptophan decarboxylase genes in *Catharanthus roseus* hairy roots. *J. Biotechnol.* 122:28–38
65. Huang FC, Kutchan TM. 2000. Distribution of morphinan and benzo[c]phenanthridine alkaloid gene transcript accumulation in *Papaver somninferum*. *Phytochemistry* 53:555–64
66. Hughes EH, Hong SB, Gibson SI, Shanks JV, San KY. 2004. Metabolic engineering of the indole pathway in *Catharanthus roseus* hairy roots and increased accumulation of tryptamine and serpentine. *Metab. Eng.* 6:268–76
67. Ikezawa N, Iwasa K, Sato F. 2007. Molecular cloning and characterization of methylenedioxy bridge-forming enzymes involved in stylopine biosynthesis in *Eschscholzia californica*. *FEBS J.* 274:1019–35
68. Ikezawa N, Tanaka M, Nagayoshi M, Shinkyo R, Sakaki T, et al. 2003. Molecular cloning and characterization of Cyp719, a methylenedioxy bridge-forming enzyme that belongs to a novel P450 family, from cultured *Coptis japonica cells*. *J. Biol. Chem.* 278:38557–65

69. Inui T, Tamura K, Fujii N, Morishige T, Sato F. 2007. Overexpression of *Coptis japonica* norcoclaurine 6-*O*-methyltransferase overcomes the rate-limiting step in benzylisoquinoline alkaloid biosynthesis in cultured *Eschscholzia californica*. *Plant Cell Physiol.* 48:252–62
70. Irmler S, Schröder G, St-Pierre B, Crouch NP, Hotze M, et al. 2000. Indole alkaloid biosynthesis in *Catharanthus roseus*: new enzyme activities and identification of cytochrome P450 Cyp72A1 as secologanin synthase. *Plant J.* 24:797–804
71. Jacobs DI, Gaspari M, van der Greef J, van der Heijden R, Verpoorte R. 2005. Proteome analysis of the medicinal plant *Catharanthus roseus*. *Planta* 221:690–704
72. Jorgensen RA, Atkinson RG, Forster RL, Lucas WJ. 1998. An RNA-based information superhighway in plants. *Science* 279:1486–87
73. Kaiser H, Richter U, Keiner R, Brabant A, Hause B, Dräger B. 2006. Immunolocalisation of two tropinone reductases in potato (*Solanum tuberosum* L.) root, stolon, and tuber sprouts. *Planta* 225:127–37
74. Kato M, Mizuno K, Crozier A, Fujimura T, Ashihara H. 2000. Caffeine synthase gene from tea leaves. *Nature* 406:956–57
75. Kato N, Dubouzet E, Kokabu Y, Yoshida S, Taniguchi Y, et al. 2007. Identification of a WRKY protein as a transcriptional regulator of benzylisoquinoline alkaloid biosynthesis in *Coptis japonica*. *Plant Cell Physiol.* 48:8–18
76. Keiner R, Kaiser H, Nakajima K, Hashimoto T, Dräger B. 2002. Molecular cloning, expression and characterization of tropinone reductase II, an enzyme of the SDR family in *Solanum tuberosum* (L.). *Plant Mol. Biol.* 48:299–308
77. Kim YS, Uefuji H, Ogita S, Sano H. 2006. Transgenic tobacco plants producing caffeine: a potential new strategy for insect pest control. *Transgenic Res.* 15:667–72
78. Kraus PF, Kutchan TM. 1995. Molecular cloning and heterologous expression of a cDNA encoding berbamunine synthase, a C-O phenol-coupling cytochrome P450 from the higher plant *Berberis stolonifera*. *Proc. Natl. Acad. Sci. USA* 92:2071–75
79. Kutchan TM. 1989. Expression of enzymatically active cloned strictosidine synthase from the higher plant *Rauvolfia serpentina* in *Escherichia coli*. *FEBS Lett.* 257:127–30
80. Laflamme P, St-Pierre B, De Luca V. 2001. Molecular and biochemical analysis of a Madagascar periwinkle root-specific minovincinine-19-hydroxy-*O*-acetyltransferase. *Plant Physiol.* 125:189–98
81. Larkin PJ, Miller JA, Allen RS, Chitty JA, Gerlach WL, et al. 2007. Increasing morphinan alkaloid production by overexpressing codeinone reductase in transgenic *Papaver somniferum*. *Plant Biotechnol. J.* 5:26–37
82. Lenz R, Zenk MH. 1995. Acetyl coenzyme A:salutaridinol-7-*O*-acetyltransferase from *Papaver somniferum* plant cell cultures. The enzyme catalyzing the formation of thebaine in morphine biosynthesis. *J. Biol. Chem.* 270:31091–96
83. Lenz R, Zenk MH. 1995. Purification and properties of codeinone reductase (NADPH) from *Papaver somniferum* cell cultures and differentiated plants. *Eur. J. Biochem.* 233:132–39
84. Li R, Reed DW, Liu E, Nowak J, Pelcher LE, et al. 2006. Functional genomic analysis of alkaloid biosynthesis in *Hyoscyamus niger* reveals a cytochrome P450 involved in littorine rearrangement. *Chem. Biol.* 13:513–20
85. Lin C, Mueller LA, McCarthy J, Crouzillat D, Petiard V, Tanksley SD. 2005. Coffee and tomato share common gene repertoires as revealed by deep sequencing of seed and cherry transcripts. *Theor. Appl. Genet.* 112:114–30
86. Liscombe DK, Facchini PJ. 2007. Molecular cloning and characterization of tetrahydroprotoberberine cis-*N*-methyltransferase, an enzyme involved in alkaloid biosynthesis in opium poppy. *J. Biol. Chem.* 282:14741–51

87. Liscombe DK, MacLeod BP, Loukanina N, Nandi OI, Facchini PJ. 2005. Evidence for the monophyletic evolution of benzylisoquinoline alkaloid biosynthesis in angiosperms. *Phytochemistry* 66:2501–20
88. Liu T, Zhu P, Cheng KD, Meng C, He HX. 2005. Molecular cloning, expression and characterization of hyoscyamine 6β-hydroxylase from hairy roots of *Anisodus tanguticus*. *Planta Med.* 71:249–53
89. Lopez-Meyer M, Nessler CL. 1997. Tryptophan decarboxylase is encoded by two autonomously regulated genes in *Camptotheca acuminata* which are differentially expressed during development and stress. *Plant J.* 11:1167–75
90. Loris EA, Panjikar S, Ruppert M, Barleben L, Unger M, et al. 2007. Structure-based engineering of strictosidine synthase: auxiliary for alkaloid libraries. *Chem. Biol.* 14:979–85
91. Luk LY, Bunn S, Liscombe DK, Facchini PJ, Tanner ME. 2007. Mechanistic studies on norcoclaurine synthase of benzylisoquinoline alkaloid biosynthesis: an enzymatic Pictet-Spengler reaction. *Biochemistry* 46:10153–61
92. Ma X, Koepke J, Bayer A, Fritzsch G, Michel H, Stöckigt J. 2005. Crystallization and preliminary X-ray analysis of native and selenomethionyl vinorine synthase from *Rauvolfia serpentina*. *Acta Crystallogr. D Biol. Crystallogr.* 61:694–96
93. Ma X, Panjikar S, Koepke J, Loris E, Stöckigt J. 2006. The structure of *Rauvolfia serpentina* strictosidine synthase is a novel six-bladed β-propeller fold in plant proteins. *Plant Cell* 18:907–20
94. Mahroug S, Courdavault V, Thiersault M, St-Pierre B, Burlat V. 2006. Epidermis is a pivotal site of at least four secondary metabolic pathways in *Catharanthus roseus* aerial organs. *Planta* 223:1191–200
95. Matsuda J, Okabe S, Hashimoto T, Yamada Y. 1991. Molecular cloning of hyoscyamine 6β-hydroxylase, a 2-oxoglutarate-dependent dioxygenase, from cultured roots of *Hyoscyamus niger*. *J. Biol. Chem.* 266:9460–64
96. Mattern-Dogru E, Ma X, Hartmann J, Decker H, Stöckigt J. 2002. Potential active-site residues in polyneuridine aldehyde esterase, a central enzyme of indole alkaloid biosynthesis, by modelling and site-directed mutagenesis. *Eur. J. Biochem.* 269:2889–96
97. McCarthy AA, McCarthy JG. 2007. The structure of two *N*-methyltransferases from the caffeine biosynthetic pathway. *Plant Physiol.* 144:879–89
98. McKnight TD, Bergey DR, Burnett RJ, Nessler CL. 1991. Expression of enzymatically active and correctly targeted strictosidine synthase in transgenic tobacco plants. *Planta* 185:148–52
99. McKnight TD, Roessner CA, Devagupta R, Scott AI, Nessler CL. 1990. Nucleotide sequence of a cDNA encoding the vacuolar protein strictosidine synthase from *Catharanthus roseus*. *Nucleic Acids Res.* 18:4939
100. Menke FL, Champion A, Kijne JW, Memelink J. 1999. A novel jasmonate- and elicitor-responsive element in the periwinkle secondary metabolite biosynthetic gene *Str* interacts with a jasmonate- and elicitor-inducible AP2-domain transcription factor, ORCA2. *EMBO J.* 18:4455–63
101. Millgate AG, Pogson BJ, Wilson IW, Kutchan TM, Zenk MH, et al. 2004. Analgesia: morphine-pathway block in *top1* poppies. *Nature* 431:413–14
102. Minami H, Dubouzet E, Iwasa K, Sato F. 2007. Functional analysis of norcoclaurine synthase in *Coptis japonica*. *J. Biol. Chem.* 282:6274–82
103. Mizuno K, Kato M, Irino F, Yoneyama N, Fujimura T, Ashihara H. 2003. The first committed step reaction of caffeine biosynthesis: 7-methylxanthosine synthase is closely homologous to caffeine synthases in coffee (*Coffea arabica* L.). *FEBS Lett.* 547:56–60

104. Mizuno K, Okuda A, Kato M, Yoneyama N, Tanaka H, et al. 2003. Isolation of a new dual-functional caffeine synthase gene encoding an enzyme for the conversion of 7-methylxanthine to caffeine from coffee (*Coffea arabica* L.). *FEBS Lett.* 534:75–81
105. Moll S, Anke S, Kahmann U, Hänsch R, Hartmann T, Ober D. 2002. Cell-specific expression of homospermidine synthase, the entry enzyme of the pyrrolizidine alkaloid pathway in *Senecio vernalis*, in comparison with its ancestor, deoxyhypusine synthase. *Plant Physiol.* 130:47–57
106. Morishige T, Dubouzet E, Choi KB, Yazaki K, Sato F. 2002. Molecular cloning of columbamine *O*-methyltransferase from cultured *Coptis japonica* cells. *Eur. J. Biochem.* 269:5659–67
107. Morishige T, Tsujita T, Yamada Y, Sato F. 2000. Molecular characterization of the *S*-adenosyl-L-methionine:3′-hydroxy-*N*-methylcoclaurine 4′-*O*-methyltransferase involved in isoquinoline alkaloid biosynthesis in *Coptis japonica*. *J. Biol. Chem.* 275:23398–405
108. Murata J, Bienzle D, Brandle JE, Sensen CW, De Luca V. 2006. Expressed sequence tags from Madagascar periwinkle (*Catharanthus roseus*). *FEBS Lett.* 580:4501–7
109. Murata J, De Luca V. 2005. Localization of tabersonine 16-hydroxylase and 16-OH tabersonine-16-*O*-methyltransferase to leaf epidermal cells defines them as a major site of precursor biosynthesis in the vindoline pathway in *Catharanthus roseus*. *Plant J.* 44:581–94
110. Nakajima K, Hashimoto T, Yamada Y. 1993. cDNA encoding tropinone reductase-II from *Hyoscyamus niger*. *Plant Physiol.* 103:1465–66
111. Nakajima K, Hashimoto T, Yamada Y. 1993. Two tropinone reductases with different stereospecificities are short-chain dehydrogenases evolved from a common ancestor. *Proc. Natl. Acad. Sci. USA* 90:9591–95
112. Nakajima K, Hashimoto T. 1999. Two tropinone reductases, that catalyze opposite stereospecific reductions in tropane alkaloid biosynthesis, are localized in plant root with different cell-specific patterns. *Plant Cell Physiol.* 40:1099–107
113. Nakajima K, Oshita Y, Kaya M, Yamada Y, Hashimoto T. 1999. Structures and expression patterns of two tropinone reductase genes from *Hyoscyamus niger*. *Biosci. Biotechnol. Biochem.* 63:1756–64
114. Nakajima K, Yamashita A, Akama H, Nakatsu T, Kato H, et al. 1998. Crystal structures of two tropinone reductases: different reaction stereospecificities in the same protein fold. *Proc. Natl. Acad. Sci. USA* 95:4876–81
115. Nawrot R, Kalinowski A, Gozdzicka-Jozefiak A. 2007. Proteomic analysis of *Chelidonium majus* milky sap using two-dimensional gel electrophoresis and tandem mass spectrometry. *Phytochemistry* 68:1612–22
116. Ober D, Hartmann T. 1999. Homospermidine synthase, the first pathway-specific enzyme of pyrrolizidine alkaloid biosynthesis, evolved from deoxyhypusine synthase. *Proc. Natl. Acad. Sci. USA* 96:14777–82
117. Ogawa M, Herai Y, Koizumi N, Kusano T, Sano H. 2001. 7-Methylxanthine methyltransferase of coffee plants. Gene isolation and enzymatic properties. *J. Biol. Chem.* 276:8213–18
118. Ogita S, Uefuji H, Morimoto M, Sano H. 2004. Application of RNAi to confirm theobromine as the major intermediate for caffeine biosynthesis in coffee plants with potential for construction of decaffeinated varieties. *Plant Mol. Biol.* 54:931–41
119. Ogita S, Uefuji H, Yamaguchi Y, Koizumi N, Sano H. 2003. Producing decaffeinated coffee plants. *Nature* 423:823

120. Oudin A, Mahroug S, Courdavault V, Hervouet N, Zelwer C, et al. 2007. Spatial distribution and hormonal regulation of gene products from methyl erythritol phosphate and monoterpene-secoiridoid pathways in *Catharanthus roseus*. *Plant Mol. Biol.* 65:13–30

121. Ounaroon A, Decker G, Schmidt J, Lottspeich F, Kutchan TM. 2003. (*R,S*)-Reticuline 7-*O*-methyltransferase and (*R,S*)-norcoclaurine 6-*O*-methyltransferase of *Papaver somniferum*—cDNA cloning and characterization of methyl transfer enzymes of alkaloid biosynthesis in opium poppy. *Plant J.* 36:808–19

122. Panicot M, Minguet EG, Ferrando A, Alcazar R, Blazquez MA, et al. 2002. A polyamine metabolon involving aminopropyl transferase complexes in *Arabidopsis*. *Plant Cell* 14:2539–51

123. Park SU, Yu M, Facchini PJ. 2002. Antisense RNA-mediated suppression of benzophenanthridine alkaloid biosynthesis in transgenic cell cultures of California poppy. *Plant Physiol.* 128:696–706

124. Park SU, Yu M, Facchini PJ. 2003. Modulation of berberine bridge enzyme levels in transgenic root cultures of California poppy alters the accumulation of benzophenanthridine alkaloids. *Plant Mol. Biol.* 51:153–64

125. Pauli HH, Kutchan TM. 1998. Molecular cloning and functional heterologous expression of two alleles encoding (*S*)-*N*-methylcoclaurine 3′-hydroxylase (Cyp80B1), a new methyl jasmonate-inducible cytochrome P-450-dependent monooxygenase of benzylisoquinoline alkaloid biosynthesis. *Plant J.* 13:793–801

126. Pauw B, Hilliou FA, Martin VS, Chatel G, de Wolf CJ, et al. 2004. Zinc finger proteins act as transcriptional repressors of alkaloid biosynthesis genes in *Catharanthus roseus*. *J. Biol. Chem.* 279:52940–48

127. Pilatzke-Wunderlich I, Nessler CL. 2001. Expression and activity of cell-wall-degrading enzymes in the latex of opium poppy, *Papaver somniferum* L. *Plant Mol. Biol.* 45:567–76

128. Reimann A, Nurhayati N, Backenköhler A, Ober D. 2004. Repeated evolution of the pyrrolizidine alkaloid-mediated defense system in separate angiosperm lineages. *Plant Cell.* 16:2772–84

129. Rischer H, Oresic M, Seppanen-Laakso T, Katajamaa M, Lammertyn F, et al. 2006. Gene-to-metabolite networks for terpenoid indole alkaloid biosynthesis in *Catharanthus roseus* cells. *Proc. Natl. Acad. Sci. USA* 103:5614–19

130. Robertson D. 2004. VIGS vectors for gene silencing: many targets, many tools. *Annu. Rev. Plant Biol.* 55:495–519

131. Ronning CM, Stegalkina SS, Ascenzi RA, Bougri O, Hart AL, et al. 2003. Comparative analyses of potato expressed sequence tag libraries. *Plant Physiol.* 131:419–29

132. Rueffer M, Zenk MH. 1987. Enzymatic formation of protopines by a microsomal cytochrome P-450 system of *Corydalis vaginans*. *Tetrahedron Lett.* 28:5307–10

133. Ruppert M, Panjikar S, Barleben L, Stöckigt J. 2006. Heterologous expression, purification, crystallization and preliminary X-ray analysis of raucaffricine glucosidase, a plant enzyme specifically involved in *Rauwolfia* alkaloid biosynthesis. *Acta Crystallogr. Sect. F Struct. Biol. Cryst. Commun.* 62:257–60

134. Ruppert M, Woll J, Giritch A, Genady E, Ma X, Stöckigt J. 2005. Functional expression of an ajmaline pathway-specific esterase from *Rauvolfia* in a novel plant-virus expression system. *Planta* 222:888–98

135. Samanani N, Alcantara J, Bourgault R, Zulak KG, Facchini PJ. 2006. The role of phloem sieve elements and laticifers in the biosynthesis and accumulation of alkaloids in opium poppy. *Plant J.* 47:547–63

136. Samanani N, Facchini PJ. 2002. Purification and characterization of norcoclaurine synthase. The first committed enzyme in benzylisoquinoline alkaloid biosynthesis in plants. *J. Biol. Chem.* 277:33878–83
137. Samanani N, Liscombe DK, Facchini PJ. 2004. Molecular cloning and characterization of norcoclaurine synthase, an enzyme catalyzing the first committed step in benzylisoquinoline alkaloid biosynthesis. *Plant J.* 40:302–13
138. Samanani N, Park SU, Facchini PJ. 2005. Cell type-specific localization of transcripts encoding nine consecutive enzymes involved in protoberberine alkaloid biosynthesis. *Plant Cell* 17:915–26
139. Schmidt D, Stöckigt J. 1995. Enzymatic formation of the sarpagan-bridge: a key step in the biosynthesis of sarpagine- and ajmaline-type alkaloids. *Planta Med.* 61:254–58
140. Schröder G, Unterbusch E, Kaltenbach M, Schmidt J, Strack D, et al. 1999. Light-induced cytochrome P450-dependent enzyme in indole alkaloid biosynthesis: tabersonine 16-hydroxylase. *FEBS Lett.* 458:97–102
141. Shoji T, Nakajima K, Hashimoto T. 2000. Ethylene suppresses jasmonate-induced gene expression in nicotine biosynthesis. *Plant Cell Physiol.* 41:1072–76
142. Shoji T, Winz R, Iwase T, Nakajima K, Yamada Y, Hashimoto T. 2002. Expression patterns of two tobacco isoflavone reductase-like genes and their possible roles in secondary metabolism in tobacco. *Plant Mol. Biol.* 50:427–40
143. Siberil Y, Benhamron S, Memelink J, Giglioli-Guivarc'h N, Thiersault M, et al. 2001. *Catharanthus roseus* G-box binding factors 1 and 2 act as repressors of strictosidine synthase gene expression in cell cultures. *Plant Mol. Biol.* 45:477–88
144. Siminszky B, Gavilano L, Bowen SW, Dewey RE. 2005. Conversion of nicotine to nornicotine in *Nicotiana tabacum* is mediated by Cyp82E4, a cytochrome P450 monooxygenase. *Proc. Natl. Acad. Sci. USA* 102:14919–24
145. Sottomayor M, Lopez-Serrano M, DiCosmo F, Ros Barcelo A. 1998. Purification and characterization of α-3′,4′-anhydrovinblastine synthase (peroxidase-like) from *Catharanthus roseus* (L.) G. Don. *FEBS Lett.* 428:299–303
146. Steffens P, Nagakura N, Zenk MH. 1985. Purification and characterization of the berberine bridge enzyme from *Berberis beaniana* cell cultures. *Phytochemistry* 24:2577–83
147. Stenzel O, Teuber M, Dräger B. 2006. Putrescine *N*-methyltransferase in *Solanum tuberosum* L., a calystegine-forming plant. *Planta* 223:200–12
148. Stevens LH, Blom TJM, Verpoorte R. 1993. Subcellular localization of tryptophan decarboxylase, strictosidine synthase and strictosidine glucosidase in suspension-cultured cells of *Catharanthus roseus* and *Tabernaemontana divaricata*. *Plant Cell Rep.* 12:573–76
149. St-Pierre B, De Luca V. 1995. A cytochrome P-450 monooxygenase catalyzes the first step in the conversion of tabersonine to vindoline in *Catharanthus roseus*. *Plant Physiol.* 109:131–139
150. St-Pierre B, Laflamme P, Alarco AM, De Luca V. 1998. The terminal *O*-acetyltransferase involved in vindoline biosynthesis defines a new class of proteins responsible for coenzyme A-dependent acyl transfer. *Plant J.* 14:703–13
151. St-Pierre B, Vazquez-Flota FA, De Luca V. 1999. Multicellular compartmentation of *Catharanthus roseus* alkaloid biosynthesis predicts intercellular translocation of a pathway intermediate. *Plant Cell* 11:887–900
152. Suzuki H, Koike Y, Murakoshi I, Saito K. 1996. Subcellular localization of acyltransferases for quinolizidine alkaloid biosynthesis in *Lupinus*. *Phytochemistry* 42:1557–62
153. Suzuki K, Yamada Y, Hashimoto T. 1999. Expression of *Atropa belladonna* putrescine *N*-methyltransferase gene in root pericycle. *Plant Cell Physiol.* 40:289–97

154. Suzuki K, Yun DJ, Chen XY, Yamada Y, Hashimoto T. 1999. An *Atropa belladonna* hyoscyamine 6β-hydroxylase gene is differentially expressed in the root pericycle and anthers. *Plant Mol. Biol.* 40:141–52

155. Takeshita N, Fujiwara H, Mimura H, Fitchen JH, Yamada Y, Sato F. 1995. Molecular cloning and characterization of *S*-adenosyl-L-methionine:scoulerine-9-*O*-methyltransferase from cultured cells of *Coptis japonica*. *Plant Cell Physiol.* 36:29–36

156. Tanahashi T, Zenk MH. 1990. Elicitor induction and characterization of microsomal protopine-6-hydroxylase, the central enzyme in benzophenanthridine alkaloid biosynthesis. *Phytochemistry* 29:1113–22

157. Teuber M, Azemi ME, Namjoyan F, Meier AC, Wodak A, et al. 2007. Putrescine *N*-methyltransferases-a structure-function analysis. *Plant Mol. Biol.* 63:787–801

158. Uefuji H, Ogita S, Yamaguchi Y, Koizumi N, Sano H. 2003. Molecular cloning and functional characterization of three distinct *N*-methyltransferases involved in the caffeine biosynthetic pathway in coffee plants. *Plant Physiol.* 132:372–80

159. Uefuji H, Tatsumi Y, Morimoto M, Kaothien-Nakayama P, Ogita S, Sano H. 2005. Caffeine production in tobacco plants by simultaneous expression of three coffee *N*-methyltrasferases and its potential as a pest repellant. *Plant Mol. Biol.* 59:221–27

160. Unterlinner B, Lenz R, Kutchan TM. 1999. Molecular cloning and functional expression of codeinone reductase: the penultimate enzyme in morphine biosynthesis in the opium poppy *Papaver somniferum*. *Plant J.* 18:465–75

161. van der Fits L, Memelink J. 2000. ORCA3, a jasmonate-responsive transcriptional regulator of plant primary and secondary metabolism. *Science* 289:295–97

162. Vazquez-Flota F, De Carolis E, Alarco AM, De Luca V. 1997. Molecular cloning and characterization of desacetoxyvindoline-4-hydroxylase, a 2-oxoglutarate dependent-dioxygenase involved in the biosynthesis of vindoline in *Catharanthus roseus* (L.) G. Don. *Plant Mol. Biol.* 34:935–48

163. Veau B, Courtois M, Oudin A, Chenieux JC, Rideau M, Clastre M. 2000. Cloning and expression of cDNAs encoding two enzymes of the MEP pathway in *Catharanthus roseus*. *Biochim. Biophys. Acta* 1517:159–63

164. Viehweger K, Schwartze W, Schumann B, Lein W, Roos W. 2006. The Gα protein controls a pH-dependent signal path to the induction of phytoalexin biosynthesis in *Eschscholzia californica*. *Plant Cell* 18:1510–23

165. Vom Endt D, Soares e Silva M, Kijne JW, Pasquali G, Memelink J. 2007. Identification of a bipartite jasmonate-responsive promoter element in the *Catharanthus roseus ORCA3* transcription factor gene that interacts specifically with AT-hook DNA-binding proteins. *Plant Physiol.* 144:1680–89

166. von Schumann G, Gao S, Stöckigt J. 2002. Vomilenine reductase–a novel enzyme catalyzing a crucial step in the biosynthesis of the therapeutically applied antiarrhythmic alkaloid ajmaline. *Bioorg. Med. Chem.* 10:1913–18

167. Walz C, Giavalisco P, Schad M, Juenger M, Klose J, Kehr J. 2004. Proteomics of curcurbit phloem exudate reveals a network of defence proteins. *Phytochemistry* 65:1795–804

168. Warzecha H, Gerasimenko I, Kutchan TM, Stöckigt J. 2000. Molecular cloning and functional bacterial expression of a plant glucosidase specifically involved in alkaloid biosynthesis. *Phytochemistry* 54:657–66

169. Wege S, Scholz A, Gleissberg S, Becker A. 2007. Highly efficient virus-induced gene silencing (VIGS) in California poppy (*Eschscholzia californica*): an evaluation of VIGS as a strategy to obtain functional data from nonmodel plants. *Ann. Bot.* 100:641–49

170. Weid M, Ziegler J, Kutchan TM. 2004. The roles of latex and the vascular bundle in morphine biosynthesis in the opium poppy, *Papaver somniferum*. *Proc. Natl. Acad. Sci. USA*. 101:13957–62
171. Weiss D, Baumert A, Vogel M, Roos W. 2006. Sanguinarine reductase, a key enzyme of benzophenanthridine detoxification. *Plant Cell Environ.* 29:291–302
172. Wink M, Hartmann T. 1982. Localization of the enzymes of quinolizidine alkaloid biosynthesis in leaf chloroplasts of *Lupinus polyphyllus*. *Plant Physiol.* 70:74–77
173. Winkel BS. 2004. Metabolic channeling in plants. *Annu. Rev. Plant Biol.* 55:85–107
174. Winkler A, Hartner F, Kutchan TM, Glieder A, Macheroux P. 2006. Biochemical evidence that berberine bridge enzyme belongs to a novel family of flavoproteins containing a bi-covalently attached FAD cofactor. *J. Biol. Chem.* 281:21276–85
175. Winkler A, Kutchan TM, Macheroux P. 2007. 6-*S*-Cysteinylation of bi-covalently attached FAD in berberine bridge enzyme tunes the redox potential for optimal activity. *J. Biol. Chem.* 282:24437–43
176. Xu D, Shen Y, Chappell J, Cui M, Nielsen M. 2007. Biochemical and molecular characterization of nicotine demethylase in tobacco. *Physiol. Plant.* 129:307–19
177. Yamamoto H, Katano N, Ooi A, Inoue K. 2000. Secologanin synthase which catalyzes the oxidative cleavage of loganin into secologanin is a cytochrome P450. *Phytochemistry* 53:7–12
178. Yamazaki Y, Sudo H, Yamazaki M, Aimi N, Saito K. 2003. Camptothecin biosynthetic genes in hairy roots of *Ophiorrhiza pumila*: cloning, characterization and differential expression in tissues and by stress compounds. *Plant Cell Physiol.* 44:395–403
179. Yun DJ, Hashimoto T, Yamada Y. 1992. Metabolic engineering of medicinal plants: transgenic *Atropa belladonna* with an improved alkaloid composition. *Proc. Natl. Acad. Sci. USA*. 89:11799–803
180. Zarate R, el Jaber-Vazdekis N, Medina B, Ravelo AG. 2006. Tailoring tropane alkaloid accumulation in transgenic hairy roots of *Atropa baetica* by overexpressing the gene encoding hyoscyamine 6β-hydroxylase. *Biotechnol. Lett.* 28:1271–77
181. Zhang L, Ding R, Chai Y, Bonfill M, Moyano E, et al. 2004. Engineering tropane biosynthetic pathway in *Hyoscyamus niger* hairy root cultures. *Proc. Natl. Acad. Sci. USA* 101:6786–91
182. Ziegler J, Diaz-Chávez ML, Kramell R, Ammer C, Kutchan TM. 2005. Comparative macroarray analysis of morphine containing *Papaver somniferum* and eight morphine free *Papaver* species identifies an *O*-methyltransferase involved in benzylisoquinoline biosynthesis. *Planta* 222:458–71
183. Ziegler J, Voigtländer S, Schmidt J, Kramell R, Miersch O, et al. 2006. Comparative transcript and alkaloid profiling in *Papaver* species identifies a short chain dehydrogenase/reductase involved in morphine biosynthesis. *Plant J.* 48:177–92
184. Zulak KG, Cornish A, Daskalchuk TE, Deyholos MK, Goodenowe DB, et al. 2007. Gene transcript and metabolite profiling of elicitor-induced opium poppy cell cultures reveals the coordinate regulation of primary and secondary metabolism. *Planta* 225:1085–106

Genetically Engineered Plants and Foods: A Scientist's Analysis of the Issues (Part I)

Peggy G. Lemaux

Department of Plant and Microbial Biology, University of California, Berkeley, California 94720; email: lemauxpg@nature.berkeley.edu

Annu. Rev. Plant Biol. 2008. 59:771–812

First published online as a Review in Advance on February 19, 2008

The *Annual Review of Plant Biology* is online at plant.annualreviews.org

This article's doi:
10.1146/annurev.arplant.58.032806.103840

1543-5008/08/0602-0771$20.00

Key Words

benefits, biotechnology, crops, food safety, genetic engineering, risks

Abstract

Through the use of the new tools of genetic engineering, genes can be introduced into the same plant or animal species or into plants or animals that are not sexually compatible—the latter is a distinction with classical breeding. This technology has led to the commercial production of genetically engineered (GE) crops on approximately 250 million acres worldwide. These crops generally are herbicide and pest tolerant, but other GE crops in the pipeline focus on other traits. For some farmers and consumers, planting and eating foods from these crops are acceptable; for others they raise issues related to safety of the foods and the environment. In Part I of this review some general and food issues raised regarding GE crops and foods will be addressed. Responses to these issues, where possible, cite peer-reviewed scientific literature. In Part II to appear in 2009, issues related to environmental and socioeconomic aspects of GE crops and foods will be covered.

Contents

1. INTRODUCTION

"Be very, very careful what you put into that head, because you will never, ever get it out," said Thomas Cardinal Wolsey (1471–1530). Although spoken centuries ago, this admonition rings true today when it comes to the impact of information people receive, particularly in the popular press, about genetically engineered (GE) crops and foods. Genetic engineering enables the introduction of genes, using the modern tools of recombinant DNA (rDNA), from the same species into an organism; of more concern to some, genes from organisms in other kingdoms can be introduced. Although much relating to GE crops and foods has been written, both pro and con, this review attempts, where possible, to address issues by linking responses to peer-reviewed literature. The intent is to present as accurate a scientific picture as possible, although this does not imply that people possessing the same scientific understanding will necessarily make the same choices about the advisability of GE crops for consumption, because different people have different values.

GE crops, and products made from them, must be evaluated on a case-by-case basis and, although scientific information should be a part of the considerations for using and consuming these crops, issues beyond the technical, science-based facts also need to be considered. Here, aspects of a number of issues related to GE crops and foods are reviewed from a detailed scientific viewpoint. Not all issues raised are discussed and not all aspects of the issues raised are addressed.

GE: genetically engineered

Recombinant DNA (rDNA): DNA that is manipulated in the laboratory using recombinant DNA technologies

GMO: genetically modified organism

2. GENERAL ISSUES

2.1. Terminology

Biotechnology literally means the use of a living organism (hence, "bio") to perform a task or function. Historically the term was used to describe processes like cheese, yogurt, wine, or beer production. In modern parlance, however, biotechnology is commonly used to refer to the newer methods of genetic engineering of organisms through the use of recombinant DNA or rDNA. People use the term GMO today to refer to a genetically modified organism, one that has been engineered using rDNA. Others refer to foods created in this manner as genetically engineered or GE foods. So, a GE or GMO food is a food modified using rDNA methods or one that contains a GE ingredient. The term LMO, for living modified organism, refers to a GE organism that is alive, such as a fresh fruit, vegetable, or seed that was created using rDNA. A seed is an LMO, whereas flour made from seeds or grain would not be an LMO. Use of the terms GMO and LMO can be confusing, especially to geneticists, given that all foods eaten today have been altered or modified genetically through natural or human-imposed mutations or crossing. Frankenfoods, or Frankenstein foods, is a term first coined by Paul Lewis in his 1992 letter to the Editor of the *New York Times* (139), arguing against GE tomatoes and calling for action against Frankenfoods. The term gained popularity after 1998 when nongovernmental organizations (NGOs) started using the term to call consumers to action against GE foods (102).

GRAS: generally recognized as safe

Classical breeding: methods used by humans to facilitate genetic exchange between one organism and another

2.2. Besides Genetically Engineered Crops, Does Genetic Engineering Play a Role in Producing Food?

Much processed food is produced using enzymes, or whole organisms with enzymes, that are responsible for altering the nature of the food—such as bacteria (e.g., yogurt), yeast (e.g., beer, wine), and multicellular fungi (e.g., blue cheese). These enzymes were modified genetically through traditional methods and in some cases rDNA methods as well. One example of the latter is the modification of an enzyme used in making cheese, rennin. This enzyme is present in rennet, historically isolated from the stomachs of slaughtered calves where it was needed to clot mother's milk to slow its digestion. In cheese-making, rennet is used to coagulate milk to separate the curds (solids) and whey (liquid). Rennin or chymosin was the first protein produced through rDNA means to be used in food (95). The chymosin gene from a cow was cloned into yeast and *Escherichia coli*, from which rennin can be made in larger quantities and with more consistent quality than from calves' stomachs. Engineered chymosin is currently used in approximately 60% of U.S. hard cheese products (27).

Other products produced by rDNA methods include food supplements, such as vitamin B2 (riboflavin) (181), α-amylase (used to produce high-fructose corn syrup and dry beer), and lactase (added to milk to reduce the lactose content for persons with lactose intolerance). The Food and Drug Administration (FDA) granted GRAS (generally recognized as safe) (See section 3.4) status for these enzymes produced by GE microorganisms prior to their use in food (125).

2.3. How Does the Creation of a Genetically Engineered Crop Differ from That of a Classically Bred Crop?

Similarities and differences exist between the modifications made in organisms by classical breeding versus those made via rDNA methods. Both approaches can involve changes in the sequence, order, and regulation of genes in an organism and can utilize many of the same enzymes. However, with the rDNA approach the amount of genetic information modified is small, one or a few genes, compared with the classical breeding approach where all the tens of thousands of genes in the organism are involved, potentially exchanging positions. Another difference is that with the rDNA approach when and where a gene product is made can be controlled precisely. Thus, if a change in seed characteristics is desired, a gene can be linked to regulatory signals that result in expression only in the seed or even in a specific compartment of the seed (43)—an outcome difficult to achieve with classical breeding.

With classical breeding approaches, crosses can only be accomplished between closely related species or genera. For example, a wild *Lycopersicon* variety can be crossed with cultivated tomato (*Lycopersicon esculentum*) varieties (42), and wheat (*Triticum aestivum*) can be crossed with rye (*Secale cereale*) to yield triticale (218). But in many crosses, wild relatives and different genera or species are not compatible or crosses can be made but the resulting embryos must be rescued by in vitro culture to obtain a plant (204). In contrast, rDNA approaches can utilize genetic material from any living organism, which permits DNA from bacterial or animal sources to be introduced into plants. Therefore, rDNA can result in gene combinations not previously seen.

2.4. Can Marker-Assisted Selection Be Used Instead of Genetic Engineering to Improve Crops?

When it is determined what genic sequences are responsible for certain traits, that information can be used to develop breeding aids. The ability to select desirable alleles and eliminate deleterious ones in a fast, reliable manner is critical to the development of improved germplasm through breeding. Genetic markers can speed identification of plants with desired (or deleterious) alleles in large populations via a process termed marker-assisted selection (MAS). Markers closely linked to desired traits are used to select indirectly for the trait (58). With the whole and partial genome sequences and other molecular tools now available, markers can now be identified in the responsible gene, rather than linked to it, which makes MAS even more valuable. Thus, a marker was found in *Xa5*, a rice (*Oryza sativa*) bacterial blight disease resistance gene, and its use prevented separation of the marker from the trait by recombination (115).

MAS is particularly valuable for traits when *a*) phenotypic screens in the field are difficult or costly, e.g., drought/frost tolerance or resistance to exotic diseases or pests; *b*) multiple alleles exist; and *c*) recessive or low heritability traits exist that require progeny testing. MAS is used for some important traits, e.g., leaf rust resistance in wheat (165), erect panicle in rice (126), soybean (*Glycine max*) rust resistance (108), drought adaptation in maize (190), and root-knot nematode resistance in cotton (*Gossypium hirsutum*) (255).

Utilization of GE crop varieties is not permitted for organic growers. National Organic Standards specify that these varieties cannot be intentionally grown by organic farmers and labeled "organic" (161) (See section 3.16); however, MAS can be used to introduce desired traits from wild or related species and these species are acceptable to organic growers. However, this approach is limited to diversity extant in sexually compatible species, which is often not sufficiently broad to provide needed traits. Utilizing MAS to create food crops has led to the term, "Super Organics" (144), crops that are grown under certified organic conditions and were created through classical breeding using genomic information and MAS, not through rDNA methods.

2.5. Does the Use of rDNA Always Involve Moving Genes from One Organism to Another?

Using rDNA methods, a gene from any living organism can be inserted into a plant and, given appropriate regulatory signals and codon usage, can be expressed efficiently in a plant cell. To introduce a gene from the same or a heterologous source, the gene must be identified in a donor organism and cloned into a bacterium to obtain sufficient DNA to build plant transformation vectors (210) and perform the transformation. Given the intermediate bacterial step, even if structural genes and regulatory sequences are from the plant, plant transformation would involve moving DNA from one organism to another.

Sources of genes to engineer plants can be derived from the same plant, a different plant, a related wild species, or from bacteria, fungi, viruses, and mammals. The capacity to introduce genes from different living organisms raises the issue of whether all engineered plants, regardless of the source of the genetic material, should be considered as a homogeneous group. Alternatively, it has been suggested that GE plants be placed in three classes: *i*) wide transfer, referring to gene movement from organisms of other kingdoms into plants; *ii*) close transfer, referring to movement between species of plants; and *iii*) tweaking, referring to the manipulation of levels or patterns of expression of genes already present in the plant (232).

Using such a classification scheme would provide some clarity to several issues relating to regulation and public perception of GE crops. A determination of substantial equivalence (See section 3.4) could then be carried out at different levels of scrutiny, depending on classification level. A GE plant created by tweaking or close transfer would result in changes unlikely to be dramatically different from those created by processes used by traditional breeders. Conversely, introduction

MAS: marker-assisted selection

Substantial equivalence: an assessment of a new food must demonstrate it is as safe as its conventional counterpart

via a wide transfer would likely require more thorough testing to establish substantial equivalence.

EPA: Environmental Protection Agency

USDA: United States Department of Agriculture

Pesticide: any substance or mixture of substances that prevents, destroys, repels, or mitigates any pest, including insects, weeds, fungi, bacteria, viruses, mice, and other animals

Bt: *Bacillus thuringiensis*

APHIS: Animal and Plant Health Inspection Service

EIS: environmental impact statement

2.6. Which U.S. Agencies Have Regulatory Authority Over Genetically Engineered and Classically Bred Crops?

In the early 1980s, the U.S. established a formal regulatory structure for GE organisms by expanding existing legislation to accommodate products created by rDNA. This approach was outlined in an Office of Science and Technology Policy document entitled *Coordinated Framework for Regulation of Biotechnology* (169), which established the concept that GE foods would be regulated on the basis of product, not process, and on a case-by-case basis.

GE foods and products made from them are under regulatory control of three federal agencies: the FDA, the Environmental Protection Agency (EPA), and the U.S. Department of Agriculture (USDA) (see 150 for a review). The FDA is responsible for the safety and labeling of foods and animal feeds from all crops, including those that are GE. The FDA requires full evaluations of GE foods containing uncharacterized DNA sequences, significantly altered nutrient levels, different composition relative to existing foods, potentially allergenic or toxic proteins, and/or new selection marker genes. The EPA evaluates food safety and environmental issues associated with new pesticides and pesticidal products. Bt corn (*Bacillus thuringiensis; Zea mays*) and the pesticidal Bt product it contains, used to control the European corn borer, for example, fall under its jurisdiction. The EPA's control also encompasses GE plants in which a small part of a pest, such as a viral regulatory sequence (e.g., 35S promoter), is used to develop the GE crop. A division of the USDA, the Animal and Plant Health Inspection Service (APHIS), oversees environmental consequences and safety of planting and field-testing GE plants; their role is to ensure that field tests of GE crops are conducted under controlled conditions and that any unusual occurrences are reported. Every GE crop will not be overseen by all three agencies; however, all three agencies have the legal power to ask for immediate removal from the market of any product, if valid scientific data show a safety concern for consumers or the environment.

The federal government considers each GE plant with a specific DNA segment introduced via rDNA methods to be a "regulated article" and each gene transfer is defined as an event. Creating a second transformed plant with an identical DNA construct inserted in a different location is considered to be a separate event, a regulated article requiring oversight, even if the first event received regulatory approval and attained nonregulated status. As of October 2007, 113 petitions have been received at APHIS; 90 petitions received nonregulation status and no longer require APHIS review for movement or release in the U.S. (113).

In 2005, an audit by the USDA Inspector General (110) indicated the USDA lacked basic information about where GE crops were grown and their fate after harvest, raising concerns particularly about the fate of crops engineered to produce pharmaceuticals (See section 3.14). Two additional concerns were raised in 2007. First, a U.S. federal court ordered the USDA to conduct more detailed reviews of applications for experimental plots of GE bent grass when pollen was found to have spread 13 miles from the original cultivation site (61). Second, in early 2007 questions were raised about the approval of deregulation status for Roundup Ready® alfalfa when a U.S. District Court Judge ruled that the USDA had erred in approving deregulation without a proper environmental impact statement (EIS). Roundup Ready® alfalfa was returned to regulated status, pending submission and review of an appropriate EIS (11).

2.7. Which Genetically Engineered Crops Are Grown Commercially?

The first GE plant was tobacco, reported in 1983 (23), but no plants were commercially grown until the FlavrSavr™ tomato was commercialized in 1994 (146). Although the FlavrSavr™ tomato was ultimately taken off the market, other commercial crops entered the market—most notably large acreage crops, such as canola (*Brassica napus*), corn, cotton, soybean, and most recently, alfalfa (*Medicago sativa*) (See section 3.20). If success is measured by increases in global acreage or farmer acceptance, certainly these GE crops have been successful. In 2005, the billionth acre of a GE crop was planted (116). In 2006 the worldwide acreage of GE crops was 252 million acres grown by 10.3 million farmers in 22 countries (117); the majority of the farmers are in the U.S. and almost none are in Europe. In the U.S. the adoption of herbicide-tolerant (HT) soybeans represented 87% of total U.S. soybean acreage in 2006. HT cotton represented 60% of total cotton acreage (71); pest-resistant (Bt) cotton was 52%, whereas Bt corn was 35% of total corn acreage.

Despite sizeable GE crop acreage, the diversity of crop types and traits in commercial production is limited. Few minor acreage GE crops are at present commercially successful, i.e., papaya (*Carica papaya*), certain types of squash (*Cucurbita* sp.), and sweet corn (117). Nearly all major-acreage, commercial releases of GE crops are based on pest protection via genes from Bt or HT, predominantly resulting in tolerance to Monsanto's RoundUp® herbicide, although some result in tolerance to Bayer's Liberty® herbicide. More recently, stacked versions of these traits were released—e.g., maize engineered for rootworm and European corn borer resistance (both Bt-based) and tolerance to RoundUp®. Except GE papaya, all commercial varieties in 2007 are from the private, not the public, sector.

2.8. How Many Foods Are Genetically Engineered?

HT: herbicide tolerant

Estimates suggest that as much as 80% of U.S. processed food may contain an ingredient from a GE crop, such as corn starch, high-fructose corn syrup, corn oil, canola oil, soybean oil, soy flour, soy lecithin, or cottonseed oil (98). Despite this percentage in processed foods, there are very few commercially available whole GE foods. The first commercial GE whole food was the FlavrSavr™ tomato, engineered to have a longer shelf life (129) so tomatoes could be kept on the vine longer to ripen, develop more flavor, and allow later shipments to stores. Although grown in California, the tomatoes were made into tomato paste, clearly labeled, and sold in the U.K. The paste gained an estimated 60% share of the canned tomato market by 1999, but left the market shortly thereafter owing to market concerns (146). Endless Summer™ tomatoes, also engineered to control ripening and introduced at approximately the same time, were commercially available for only a short time.

GE papaya is the only engineered fruit commercially available in the U.S. today. This occurred because in Hawaii, where most papayas for the U.S. are grown, production fell owing to losses to papaya ringspot virus, PRSV (93). PRSV, discovered in Hawaii in the 1940s, virtually eliminated large-scale production on Oahu in the 1950s, forcing the industry to relocate in the early 1960s to the island of Hawaii. There it thrived, which led to 95% of Hawaii's papaya being produced there by the 1980s. Delay in spread of the disease gave researchers time to look at possibilities to protect against the virus. Infecting papaya with milder virus strains (205) met with limited success owing to a more aggressive PRSV, but a GE papaya containing a viral coat protein gene was successful (92, 141). In 2006 the GE varieties "Rainbow" and "SunUp" accounted for >50% of papaya production in Hawaii, although much of the papaya consumed in the U.S. is from Brazil, Mexico, and the Caribbean, where PRSV is not a serious problem.

Another commercial whole food available in the U.S. is GE squash (yellow crookneck, straightneck, and zucchini). The first variety of GE yellow squash, termed Freedom II, was the second GE crop to be cleared by U.S. regulators. Freedom II was engineered with viral coat protein genes to be resistant to two viruses—Watermelon Mosaic Virus 2 (WMV2) and Zucchini Yellow Mosaic Virus (ZYMV) (238). Freedom II reached the market in 1995 but was not labeled like the FlavrSavr™ tomato. Viral resistance was transferred to zucchini by breeding and, because squash is usually infected with a third virus, Cucumber Mosaic Virus (CMV), a GE squash resistant to all three viruses was developed. Six varieties of GE yellow squash and zucchini, bearing various names, e.g., Independence II, Liberator III, Freedom III, and Destiny III, are currently being sold. U.S. acreage is limited in part because of the negative effects of other viruses against which the GE varieties are not protected, but resistance to the original three viruses remains strong (88).

The last whole GE food available in the U.S. is GE sweet corn, engineered with a Bt gene to protect against earworms (*Helicoverpa zea*), one of the most costly crop pests in North America. Earworm damage results in subsequent fungal and bacterial attack and quality loss (107). Expressing Bt in corn results in reductions in insect attack. By reducing insect damage, mycotoxigenic fungi numbers are decreased and this results in lower levels of mycotoxins, such as fumonisins, which have toxic effects on humans such as elevated rates of liver and/or esophageal cancer (243). Comparing fumonisin levels in corn from Bt hybrids versus control hybrids, Bt hybrids give higher percentages of grain suitable for human and animal use (99).

2.9. What Is in the Crop Biotechnology Pipeline?

Although commercialized GE crops are limited in trait diversity, proof-of-concept for many other traits has been reported in laboratory experiments and small-scale field trials. These traits fit into several categories: pest resistance, agronomic performance, abiotic stress tolerance, medical applications, biofuels, and improved food, feed, and environment.

Pest resistance traits are aimed at improving crop performance by protecting against pests. For example, researchers found a gene in the genome of a wild Mexican potato (*Solanum tuberosum*) variety that was subsequently engineered into cultivated potato, allowing the GE potato to survive exposure to the many races of *Phytophthora infestans*, the fungus responsible for the Irish potato famine (215). A native gene, *Mi*, from tomato was upregulated to protect the roots against root knot nematode (196). Although Europe has been reluctant to embrace engineered crops, the first field trial of GE grapes (*Vitis vinifera*) took place in the northern Alsace region of France in 2005. A coat protein gene from fanleaf virus was inserted into the grape rootstock (29), but not in the scion, the portion of the plant that bears fruit.

Some traits aimed at improving field performance of crops for farmers could, given responsible usage, also positively impact the environment. One key aspect of crop performance is yield. In 2001, transgenic rice plants expressing the maize proteins pyruvate orthophosphate dikinase (PPDK) and phosphoenolpyruvate carboxylase (PEPC) exhibited a higher photosynthetic capacity ($\geq$35%) compared with untransformed plants (130). Another agronomic improvement focuses on nitrogen use efficiency, aimed at reducing fertilizer usage and increasing sustainability. The plant-specific transcription factor Dof1, when introduced into the model plant species *Arabidopsis*, increased nitrogen content by ~30%, improving growth under low-nitrogen conditions (253).

Another focus is on improving abiotic stress tolerance, e.g., high salt, high and low water availability, and temperature extremes. Constitutive expression of *CBF* genes from the cold response pathway in GE *Arabidopsis* induces expression of target *COR* (cold-regulated) genes and enhances freezing tolerance in nonacclimated plants (140). Transgenic tomato plants overexpressing a vacuolar Na^+/H^+ antiport produce fruit when grown in 200 mM sodium chloride, ~40% of sea water concentration (257), and the tomato fruits display very low sodium content. The first use of GE to alter nutritional quality was the introduction of three genes into rice to create the much publicized Golden Rice variety, enriched in provitamin A (254) (See section 3.21). Efforts have also been successful in increasing calcium levels threefold in potato (174), as well as increasing folate levels in tomato (54).

Approaches utilizing GE plants have also focused on combating human diseases and include the development of a subunit vaccine against pneumonic and bubonic plague that is immunogenic in mice (6); a potato-based vaccine for hepatitis B, shown to raise immunological responses in humans (233); a GE pollen vaccine that reduces allergy symptoms (164); and an edible rice-based vaccine targeted at alleviating allergic diseases such as asthma, seasonal allergies, and atopic dermatitis (225) (See section 3.14).

The utilization of plants to produce alternative energy sources is a present focus of attention, given the global rise in nonrenewable energy usage and greenhouse gas emissions. One approach involves engineering the green alga, *Chlamydomonas reinhardtii*, to produce hydrogen gas, a clean, renewable fuel source (151). Paper waste, particularly from newspapers, is a major environmental pollutant that because of compaction remains in landfills for decades without decomposition. GE bacteria engineered with trifunctional designer cellulosomes or bifunctional systems can degrade microcrystalline cellulose and straw (72). Efforts are also aimed at improving the ability of engineered plants and microbes to process cellulosic biomass into usable biofuels (For reviews, see 221 and 237).

Allergenicity: reaction to a substance that is foreign to the body and can cause a hypersensitive or allergic reaction in certain people

Nutritional composition: includes protein, carbohydrate, fat, vitamins, minerals, fiber, moisture, and phytochemical levels

3. FOOD ISSUES

The topics addressed in this section represent some major issues that have been raised regarding GE foods. These include food safety of GE plants and animals, pharma crops, labeling, allergenicity, nutritional composition, organic foods, and food safety testing.

3.1. Did People Die After Consuming Tryptophan Made By Genetically Engineered Bacteria?

In 1989 claims surfaced that a nutritional supplement, L-tryptophan, used to treat insomnia, premenstrual syndrome, and depression, caused an epidemic of eosinophilia-myalgia syndrome (EMS) in the U.S.; the number affected was reported to be "between 5000 and 10,000 people and the number of deaths near 40" (213). All affected people had consumed tryptophan made by one Japanese company (197) that had produced L-tryptophan using GE bacteria without incident prior to 1989. However, in 1989 the company changed GE bacterial strains and manufacturing processes, eliminating some filtration steps and reducing by half the amount of active carbon used for purification. Although the final product was 99.6% pure, it still contained 60 different impurities (148), any one of which could have caused the illness, although the cause of the problems was never conclusively linked to the organism or the manufacturing process. But reconstruction experiments (148) make it likely that the presence of the causative impurity was not due to the GE bacterium, but to the changes in processing. In a legal summation, it was stated that "the fermentation and later cooking of industrial sized lots of L-tryptophan generated the contaminant" that was legally responsible for the

GM: genetically modified

Toxicity: adverse physiological effects following exposure to a substance

autoimmune EMS disease (234). Procedures should have been conducted to assess safety after changes were made in the strains and production methods.

3.2. Were Potatoes Genetically Engineered with a Lectin Protein Unsafe to Eat?

In the late 1990s, Ewen & Pusztai (69) conducted studies on rats fed potatoes engineered to express an introduced lectin gene from a snowdrop plant (*Galanthus nivalis*), intended to reduce insect damage. After feeding, they observed stomach lesions in the rats and concluded that "the damage to the rats did not come from the lectin, but apparently from the same process of genetic engineering that is used to create the GM foods everyone was already eating" (211). This study and its conclusions were strongly criticized by the scientific community (186), because the study was conducted with too few animals and inadequate controls. Following the initial announcement of the findings to the popular press, the original study was published in the *Lancet* to provide researchers an opportunity to view the data. But the data in the paper left researchers unable to draw firm conclusions (134) or confirm or deny results. The U.K.'s Royal Society criticized the study for lack of proper controls. In the same issue of *Lancet* in which the paper was published, Dutch scientists concluded the observed toxic effects might be due to nutritional differences between control and GE potatoes, not from the GE process (133). To reach firm conclusions, experiments should be repeated on larger numbers of animals with proper controls. Notably, this product was not marketed and the results do not extend to safety analyses of other GE crops. (See section 3.4)

3.3. Were Fish Genes Introduced into Strawberries?

An antifreeze gene from Artic flounder was introduced into tobacco and tomato (103) and field-tested in tobacco (*Nicotiana tobacum*) (137) and tomato (114); it was not introduced into other crops, like strawberries (*Fragaria* × *ananassa*), nor was it commercialized. The gene used, *afa3*, encoded an antifreeze protein, which in the blood of polar fish was found to inhibit ice recrystallization; however, despite high mRNA levels in the leaves of transformed tobacco, no inhibition of ice recrystallization was detected. If the approach had been pursued, additional environmental and food safety tests would have been conducted to study the impacts of this gene on the plant, the environment, and consumers. Although humans consume flounder and this protein, substantial equivalence and allergenicity and toxicity tests (See section 3.4) would have been done to assure the safety of the gene product in new foods.

However, issues with foods such as those engineered with a fish gene go beyond scientific risk, they raise questions of whether exchanges between certain organisms should be carried out. Cross-kingdom transfer of animal genes to plants is not popular with consumers worldwide (143), who are more comfortable with gene transfer among plants or between plants and bacteria (118). In fact, in a 2001 poll, 33% of U.S. respondents believed that it was not possible to transfer animal genes into plants and 16% weren't sure (199). To date, no human or animal genes have been introduced into any commercialized GE crops in the U.S., but rice engineered with human lysostaphin and lysozyme to combat childhood diarrhea (256) has been grown in the field (87).

3.4. Are Food Safety Studies Conducted on GE Foods?

GE foods and products made from GE crops that are used in foods today have undergone safety testing by the companies or institutions that developed them (See sections 3.6 and 3.7). The data were then reviewed by federal regulatory agencies. Frequently GE foods and products made from GE crops are also tested by outside groups and the results published in peer-reviewed journals. This process is comparable to safety assessments done for pharmaceutical drugs and biomarkers; pharmaceutical companies provide safety data that are subsequently reviewed by FDA scientists (82). Consultation with and submission to regulatory agencies of certain safety data for GE foods is voluntary, as are some data for pharmaceutical products (82); however, the legal requirements that foods (and pharmaceuticals) have to meet are not voluntary. Although GE foods can be marketed without certain regulatory approvals, to date all products in the marketplace have undergone full review by regulatory agencies regarding safety and content relative to unmodified forms (searchable data on specific events available at 84). Submitting the safety data is in the developer's best interests, however, given the legal liabilities incurred should a problem with the food arise following market introduction (See section 3.14).

The EPA focuses on environmental and human health impacts of pesticides and therefore evaluates GE plants with altered pesticide traits. The EPA's regulatory oversight of Bt crops is based on the presence in the plant of Cry proteins from *B. thuringiensis* (See section 3.7), which are termed plant-incorporated protectants (PIPs), substances that alter the crop's pesticidal properties (65).

Cry: crystal protein

Health safety assessments of GE foods are based in part on the concept of substantial equivalence (132). If the food and/or its new ingredient(s) is substantially equivalent to existing foods or food ingredients, it is treated like conventional foods with respect to certain aspects of its safety (124). Food or food ingredients used safely for long periods or foods substantially equivalent to these foods in nutritional characteristics do not require additional extensive safety testing. Substances that result in scientifically based safety issues require additional testing in the laboratory or in animal models.

A determination of substantial equivalence requires analysis of GE foods relative to comparable existing foods in terms of protein, fat, starch, amino acid, vitamin, mineral, and phytonutrient composition (20, 209, 229). GE foods can be designated substantially equivalent to their existing counterparts, substantially equivalent except for certain defined differences (on which safety assessments are then needed), or not substantially equivalent, meaning more safety testing and further review are necessary. When making such comparisons, it is important to note that the composition of components varies across a range—whether conventional, organic, or GE. For example, when polyphenol profiles of fresh apple juices from various apple (*Malus domestica*) cultivars and commercially available apple juices were compared, significant differences were found in total polyphenol content, as well as in profiles of individual polyphenols, as analyzed by high-performance liquid chromatography (HPLC)-photodiode array detection and HPLC-electrospray ionization-tandem mass spectrometry (123).

Large numbers of animal tests on GE foods and GE ingredients have been conducted and published in the literature (See 40, 76, 127, 185, and 244 for reviews). In the studies reported in these reviews, both chemical analyses and studies in a variety of animals (e.g., dairy cows, beef cattle, pigs, laying hens, broilers, fish, and rabbits) revealed no significant, unintended differences between GE and conventional varieties in composition, digestibility, or animal health and performance. The lack of significant differences between GE food and feed and isogenic counterparts in these tests strongly supports their substantial equivalence.

Food safety testing in animals is used to determine toxicity and allergenicity of the GE food or ingredient; however, such testing of whole GE foods and feeds is difficult or impossible owing to the need for animals to consume large amounts of food to obtain sufficient quantities of the GE ingredient. Compositional analyses and toxicity testing of individual components are actually more sensitive and accurate in assessing safety (40). Therefore, in addition to whole foods, safety tests are conducted on individual products of introduced genes, both target and selectable marker genes, on the basis of the food additive provision (Section 409) of the 1992 Federal Food, Drug, and Cosmetic Act (83). This act states that substances intentionally added to food are food additives, unless they are GRAS or are exempt, as with a pesticide, and are then the responsibility of the EPA. GRAS status is established by a long history of food use or when the nature of the substance does not raise significant, scientifically based safety issues (77). For example, the FlavrSavr™ tomato (See section 2.8) was created using a kanamycin resistance selectable marker gene; data on the selection gene and its product were submitted by the company and, following review, the gene and its product were granted GRAS status (188).

Transgene: a gene that is manipulated using recombinant DNA technologies and reintroduced into a host organism

3.5. What Happens to the DNA in Foods When They Are Eaten?

The daily human intake of DNA in food is estimated at 0.1–1 g (75). Estimates of the total daily transgene DNA intake can be calculated, assuming 50% of the diet is from GE foods and transgenes represent an estimated 0.0005% of total DNA in food, as 0.5–5 μg/day. DNA is chemically identical regardless of its source and is mostly degraded during industrial processing and in the digestive tract. Small fragments can be detected in certain body tissues, such as leukocytes, liver, and spleen. For example, fragments of orally administered phage M13 and plant DNA were taken up by phagocytes as a part of their normal function as immune system cells (200, 201). In rare instances fragments could pass into other organs, including the fetus, but were never demonstrated to be intact. Others reviewing the published data in these papers argued that the rare events observed more likely resulted from contamination (18, 91, 120).

In July 2007, the European Food Safety Authority released statements on the fate of genes and proteins in food and feed: "After ingestion, a rapid degradation into short DNA or peptide fragments is observed in the gastrointestinal tract of animals and humans" and "To date a large number of experimental studies with livestock have shown that rDNA fragments or proteins derived from GM plants have not been detected in tissues, fluids or edible products of farm animals" (68).

No reproducible data exist to show that transgene DNA in commercialized GE crops has unique behavior relative to native plant DNA. However, in late 2005 Dr. Irina Ermakova (184) of the Russian Academy of Sciences publicly announced her study, describing stunted development and higher infant mortality in rats fed diets containing Roundup Ready® soybeans (55.6% mortality) compared with rats fed conventional soybeans (9% mortality). Among the possibilities, she claimed that animals died of mutations induced solely by the transgene DNA—on the basis of earlier claims that DNA insertion in the plant genome is highly mutagenic (136). Her results were not published in a peer-reviewed scientific journal, but were presented at international symposia (184) and during parliamentary debate in New South Wales, where the data were used to push for a ban on GE crop cultivation in the European Union (E.U.) (175).

The results of the Ermakova study contradict the results from a number of other, sometimes multigenerational, studies on rats and mice fed Roundup Ready® soybeans that revealed no adverse effects on litter size, histological appearance of tissues, or numbers of deaths of progeny (30, 231, 259; For review, see 217). Differences between these studies and those of Ermakova likely relate to aspects of her experimental procedure: *i*) the conventional diet was from an uncharacterized soy variety, *ii*) the number of pups in the litters was small, and *iii*) reproductive rates in rats fed conventional soy were low. In an attempt to understand her studies, the editor of *Nature Biotechnology* invited Dr. Ermakova to provide a detailed account of her work (145). In this dialogue, Ermakova admits to having questions about her own results, making the need for peer-review and controlled repetition of her studies using proper controls essential.

3.6. Do Genetically Engineered Foods Have Changes in Nutritional Content?

Preventing adverse health effects of foods requires the application of appropriate scientific methods to predict and identify unintended compositional changes resulting from genetic modification of plants, animals, and microbes—whether by classical or rDNA methods. It is the final product, rather than the means by which it is modified, that is more likely to result in unintended effects (50). Nonetheless, the nutritional composition of GE foods, including levels of protein, carbohydrate, fat, vitamin, mineral, fiber, moisture, and phytochemicals, is analyzed for substantial equivalence, and levels of individual nutrients and antinutrients in GE foods are compared with levels in conventional counterparts (See section 3.4).

When considering substantial equivalence, it is important to note that a range of natural variation is observed in conventionally bred cultivars when grown under similar conditions (208). Therefore, comparisons of nutritional content of GE foods must be measured against variation in conventional foods grown under comparable conditions. For example, nutrient composition of GE potato tubers was compared with control wild-type and tissue culture–derived non-GE potato tubers of two cultivars, cv. Record and cv. Desiree, grown under the same conditions. Data were analyzed using targeted compositional analyses (207). An analysis of variance (ANOVA) for the major consensus nutrient compounds, recommended by the Organization of Economic Cooperation and Development (171) as being appropriate for safety assessment of novel foods, was conducted and no consistent differences, outside normal variation, were found among the tubers.

Extensive nutritional equivalence studies of Roundup Ready® soybeans have been conducted. These studies include analyses of protein, oil, fiber, carbohydrate, ash, and moisture content and the amino acid and fatty acid composition in both seeds and toasted soybean meal; the values were compared with those from conventional soybeans. Special attention was given to levels of antinutrients and phytonutrients typical for soybeans, e.g., trypsin inhibitors, lectins, and isoflavones (172). One significant difference was detected in defatted, nontoasted soybean meal, the starting material for the production of commercially utilized soybean protein. The variation was in trypsin inhibitor levels, which were 11%–26% higher in GE soybeans than in wild-type. However, levels in seeds and defatted, toasted soybean meal, the form used in foods, were similar for all lines. The results demonstrated that the composition of these GE lines is equivalent to that of conventional soybean cultivars in the form consumed by humans. Equivalence of the feeding value of this GE soy was also demonstrated by feeding it to rats, chicken, catfish, and dairy cattle (100). A broader study using Bt corn and Roundup Ready® corn and soybean to look at composition, digestibility, and feeding value for sheep, chickens, and beef and dairy cattle concluded that seeds of the GE varieties were substantially equivalent to seeds from isolines of non-GE varieties (46).

A 1999 study of nutritional equivalence by Lappé and others (135), often cited by those concerned about GE crops, showed that Roundup Ready® soybeans had reduced levels of isoflavones, notably genistin and daidzin, and thus had significant implications for human health given the potential positive health benefits of the two compounds. The American Soybean Association published a response to this study indicating the variation in phytoestrogen levels was within the limits of variability for conventional soybean varieties (1). In fact, not all comparisons in the Lappé study of the two compounds in conventional versus transgenic varieties showed reduced levels; some showed significant increases (128, table 1). Another phytoestrogen, glycitin, showed significant decreases in only two of seven samples. These results underscore the variability of phytoestrogen levels from sample to sample. A premise of the Lappé study (128) was that other studies on Roundup Ready® soybean used seeds from non-herbicide-treated plants and this raised concerns on the basis of preliminary data from *Phaseolus* that herbicide treatment might generate increased levels of phytoestrogens (198). However, the original 1999 study on Roundup Ready® soybean safety was performed on seed from herbicide-treated plants and no differences in phytoestrogen levels were observed (229).

It is important to note that genetic engineering can purposefully be used to change the nutritional profiles of foods. In these cases studies similar to those described above would be conducted; the mandate for substantial equivalence would apply only to compounds unrelated to the introduced trait. Examples of such foods include those with increased β-carotene (173, 254), flavinoids (53, 189), calcium (174), folate (54), and iron availability (57) (See section 2.9). According to FDA policy, GE foods with altered nutritional traits must be labeled to indicate nutritional differences; one example is Vistive™, a low-linoleic oil from GE soybeans that can be used instead of trans fat–containing oils (157).

3.7. Is the Bt Protein Safe for Human Consumption?

Bt proteins, naturally occurring insecticides produced by the soil bacterium, *B. thuringiensis*, have been used to control crop pests since the 1920s (89), generally as microbial products. Many strains of *B. thuringiensis* exist that produce different Bt proteins varying in the insects they target, e.g., larvae of butterflies and moths, beetles, and mosquitoes. The insecticidal Bt proteins form crystalline protein bodies inside the bacterium, hence the name Cry proteins. Full-sized Cry proteins are inactive until eaten by target insect larva, and inside the midgut they are cleaved and become active. The smaller, active peptides bind to specialized receptors, creating holes in the gut membrane that cause contents to leak and kill the larvae. The precision of different Bt proteins for their targets resides in the specificity of their tight binding to companion receptors in the insect gut (70).

Bt microbial products have a long history of safe use (~40 years) with only two reports prior to 1995 of possible adverse human effects, neither of which was due to exposure to Cry proteins (149). In a 1991 study that focused on exposure via inhalation of Bt sprays, results showed immune responses and skin sensitization to Bt in 2 of 123 farm workers (21). In a 2006 article, the Organic Consumers Association linked this observation to possible impacts of Bt in GE foods, warning that "Bt crops threaten public health" (38). But the respiratory sensitization observed in the farm workers does not provide validation that oral exposure to Bt would result in allergic responses.

In recent years a variety of safety studies were conducted specifically on native Bt proteins to show that they do not have characteristics of food allergens or toxins (See 64, 70, and 152 for reviews). In its review of Bt proteins, the EPA stated that, "several types of data are required for Bt plant pesticides to provide a reasonable certainty that no harm will result from the aggregate exposure of these proteins." The data must show that Bt proteins "behave as would be expected of a dietary protein, are not structurally related to any known food allergen or protein toxin, and do not display any oral toxicity when administered at high doses" (64). The EPA does not require long-term studies because the protein's instability in digestive fluids makes such studies meaningless in terms of consumer health (206). In vitro digestion assays were used to confirm degradation characteristics of Bt proteins, whereas murine feeding studies were used to assess acute oral toxicity (22, 64). Data on *Cry1Ab* in maize and cotton and *Cry1Ac* in tomato, maize, and cotton have been carefully reviewed by regulatory agencies in numerous countries, including the U.S., Canada, Japan, U.K., E.U., Russia, and South Africa (4).

The possibility for allergenic effects of four maize Bt varieties was specifically investigated in potentially sensitive populations (16). Skin prick tests were performed with protein extracts from MON810, Bt11, T25, and Bt176 and from nontransgenic control samples in two sensitive groups: children with food and inhalant allergies and individuals with asthma-rhinitis. Immunoglobulin E immunoblot reactivity of sera from patients with food allergies was tested versus Bt maize and pure Cry1Ab protein. No individual reacted differently to transgenic and nontransgenic samples; none had detectable IgE antibodies against pure transgenic proteins.

A truncated version of the full-length 131-kDa Bt protein, containing only the insect-toxic fragment, is used to engineer some crops. For example, Mon810 maize contains a truncated *cry1Ab* gene that codes for a 91-kDa protein. The potential for mammalian toxicity of the truncated protein was assessed by administering purified, truncated Cry1Ab protein from *E. coli* to groups of ten male and female CD-1 mice at $\leq$4000 mg/kg body weight (2). These doses represented a 200–1000-fold excess over the exposure level predicted on the basis of human consumption of MON810 grain. Mice were observed up to 9 days after dosing; no treatment-related effects on body weight, food consumption, survival, or gross pathology upon necropsy were observed for mice administered Cry1Ab truncated protein.

Despite extensive evaluations of Bt food safety, in June 2005 a Greenpeace press release, published in the *New York Times* and other international newspapers, stated, "There are strong warning signs that this GE Bt rice could cause allergenic reactions, as it did when tested on mice based on a study (158) and references therein". However, in the Moreno-Fierros study (158) referred to in the press release, *Cry1Ac* was being tested as an oral adjuvant to boost vaccine titers. As such, the protein was used in large amounts and the stomach pH was raised to prevent degradation of Cry1Ac. It had been chosen as an adjuvant precisely because it is nontoxic to vertebrates (193).

The native Cry9c, a protein effective against lepidopteran insects, was engineered into a variety of corn called Starlink™. Researchers knew the Cry9C protein did not originate from an allergenic source and had no amino acid homology with known toxins or allergens in available protein databases. However, when Starlink™ corn was created, the Cry9C protein had no history of human dietary exposure, and in addition it was not readily digestible and was stable at 90°C (62), both hallmarks of certain allergens (See section 3.9); Cry9C also had biochemical characteristics that differentiated it from other previously reviewed Cry proteins (63). To determine with reasonable certainty that no harm would result from human exposure to this protein, it was necessary for the EPA to determine if proteins with these biochemical characteristics were likely to affect the safety of a food. Because it was slow to digest, it provided longer lasting protection against insect damage, but the altered digestibility characteristics in humans and its relative stability to heat caused regulators to delay approval of the crop for human consumption (although it was approved for animals) so that they could reexamine its potential as a human allergen (See section 3.9).

A positive aspect of safety regarding Bt corn is the lower levels of mycotoxins compared with non-Bt corn. Mycotoxins are toxic and carcinogenic chemicals produced as secondary metabolites of fungal colonization (252) that occur as a result of insects such as the corn earworm carrying the mycotoxin-containing fungi that infest the kernels following wounding. In some cases, the reduction of mycotoxins in Bt corn results in a positive economic impact on U.S. domestic and international markets. More importantly, in less-developed countries certain mycotoxins are significant contaminants of food and their reduction in Bt corn could improve human and animal health.

In 2002, APHIS announced the deregulation of a corn variety, Mon 863, with increased rootworm (*Diabrotica* spp.) resistance. Food safety assessments by the company used 90-day mouse feeding trials to demonstrate safety (156); independent assessments also demonstrated the safety of Mon 863 (94, 109, 228). Mon 863 contains a variant Cry3Bb1 with seven amino acid differences from wild-type Cry3Bb1 to enhance plant expression and insecticidal activity against corn rootworm (3). A 2007 paper (203) contained a statistical reanalysis of the original data that was different from the earlier risk assessment analyses, which caused the authors to conclude that "with the present data it cannot be concluded that GM corn MON 863 is a safe product." After the 2007 peer-reviewed publication, the European Commission requested the European Food Safety Authority (EFSA) to determine what impact the reanalysis had on their earlier decision. The EFSA concluded that the reanalysis did not raise new safety concerns (67).

3.8. Have Allergens Been Introduced into Foods Through Genetic Engineering?

The use of genetic engineering to introduce genes into an organism raises the possibility of the introduction of allergens. Under the FDA's biotechnology food policy, GE foods must be labeled if the source of the gene is one of the common allergy-causing foods [e.g., cow's milk, eggs, fish and shellfish, tree nuts, wheat, soybeans, and especially peanuts (47)], unless the gene product is proven not to be allergenic through additional safety testing. Although not mandatory, to date all companies marketing new GE foods have consulted with the FDA and performed recommended analyses to determine if introduced proteins have properties that indicate possible allergenicity, i.e., similarities to known allergens, small size, slow digestibility, and/or high heat stability (230). Although there are exceptions in each category, these characteristics indicate the protein might be allergenic and therefore merits further study.

One example of an introduced allergen that was forestalled by this process was the attempt to engineer soybean with a Brazil nut protein, the methionine-rich 2S albumin, to improve soy protein's deficiency in the essential amino acid, methionine. Attempts to manipulate this nutrient through traditional breeding had failed because of lower yields or grain quality. In the development of the GE soybean researchers recognized that allergies to nuts are among the most common types of allergies and allergies specific to Brazil nut had been documented (14). Therefore, testing of the new soybeans for allergenicity was conducted in university and industrial labs during product development. Sera from people allergic to Brazil nut reacted with the new soybean (166), so development of the new soybean was halted and it was never marketed.

Foods can also be engineered to remove offending allergens to create, for example, more hypoallergenic foods (See section 3.11).

3.9. Were Foods Made From Bt Corn Removed from the Market Because of Allergenicity Concerns?

An example of a commercialized GE crop that was recalled owing to concerns about allergenicity is Starlink™ corn, a variety engineered to express the Bt *Cry9C* protein (See section 3.7). The EPA did not approve use of StarLink™ corn for for human consumption; animal consumption was approved because farm animals do not have food allergies. The concern was that the Cry9c protein shared several molecular properties with proteins that are known food allergens (39)—namely, increased heat stability and slower digestibility characteristics. While additional testing was being conducted to determine human safety, Starlink^{TM} entered the human food supply because of problems encountered with segregating feed and food corn. As a result, the FDA issued a recall of numerous food products containing Starlink^{TM} corn.

In October 2000 the FDA asked the Centers for Disease Control and Prevention (CDCP) to investigate 51 reports of human illness that individuals claimed were related to consumption of products containing Starlink^{TM} corn. Of the 51 reports, 28 described symptoms consistent with a possible allergic reaction to corn products. Blood serum samples from 17 patients were tested using an enzyme-linked immunosorbent assay (ELISA) to detect antibodies to the Bt protein. The CDCP study (39) concluded that Starlink^{TM}-specific antibodies were not detected in those human sera; however, the study was not conclusive for two reasons. First, food allergies can occur in individuals even if they have no detectable allergy-specific antibodies that bind to the allergen (170). Second, the source of the protein to make antibodies was of bacterial origin, not plant, and this could have changed the conformational shape of the protein, compromising the ability of the antibodies to recognize the plant-made protein. However, researchers analyzed the corn-containing foods consumed by 10 of the 17 test subjects who reported allergic reactions. Detection of Bt protein was negative in 9 of 10 samples; the tenth was inconclusive (74)

Taken together, these results suggest that the Bt protein in Starlink^{TM} was not involved in the allergic reactions of the 17 individuals tested. But uncertainty still exists because blood and food samples were not received from all 28 individuals who experienced a true allergic reaction. In separate studies, an EPA scientific advisory panel concluded that the Bt in Starlink^{TM} had a moderate chance to cause allergies, on the basis of its biochemical nature. But the level of its presence in food at that time was low; Starlink corn represented between 0.4–0.5% of U.S. corn production (202) and levels of protein also influence its potential for allergenicity (73). Starlink^{TM} corn was removed from the market in 2000 and, on the basis of USDA monitoring, the food supply is now 99.99% Starlink-free (242) and Starlink^{TM} corn therefore is not currently likely to cause allergy-related problems.

3.10. Do Only Genetically Engineered Foods Cause Food Allergies?

Allergies are present in conventional foods such as milk, eggs, fish, shellfish, tree nuts, soybeans, wheat, and peanuts, termed the "big eight"—the foods that are the major allergen sources for adults and children in the U.S. Another example of a conventionally bred food, not considered to be allergenic when introduced in the U.S. in the 1960s but now known to cause allergenic responses, is the kiwi (*Actinidia arguta*). No allergenicity testing or screening was conducted on the fruit when introduced; however, today kiwi is known to cause allergic reactions (222), some of them lethal due to cross allergies with latex (245). This raises the question of how much testing introduced foods, GE or classically bred, should undergo in the U.S. before being offered to consumers.

Given that food safety testing conducted on GE foods focuses on the introduced gene and its protein product (See section 3.4), it seems unlikely that allergenicity issues related to a commercialized GE food that has undergone FDA scrutiny will be greater than that of conventional foods, created by classical breeding and mutation, that have not undergone such scrutiny (50). Does this mean GE foods are 100% safe? No, a statement that a food is 100% safe cannot be made about any food—be it conventional, GE, or organic. For example, a peanut—whether grown conventionally or organically, whether GE or non-GE—can cause severe allergies in sensitive individuals (178).

CaMV: cauliflower mosaic virus

3.11. Can Genetically Engineered Foods Have Fewer Allergens than Non-GE Foods?

On the basis of data from the third National Health and Nutrition Examination Survey (160), 54.3% of individuals aged 6–59 had a positive skin test to at least one of the ten allergens tested (12). The highest prevalence was for dust mite, rye, ragweed, and cockroach; approximately 25% of the population tested positive to each allergen. Peanut allergy was the least common—only 9% of the population—but it is one of the most severe and durable allergies. Other food allergies include those to milk, eggs, fish, shellfish, tree nuts, soybeans, and wheat (See section 3.10). The nature of the proteins causing these allergic reactions is well characterized in certain cases, thus making it is possible to engineer the organism to make lower levels of the proteins responsible for the allergies or change their conformation to reduce allergic responses (33). Reported successful examples of engineering approaches that reduce allergenicity include those aimed at grass pollen (24, 25) and foods such as wheat (34, 35), rice (224), and peanuts (*Arachis hypogaea*) (219).

3.12. Do Viral Sequences Used in Plant Genetic Engineering Create a Human Health Risk?

Introduced transgenes are regulated by promoter sequences that determine how much, where, and when the encoded protein is expressed. The 35S promoter from the cauliflower mosaic virus (CaMV) (168) was used in some commercial GE crops, e.g., Bt11, Bt176, Mon810 maize, and Roundup Ready® soybean (4). This promoter was used to obtain strong expression of the linked gene throughout the plant (19). In other GE crops such as high laurate canola, a native promoter (*Brassica napin* storage protein promoter) led to expression of the California laurel (*Umbellularia californica*) thioesterase in embryos, but not in leaves or pollen (187).

It has been claimed that the 35S promoter may be unstable and prone to transfer and insertion into DNA of other cells, on the basis of a recombinational hotspot in the promoter (104). This theory led to claims that use of the 35S and other viral promoters in GE crops might increase human cancer rates by activating nonviral genes in the species into which it was transferred (humans) by horizontal transfer. Although not based on direct scientific experimentation, Stanley Ewen, who collaborated with A. Pusztai on the snowdrop lectin studies in potato (69), speculated that the CaMV promoter "could affect stomach and colonic lining by causing a growth factor effect with the unproven possibility of hastening cancer formation in those organs" (212).

These speculations have been extensively rebutted by the scientific community, as summarized in 105. One major thrust of the rebuttals is that the 35S promoter is ubiquitous in nature. In the U.K. an estimated ~14–25% of oilseed rape in the field is infected with CaMV (101); similar numbers have been estimated for cauliflower and cabbage. Because of its prevalence in foods, humans have consumed CaMV and its promoter at high levels for decades with no observable effects. The presence of the CaMV promoter in GE plants does not in principle present a different situation. Additionally, DNA in food is rapidly broken down during digestion, giving it little time to interact with the stomach and colonic linings (See section 3.5).

A documented issue with this promoter in the laboratory is that it can become inactivated if CaMV infects the GE plant with a CaMV-driven transgene. This inactivation was demonstrated when CaMV-driven herbicide resistance in oilseed rape was compromised, causing the virally infected plants to become susceptible to the herbicide (5). Although not related to human safety, this situation should be carefully monitored in the field to avoid unexpected situations. At present other promoters that are not derived from plant viruses are being used in GE plants (45, 183, 247).

3.13. Can Genetically Engineered Foods Increase Antibiotic Resistance in Human and Animal Intestinal Flora?

The frequency of resistance to antibiotics in bacteria and the numbers of drugs to which they are resistant is increasing. Several factors have been suggested as exacerbating this problem (163). One potential causative factor is the widespread use of antibiotics in human therapy (90, 119). Another potential causative factor is the subtherapeutic use of antibiotics for growth promotion in farm animals (41, 138, 216). In a 2007 report on levels of antibiotics in the manure of animals fed antibiotics, data were presented on the passage of antibiotics to foods, especially root crops, when manure was used as fertilizer (56). This is of potential importance to all farmers who utilize animal manure as a primary source of fertilizer.

Antibiotic-resistance genes—sometimes used as markers to identify GE plant cells that receive transgenes—might add to the problem of antibiotic-resistant bacteria. For marker genes in GE foods to increase antibiotic resistance in humans or animals, they must be transferred to bacteria in the respective digestive tracts. Functional transfer of plant DNA into microorganisms is directly impacted by intactness of DNA. Complete transfer of the antibiotic resistance gene, and possibly its controlling elements, and its integration in the bacterial chromosome must occur to make a bacterium antibiotic-resistant.

During chewing, cells in food are broken down. As cells are destroyed, DNA is released and highly active enzymes in saliva and in the plant start degrading DNA (153)—a process that continues in the digestive tract, where other enzymes further break down DNA and proteins (See section 3.5). In mouse studies, fragments but not intact pieces of M13mp18 DNA were found in 0.1% of white blood cells and spleen or liver cells at 2–24 h after feeding, but not later (201). In humans, foods remain in the stomach for ~2 h, where the remaining DNA is fragmented into small pieces. To demonstrate the fate of transgene DNA in humans, the antibiotic resistance gene from GE maize was shown not to transfer to gut bacteria in chickens fed GE maize (48).

Although GE crops are not likely to be significant factors in increasing the incidence of antibiotic-resistant bacteria, new selection strategies for identifying engineered plants were developed, in part as a response to public concerns, and these offer alternatives to the use of antibiotic resistance genes as selectable markers. These approaches include genes such as phosphomannose and xylose isomerase that facilitate selection by giving transgenic cells a metabolic advantage over nontransgenic cells (180). Also, means exist to segregate marker genes so they do not remain in the commercial product (128, 258). An *Agrobacterium*-mediated method is available that uses plant-derived transfer DNA and a novel transient selection system that can result in only native DNA in GE plants (194).

3.14. Can Genetically Engineered Food Crops Be Used to Make Pharmaceuticals? Could They Contaminate the Food Supply?

In the early 1990s, efforts were made to evaluate the effectiveness of plants and foods to deliver pharmaceuticals, particularly vaccines. These efforts involved using tobacco to express a bacterial surface protein to prevent dental caries and to express the hepatitis B surface antigen (52, 147). Since then, maize, potato, rice, soybean, and tomato have been used to produce vaccines for both humans and animals (177). These include subunit vaccines against pneumonic and bubonic plague, shown to be immunogenic in mice (6); a potato-based vaccine for hepatitis B that raises an immunological response in humans (233); a GE pollen vaccine that reduces symptoms in allergy sufferers (164); and an edible rice-based vaccine targeted to allergic diseases such as asthma, seasonal allergies, and atopic dermatitis (225) (See section 2.9).

Plant vaccines have the advantage of being readily consumed with limited or no processing and of obviating the need for cold storage, clear advantages in developing countries. However, with this ease of delivery comes the possibility that such products could enter the food supply if food crops are engineered. Under U.S. regulations, GE plants containing pharmaceutical or industrial products are not permitted to enter the food supply. The FDA prohibits "adulterated" foods in the supply chain, including foods from GE crops that might contain potentially harmful proteins (81). APHIS, which regulates the movement and field testing of GE plants (See section 3.6), requires special steps to prevent plants that produce drugs or industrial enzymes from contaminating food crops: *i*) labeling, packaging, and segregating regulated plant materials; *ii*) reproductive isolation to prevent GE pollen from fertilizing conventional plants; *iii*) postharvest monitoring to remove volunteer plants; and (*iv*) proper disposal of the transgenic material.

In 2005 these rules were tightened to include the following: *i*) exclude field growth without a permit; *ii*) include crop inspections seven times/year, twice after harvest; *iii*) increase field isolation distances; and *iv*) use dedicated farm equipment (9). This tightening resulted from early violations of field-testing permits. For example, in two cases regulators found volunteer engineered corn plants producing a pharmaceutical protein (8) that had tassled in a soybean field.

Cases like these demonstrate that "pharming" in food plants can result in mixing with food. The Grocery Manufacturers of America urged the USDA to restrict plant-made pharmaceutical production to nonfood crops (96). The National Corn Growers Association countered by proposing safeguards such as *i*) using plants that are male-sterile or that produce non-GE pollen, *ii*) dedicated production systems that isolate pharma crops, *iii*) third-party verification, and *iv*) grower training programs (159). In September 2002, the FDA released a guidance document that recommends multiple strategies to prevent pharma crops from contaminating human or animal feed (79). This document suggests that those who are growing drug-producing plants that cross pollinate, such as corn and canola, strengthen containment procedures by growing plants in geographical regions where little or none of that crop is grown for food. Following this strategy, Ventria, a company that developed self-pollinating rice engineered to produce human lysostaphin and lysozyme to shorten the duration of childhood diarrhea, relocated their fields from their home rice-growing state, California, to Kansas, where commercial rice is not grown (87).

3.15. Why Doesn't the FDA Require Labeling of Genetically Engineered Foods?

The FDA's labeling policy for GE foods is the same as for conventional foods and it assures that consumers are given information about nutritional, health safety, or food quality changes in the end product. FDA-mandated labels are not used to provide information about the process by which the food is made. If a GE food is significantly different from its conventional counterpart, the food must be labeled to indicate the difference. Instances where the nutritional profile changes are included, for example if the GE food is created using genetic information from a previously recognized allergenic source, such as peanut, soy, or wheat, or if the new protein has characteristics of known allergens. For example, oils made from GE soybean and canola varieties with changes in fatty acid composition must be labeled; foods containing those oils must be labeled and companies producing that oil must use a new name. For example, Monsanto is using the name Vistive™ to market its low–linoleic acid product from GE soybean oils (157). If a food contains a new, potentially allergy-causing introduced protein, the label must state that the product contains the allergen and name its source.

3.16. Are Organic Foods Healthier or Safer?

Organic farming is a method of agricultural production that does not allow the use of synthetic pesticides, fertilizers, or growth enhancers. Foods grown under organic certification differ from conventionally produced food by the manner in which they are grown, handled, and processed, but an "organic" label does not guarantee the nature of the product, the food, or ingredient, only its production method. The important factors for many people who consume organic foods relate to the perceptions that they are healthier, taste better, are better for the environment, have lower pesticide levels and fewer food additives, and are better for animal welfare (214). However, organic certification does not imply that foods produced using organic methods are more nutritious or safer than those produced without organic methods (195).

A 2007 review by the British Nutrition Foundation stated, "There appears to be a perception among many consumers that organic foods are more nutritious and therefore healthier than conventionally produced foods. However, to date there are limited data to support this view" (248). This perception has led in part to increases in the world market for certified organic foods to ~$34 billion in 2005 (111). A 2007 poll showed that 57% of polled consumers strongly believed that science had proven that organic food was healthier than conventional (182, figure 17). Because of the paucity of scientific data, the UK Food Standards Agency decided in October 2007 to seek a contractor who will evaluate relevant studies and compare the nutrient and non-nutrient content of organic and conventional foods to determine if any compositional differences have nutritional or other health effects in the context of the complete diet (86).

In general, only a small number of peer-reviewed studies exist that analyze nutritional differences between foods produced conventionally and organically. Although statistically significant differences have been observed for a limited number of metabolites for a few foods grown under differing environmental conditions using conventional and organic production systems, more research is required to determine if any of these differences have actual health-promoting effects. Some examples of such studies follow.

i. Zörb and colleagues (260) looked at the profiles of 44 metabolites in wheat grown under comparable organic and conventional conditions as a part of a long-term biodynamic, bioorganic, and conventional farming system in Switzerland. Statistical analyses of data, obtained with high-throughput gas chromatography-mass spectrometry, showed that metabolite status of wheat grain from organic and conventional farming did not differ in the levels of 44 metabolites, which indicates low or no impact of farming systems on wheat metabolite composition.

ii. Another study found increases in vitamin C in organically grown kiwifruit compared with conventionally grown fruits, both before and after storage. Postharvest performance was measured for both types of kiwifruit, grown on the same farm and harvested at the same maturity stage (7). Total phenolics and antioxidant activity were also higher in organic fruit.

iii. In tomatoes, levels of the flavonoids quercitin and kaempferol aglycones in archived samples of organically produced tomatoes, grown from 1994–2004 in the Long-Term Research on Agricultural Systems project at University of California, Davis, were at statistically higher levels than those grown in the same tract using conventional production practices (155). Flavonoid levels increased over time in the tomatoes grown organically, but not in those grown conventionally.

iv. Increases in total antioxidant activity were also found in a 2005 study of red oranges (*Citrus aurantium*). Organic oranges had significantly higher total phenolics, total anthocyanins and ascorbic acid levels, and total antioxidant activity versus corresponding nonorganic oranges (227). Four lots of fruits, purchased from certified producers grown under statutory European Community regulations at the same time of year, were analyzed; however, no assurances were given that the two sources of oranges were grown under comparable environmental conditions. Also, no indications of the natural variation in these phytonutrients were given for comparison.

v. There are "moderately strong and consistent data showing that organic potatoes are richer sources of vitamin C than their conventionally grown counterparts"; no studies have shown lower levels of vitamin C in organic potatoes (248).

Several studies of nutritional differences between organically and conventionally produced dairy products have been reported.

i. Several small-scale studies reported different conclusions when comparing the effects of farming systems on the content in milk of conjugated linoleic acid content, known for its health-promoting effects (cited in 60).

ii. In one large-scale study a higher proportion of polyunsaturated fatty acids and n-3 fatty acids relative to monounsaturated fatty acids was observed in milk from cows raised under organic production methods, compared with those that were conventionally raised (60). No differences were seen in the proportion of conjugated linoleic acid or vaccenic acid, but factors other than farming systems, e.g., time of year, breed, type of feed, and access to fresh grazing, are known to affect the fatty acid content of milk.

iii. A 2007 study conducted on 312 breast-feeding mothers demonstrated that mothers' milk from women eating a diet that consisted of 89% or more of organic dairy and meat products was measurably higher in conjugated linoleic acid (192).

iv. Kuhnert and coworkers (131) looked at the incidence of *E. coli*, particularly Shiga toxigenic and 0157:H7 strains, in milk. Although levels were relatively high in cattle feces, no differences in prevalence of the two types of organisms in milk were found between those raised using organic practices versus conventional farming systems.

Differences reported in nutrient composition between organically and conventionally produced foods are interesting but, as seen in the examples given, it is very difficult to control all variables that might affect nutritional quality and ensure that the observed variations are significant and reproducible. In addition, there are many important nutrients for which no significant differences have been found. For example, in milk no significant differences have been reported in other major nutrients such as calcium, zinc, vitamin B2, or vitamin B12 (248). Much more research is needed to determine whether the nutritional differences observed between organic and conventional food products are reproducible and have a significant impact on human health.

One notable difference between conventional and organic production methods, which may be perceived by consumers as healthier, is the ban on the use of synthetic pesticides in organic agriculture. Synthetic pesticides can only be used in organic farming when an efficacious, natural version is not available and no organic substitutes exist. Lists of chemicals approved for organic agriculture are available (162). With regard to this aspect of food safety of organics, very little peer-reviewed research has been conducted. A small-scale study looked at levels of certain pesticides in children's urine following consumption of conventional and organic foods. Researchers looked at contributions of daily dietary pesticide intake on overall pesticide exposure during a 15-day period in 23 children, aged 3–11 (142). Children ate conventional foods on days 1–3 and 9–15 and organic foods on days 4–8; attempts were made to substitute comparable food items so as not to change their diets. Analysis of urine specimens collected twice daily showed that concentrations of the organophosphate pesticides malathion and chlorpyrifos decreased to undetectable levels immediately after organic diets were consumed and remained undetectable until conventional diets resumed. However, no direct determinations of levels of organophosphates in the foods were carried out and it was not stated whether the already low levels of organophosphates in the conventional foods would have adverse impacts on health.

Strictly from a nutritional perspective not enough data exist at present to show nutritional benefits from conventionally or organically produced foods that favors consuming either for health benefits. However, if the goal is to promote healthy eating, it is more important for consumers to focus on eating a healthy, balanced diet, rich in fruits and vegetables, than focusing on foods that are produced by particular methods. Convincing epidemiological evidence shows that diets rich in fresh fruits and vegetables, regardless of the methods used to produce them, improve health and are associated with reduced frequency and severity of a number of health conditions (191).

3.17. Should Genetically Engineered Crops and Foods Be Banned Until They Are Proven to Be 100% Safe?

Acceptance of the new GE foods depends on several factors, including perception of risk and benefit, assurance of safety, and one's own values. Nearly everything in our technologically complex world comes with risks. The introduction of the automobile, hybrid crops, margarine, pasteurized milk, and vaccines all came with attendant risks. Only after individuals gained experience with these new products did they become comfortable with choosing those products for which the benefits for them outweighed the risks.

The first GE crops to be released commercially benefited farmers, the companies that produced them, and in some cases the environment, but consumers saw little benefit. In the development pipeline are GE crops and foods that might be attractive to consumers and have greater benefit for the environment (See section 2.9), but benefits realized depend on which products are developed, how they are deployed, and how different individuals value them. Potential advantages from GE crops and foods could be substantial in terms of the environment and human health. In fact, continuing to deplete our resources as we do now is likely to be more harmful than making the best possible use of all available technologies (31).

The second factor relating to acceptance of GE food has to do with assurance of safety. GE foods that make it to the market go through extensive safety testing, the data from which are reviewed by the USDA, FDA, and/or EPA (See sections 2.6 and 3.4). GE foods cannot be guaranteed to be 100% safe, just as foods created by conventional breeding or grown using conventional or organic practices cannot be guaranteed to be completely safe (15). Given that safety testing of GE foods focuses on the introduced gene and its product and a determination of substantial equivalence, food safety issues with a commercialized GE food that are greater than those experienced with conventionally modified foods are unlikely to arise (50).

The third factor relating to acceptance of GE foods has to do with individual values. This aspect cannot be addressed with scientific data.

3.18. Are Milk and Meat from Cloned Cows Safe to Eat?

bGH: bovine growth hormone

IGF-I: insulin-like growth factor I

rbGH: recombinant bovine growth hormone

A clone of an organism is genetically identical to a single common ancestor. Cloning of animals can be achieved by splitting an early-stage multicellular embryo to create twins; the first split-embryo calves were produced in 1981. Clones are also produced by nuclear transfer, in which DNA from the nucleus of one cell is introduced into a recipient unfertilized egg from which the nucleus was removed (223). Nuclear transfer has been performed successfully since the mid-1980s, but Dolly the sheep was different—she represented the first successful nuclear transfer to an adult cell (249). Since then, several adult tissues have been used to produce clones of cattle, pigs, horses, cats, rabbits, goats, and fish (59). Cloning animals is one of many methods used to assist animal reproduction (154).

One of the food safety issues raised regarding consumption of food from cloned animals is whether the process causes changes in the composition of food derived from the animal. The Center of Veterinary Medicine in the FDA has the responsibility to evaluate food safety and animal health issues. In their draft risk assessment of the safety of food from cloned animals, they state it is "highly unlikely that 'silent' pathways producing intrinsic toxicants exist in food animals" and that the only hazards that could arise "would be from incomplete or inappropriate reprogramming of the genetic information from the donor somatic nucleus (i.e., epigenetic effects)" (80). With regard to compositional differences in meat from cloned cows, numerous studies found no obvious differences in milk or meat (167, 226, 235, 236, 246). The FDA draft risk assessment on livestock cloning states, "the current weight of evidence suggests that there are no biological reasons, either based on underlying scientific assumptions or empirical studies, to indicate that consumption of edible products from clones of cattle, pigs, sheep or goats poses a greater risk than consumption of those products from their non-clone counterparts" (80).

3.19. Is Milk from rbGH-Injected Cows Safe? Why Isn't It Labeled?

Bovine growth hormone (bGH), also called bovine somatotropin (bST), is unrelated to steroid hormones. bGH, produced in the pituitary glands of dairy cows, is a naturally occurring protein hormone in milk, which stimulates the liver to produce insulin-like growth factor-I (IGF-I). The structure of human somatotropin differs from bGH, and the latter is not biologically active in humans (176). Upon pasteurization, 90% of bGH is destroyed; digestive enzymes degrade the remainder. Other growth factors in milk (e.g., the cytokines IL-1 and IL-2), though sometimes slightly elevated in milk from bGH-injected cows, are inactive in other mammals (122).

Since the late 1920s it was known that lactating mammals produce more milk when treated with extracts of the pituitary hormone bGH, but because that hormone could only be isolated from the pituitary glands of slaughtered cattle, bGH was not available in sufficient quantities for commercial use in the dairy industry (37). Sufficient quantities were made available when a synthetic gene for bGH was inserted into a bacterium to produce recombinant bGH (rbGH or rbST), which is chemically identical to bGH. When rbGH is injected into cows, the efficiency of conversion of feed to milk is increased and milk yields can be increased by 15% to 20% (17, 55). Trace amounts of bGH is found in all milk; cows given rbGH contain no more bGH than unsupplemented cows (122). Published data indicate that the use of rbGH to increase milk production does not impact its nutritional quality.

Extensive studies of rbGH safety have been conducted worldwide and reviewed by the FDA, after which both milk and meat from rbGH-injected cows were deemed safe (78). Separate reviews of the data by the National Institutes of Health, the World Health Organization, the Office of the Inspector General of the Department of Health and Human Services, and reviews by the Journal of the American Medical Association and the Journal of the American Dietetic Association all independently concluded that milk from rbGH-injected cows is safe.

Despite these safety assurances, claims were made as recently as 2001 (66) that milk from rbGH-treated cows contains elevated levels of IGF-I, a protein hormone normally present in milk (44). An elevated content of IGF-I has been suggested to have adverse implications for human health and cancer frequency. Comparisons of marketed milk indicate that there are no differences in IGF-I concentrations between milk derived from cows treated or not with rbGH (240), and levels are within the limits of natural variation (for review, see 85). In fact, IGF-I levels in human breast milk and saliva are higher than in cow's milk. Additionally, IGF-I is digested as other food proteins are and is inactive when consumed (for review, see 85). IGF-I content of milk from rbGH-treated cows has been extensively reviewed and its safety confirmed (78, 97, 240).

The FDA concluded that the use of rbGH in dairy cattle presents no confirmed health risks to consumers and the milk is substantially equivalent to milk from cows not treated with rbGH (See section 3.4). However, aside from safety issues, some consumers view the use of rbGH to increase milk production as "unnatural" and this has been promoted as a reason to oppose milk from cows injected with rbGH (37). This perspective led some dairies to voluntarily, although not legally, label milk as being from cows not injected with rbGH, even though FDA labeling policy for foods produced from GE ingredients (which is the same as for all other foods and food ingredients) specifies no label is needed if the food is substantially equivalent to non-GE foods in safety, composition, and nutrition. Of note, in January 2008, the Pennsylvania Department of Agriculture issued a new labeling standard indicating that milk could be labeled as coming from cows not treated with rbGH as long as the labeling was uniform (179).

Outside the U.S., countries that are signatories to the World Trade Organization cannot bar milk from cows injected with rbGH based solely on its production method, unless there is scientific evidence that it affects human health or safety (37). But the E.U. has been staunch in its opposition to such milk in part due to consumer concerns that arose in the 1990s as a result of certain food safety outbreaks, such as bovine spongiform encephalopathy (32), that were not effectively handled by existing regulatory systems. In 1999 the E.U. decided not to approve sales of milk from rbGH-treated cows in E.U. member countries, based not on human health concerns but on animal welfare issues (51). Today milk and milk products from rbGH-treated cows are recognized as safe in the E.U. and can be marketed in E.U. countries (49, 97), but the use of rbST in their dairy herds is not approved.

With regard to animal health, some studies have reported an increased frequency of mastitis in groups of rbGH-treated cows. This increase has been attributed mainly to increased milk volume in the mammary glands of treated cows and no convincing data are available that show a decrease in secretion of mammary gland immune factors as a result of growth hormone treatments (36). A 1999 study (106) indicated the rbGH can actually provide a protective effect against *Streptococcus uberis* mastitis following experimental infection.

3.20. Can the USDA Stop the Planting of Genetically Engineered Crops that Pose Health or Environmental Risks?

After the commercialization process for a GE crop is complete, including deregulation, all federal regulatory agencies (FDA, EPA, and

USDA) have the legal authority to demand the immediate removal of any product from the marketplace. Removal can be demanded if new, science-based evidence raises questions about consumer or environmental safety (10). A case in point is the rescinding of deregulatory status of Roundup Ready® alfalfa by a U.S. District Court Judge in 2007, on the basis of the lack of a full EIS (112). A concern was that cultivation of GE alfalfa would result in the spread of the Roundup Ready® gene to "natural alfalfa" causing a "significant environmental impact" (121). After a specified date in 2007, farmers were not able to plant Roundup Ready® alfalfa and will have to await more evaluation and approval of the EIS.

Bioavailability: degree to or rate at which substance is absorbed and becomes available for physiological activity

Recommended daily allowance (RDA): amounts of vitamins and minerals to be consumed to maintain good health, specified by the Food and Nutrition Board of the National Research Council

3.21. Is Golden Rice the Only Way to Provide Vitamin A to People in Developing Countries?

Vitamin A deficiency, along with iron and zinc deficiencies, pose the greatest public health consequences of all micronutrient deficiencies. Vitamin A deficiency is most common in young children and pregnant women and can lead to blindness, susceptibility to infectious diseases, and death (251). The Food and Agricultural Organization and the United Nations have developed different strategies to overcome deficiency of vitamin A, including dietary diversification, food fortification, and vitamin supplementation. When applied, there has been varying success in different regions of the developing world with the various approaches, e.g., distribution of vitamin A pills in Nepal (241), the fortification of sugar with vitamin A in Guatemala (13), and gardening projects in Bangladesh and Thailand (239). All these efforts required continuous public education and financial support from the public and private sector. For example, vitamin A fortification of sugar was temporarily suspended owing to an economic downturn that increased vitamin A prices and at that point vitamin A deficiency reappeared (239).

Despite these various efforts, ~250,000 to 500,000 children deficient in vitamin A become blind each year; half of them die within twelve months (250). Recent studies indicate that biofortification, i.e., incorporating micronutrients into food, has the potential to control deficiencies and is cost-effective and efficient compared with alternative public health and agricultural measures when coupled with other micronutrient interventions (220). To develop a biofortification strategy to address vitamin A deficiency, researchers developed the first variety of Golden Rice (GR1), a GE variety with increased levels of β-carotene, a precursor to vitamin A, compared with non-GE rice (254). The rice contained three new genes, two from daffodil (*Narcissus pseudonarcissus*) and one from a bacterium (*Erwinia uredovora*). In 2005 the development of a new Golden Rice variety, GR2, was published; in GR2 a maize gene is substituted for the daffodil genes, boosting β-carotene levels to 37 μg/g—estimated to provide 50% of a child's RDA of vitamin A in 72 g of dry GR2 rice (173). However, the actual impact of this rice also depends on several other variables, e.g., uptake and conversion to vitamin A, amount consumed, bioavailability, effects of cooking, and consumer acceptance (28).

The GR1 and GR2 rice varieties are in use in breeding programs in the Philippines, India, Bangladesh, China, and Vietnam; the use of Golden Rice is being governed by the Golden Rice Humanitarian Board and is based on full regulatory compliance (G. Berry, personal communication). Although perhaps not legally needed, because often no intellectual property restrictions exist in these countries on commonly employed genes [e.g., 35S promoter, hygromycin resistance gene (26)], all companies with patents applying to Golden Rice licensed them at no charge for use in resource-poor countries.

Golden Rice might increase vitamin A sufficiency for people in areas difficult to reach with other vitamin A distribution efforts or for people with limited opportunities to grow or purchase sufficient amounts of fresh vegetables or fruits. Golden Rice will not be the single solution to vitamin A deficiency worldwide, but it is another tool that can be used in public health programs to combat vitamin A deficiency.

4. CONCLUDING REMARKS

Researchers using rDNA methods now have the technology to transfer genes, not only within a species, but also from one kingdom to another. This technology opens the door to changing agricultural crops in ways not previously possible. These changes can result in plants that are better able to survive pest attack and abiotic stresses, can be enhanced nutritionally, or can be used to immunize humans and animals. But, with this capacity to change comes the responsibility to proceed with caution, investigating possible outcomes carefully. Conversely, there is also a responsibility to utilize the technology where it can provide improvements to human health and the environment and make farmers' efforts more productive.

On the basis of the intensive look at the data and the peer-reviewed research in this review, the development of GE crops to date seems to have been responsible and regulatory agencies have, in general, proceeded with caution in releasing GE varieties. Although no human activity can be guaranteed 100% safe, the commercial GE crops and products available today are at least as safe in terms of food safety as those produced by conventional methods. This does not mean we should relax our vigilance in investigating products resulting from this new technology as well as the time-honored methods. But, we should not hold the new GE products to standards not required for food and feed products produced by other technologies and methods.

With the proper balance of caution and scrutiny, we can take advantage of the power of this technology without compromising the health of humans, animals, or the environment. To achieve that proper balance it is important to know the facts about the technology and its products. This is the information that I have attempted to provide in Part I of this review on general and food issues. In Part II, I will cover environmental and socioeconomic issues. In this way, paraphrasing Cardinal Wolsey, I hope that this will help us to be "very, very careful what we put into our heads"!

SUMMARY POINTS

1. Foods consumed today are derived from plants and animals whose genetic makeup has been modified by sexual crosses and mutation. Recombinant DNA provides a new tool to make genetic modifications, and this technology is termed genetic engineering or biotechnology.
2. Technically, researchers are now able to transfer genes using recombinant DNA methods, not only within a species, but also from one kingdom to another, which can lead to significant changes in various attributes of agricultural crops.
3. The safety of genetically engineered crops and foods, just as those created by classical breeding and mutation and grown conventionally or organically, needs to be evaluated on a case-by-case basis so that informed decisions can be made about their utility, safety, and appropriateness.
4. Data and information from peer-reviewed science on the safety of these products should be a part of the information considered when growing and consuming foods from these crops.
5. Factors beyond the technical, science-based facts should also be considered during the decision-making process.

6. Although scientific testing and governmental regulation can reduce the safety risks of conventionally and organically produced and genetically engineered crops and food, 100% safety is not achievable.
7. To date, no scientifically valid demonstrations have shown that food safety issues of foods containing genetically engineered (GE) ingredients are greater than those from conventionally or organically produced foods.
8. In commercial fields only a few crops have been modified using rDNA technologies (i.e., canola, corn, cotton, papaya, squash, and soy), but many others are in development.

FUTURE ISSUES

1. The introduction of pharmaceutical and industrial proteins into edible genetically engineered crops raises issues that require additional safety and regulatory scrutiny.
2. Measures that permit farmers to use their production techniques of choice, while respecting their neighbors' rights to do the same, must be pursued to achieve economic coexistence.
3. Interest in and funding for independent peer-reviewed studies on the food safety of conventional, organic, and GE foods must be encouraged.
4. Rigorous, fact-based governmental regulatory policy should be in place to allow public- and private-sector scientists to play a role in the creation and evaluation of genetically engineered crops.

DISCLOSURE STATEMENT

The author is not aware of any biases that might be perceived as affecting the objectivity of this review.

ACKNOWLEDGMENTS

The author thanks Dr. Wilhelm Gruissem for encouragment fifteen years ago to begin the process of addressing the issues related to agricultural biotechnology in a scholarly manner, linking responses to the peer-reviewed scientific literature. The author also expresses gratitude to Dr. Petra Baettig-Frey for providing the first draft of these efforts—available for the past ten years in the biotechnology information section of **http://ucbiotech.org**. The author is also indebted to the dedication of Ms. Barbara Alonso, who helped in the preparation of this manuscript and has maintained a scientific database that made the writing of this article possible.

LITERATURE CITED

1. Ag BioTech InfoNet. 1999. *ASA response to: "Alterations in clinically important phytoestrogens in genetically modified, herbicide-tolerant soybeans."* **http://www.biotech-info.net/ASA_response.html**

2. AGBIOS. 2005. *Database Product Description: MON-ØØ81Ø-6 (MON810)*. **http://www.agbios.com/dbase.php?action=ShowProd&data=MON810&frmat=LONG**
3. AGBIOS. 2006. *Database Product Description: MON-ØØ863-5 (MON863)*. **http://www.agbios.com/dbase.php?action=ShowProd&data=MON863&frmat=LONG**
4. **AGBIOS. 2007. *GM Crop Database Product Description*. http://agbios.com/dbase.php.**

4. Database for querying safety information on genetically engineered plants and plants with novel traits produced using accelerated mutagenesis and plant breeding.

5. Al-Kaff NS, Kreike MM, Covey SN, Pitcher R, Page AM, Dale PJ. 2000. Plants rendered herbicide-susceptible by cauliflower mosaic virus-elicited suppression of a 35S promoter regulated transgene. *Nat. Biotechnol.* 18:995–99
6. Alvarez ML, Pinyerd HL, Crisantes JD, Rigano MM, Pinkhasov J, et al. 2006. Plant-made subunit vaccine against pneumonic and bubonic plague is orally immunogenic in mice. *Vaccine* 24:2477–90
7. Amodio ML, Colelli G, Hasey JK, Kader AA. 2007. A comparative study of composition and postharvest performance of organically and conventionally grown kiwifruits. *J. Sci. Food Agric.* 87:1228–36
8. Animal Plant Health Insp. Serv., USDA. 2002. *USDA Investigates Biotech Company for Possible Permit Violations*. **http://www.aphis.usda.gov/lpa/news/2002/11/prodigene.html**
9. Animal Plant Health Insp. Serv., USDA. 2005. Introductions of plants genetically engineered to produce industrial compounds. Docket No. 03–038–2. *Fed. Regist.* 70:85
10. Animal Plant Health Insp. Serv., USDA. 2005. USDA's biotechnology deregulation process. **http://www.aphis.usda.gov/lpa/pubs/fsheet_faq_notice/fs_biodereg.html**
11. Animal Plant Health Insp. Serv., USDA. 2007. Return to regulated status of alfalfa genetically engineered for tolerance to the herbicide glyphosate. *Fed. Regist.* 72:56
12. Arbes SJ Jr, Gergen PJ, Elliott L, Zeldin DC. 2005. Prevalences of positive skin test responses to 10 common allergens in the US population: Results from the Third National Health and Nutrition Examination Survey. *J. Allergy Clin. Immunol.* 116:377–83
13. Arroyave G, Aguilar JR, Flores M, Guzman MA. 1995. Fortification of sugar with vitamin A. *UN Univ.* 192(Chapter 7):1–82
14. Arshad SH, Malmberg E, Krapf K, Hide DW. 1991. Clinical and immunological characteristics of Brazil nut allergy. *Clin. Exp. Allergy* 21:373–76
15. Avery AA. 2006. *The Truth about Organic Foods*. Chesterfield, MO: Henderson Commun.
16. Batista R, Nunes B, Carmo M, Cardoso C, José HS, et al. 2005. Lack of detectable allergenicity of transgenic maize and soya samples. *J. Allergy Clin. Immunol.* 116:403–10
17. Bauman DE, Eppared PJ, DeGeeter MJ, Lanza GM. 1985. Responses of high-producing dairy cows to long-term treatment with pituitary somatotropin and recombinant somatotropin. *J. Dairy Sci.* 68:1352–62
18. Beever DE, Kemp CF. 2000. Safety issues associated with the DNA in animal feed derived from genetically modified crops. A review of scientific and regulatory procedures. *Nutr. Abstr. Rev. Ser. B: Livestock Feeds Feed.* 70:175–82
19. Benfey PN, Chua N-H. 1990. The Cauliflower Mosaic Virus 35S promoter: Combinatorial regulation of transcription in plants. *Science* 250:959–66
20. Berberich SA, Ream JE, Jackson TL, Wood R, Stipanovic R, et al. 1996. The composition of insect-protected cottonseed is equivalent to that of conventional cottonseed. *J. Agric. Food Chem.* 44:365–71
21. Bernstein L, Bernstein JA, Miller M, Tierzieva S, Bernstein DI, et al. 1999. Immune responses in farm workers after exposure to *Bacillus thuringiensis* pesticides. *Environ. Health Perspect.* 107:575–82
22. Betz FS, Hammond BF, Fuchs RL. 2000. Safety and advantages of *Bacillus thuringiensis* protected plants to control insect pests. *Regul. Toxicol. Pharmacol.* 32:156–73

23. Bevan MW, Flavell RB, Chilton MD. 1983. A chimeric antibiotic resistance gene as a selectable marker for plant cell transformation. *Nature* 304:184–87
24. Bhalla PL, Singh MB. 2004. Knocking out expression of plant allergen genes. *Methods* 32:340–45
25. Bhalla PL, Swoboda I, Singh MB. 2001. Reduction in allergenicity of grass pollen by genetic engineering. *Int. Arch. Allergy Immunol.* 124:51–54
26. Binenbaum E, Nottenburg C, Pardey PG, Wright BD, Zambrano P. 2000. South-north trade, intellectual property jurisdictions, and *Freedom to Operate* in agricultural research on staple crops. *Environ. Prod. Technol. Div., Int. Food Policy Res. Inst.* Discuss. Pap. No. 70
27. Biotechnol. Ind. Organ. (BIO). 2007. *Guide to Biotechnology 2007*, p. 83. **http://bio.org/speeches/pubs/er/BiotechGuide.pdf**
28. Bouis H. 2004. *Hidden hunger: the role of nutrition, fortification and biofortification.* Presented at World Food Prize Int. Symp., Des Moines, IA
29. Bouquet A, Marck G, Pistagna D, Torregrosa L. 2003. *Transfer of grape fanleaf virus coat protein gene through hybridization with Xiphinema index resistant genotypes to obtain rootstocks resistant to virus spread.* Presented at VIII Int. Conf. Grape Genet. Breed., Int. Soc. Horticult. Sci., *Acta Horticult.* 603:325–36
30. Brake DG, Evenson DP. 2004. A generational study of glyphosate-tolerant soybeans on mouse fetal, postnatal, pubertal and adult testicular development. *Food Chem. Toxicol.* 42:29–36
31. Brown LR, Renner M, Halweil B. 2000. *Vital Signs 2000.* New York/London: Norton. 191 pp.
32. Brown P, Will RG, Bradley R, Asher DM, Detwiler L. 2001. Bovine spongiform encephalopathy and variant Creutzfeldt-Jakob disease: Background, evolution and current concerns. *Emerg. Infect. Dis.* 7(1):Jan-Feb. **http://www.cdc.gov/ncidod/EID/vol7no1/brown.htm**
33. Buchanan BB. 2001. Genetic engineering and the allergy issue. *Plant Physiol.* 126:5–7
34. Buchanan BB, Adamidi C, Lozano RM, Yee BC, Momma M, et al. 1997. Thioredoxin-linked mitigation of allergic responses to wheat. *Proc. Natl. Acad. Sci. USA* 94:5372–77
35. Buchanan BB, del Val G, Frick OL. 1999. *Thioredoxin: A photosynthetic regulatory protein mitigating food allergies.* Am. Soc. Plant Biol. Annu. Meet., Abstr. 42002. **http://abstracts.aspb.org/pb1999/public/M20/0952.shtml**
36. **Burton JL, McBride BW, Block E, Glimm DR, Kennelly JJ. 1994. A review of bovine growth hormone. *Can. J. Anim. Sci.* 74:167–201**

36. Review of safety studies on effects of long-term rBST treatment of cows.

37. Buttel FH. 2004. The recombinant BGH controversy in the United States: Toward a new consumption politics of food? *Agric. Hum. Values* 17:5–20
38. Carman NJ. 2006. *Gene-altered Bt crops threaten public health: Immune responses and skin sensitization to Bt in farm workers and presence of Bt in many genetically engineered foods.* **http://www.organicconsumers.org/ge/BT031706.cfm**
39. Cent. Dis. Control Prev. 2001. *CDC report to FDA: Investigation of human health effects associated with potential exposure to genetically modified corn. June 11.* **http://www.cdc.gov/nceh/ehhe/Cry9cReport/pdfs/cry9creport.pdf**
40. **Chassy B, Hlywka JJ, Kleter GA, Kok EJ, Kuiper HA, et al. 2004. Nutritional and safety assessments of foods and feeds nutritionally improved through biotechnology: An executive summary. *Compr. Rev. Food Sci. Food Saf.* 3:25–104**

40. Provides scientific information and recommendations on safety and nutritional aspects of crops with improved nutritional qualities.

41. Chee-Sanford JC, Aminov RI, Krapac IJ, Garrigues-Jeanjean N, Mackie RI. 2001. Occurrence and diversity of tetracycline resistance genes in lagoons and groundwater underlying two swine production facilities. *Appl. Environ. Microbiol.* 67:1494–502

42. Chetelat RT, Deverna JW, Bennett AB. 1995. Introgression into tomato (*Lycopersicon esculentum*) of the *L. chmielewskii* sucrose accumulator gene (*sucr*) controlling fruit sugar composition. *Theor. Appl. Genet.* 91:327–33
43. Cho M-J, Kim HK, Choi H-W, Buchanan BB, Lemaux PG. 2000. Endosperm-specific GFP expression driven by barley D-hordein promoter and its inheritance in transgenic barley and wheat plants. *In Vitro Cell. Dev. Biol. Anim.* 36:A63
44. Chopra S, Feeley M, Lambert G, Mueller T. 1998. *rBST (Nutrilac) "Gaps Analysis" Report.* Health Prot. Branch, Health Can. **http://www.nfu.ca/gapsreport.html**
45. Christensen AH, Quail PH. 1996. Ubiquitin promoter-based vectors for high-level expression of selectable and/or screenable marker genes in monocotyledonous plants. *Transgenic Res.* 5:213–18
46. Clark JH, Ipharraguerre IR. 2001. Livestock performance: Feeding Biotech Crops. *J. Dairy Sci.* 84:E9–18
47. Clydesdale FM. 1996. Allergenicity of foods produced by genetic modification. *Food Sci. Nutr.* 36:1–186
48. Coghlan A. 2000. So far so good—For the moment, the gene genie is staying in its bottle. *New Sci.* 165:4
49. Collier RJ, Bauman DE. 2001. Re: Re: Role of the insulin-like growth factors in cancer development and progression. *J. Natl. Cancer Inst.* 93:876
50. Comm. Identifying Assessing Unintended Effects Genet. Eng. Foods Human Health. 2004. *Safety of Genetically Engineered Foods: Approaches to Assessing Unintended Health Effects.* Washington, DC: Natl. Acad.
51. Counc. Decis. 17 Dec. 1999. Concerning the placing on the market and administration of bovine somatotrophin (BST) and repealing decision 90/218/EEC 1999/880/EC. *Off. J. Eur. Communities* 42:71–73 **http://eurlex.europa. eu/LexUriServ/LexUriServ.do?uri=OJ:L:1999:331:0071:0072:EN:PDF**
52. Curtiss RI III, Cardineau CA. 1990. Genetically modified plants for use as oral immunogens. *World Patent Appl. WO 90/02484*
53. Deavours BE, Dixon RA. 2005. Metabolic engineering of isoflavonoid biosynthesis in alfalfa. *Plant Physiol.* 138:2245–59
54. Diaz de la Garza RI, Gregory JF III, Hanson AD. 2007. Folate biofortification of tomato fruit. *Proc. Natl. Acad. Sci. USA* 104:4218–22
55. Dohoo IR, Leslie K, DesCôteaux L, Fredeen A, Dowling P, et al. 2003. A meta-analysis review of the effects of rBST 1. Methodology and effects on production. *Can. J. Vet. Res.* 67:241–51
56. Dolliver H, Kumar K, Gupta S. 2007. Sulfamethazine uptake by plants from manure-amended soil. *J. Environ. Q.* 36:1224–30
57. Drakakaki G, Marcel S, Glahn RP, Lund EK, Pariagh S, et al. 2005. Endosperm-specific coexpression of recombinant soybean ferritin and *Aspergillus* phytase in maize results in significant increases in the levels of bioavailable iron. *Plant Mol. Biol.* 59:869–80
58. Dubcovsky J. 2004. Marker-assisted selection in public breeding programs: the wheat experience. *Crop Sci.* 44:1895–98
59. Edwards JL, Schrick FN, McCracken MD, van Amstel SR, Hopkins FM, et al. 2003. Cloning adult farm animals: A review of the possibilities and problems associated with somatic cell nuclear transfer. *Am. J. Reprod. Immunol.* 50:113–23
60. Ellis KA, Innocent G, Grove-White D, Cripps P, McLean WG, et al. 2006. Comparing the fatty acid composition of organic and conventional milk. *J. Dairy Sci.* 89:1938–50
61. Ellstrand NC. 2006. *Genetic Eng. Pollen Flow.* Univ. Calif. Agric. Nat. Resour., Agric. Genet. Eng. Fact Sheet 5. Agric. Biotechnol. Calif. Ser., Publ. 8182

62. Environ. Prot. Agency (EPA). 1998. *Bacillus thuringiensis* subspecies tolworthi Cry9C protein and the genetic material necessary for its production in corn; Exemption from the requirement of a tolerance. *Fed. Regist.* 63(99):28258–61
63. Environ. Prot. Agency (EPA). 2007. *Cry9C food allergenicity assessment background document.* **http://www.epa.gov/oppbppd1/biopesticides/pips/old/cry9c/cry9c-epa-background.htm**
64. Environ. Prot. Agency Off. Pestic. Programs Biopesticides Pollut. Prev. Div. 2000. *Biopesticides registration document, preliminary risks and benefits section, Bacillus thuringiensis plant-pesticides.* Washington, DC: EPA
65. Environ. Prot. Agency Off. Sci. Coord. Policy Biotechnol. Team. 2006. *Regulatory framework.* **http://www.epa.gov/scipoly/biotech/pubs/framework.htm**
66. Epstein SS. 2001. Role of the insulin-like growth factors in cancer development and progression. *J. Natl. Cancer Inst.* 93:238
67. Eur. Food Saf. Auth. 2007. *EFSA review of statistical analyses conducted for the assessment of the MON 863 90-day rat feeding study.* **http://www.efsa.europa.eu/EFSA/efsa_locale-1178620753812_1178621342614.htm**
68. Eur. Food Saf. Auth. 2007. *EFSA statement of the fate of recombinant DNA or proteins in meat, milk and eggs from animals.* **http://www.efsa.europa.eu/EFSA/Statement/gmo_EFSA_statement_DNA_proteins_gastroint,0.pdf**
69. Ewen SWB, Pusztai A. 1999. Effect of diets containing genetically modified potatoes expressing *Galanthus nivalis* lectin on rat small intestine. *Lancet* 354:1353–54
70. Federici B. 2002. Case study: Bt crops a novel mode of insect control. In *Genetically Modified Crops: Assessing Safety*, ed. KT Atherton, pp. 164–200. London: Taylor & Francis
71. Fernandez-Cornejo J, Caswell M. 2006. The first decade of genetically engineered crops in the United States. *USDA Econ. Res. Serv., Econ. Inf. Bull. No. EIB-11*
72. Fierobe HP, Mingardon F, Mechaly A, Belaich A, Rincon MT, et al. 2005. Action of designer cellulosomes on homogeneous versus complex substrates: controlled incorporation of three distinct enzymes into a defined trifunctional scaffoldin. *J. Biol. Chem.* 280:16325–34
73. FIFRA Sci. Advis. Panel Meet. 2000. *A set of scientific issues being considered by the Environmental Protection Agency regarding: Assessment of Scientific Information Concerning StarLink™ Corn. SAP Rep. No. 2000–06, Dec. 1.* **http://www.agbios.com/docroot/articles/2000341-A.pdf**
74. FIFRA Sci. Advisory Panel Meet. 2001. *A Set of Scientific Issues Being Considered by the Environmental Protection Agency Regarding: Assessment of Additional Scientific Information Concerning StarLink™ Corn. SAP Rep. No. 2001–09, July 25.* **http://www.epa.gov/scipoly/sap/meetings/2001/index.htm#july**
75. Flachowsky G. 2007. Feeds from genetically engineering plants—Results and future challenges. *ISB News Rep.* March:4–7
76. Flachowsky G, Aulrich K, Böhme H, Halle I. 2007. Studies on feeds from genetically modified plants (GMP)—Contributions to nutritional and safety assessment; Table 3. *Anim. Feed Sci. Technol.* 133:2–30
77. Food Drug Adm. (FDA). 1995. *FDA'S policy for foods developed by biotechnology.* **http://vm.cfsan.fda.gov/~lrd/biopolcy.html**
78. Food Drug Adm. (FDA). 2000. FDA responds to citizen petition on BST. *FDA Vet. Newsl.* XV:8. **http://www.fda.gov/cvm/CVM_Updates/cpetup.html**

79. Food Drug Adm. (FDA). 2002. *Guidance for industry: Drugs, biologics, and medical devices derived from bioengineered plants for use in humans and animals.* **http://www.fda.gov/cber/gdlns/bioplant.htm**
80. Food Drug Adm. (FDA). 2003. *Animal cloning: A risk assessment.* **http://www.fda.gov/cvm/Documents/CLRAES.pdf**
81. Food Drug Adm. (FDA). 2004. *Federal Food, Drug, and Cosmetic Act: Chapter IV—Food.* **http://www.fda.gov/opacom/laws/fdcact/fdcact4.htm**
82. Food Drug Adm. (FDA). 2005. *Guidance for industry: Pharmacogenomic data submissions.* **http://www.fda.gov/Cder/guidance/6400fnl.pdf**
83. Food Drug Adm. Cent. Food Saf. Appl. Nutr. 1996. *Safety assurance of foods derived by modern biotechnology in the United States.* **http://www.cfsan.fda.gov/~lrd/biojap96.html**
84. Food Drug Adm. Cent. Food Saf. Appl. Nutr. 2007. *Biotechnology.* **http://vm.cfsan.fda.gov/%7Elrd/biotechm.html**
85. Food Drug Adm. Cent. Vet. Med. 1993. *Report on the Food and Drug Administration's Review of the Safety of Recombinant Bovine Somatotropin.* **http://www.fda.gov/cvm/RBRPTFNL.htm**
86. Food Standards Agency. 2007. *Agency seeks contractor to review scientific literature.* **http://www.food.gov.uk/news/newsarchive/2007/oct/contractorliterature**
87. Fox JL. 2006. Turning plants into factories. *Nat. Biotechnol.* 24:1191–93
88. Gaba V, Zelcer A, Gal-On A. 2004. Cucurbit biotechnology—the importance of virus resistance. *In Vitro Cell. Dev. Biol. Plant* 40:346–58
89. Glazer AN, Nikaido H. 1995. *Microbial Biotechnology: Fundamentals of Applied Microbiology.* New York: Freeman
90. Gold HS, Moellering RC Jr. 1996. Antimicrobial-drug resistance. *N. Engl. J. Med.* 335:1445–53
91. Goldstein DA, Tinland B, Gilbertson LA, Staub JM, Bannon GA, et al. 2005. Human safety and genetically modified plants: a review of antibiotic resistance markers and future transformation selection technologies. *J. Appl. Microbiol.* 99:7–23
92. Gonsalves D. 1998. Control of papaya ringspot virus in papaya: A case study. *Annu. Rev. Phytopathol.* 36:165–205
93. Gonsalves D, Ferriera S, Manshardt R, Fitch M, Slightom J. 2000. Transgenic virus resistant Papaya: New hope for controlling Papaya Ringspot Virus in Hawaii. *Plant Health Progress. (plant Health Reviews)*, 21 June
94. Grant RJ, Fanning KC, Kleinschmit D, Stanisiewski EP, Hartnell GF. 2003. Influence of glyphosate-tolerant (event NK603) and corn rootworm protected (event MON863) corn silage and grain on feed consumption and milk production in Holstein cattle. *J. Dairy Sci.* 89:1707–15
95. Green ML, Angal S, Lowe PA, Marston FAO. 1985. Cheddar cheesemaking with recombinant calf chymosin (EC 3.4.23.4) synthesized in *Escherichia coli*. *J. Dairy Res.* 52:281–86
96. Grocery Manuf. Am. 2002. *GMA urges the use of non-food crops for biotech drugs: ProdiGene's errors raise serious concerns, say GMA.* **http://www.gmabrands.com/news/docs/NewsRelease.cfm?DocID=1029**
97. Haligaard P, Gaspard I, Abraam D. 1999. No need for maximum residue limit for risk-free BST, says commission. Brussels Belgium. *La Prensa* 1999:954
98. Hallman WK, Hebden WC, Aquino HL, Cutie CL, Lang JT. 2003. *Public Perceptions of Genetically Modified Foods: A National Study of American Knowledge and Opinion.* Food Policy Inst. Publ. RR-1003-004. New Brunswick, NJ: Rutgers Univ.

99. Hammond BG, Campbell KW, Pilcher CD, Degooyer TA, Robinson AE, et al. 2004. Lower fumonisin mycotoxin levels in the grain of Bt-corn grown in the United States in 2000–2002. *J. Agric. Food Chem.* 52:1390–97
100. Hammond BG, Vicini JL, Hartnell GF, Naylor MW, Knight CD, et al. 1996. The feeding value of soybeans fed to rats, chickens, catfish and dairy cattle is not altered by genetic incorporation of glyphosate tolerance. *J. Nutr.* 126:717–27
101. Hardwick NV, Davies JML, Wright DM. 1994. The incidence of three virus diseases of winter oilseed rape in England and Wales in the 1991/02 and 1992/93 growing season. *Plant Pathol.* 43:1045–49
102. Hellsten I. 2003. Focus on metaphors: The case of Frankenfood on the Web. *J. Comput.-Med. Commun.* 8(4)
103. Hightower R, Baden C, Penzes E, Lund P, Dunsmuir P. 1991. Expression of antifreeze proteins in transgenic plants. *Plant Mol. Biol.* 17:1013–21
104. Ho M-W, Ryan A, Cummins J. 1999. Cauliflower mosaic viral promoter—A recipe for disaster? *Microb. Ecol. Health Dis.* 11:194–97
105. Hodgson J. 2000. Scientists avert new GMO crisis. *Nat. Biotechnol.* 18:13
106. Hoeben D, Burvenich D, Eppard PJ, Hard DL. 1999. Effect of rBST on milk production and composition of cows with *Streptococcus uberis* mastitis. *J. Dairy Sci.* 82:1671–83
107. Horvath Z. 2003. Damage in corn production and in hybrid multiplication caused by species of Coleoptera. *Cereal Res. Commun.* 31:421–27
108. Hyten DL, Hartman GL, Nelson RL, Frederick RD, Concibido VC, et al. 2007. Map location of the *Rpp1* locus that confers resistance to soybean rust in soybean. *Crop Sci.* 47:837–40
109. Hyun Y, Bressner GE, Fischer RL, Miller PS, Ellis M, et al. 2005. Performance of growing-finishing pigs fed diets containing YieldGard Rootworm corn (MON 863), a nontransgenic genetically similar corn, or conventional corn hybrids. *J. Anim. Sci.* 83:1581–90
110. Insp. Gen. USDA. 2005. *Audit Report: Animal Plant Health Inspect. Serv. Controls over Issuance of Genet. Eng. Organism Release Permits.* Audit 50601-8-Te
111. Int. Fed. Org. Agric. Mov. (IFOAM). 2007. *Nearly 31 Million Certified Organic Hectares Worldwide: IFOAM, FiBL and SÖL present new facts and figures about the organic sector at BioFach 2007.* **http://www.ifoam.org/press/press/Statistics_2007.html**
112. IPSA. 2007. Federal judge rules USDA approval of RR alfalfa illegal. *Independent Prof. Seed Assoc. Newsl.* 5:6–7
113. ISB (Inf. Syst. Biotechnol.). 2007. *Petitions of nonregulated status granted or pending by APHIS.* **http://www.aphis.usda.gov/brs/not_reg.html**
114. ISB (Inf. Syst. Biotechnol.). 2007. *Search results for tomato, field test release permits database for the U.S.* **http://www.isb.vt.edu/CFDOCS/fieldtests3.cfm?FIELDNAMES=NUM_VAL,LIST_AS,SELECT_ASCDESC,DB_CHOICE&num_val=91-079-01r&db_choice=com&list_as=detail&select_ascdesc=sort_date**
115. Iyer-Pascuzzi AS, McCouch SR. 2007. Functional markers for xa5-mediated resistance in rice. *Mol. Breed.* 19:291–96
116. James C. 2005. Global status of commercialized biotech/GM crops: 2005. *ISAAA Briefs* No. 34

116. Comprehensive review of current status of acreage of genetically engineered crops grown worldwide.

117. James C. 2006. Global status of commercialized biotech/GM crops: 2006. *ISAAA Briefs* No. 35
118. James S, Burton M. 2003. Consumer preferences for GM food and other attributes of the food system. *Aust. J. Agric. Res. Econ.* 47:501–18

119. Jeljaszewicz J, Mlynarczyk G, Mlynarczyk A. 2000. Antibiotic resistance in gram-positive cocci. *Int. J. Antimicrob. Agents* 16:473–78

120. Jonas DA, Elmadfa I, Engel KH, Heller KJ, Kozianowski G, et al. 2001. Safety considerations of DNA in food. *Ann. Nutr. Metabol.* 45:235–54

121. Jones P. 2007. Judge concerned that alfalfa may be a little rascal—and other legal news. *ISB News Rep.* July 2007:9–10

122. Juskevich JC, Guyer CG. 1990. Bovine growth hormone: Human food safety evaluation. *Science* 249:875–84

123. Kahle K, Kraus M, Richling E. 2005. Polyphenol profiles of apple juices. *Mol. Nutr. Food Res.* 49:797–806

124. Kessler DA, Taylor MR, Maryanski JH, Flamm EL, Kahl LS. 1992. The safety of foods developed by biotechnology. *Science* 256:1747–49

125. Klibanov AM. 1989. Advances in enzymes. In *Biotechnology Challenges in the Flavor and Food Industry*, ed. RD Lindsay, BJ Willis, pp. 25–43. New York: Elsevier Appl. Sci.

126. Kong FN, Wang JY, Zou JC, Shi LX, Jin MD, et al. 2007. Molecular tagging and mapping of the erect panicle gene in rice. *Mol. Breed.* 19:297–304

127. Konig A, Cockburn A, Crevel RWR, Debruyne E, Grafstroem R, et al. 2004. Assessment of the safety of foods derived from genetically modified (GM) crops. *Food Chem. Toxicol.* 42:1047–88

127. Provides guidance on how to assess the safety of foods derived from genetically engineered crops.

128. Koprek T, McElroy D, Louwerse J, Williams-Carrier R, Lemaux PG. 2000. An efficient method for dispersing *Ds* elements in the barley genome as a tool for determining gene function. *Plant J.* 24:253–63

129. Kramer MG, Redenbaugh K. 1994. Commercialization of a tomato with an antisense polygalacturonase gene—the Flavr Savr^{TM} story. *Euphytica* 9:293–97

130. Ku MS, Cho D, Li X, Jiao DM, Pinto M, et al. 2001. Introduction of genes encoding C4 photosynthesis enzymes into rice plants: Physiological consequences. *Novartis Found. Symp., Rice Biotechnol.: Improv. Yield, Stress Toler. Grain Qual.* 236:100–11

131. Kuhnert P, Cubosson DR, Roesch M, Homeld E, Doherr MG, Blum JW. 2005. Prevalence and risk-factor analysis of Shiga toxigenic *E. coli* in faecal samples of organically and conventionally farmed dairy cattle. *Vet. Microbiol.* 109:37–45

132. Kuiper HA, Kleter GA, Noteborn HPJM, Kok EJ. 2001. Assessment of the food safety issues related to genetically modified foods. *Plant J.* 27:503–28

133. Kuiper HA, Noteborn HPJM, Peijnenburg AACM. 1999. Adequacy of methods for testing the safety of genetically modified foods. *Lancet* 354:1315–16

134. Lachmann A. 1999. GM food debate. *Lancet* 354:1726

135. Lappé MA, Bailey EB, Childress C, Setchell KDR. 1999. Alterations in clinically important phytoestrogens in genetically modified, herbicide tolerant soybeans. *J. Med. Food* 1:241–45

136. Latham JR, Wilson AK, Steinbrecher RA. 2005. Mutational consequences of plant transformation. *J. Biomed. Biotech.* 2006:1–7

137. Lee J, Cetiner MS, Blackmon WJ, Jaynes JM. 1990. The reduction of the freezing point of tobacco plants transformed with the gene encoding for the antifreeze protein from winter flounder. *J. Cell. Biochem. Suppl.* 14(Pt. E):303

138. Levy SB. 1998. Multidrug resistance: a sign of the times. *N. Engl. J. Med.* 338:1376–78

139. Lewis P. 1992. Mutant foods create risks we can't yet guess. *The New York Times*, June 16

140. Liu F-X, Tan Z-B, Zhu J-Q, Deng X-J. 2004. *Arabidopsis* CBF1 in plant tolerance to low temperature and drought stresses. *Yi Chuan* 26:394–98 (In Chinese)

141. Lius S, Manshardt RM, Fitch MMM, Slightom JL, Sanford JC, Gonsalves D. 1997. Pathogen-derived resistance provides papaya with effective protection against papaya ringspot virus. *Mol. Breed.* 3:161–68
142. Lu C, Toepel K, Irish R, Fenske RA, Barr DB, Bravo R. 2005. Organic diets significantly lower children's dietary exposure to organophosphorus pesticides. *Environ. Health Perspect.* 114:260–63
143. Macer DRJ. 2003. Genetic engineering: Cross species and cross cultural perspectives, Table 2. In *Dialog der Kulturen*, ed. S Fritsch-Oppermann, pp. 159–80. Loccum: Evangelische Akad.
144. Manning R. 2004. Super organics. *Wired*, May, Issue 1205. **http://www.wired.com/wired/archive/12.05/food.html**
145. Marshall A. 2007. GM soybeans and health safety—a controversy reexamined. *Nat. Biotechnol.* 25:981–87
146. Martineau B. 2001. *First Fruit: The Creation of the Flavr Savr Tomato and the Birth of Biotech Foods.* New York: McGraw-Hill
147. Mason HS, Lam DM, Arntzen CJ. 1992. Expression of hepatitis B surface antigen in transgenic plants. *Proc. Natl. Acad. Sci. USA* 89:11745–49
148. Mayeno AN, Gleich GJ. 1994. Eosinophilia-myalgia syndrome and tryptophan production: A cautionary tale. *Trends Biotechnol.* 12:346–52
149. McClintock JT, Schaffer CR, Sjoblad RD. 1995. A comparative review of the mammalian toxicity of *Bacillus thuringiensis*-based pesticides. *Pestic. Sci.* 45:95–105
150. McHughen A. 2006. *Plant Genetic Engineering and Regulation in the U.S.* Univ. Calif. Agric. Nat. Resour., Agric. Biotechnol. Calif. Ser., Publ. 8179
151. Melis A, Happe T. 2001. Hydrogen production. Green algae as a source of energy. *Plant Physiol.* 127:740–48
152. Mendelsohn M, Kough J, Vaituzis Z, Matthews K. 2003. Are Bt crops safe? *Nat. Biotechnol.* 21:1003–9
153. Mercer DK, Scott KP, Bruce-Johnson WA, Glover A, Flint HJ. 1999. Fate of free DNA and transformation of the oral bacterium *Streptococcus gordonii* DL1 by plasmid DNA in human saliva. *Appl. Environ. Microbiol.* 65:6–10
154. Mirando MA, Hamernik DL. 2006. Funding priorities in animal reproduction at the USDA Coop. State Res. Educ. Ext. Serv. *Biol. Reprod.* 74:459–62
155. Mitchell AE, Hong Y-J, Koh E, Barrett DM, Bryant DE, et al. 2007. Ten-year comparison of the influence of organic and conventional crop management practices on the content of flavonoids in tomatoes. *J. Agric. Food Chem.* 55:6154–59
156. Monsanto. 2003. *Safety Assessment of YieldGard Rootworm™ Corn.* **http://www.monsanto.com/pdf/products/yieldgard_rw_es.pdf**
157. Monsanto. 2007. *Vistive™ brochure.* **http://www.monsanto.com/monsanto/ag_products/pdf/output_traits/vistive_full_brochure.pdf**
158. Moreno-Fierros L, García N, Gutiérrez R, López-Revilla R, Vázquez-Padrón RI. 2000. Intranasal, rectal and intraperitoneal immunization with protoxin Cry1Ac from *Bacillus thuringiensis* induces compartmentalized serum, intestinal, vaginal and pulmonary immune responses in Balb/c mice. *Microbes Infect.* 2:885–90
159. Natl. Corn Growers Assoc. 2002. *NCGA commends APHIS on quick action concerning biotech compliance infractions.* **http://www.ncga.com/news/notd/2002/november/112702.htm**
160. Natl. Health Nutr. Exam. Surv. III. 2004. *Training manual for allergy component.* **http://www.cdc.gov/nchs/data/nhanes/nhanes3/cdrom/nchs/manuals/train.pdf**
161. Natl. Org. Program (NOP). 2006. *NOP regulations and guidelines.* **http://www.ams.usda.gov/nop/NOP/NOPhome.html**

146. Historical perspective on the challenges faced by the first genetically engineered whole food.

162. Natl. Org. Program (NOP). 2007. *National List Information*. **http://www.ams.usda.gov/nop/NationalList/ListHome.html**
163. Nawaz MS, Erickson BD, Khan AA, Khan SA, Pothuluri JV, et al. 2001. Human health impact and regulatory issues involving antimicrobial resistance in the food animal production environment. *Regul. Res. Perspect.* 1:1–10
164. Niederberger V, Horak F, Vrtala S, Spitzauer S, Krauth M-T, et al. 2004. Vaccination with genetically engineered allergens prevents progression of allergic disease. *Proc. Natl. Acad. Sci. USA* 101:14677–82
165. Nocente F, Gazza L, Pasquini M. 2007. Evaluation of leaf rust resistance genes *Lr1*, *Lr9*, *Lr24*, *Lr47* and their introgression into common wheat cultivars by marker-assisted selection. *Euphytica* 155:329–36
166. Nordlee JA, Taylor SL, Townsend JA, Thomas LA, Bush RK. 1996. Identification of a Brazil-nut allergen in transgenic soybeans. *N. Engl. J. Med.* 334:688–92
167. Norman HD, Walsh MK. 2004. Performance of dairy cattle clones and evaluation of their milk composition. *Cloning Stem Cells* 6:157–64
168. Odell JT, Nagy F, Chua N-H. 1985. Identification of DNA sequences required for activity of the cauliflower mosaic virus 35S promoter. *Nature* 313:810–14
169. Off. Sci. Technol. 1984. Proposal for a coordinated framework for regulation of biotechnology. *Fed. Regist.* 49:50
170. Ogura Y, Ogura H, Zushi N, Morita H, Kurashige T. 1993. The usefulness and the limitations of the radioallerosorbent test in diagnosing food allergy in atopic dermatitis. *Arerugi—Jpn. J. Allergol.* 46:748–56
171. Org. Econ. Coop. Dev. 2007. *Consensus document on compositional considerations for new varieties of potatoes: Key food and feed nutrients, anti-nutrients and toxicants*. **http://www.oecd.org/LongAbstract/0,3425,en_2649_34385_1811544_1_1_1_37465,00.html**
172. Padgette SR, Taylor NB, Nida DL, Bailey MR, MacDonald J, et al. 1996. The composition of glyphosate-tolerant soybean seeds is equivalent to that of conventional soybeans. *J. Nutr.* 126:702–16
173. Paine JA, Shipton CA, Chaggar S, Howells RM, Kennedy MJ, et al. 2005. Improving the nutritional value of Golden Rice through increased provitamin A content. *Nat. Biotechnol.* 23:429–30
174. Park S, Kang T-S, Kim C-K, Han J-S, Kim S, et al. 2005. Genetic manipulation for enhancing calcium content in potato tuber. *J. Agric. Food Chem.* 53:5598–603
175. Parliam NSW. 2005. *Gene technology (GM Crop Moratorium) amendment (Postponement of Expiry) bill*. **http://www.parliament.nsw.gov.au/prod/PARLMENT/hansArt.nsf/V3Key/LC20051109040**
176. Parodi PW. 2005. Dairy product consumption and the risk of breast cancer. *J. Am. Coll. Nutr.* 24:S556–58
177. Pascual DW. 2007. Vaccines are for dinner. *Proc. Natl. Acad. Sci. USA* 104:10757–58
178. Peeters KABM, Koppelman SJ, van Hoffen E, van der Tas CWH, den Hartog Jager CF, et al. 2007. Does skin prick test reactivity to purified allergens correlate with clinical severity of peanut allergy? *Clin. Exp. Allergy* 37:108–15
179. Penn. Dep. Agric. 2008. *Milk Labeling Standards* 2.0.1.17.2008. **http://www.agriculture.state.pa.us/agriculture/lib/agriculture/foodsafetyfiles/labeling/milk_labeling_standards_new.pdf**
180. Penna S, Sági L, Swennen R. 2002. Positive selectable marker genes for routine plant transformation. *In Vitro Cell. Dev. Biol. Plant* 38:125–28

172. First peer-reviewed report on equivalence of genetically engineered and conventional soybean.

173. Seminal paper describing second-generation, nutritionally enhanced Golden Rice.

181. Perkins JB, Sloma A, Hermann T, Theriault K, Zachgo E, et al. 1999. Genetic engineering of *Bacillus subtilis* for the commercial production of riboflavin. *J. Ind. Microbiol. Biotechnol.* 22:8–18

182. Pirog R, Larson A. 2007. *Consumer perceptions of the safety, health and environmental impacts of various scales and geographic origin of food supply chains.* **http://www.leopold.iastate.edu/pubs/staff/consumer/consumer_0907.pdf**

183. Potenza C, Aleman L, Sengupta-Gopalan C. 2004. Targeting transgene expression in research, agricultural and environmental applications: Promoters used in plant transformation. *In Vitro Cell. Dev. Biol.* 40:1–22

184. Pravda (Online). 2005. *People eating genetically modified food may have rat-short lifespan, Nov. 27.* **http://english.pravda.ru/science/19/94/377/16372_GMF.html**

185. Preston C. 2005. Peer reviewed publications on safety of GM foods. *AgBioWorld.* http://www.agbioworld.org/biotech-info/articles/biotech-art/peer-reviewed-pubs.html

185. Extensive listing of peer-reviewed publications on food safety of genetically engineered foods.

186. R. Soc. 1999. Review *of data on possible toxicity of GM potatoes, May 18.* **http://royalsociety.org/displaypagedoc.asp?id=6170**

187. Radke SE, Andrews BM, Moloney MM, Crouch ML, Kridl JC, Knauf VC. 1988. Transformation of *Brassica napus* L. using *Agrobacterium tumefaciens*: developmentally regulated expression of a reintroduced napin gene. *Theor. Appl. Genet.* 75:685–94

188. Redenbaugh K, Hiatt W, Martineau B, Kramer M, Sheehy R, et al. 1992. *Safety Assessment of Genetically Engineered Fruits and Vegetables: A Case Study of the FLAVR SAVR Tomato.* Boca Raton, FL: CRC Press. 267 pp.

189. Rein D, Schijlen E, Kooistra T, Herbers K, Verschuren L, et al. 2006. Transgenic flavonoid tomato intake reduces C-reactive protein in human C-reactive protein transgenic mice more than wild-type tomato. *J. Nutr.* 136:2331–37

190. Ribaut J-M, Ragot M. 2007. MAS to improve drought adaptation in maize. *J. Exp. Bot.* 58:351–60

191. Riboli E, Norat T. 2003. Epidemiologic evidence of the protective effect of fruit and vegetables on cancer risk. *Am. J. Clin. Nutr.* 78:S559–69

192. Rist L, Mueller A, Barthel C, Snijders B, Jansen M, et al. 2007. Influence of organic diet on the amount of conjugated linoleic acids in breast milk of lactating women in the Netherlands. *Br. J. Nutr.* 97:735–43

193. Rojas-Hernández S, Rodríguez-Monroy MA, López-Revilla R, Reséndiz-Albor AA, Moreno-Fierros L. 2004. Intranasal coadministration of the Cry1Ac protoxin with amoebal lysates increases protection against *Naegleria fowleri* meningoencephalitis. *Infect. Immun.* 72:4368–75

194. Rommens CM, Humara JM, Ye J, Yan H, Richael C, et al. 2004. Crop improvement through modification of the plant's own genome. *Plant Physiol.* 135:1–11

195. Ronald P, Fouche B. 2006. *Genetic Engineering and Organic Production Systems.* Univ. Calif. Div. Agric. Nat. Resour., Agric. Biotechnol. Calif. Ser., Publ. 8188

196. Rossi M, Goggin FL, Milligan SB, Kaloshian I, Ullman DE, Williamson VM. 1998. The nematode resistance gene *Mi* of tomato confers resistance against the potato aphid. *Proc. Natl. Acad. Sci. USA* 95:9750–54

197. Roufs JB. 1992. Review of L-tryptophan and eosinophilia-mylagia syndrome. *J. Am. Diet. Assoc.* 92:844–50

198. Sandermann H, Wellmann E. 1998. Risikobewertung der kunstlichen herbizidresistenz. *Biol. Sicherheit* 1:285–92

199. Schilling BJ, Hallman WK, Adelaja AO, Marxen LJ. 2002. *Consumer Knowledge of Food Biotechnology: A Descriptive Study of U.S. Residents*. Food Policy Inst. Rep. RR-0602-002. New Brunswick, NJ: Rutgers Univ.
200. Schubbert R, Hohlweg U, Renz D, Doerfler W. 1998. On the fate of orally ingested foreign DNA in mice: chromosomal association and placental transmission in the fetus. *Mol. Gen. Genet.* 259:569–76
201. Schubbert R, Renz B, Schmitz B, Doerfler W. 1997. Foreign (M13) DNA ingested by mice reaches peripheral leukocytes, spleen, and liver via the intestinal wall mucosa and can be covalently linked to mouse DNA. *Proc. Natl. Acad. Sci. USA* 94:961–66
202. Segarra AE, Rawson JM. 2001. *Starlink™ Corn Controversy: Background. CRC Report for Congress RS20732.* **http://ncseonline.org/NLE/CRSreports/Agriculture/ag-101.cfm**
203. Séralini GE, Cellier D, de Vendomois JS. 2007. New analysis of a rat feeding study with a genetically modified maize reveals signs of hepatorenal toxicity. *Arch. Environ. Contam. Toxicol.* 52:596–602
204. Sharma DR, Kaur R, Kumar K. 1996. Embryo rescue in plants-a review. *Euphytica* 89:325–37
205. Sheen TF, Wang HL, Wang DN. 1998. Control of papaya ringspot virus by cross protection and cultivation techniques. *J. Jpn. Soc. Horticult. Sci.* 67:1232–35
206. Shelton AM, Zhao J-Z, Roush RT. 2002. Economic, ecological, food safety and social consequences of the deployment of Bt transgenic plants. *Annu. Rev. Entomol.* 47:845–81
207. Shepherd LVT, McNicol JW, Razzo R, Taylor MA, Davies HV. 2006. Assessing potential for unintended effects in genetically modified potatoes perturbed in metabolic and developmental processes. Targeted analysis of key nutrients and antinutrients. *Transgenic Res.* 15:409–25
208. Shewry PR, Baudo M, Lovegrove A, Powers S, Napiera JA, et al. 2006. Are GM and conventionally bred cereals really different? *Trends Food Sci. Technol.* 18:201–9
209. Sidhu RS, Hammond BG, Fuchs RL, Mutz J-N, Holden LR, et al. 2000. Glyphosate-tolerant corn: The composition and feeding value of grain from glyphosate-tolerant corn is equivalent to that of conventional corn (*Zea mays* L.). *J. Agric. Food Chem.* 48:2305–12
210. Slater A, Scott NW, Fowler MW. 2003. *Plant Biotechnology: The Genetic Manipulation of Plants*. New York: Oxford Univ. Press
211. Smith JM. 2003. *Seeds of Deception*. p. 19. Fairfield, IA: Yes! Books.
212. See Ref. 211, p. 65
213. See Ref. 211, pp. 105–22
214. Soil Assoc. 2007. *10 reasons to eat organic food.* **http://www.whyorganic.org/healthy_tenReasons.asp**
215. Song J, Bradeen JM, Naess KS, Raasch JA, Wielgus SM, et al. 2003. Gene *RB* cloned from *Solanum bulbocastanum* confers broad spectrum resistance to potato late blight. *Proc. Natl. Acad. Sci. USA* 100:9128–33
216. Sørensen TL, Blom M, Monnet DL, Frimodt-Møller N, Poulsen RL, Espersen F. 2001. Transient intestinal carriage after ingestion of antibiotic-resistant *Enterococcus faecium* from chicken and pork. *N. Engl. J. Med.* 345:1161–66
217. Soybean Tissue Cult. Genet. Eng. Cent. 2007. *Roundup Ready® soybean selected references.* **http://www.cropsoil.uga.edu/soy-engineering/RoundupReady.html**
218. Stallknecht GF, Gilbertson KM, Ranney JE. 1996. Alternative wheat cereals as food grains: Einkorn, emmer, spelt, kamut, and triticale. In *Progress in New Crops*, ed. J Janick, pp. 156–70. Alexandria, VA: ASHS Press

207. Demonstration of substantial equivalence of key nutrients and antinutrients in genetically engineered potatoes.

211. Frequently referenced book describing perceived dangers of genetically engineered crops and foods.

219. Stanley JS, King N, Burks AW, Huang SK, Sampson H, et al. 1997. Identification and mutational analysis of the immunodominant IgE binding epitopes of the major peanut allergen Ara h 2. *Arch. Biochem. Biophys.* 342:244–53

220. Stein AJ. 2006. *Micronutrient malnutrition and the impact of modern plant breeding on public health in India: How cost-effective is biofortification*? Gőttingen: Cuvillier Verlag

221. Stephanopoulos G. 2007. Challenges in engineering microbes for biofuels production. *Science* 315:801–4

222. Steurich F, Feyerabend R. 1996. Allergy to kiwi fruit. *Allergologie* 19:367–78

223. Strachan T, Read AP. 1999. *Genetic Manipulation of Animals*. New York: Wiley

224. Tada Y, Nakase M, Adachi T, Nakamura R, Shimada H, et al. 1996. Reduction of 14–16 kDa allergenic proteins in transgenic rice plants by antisense gene. *FEBS Lett.* 391:341–45

225. Takagi H, Hiro T, Yang L, Tada Y, Yuki Y, et al. 2006. A rice-based edible vaccine expressing multiple T cell epitopes induces oral tolerance for inhibition of Th2-mediated IgE responses. *Proc. Natl. Acad. Sci. USA* 102:17525–30

226. Takahashi S, Ito Y. 2004. Evaluation of meat products from cloned cattle: Biological and biochemical properties. *Cloning Stem Cells* 6:165–71

227. Tarozzi A, Hrelia S, Angeloni C, Morroni F, Biagi P, et al. 2005. Antioxidant effectiveness of organically and nonorganically grown red oranges in cell culture systems. *Eur. J. Nutr.* 45:152–58

228. Taylor ML, Hyun Y, Hartnell GF, Riordan SG, Nemeth MA, et al. 2003. Comparison of broiler performance when fed diets containing grain from YieldGard Rootworm (MON863), YieldGard Plus (MON810 × MON863), nontransgenic control, or commercial reference corn hybrids. *Poult. Sci.* 82:1948–56

229. Taylor NB, Fuchs RL, MacDonald J, Shariff AR, Padgette SR. 1999. Compositional analysis of glyphosate-tolerant soybeans treated with glyphosate. *J. Agric. Food Chem.* 47:4469–73

230. Taylor SL, Hefle SL. 2002. Genetically engineered foods: implications for food allergy. *Curr. Opin. Allergy Clin. Immunol.* 2:249–52

231. Teshima R, Akiyama H, Okunuki H, Sakushima J, Goda Y, et al. 2000. Effect of GM and non-GM soybeans on the immune system of BN rats and B10A mice. *J. Food Hyg. Soc. Jpn.* 41:188–93

232. Tester M. 1999. Seeking clarity in the debate over the safety of GM foods. *Nature* 402:575

233. Thanavala Y, Mahoney M, Pal S, Scott A, Richter L, et al. 2005. Immunogenicity in humans of an edible vaccine for hepatitis B. *Proc. Natl. Acad. Sci. USA* 102:3378–82

234. The Consumer Law Page. 1998. *Contaminated L-tryptophan and 5-hydroxy-L-tryptophan, eosinophilia myalgia syndrome [EMS]: The 1989 epidemic and the 1998 warning.* **http://consumerlawpage.com/article/tryptophan.shtml**

235. Tian XC, Kubota C, Sakashita K, Izaike Y, Okano R, et al. 2005. Meat and milk compositions of bovine clones. *Proc. Natl. Acad. Sci. USA* 102:6261–66

235. Provides science-based information to address public concerns about the safety of meat and milk from somatic animal clones.

236. Tomé D, Dubarry M, Fromentin G. 2004. Nutritional value of milk and meat products derived from cloning. *Cloning Stem Cells* 6:172–77

237. Tomey F, Moeller I, Scarpa A, Wang K. 2007. Genetic engineering approaches to improve bioethanol production from maize. *Curr. Opin. Biotechnol.* 18:193–99

238. Tricoli DM, Carney KJ, Russell PF, McMaster JR, Groff DW, et al. 1995. Field evaluation of transgenic squash containing single or multiple virus coat protein gene constructs for resistance to cucumber mosaic virus, watermelon mosaic virus 2 and zucchini yellow mosaic virus. *Bio/Technology* 13:1458–65

239. Underwood BA, Smitasiri S. 1999. Micronutrient malnutrition: Policies and programs for control and their implications. *Annu. Rev. Nutr.* 19:303–24
240. Ungemach FR, Weber NE. 1998. *Toxicological evaluation of certain veterinary drug residues in food*. Presented at 15th Meet. Jt. FAO/WHO Expert Comm. Food Addit., Geneva, Switz.
241. UNICEF. 2001. *A million children saved through vitamin A supplementation*. **http://www.unicef.org/newsline/01pr13.htm**
242. US EPA Off. Pesticide Programs. 2007. (Draft White Pap.) *Concerning Dietary Exposure To Cry9c Protein Produced By Starlink® Corn And The Potential Risks Associated With Such Exposure, Oct. 16*
243. Van der Westhuizen L, Shephard GS, Scussel VM, Costa LLF, Vismer HF, et al. 2003. Fumonisin contamination and *Fusarium* incidence in corn from Santa Carina, Brazil. *J. Agric. Food Chem.* 51:5574–78
244. van Eenennaam A. 2006. *Genetic Engineering and Animal Agriculture*. Univ. Calif. Agric. Nat. Resour., Agric. Biotechnol. Calif. Ser., Publ. 8184
245. Vozza I, Ranghi G, Quaranta A. 2005. Allergy and desensitization to latex. Clinical study on 50 dentistry subjects. *Minerva Stomatol.* 54:237–45
246. Walsh MK, Lucey JA, Govindasamy-Lucey S, Pace MM, Bishop MD. 2003. Comparison of milk produced by cows cloned by nuclear transfer with milk from non-cloned cows. *Cloning Stem Cells* 5:213–19
247. Wang Y, Zhang W, Cao J, McElroy D, Wu R. 1992. Characterization of *cis*-acting elements regulating transcription from the promoter of a constitutively active rice actin gene. *Mol. Cell. Biol.* 12:3399–406
248. Williamson C. 2007. Is organic food better for our health? *Nutr. Bull.* 32:104–8
249. Wilmut I, Schnieke AF, McWhir J, Kind AJ, Campbell KH. 1997. Viable offspring derived from fetal and adult mammalian cells. *Nature* 385:810–13
250. World Health Org. (WHO). 2007. *Micronutrient deficiencies, Vitamin A deficiency*. **http://www.who.int/nutrition/topics/vad/en/**
251. World Health Org. (WHO). 2007. *Micronutrients*. **http://www.who.int/nutrition/topics/micronutrients/en/**
252. Wu F. 2006. Mycotoxin reduction in Bt corn: potential economic, health, and regulatory impacts. *Transgenic Res.* 15:277–89
253. Yanagisawa S, Akiyama A, Kisaka H, Uchimiya H, Miwa T. 2004. Metabolic engineering with Dof1 transcription factor in plants: Improved nitrogen assimilation and growth under low-nitrogen conditions. *Proc. Natl. Acad. Sci. USA* 101:7833–38
254. Ye X, Al-Babili S, Kloti A, Zhang J, Lucca P, et al. 2000. Engineering the provitamin A (β-carotene) biosynthetic pathway into (carotenoid-free) rice endosperm. *Science* 287:303–5
255. Ynturi P, Jenkins JN, McCarty JC Jr., Gutierrez OA, Saha S. 2006. Association of root-knot nematode resistance genes with simple sequence repeat markers on two chromosomes in cotton. *Crop Sci.* 46:2670–74
256. Zavaleta N, Figueroa D, Rivera J, Sanchez J, Alfaro S, Lonnerdal B. 2007. Efficacy of rice-based oral rehydration solution containing recombinant human lactoferrin and lysozyme in Peruvian children with acute diarrhea. *J. Pediatr. Gastroenterol. Nutr.* 44:258–26
257. Zhang H-X, Hodson JN, Williams JP, Blumwald E. 2001. Engineering salt-tolerant *Brassica* plants: Characterization of yield and seed oil quality in transgenic plants with increased vacuolar sodium accumulation. *Proc. Natl. Acad. Sci. USA* 98:12832–36

258. Zhang W, Subbarao S, Addae P, Shen A, Armstrong C, et al. 2003. Cre/lox-mediated marker gene excision in transgenic maize (*Zea mays* L.) plants. *Theor. Appl. Genet.* 107:1157–68
259. Zhu YZ, Li DF, Wang FL, Yin JD, Jin H. 2004. Nutritional assessment and fate of DNA of soybean meal from roundup ready or conventional soybeans using rats. *Arch. Anim. Nutr.* 58:295–310
260. Zörb C, Langenkämper G, Betxche T, Niehaus K, Barsch A. 2006. Metabolite profiling of wheat grains (*Triticum aestivum* L.) from organic and conventional agriculture. *J. Agric. Food Chem.* 54:8301–6

Cumulative Indexes

Contributing Authors, Volumes 49–59

D

E

F

G

H

U

V

W

X

Y

Z

Chapter Titles, Volumes 49–59

Genetics and Molecular Biology

Tissue, Organ, and Whole Plant Events

Acclimation and Adaptation

ANNUAL REVIEWS
Intelligent Synthesis of the Scientific Literature

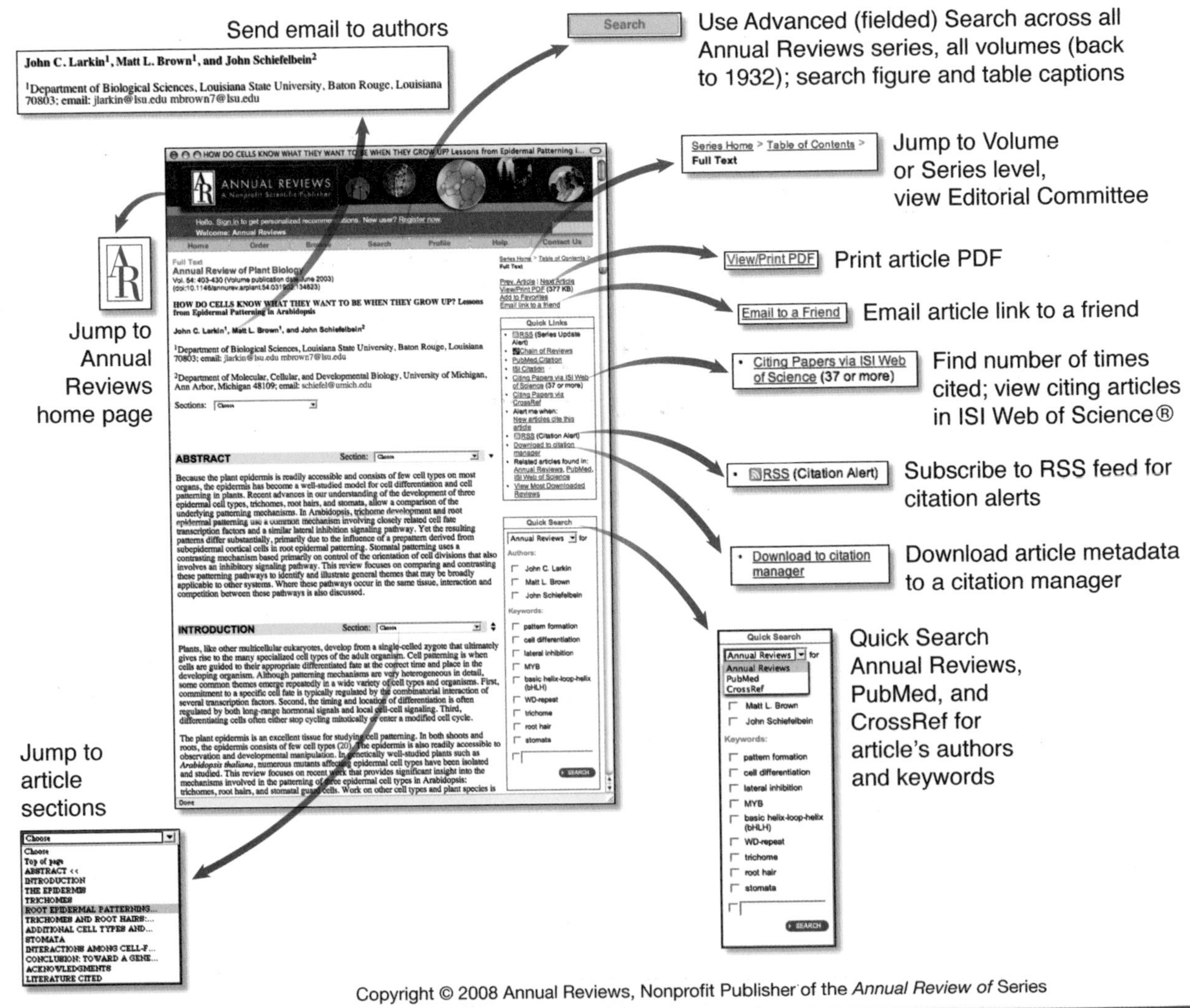